Student's Solutions Manual to Accompany

PRECALCULUS
A PROBLEMS-ORIENTED APPROACH

THIRD EDITION

David Cohen
Department of Mathematics
University of California
Los Angeles

Prepared by
Ross Rueger
Department of Mathematics
College of the Sequoias

West Publishing Company
St. Paul   New York   Los Angeles   San Francisco

CONTENTS

CHAPTER 10 ADDITIONAL TOPICS IN ALGEBRA AND TRIGONOMETRY

APPENDIX

PREFACE

This solutions manual contains complete solutions to all odd exercises of David Cohen's <u>Precalculus: A Problems-Oriented Approach</u> (third edition). It also contains complete solutions to odd and even exercises designated as a chapter test, at the beginning of the review exercises for each chapter. I have attempted to format solutions for readability and accuracy, and apologize to you for any errors that you may encounter. I would be more than happy to hear from you with any comments or suggestions for changes (your instructor has my address in this same section of her manual).

Please use this manual with some degree of caution. Be sure that you have attempted a solution, and re-attempted it, before you look it up in this manual. Mathematics can only be learned by **doing**, and not by observing! As you use this manual, do not just read the solution but work it along with the manual, using my solution to check your work. If you use this manual in that fashion, then it should be helpful to you in your studying. Solutions have been written in the same format as the textbook, however your instructor may prefer an alternate method.

I would like to thank a number of people for their assistance in preparing this manual. Thanks go to Peter Marshall, Deanna Quinn, and Maralene Bates of West Educational Publishing. Special thanks to Chuck Heuer for his meticulous error-checking of my work. I also thank Susan Schnelbach for her much-needed help in typing the Analytic Geometry chapter, and Susan Gerstein for her excellent editing suggestions.

Finally, I wish to express my deepest thanks to David Cohen who has authored such a fine textbook. Please read it and work as many problems as you possibly can (yes, even if they're **not** assigned!), for this book provides you with the fundamental tools to study calculus.

For Nanny - I'll always remember her smile.

Ross Rueger
January, 1990

CHAPTER ONE
ALGEBRA AND COORDINATE GEOMETRY
FOR PRECALCULUS

1.1 The Real Numbers

1. (a) natural number, integer, rational number
    (b) integer, rational number

3. (a) rational number
    (b) irrational number

5. (a) natural number, integer, rational number
    (b) rational number

7. (a) rational number
    (b) rational number

9. irrational number

11. natural number, integer, rational number

13. (a) $\dfrac{54}{10} = \dfrac{27}{5}$
    (b) Let x = 5.444...   Then 10x = 54.444... and 10x - x = 49.
         Thus 9x = 49, and consequently $x = \dfrac{49}{9}$.

15. (a) 99/100
    (b) Let x = 0.999... Then 10x = 9.999... , and 10x - x = 9.
         Thus 9x = 9, and consequently x = 1.

17. Since $\frac{11}{4}$ = 3.75, we have the following graph:

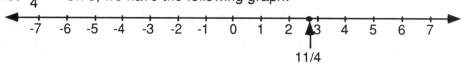

11/4

19. Since $1 + \sqrt{2} \approx 2.4$, we have the following graph:

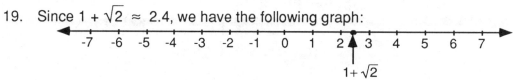

$1+\sqrt{2}$

21. Since $\sqrt{2} - 1 \approx 0.4$, we have the following graph:

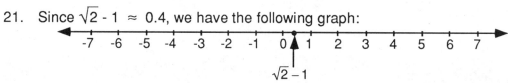

$\sqrt{2}-1$

23. Since $\sqrt{2} + \sqrt{3} \approx 2.7$, we have the following graph:

$\sqrt{2}+\sqrt{3}$

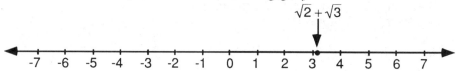

25. Since $\frac{1 + \sqrt{2}}{2} \approx \frac{2.4}{2} \approx 1.2$, we have the following graph:

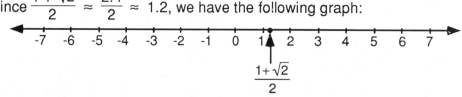

$\frac{1+\sqrt{2}}{2}$

27. Since $\frac{\pi}{2} \approx 1.57$, we have the following graph:

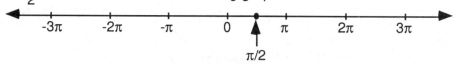

$\pi/2$

29. Since $\dfrac{\pi}{6} \approx 0.52$, we have the following graph:

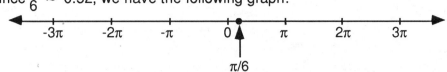

31. We draw the graph:

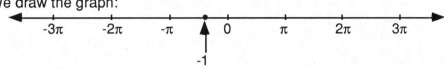

33. Since $\dfrac{\pi}{3} \approx 1.05$, we have the following graph:

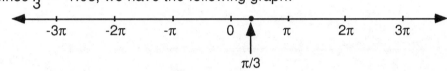

35. Since $2\pi + 1 \approx 7.28$, we have the following graph:

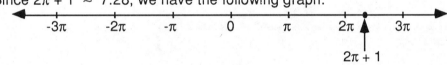

37. Since $\dfrac{\sqrt{139} - 5}{3} \approx 2.26$, we have the following graph:

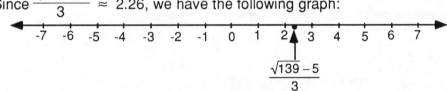

39. false

41. true (since -2 = -2, then it is also true that $-2 \le -2$)

43. false

45. false (since $2\pi \approx 6.2$)

47. true (since $2\sqrt{2} \approx 2.8$)

49. We graph the interval (2, 5):

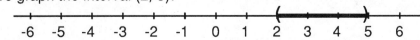

51. We graph the interval [1, 4]:

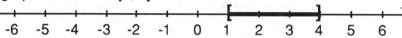

53. We graph the interval [0, 3):

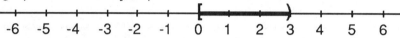

55. We graph the interval (-3, ∞):

57. We graph the interval [-1, ∞):

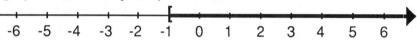

59. We graph the interval (-∞, ∞):

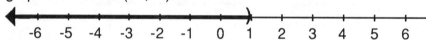

61. We graph the interval (-∞, π]:

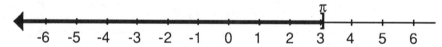

63. Let x = 0.191919...
     Then 100x - x = 19.191919... - 0.191919... = 19.
     Thus 99x = 19   and x = 19/99.

65. Let x = 0.3121212...
     Then 1000x - 10x = 312.121212... - 3.121212... = 309.
     Thus 990x = 309 and x = $\dfrac{309}{990}$, which reduces to $\dfrac{103}{330}$.

67. (a)   The common value to six decimal places is 3.863703
     (b)   The common value to six decimal places is 3.162277
     (c)   The common value to six decimal places is 1.847759
     (d)   The common value to six decimal places is 2.000000

69. (a) $a = \sqrt{2}$, $b = -\sqrt{2}$
     (b) $a = \sqrt{2}$, $b = \sqrt{3}$

71. (a) $a = \sqrt{12}$, $b = \sqrt{3}$
    (b) $a = \sqrt{2}$, $b = \sqrt{3}$

73. (a) If A is rational, then it already represents an irrational number raised to an irrational power.
    (b) Using the hint and rules of exponents, we obtain $(\sqrt{2})^2 = 2$, which is rational. The argument used here is intriguing, we have showed that either A is rational, or that we can raise it to an irrational number to result in a rational. In either case, we have shown the desired result.

1.2 Absolute Value

1. $|3| = 3$

3. $|-6| = 6$

5. $|-1 + 3| = |2| = 2$

7. $\left|-\dfrac{4}{5}\right| - \dfrac{4}{5} = \dfrac{4}{5} - \dfrac{4}{5} = 0$

9. $|-6 + 2| - |4| = |-4| - |4| = 4 - 4 = 0$

11. $\big| |-8| + |-9| \big| = |8 + 9| = |17| = 17$

13. $\left|\dfrac{27 - 5}{5 - 27}\right| = \left|\dfrac{22}{-22}\right| = |-1| = 1$

15. $|7(-8)| - |7| \, |-8| = |-56| - 7(8) = 56 - 56 = 0$

17. $|\sqrt{2} - 1| = \sqrt{2} - 1$ since $\sqrt{2} > 1$

19. If $x \geq 3$, then $|x - 3| = x - 3$

21. If $x < 3$, then $|x - 3| = -(x - 3) = -x + 3$ or $3 - x$

23. $|t^2 + 1| = t^2 + 1$, since $t^2 + 1 > 0$

25. Since $-\sqrt{3} - 4 < 0$, then $|-\sqrt{3} - 4| = -(-\sqrt{3} - 4) = \sqrt{3} + 4$

27. (a) If $x < 3$, then $x - 3 < 0$ and $x - 4 < 0$. So:
$$|x - 3| + |x - 4| = -(x - 3) - (x - 4)$$
$$= -x + 3 - x + 4$$
$$= -2x + 7$$

(b) If $x > 4$, then $x - 3 > 0$ and $x - 4 > 0$. So:
$$|x - 3| + |x - 4| = (x - 3) + (x - 4)$$
$$= x - 3 + x - 4$$
$$= 2x - 7$$

(c) If $3 < x < 4$, then $x - 3 > 0$ and $x - 4 < 0$. So:
$$|x - 3| + |x - 4| = (x - 3) - (x - 4)$$
$$= x - 3 - x + 4$$
$$= 1$$

(d) If $x = 4$, then $|x - 3| + |x - 4| = 1 + 0 = 1$
(e) If $x = 3$, then $|x - 3| + |x - 4| = 0 + 1 = 1$

29. If $-\dfrac{5}{2} < x < -\dfrac{3}{2}$, then $x + 1 < 0$ and $x + 3 > 0$. Thus:
$$|x + 1| + 4|x + 3| = -(x + 1) + 4(x + 3)$$
$$= -x - 1 + 4x + 12$$
$$= 3x + 11$$

31. $|x - 4| = 8$

33. $|x - (-3)| = 1$, or $|x + 3| = 1$

35. (a) $|x - 2| = \dfrac{1}{2}$

    (b) $|x - 2| < \dfrac{1}{2}$

    (c) $|x - 2| \geq \dfrac{1}{2}$

    (d) $|x - 2| > \dfrac{1}{2}$

37. $|y| < 3$

39. $|x^2 - a^2| < M$

41. $|x - a| < \delta$

43. We graph the interval:

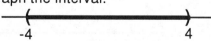

-4   4

45. We graph the interval:

-1   1

47. We graph the interval:

2   8

49. We graph the interval:

-1   7

51. We graph the interval:

-11/6   7/6

53. We graph the interval:

3   7

55. (a) We graph the interval:

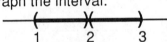

1   3

(b) We graph the interval:

1   2   3

(c) The interval in part (b) does not include the number 2.

57. (a) min (6,1) = 1

$$\min(6,1) = \frac{6 + 1 - |6 - 1|}{2} = \frac{7 - 5}{2} = \frac{2}{2} = 1$$

(b) min (1,-6) = -6

$$\min(1,-6) = \frac{1 + (-6) - |1 - (-6)|}{2}$$

$$= \frac{-5 - |1 + 6|}{2}$$

$$= \frac{-5 - 7}{2}$$

$$= \frac{-12}{12}$$

$$= -6$$

(c)   min $(-6,-6)$ $= -6$

min $(-6,-6)$ $= \dfrac{-6 + (-6) - |-6 - (-6)|}{2}$

$= \dfrac{-12 - |-6 + 6|}{2}$

$= \dfrac{-12}{2}$

$= -6$

59. $|a + b + c| = |a + (b + c)|$

$\leq |a| + |b + c|$ by the triangle inequality

$\leq |a| + |b| + |c|$ by the triangle inequality

61.   <u>case 1</u>: $a = b$

Then max $(a,b) = a$ and $\dfrac{a + b + |a - b|}{2} = \dfrac{a + a + |a - a|}{2}$

$= \dfrac{2a}{2}$

$= a$, which checks.

<u>case 2</u>: $a > b$

Then max $(a,b) = a$ and $\dfrac{a + b + |a - b|}{2} = \dfrac{a + b + a - b}{2}$ since $a - b > 0$

$= \dfrac{2a}{2}$

$= a$,   which checks.

<u>case 3</u>: $a < b$

Then max $(a,b) = b$ and $\dfrac{a + b + |a - b|}{2} = \dfrac{a + b + -(a - b)}{2}$ since $a - b < 0$

$= \dfrac{a + b - a + b}{2}$

$= \dfrac{2b}{2}$

$= b$, which checks.

63.   (a)   Property 1(b)

(b) $a + b \leq |a| + |b|$

(c) $(-a) + (-b) \leq |a| + |b|$, so $-(a + b) \leq |a| + |b|$

(d)   Since $a + b \leq |a| + |b|$ and $-(a + b) \leq |a| + |b|$, then
$|a + b| \leq |a| + |b|$ since $|a + b|$ is either $a + b$ or $-(a + b)$

1.3 Integer Exponents and Nth Roots

1.   (a) $x^3 x^{12} = x^{15}$
      (b) $\left(x^3\right)^{12} = x^{36}$
      (c) $(x + 1)^3 (x + 1)^{12} = (x + 1)^{15}$
      (d) $\left[(x + 1)^3\right]^{12} = (x + 1)^{36}$

3.   (a) $\dfrac{a^{15}}{a^9} = a^6$

      (b) $\dfrac{(a + 1)^{15}}{(a + 1)^9} = (a + 1)^6$

      (c) $\dfrac{(a + 2)^6 (a + 1)^{15}}{[(a + 2)(a + 1)]^5} = \dfrac{(a + 2)^6 (a + 1)^{15}}{(a + 2)^5 (a + 1)^5} = (a + 2)(a + 1)^{10}$

5.   (a) $(64)^0 = 1$
      (b) $\left(64^3\right)^0 = 1$
      (c) $\left(64^0\right)^3 = 1$

7.   (a) $10^{-1} + 10^{-2} = \dfrac{1}{10} + \dfrac{1}{100}$

                    $= \dfrac{10}{100} + \dfrac{1}{100}$

                    $= \dfrac{11}{100}$

      (b) $\left(10^{-1} + 10^{-2}\right)^{-1} = \left(\dfrac{11}{100}\right)^{-1} = \dfrac{100}{11}$

      (c) $\left(10^{-1}\right)^{-2} = 10^2 = 100$

9.   (a) $\left(a^2 b c^0\right)^{-3} = \dfrac{1}{\left(a^2 b\right)^3} = \dfrac{1}{a^6 b^3}$

      (b) $\left(a^3 b\right)^3 \left(a^2 b^4\right)^{-1} = a^9 b^3 a^{-2} b^{-4} = a^7 b^{-1} = \dfrac{a^7}{b}$

      (c) $\left(a^{-3} b^{-1} c^3\right)^{-2} = a^6 b^2 c^{-6} = \dfrac{a^6 b^2}{c^6}$

11. $\left(2^{-2} + 2^{-1} + 2^0\right)^{-2} = \left(\dfrac{1}{4} + \dfrac{1}{2} + 1\right)^{-2} = \left(\dfrac{7}{4}\right)^{-2} = \dfrac{16}{49}$

13. $\left(\dfrac{x^3y^{-2}z}{xy^2z^{-3}}\right)^{-3} = \dfrac{x^{-9}y^6z^{-3}}{x^{-3}y^{-6}z^9} = \dfrac{y^{6-(-6)}}{x^{-3+9}z^{9+3}} = \dfrac{y^{12}}{x^6z^{12}}$

15. $\left(\dfrac{x^4y^{-8}z^2}{xy^2z^{-6}}\right)^{-2} = \dfrac{x^{-8}y^{16}z^{-4}}{x^{-2}y^{-4}z^{12}} = \dfrac{y^{16+4}}{x^{-2+8}z^{12+4}} = \dfrac{y^{20}}{x^6z^{16}}$

17. $\left(\dfrac{a^{-2}b^{-3}c^{-4}}{a^2b^3c^4}\right)^2 = \dfrac{a^{-4}b^{-6}c^{-8}}{a^4b^6c^8} = \dfrac{1}{a^{4+4}b^{6+6}c^{8+8}} = \dfrac{1}{a^8b^{12}c^{16}}$

19. $\dfrac{x^2}{y^{-3}} \div \dfrac{x^2}{y^3} = \dfrac{x^2}{y^{-3}} \cdot \dfrac{y^3}{x^2} = \dfrac{x^2y^3}{x^2y^{-3}} = y^6$

21. (a)   false (since $\sqrt{81} = 9$)
     (b)   true
     (c)   true

23. (a)   false (since $\sqrt{9 + 16} = 5$ while $\sqrt{9} + \sqrt{16} = 3 + 4 = 7$)
     (b)   true

25. (a)   false (since $\sqrt{(-5)^2} = \sqrt{25} = 5$)
     (b)   false (since $\sqrt{x^2} = -x$ if $x < 0$)

27. (a) $\sqrt[3]{-64} = -4$
     (b) $\sqrt[4]{-64}$ is undefined

29. (a) $\sqrt[3]{\dfrac{8}{125}} = \dfrac{2}{5}$
     (b) $\sqrt[3]{-\dfrac{8}{125}} = -\dfrac{2}{5}$

31. (a) $\sqrt{-16}$ is undefined
     (b) $\sqrt[4]{-16}$ is undefined

33. (a) $\sqrt[4]{\dfrac{256}{81}} = \dfrac{4}{3}$

    (b) $\sqrt[3]{-\dfrac{27}{125}} = -\dfrac{3}{5}$

35. (a) $\sqrt[5]{-32} = -2$

    (b) $-\sqrt[5]{-32} = -(-2) = 2$

37. (a) $\sqrt{18} = \sqrt{9}\,\sqrt{2} = 3\sqrt{2}$

    (b) $\sqrt[3]{54} = \sqrt[3]{27}\,\sqrt[3]{2} = 3\sqrt[3]{2}$

39. (a) $\sqrt{98} = \sqrt{49}\,\sqrt{2} = 7\sqrt{2}$

    (b) $\sqrt[5]{-64} = \sqrt[5]{-32}\,\sqrt[5]{2} = -2\sqrt[5]{2}$

41. (a) $\sqrt{\dfrac{25}{4}} = \dfrac{5}{2}$

    (b) $\sqrt[4]{\dfrac{16}{625}} = \dfrac{2}{5}$

43. (a) $\sqrt{2} + \sqrt{8} = \sqrt{2} + \sqrt{4}\,\sqrt{2} = \sqrt{2} + 2\sqrt{2} = 3\sqrt{2}$

    (b) $\sqrt[3]{2} + \sqrt[3]{16} = \sqrt[3]{2} + \sqrt[3]{8}\,\sqrt[3]{2} = \sqrt[3]{2} + 2\sqrt[3]{2} = 3\sqrt[3]{2}$

45. (a) $4\sqrt{50} - 3\sqrt{128} = 4\sqrt{25}\,\sqrt{2} - 3\sqrt{64}\,\sqrt{2} = 20\sqrt{2} - 24\sqrt{2} = -4\sqrt{2}$

    (b) $\sqrt[4]{32} + \sqrt[4]{162} = \sqrt[4]{16}\,\sqrt[4]{2} + \sqrt[4]{81}\,\sqrt[4]{2} = 2\sqrt[4]{2} + 3\sqrt[4]{2} = 5\sqrt[4]{2}$

47. (a) 0.3 [because $(0.3)^2 = 0.09$]
    (b) 0.2 [because $(0.2)^3 = 0.008$]

49. $4\sqrt{24} - 8\sqrt{54} + 2\sqrt{6} = 4\sqrt{4}\,\sqrt{6} - 8\sqrt{9}\,\sqrt{6} + 2\sqrt{6}$
    $$= 8\sqrt{6} - 24\sqrt{6} + 2\sqrt{6}$$
    $$= -14\sqrt{6}$$

51. $\sqrt{\sqrt{64}} = \sqrt{8} = \sqrt{4}\,\sqrt{2} = 2\sqrt{2}$

53. (a) $\sqrt{36x^2} = 6x$

    (b) $\sqrt{36y^2} = -6y$, since $y < 0$

55. (a) $\sqrt{ab^2}\,\sqrt{a^2b} = \sqrt{a^3b^3} = ab\sqrt{ab}$

    (b) $\sqrt{ab^3}\,\sqrt{a^3b} = \sqrt{a^4b^4} = a^2b^2$

57. $\sqrt{72a^3b^4c^5} = \sqrt{36a^2b^4c^4}\,\sqrt{2ac} = 6ab^2c^2\,\sqrt{2ac}$

59. $\sqrt[4]{16a^4b^5} = \sqrt[4]{16a^4b^4} \cdot \sqrt[4]{b} = -2ab\sqrt[4]{b}$ (since $a < 0$)

61. $\sqrt{18a^3b^2} = \sqrt{9a^2b^2}\,\sqrt{2a} = 3ab\sqrt{2a}$

63. $\sqrt[3]{\dfrac{16a^{12}b^2}{c^9}} = \dfrac{\sqrt[3]{8a^{12}}\,\sqrt[3]{2b^2}}{\sqrt[3]{c^9}} = \dfrac{2a^4\,\sqrt[3]{2b^2}}{c^3}$

65. $\sqrt[6]{\dfrac{5a^7}{a^{-5}b^6}} = \sqrt[6]{\dfrac{5a^{12}}{b^6}} = \dfrac{\sqrt[6]{5}\,\sqrt[6]{a^{12}}}{\sqrt[6]{b^6}} = -\dfrac{a^2\,\sqrt[6]{5}}{b}$ (since $a < 0$)

67. (a) $\dfrac{4}{\sqrt{7}} \cdot \dfrac{\sqrt{7}}{\sqrt{7}} = \dfrac{4\sqrt{7}}{7}$

    (b) $\dfrac{3}{\sqrt{3}} \cdot \dfrac{\sqrt{3}}{\sqrt{3}} = \dfrac{3\sqrt{3}}{3} = \sqrt{3}$

    (c) $\dfrac{\sqrt{2}}{\sqrt{5}} \cdot \dfrac{\sqrt{5}}{\sqrt{5}} = \dfrac{\sqrt{10}}{5}$

69. (a) $\dfrac{1}{1+\sqrt{5}} \cdot \dfrac{1-\sqrt{5}}{1-\sqrt{5}} = \dfrac{1-\sqrt{5}}{1-5} = \dfrac{1-\sqrt{5}}{-4}$ or $\dfrac{\sqrt{5}-1}{4}$

    (b) $\dfrac{1}{1-\sqrt{5}} \cdot \dfrac{1+\sqrt{5}}{1+\sqrt{5}} = \dfrac{1+\sqrt{5}}{1-5} = \dfrac{1+\sqrt{5}}{-4}$ or $\dfrac{-1-\sqrt{5}}{4}$

    (c) $\dfrac{1+\sqrt{5}}{1-\sqrt{5}} \cdot \dfrac{1+\sqrt{5}}{1+\sqrt{5}} = \dfrac{1+\sqrt{5}+\sqrt{5}+5}{1-5} = \dfrac{6+2\sqrt{5}}{-4} = \dfrac{-3-\sqrt{5}}{2}$

71. $\dfrac{1}{\sqrt{5}} + 4\sqrt{45} = \dfrac{1}{\sqrt{5}} \cdot \dfrac{\sqrt{5}}{\sqrt{5}} + 4\sqrt{9}\,\sqrt{5}$

$$= \dfrac{\sqrt{5}}{5} + 12\sqrt{5}$$

$$= \dfrac{\sqrt{5}}{5} + \dfrac{60\sqrt{5}}{5}$$

$$= \dfrac{61\sqrt{5}}{5}$$

73. $\dfrac{1}{\sqrt[3]{25}} \cdot \dfrac{\sqrt[3]{5}}{\sqrt[3]{5}} = \dfrac{\sqrt[3]{5}}{\sqrt[3]{125}} = \dfrac{\sqrt[3]{5}}{5}$

75. $\dfrac{3}{\sqrt[4]{3}} \cdot \dfrac{\sqrt[4]{3^3}}{\sqrt[4]{3^3}} = \dfrac{3\sqrt[4]{27}}{3} = \sqrt[4]{27}$

77. $\dfrac{1}{\sqrt[4]{2ab^5}} \cdot \dfrac{\sqrt[4]{8a^3b^3}}{\sqrt[4]{8a^3b^3}} = \dfrac{\sqrt[4]{8a^3b^3}}{\sqrt[4]{16a^4b^8}} = \dfrac{\sqrt[4]{8a^3b^3}}{2ab^2}$

79. $\dfrac{3}{\sqrt[5]{16a^4b^9}} \cdot \dfrac{\sqrt[5]{2ab}}{\sqrt[5]{2ab}} = \dfrac{3\sqrt[5]{2ab}}{\sqrt[5]{32a^5b^{10}}} = \dfrac{3\sqrt[5]{2ab}}{2ab^2}$

81. $\dfrac{x}{\sqrt{x}-2} \cdot \dfrac{\sqrt{x}+2}{\sqrt{x}+2} = \dfrac{x(\sqrt{x}+2)}{x-4}$

83. $\dfrac{\sqrt{x}-\sqrt{a}}{\sqrt{x}+\sqrt{a}} \cdot \dfrac{\sqrt{x}-\sqrt{a}}{\sqrt{x}-\sqrt{a}} = \dfrac{x-2\sqrt{ax}+a}{x-a}$

85. $\dfrac{\sqrt{x}-\sqrt{5}}{x-5} \cdot \dfrac{\sqrt{x}+\sqrt{5}}{\sqrt{x}+\sqrt{5}} = \dfrac{x-5}{(x-5)(\sqrt{x}+\sqrt{5})} = \dfrac{1}{\sqrt{x}+\sqrt{5}}$

87. $\dfrac{\sqrt{2+h} - \sqrt{2}}{h} \cdot \dfrac{\sqrt{2+h} + \sqrt{2}}{\sqrt{2+h} + \sqrt{2}} = \dfrac{2+h-2}{h(\sqrt{2+h} + \sqrt{2})}$

$= \dfrac{h}{h(\sqrt{2+h} + \sqrt{2})}$

$= \dfrac{1}{\sqrt{2+h} + \sqrt{2}}$

89. 9^{10}

91. (a)   To six decimal places, both values are 1.645751.

(b) $(\sqrt{7} - 1)^2 = (\sqrt{7})^2 - 2\sqrt{7} + 1 = 8 - 2\sqrt{7}$, thus since $\sqrt{7} - 1 > 0$ the square roots are equal also.

93. For the first of the two given equations, the common value of both sides to six places (not rounding off) is 1.414213. For the second equation, the value of both sides to six decimal places is 3.141592. (Actually, the values in the second equation agree to nine decimal places; this approximation for π was discovered by Ramanujan.)

95. First rationalize the denominator in $\dfrac{\sqrt{a}}{\sqrt{a} + \sqrt{b}}$:

$\dfrac{\sqrt{a}}{\sqrt{a} + \sqrt{b}} \cdot \dfrac{\sqrt{a} - \sqrt{b}}{\sqrt{a} - \sqrt{b}} = \dfrac{a - \sqrt{ab}}{a - b}$

Next rationalize the denominator in $\dfrac{\sqrt{b}}{\sqrt{a} - \sqrt{b}}$:

$\dfrac{\sqrt{b}}{\sqrt{a} - \sqrt{b}} \cdot \dfrac{\sqrt{a} + \sqrt{b}}{\sqrt{a} + \sqrt{b}} = \dfrac{\sqrt{ab} + b}{a - b}$

Thus, we have:

$\dfrac{\sqrt{a}}{\sqrt{a} + \sqrt{b}} \cdot \dfrac{\sqrt{b}}{\sqrt{a} - \sqrt{b}} = \dfrac{a - \sqrt{ab}}{a - b} + \dfrac{\sqrt{ab} + b}{a - b}$

$= \dfrac{a - \sqrt{ab} + \sqrt{ab} + b}{a - b}$

$= \dfrac{a + b}{a - b}$

97. $\dfrac{x^{3a+2b-c}}{(x^{2a})(x^b)} \cdot x^{3c-a-b} = \dfrac{x^{2a+b+2c}}{x^{2a+b}} = x^{2c}$

99. We square the right-hand side of the equality:

$$(\sqrt{p-r} + \sqrt{q})^2 = (\sqrt{p-r} + \sqrt{q})(\sqrt{p-r} + \sqrt{q})$$
$$= (p-r) + 2\sqrt{q(p-r)} + q$$
$$= p + q - r + 2\sqrt{q(p-r)}$$

Taking square roots verifies the identity.

1.4 Rational Exponents

1. $16^{1/2} = \sqrt{16} = 4$

3. $\left(\dfrac{1}{36}\right)^{1/2} = \sqrt{\dfrac{1}{36}} = \dfrac{1}{6}$

5. $(-16)^{1/2} = \sqrt{-16}$, which is undefined.

7. $625^{1/4} = \sqrt[4]{625} = 5$

9. $8^{1/3} = \sqrt[3]{8} = 2$

11. $8^{2/3} = \left(\sqrt[3]{8}\right)^2 = (2)^2 = 4$

13. $(-32)^{1/5} = \sqrt[5]{-32} = -2$

15. $(-1000)^{1/3} = \sqrt[3]{-1000} = -10$

17. $49^{-1/2} = \left(\sqrt{49}\right)^{-1} = 7^{-1} = \dfrac{1}{7}$

19. $(-49)^{-1/2} = \left(\sqrt{-49}\right)^{-1}$, which is undefined.

21. $(36)^{-3/2} = \left(\sqrt{36}\right)^{-3} = 6^{-3} = \dfrac{1}{6^3} = \dfrac{1}{216}$

23. $125^{2/3} = \left(\sqrt[3]{125}\right)^2 = (5)^2 = 25$

25. $(-1)^{3/5} = \left(\sqrt[5]{-1}\right)^3 = (-1)^3 = -1$

27. $32^{4/5} - 32^{-4/5} = \left(\sqrt[5]{32}\right)^4 - \left(\sqrt[5]{32}\right)^{-4}$

$= 2^4 - 2^{-4}$

$= 16 - \dfrac{1}{16}$

$= \dfrac{255}{16}$

29. $\left(\dfrac{9}{16}\right)^{-5/2} - \left(\dfrac{1000}{27}\right)^{4/3} = \left(\dfrac{16}{9}\right)^{-5/2} - \left(\dfrac{1000}{27}\right)^{4/3}$

$= \left(\sqrt{\dfrac{16}{9}}\right)^5 - \left(\sqrt[3]{\dfrac{1000}{27}}\right)^4$

$= \left(\dfrac{4}{3}\right)^5 - \left(\dfrac{10}{3}\right)^4$

$= \dfrac{1024}{243} - \dfrac{10000}{81}$

$= -\dfrac{28976}{243}$

31. $(2a^{1/3})(3a^{1/4}) = 6a^{7/12}$, since $\dfrac{1}{3} + \dfrac{1}{4} = \dfrac{4}{12} + \dfrac{3}{12} = \dfrac{7}{12}$

33. $\sqrt[4]{\dfrac{64a^{2/3}}{a^{1/3}}} = \sqrt[4]{64a^{1/3}}$

$= (16 \cdot 4a^{1/3})^{1/4}$

$= 2(4a^{1/3})^{1/4}$

$= 2(4^{1/4})a^{1/12}$, or $2^{3/2}a^{1/12}$

35. $\dfrac{(x^2 + 1)^{3/4}}{(x^2 + 1)^{-1/4}} = (x^2 + 1)^{4/4} = x^2 + 1$

37. (a) $\sqrt{3}\ \sqrt[3]{6} = 3^{1/2}\,6^{1/3} = 2^{1/3}\,3^{5/6}$

(b) $3^{1/2}\,6^{1/3} = 3^{3/6}\,6^{2/6} = \sqrt[6]{3^3 6^2} = \sqrt[6]{972}$

39. (a) $\sqrt[3]{6}\,\sqrt[4]{2} = 6^{1/3}\,2^{1/4} = 2^{7/12}\,3^{1/3}$

    (b) $6^{1/3}\,2^{1/4} = 6^{4/12}\,2^{3/12} = \sqrt[12]{6^4 2^3} = \sqrt[12]{10368}$

41. (a) $\sqrt[3]{x^2}\,\sqrt[5]{y^4} = x^{2/3}\,y^{4/5}$

    (b) $x^{2/3}\,y^{4/5} = x^{10/15}\,y^{12/15} = \sqrt[15]{x^{10}y^{12}}$

43. (a) $\sqrt[4]{x^a}\,\sqrt[3]{x^b}\,\sqrt{x^{a/6}}$
    $\begin{aligned} &= x^{a/4}\,x^{b/3}\,x^{a/12} \\ &= x^{3a/12}\,x^{4b/12}\,x^{a/12} \\ &= x^{(4a+4b)/12} \\ &= x^{(a+b)/3} \end{aligned}$

    (b) $x^{(a+b)/3} = \sqrt[3]{x^{a+b}}$

45. $\sqrt[3]{(x+1)^2} = (x+1)^{2/3}$

47. $\left(\sqrt[5]{x+y}\right)^2 = (x+y)^{2/5}$

49. $\sqrt[3]{\sqrt{x}} + \sqrt{\sqrt[3]{x}} = (x^{1/2})^{1/3} + (x^{1/3})^{1/2} = x^{1/6} + x^{1/6} = 2x^{1/6}$

51. $\sqrt{\sqrt[3]{x}\,\sqrt[4]{y}} = (x^{1/2}\,y^{1/4})^{1/2} = x^{1/6}\,y^{1/8}$

53. $9^{10/9} \approx 11.5$; $10^{9/10} \approx 7.9$. Thus $9^{10/9}$ is larger.

55. We complete the table:

n	2	5	10	100	10^3	10^4	10^5	10^6
$n^{1/n}$	1.4142	1.3797	1.2589	1.0471	1.0069	1.0009	1.0001	1.0000

57. (a) $2^{2/3}$ is less than 2; $2^{3/2}$ is greater than 2. Thus, $2^{3/2}$ is the larger number.

    (b) $5^{1/2} = \sqrt{5}$; $5^{-2} = \dfrac{1}{25}$; thus $5^{1/2}$ is the larger number.

(c) $2^{1/2}$ is larger. (One way to see this is to raise both numbers to the sixth power)

(d) $(1/2)^{1/3}$ is larger. (One way to see this is to raise both numbers to the sixth power.)

(e) $10^{1/10}$ is larger than 1, but $(1/10)^{10}$ is much less than 1. Thus $10^{1/10}$ is the larger number.

59.   (a) $2^{1/2} = \sqrt{2}$, which is irrational.

(b) $\left(\sqrt{2}\right)^2 = 2$, which is rational.

61. $(-0.5)^{1/3} \approx -0.7937$ while $(-0.4)^{1/3} \approx -0.7368$, so $(-0.5)^{1/3}$ is smaller. Without a calculator, we only need to see that -0.5 is smaller, and since both numbers are raised to the same exponent, then $(-0.5)^{1/3}$ is smaller.

63.

$$\frac{a-b}{a+b}\sqrt{\frac{a+b}{a-b}} = \frac{a-b}{a+b} \bullet \frac{(a+b)^{1/2}}{(a-b)^{1/2}}$$

$$= \frac{a-b}{(a-b)^{1/2}} \bullet \frac{(a+b)^{1/2}}{a+b}$$

$$= \frac{(a-b)^{1/2}}{(a+b)^{1/2}}$$

$$= \left(\frac{a-b}{a+b}\right)^{1/2}, \text{ as required.}$$

1.5 Polynomials and Factoring

1.   (a)   all real numbers, or $(-\infty, \infty)$
(b)   non-negative real numbers, or $[0, \infty)$

3.   (a)   all real numbers, or $(-\infty, \infty)$
(b)   all real numbers, or $(-\infty, \infty)$

5.   (a)   non-negative real numbers, or $[0, \infty)$
(b)   positive real numbers except 1, or $(0, 1) \cup (1, \infty)$

7.   (a)   degree: 0; coefficients: 4
(b)   degree: 3; coefficients: 4
(c)   degree: 6; coefficients: 1, 4, -1, 2

9.　1　　$(A - B)(A + B) = A^2 + AB - AB - B^2$
$$= A^2 - B^2$$

2(a)　$(A + B)^2 = (A + B)(A + B)$
$$= A^2 + AB + AB + B^2$$
$$= A^2 + 2AB + B^2$$

2(b)　$(A - B)^2 = (A - B)(A - B)$
$$= A^2 - AB - AB + B^2$$
$$= A^2 - 2AB + B^2$$

11.　(a)　$x^2 - y^2$
(b)　$(x^2)^2 - 5^2 = x^4 - 25$

13.　$A^2 - 16$

15.　$\left(\sqrt{ab}\right)^2 - \left(\sqrt{c}\right)^2 = ab - c$

17.　$x^2 - 16x + 64$

19.　$(2^m)^2 + 2(2^m) + 1 = 2^{2m} + 2^{m+1} + 1$

21.　$\left(\sqrt{x}\right)^2 + 2\sqrt{xy} + \left(\sqrt{y}\right)^2 = x + 2\sqrt{xy} + y$

23.　$(2x + y)^3 = (2x)^3 + 3(2x)^2 y + 3(2x)y^2 + y^3 = 8x^3 + 12x^2 y + 6xy^2 + y^3$

25.　$(a + 1)^3 = a^3 + 3a^2(1) + 3a(1)^2 + 1^3 = a^3 + 3a^2 + 3a + 1$

27.　$x^3 - y^3$

29.　$x^3 + 1^3 = x^3 + 1$

31.　$(x^{1/3})^3 - (y^{1/3})^3 = x - y$

33.　(a)　$x^2 - 64 = (x + 8)(x - 8)$
(b)　$7x^4 + 14x^2 = 7x^2(x^2 + 2)$
(c)　$121z - z^3 = z(121 - z^2) = z(11 + z)(11 - z)$
(d)　$a^2 b^2 - c^2 = (ab + c)(ab - c)$

35.　(a)　$x^2 + 2x - 3 = (x + 3)(x - 1)$
(b)　$x^2 - 2x - 3 = (x - 3)(x + 1)$
(c)　$x^2 - 2x + 3$ is irreducible
(d)　$-x^2 + 2x + 3 = (-x + 3)(x + 1)$ or $-(x - 3)(x + 1)$

37. (a) $x^3 + 1 = (x + 1)(x^2 - x + 1)$

(b) $x^3 + 216 = (x + 6)(x^2 - 6x + 36)$

(c) $1000 - 8x^6 = 8(125 - x^6)$
$$= 8[5^3 - (x^2)^3]$$
$$= 8(5 - x^2)(25 + 5x^2 + x^4)$$

(d) $64a^3x^3 - 125 = (4ax)^3 - 5^3 = (4ax - 5)(16a^2x^2 + 20ax + 25)$

39. $2x - 2x^3 = 2x(1 - x^2) = 2x(1 - x)(1 + x)$

41. $100x^3 - x^5 = x^3(100 - x^2) = x^3(10 - x)(10 + x)$

43. $2x^4 + 3x^3 - 9x^2 = x^2(2x^2 + 3x - 9) = x^2(2x - 3)(x + 3)$

45. $4x^3 - 20x^2 + 25x = x(4x^2 - 20x + 25) = x(2x - 5)^2$

47. $x^2z^2 + xzt + xyz + yt = xz(xz + t) + y(xz + t) = (xz + t)(xz + y)$

49. $a^2t^2 + b^2t^2 - cb^2 - ca^2 = t^2(a^2 + b^2) - c(b^2 + a^2) = (a^2 + b^2)(t^2 - c)$

51. $x^3 - 13x^2 - 90x = x(x^2 - 13x - 90) = x(x - 18)(x + 5)$

53. $4x^2 - 29xy - 24y^2 = (4x + 3y)(x - 8y)$

55. $x^2 + 2x + 16$ is irreducible

57. $1 - (x + y)^2 = \left(1 + (x + y)\right)\left(1 - (x + y)\right) = (1 + x + y)(1 - x - y)$

59. $x^8 - 1 = (x^4 - 1)(x^4 + 1)$
$$= (x^2 - 1)(x^2 + 1)(x^4 + 1)$$
$$= (x - 1)(x + 1)(x^2 + 1)(x^4 + 1)$$

61. $x^3 + 3x^2 + 3x + 1 = (x^3 + 1) + (3x^2 + 3x)$
$$= (x + 1)(x^2 - x + 1) + 3x(x + 1)$$
$$= (x + 1)(x^2 - x + 1 + 3x)$$
$$= (x + 1)(x^2 + 2x + 1)$$
$$= (x + 1)(x + 1)^2$$
$$= (x + 1)^3$$

63. $27x^3 + 108x^2 + 144x + 64$

$= (27x^3 + 64) + 36x(3x + 4)$

$= (3x + 4)(9x^2 - 12x + 16) + 36x(3x + 4)$

$= (3x + 4)(9x^2 - 12x + 16 + 36x)$

$= (3x + 4)(9x^2 + 24x + 16)$

$= (3x + 4)(3x + 4)^2$

$= (3x + 4)^3$

65. $x^4 - 25x^2 + 144 = (x^2 - 9)(x^2 - 16) = (x - 3)(x + 3)(x - 4)(x + 4)$

67. $x^2 + 16y^2$ is irreducible

69. $x^3 - 2x^2 - 255x = x(x^2 + 2x - 255) = x(x + 17)(x - 15)$

71. $x^3 + a^3 + x + a = (x + a)(x^2 - xa + a^2) + (x + a) \bullet 1$

$= (x + a)(x^2 - xa + a^2 + 1)$

73. $a^4 - (b + c)^4 = \left(a^2 - (b + c)^2\right)\left(a^2 + (b + c)^2\right)$

$= \left(a - (b + c)\right)\left(a + (b + c)\right)\left(a^2 + b^2 + 2bc + c^2\right)$

$= (a - b - c)(a + b + c)(a^2 + b^2 + 2bc + c^2)$

75. $x^3a^2 - 8y^3a^2 - 4x^3b^2 + 32y^3b^2 = a^2(x^3 - 8y^3) - 4b^2(x^3 - 8y^3)$

$= (x^3 - 8y^3)(a^2 - 4b^2)$

$= (x - 2y)(x^2 + 2xy + 4y^2)(a - 2b)(a + 2b)$

77. $ax^2 + (1 + ab)xy + by^2 = ax^2 + xy + abxy + by^2$

$= x(ax + y) + by(ax + y)$

$= (ax + y)(x + by)$

79. $(5a^2 - 11a + 10)^2 - (4a^2 - 15a + 6)^2$

$= \left((5a^2-11a+10) - (4a^2-15a+6)\right)\left((5a^2-11a+10) + (4a^2-15a+6)\right)$

$= (a^2 + 4a + 4)(9a^2 - 26a + 16)$

$= (a + 2)^2(9a - 8)(a - 2)$

81. $(x + 1)^{1/2} - (x + 1)^{3/2} = (x + 1)^{1/2}\left(1 - (x + 1)^{2/2}\right)$

$= (x + 1)^{1/2}(1 - x - 1)$

$= (x + 1)^{1/2}(-x)$

$= -x(x + 1)^{1/2}$

83. $(x + 1)^{-1/2} - (x + 1)^{-3/2}$
$$= (x + 1)^{-3/2}\left((x + 1)^1 - 1\right)$$
$$= (x + 1)^{-3/2}(x)$$
$$= x(x + 1)^{-3/2} \quad \text{or} \quad \frac{x}{(x + 1)^{3/2}}$$

85. $x^2(a^2 - x^2)^{-1/2} + (a^2 - x^2)^{1/2}$
$$= (a^2 - x^2)^{-1/2}\left(x^2 + (a^2 - x^2)^1\right)$$
$$= a^2(a^2 - x^2)^{-1/2}$$
$$= \frac{a^2}{(a^2 - x^2)^{1/2}}$$

87. (a)   We have the following charts:

x	$\dfrac{x^2 - 16}{x - 4}$		x	$\dfrac{x^2 - 16}{x - 4}$
3.9	7.9		4.1	8.1
3.99	7.99		4.01	8.01
3.999	7.999		4.001	8.001
3.9999	7.9999		4.0001	8.0001
3.99999	7.99999		4.00001	8.00001

(b)   As x approaches 4, the value of the expression $\dfrac{x^2 - 16}{x - 4}$ approaches 8.

(c) $\dfrac{x^2 - 16}{x - 4} = \dfrac{(x + 4)(x - 4)}{x - 4} = x + 4$, which approaches 8 as x approaches 4.

89. $x^4 + 64$
$$= x^4 + 16x^2 - 16x^2 + 64$$
$$= (x^4 + 16x^2 + 64) - 16x^2$$
$$= (x^2 + 8)^2 - (4x)^2$$
$$= (x^2 + 8 - 4x)(x^2 + 8 + 4x)$$
$$= (x^2 - 4x + 8)(x^2 + 4x + 8)$$

91. $(x + y)^2 + (x + z)^2 - (z + t)^2 - (y + t)^2$

$$= \left((x + y)^2 - (y + t)^2\right) + \left((x + z)^2 - (z + t)^2\right)$$

$$= \left(x + y - (y+t)\right)\left(x + y + (y+t)\right) + \left(x + z - (z+t)\right)\left(x + z + (z+t)\right)$$

$$= (x - t)(x + 2y + t) + (x - t)(x + 2z + t)$$

$$= (x - t)(x + 2y + t + x + 2z + t)$$

$$= (x - t)(2x + 2y + 2z + 2t)$$

$$= 2(x - t)(x + y + z + t)$$

93. $(b - c)^3 + (c - a)^3 + (a - b)^3$

$$= b^3 - 3b^2c + 3bc^2 - c^3 + c^3 - 3c^2a + 3ca^2 - a^3 + a^3 - 3a^2b + 3ab^2 - b^3$$

$$= -3b^2c + 3bc^2 - 3c^2a + 3ca^2 - 3a^2b + 3ab^2$$

$$= (3bc^2 - 3c^2a) + (3ca^2 - 3b^2c) + (3ab^2 - 3a^2b)$$

$$= 3c^2(b - a) + 3c(a^2 - b^2) + 3ab(b - a)$$

$$= 3c^2(b - a) - 3c(b^2 - a^2) + 3ab(b - a)$$

$$= 3(b - a)[c^2 - c(b + a) + ab]$$

$$= 3(b - a)[c^2 - c\,b - ca + ab]$$

$$= 3(b - a)[c(c - b) - a(c - b)]$$

$$= 3(b - a)[\,(c - b)(c - a)\,]$$

$$= 3(b - a)(c - a)(c - b)$$

1.6 Quadratic Equations

1. $2(-3)^2 - 6(-3) - 36 = 0$

$\qquad 18 + 18 - 36 = 0$, which is true

So $x = -3$ is a solution.

3. $4(-1/4)^2 - 1 = 0$

$\quad 4(1/16) - 1 = 0$

$\qquad \dfrac{1}{4} - 1 = 0$, which is false

So $x = -1/4$ is not a solution.

5. $(-1 - \sqrt{7})^2 - 2(-1 - \sqrt{7}) - 6 = 0$

$\quad 1 + 2\sqrt{7} + 7 + 2 + 2\sqrt{7} - 6 = 0$

$\qquad\qquad\qquad 4\sqrt{7} + 4 = 0$, which is false

So $x = -1 - \sqrt{7}$ is not a solution.

7. $x^2 - 5x - 6 = 0$

$\quad (x - 6)(x + 1) = 0$

$\qquad\qquad x = 6$ or $x = -1$

9.
$$x^2 - 100 = 0$$
$$(x - 10)(x + 10) = 0$$
$$x = \pm 10$$

11.
$$25x^2 - 60x + 36 = 0$$
$$(5x - 6)^2 = 0$$
$$5x - 6 = 0$$
$$x = 6/5 \ \text{(double root)}$$

13.
$$10z^2 - 13z - 3 = 0$$
$$(5z + 1)(2z - 3) = 0$$
$$z = -1/5 \ \text{or} \ z = 3/2$$

15.
$$(x + 1)^2 - 4 = 0$$
$$(x + 1)^2 - 2^2 = 0$$
$$(x + 1 - 2)(x + 1 + 2) = 0$$
$$(x - 1)(x + 3) = 0$$
$$x = 1 \ \text{or} \ x = -3$$

17.
$$2x^2 - 15x - 8 = 0$$
$$(2x + 1)(x - 8) = 0$$
$$x = -1/2 \ \text{or} \ x = 8$$

19.
$$x(2x - 13) = -6$$
$$2x^2 - 13x + 6 = 0$$
$$(2x - 1)(x - 6) = 0$$
$$x = 1/2 \ \text{or} \ x = 6$$

21.
$$x(x + 1) = 156$$
$$x^2 + x - 156 = 0$$
$$(x + 13)(x - 12) = 0$$
$$x = -13 \ \text{or} \ x = 12$$

23. $a = 1, b = 10, c = 9$
$$x = \frac{-10 \pm \sqrt{100 - 36}}{2} = \frac{-10 \pm \sqrt{64}}{2} = \frac{-10 \pm 8}{2}$$
$$x = \frac{-10 + 8}{2} = \frac{-2}{2} = -1 \ \text{or} \ x = \frac{-10 - 8}{2} = \frac{-18}{2} = -9$$

25. $a = 1, b = -1, c = -5$
$$x = \frac{1 \pm \sqrt{1 - 4(1)(-5)}}{2(1)} = \frac{1 \pm \sqrt{21}}{2}$$

27. $a = 2, b = 3, c = -4$

$$x = \frac{-3 \pm \sqrt{9 - 4(2)(-4)}}{2(2)} = \frac{-3 \pm \sqrt{41}}{4}$$

29. $a = 12, b = 32, c = 5$

$$x = \frac{-32 \pm \sqrt{(32)^2 - 4(12)(5)}}{2(12)} = \frac{-32 \pm \sqrt{784}}{24} = \frac{-32 \pm 28}{24}$$

$x = -1/6$ or $x = -5/2$

31. $a = 2, b = -1, c = -5$

$$x = \frac{1 \pm \sqrt{1 - 4(2)(-5)}}{2(2)} = \frac{1 \pm \sqrt{41}}{4}$$

33. $a = -6, b = 12, c = 1$

$$x = \frac{-12 \pm \sqrt{144 - 4(-6)(1)}}{2(-6)}$$

$$= \frac{-12 \pm \sqrt{168}}{-12}$$

$$= \frac{-12 \pm \sqrt{(4)(42)}}{-12}$$

$$= \frac{-12 \pm 2\sqrt{42}}{-12}$$

$$x = \frac{-6 \pm \sqrt{42}}{-6} \quad \text{or} \quad x = \frac{6 \pm \sqrt{42}}{6}$$

35. $x^2 + 3x + 2.249 = 0$

Using the quadratic formula, we have:

$$x = \frac{-3 \pm \sqrt{9 - 4(1)(2.249)}}{2(1)}$$

$$x \approx -1.47 \text{ or } x \approx -1.53$$

37. $x^2 + 156x + 5963 = 0$

$$x = \frac{-156 \pm \sqrt{156^2 - 4(5963)}}{2} = \frac{-156 \pm \sqrt{484}}{2} = \frac{-156 \pm 22}{2}$$

So $x = \dfrac{-156 + 22}{2} = -67$ or $x = \dfrac{-156 - 22}{2} = -89$

39. $(3x - 2)^2 = 3x - 2$

$9x^2 - 12x + 4 = 3x - 2$

$9x^2 - 15x + 6 = 0$

$3(3x - 2)(x - 1) = 0$

$x = \dfrac{2}{3}$ or $x = 1$

41. $1 - 2x^2 = x$

$0 = 2x^2 + x - 1$

$0 = (2x - 1)(x + 1)$

$x = \dfrac{1}{2}$ or $x = -1$

43. $3x^2 + 4x - 3 = 0$

$x = \dfrac{-4 \pm \sqrt{16 - 4(3)(-3)}}{2(3)} = \dfrac{-4 \pm \sqrt{52}}{6} = \dfrac{-4 \pm 2\sqrt{13}}{6} = \dfrac{-2 \pm \sqrt{13}}{3}$

45. $x^2 = 24$

$x^2 - 24 = 0$

$x = \dfrac{0 \pm \sqrt{0 - 4(-24)}}{2} = \dfrac{\pm\sqrt{96}}{2} = \dfrac{\pm 4\sqrt{6}}{2} = \pm 2\sqrt{6}$

47. $x(x - 1) = 1$

$x^2 - x = 1$

$x^2 - x - 1 = 0$

$x = \dfrac{1 \pm \sqrt{1 - 4(-1)}}{2} = \dfrac{1 \pm \sqrt{5}}{2}$

49. $\dfrac{1}{2}x^2 - x - \dfrac{1}{3} = 0$

We multiply by 6 to clear fractions:

$6\left(\dfrac{1}{2}x^2 - x - \dfrac{1}{3} \right) = 6(0)$

$3x^2 - 6x - 2 = 0$

$x = \dfrac{6 \pm \sqrt{36 - 4(3)(-2)}}{2(3)} = \dfrac{6 \pm \sqrt{60}}{6} = \dfrac{6 \pm 2\sqrt{15}}{6} = \dfrac{3 \pm \sqrt{15}}{3}$

51. $2\sqrt{5}\,x^2 - x - 2\sqrt{5} = 0$

    We multiply by $\sqrt{5}$ to simplify the equation:

    $$\sqrt{5}\left(2\sqrt{5}\,x^2 - x - 2\sqrt{5}\right) = \sqrt{5}\,(0)$$

    $$10x^2 - \sqrt{5}\,x - 10 = 0$$

    $$x = \frac{\sqrt{5} \pm \sqrt{5 - 4(10)(-10)}}{2(10)} = \frac{\sqrt{5} \pm \sqrt{405}}{20} = \frac{\sqrt{5} \pm 9\sqrt{5}}{20}$$

    So $x = \dfrac{\sqrt{5} + 9\sqrt{5}}{20} = \dfrac{10\sqrt{5}}{20} = \dfrac{\sqrt{5}}{2}$ or $x = \dfrac{\sqrt{5} - 9\sqrt{5}}{20} = \dfrac{-8\sqrt{5}}{20} = -\dfrac{2\sqrt{5}}{5}$

53. $2y^2x^2 - 3yx + 1 = 0$

    $(2yx - 1)(yx - 1) = 0$

    $$x = \frac{1}{2y} \text{ or } x = \frac{1}{y}$$

55. $(x - p)^2 + (x - q)^2 = p^2 + q^2$

    $x^2 - 2px + p^2 + x^2 - 2qx + q^2 = p^2 + q^2$

    $2x^2 - 2px - 2qx = 0$

    $x^2 - px - qx = 0$

    $x(x - p - q) = 0$

    $x = 0$ or $x = p + q$

57. $12x^2 = ax + 20a^2$

    $12x^2 - ax - 20a^2 = 0$

    $(4x + 5a)(3x - 4a) = 0$

    $$x = -\frac{5a}{4} \text{ or } x = \frac{4a}{3}$$

59. $2\pi r^2 + 2\pi rh = 20\pi$

    $2\pi r^2 + 2\pi rh - 20\pi = 0$

    $2\pi(r^2 + rh - 10) = 0$

    $$r = \frac{-h \pm \sqrt{h^2 - 4(-10)}}{2(1)} = \frac{-h \pm \sqrt{h^2 + 40}}{2}$$

61. $-16t^2 + v_0 t = 0$

    $t(-16t + v_0) = 0$

    $$t = 0 \text{ or } t = \frac{v_0}{16}$$

63. $x^3 + bx^2 - 2b^2x = 0$
$x(x^2 + bx - 2b^2) = 0$
$x(x + 2b)(x - b) = 0$
$x = 0, -2b, b$

65. $a = 1, \ b = -12, \ c = 16$
We compute the discriminant:
$$b^2 - 4ac = 144 - 4(1)(16) = 80 > 0$$
The equation has two real roots.

67. $a = 4, \ b = -5, \ c = -\dfrac{1}{2}$
We compute the discriminant:
$$b^2 - 4ac = 25 - 4\,(4)\left(-\dfrac{1}{2}\right) = 33 > 0$$
The equation has two real roots.

69. $a = 1, \ b = \sqrt{3}, \ c = \dfrac{3}{4}$
We compute the discriminant:
$$b^2 - 4ac = 3 - 4\,(1)\left(\dfrac{3}{4}\right) = 0$$
The equation has one real root.

71. $a = 1, \ b = -\sqrt{5}, \ c = 1$
We compute the discriminant:
$$b^2 - 4ac = 5 - 4(1)(1) = 1 > 0$$
The equation has two real roots.

73. $$\begin{aligned} b^2 - 4ac &= 0 \\ 144 - 4(1)(k) &= 0 \\ 4k &= 144 \\ k &= 36 \end{aligned}$$

75. $$\begin{aligned} b^2 - 4ac &= 0 \\ k^2 - 4(1)(5) &= 0 \\ k &= \pm\sqrt{20} = \pm 2\sqrt{5} \end{aligned}$$

77.   (a) $\sqrt{x - 8} = 4$
Squaring each side, we have:
$$\begin{aligned} x - 8 &= 16 \\ x &= 24 \end{aligned}$$
Check: $\sqrt{24 - 8} = \sqrt{16} = 4$
Solution: 24

(b) $\sqrt{x-8} = 2x+1$

Squaring each side, we have:

$$x-8 = 4x^2 + 4x + 1$$

$$0 = 4x^2 + 3x + 9$$

$$x = \frac{-3 \pm \sqrt{9-4(4)(9)}}{2(4)} = \frac{-3 \pm \sqrt{-135}}{8}$$

So there are no real solutions.

79. $\sqrt{1-3x} = 2$

Squaring both sides yields:

$$1 - 3x = 4$$

$$-3x = 3$$

$$x = -1$$

Check: $\sqrt{1-3(-1)} = \sqrt{4} = 2$, which is true.

Solution: -1

81. $\sqrt{x^4 - 13x^2 + 37} = 1$

After squaring both sides we obtain:

$$x^4 - 13x^2 + 36 = 0$$

$$(x^2 - 4)(x^2 - 9) = 0$$

$$(x-2)(x+2)(x-3)(x+3) = 0$$

$$x = \pm 2 \quad \text{or} \quad x = \pm 3$$

Upon checking, we find that all four of these numbers satisfy the original equation.

Solutions: $\pm 2, \pm 3$

83. $\sqrt{1-2x} + \sqrt{x+5} = 4$

$$\left(\sqrt{1-2x}\right)^2 = \left(4 - \sqrt{x+5}\right)^2$$

$$1 - 2x = 16 - 8\sqrt{x+5} + x + 5$$

$$8\sqrt{x+5} = 3x + 20$$

After squaring both sides again, and then simplifying, we obtain:

$$9x^2 + 56x + 80 = 0$$

$$(x+4)(9x+20) = 0$$

$$x = -4 \quad \text{or} \quad x = -20/9$$

Upon checking, we find that both of these values satisfy the original equation.

Solutions: -4, -20/9

85. $\sqrt{3 + 2t} + \sqrt{-1 + 4t} = 1$

$$\left(\sqrt{3 + 2t}\right)^2 = \left(1 - \sqrt{-1 + 4t}\right)^2$$

$$3 + 2t = 1 - 2\sqrt{-1 + 4t} - 1 + 4t$$

$$2\sqrt{-1 + 4t} = 2t - 3$$

After squaring both sides again, and then simplifying, we obtain:

$$4t^2 - 28t + 13 = 0$$

$$(2t - 1)(2t - 13) = 0$$

$$t = 1/2 \quad \text{or} \quad t = 13/2$$

Upon checking, however, we find that neither of these values satisfies the original equation. So there is no solution to the equation.

87. $\sqrt{2y - 3} - \sqrt{3y + 3} + \sqrt{3y - 2} = 0$

$$\left(\sqrt{2y - 3} - \sqrt{3y + 3}\right)^2 = \left(-\sqrt{3y - 2}\right)^2$$

$$2y - 3 - 2\sqrt{2y - 3}\sqrt{3y + 3} + 3y + 3 = 3y - 2$$

$$2y + 2 = 2\sqrt{2y - 3}\sqrt{3y + 3}$$

$$y + 1 = \sqrt{2y - 3}\sqrt{3y + 3}$$

After squaring this last equation and then simplifying, we obtain:

$$y^2 - y - 2 = 0$$

$$(y - 2)(y + 1) = 0$$

$$y = 2 \quad \text{or} \quad y = -1$$

Upon checking, we find that only $y = 2$ satisfies the original equation.
Solution: 2

89. $\sqrt{2x + 1} + \sqrt{x + 4} = 1$

$$\left(\sqrt{2x + 1}\right)^2 = \left(1 - \sqrt{x + 4}\right)^2$$

$$2x + 1 = 1 - 2\sqrt{x + 4} + x + 4$$

$$x - 4 = -2\sqrt{x + 4}$$

After squaring this last equation and then simplifying, we obtain:

$$x^2 - 12x = 0$$

$$x(x - 12) = 0$$

$$x = 0 \quad \text{or} \quad x = 12$$

Upon checking, we find that neither of these values satisfies the original equation. So there is no solution to the equation.

91. $\dfrac{3}{x+5} + \dfrac{4}{x} = 2$

Multiplying through by the least common denominator $x(x + 5)$ gives us:

$$3x + 4(x + 5) = 2x(x + 5)$$
$$7x + 20 = 2x^2 + 10x$$
$$-2x^2 - 3x + 20 = 0$$
$$2x^2 + 3x - 20 = 0$$
$$(2x - 5)(x + 4) = 0$$
$$x = 5/2 \quad \text{or} \quad x = -4$$

Both of these values check in the original equation.

93. $1 - x - \dfrac{2}{6x+1} = 0$

Multiplying through by the least common denominator $6x + 1$ gives us:

$$-6x^2 + 5x - 1 = 0$$
$$6x^2 - 5x + 1 = 0$$
$$(3x - 1)(2x - 1) = 0$$
$$x = 1/3 \quad \text{or} \quad x = 1/2$$

Both values check in the original equation.

95. $\dfrac{3x^2 - 6x - 3}{(x+1)(x-2)(x-3)} + \dfrac{5 - 2x}{x^2 - 5x + 6} = 0$

$\dfrac{3x^2 - 6x - 3}{(x+1)(x-2)(x-3)} + \dfrac{5 - 2x}{(x-3)(x-2)} = 0$

Multiplying through by the least common denominator $(x + 1)(x - 2)(x - 3)$ gives us:

$$3x^2 - 6x - 3 + (5 - 2x)(x + 1) = 0$$
$$3x^2 - 6x - 3 - 2x^2 + 3x + 5 = 0$$
$$x^2 - 3x + 2 = 0$$
$$(x - 2)(x - 1) = 0$$
$$x = 2 \quad \text{or} \quad x = 1$$

Of these two values, only $x = 1$ checks in the original equation.

97.

$$\frac{2x}{x^2 - 1} - \frac{1}{x + 3} = 0$$

$$\frac{2x}{(x - 1)(x + 1)} - \frac{1}{(x - 3)} = 0$$

Multiplying through by the least common denominator $(x - 1)(x + 1)(x - 3)$ gives us:

$$2x(x + 3) - (x - 1)(x + 1) = 0$$
$$2x^2 + 6x - x^2 + 1 = 0$$
$$x^2 + 6x + 1 = 0$$
$$x = \frac{-6 \pm \sqrt{36 - 4}}{2}$$
$$x = \frac{-6 \pm 4\sqrt{2}}{2}$$
$$x = -3 \pm 2\sqrt{2}$$

Both values check in the original equation.

99.   We factor each denominator to yield:

$$\frac{x - 1}{x + 1} - \frac{x + 1}{x + 3} + \frac{4}{(x + 1)(x + 3)} = 0$$

Multiply each side of the equation by $(x + 1)(x + 3)$ to yield:

$$(x - 1)(x + 3) - (x + 1)(x + 1) + 4 = 0$$
$$x^2 + 2x - 3 - x^2 - 2x - 1 + 4 = 0$$
$$0 = 0$$

So any value of x (except $x = -1$ or $x = -3$) is a solution to the equation.

101.

$$\sqrt{\sqrt{x} + \sqrt{a}} + \sqrt{\sqrt{x} - \sqrt{a}} = \sqrt{2\sqrt{x} + 2\sqrt{b}}$$

$$\left(\sqrt{\sqrt{x} + \sqrt{a}} + \sqrt{\sqrt{x} - \sqrt{a}}\right)^2 = \left(\sqrt{2\sqrt{x} + 2\sqrt{b}}\right)^2$$

$$\sqrt{x} + \sqrt{a} + 2\sqrt{\sqrt{x} + \sqrt{a}}\sqrt{\sqrt{x} - \sqrt{a}} + \sqrt{x} - \sqrt{a} = 2\sqrt{x} + 2\sqrt{b}$$

$$\sqrt{\sqrt{x} + \sqrt{a}}\sqrt{\sqrt{x} - \sqrt{a}} = \sqrt{b}$$

Squaring both sides of this last equation yields:

$$\left(\sqrt{x} + \sqrt{a}\right)\left(\sqrt{x} - \sqrt{a}\right) = b$$
$$x - a = b$$
$$x = a + b$$

Upon checking, we find that this value of x satisfies the original equation. (Note: the following fact is useful in carrying out the check. Two non-negative quantities are equal if and only if their squares are equal.)
Solution: $a + b$

103. $\dfrac{\sqrt{x} - a}{\sqrt{x}} - \dfrac{\sqrt{x} + a}{\sqrt{x} - b} = 0$ $(a, b > 0)$

Let $t = \sqrt{x}$. Then the given equation can be written as:

$$\frac{t - a}{t} = \frac{t + a}{t - b}$$

$$t^2 + at = t^2 - at - bt + ab$$

$$2at + bt = ab$$

$$t(2a + b) = ab$$

$$t = \frac{ab}{2a + b}$$

Thus, $x = t^2 = \dfrac{a^2 b^2}{(2a + b)^2}$

Upon checking, we find that this value of x satisfies the original equation.

Solution: $\dfrac{a^2 b^2}{(2a + b)^2}$

105. $\sqrt{x^2 - x - 1} - \dfrac{2}{\sqrt{x^2 - x - 1}} = 1$

Let $t = x^2 - x - 1$. Then the given equation becomes:

$$\sqrt{t} - \frac{2}{\sqrt{t}} = 1 \qquad (1)$$

$$t - 2 = \sqrt{t} \quad \text{(multiplying by } \sqrt{t}\text{)}$$

$$t^2 - 4t + 4 = t \quad \text{(squaring)}$$

$$t^2 - 5t + 4 = 0$$

$$(t - 4)(t - 1) = 0$$

$$t = 4 \quad \text{or} \quad t = 1$$

Upon checking, we find that $t = 4$ satisfies Equation (1), but $t = 1$ does not. With $t = 4$ we have:

$$x^2 - x - 1 = 4$$

$$x^2 - x - 5 = 0$$

After applying the quadratic formula:

$$x = \frac{1 \pm \sqrt{21}}{2}$$

Solutions: $\dfrac{1 \pm \sqrt{21}}{2}$

107. $\sqrt{\dfrac{x-a}{x}} + 4\sqrt{\dfrac{x}{x-a}} = 5 \quad (a \neq 0)$

With $t = \dfrac{x-a}{x}$ the given equation becomes:

$$\sqrt{t} + \dfrac{4}{\sqrt{t}} = 5$$

$$t + 4 = 5\sqrt{t} \qquad \text{(multiplying by } \sqrt{t})$$

After squaring and rearranging terms, we obtain:

$$t^2 - 17t + 16 = 0$$
$$(t-1)(t-16) = 0$$
$$t = 1 \quad \text{or} \quad t = 16$$

After checking, we find that both of these values satisfy the equation:

$$\sqrt{t} + \dfrac{4}{\sqrt{t}} = 5$$

If $t = 1$, we have:

$$1 = \dfrac{x-a}{x}$$
$$x = x - a$$
$$0 = -a$$

But since $a \neq 0$, we discard this case.

If $t = 16$, we have:

$$16 = \dfrac{x-a}{x}$$
$$16x = x - a$$
$$x = -a/15$$

Solution: $\dfrac{-a}{15}$

109.   Replacing h by 3 and S by 8π in the given formula yields:

$$2\pi r^2 + 2\pi r(3) = 8\pi$$
$$r^2 + 3r = 4$$
$$r^2 + 3r - 4 = 0$$
$$(r+4)(r-1) = 0$$
$$r = -4 \quad \text{or} \quad r = 1$$

We choose the positive root here because $r > 0$. Thus, $r = 1$ meter.

111.   (a)   Replacing t by 10 in the equation yields:

$$P = -(10)^2 + 26(10) + 106$$
$$= -100 + 260 + 106$$
$$= 266$$

So after 10 days, approximately 266 people will have caught the flu.

(b) With P = 250, the equation yields:
$$-t^2 + 26t + 106 = 250$$
$$t^2 - 26t + 144 = 0$$
$$(t - 8)(t - 18) = 0$$

Thus, t = 8 days or t = 18 days. We discard the value t = 18 because the problem states that $t \le 13$. So after 8 days, approximately 250 people will have caught the flu.

113. Denoting the lengths of the two pieces by x and L - x, we have:
$$\left(\frac{x}{4}\right)^2 + \left(\frac{L-x}{4}\right)^2 = \frac{5L^2}{128}$$
$$\frac{x^2}{16} + \frac{L^2 - 2Lx + x^2}{16} = \frac{5L^2}{128}$$

After multiplying both sides by 128 and then simplifying, we obtain:
$$16x^2 - 16Lx + 3L^2 = 0$$
$$(4x - 3L)(4x - L) = 0$$
$$x = \frac{3L}{4} \quad \text{or} \quad x = \frac{L}{4}$$

If x = 3L/4, then L - x = L/4. Similarly, if x = L/4, then L - x = 3L/4. So in either case, the lengths of the two pieces are L/4 inches and 3L/4 inches.

115. Dividing $ax^2 + bx + c = 0$ by a, we have $x^2 + \frac{b}{a}x + \frac{c}{a} = 0$.

Thus $p = \frac{b}{a}$ and $q = \frac{c}{a}$, and thus:

$$\text{sum} = -\frac{b}{a} \quad \text{and} \quad \text{product} = \frac{c}{a}$$

117.
$$-x = \sqrt{1 - \sqrt{1 + x}}$$
$$x^2 = 1 - \sqrt{1 + x} \quad \text{(squaring)}$$
$$x^2 - 1 = -\sqrt{1 + x}$$
$$(x - 1)(x + 1) = -\sqrt{x + 1}$$
$$(x - 1)\sqrt{x + 1}\sqrt{x + 1} + \sqrt{x + 1} = 0$$
$$\sqrt{x + 1}\left((x - 1)\sqrt{x + 1} + 1\right) = 0$$

$$\sqrt{x + 1} = 0 \quad \text{or} \quad (x - 1)\sqrt{x + 1} + 1 = 0$$
$$x + 1 = 0 \qquad\qquad (x - 1)\sqrt{x + 1} = -1$$
$$x = -1 \qquad\qquad (x - 1)^2(x + 1) = 1$$

After multiplying out the left-hand side, we obtain:
$$x^3 - x^2 - x + 1 = 1$$
$$x^3 - x^2 - x = 0$$
$$x(x^2 - x - 1) = 0$$
$$x = 0 \quad \text{or} \quad x^2 - x - 1 = 0$$

Now use the quadratic formula to obtain:

$$x = \frac{1 \pm \sqrt{5}}{2}$$

We discard the solution involving the positive root, since it doesn't check in the original equation.

Solutions: -1, 0, $\dfrac{1 - \sqrt{5}}{2}$

119.   Let x and $16 - x$ denote the lengths of the two pieces. Therefore, the two circumferences are x and $16 - x$, respectively. We can find the corresponding radii by writing the formula $C = 2\pi r$ as $r = \dfrac{C}{2\pi}$. Thus the corresponding radii are $\dfrac{x}{2\pi}$ and $\dfrac{16 - x}{2\pi}$, respectively. Now if the sum of the two areas is 12 cm², we have:

$$\pi \left(\frac{x}{2\pi}\right)^2 + \pi \left(\frac{16 - x}{2\pi}\right)^2 = 12$$

$$\frac{x^2}{4\pi} + \frac{256 - 32x + x^2}{4\pi} = 12$$

$$2x^2 - 32x + 256 = 48\pi$$

$$x^2 - 16x + 128 = 24\pi$$

$$x^2 - 16x + (128 - 24\pi) = 0$$

Applying the quadratic formula with $a = 1$, $b = -16$, and $c = 128 - 24\pi$ yields:

$$x = \frac{16 \pm \sqrt{256 - 4(128 - 24\pi)}}{2}$$

$$= \frac{16 \pm \sqrt{96\pi - 256}}{2}$$

$$= \frac{16 \pm 4\sqrt{6\pi - 16}}{2}$$

$$= 8 \pm 2\sqrt{6\pi - 16}$$

Both roots here yield positive values for x. First consider the positive sign. Then $x = 8 + 2\sqrt{6\pi - 16}$ and consequently $16 - x = 8 - 2\sqrt{6\pi - 16}$ (which is the same as the value obtained for x using the negative root). Similarly, if we begin with $x = 8 - 2\sqrt{6\pi - 16}$, we find that $16 - x$ is $8 + 2\sqrt{6\pi - 16}$. So in either case, the lengths are:

$$8 + 2\sqrt{6\pi - 16} \quad \text{and} \quad 8 - 2\sqrt{6\pi - 16}$$

The smaller of these two numbers is $8 - 2\sqrt{6\pi - 16}$. Using a calculator now and rounding off to two decimal places, we find the required length to be 4.62 cm.

1.7 Inequalities

1. $x + 5 < 4$

    $x < -1$

    Solution set: $(-\infty, -1)$

3. $1 - 3x \leq 0$

    $-3x \leq -1$

    $x \geq 1/3$

    Solution set: $[1/3, \infty)$

5. $4x + 6 < 3(x - 1) - x$

    $4x + 6 < 2x - 3$

    $2x < -9$

    $x < -9/2$

    Solution set: $(-\infty, -9/2)$

7. $1 - 2(t + 3) - t \leq 1 - 2t$

    $1 - 2t - 6 - t \leq 1 - 2t$

    $-6 - t \leq 0$

    $-t \leq 6$

    $t \geq -6$

    Solution set: $[-6, \infty)$

9. $\dfrac{3x}{5} - \dfrac{x - 1}{3} < 1$

    $9x - 5(x - 1) < 15$

    $4x + 5 < 15$

    $4x < 10$

    $x < 5/2$

    Solution set: $(-\infty, 5/2)$

11. $\dfrac{x - 1}{4} - \dfrac{2x + 3}{5} \leq x$

    $5(x - 1) - 4(2x + 3) \leq 20x$

    $5x - 5 - 8x - 12 \leq 20x$

    $-23x \leq 17$

    $x \geq -17/23$

    Solution set: $[-17/23, \infty)$

13. $-2 \leq x - 6 \leq 0$

    $4 \leq x \leq 6$

    Solution set: $[4, 6]$

15. $-1 \leq \dfrac{1 - 4t}{3} \leq 1$

$-3 \leq 1 - 4t \leq 3$

$-4 \leq -4t \leq 2$

$1 \geq t \geq -\dfrac{1}{2}$

Or equivalently: $-\dfrac{1}{2} \leq t \leq 1$

Solution set: [-1/2, 1]

17. $.99 < \dfrac{x}{2} - 1 < .999$

$1.98 < x - 2 < 1.998$

$3.98 < x < 3.998$

Solution set: (3.98, 3.998)

19.   (a) $|x| \leq 1/2$

$-\dfrac{1}{2} \leq x \leq \dfrac{1}{2}$

Solution set: [-1/2, 1/2]

(b) $|x| > 1/2$

$x > 1/2$ or $x < -1/2$

Solution set: $(-\infty, -1/2] \cup [1/2, \infty)$

21.   (a)   Every number except zero has a positive distance from the origin.

Solution set: $(-\infty, 0) \cup (0, \infty)$

(b)   No number satisfies this inequality.

Solution set: None

23.   (a) $|x - 2| < 1$

$-1 < x - 2 < 1$

$1 < x < 3$

Solution set: (1, 3)

(b) $|x - 2| > 1$

$x - 2 > 1$ or $x - 2 < -1$

$x > 3$ or $x < 1$

Solution set: $(-\infty, 1) \cup (3, \infty)$

25.   (a) $|1 - x| \leq 5$

$-5 \leq 1 - x \leq 5$

$-6 \leq -x \leq 4$

$6 \geq x \geq -4$

Solution set: [-4, 6]

(b) $|1 - 4x| \leq 5$

$-5 \leq 1 - 4x \leq 5$

$-6 \leq -4x \leq 4$

$3/2 \geq x \geq -1$

Solution set: $[-1, 3/2]$

(c) $|1 - 4x| > 5$

$1 - 4x > 5$ or $1 - 4x < -5$

$-4x > 4$ or $-4x < -6$

$x < -1$ or $x > 3/2$

Solution set: $(-\infty, -1) \cup (3/2, \infty)$

27. $|x - a| < c$

$-c < x - a < c$

$a - c < x < a + c$

Solution set: $(a - c, a + c)$

29. $\left|\dfrac{x - 2}{3}\right| < 4$

$-4 < \dfrac{x - 2}{3} < 4$

$-12 < x - 2 < 12$

$-10 < x < 14$

Solution set: $(-10, 14)$

31. $\left|\dfrac{x + 1}{2}\right| - \left|\dfrac{x - 1}{3}\right| < 1$

$-1 < \dfrac{x + 1}{2} - \dfrac{x - 1}{3} < 1$

$-6 < 3(x + 1) - 2(x - 1) < 6$

$-6 < x + 5 < 6$

$-11 < x < 1$

Solution set: $(-11, 1)$

33. (a) $|(x + h)^2 - x^2| < 3h^2$ $\qquad (h > 0)$

$-3h^2 < 2xh + h^2 < 3h^2$

$-2h < x < h$

Solution set: $(-2h, h)$

(b) $|(x + h)^2 - x^2| < 3h^2$ $\qquad (h < 0)$

$-3h^2 < 2xh + h^2 < 3h^2$

$-4h^2 < 2xh < 2h^2$

Now we divide through by the negative quantity $2h$ to obtain

$-2h > x > h$

Solution set: $(h, -2h)$

35. $x^2 + x - 6 = (x + 3)(x - 2)$, so the key numbers are -3 and 2.

Interval	Test Number	$x + 3$	$x - 2$	$(x + 3)(x - 2)$
$(-\infty, -3)$	-4	neg.	neg.	pos.
$(-3, 2)$	0	pos.	neg.	neg.
$(2, \infty)$	3	pos.	pos.	pos.

Solution set for $x^2 + x - 6 < 0$: $(-3, 2)$

37. $x^2 - 11x + 18 = (x - 2)(x - 9)$, so the key numbers are 2 and 9.

Interval	Test Number	$x - 2$	$x - 9$	$(x - 2)(x - 9)$
$(-\infty, 2)$	0	neg.	neg.	pos.
$(2, 9)$	3	pos.	neg.	neg.
$(9, \infty)$	10	pos.	pos.	pos.

Solution set for $x^2 - 11x + 18 > 0$: $(-\infty, 2) \cup (9, \infty)$

39. $9x - x^2 \le 20 \iff -x^2 + 9x - 20 \le 0 \iff x^2 - 9x + 20 \ge 0$

Thus, the given inequality is equivalent to $x^2 - 9x + 20 \ge 0$, or $(x - 4)(x - 5) \ge 0$; so the key numbers are 4 and 5.

Interval	Test Number	$x - 4$	$x - 5$	$(x - 4)(x - 5)$
$(-\infty, 4)$	0	neg.	neg.	pos.
$(4, 5)$	9/2	pos.	neg.	neg.
$(5, \infty)$	6	pos.	pos.	pos.

The solution set for $x^2 - 9x + 20 \ge 0$ (and consequently for the original inequality also) is: $(-\infty, 4] \cup [5, \infty)$

41. $x^2 - 16 = (x - 4)(x + 4)$, so the key numbers are ± 4.

Interval	Test Number	$x - 4$	$x + 4$	$(x - 4)(x + 4)$
$(-\infty, -4)$	-5	neg.	neg.	pos.
$(-4, 4)$	0	neg.	pos.	neg.
$(4, \infty)$	5	pos.	pos.	pos.

Solution set for $x^2 - 16 \geq 0$: $(-\infty, -4] \cup [4, \infty)$

43. $16x^2 + 24x + 9 = (4x + 3)^2$, so the only key number is -3/4.

Interval	Test Number	$4x + 3$	$(4x + 3)^2$
$(-\infty, -3/4)$	-1	neg.	pos.
$(-3/4, \infty)$	1	pos.	pos.

The polynomial $16x^2 + 24x + 9$ is positive for all values of x except $x = -3/4$. The polynomial is zero when $x = -3/4$. Thus the inequality $16x^2 + 24x + 9 < 0$ (and consequently the original inequality also) has no solution. <u>Alternate Method:</u> The inequality $(4x + 3)^2 < 0$ has no solution, since the square of a real number is never negative.

45. $x^3 + 13x^2 + 42x = x(x^2 + 13x + 42) = x(x + 7)(x + 6)$
Thus the key numbers are 0, -7, and -6.

Interval	Test Number	x	$x + 7$	$x + 6$	$x(x + 7)(x + 6)$
$(-\infty, -7)$	-8	neg.	neg.	neg.	neg.
$(-7, -6)$	-13/2	neg.	pos.	neg.	pos.
$(-6, 0)$	-1	neg.	pos.	pos.	neg.
$(0, \infty)$	1	pos.	pos.	pos.	pos.

Solution set for $x^3 + 13x^2 + 42x > 0$: $(-7, -6) \cup (0, \infty)$

47. There are no key numbers since the equation $2x^2 + 1 = 0$ has no real solutions. So the only interval is $(-\infty, \infty)$, and any number will suffice as a test number. With $x = 0$, we have $2(0)^2 + 1 = 2 > 0$. Consequently, the polynomial is positive for all values of x, and the solution set is $(-\infty, \infty)$. [Note: this answer is obvious from the start; the techniques of this section aren't really needed.]

49. The key numbers are -4, -3, and 1.

Interval	Test Number	x - 1	x + 3	x + 4	(x - 1)(x + 3)(x + 4)
$(-\infty, -4)$	-5	neg.	neg.	neg.	neg.
$(-4, -3)$	-7/2	neg.	neg.	pos.	pos.
$(-3, -1)$	0	neg.	pos.	pos.	neg.
$(-1, \infty)$	2	pos.	pos.	pos.	pos.

Solution set of the inequality $(x - 1)(x + 3)(x + 4) \geq 0$: $[-4, -3] \cup [1, \infty)$

51. The key numbers are $\pm 1/3$ and 2.

Interval	Test Number	x - 2	3x + 1	3x - 1	$(x - 2)^2(3x + 1)^3(3x - 1)$
$(-\infty, -1/3)$	-1	neg.	neg.	neg.	pos.
$(-1/3, 1/3)$	0	neg.	pos.	neg.	neg.
$(1/3, 2)$	1	neg.	pos.	pos.	pos.
$(2, \infty)$	3	pos.	pos.	pos.	pos.

Solution set for $(x - 2)^2(3x + 1)^3(3x - 1) > 0$: $(-\infty, -1/3) \cup (1/3, 2) \cup (2, \infty)$

53.
$$x^4 - 25x^2 + 144 \leq 0$$
$$(x^2 - 9)(x^2 - 16) \leq 0$$
$$(x - 3)(x + 3)(x - 4)(x + 4) \leq 0$$
Thus, the key numbers are ± 3 and ± 4.

Interval	Test Number	$x-4$	$x-3$	$x+3$	$x+4$	$(x-3)(x+3)(x-4)(x+4)$
$(-\infty,-4)$	-6	neg.	neg.	neg.	neg.	pos.
$(-4,-3)$	-3.5	neg.	neg.	neg.	pos.	neg.
$(-3,3)$	0	neg.	neg.	pos.	pos.	pos.
$(3,4)$	3.5	neg.	pos.	pos.	pos.	neg.
$(4,\infty)$	6	pos.	pos.	pos.	pos.	pos.

Solution set for $x^4 - 25x^2 + 144 \leq 0$: $[-4, -3] \cup [3, 4]$

55.
$$x^3 + 2x^2 - x - 2 > 0$$
$$x^2(x + 2) - (x + 2) > 0$$
$$(x + 2)(x^2 - 1) > 0$$
$$(x + 2)(x + 1)(x - 1) > 0$$
The key numbers are -2 and ± 1.

Interval	Test Number	$x - 1$	$x + 1$	$x + 2$	$(x - 1)(x + 1)(x + 2)$
$(-\infty, -2)$	-3	neg.	neg.	neg.	neg.
$(-2, -1)$	-1.5	neg.	neg.	pos.	pos.
$(-1, 1)$	0	neg.	pos.	pos.	neg.
$(1, \infty)$	2	pos.	pos.	pos.	pos.

Solution set for $(x + 2)(x - 1)(x + 1) > 0$ (and for original inequality):
    $(-2, -1) \cup (1, \infty)$

57.   Key numbers: ± 1

Interval	Test Number	x + 1	x - 1	$\dfrac{x-1}{x+1}$
$(-\infty, -1)$	-2	neg.	neg.	pos.
$(-1, 1)$	0	pos.	neg.	neg.
$(1, \infty)$	2	pos.	pos.	pos.

Thus, the quotient is negative on $(-1, 1)$, and it is zero when $x = 1$. So the solution set for $\dfrac{x-1}{x+1} \leq 0$ is $(-1, 1]$.

59.   Key numbers: 2 and 3/2

Interval	Test Number	2 - x	3 - 2x	$\dfrac{2-x}{3-2x}$
$(-\infty, 3/2)$	0	pos.	pos.	pos.
$(3/2, 2)$	7/4	pos.	neg.	neg.
$(2, \infty)$	3	neg.	neg.	pos.

Thus, the quotient is positive on $(-\infty, 3/2)$ and $(2, \infty)$. Also, the quotient is zero when $x = 2$. So the solution set for $\dfrac{2-x}{3-2x} \geq 0$ consists of the two intervals: $(-\infty, 3/2) \cup [2, \infty)$.

61. $\dfrac{2x^3 + 5x^2 - 7x}{3x^2 + 7x + 4} > 0$

$\dfrac{x(2x^2 + 5x - 7)}{(3x + 4)(x + 1)} > 0$

$\dfrac{x(2x + 7)(x - 1)}{(3x + 4)(x + 1)} > 0$

Thus, the key numbers are 0, -7/2, 1, -4/3, and -1.

Interval	Test Number	x - 1	x	x + 1	3x + 4	2x + 7	$\dfrac{x(2x + 7)(x - 1)}{(3x + 4)(x + 1)}$
$(-\infty, -7/2)$	-4	neg.	neg.	neg.	neg.	neg.	neg.
$(-7/2, -4/3)$	-2	neg.	neg.	neg.	neg.	pos.	pos.
$(-4/3, -1)$	-7/6	neg.	neg.	neg.	pos.	pos.	neg.
$(-1, 0)$	-1/2	neg.	neg.	pos.	pos.	pos.	pos.
$(0, 1)$	1/2	neg.	pos.	pos.	pos.	pos.	neg.
$(1, \infty)$	2	pos.	pos.	pos.	pos.	pos.	pos.

Solution set: $(-7/2, -4/3) \cup (-1, 0) \cup (1, \infty)$

63.

$$\frac{1}{x - 2} - \frac{1}{x - 1} \geq \frac{1}{6}$$

$$\frac{1}{x - 2} - \frac{1}{x - 1} - \frac{1}{6} \geq 0$$

$$\frac{6(x - 1) - 6(x - 2) - (x - 2)(x - 1)}{6(x - 2)(x - 1)} \geq 0$$

$$\frac{-x^2 + 3x + 4}{6(x - 2)(x - 1)} \geq 0$$

$$\frac{x^2 - 3x - 4}{6(x - 2)(x - 1)} \leq 0$$

$$\frac{(x - 4)(x + 1)}{6(x - 2)(x - 1)} \leq 0$$

Thus, the key numbers are -1, 1, 2, and 4.

Interval	Test Number	x - 4	x - 2	x - 1	x + 1	$\dfrac{(x - 4)(x + 1)}{6(x - 2)(x - 1)}$
$(-\infty, -1)$	-2	neg.	neg.	neg.	neg.	pos.
$(-1, 1)$	0	neg.	neg.	neg.	pos.	neg.
$(1, 2)$	3/2	neg.	neg.	pos.	pos.	pos.
$(2, 4)$	3	neg.	pos.	pos.	pos.	neg.
$(4, \infty)$	5	pos.	pos.	pos.	pos.	pos.

The initial sequence of steps shows that the original inequality is equivalent to:

$$\frac{(x - 4)(x + 1)}{6(x - 2)(x - 1)} \leq 0$$

This quotient is negative on the intervals $(-1, 1)$ and $(2, 4)$. It is zero when $x = -1$ and 4. Thus, the required solution set is $[-1, 1) \cup (2, 4]$.

65.

$$\frac{1 + x}{1 - x} - \frac{1 - x}{1 + x} < -1$$

$$\frac{1 + x}{1 - x} - \frac{1 - x}{1 + x} + 1 < 0$$

$$\frac{(1 + x)^2 - (1 - x)^2 + (1 - x^2)}{(1 - x)(1 + x)} < 0$$

$$\frac{-x^2 + 4x + 1}{(1 - x)(1 + x)} < 0$$

The denominator is zero when $x = \pm 1$. Using the quadratic formula, we find the numerator is zero when $x = 2 \pm \sqrt{5}$. Thus, the key numbers are ± 1 and $2 \pm \sqrt{5}$. For purposes of picking appropriate test numbers, note that $2 + \sqrt{5} \approx 4.2$ and that $2 - \sqrt{5} \approx -0.2$.

Interval	Test Number	$x - 4.2$	$x - 1$	$x + 0.2$	$x + 1$	$\dfrac{-x^2 + 4x + 1}{1 - x^2}$
$(-\infty, -1)$	-2	neg.	neg.	neg.	neg.	pos.
$(-1, -0.2)$	-0.5	neg.	neg.	neg.	pos.	neg.
$(-0.2, 1)$	0	neg.	neg.	pos.	pos.	pos.
$(1, 4.2)$	2	neg.	pos.	pos.	pos.	neg.
$(4.2, \infty)$	5	pos.	pos.	pos.	pos.	pos.

Solution set: $(-1, 2 - \sqrt{5}) \cup (1, 2 + \sqrt{5})$

67.

$$\frac{3 - 2x}{3 + 2x} > \frac{1}{x}$$

$$\frac{3 - 2x}{3 + 2x} - \frac{1}{x} > 0$$

$$\frac{x(3 - 2x) - (3 + 2x)}{x(3 + 2x)} > 0$$

$$\frac{x - 2x^2 - 3}{x(3 + 2x)} > 0$$

$$\frac{2x^2 - x - 3}{x(3 + 2x)} < 0$$

The denominator is zero when $x = 0$ and $x = -3/2$. By using the quadratic formula, we find that there are no real numbers for which the numerator is zero. Thus, 0 and -3/2 are the only key numbers.

Interval	Test Number	$2x + 3$	x	$\dfrac{2x^2 - x + 3}{x(2x + 3)}$
$(-\infty, -3/2)$	-2	neg.	neg.	pos.
$(-3/2, 0)$	-1	pos.	neg.	neg.
$(0, \infty)$	1	pos.	pos.	pos.

The initial steps show that the given inequality is equivalent to:

$$\frac{2x^2 - x - 3}{x(3 + 2x)} < 0$$

The solution set is, therefore, (-3/2, 0).

69. First solve the equation $F = \frac{9}{5}C + 32$ for C. This yields:

$$C = \frac{5F - 160}{9}$$

The following inequalities are then equivalent:

$$-183 \le C \le 112$$
$$-183 \le \frac{5F - 160}{9} \le 112$$
$$-1647 \le 5F - 160 \le 1008$$
$$-1487 \le 5F \le 1168$$
$$\frac{-1487}{5} \le F \le \frac{1168}{5}$$

After carrying out the arithmetic and rounding off to the nearest integer, we obtain $-297° \le F \le 234°$, or $[-297°, 234°]$.

71.
$$50 \ge v \ge 40$$
$$50 \ge -32t + 60 \ge 40$$
$$-10 \ge -32t \ge -20$$
$$\frac{10}{32} \le t \le \frac{20}{32}$$
$$\frac{5}{16} \le t \le \frac{5}{8}$$

The velocity will be in the required range during the time interval $\frac{5}{16} \le t \le \frac{5}{8}$, or [5/16, 5/8].

73. (a) We solve the inequality:

$$x^2 - 4x - 5 \geq 0$$
$$(x - 5)(x + 1) \geq 0$$

The key numbers here are 5 and -1.

Interval	Test Number	x - 5	x + 1	(x - 5)(x + 1)
$(-\infty, -1)$	-2	neg.	neg.	pos.
$(-1, 5)$	0	neg.	pos.	neg.
$(5, \infty)$	6	pos.	pos.	pos.

The solution set for $(x - 5)(x + 1) \geq 0$, therefore, is $(-\infty, -1] \cup [5, \infty)$.

(b) We solve the inequality: $\dfrac{1}{x^2 - 4x - 5} \geq 0$

This will have the same solutions as in (a), except the endpoints x = -1 and x = 5 are not included. The solution set for this is $(-\infty, -1) \cup (5, \infty)$.

75. The solutions will be real provided the discriminant $b^2 - 4ac$ is non-negative. Thus, we have:

$$b^2 - 4 \geq 0$$
$$(b - 2)(b + 2) \geq 0$$

The key numbers here are ± 2.

Interval	Test Number	b - 2	b + 2	(b - 2)(b + 2)
$(-\infty, -2)$	-3	neg.	neg.	pos.
$(-2, 2)$	0	neg.	pos.	neg.
$(2, \infty)$	3	pos.	pos.	pos.

Thus, the solution set consists of the two intervals $(-\infty, -2] \cup [2, \infty)$. For values of b in either of these two intervals, the equation $x^2 + bx + 1 = 0$ will have real solutions. [Note: A more efficient way to solve the inequality $b^2 - 4 \geq 0$ is to write it as $b^2 \geq 4$, and then take the square roots of both (nonnegative) sides to obtain $|b| \geq 2$]

77. If $x = 1$ is a solution of $\dfrac{2a + x}{x - 2a} < 1$, then we have:

$$\frac{2a + 1}{1 - 2a} < 1$$

$$\frac{2a + 1}{1 - 2a} - 1 < 0$$

$$\frac{2a + 1 - (1 - 2a)}{1 - 2a} < 0$$

$$\frac{4a}{1 - 2a} < 0$$

Thus, the key numbers are 0 and 1/2.

Interval	Test Number	a	1 - 2a	$\dfrac{4a}{1 - 2a}$
$(-\infty, 0)$	-1	neg.	pos.	neg.
$(0, 1/2)$	1/4	pos.	pos.	pos.
$(1/2, \infty)$	1	pos.	neg.	neg.

The allowable values of a are, therefore, those numbers in either of the intervals $(-\infty, 0)$ or $(1/2, \infty)$. In other words $a < 0$ or $a > 1/2$.

79. Using the Pythagorean Theorem, we find the hypotenuse is $\sqrt{x^2 + (1 - x)^2}$, or $\sqrt{2x^2 - 2x + 1}$. If this is less than $\sqrt{17}/5$, then we have:

$$\sqrt{2x^2 - 2x + 1} < \sqrt{17}/5$$

$$\left(5\sqrt{2x^2 - 2x + 1}\right)^2 < \left(\sqrt{17}\right)^2$$

$$50x^2 - 50x + 25 < 17$$

$$50x^2 - 50x + 8 < 0$$

$$25x^2 - 25x + 4 < 0$$

$$(5x - 1)(5x - 4) < 0$$

The key numbers here are 1/5 and 4/5.

Interval	Test Number	5x - 1	5x - 4	(5x - 1)(5x - 4)
$(-\infty, 1/5)$	0	neg.	neg.	pos.
$(1/5, 4/5)$	2/5	pos.	neg.	neg.
$(4/5, \infty)$	1	pos.	pos.	pos.

The solution set is the interval $(1/5, 4/5)$. In other words, if $\dfrac{1}{5} < x < \dfrac{4}{5}$, then the hypotenuse will be less than $\sqrt{17}/5$.

81.   For the cylinder, we have:

$$\frac{V}{S} = \frac{\pi r^2 h}{2\pi r^2 + 2\pi rh} = \frac{\pi r^2}{2\pi r^2 + 2\pi r} = \frac{r}{2r + 2}$$

The condition $\frac{V}{S} < \frac{1}{3}$ then becomes:

$$\frac{r}{2r + 2} < \frac{1}{3}$$

Since r is positive here, we can multiply through by the positive quantity $3(2r + 2)$. This yields:

$$3r < 2r + 2$$
$$r < 2$$

So $0 < r < 2$.

83.   We complete the table:

a	b	$\sqrt{ab}$	$\frac{a+b}{2}$	$\sqrt{\frac{a^2 + b^2}{2}}$	largest	smallest
1	2	1.4142	1.5	1.5811	R.M.	G.M.
1	3	1.7320	2.0	2.2361	R.M.	G.M.
1	4	2.0000	2.5	2.9155	R.M.	G.M.
2	3	2.4495	2.5	2.5495	R.M.	G.M.
3	4	3.4641	3.5	3.5355	R.M.	G.M.
9	10	9.4868	9.5	9.5131	R.M.	G.M.
99	100	99.4987	99.5	99.5012	R.M.	G.M.
999	1000	999.4999	999.5	999.5001	R.M.	G.M.

85. (a) Since a + b is the diameter of the circle, then CE = EF = $\frac{a+b}{2}$, as they are radii of the circle.

(b) Consider the triangle:

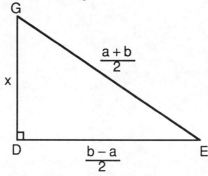

where DE = $b - \frac{a+b}{2} = \frac{b-a}{2}$

So:

$$\left(\frac{b-a}{2}\right)^2 + x^2 = \left(\frac{a+b}{2}\right)^2$$

$$\frac{b^2 - 2ab + a^2}{4} + x^2 = \frac{a^2 + 2ab + b^2}{4}$$

$$-2ab + 4x^2 = 2ab$$

$$4x^2 = 4ab$$

$$x^2 = ab$$

$$x = \sqrt{ab}$$

Thus DG = $\sqrt{ab}$

Now consider the triangle:

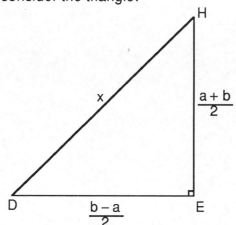

So:
$$\left(\frac{b-a}{2}\right)^2 + \left(\frac{a+b}{2}\right)^2 = x^2$$

$$\frac{b^2 - 2ab + a^2}{4} + \frac{a^2 + 2ab + b^2}{4} = x^2$$

$$\frac{2a^2 + 2b^2}{4} = x^2$$

$$\frac{a^2 + b^2}{2} = x^2$$

$$\sqrt{\frac{a^2 + b^2}{2}} = x$$

Thus $DH = \sqrt{\dfrac{a^2 + b^2}{2}}$

(c)   That $DG \leq EH$ is clear, as is $EH \leq DH$, since $\overline{DH}$ is the hypotenuse of the above triangle. So $\sqrt{ab} \leq \dfrac{a+b}{2} \leq \sqrt{\dfrac{a^2 + b^2}{2}}$

87. (a)   Let l be the length, so $2x + 2l = 30$
$x + l = 15$, thus $l = 15 - x$
Thus the area is given by $A = x(15 - x)$.

(b) $x(15 - x) \leq \left(\dfrac{x + 15 - x}{2}\right)^2 = \left(\dfrac{15}{2}\right)^2 = \dfrac{225}{4}$

(c)   Solve: $x(15 - x) = \dfrac{225}{4}$

$15x - x^2 = \dfrac{225}{4}$

$60x - 4x^2 = 225$

$4x^2 - 60x + 225 = 0$

$(2x - 15)^2 = 0$

So $x = \dfrac{15}{2}$

Since the length is also $\dfrac{15}{2}$, the rectangle is a square of dimensions $\dfrac{15}{2}$ ft by $\dfrac{15}{2}$ ft.

89. If we compute the key numbers by the quadratic formula, we have:

$$x = \frac{-2c \pm \sqrt{4c^2 - 4(-6c)}}{2} = \frac{-2c \pm 2\sqrt{c^2 + 6c}}{2} = -c \pm \sqrt{c^2 + 6c}$$

Since these key numbers must be equal to -3c and c, respectively, we have:

$$-c - \sqrt{c^2 + 6c} = -3c \qquad \text{and} \qquad -c + \sqrt{c^2 + 6c} = c$$
$$\sqrt{c^2 + 6c} = 2c \qquad\qquad\qquad \sqrt{c^2 + 6c} = 2c$$

Squaring, we have:

$$c^2 + 6c = 4c^2$$
$$3c^2 - 6c = 0$$
$$3c(c - 2) = 0$$
$$c = 0, \ c = 2$$

Thus a (non-zero) value is $c = 2$.

1.8 Rectangular Coordinates

1.   We plot the points:

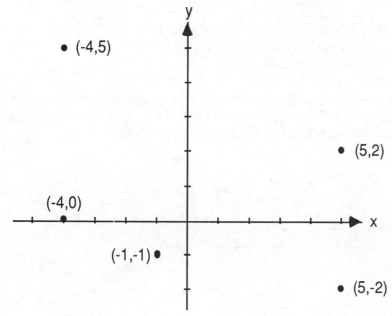

3.   (a)   We draw the figure:

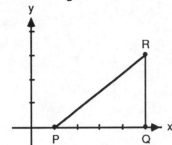

(b)   Since b = 5 - 1 = 4 and h = 3 - 0 = 3, then:
      A = (1/2) bh = (1/2)(4)(3) = 6

5.   (a)   Here $(x_1, y_1) = (0, 0)$ and $(x_2, y_2) = (-3, 4)$, so by the distance formula:
$$d = \sqrt{(-3 - 0)^2 + (4 - 0)^2} = \sqrt{9 + 16} = \sqrt{25} = 5$$
      (b)   Here $(x_1, y_1) = (2, 1)$ and $(x_2, y_2) = (7, 13)$, so:
$$d = \sqrt{(7 - 2)^2 + (13 - 1)^2} = \sqrt{25 + 144} = \sqrt{169} = 13$$

7.   (a)   Here $(x_1, y_1) = (-5, 0)$ and $(x_2, y_2) = (5, 0)$, so:
$$d = \sqrt{\left(5 - (-5)\right)^2 + (0 - 0)^2} = \sqrt{100 + 0} = \sqrt{100} = 10$$
      (b)   Here $(x_1, y_1) = (0, -8)$ and $(x_2, y_2) = (0, 1)$, so:
$$d = \sqrt{(0 - 0)^2 + \left(1 - (-8)\right)^2} = \sqrt{0 + 81} = \sqrt{81} = 9$$

Note that we really don't need to use the distance formula for either (a) or (b), since in each case one of the coordinates (either x or y) is the same. Draw quick graphs and you can find the distance by inspection:

(a)

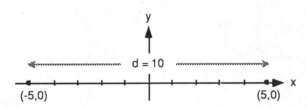

(b)

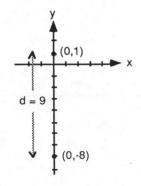

9. Here $(x_1, y_1) = (1, \sqrt{3})$ and $(x_2, y_2) = (-1, -\sqrt{3})$, so:

$$d = \sqrt{(-1 - 1)^2 + (-\sqrt{3} - \sqrt{3})^2} = \sqrt{(-2)^2 + (-2\sqrt{3})^2} = \sqrt{4 + 12} = 4$$

11. (a) We calculate the distance of each point from the origin:

$(3, -2)$: $d = \sqrt{(3 - 0)^2 + (-2 - 0)^2} = \sqrt{9 + 4} = \sqrt{13}$

$(4, 1/2)$: $d = \sqrt{(4 - 0)^2 + (1/2 - 0)^2} = \sqrt{16 + 1/4} = \sqrt{16.25}$

So $(4, 1/2)$ is farther from the origin.

(b) We calculate the distance of each point from the origin:

$(-6, 7)$: $d = \sqrt{(-6 - 0)^2 + (7 - 0)^2} = \sqrt{36 + 49} = \sqrt{85}$

$(9, 0)$: $d = \sqrt{(9 - 0)^2 + (0 - 0)^2} = \sqrt{81 + 0} = \sqrt{81}$

So $(-6, 7)$ is farther from the origin.

13. The hint is a good one. We will graph the triangle and then determine (using $a^2 + b^2 = c^2$) whether the triangle is a right triangle (we are using the <u>converse</u> of the Pythagorean Theorem.)

(a) We graph the points:

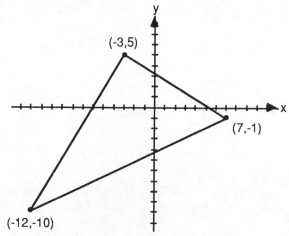

$$a = \sqrt{(-3 - 7)^2 + \big(5 - (-1)\big)^2} = \sqrt{100 + 36} = \sqrt{136}$$

$$b = \sqrt{\big(-12 - (-3)\big)^2 + (-10 - 5)^2} = \sqrt{81 + 225} = \sqrt{306}$$

$$c = \sqrt{(-12 - 7)^2 + \big(-10 - (-1)\big)^2} = \sqrt{361 + 81} = \sqrt{442}$$

We check: $a^2 + b^2 = 136 + 306 = 442 = c^2$

So the triangle is a right triangle.

Note: By graphing the triangle you can get a good guess as to what a, b, and c <u>should</u> be. Don't be afraid to draw the figure, it really helps!

(b)   We graph the points:

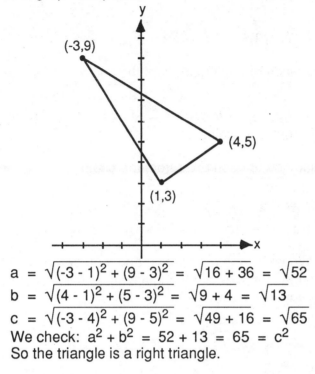

$$a = \sqrt{(-3 - 1)^2 + (9 - 3)^2} = \sqrt{16 + 36} = \sqrt{52}$$
$$b = \sqrt{(4 - 1)^2 + (5 - 3)^2} = \sqrt{9 + 4} = \sqrt{13}$$
$$c = \sqrt{(-3 - 4)^2 + (9 - 5)^2} = \sqrt{49 + 16} = \sqrt{65}$$

We check: $a^2 + b^2 = 52 + 13 = 65 = c^2$
So the triangle is a right triangle.

(c)   We graph the points:

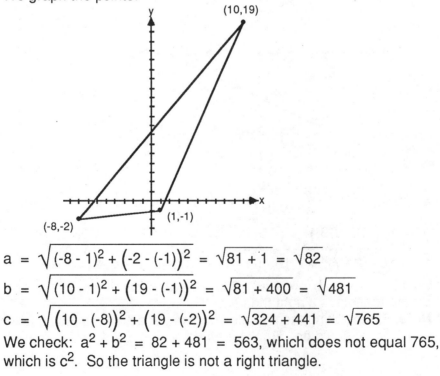

$$a = \sqrt{(-8 - 1)^2 + \left(-2 - (-1)\right)^2} = \sqrt{81 + 1} = \sqrt{82}$$
$$b = \sqrt{(10 - 1)^2 + \left(19 - (-1)\right)^2} = \sqrt{81 + 400} = \sqrt{481}$$
$$c = \sqrt{\left(10 - (-8)\right)^2 + \left(19 - (-2)\right)^2} = \sqrt{324 + 441} = \sqrt{765}$$

We check: $a^2 + b^2 = 82 + 481 = 563$, which does not equal 765,
which is c^2. So the triangle is not a right triangle.

15. We let $(x_1, y_1) = (1, -4)$, $(x_2, y_2) = (5, 3)$, and $(x_3, y_3) = (13, 17)$,
so using the formula from exercise #14(b) we have:

$$\text{Area} = (1/2) \left| 1(3) - 5(-4) + 5(17) - 13(3) + 13(-4) - 1(17) \right|$$
$$= (1/2) \left| 3 + 20 + 85 - 39 - 52 - 17 \right|$$
$$= (1/2) \left| 0 \right|$$
$$= 0$$

For the area of the triangle to be 0 it must be that these three points do not form a triangle. The only way that could occur is if the three points are collinear, that is, they all lie on the same line.

17. $(x - 3)^2 + (y - 1)^2 = 25$

The circle is in standard form, so its center is $(3, 1)$ and its radius is $\sqrt{25} = 5$.

y-intercepts: $x = 0$
$$9 + (y - 1)^2 = 25$$
$$(y - 1)^2 = 16$$
$$y - 1 = \pm 4$$
$$y = 1 \pm 4 = 5 \text{ or } -3$$

19. $x^2 + y^2 = \sqrt{2}$

The circle is in standard form, so its center is $(0, 0)$ and its radius is

$$\sqrt{\sqrt{2}} = \sqrt[4]{2}.$$

y-intercepts: $x = 0$
$$y^2 = \sqrt{2}$$
$$y = \pm \sqrt{\sqrt{2}} = \pm \sqrt[4]{2}$$

21. $x^2 + y^2 + 8x - 6y = -24$

We must complete the square:
$$x^2 + 8x + y^2 - 6y = -24$$
$$(x^2 + 8x + 16) + (y^2 - 6y + 9) = -24 + 16 + 9$$
$$(x + 4)^2 + (y - 3)^2 = 1$$

The center is $(-4, 3)$ and the radius is $\sqrt{1} = 1$.

y-intercepts: $x = 0$
$$16 + (y - 3)^2 = 1$$
$$(y - 3)^2 = -15$$
Impossible!
There are no y-intercepts.

23. $9x^2 + 54x + 9y^2 - 6y + 64 = 0$
We divide by 9 and complete the square:
$$x^2 + 6x + y^2 - \frac{2}{3}y = -\frac{64}{9}$$
$$(x^2 + 6x + 9) + \left(y^2 - \frac{2}{3}y + \frac{1}{9}\right) = -\frac{64}{9} + 9 + \frac{1}{9}$$
$$(x + 3)^2 + (y - 1/3)^2 = 2$$
The center is (-3, 1/3) and the radius is $\sqrt{2}$.
y-intercepts: x = 0
$$9 + (y - 1/3)^2 = 2$$
$$(y - 1/3)^2 = -7$$
Impossible!
There are no y-intercepts.

25. $2x^2 + 2y^2 = 2x + 6y - 3$
We divide by 2 and complete the square:
$$x^2 + y^2 = x + 3y - 3/2$$
$$(x^2 - x) + (y^2 - 3y) = -3/2$$
$$(x^2 - x + 1/4) + (y^2 - 3y + 9/4) = -3/2 + 1/4 + 9/4$$
$$(x - 1/2)^2 + (y - 3/2)^2 = 1$$
The center is (1/2, 3/2) and the radius is 1.
y-intercepts: x = 0
$$2y^2 = 6y - 3$$
$$2y^2 - 6y + 3 = 0$$
$$y = \frac{6 \pm \sqrt{36 - 24}}{4} = \frac{6 \pm 2\sqrt{3}}{4} = \frac{3 \pm \sqrt{3}}{2}$$

27.   The midpoint of PQ = (1, 1) is the center of the circle. We use the distance formula to find the radius:
$$r = \sqrt{(6 - 1)^2 + (4 - 1)^2} = \sqrt{25 + 9} = \sqrt{34}$$
So the equation is $(x - 1)^2 + (y - 1)^2 = 34$.

29.   (a)   Here $(x_1, y_1) = (3, 2)$ and $(x_2, y_2) = (9, 8)$, so by the midpoint formula:
$$M = \left(\frac{3 + 9}{2}, \frac{2 + 8}{2}\right) = \left(\frac{12}{2}, \frac{10}{2}\right) = (6, 5)$$
(b)   Here $(x_1, y_1) = (-4, 0)$ and $(x_2, y_2) = (5, -3)$, so:
$$M = \left(\frac{-4 + 5}{2}, \frac{0 - 3}{2}\right) = \left(\frac{1}{2}, \frac{-3}{2}\right)$$
(c)   Here $(x_1, y_1) = (3, -6)$ and $(x_2, y_2) = (-1, -2)$, so:
$$M = \left(\frac{3 - 1}{2}, \frac{-6 - 2}{2}\right) = \left(\frac{2}{2}, \frac{-8}{2}\right) = (1, -4)$$

31. Let's call $C(x, y)$. Since B is the midpoint of AC, then:

$$\frac{-1 + x}{2} = 5 \qquad \text{and} \qquad \frac{2 + y}{2} = -3$$

We solve each of these for x and y:

$$\frac{-1 + x}{2} = 5 \qquad \text{and} \qquad \frac{2 + y}{2} = -3$$
$$-1 + x = 10 \qquad\qquad 2 + y = -6$$
$$x = 11 \qquad\qquad\qquad y = -8$$

So the coordinates of C must be $(11, -8)$.

33. (a) We draw the figure:

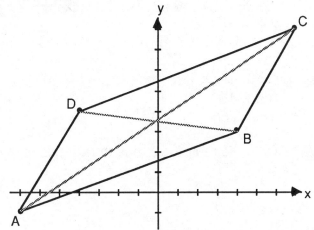

(b) For AC, let $(x_1, y_1) = (-7, -1)$ and $(x_2, y_2) = (7, 8)$, so the midpoint is:

$$M_1 = \left(\frac{-7 + 7}{2}, \frac{-1 + 8}{2} \right) = (0, 7/2)$$

For BD, let $(x_1, y_1) = (4, 3)$ and $(x_2, y_2) = (-4, 4)$, so the midpoint is:

$$M_2 = \left(\frac{4 - 4}{2}, \frac{3 + 4}{2} \right) = (0, 7/2)$$

(c) It appears that the midpoints of the two diagonals of a parallelogram are the same. Or, stated more clearly, the diagonals of a parallelogram bisect each other.

35. (a) Since $(AB)^2 = 68$, $(BC)^2 = 40$, and $(AC)^2 = 20$, then:

$$(AB)^2 + (BC)^2 + (AC)^2 = 128$$

(b) Let the midpoints be X, Y, and Z, so:

$$X = M_{AB} = (5, 2)$$
$$Y = M_{BC} = (6, 4)$$
$$Z = M_{AC} = (2, 3)$$

Then the medians are:

$$AY = \sqrt{(6-1)^2 + (4-1)^2} = \sqrt{25+9} = \sqrt{34}$$
$$BZ = \sqrt{(2-9)^2 + (3-3)^2} = \sqrt{49+0} = \sqrt{49} = 7$$
$$CX = \sqrt{(5-3)^2 + (2-5)^2} = \sqrt{4+9} = \sqrt{13}$$

So, the required value is:

$$(AY)^2 + (BZ)^2 + (CX)^2 = 34 + 49 + 13 = 96$$

(c)   This ratio is $\dfrac{128}{96} = \dfrac{4}{3}$

37.   Since the center is $(3, 2)$, we know the equation will take the form:

$$(x-3)^2 + (y-2)^2 = R^2$$

We can find R since the point $(-2, -10)$ must satisfy this equation:

$$(-2-3)^2 + (-10-2)^2 = R^2$$
$$25 + 144 = R^2$$
$$169 = R^2$$

So the equation of the circle is $(x-3)^2 + (y-2)^2 = 169$.

39.   From a sketch, we see that the radius is 3, and thus equation of the circle is:

$$(x-3)^2 + (y-5)^2 = 9$$

41. $a^2 = 1^2 + 1^2 = 2$, so $a = \sqrt{2}$
$b^2 = 1^2 + (\sqrt{2})^2 = 1 + 2 = 3$, so $b = \sqrt{3}$
$c^2 = 1^2 + (\sqrt{3})^2 = 1 + 3 = 4$, so $c = 2$
$d^2 = 1^2 + 2^2 = 1 + 4 = 5$, so $d = \sqrt{5}$
$e^2 = 1^2 + (\sqrt{5})^2 = 1 + 5 = 6$, so $e = \sqrt{6}$
$f^2 = 1^2 + (\sqrt{6})^2 = 1 + 6 = 7$, so $f = \sqrt{7}$
$g^2 = 1^2 + (\sqrt{7})^2 = 1 + 7 = 8$, so $g = \sqrt{8} = 2\sqrt{2}$

43.   If the circle is concentric with $x^2 - 6x + y^2 - 4y + 4 = 0$, then its center will be the same. We complete the square:

$$x^2 - 6x + y^2 - 4y = -4$$
$$x^2 - 6x + 9 + y^2 - 4y + 4 = -4 + 9 + 4$$
$$(x-3)^2 + (y-2)^2 = 9$$

So the center is $(3, 2)$. Since its equation is $(x-3)^2 + (y-2)^2 = r^2$, and $(0, 0)$ lies on the circle, we have:

$$(-3)^2 + (-2)^2 = r^2$$
$$13 = r^2$$

So the equation is $(x-3)^2 + (y-2)^2 = 13$.

45.   We definitely use the hint: $13 = \sqrt{144 + (t-2)^2}$
Squaring each side, we get: $169 = 144 + (t-2)^2$
$$25 = (t-2)^2$$
Taking square roots: $t - 2 = 5$ or $t - 2 = -5$
$$t = 7 \quad \text{or} \quad t = -3$$
Thus there are two real solutions for t, 7 and -3

47.   (a)   Call (x, y) the coordinates of B. Clearly $y = c$, since the top and bottom of the parallelogram must be parallel, and since the bottom is horizontal the top must be also. Now also OC = AB (opposite sides are equal):
$$OC = \sqrt{(b-0)^2 + (c-0)^2} = \sqrt{b^2 + c^2}$$
$$AB = \sqrt{(x-a)^2 + (c-0)^2} = \sqrt{(x-a)^2 + c^2}$$
Since OC = AB: $\sqrt{b^2 + c^2} = \sqrt{(x-a)^2 + c^2}$
Squaring each side: $b^2 + c^2 = (x-a)^2 + c^2$
$$b^2 = (x-a)^2$$
Taking roots, we get: $x - a = b$ or $x - a = -b$
$$x = a + b \quad \text{or} \quad x = a - b$$
But clearly $x = a - b$ doesn't make sense (look at the diagram), so $x = a + b$. So the coordinates of B must be $(a + b, c)$.

(b)   For $O(0, 0)$ and $B(a + b, c)$, $M_{OB} = \left(\dfrac{a+b}{2}, \dfrac{c}{2}\right)$.

For $A(a, 0)$ and $C(b, c)$, $M_{AC} = \left(\dfrac{a+b}{2}, \dfrac{c}{2}\right)$.

(c)   Clearly our two midpoints from (b) are equal. Since the two midpoints on the diagonals are equal, they must bisect each other.

49.   Using the hint and the lengths of our diagonals from #48, we have:
$$\sqrt{(a+b)^2 + c^2} = \sqrt{(b-a)^2 + c^2}$$
Squaring each side: $(a+b)^2 + c^2 = b^2 - 2ab + a^2 + c^2$
$$2ab = -2ab$$
$$4ab = 0$$
$$a = 0 \text{ or } b = 0$$
Now $a = 0$ is impossible, since our figure would no longer be a parallelgram. So $b = 0$. But if $b = 0$, then we must have a rectangle (look at the figure). This proves the desired result.

51. We first compute the left-hand side of the equality:

$$AB = \sqrt{(2-0)^2 + (0-0)^2} = \sqrt{4} = 2$$
$$AC = \sqrt{(2a-0)^2 + (2b-0)^2} = \sqrt{4a^2 + 4b^2}$$

So $AB^2 + AC^2 = 4 + 4a^2 + 4b^2$

Now for the right-hand side. We first find $M = \left(\dfrac{2a+a}{2}, \dfrac{2b+0}{2}\right) = (a+1, b)$

$$BM = \sqrt{(a+1-2)^2 + (b-0)^2} = \sqrt{(a-1)^2 + b^2}$$
$$AM = \sqrt{(a+1-0)^2 + (b-0)^2} = \sqrt{(a+1)^2 + b^2}$$

So $2(BM^2 + AM^2) = 2[(a-1)^2 + b^2 + (a+1)^2 + b^2]$
$$= 2(a^2 - 2a + 1 + b^2 + a^2 + 2a + 1 + b^2)$$
$$= 2(2a^2 + 2b^2 + 2)$$
$$= 4a^2 + 4b^2 + 4$$

So $AB^2 + AC^2 = 2(BM^2 + AM^2)$

53. (a) $PM = \sqrt{\left(\dfrac{x_1 + x_2}{2} - x_1\right)^2 + \left(\dfrac{y_1 + y_2}{2} - y_1\right)^2}$

$$= \sqrt{\left(\dfrac{x_2 - x_1}{2}\right)^2 + \left(\dfrac{y_2 - y_1}{2}\right)^2}$$

$$= \dfrac{\sqrt{(x_2 - x_1)^2 + (y_2 - y_1)^2}}{2}$$

$MQ = \sqrt{\left(x_2 - \dfrac{x_1 + x_2}{2}\right)^2 + \left(y_2 - \dfrac{y_1 + y_2}{2}\right)^2}$

$$= \sqrt{\left(\dfrac{x_2 - x_1}{2}\right)^2 + \left(\dfrac{y_2 - y_1}{2}\right)^2}$$

$$= \dfrac{\sqrt{(x_2 - x_1)^2 + (y_2 - y_1)^2}}{2}$$

Thus, $PM = MQ$

(b) $PM + MQ = \sqrt{(x_2 - x_1)^2 + (y_2 - y_1)^2} = PQ$

55. (a) We compute the areas:

Rectangle: (length)(width) = (5)(4) = 20

Triangles: (1) $= \dfrac{1}{2}$ (base)(height) $= \dfrac{1}{2}$ (4)(4) = 8

(2) $= \dfrac{1}{2}$ (base)(height) $= \dfrac{1}{2}$(5)(1) = 5/2

(3) $= \dfrac{1}{2}$ (base)(height) $= \dfrac{1}{2}$ (3)(1) = 3/2

So Area ($\triangle ABC$) = 20 - 8 - 5/2 - 3/2 = 8 sq. units

(b)   We compute the areas:

Rectangle: (length)(width) = (9)(3) = 27

Triangles: (1) $= \frac{1}{2}$ (base)(height) $= \frac{1}{2}$ (9)(1) = 9/2

(2) $= \frac{1}{2}$ (base)(height) $= \frac{1}{2}$ (2)(3) = 3

(3) $= \frac{1}{2}$ (base)(height) $= \frac{1}{2}$ (6)(3) = 9

So Area($\triangle ABC$) = $27 - \frac{9}{2} - 3 - 9 = \frac{21}{2}$ or $10\frac{1}{2}$

(c)   We compute the areas:

Rectangle:
   (length)(width) $= (x_2 - x_1)(y_3 - y_1) = x_2 y_3 - x_1 y_3 - x_2 y_1 + x_1 y_1$

Triangles:

(1) $= \frac{1}{2}$ (base)(height) $= \frac{1}{2}(y_3 - y_1)(x_3 - x_1) = \frac{1}{2}(x_3 y_3 - x_3 y_1 - x_1 y_3 + x_1 y_1)$

(2) $= \frac{1}{2}$(base)(height) $= \frac{1}{2}(y_3 - y_2)(x_2 - x_3) = \frac{1}{2}(x_2 y_3 - x_2 y_2 - x_3 y_3 + x_3 y_2)$

(3) $= \frac{1}{2}$(base)(height) $= \frac{1}{2}(x_2 - x_1)(y_2 - y_1) = \frac{1}{2}(x_2 y_2 - x_2 y_1 - x_1 y_2 + x_1 y_1)$

So Area($\triangle ABC$)
   = Rectangle - Triangles
   $= \frac{1}{2}\big(2x_2 y_3 - 2x_1 y_3 - 2x_2 y_1 + 2x_1 y_1 - x_3 y_3 + x_3 y_1 + x_1 y_3 - x_1 y_1 - x_2 y_3$
   $+ x_2 y_2 + x_3 y_3 - x_3 y_2 - x_2 y_2 + x_2 y_1 - x_1 y_2 - x_1 y_1\big)$
   $= \frac{1}{2} (x_2 y_3 - x_1 y_3 - x_2 y_1 + x_3 y_1 - x_3 y_2 + x_1 y_2)$

This is the desired result.

57. (a) We apply the Pythagorean Theorem:

$$u^2 + v^2 = \frac{4(m+n)^2}{n^2} + \frac{16m^2}{(m-n)^2}$$

$$= \frac{4(m+n)^2(m-n)^2 + 16m^2n^2}{(m-n)^2n^2}$$

$$= \frac{4\left(m^2 - n^2\right)^2 + 16m^2n^2}{(m-n)^2n^2}$$

$$= \frac{4m^4 - 8m^2n^2 + 4n^4 + 16m^2n^2}{(m-n)^2n^2}$$

$$= \frac{4m^4 + 8m^2n^2 + 4n^4}{(m-n)^2n^2}$$

$$= \frac{4\left(m^2 + n^2\right)^2}{(m-n)^2n^2}$$

Taking roots, we have:

$$w = \sqrt{u^2 + v^2} = \frac{2(m^2 + n^2)}{(m-n)n}$$

(b) We compute the right-hand side:

$$u + v + w = \frac{2m + 2n}{n} + \frac{4m}{m-n} + \frac{2m^2 + 2n^2}{(m-n)n}$$

$$= \frac{(2m+2n)(m-n) + 4mn + 2m^2 + 2n^2}{(m-n)n}$$

$$= \frac{2m^2 - 2n^2 + 4mn + 2m^2 + 2n^2}{(m-n)n}$$

$$= \frac{4m^2 + 4mn}{(m-n)n}$$

$$= \frac{4m(m+n)}{(m-n)n}$$

But this is exactly $\frac{1}{2}$ uv, thus proving the desired result.

(c) We simply choose m and n such that u, v, and w will be integers, say m = 3 and n = 2. Then u = 5, v = 12, and w = 13. As a check, we compute:

$$\text{area} = \frac{1}{2}(5)(12) = 30$$
$$\text{perimeter} = 5 + 12 + 13 = 30$$

1.9 The Complex Number System

1. We complete the table:

i^2	i^3	i^4	i^5	i^6	i^7	i^8
-1	$-i$	1	i	-1	$-i$	1

3. (a) real: 4; imaginary: 5
    (b) real: 4; imaginary: -5
    (c) real: 1/2; imaginary: -1
    (d) real: 0; imaginary: 16

5. Equating the real parts gives $2c = 8$, and therefore $c = 4$.
    Similarly, equating the imaginary parts yields $d = -3$.

7. (a) $(5 - 6i) + (9 + 2i) = (5 + 9) + (-6 + 2)i = 14 - 4i$
    (b) $(5 - 6i) - (9 + 2i) = (5 - 9) + (-6 - 2)i = -4 - 8i$

9. (a) $(3 - 4i)(5 + i) = 15 - 17i - 4i^2 = 19 - 17i$
    (b) $(5 + i)(3 - 4i) = 19 - 17i$, from part (a)

    (c) $$\frac{3 - 4i}{5 + i} \bullet \frac{5 - i}{5 - i} = \frac{15 - 23i + 4i^2}{25 - i^2}$$
    $$= \frac{11 - 23i}{26}$$
    $$= \frac{11}{26} - \frac{23}{26} i$$

    (d) $$\frac{5 + i}{3 - 4i} \bullet \frac{3 + 4i}{3 + 4i} = \frac{15 + 23i + 4i^2}{9 - 16i^2}$$
    $$= \frac{11 + 23i}{25}$$
    $$= \frac{11}{25} + \frac{23}{25} i$$

11. (a) $z + w = (2 + 3i) + (9 - 4i) = 11 - i$
     (b) $\overline{z} + w = (2 - 3i) + (9 - 4i) = 11 - 7i$
     (c) $z + \overline{z} = (2 + 3i) + (2 - 3i) = 4$

13. $(z + w) + w_1 = \big((2 + 3i) + (9 - 4i)\big) + (-7 - i)$
     $$= (11 - i) + (-7 - i)$$
     $$= 4 - 2i$$

15. $zw = (2 + 3i)(9 - 4i) = 18 + 19i - 12i^2 = 30 + 19i$

17. $z\overline{z} = (2 + 3i)(2 - 3i) = 4 - 9i^2 = 13$

19. $ww_1 = (9 - 4i)(-7 - i) = -63 + 19i + 4i^2 = -67 + 19i$, so
     $z(ww_1) = (2 + 3i)(-67 + 19i) = -134 - 163i + 57i^2 = -191 - 163i$

21. $w + w_1 = (9 - 4i)(-7 - i) = 2 - 5i$, so
     $z(w + w_1) = (2 + 3i)(2 - 5i) = 4 - 4i - 15i^2 = 19 - 4i$

23. $z^2 = (2 + 3i)(2 + 3i) = 4 + 12i + 9i^2 = -5 + 12i$, and
     $w^2 = (9 - 4i)(9 - 4i) = 81 - 72i + 16i^2 = 65 - 72i$, so
     $z^2 - w^2 = (-5 + 12i) - (65 - 72i) = -70 + 84i$

25. $zw = 30 + 19i$ (from # 15), so $(zw)^2 = (30 + 19i)(30 + 19i)$
     $= 900 + 1140i + 361i^2$
     $= 539 + 1140i$

27. $z^2 = -5 + 12i$ (from #23), so
     $z^3 = z \bullet z^2 = (2 + 3i)(-5 + 12i) = -10 + 9i + 36i^2 = -46 + 9i$

29. $\dfrac{z}{w} = \dfrac{2 + 3i}{9 - 4i} \bullet \dfrac{9 + 4i}{9 + 4i}$

     $= \dfrac{18 + 35i + 12i^2}{81 - 16i^2}$

     $= \dfrac{6 + 35i}{97}$

     $= \dfrac{6}{97} + \dfrac{35}{97}i$

31. By first calculating $\overline{z}$ and $\overline{w}$, we have:

     $\dfrac{2 - 3i}{9 + 4i} \bullet \dfrac{9 - 4i}{9 - 4i} = \dfrac{18 - 35i + 12i^2}{81 - 16i^2}$

     $= \dfrac{6 - 35i}{97}$

     $= \dfrac{6}{97} - \dfrac{35}{97}i$

33. By first calculating $\overline{z}$, we have:

$$\frac{2+3i}{2-3i} \cdot \frac{2+3i}{2+3i} = \frac{4+12i+9i^2}{4-9i^2}$$

$$= \frac{-5+12i}{13}$$

$$= -\frac{5}{13} + \frac{12}{13}i$$

35. $w - \overline{w} = (9-4i) - (9+4i) = -8i$, so the fraction becomes $\dfrac{-8i}{2i} = -4$

37. $\dfrac{i}{5+i} \cdot \dfrac{5-i}{5-i} = \dfrac{5i-i^2}{25-i^2}$

$$= \frac{1+5i}{26}$$

$$= \frac{1}{26} + \frac{5}{26}i$$

39. $\dfrac{1}{i} \cdot \dfrac{i}{i} = \dfrac{i}{i^2} = \dfrac{i}{-1} = -i$

41. $\sqrt{-49} + \sqrt{-9} + \sqrt{-4} = 7i + 3i + 2i = 12i$

43. $\sqrt{-20} - 3\sqrt{-45} + \sqrt{-80} = \sqrt{4}\sqrt{-5} - 3\sqrt{9}\sqrt{-5} + \sqrt{16}\sqrt{-5}$

$$= 2\sqrt{5}\,i - 9\sqrt{5}\,i + 4\sqrt{5}\,i$$

$$= -3\sqrt{5}\,i$$

45. $1 + \sqrt{-36}\sqrt{-36} = 1 + (6i)(6i) = 1 + 36i^2 = -35$

47. $3\sqrt{-128} - 4\sqrt{-18} = 3\sqrt{-64}\sqrt{2} - 4\sqrt{-9}\sqrt{2}$

$$= 3(8i)\sqrt{2} - 4(3i)\sqrt{2}$$

$$= 24\sqrt{2}\,i - 12\sqrt{2}\,i$$

$$= 12\sqrt{2}\,i$$

49. (a) $z + w = (a+bi) + (c+di) = (a+c) + (b+d)i$

(b) $z - w = (a+bi) - (c+di) = (a-c) + (b-d)i$

(c) $zw = (a+bi)(c+di)$

$$= ac + bci + adi + bdi^2$$

$$= (ac - bd) + (bc + ad)i$$

(d) $\dfrac{z}{w} = \dfrac{a+bi}{c+di} \bullet \dfrac{c-di}{c-di} = \dfrac{ac+bci-adi-bdi^2}{c^2-d^2i^2} = \dfrac{ac+bd}{c^2+d^2} + \dfrac{bc-ad}{c^2+d^2}i$

51. (a)

$$z^3 = \left(\dfrac{-1+i\sqrt{3}}{2}\right)^3 \qquad\qquad w^3 = \left(\dfrac{-1-i\sqrt{3}}{2}\right)^3$$

$$= \dfrac{(-1+i\sqrt{3})^3}{8} \qquad\qquad = \dfrac{(-1-i\sqrt{3})^3}{8}$$

$$= \dfrac{(-1+i\sqrt{3})(-1+i\sqrt{3})^2}{8} \qquad\qquad = \dfrac{(-1-i\sqrt{3})(-1-i\sqrt{3})^2}{8}$$

$$= \dfrac{(-1+i\sqrt{3})(1-2i\sqrt{3}+3i^2)}{8} \qquad\qquad = \dfrac{(-1-i\sqrt{3})(1+2i\sqrt{3}+3i^2)}{8}$$

$$= \dfrac{(-1+i\sqrt{3})(-2-2i\sqrt{3})}{8} \qquad\qquad = \dfrac{(-1-i\sqrt{3})(-2+2i\sqrt{3})}{8}$$

$$= \dfrac{2-2i\sqrt{3}+2i\sqrt{3}-6i^2}{8} \qquad\qquad = \dfrac{2+2i\sqrt{3}-2i\sqrt{3}-6i^2}{8}$$

$$= \dfrac{8}{8} \qquad\qquad\qquad\qquad\qquad = \dfrac{8}{8}$$

$$= 1 \qquad\qquad\qquad\qquad\qquad\quad = 1$$

(b) $zw = \left(\dfrac{-1+i\sqrt{3}}{2}\right)\left(\dfrac{-1-i\sqrt{3}}{2}\right) = \dfrac{1-i\sqrt{3}+i\sqrt{3}-3i^2}{4} = \dfrac{4}{4} = 1$

(c)

$$w^2 = \left(\dfrac{-1-i\sqrt{3}}{2}\right)^2 \qquad\qquad z^2 = \left(\dfrac{-1+i\sqrt{3}}{2}\right)^2$$

$$= \dfrac{1+2i\sqrt{3}+3i^2}{4} \qquad\qquad = \dfrac{1-2i\sqrt{3}+3i^2}{4}$$

$$= \dfrac{-2+2i\sqrt{3}}{4} \qquad\qquad\quad = \dfrac{-2-2i\sqrt{3}}{4}$$

$$= \dfrac{-1+i\sqrt{3}}{2} \qquad\qquad\quad = \dfrac{-1-i\sqrt{3}}{2}$$

$$= z \qquad\qquad\qquad\qquad = w$$

(d) $(1-z+z^2)(1+z-z^2)$

$$= (1-z+w)(1+z-w)$$

$$= \left(\dfrac{2}{2}-\dfrac{-1+i\sqrt{3}}{2}+\dfrac{-1-i\sqrt{3}}{2}\right)\left(\dfrac{2}{2}+\dfrac{-1+i\sqrt{3}}{2}-\dfrac{-1-i\sqrt{3}}{2}\right)$$

$$= \left(\dfrac{2-2i\sqrt{3}}{2}\right)\left(\dfrac{2+2i\sqrt{3}}{2}\right)$$

$$= (1-i\sqrt{3})(1+i\sqrt{3})$$

$$= 1-3i^2$$

$$= 4$$

53. (a) Let $z = a + bi$, then $0 + z = (0 + 0i) + (a + bi) = a + bi = z$, and
$z + 0 = (a + bi) + (0 + 0i) = a + bi = z$.

(b) $0 \cdot z = (0 + 0i)(a + bi) = 0 + 0i = 0$, and
$z \cdot 0 = (a + bi)(0 + 0i) = 0$.

55. (a) $z + w = (a + bi) + (c + di) = (a + c) + (b + d)i$
$w + z = (c + di) + (a + bi) = (c + a) + (b + d)i = z + w$

(b) $zw = (a + bi)(c + di)$
$= ac + bci + adi + bdi^2$
$= (ac - bd) + (bc + ad)i$
$wz = (c + di)(a + bi)$
$= ac + adi + bci + bdi^2$
$= (ac - bd) + (bc + ad)i$
$= zw$

57. $\dfrac{a + bi}{a - bi} + \dfrac{a - bi}{a + bi} = \dfrac{a + bi}{a - bi} \cdot \dfrac{a + bi}{a + bi} + \dfrac{a - bi}{a + bi} \cdot \dfrac{a - bi}{a - bi}$

$= \dfrac{(a + bi)^2}{a^2 + b^2} + \dfrac{(a - bi)^2}{a^2 + b^2}$

$= \dfrac{a^2 + 2abi - b^2 + a^2 - 2abi - b^2}{a^2 + b^2}$

$= \dfrac{2a^2 - 2b^2}{a^2 + b^2}$

Thus the real part is $\dfrac{2a^2 - 2b^2}{a^2 + b^2}$, and the imaginary part is 0.

59. $\dfrac{(a + bi)^2}{a - bi} - \dfrac{(a - bi)^2}{a + bi}$

$= \dfrac{(a + bi)^3 - (a - bi)^3}{(a - bi)(a + bi)}$

$= \dfrac{(a^3 + 3a^2bi + 3ab^2i^2 + b^3i^3) - (a^3 - 3a^2bi + 3ab^2i^2 - b^3i^3)}{a^2 - b^2i^2}$

$= \dfrac{(a^3 - 3ab^2) + (3a^2b - b^3)i - (a^3 - 3ab^2) + (3a^2b - b^3)i}{a^2 + b^2}$

$= \dfrac{(6a^2b - 2b^3)}{a^2 + b^2} i$

Thus the real part is 0.

Chapter 1 Review Exercises

1. (a) $x - 81x^3 = x(1 - 81x^2)$
$$= x(1 + 9x)(1 - 9x)$$

(b) $(x^2 + a^2)(x^3 + 3b^3 + 1) - (x^2 + a^2)(2b^3 + 1)$
$$= (x^2 + a^2)(x^3 + 3b^3 + 1 - 2b^3 - 1)$$
$$= (x^2 + a^2)(x^3 + b^3)$$
$$= (x^2 + a^2)(x + b)(x^2 - bx + b^2)$$

(c) $2(x^2 + 4)^{1/2} - 2x^2(x^2 + 4)^{-3/2} = 2(x^2 + 4)^{-3/2}\left[(x^2 + 4)^2 - 2x^2\right]$
$$= 2(x^2 + 4)^{-3/2}(x^4 + 8x^2 + 16 - 2x^2)$$
$$= 2(x^2 + 4)^{-3/2}(x^4 + 6x^2 + 16)$$

2. $|x - 3| < 5$

3. (a) $\sqrt[3]{16} - \sqrt[3]{-250} + \sqrt[3]{-2} = 2\sqrt[3]{2} - (-5)\sqrt[3]{2} + (-1)\sqrt[3]{2}$
$$= 2\sqrt[3]{2} + 5\sqrt[3]{2} - \sqrt[3]{2}$$
$$= 6\sqrt[3]{2}$$

(b) $\left(\dfrac{a^{-3}b^4c^5}{b^0ca^{-1}}\right)^{-3/2} = \left(\dfrac{b^4c^4}{a^2}\right)^{-3/2} = \dfrac{b^{-6}c^{-6}}{a^{-3}} = \dfrac{a^3}{b^6c^6}$

(c) $8^{2/3} + 4^0 + \left(\dfrac{4}{9}\right)^{-3/2} = 2^2 + 1 + \left(\dfrac{2}{3}\right)^{-3}$
$$= 4 + 1 + \left(\dfrac{3}{2}\right)^3$$
$$= 5 + \dfrac{27}{8}$$
$$= \dfrac{67}{8}$$

4. (a) $\dfrac{\sqrt{2}}{\sqrt{5}} \bullet \dfrac{\sqrt{5}}{\sqrt{5}} = \dfrac{\sqrt{10}}{5}$

(b) $\dfrac{1}{1 + \sqrt{2}} \bullet \dfrac{1 - \sqrt{2}}{1 - \sqrt{2}} = \dfrac{1 - \sqrt{2}}{1 - 2} = -1 + \sqrt{2}$

(c) $\dfrac{4}{\sqrt[3]{4}} \bullet \dfrac{\sqrt[3]{2}}{\sqrt[3]{2}} = \dfrac{4\sqrt[3]{2}}{\sqrt[3]{8}} = \dfrac{4\sqrt[3]{2}}{2} = 2\sqrt[3]{2}$

5.   We use the distance formula:

$$d = \sqrt{(-12 - 4)^2 + (-4 + 6)^2} = \sqrt{256 + 4} = \sqrt{260} = 2\sqrt{65}$$

6.   (a)
$$8x^2 - 10x = 3$$
$$8x^2 - 10x - 3 = 0$$
$$(4x + 1)(2x - 3) = 0$$
$$x = -1/4 \text{ or } x = 3/2$$
Solutions: -1/4, 3/2

   (b) $3x^2 + x - 1 = 0$
We use the quadratic formula:

$$x = \frac{-1 \pm \sqrt{1 - 4(3)(-1)}}{2(3)} = \frac{-1 \pm \sqrt{13}}{6}$$

Solutions: $\dfrac{-1 \pm \sqrt{13}}{6}$

   (c)
$$2 - \sqrt{4 + 3x} - \sqrt{3 + 2x} = 0$$
$$2 - \sqrt{4 + 3x} = \sqrt{3 + 2x}$$
Squaring each side, we get:
$$4 - 4\sqrt{4 + 3x} + 4 + 3x = 3 + 2x$$
$$8 + 3x - 4\sqrt{4 + 3x} = 3 + 2x$$
$$-4\sqrt{4 + 3x} = -5 - x$$
Squaring each side again, we get:
$$16(4 + 3x) = 25 + 10x + x^2$$
$$64 + 48x = 25 + 10x + x^2$$
$$0 = x^2 - 38x - 39$$
$$0 = (x - 39)(x + 1)$$
$$x = 39 \text{ or } x = -1$$
Check:
$$x = 39: \quad 2 - \sqrt{121} - \sqrt{81} = 2 - 11 - 9 = -18 \neq 0$$
$$x = -1: \quad 2 - \sqrt{1} - \sqrt{1} = 2 - 1 - 1 = 0$$
Solution: -1

7.   If $-3 < x < -2$, then $x + 3 > 0$ and $x + 2 < 0$. Therefore:
$$|x + 3| - |x + 2| = (x + 3) - \big(-(x + 2)\big)$$
$$= x + 3 + x + 2$$
$$= 2x + 5$$

8. $i^3 - i^4 + \dfrac{1}{i} = (-i) - (1) + \dfrac{1}{i} \bullet \dfrac{i}{i} = -i - 1 - i = -1 - 2i$

9. (a) $z^2 = (2 + 3i)(2 + 3i) = 4 + 12i + 9i^2 = -5 + 12i$, and
    $w^2 = (1 - 4i)(1 - 4i) = 1 - 8i + 16i^2 = -15 - 8i$, so:
    $$z^2 + w^2 = (-5 + 12i) + (-15 - 8i) = -20 + 4i$$

    (b) $\dfrac{w}{z} = \dfrac{1 - 4i}{2 + 3i} \bullet \dfrac{2 - 3i}{2 - 3i} = \dfrac{2 - 11i + 12i^2}{4 - 9i^2} = \dfrac{-10 - 11i}{13} = -\dfrac{10}{13} - \dfrac{11}{13}i$

    (c) $\overline{z} = 2 - 3i$ and $3w = 3 - 12i$, so:
    $$\overline{z} + 3w = (2 - 3i) + (3 - 12i) = 5 - 15i$$

10. To have exactly one real solution, the discriminant must be equal to 0. Thus:
    $$(-k)^2 - 4(3)(5) = 0$$
    $$k^2 - 60 = 0$$
    $$k^2 = 60$$
    $$k = \pm\sqrt{60} = \pm2\sqrt{15}$$
    Since we are asked to find a positive value for k, we have $k = 2\sqrt{15}$.

11. The midpoint of AB must be the center, so the center is (-1, -2). We can find
    the radius R by the distance from the center to the point (4, -5):
    $$R = \sqrt{(4 + 1)^2 + (-5 + 2)^2} = \sqrt{25 + 9} = \sqrt{34}$$
    So the equation of the circle is $(x + 1)^2 + (y + 2)^2 = 34$.

12. (a) $3 \leq \dfrac{2 - 3x}{2} \leq 5$
    $$6 \leq 2 - 3x \leq 10$$
    $$4 \leq -3x \leq 8$$
    $$-4/3 \geq x \geq -8/3$$
    Solution set: [-8/3, -4/3]

    (b) $|x - 6| < 1$
    $$-1 < x - 6 < 1$$
    $$5 < x < 7$$
    Solution set: (5, 7)

    (c) $|2x - 4| \geq 2$
    $$2x - 4 \geq 2 \quad \text{or} \quad 2x - 4 \leq -2$$
    $$2x \geq 6 \quad \text{or} \quad 2x \leq 2$$
    $$x \geq 3 \quad \text{or} \quad x \leq 1$$
    Solution set: $(-\infty, 1] \cup [3, \infty)$

13.   (a) $6x^3 + 11x^2 - 7x < 0$
       $x(6x^2 + 11x - 7) < 0$
       $x(3x + 7)(2x - 1) < 0$
       Key numbers: 0, -7/3, 1/2

Interval	Test Number	x	$3x+7$	$2x-1$	$x(3x+7)(2x-1)$
$\left(-\infty, -\dfrac{7}{3}\right)$	-10	neg.	neg.	neg.	neg.
$\left(-\dfrac{7}{3}, 0\right)$	-1	neg.	pos.	neg.	pos.
$\left(0, \dfrac{1}{2}\right)$	$\dfrac{1}{4}$	pos.	pos.	neg.	neg.
$\left(\dfrac{1}{2}, \infty\right)$	5	pos.	pos.	pos.	pos.

Solution set: $(-\infty, -7/3) \cup (0, 1/2)$

   (b) $\dfrac{x+3}{x-4} \geq 0$
       Key numbers: -3, 4

Interval	Test Number	$x+3$	$x-4$	$\dfrac{x+3}{x-4}$
$(-\infty, -3)$	-5	neg.	neg.	pos.
$(-3, 4)$	0	pos.	neg.	neg.
$(4, \infty)$	10	pos.	pos.	pos.

Note that $x = -3$ is also a solution to the inequality.
Solution set: $(-\infty, -3] \cup (4, \infty)$

(c)
$$\frac{1}{x} - \frac{x}{x-1} < 3$$

$$\frac{1}{x} - \frac{x}{x-1} - 3 < 0$$

$$\frac{1(x-1) - x(x) - 3x(x-1)}{x(x-1)} < 0$$

$$\frac{x - 1 - x^2 - 3x^2 + 3x}{x(x-1)} < 0$$

$$\frac{-4x^2 + 4x - 1}{x(x-1)} < 0$$

$$\frac{-(2x-1)^2}{x(x-1)} < 0$$

Key numbers: 1/2, 0, 1

Interval	Test Number	$-(2x-1)^2$	x	$x-1$	$\dfrac{-(2x-1)^2}{x(x-1)}$
$(-\infty, 0)$	-3	neg.	neg.	neg.	neg.
$\left(0, \dfrac{1}{2}\right)$	$\dfrac{1}{4}$	neg.	pos.	neg.	pos.
$\left(\dfrac{1}{2}, 1\right)$	$\dfrac{3}{4}$	neg.	pos.	neg.	pos.
$(1, \infty)$	4	neg.	pos.	pos.	neg.

Solution set: $(-\infty, 0) \cup (1, \infty)$

14.　Let $x = 5.777...$, so $10x = 57.777...$.

Then $10x - x = 57.777... - 5.777... = 52$, thus $9x = 52$ and $x = \dfrac{52}{9}$.

So $5.777... = \dfrac{52}{9}$.

15.　(a)　$\sqrt{a} \cdot \sqrt[4]{b^3} = a^{1/2}b^{3/4}$

　　(b)　$a^{1/2}b^{3/4} = a^{2/4}b^{3/4} = \left(a^2b^3\right)^{1/4} = \sqrt[4]{a^2b^3}$

17.　$x^2 + ax + yx + ay = x(x+a) + y(x+a) = (x+a)(x+y)$

19.　$x^2 - 18x + 81 = (x-9)^2$

21. $8a^2x^2 + 16a^3 = 8a^2(x^2 + 2a)$

23. $12x^2 - 2x - 4 = 2(6x^2 - x - 2) = 2(3x - 2)(2x + 1)$

25. $2x^2 - 2bx + ax - ab = 2x(x - b) + a(x - b) = (x - b)(2x + a)$

27. $(x^2 + 2x - 8)^2 - (2x + 1)^2$
$$= \big((x^2 + 2x - 8) - (2x + 1)\big)\big((x^2 + 2x - 8) + (2x + 1)\big)$$
$$= (x^2 - 9)(x^2 + 4x - 7)$$
$$= (x + 3)(x - 3)(x^2 + 4x - 7)$$

29. $(x + y - 1)^2 - (x - y + 1)^2$
$$= \big((x - y - 1) - (x - y + 1)\big)\big((x + y - 1) + (x - y + 1)\big)$$
$$= (2y - 2)(2x)$$
$$= 4x(y - 1)$$

31. $12x^3 + 44x^2 - 16x = 4x(3x^2 + 11x - 4) = 4x(3x - 1)(x + 4)$

33. $a^2 - b^2 + ac - bc + a^2b - b^2a = (a - b)(a + b) + c(a - b) + ab(a - b)$
$$= (a - b)(a + b + c + ab)$$

35. $4^{3/2} = (\sqrt{4})^3 = 2^3 = 8$

37. $\big((3025)^{1/2}\big)^0 = 1$

39. $8^{-4/3} = \left(\sqrt[3]{8}\right)^{-4} = 2^{-4} = \dfrac{1}{2^4} = \dfrac{1}{16}$

41. $(-243)^{-2/5} = \left(\sqrt[5]{-243}\right)^{-2} = (-3)^{-2} = \dfrac{1}{(-3)^2} = \dfrac{1}{9}$

43. $(a^2b^6c^8)^{1/2} = a^{2/2}b^{6/2}c^{8/2} = ab^3c^4$

45. $\sqrt{a^3b^5}\,\sqrt{4ab^3} = \sqrt{4a^4b^8} = 2a^2b^4$

47. $\sqrt[3]{16} - \sqrt[3]{-54} = \sqrt[3]{8}\,\sqrt[3]{2} - \sqrt[3]{-27}\,\sqrt[3]{2}$
$$= 2\sqrt[3]{2} - (-3)\,\sqrt[3]{2}$$
$$= 5\sqrt[3]{2}$$

49. $\sqrt{24a^2b^3} + ba\sqrt{54b} = \sqrt{4a^2b^2}\sqrt{6b} + ba\sqrt{9}\sqrt{6b}$
$= 2ab\sqrt{6b} + 3ab\sqrt{6b}$
$= 5ab\sqrt{6b}$

51. $\sqrt{t^2} = |t|$

53. $\sqrt[4]{16x^4} = |2x| = 2|x|$

55. (a) $\sqrt[3]{x}\,\sqrt[4]{x^3} = x^{1/3}x^{3/4} = x^{4/12}x^{9/12} = x^{13/12}$

   (b) $x^{13/12} = \sqrt[12]{x^{13}} = x\,\sqrt[12]{x}$

57. (a) $\sqrt{\sqrt[3]{t}\,\sqrt[5]{t^4}} = (t^{1/3}\,t^{4/5})^{1/2}$
$= (t^{5/15}\,t^{12/15})^{1/2}$
$= (t^{17/15})^{1/2}$
$= t^{17/30}$

   (b) $t^{17/30} = \sqrt[30]{t^{17}}$

59. $\dfrac{6}{\sqrt{3}} \cdot \dfrac{\sqrt{3}}{\sqrt{3}} = \dfrac{6\sqrt{3}}{3} = 2\sqrt{3}$

61. $\dfrac{1}{\sqrt{6}-\sqrt{3}} \cdot \dfrac{\sqrt{6}+\sqrt{3}}{\sqrt{6}+\sqrt{3}} = \dfrac{\sqrt{6}+\sqrt{3}}{6-3} = \dfrac{\sqrt{6}+\sqrt{3}}{3}$

63. $\dfrac{\sqrt{a^2+x^2}+\sqrt{a^2-x^2}}{\sqrt{a^2+x^2}-\sqrt{a^2-x^2}} \cdot \dfrac{\sqrt{a^2+x^2}+\sqrt{a^2-x^2}}{\sqrt{a^2+x^2}+\sqrt{a^2-x^2}}$
$= \dfrac{(a^2+x^2)+2\sqrt{a^4-x^4}+(a^2-x^2)}{(a^2+x^2)-(a^2-x^2)}$
$= \dfrac{2a^2+2\sqrt{a^4-x^4}}{2x^2}$
$= \dfrac{a^2+\sqrt{a^4-x^4}}{x^2}$

65. $\dfrac{\sqrt{x}-5}{x-25} \cdot \dfrac{\sqrt{x}+5}{\sqrt{x}+5} = \dfrac{x-25}{(x-25)(\sqrt{x}+5)} = \dfrac{1}{\sqrt{x}+5}$

67. $\dfrac{\sqrt{a^2 + x^2} - \sqrt{a^2 - x^2}}{\sqrt{a^2 + x^2} + \sqrt{a^2 - x^2}} \cdot \dfrac{\sqrt{a^2 + x^2} + \sqrt{a^2 - x^2}}{\sqrt{a^2 + x^2} + \sqrt{a^2 - x^2}}$

$= \dfrac{(a^2 + x^2) - (a^2 - x^2)}{(a^2 + x^2) + 2\sqrt{a^4 - x^4} + (a^2 - x^2)}$

$= \dfrac{2x^2}{2a^2 + 2\sqrt{a^4 - x^4}}$

$= \dfrac{x^2}{a^2 + \sqrt{a^4 - x^4}}$

69. $(9x - y)(9x + y) = (9x)^2 - y^2 = 81x^2 - y^2$

71. $(3x^2 + y^2)^2 = (3x^2)^2 + 2(3x^2)(y^2) + (y^2)^2$
$= 9x^4 + 6x^2y^2 + y^4$

73. $(1 - 3a)(1 + 3a + 9a^2) = 1^3 - (3a)^3 = 1 - 27a^3$

75. $(x^{1/2} - y^{1/2})(x^{1/2} + y^{1/2}) = (x^{1/2})^2 - (y^{1/2})^2 = x$

77. $(x^{1/3} + y^{1/3})(x^{2/3} - x^{1/3}y^{1/3} + y^{2/3}) = (x^{1/3})^3 + (y^{1/3})^3 = x + y$

79. $(3 - 2i)(3 + 2i) + (1 + 3i)^2 = 9 - 4i^2 + 1 + 6i + 9i^2$
$= 9 + 4 + 1 + 6i - 9$
$= 5 + 6i$

81. $(1 + i\sqrt{2})(1 - i\sqrt{2}) + (\sqrt{2} + i)(\sqrt{2} - i) = 1 - 2i^2 + 2 - i^2$
$= 1 + 2 + 2 + 1$
$= 6$

83. $\dfrac{3 - i\sqrt{3}}{3 + i\sqrt{3}} \cdot \dfrac{3 - i\sqrt{3}}{3 - i\sqrt{3}} = \dfrac{9 - 6i\sqrt{3} - 3}{9 + 3}$

$= \dfrac{6 - 6i\sqrt{3}}{12}$

$= \dfrac{1 - i\sqrt{3}}{2}$

$= \dfrac{1}{2} - \dfrac{\sqrt{3}}{2}i$

85. $-\sqrt{-2}\,\sqrt{-9} + \sqrt{-8} - \sqrt{-72} = -(i\sqrt{2})(3i) + 2i\sqrt{2} - 6i\sqrt{2}$
$= 3\sqrt{2} - 4i\sqrt{2}$
$= 3\sqrt{2} - 4\sqrt{2}\,i$

87. (a)   Let $z = a + bi$, so $\overline{z} = a - bi$. Then:

$$\frac{z + \overline{z}}{2} = \frac{a + bi + a - bi}{2} = \frac{2a}{2} = a = \text{Re}(z)$$

(b)   Let $z = a + bi$, so $\overline{z} = a - bi$. Then:

$$\frac{z - \overline{z}}{2i} = \frac{a + bi - a + bi}{2i} = \frac{2bi}{2i} = b = \text{Im}(z)$$

89. $|x - 6| = 2$

91. $|a - b| = 3$

93. $|x - 0| > 10$, so $|x| > 10$

95. $|\sqrt{6} - 2| = \sqrt{6} - 2$, since $\sqrt{6} - 2 > 0$

97. $|x^4 + x^2 + 1| = x^4 + x^2 + 1$, since $x^4 + x^2 + 1 > 0$

99. (a)   If $x < 2$, then $x - 2 < 0$ and $x - 3 < 0$, so:
$$|x - 2| + |x - 3| = -(x - 2) - (x - 3) = -2x + 5$$
(b)   If $2 < x < 3$, then $x - 2 > 0$ and $x - 3 < 0$, so:
$$|x - 2| + |x - 3| = x - 2 - (x - 3) = x - 2 - x + 3 = 1$$
(c)   If $x > 3$, then $x - 2 > 0$ and $x - 3 > 0$, so:
$$|x - 2| + |x - 3| = x - 2 + x - 3 = 2x - 5$$

101. (a)   T
(b)   F   (for instance: $x = -2, y = -1$)
(c)   F
(d)   T
(e)   F
(f)   F   (for instance: $x = 1/2$)

103.   We first re-draw the figure:

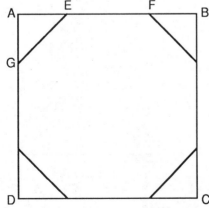

$$AE + EF + FB = 1 \qquad \text{(given)}$$
$$EF + 2AE = 1 \qquad (AE = FB)$$
$$AE = \frac{1 - EF}{2}$$

By the Pythagorean Theorem we have:

$$(AG)^2 + (AE)^2 = (GE)^2$$
$$(AE)^2 + (AE)^2 = (EF)^2 \qquad \text{(because } AG = AE \text{ and } EF = GE)$$
$$2(AE)^2 = (EF)^2$$
$$2\left(\frac{1 - EF}{2}\right)^2 = EF^2 \qquad \text{(substituting for AE)}$$

Now, for convenience, let $EF = x$. Then we have:

$$2\left(\frac{1 - 2x + x^2}{4}\right) = x^2$$
$$1 - 2x + x^2 = 2x^2$$
$$0 = x^2 + 2x - 1$$

The quadratic formula then gives us:

$$x = \frac{-2 \pm \sqrt{4 + 4}}{2} = \frac{-2 \pm \sqrt{8}}{2} = \frac{-2 \pm 2\sqrt{2}}{2} = -1 \pm \sqrt{2}$$

We choose the positive root, since $x > 0$. Thus, $x = EF = -1 + \sqrt{2}$ cm

105.   We draw a figure with the side labeled as $\frac{x}{4}$:

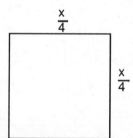

We compute the area and the perimeter:

$$\text{area} = \left(\frac{x}{4}\right)^2 = \frac{x^2}{16}$$
$$\text{perimeter} = x$$

If the area is numerically greater than the perimeter, then we have:

$$\frac{x^2}{16} > x$$
$$x^2 > 16x$$
$$x^2 - 16x > 0$$
$$x(x - 16) > 0$$

The key numbers here are 0 and 4. Since x itself must be positive, we obtain the two intervals (0, 16) and (16, ∞):

Interval	Test Number	x	x - 16	x(x - 16)
(0, 16)	1	pos.	neg.	neg.
(16, ∞)	17	pos.	pos.	pos.

From this, we conclude that the area will be numerically greater than the perimeter when x > 16 cm.

107. $t^2 - 2t - 99 = 0$
$(t - 11)(t + 9) = 0$
$t = 11$ or $t = -9$
Solutions: 11, -9

109. $4y^2 - 21y = 18$
$4y^2 - 21y - 18 = 0$
$(4y + 3)(y - 6) = 0$
$y = -3/4$ or $y = 6$
Solutions: -3/4, 6

111. $\dfrac{1}{1 - x} + \dfrac{4}{2 - x} = \dfrac{11}{6}$
$6(2 - x) + 4(6)(1 - x) = 11(1 - x)(2 - x)$
$12 - 6x + 24 - 24x = 22 - 33x + 11x^2$
$-11x^2 + 3x + 14 = 0$
$11x^2 - 3x - 14 = 0$
$(11x - 14)(x + 1) = 0$
$x = 14/11$ or $x = -1$ (both answers check)
Solutions: 14/11, -1

113. $\dfrac{x^2}{(x - 1)(x + 1)} = \dfrac{4}{x + 1} + \dfrac{4}{(x - 1)(x + 1)}$
$x^2 = 4(x - 1) + 4$
$x^2 - 4x = 0$
$x(x - 4) = 0$
$x = 0$ or $x = 4$ (both answers check)
Solutions: 0, 4

115. $y^4 - 8y^2 + 11 = 0$

Let $t = y^2$ and $t^2 = y^4$. Then the equation becomes:

$t^2 - 8t + 11 = 0$

$$t = \frac{8 \pm \sqrt{64 - 44}}{2} = \frac{8 \pm \sqrt{20}}{2} = \frac{8 \pm 2\sqrt{5}}{2} = 4 \pm \sqrt{5}$$

Thus $y^2 = 4 \pm \sqrt{5}$ and $y = \pm\sqrt{4 \pm \sqrt{5}}$

Solutions: $\pm\sqrt{4 \pm \sqrt{5}}$

117. $1 + 14x^{-1} + 48x^{-2} = 0$

$x^2 + 14x + 48 = 0$ (multiplying by x^2)

$(x + 6)(x + 8) = 0$

$x = -6$ or $x = -8$ (both values check)

Solutions: -6, -8

119. $\sqrt{4x + 3} = \sqrt{11 - 8x} - 1$

$4x + 3 = 11 - 8x - 2\sqrt{11 - 8x} + 1$

$12x - 9 = -2\sqrt{11 - 8x}$

$144x^2 - 216x + 81 = 44 - 32x$

$144x^2 - 184x + 37 = 0$

$(4x - 1)(36x - 37) = 0$

$x = 1/4$ or $x = 37/36$ (which does not check)

Solution: 1/4

121. $\sqrt{5 - 2x} - \sqrt{2 - x} - \sqrt{3 - x} = 0$

$\sqrt{5 - 2x} = \sqrt{2 - x} + \sqrt{3 - x}$

$5 - 2x = 2 - x + 2\sqrt{2 - x}\sqrt{3 - x} + 3 - x$

$0 = 2\sqrt{2 - x}\sqrt{3 - x}$

Thus $\sqrt{2 - x} = 0$ and consequently $x = 2$, or $\sqrt{3 - x} = 0$ and consequently $x = 3$. The value $x = 2$ checks in the original equation. But (considering only the real number system) the value $x = 3$ does not check.
Solution: 2

123. $\sqrt{x + 48} - \sqrt{x} = 4$

$\sqrt{x + 48} = \sqrt{x} + 4$

$x + 48 = x + 8\sqrt{x} + 16$

$32 = 8\sqrt{x}$

$4 = \sqrt{x}$

$16 = x$ (which checks)

Solution: 16

125. $3(4t - 1)^{1/2} - (2t)^{1/2} = (3 + 2t)^{1/2}$

$3\sqrt{4t - 1} = \sqrt{3 + 2t} + \sqrt{2t}$

Squaring each side, we have:

$9(4t - 1) = (3 + 2t) + 2\sqrt{6t + 4t^2} + 2t$

$36t - 9 = (3 + 4t) + 2\sqrt{6t + 4t^2}$

$32t - 12 = 2\sqrt{6t + 4t^2}$

$16t - 6 = \sqrt{6t + 4t^2}$

Squaring each side again, we have:

$256t^2 - 192t + 36 = 6t + 4t^2$

$252t^2 - 198t + 36 = 0$

$18(7t - 2)(2t - 1) = 0$

$t = 2/7 \text{ or } t = 1/2$

Upon checking, we find that only $t = 1/2$ checks in the original equation.
Solution: 1/2

127. $\dfrac{2}{\sqrt{x^2 - 36}} + \dfrac{1}{\sqrt{x + 6}} - \dfrac{1}{\sqrt{x - 6}} = 0$

$2 + \sqrt{x - 6} - \sqrt{x + 6} = 0$ (multiplying by $\sqrt{x + 6}\ \sqrt{x - 6}$)

$2 + \sqrt{x - 6} = \sqrt{x + 6}$

$4 + 4\sqrt{x - 6} + x - 6 = x + 6$

$4\sqrt{x - 6} = 8$

$\sqrt{x - 6} = 2$

$x - 6 = 4$

$x = 10$ (which checks)

Solution: 10

129. $\dfrac{1}{4}x^2 + bx - 8b^2 = 0$

Multiply by 4 to clear fractions:

$x^2 + 4bx - 32b^2 = 0$

$(x + 8b)(x - 4b) = 0$

$x = -8b \text{ or } x = 4b$

Solutions: -8b, 4b

131. $4x^2y^2 - 4xy = -1$ $(y \neq 0)$

$4x^2y^2 - 4xy + 1 = 0$

$(2xy - 1)^2 = 0$

$2xy - 1 = 0$

$x = \dfrac{1}{2y}$ (double root)

Solution: $\dfrac{1}{2y}$

133. $x + \dfrac{1}{a} - \dfrac{1}{b} = \dfrac{2}{a^2x} + \dfrac{2}{abx}$

Multiplying through by a^2bx yields:

$$a^2bx^2 + abx - a^2x = 2b + 2a$$

$$a^2bx^2 + (ab - a^2)x - 2(b + a) = 0$$

Applying the quadratic equation:

$$x = \dfrac{-(ab - a^2) \pm \sqrt{(ab - a^2)^2 - 4(a^2b)[-2(b + a)]}}{2(a^2b)}$$

$$= \dfrac{-ab + a^2 \pm \sqrt{a^4 + 6a^3b + 9a^2b^2}}{2a^2b} \quad \text{(simplifying)}$$

$$= \dfrac{-ab + a^2 \pm \sqrt{(a^2 + 3ab)^2}}{2a^2b}$$

$$= \dfrac{-ab + a^2 \pm (a^2 + 3ab)}{2a^2b}$$

Using the Plus Sign

$$x = \dfrac{-ab + a^2 + a^2 + 3ab}{2a^2b}$$

$$= \dfrac{2a^2 + 2ab}{2a^2b}$$

$$= \dfrac{2a(a + b)}{2a^2b}$$

$$= \dfrac{a + b}{ab}$$

Using the MInus Sign

$$x = \dfrac{-ab + a^2 - a^2 - 3ab}{2a^2b}$$

$$= \dfrac{-4ab}{2a^2b}$$

$$= \dfrac{-2}{a}$$

Both of these values satisfy the original equation.

Solutions: $\dfrac{a + b}{ab}$, $-\dfrac{2}{a}$

135. $\dfrac{1}{x + a + b} = \dfrac{1}{x} + \dfrac{1}{a} + \dfrac{1}{b}$

$$abx = ab(x + a + b) + bx(x + a + b) + ax(x + a + b)$$

$$abx = abx + a^2b + ab^2 + bx^2 + abx + b^2x + ax^2 + a^2x + abx$$

$$0 = (a + b)x^2 + (a^2 + 2ab + b^2)x + (a^2b + ab^2)$$

$$0 = (a + b)x^2 + (a + b)^2x + ab(a + b)$$

$$0 = x^2 + (a + b)x + ab$$

$$0 = (x + a)(x + b)$$

$$x = -a \quad \text{or} \quad x = -b \quad \text{(both values check)}$$

Solutions: $-a$, $-b$

137. $x^2 - 21x + 108 \leq 0$
        $(x - 9)(x - 12) \leq 0$
        Key numbers: 9, 12
            $(-\infty, 9)$:   positive
            $(9, 12)$:   negative
            $(12, \infty)$:   positive
        Solution set: $[9, 12]$

139. $x^2 \geq 15x$
        $x^2 - 15x \geq 0$
        $x(x - 15) \geq 0$
        Key numbers: 0 and 15
            $(-\infty, 0)$:   positive
            $(0, 15)$:   negative
            $(15, \infty)$:   positive
        Solution set: $(-\infty, 0] \cup [15, \infty)$

141. $(x - 4)^2(x + 8)^3 \geq 0$
        Key numbers: 4, -8

Interval	Test Number	$x + 8$	$x - 4$	$(x-4)^2(x+8)^3$
$(-\infty, -8)$	-9	neg.	neg.	neg.
$(-8, 4)$	0	pos.	neg.	pos.
$(4, \infty)$	5	pos.	pos.	pos.

Solution set: $[-8, 4] \cup [4, \infty)$, which simplifies to $[-8, \infty)$

143. $\dfrac{x + 12}{x - 5} > 0$
        Key numbers: -12, 5
            $(-\infty, -12)$:   positive
            $(-12, 5)$:   negative
            $(5, \infty)$:   positive
        Solution set: $(-\infty, -12) \cup (5, \infty)$

145. $\dfrac{x^2 - 10x + 9}{x^3 + 1} \le 0$

$\dfrac{(x - 1)(x - 9)}{(x + 1)(x^2 - x + 1)} \le 0$

Key numbers: $\pm 1, 9$

Interval	Test Number	x - 9	x - 1	x + 1	$\dfrac{(x - 1)(x - 9)}{x^3 + 1}$
$(-\infty, -1)$	-2	neg.	neg.	neg.	neg.
$(-1, 1)$	0	neg.	neg.	pos.	pos.
$(1, 9)$	2	neg.	pos.	pos.	neg.
$(9, \infty)$	10	pos.	pos.	pos.	pos.

Solution set: $(-\infty, -1) \cup [1, 9]$

147. $\dfrac{1 - 2x}{1 + 2x} \le \dfrac{1}{2}$

$\dfrac{1 - 2x}{1 + 2x} - \dfrac{1}{2} \le 0$

$\dfrac{2(1 - 2x) - (1 + 2x)}{2(1 + 2x)} \le 0$

$\dfrac{-6x + 1}{2(1 + 2x)} \le 0$

Key numbers: $1/6, -1/2$

Interval	Test Number	2x + 1	-6x + 1	$\dfrac{-6x + 1}{2(2x + 1)}$
$(-\infty, -1/2)$	-1	neg.	pos.	neg.
$(-1/2, 1/6)$	0	pos.	pos.	pos.
$(1/6, \infty)$	1	pos.	neg.	neg.

Solution set: $(-\infty, -1/2) \cup [1/6, \infty)$

149.
$$x^2 + \frac{1}{x^2} > 3$$

$$x^2 + \frac{1}{x^2} - 3 > 0$$

$$\frac{x^4 + 1 - 3x^2}{x^2} > 0$$

$$\frac{x^4 - 3x^2 + 1}{x^2} > 0$$

One key number is $x = 0$. The others are found by solving $x^4 - 3x^2 + 1 = 0$.
Letting $t = x^2$ and $t^2 = x^4$ we have:

$$t^2 - 3t + 1 = 0$$

$$t = \frac{3 \pm \sqrt{9 - 4}}{2} = \frac{3 \pm \sqrt{5}}{2}$$

Therefore, $x = \pm \sqrt{\dfrac{3 \pm \sqrt{5}}{2}}$

We use test numbers to find the signs on each of the intervals formed:

$\left(-\infty, -\sqrt{\frac{1}{2}(3 + \sqrt{5})} \ \right)$:   positive

$\left(-\sqrt{\frac{1}{2}(3 + \sqrt{5})} \ , \ -\sqrt{\frac{1}{2}(3 - \sqrt{5})} \ \right)$:   negative

$\left(-\sqrt{\frac{1}{2}(3 - \sqrt{5})} \ , 0 \ \right)$:   positive

$\left(0, \sqrt{\frac{1}{2}(3 - \sqrt{5})} \ \right)$:   positive

$\left(\sqrt{\frac{1}{2}(3 - \sqrt{5})} \ , \ \sqrt{\frac{1}{2}(3 + \sqrt{5})} \ \right)$:   negative

$\left(\sqrt{\frac{1}{2}(3 + \sqrt{5})} \ , \ \infty \ \right)$:   positive

Solution set: $\left(-\infty, -\sqrt{\frac{1}{2}(3 + \sqrt{5})} \ \right) \cup \left(-\sqrt{\frac{1}{2}(3 - \sqrt{5})} \ , 0 \ \right) \cup$

$\left(0, \sqrt{\frac{1}{2}(3 - \sqrt{5})} \ \right) \cup \left(\sqrt{\frac{1}{2}(3 + \sqrt{5})} \ , \ \infty \ \right)$

151. $kx^2 - 6x + 5 = 0$
discriminant $= b^2 - 4ac = 36 - 4(k)5 \geq 0$

$$36 - 20k \geq 0$$

$$-20k \geq -36$$

$$k \leq \frac{-36}{-20} = \frac{9}{5}$$

153. $kx(x + 2) = -1$
        $kx^2 + 2kx + 1 = 0$
        discriminant $= 4k^2 - 4k \geq 0$
                        $4k^2 - 4k \geq 0$
                        $4k(k - 1) \geq 0$
The key numbers are 0 and 1.
        $(-\infty, 0)$:   positive
        $(0, 1)$:   negative
        $(1, \infty)$:   positive
Thus, the given equation will have real roots when either $k < 0$ or $k \geq 1$.
(Notice that when $k = 0$, the original equation has no solutions, for then it becomes $0 = -1$)

155.   We must prove that $BC^2 = \dfrac{9}{5}(PA^2 + QA^2)$. Using the coordinates given in the hint, where $B(0,3b)$, $C(3c,0)$, $P(c,2b)$, and $Q(2c,b)$, we have:
        $BC^2 = (3c - 0)^2 + (0 - 3b)^2 = 9c^2 + 9b^2 = 9(b^2 + c^2)$
        $PA^2 = (c - 0)^2 + (2b - 0)^2 = 4b^2 + c^2$
        $QA^2 = (2c - 0)^2 + (b - 0)^2 = b^2 + 4c^2$
So $\dfrac{9}{5}(PA^2 + QA^2) = \dfrac{9}{5}(4b^2 + c^2 + b^2 + 4c^2)$

$$= \dfrac{9}{5}(5b^2 + 5c^2)$$

$$= 9(b^2 + c^2)$$

$$= BC^2$$

157.   (a)   With $V_o = 64$ ft/sec and $h_o = 0$, the formula is $h = -16t^2 + 64t$.
            Setting $h = 15$ ft yields:
                    $-16t^2 + 64t = 15$
                $-16t^2 + 64t - 15 = 0$
                $16t^2 - 64t + 15 = 0$
                $(4t - 1)(4t - 15) = 0$
                        $t = 1/4$ or $t = 15/4$
        The height of the ball is 15 ft when $t = 1/4$ sec (on the way up) and again when $t = 15/4$ sec (on the way down).

        (b)   If $h > 63$ ft, then we have:
                $-16t^2 + 64t > 63$
            $16t^2 - 64t + 63 < 0$ (multiplying by -1)
        The key numbers are found by solving the equation
        $16t^2 - 64t + 63 = 0$. By factoring the left-hand side, we obtain:
                $(4t - 9)(4t - 7) = 0$
                        $t = 9/4$ or $t = 7/4$

Since t > 0, these key numbers determine the intervals (0, 7/4), (7/4, 9/4), and (9/4, ∞). Using test numbers, we find that the solution set for the inequality is the open interval (7/4, 9/4). Thus, the height exceeds 63 ft when 7/4 < t < 9/4. (In other words, the height exceeds 63 ft for times between 1.75 sec and 2.25 sec.)

(c)   First Ball:

$$16t^2 + 40t + 50 = h$$

Setting h = 0 yields:

$$-16t^2 + 40t + 50 = 0$$

$$8t^2 - 20t - 25 = 0$$

$$t = \frac{20 \pm \sqrt{400 + 32(25)}}{2(8)}$$

$$t = \frac{20 \pm 20\sqrt{3}}{16}$$

$$t = \frac{5 \pm 5\sqrt{3}}{4}$$

$$t = \frac{5 + 5\sqrt{3}}{4} \quad \text{(positive root)}$$

$$t \approx 3.4 \text{ sec}$$

Second Ball:

$$-16t^2 + 5t + 100 = h$$

Setting h = 0 yields:

$$-16t^2 + 5t + 100 = 0$$

$$16t^2 - 5t - 100 = 0$$

$$t = \frac{5 \pm \sqrt{25 + 6400}}{2(16)}$$

$$t = \frac{5 \pm \sqrt{6425}}{32}$$

$$t = \frac{5 \pm 5\sqrt{257}}{32}$$

$$t = \frac{5 + 5\sqrt{257}}{32} \quad \text{(positive root)}$$

$$t \approx 2.7 \text{ sec}$$

Therefore, the second ball (the one thrown from 100 ft) hits the ground first.

159.   Call x the radius of the inscribed circle. Then note the diagonal (drawn from the center of this circle to the right angle) is:

$$\sqrt{x^2 + x^2} = \sqrt{2x^2} = x\sqrt{2}$$

But tracing along this diagonal, we know the full length is equal to r, thus:

$$x\sqrt{2} + x = r$$

$$x(1 + \sqrt{2}) = r$$

$$x = \frac{r}{1 + \sqrt{2}}$$

So the radius of the inscribed circle is $\frac{r}{1 + \sqrt{2}}$.

161.− (a)

$$\sqrt{a - \sqrt{a + x}} = x$$

$$a - \sqrt{a + x} = x^2$$

$$-\sqrt{a + x} = x^2 - a$$

Squaring again, we get:

$$a + x = (x^2 - a)^2$$

$$a + x = x^4 - 2ax^2 + a^2$$

$$0 = x^4 - 2ax^2 - x + a^2 - a$$

(b) Rewriting, we have $a^2 - (2x^2 + 1)\,a + (x^4 - x) = 0$
Using the quadratic, we have:

$$a = \frac{(2x^2 + 1) \pm \sqrt{(2x^2 + 1)^2 - 4(x^4 - x)}}{2}$$

$$a = \frac{(2x^2 + 1) \pm \sqrt{4x^4 + 4x^2 + 1 - 4x^4 + 4x}}{2}$$

$$a = \frac{(2x^2 + 1) \pm \sqrt{4x^2 + 4x + 1}}{2}$$

$$a = \frac{(2x^2 + 1) \pm (2x + 1)}{2}$$

So:

$$a = \frac{2x^2 + 1 + 2x + 1}{2} = \frac{2x^2 + 2x + 2}{2} = x^2 + x + 1,$$

or

$$a = \frac{2x^2 + 1 - 2x - 1}{2} = \frac{2x^2 - 2x}{2} = x^2 - x \text{ , as desired.}$$

(c)
$a = x^2 + x + 1$ or $a = x^2 - x$

$x^2 + x + (1 - a) = 0$ $x^2 - x - a = 0$

$$x = \frac{-1 \pm \sqrt{1 - 4(1 - a)}}{2} \qquad\qquad x = \frac{1 \pm \sqrt{1 - 4(-a)}}{2}$$

$$x = \frac{-1 \pm \sqrt{4a - 3}}{2} \qquad\qquad\quad x = \frac{1 \pm \sqrt{4a + 1}}{2}$$

(d) We now (painfully) check each solution in our original equation.

(1) $x = \dfrac{-1 - \sqrt{4a - 3}}{2}$

Since $x < 0$, this cannot be a solution.

(2) $x = \dfrac{-1 + \sqrt{4a - 3}}{2}$

$$\sqrt{a - \sqrt{a + \frac{-1 + \sqrt{4a - 3}}{2}}} = \frac{-1 + \sqrt{4a - 3}}{2}$$

Since $a \geq 1$, both values are positive, so we can square each side to get:

$$a - \sqrt{\frac{2a - 1 + \sqrt{4a - 3}}{2}} = \frac{1 + 4a - 3 - 2\sqrt{4a - 3}}{4}$$

Multiplying by 4, we have:

$$4a - 2\sqrt{4a - 2 + 2\sqrt{4a - 3}} = 4a - 2 - 2\sqrt{4a - 3}$$

$$-\sqrt{4a - 2 + 2\sqrt{4a - 3}} = -1 - \sqrt{4a - 3}$$

Squaring again (both sides are negative, so this preserves equality):

$$4a - 2 + 2\sqrt{4a - 3} = 1 + 2\sqrt{4a - 3} + 4a - 3$$

$$4a - 2 = 4a - 2$$

It checks!

(3) $x = \dfrac{1 - \sqrt{4a + 1}}{2}$

Since $a \geq 1$, $x < 0$, thus this cannot be a solution.

(4) $x = \dfrac{1 + \sqrt{4a + 1}}{2}$

$$\sqrt{a - \sqrt{a + \dfrac{1 + \sqrt{4a + 1}}{2}}} = \dfrac{1 + \sqrt{4a + 1}}{2}$$

Since $a \geq 1$, both values are positive, so we can square each side to get:

$$a - \sqrt{\dfrac{2a + 1 + \sqrt{4a + 1}}{2}} = \dfrac{1 + 4a + 1 + 2\sqrt{4a + 1}}{4}$$

Multiplying by 4, we have:

$$4a - 2\sqrt{4a + 2 + 2\sqrt{4a + 1}} = 4a + 2 + 2\sqrt{4a + 1}$$

$$-\sqrt{4a + 2 + 2\sqrt{4a + 1}} = 2a + 1 + \sqrt{4a + 1}$$

But the left hand side is non-positive and the right hand side is non-negative, thus:

$$2a + 1 + \sqrt{4a + 1} = 0$$

$$\sqrt{4a + 1} = -2a - 1$$

But $a \geq 1$, and this is impossible.

Thus the only value that checks is $x = \dfrac{-1 + \sqrt{4a - 3}}{2}$

OK, now how many of you *really* checked these values?

CHAPTER TWO
FUNCTIONS AND GRAPHS

2.1 Graphs and Symmetry

1. 3x + 4y = 12
    x-intercept: 4; y-intercept: 3

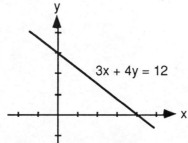

3. y = 2x - 4
    x-intercept: 2; y-intercept: -4

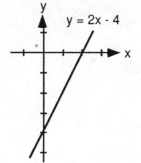

5.   x + y = 1
      x-intercept: 1; y-intercept: 1

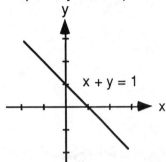

7.   (a) $y = x^2 + 3x + 2$
             y-intercepts: Let x = 0
                    y = 0 + 0 + 2 = 2
             x-intercepts: Let y = 0
                    $0 = x^2 + 3x + 2$
                    $0 = (x + 2)(x + 1)$
                    x = -1, -2
             y-intercept: 2; x-intercepts: -1, -2

      (b) $y = x^2 + 2x + 3$
             y-intercepts: Let x = 0
                    y = 0 + 0 + 3 = 3
             x-intercepts: Let y = 0
                    $0 = x^2 + 2x + 3$
                    $x = \dfrac{-2 \pm \sqrt{4 - 4(3)}}{2} = \dfrac{-2 \pm \sqrt{-8}}{2}$
             There are no x-intercepts.
             y-intercept: 3; x-intercept: none

9.   (a) $y = x^2 + x - 1$
             y-intercepts: Let x = 0
                    y = 0 + 0 - 1 = -1
             x-intercepts: Let y = 0
                    $x^2 + x - 1 = 0$
                    $x = \dfrac{-1 \pm \sqrt{1 - 4(1)(-1)}}{2} = \dfrac{-1 \pm \sqrt{5}}{2}$
             y-intercept: -1; x-intercepts: $\dfrac{-1 \pm \sqrt{5}}{2}$

(b) $y = x^2 + x + 1$
  y-intercepts: Let $x = 0$
    $y = 0 + 0 + 1 = 1$
  x-intercepts: Let $y = 0$
    $x^2 + x + 1 = 0$

$$x = \frac{-1 \pm \sqrt{1 - 4(1)}}{2} = \frac{-1 \pm \sqrt{-3}}{2}$$

  y-intercept: 1; x-intercept: none

11. $\dfrac{x}{2} + \dfrac{y}{3} = 1$
  y-intercepts: Let $x = 0$
    $\dfrac{y}{3} = 1$
    $y = 3$
  x-intercepts: Let $y = 0$
    $\dfrac{x}{2} = 1$
    $x = 2$
  y-intercept: 3; x-intercept: 2

13. $3x - 5y = 10$
  y-intercepts: Let $x = 0$
    $-5y = 10$
    $y = -2$
  x-intercepts: Let $y = 0$
    $3x = 10$
    $x = \dfrac{10}{3}$
  y-intercept: -2; x-intercept: 10/3

15. $y = x^3 - 8$
  y-intercepts: Let $x = 0$
    $y = 0 - 8 = -8$
  x-intercepts: Let $y = 0$
    $x^3 - 8 = 0$
    $x^3 = 8$
    $x = 2$
  y-intercept: -8; x-intercept: 2

17. (a) $(x - 2)^2 + (y - 3)^2 = 1$
        y-intercepts: Let $x = 0$
$$(-2)^2 + (y - 3)^2 = 1$$
$$4 + (y - 3)^2 = 1$$
$$(y - 3)^2 = -3$$
        There are no y-intercepts.
        x-intercepts: Let $y = 0$
$$(x - 2)^2 + (-3)^2 = 1$$
$$(x - 2)^2 + 9 = 1$$
$$(x - 2)^2 = -8$$
        There are no x-intercepts.
        y-intercept: none; x-intercept: none

     (b) $(x - 2)^2 + (y - 3)^2 = 4$
        y-intercepts: Let $x = 0$
$$(-2)^2 + (y - 3)^2 = 4$$
$$4 + (y - 3)^2 = 4$$
$$(y - 3)^2 = 0$$
$$y = 3$$
        x-intercepts: Let $y = 0$
$$(x - 2)^2 + (-3)^2 = 4$$
$$(x - 2)^2 + 9 = 4$$
$$(x - 2)^2 = -5$$
        There are no x-intercepts.
        y-intercept: 3; x-intercept: none

     (c) $(x - 2)^2 + (y - 3)^2 = 9$
        y-intercepts: Let $x = 0$
$$(-2)^2 + (y - 3)^2 = 9$$
$$4 + (y - 3)^2 = 9$$
$$(y - 3)^2 = 5$$
$$y - 3 = \pm\sqrt{5}$$
$$y = 3 \pm \sqrt{5}$$
        x-intercepts: Let $y = 0$
$$(x - 2)^2 + (-3)^2 = 9$$
$$(x - 2)^2 + 9 = 9$$
$$(x - 2)^2 = 0$$
$$x = 2$$
        y-intercepts: $3 \pm \sqrt{5}$; x-intercept: 2

(d) $(x - 2)^2 + (y - 3)^2 = 16$

y-intercepts: Let $x = 0$

$$(-2)^2 + (y - 3)^2 = 16$$
$$4 + (y - 3)^2 = 16$$
$$(y - 3)^2 = 12$$
$$y - 3 = \pm\sqrt{12} = \pm 2\sqrt{3}$$
$$y = 3 \pm 2\sqrt{3}$$

x-intercepts: Let $y = 0$

$$(x - 2)^2 + (-3)^2 = 16$$
$$(x - 2)^2 + 9 = 17$$
$$(x - 2)^2 = 7$$
$$x - 2 = \pm\sqrt{7}$$
$$x = 2 \pm \sqrt{7}$$

y-intercepts: $3 \pm 2\sqrt{3}$; x-intercepts: $2 \pm \sqrt{7}$

19. $y = \sqrt{x - 1} - x + 3$

y-intercepts: Let $x = 0$

$$y = \sqrt{-1} - 0 + 3$$

There are no y-intercepts.

x-intercepts: Let $y = 0$

$$0 = \sqrt{x - 1} - x + 3$$
$$x - 3 = \sqrt{x - 1}$$

We square each side of the equation:

$$(x - 3)^2 = x - 1$$
$$x^2 - 6x + 9 = x - 1$$
$$x^2 - 7x + 10 = 0$$
$$(x - 2)(x - 5) = 0$$
$$x = 2, 5 \quad (x = 2 \text{ doesn't check})$$

y-intercept: none; x-intercept: 5

21. $y = 11x - 2x^2 - x^3$

y-intercepts: Let $x = 0$

$$y = 0 - 0 - 0 = 0$$

x-intercepts: Let $y = 0$

$$0 = 11x - 2x^2 - x^3$$
$$0 = x(11 - 2x - x^2)$$

$$x = 0 \quad \text{or} \quad x = \frac{2 \pm \sqrt{4 - 4(11)(-1)}}{2(-1)} = \frac{2 \pm \sqrt{48}}{-2} = -1 \pm 2\sqrt{3}$$

A calculator yields these values to be 2.46 and -4.46.
(Note that these values agree with the graph)

y-intercept: 0; x-intercepts: $-1 + 2\sqrt{3} \approx 2.46$, $-1 - 2\sqrt{3} \approx -4.46$

23. $y = x^4 - 2x^2 - 3$
   y-intercepts: Let x = 0
       $y = 0 - 0 - 3 = -3$
   x-intercepts: Let y = 0
       $0 = x^4 - 2x^2 - 3$
       $0 = (x^2 - 3)(x^2 + 1)$
       $x^2 = 3$ (since $x^2 + 1 \neq 0$)
       $x = \pm\sqrt{3} \approx 1.73$
       (Note that these values agree with the graph)
   y-intercept: -3; x-intercepts: $\sqrt{3} \approx 1.73$, $-\sqrt{3} \approx -1.73$

25. (a)   The graph is symmetric about the x-axis:

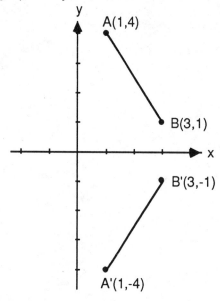

   (b)   The graph is symmetric about the y-axis:

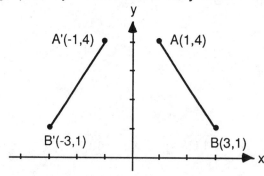

(c)   The graph is symmetric about the origin:

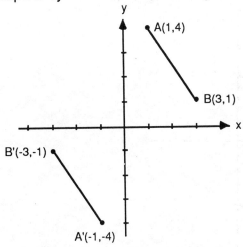

27.   (a)   The graph is symmetric about the x-axis:

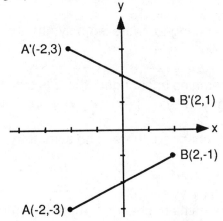

(b)   The graph is symmetric about the y-axis:

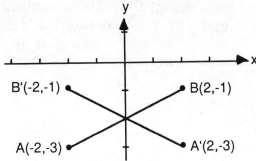

(c)   The graph is symmetric about the origin:

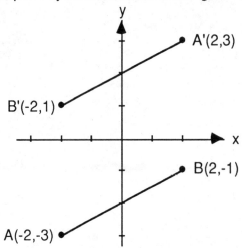

29.   (a)   x-axis: Replace y by -y: $3x^2 + (-y) = 16$
                                          $3x^2 - y = 16$
                    Since the equation is changed, there is no symmetry.
            y-axis: Replace x by - x: $3(-x)^2 + y = 16$
                                          $3x^2 + y = 16$
                    Since the equation remains unchanged, there is symmetry.
            origin: Replace x by -x <u>and</u> y by -y: $3(-x)^2 + (-y) = 16$
                                                          $3x^2 - y = 16$
                    Since the equation is changed, there is no symmetry.

        (b)   x-axis: Replace y by -y: $3x + (-y)^2 = 16$
                                          $3x + y^2 = 16$
                    Since the equation remains unchanged, there is symmetry.
            y-axis: Replace x by - x: $3(-x) + y^2 = 16$
                                          $-3x + y^2 = 16$
                    Since the equation is changed, there is no symmetry.
            origin: Replace x by -x <u>and</u> y by -y: $3(-x) + (-y)^2 = 16$
                                                          $-3x + y^2 = 16$
                    Since the equation is changed, there is no symmetry.

31. (a)   x-axis: Replace y by -y: $(-y) = x^4 - 3$
$$y = -x^4 + 3$$
Since the equation is changed, there is no symmetry.

y-axis: Replace x by -x: $y = (-x)^4 - 3$
$$y = x^4 - 3$$
Since the equation remains unchanged, there is symmetry.

origin: Replace y by -y and x by -x: $(-y) = (-x)^4 - 3$
$$-y = x^4 - 3$$
$$y = -x^4 + 3$$
Since the equation is changed, there is no symmetry.

(b)   x-axis: Replace y by -y: $(-y) = x^3 - 3$
$$y = -x^3 + 3$$
Since the equation is changed, there is no symmetry.

y-axis: Replace x by -x: $y = (-x)^3 - 3$
$$y = -x^3 - 3$$
Since the equation is changed, there is no symmetry.

origin: Replace y by -y and x by -x: $(-y) = (-x)^3 - 3$
$$-y = -x^3 - 3$$
$$y = x^3 + 3$$
Since the equation is changed, there is no symmetry.

(c)   x-axis: Replace y by -y: $(-y)^2 = x^3 - 3$
$$y^2 = x^3 - 3$$
Since the equation remains unchanged, there is symmetry.

y-axis: Replace x by -x: $y^2 = (-x)^3 - 3$
$$y^2 = -x^3 - 3$$
Since the equation is changed, there is no symmetry.

origin: Replace y by -y and x by -x: $(-y)^2 = (-x)^3 - 3$
$$y^2 = -x^3 - 3$$
Since the equation is changed, there is no symmetry.

(d)   x-axis: Replace y by -y: $(-y)^3 = x$
$$-y^3 = x$$
$$y^3 = -x$$
Since the equation is changed, there is no symmetry.

y-axis: Replace x by -x: $y^3 = -x$
Since the equation is changed, there is no symmetry.

origin: Replace y by -y and x by -x: $(-y)^3 = -x$
$$-y^3 = -x$$
$$y^3 = x$$
Since the equation remains unchanged, there is symmetry.

33. x-axis: Replace y by -y: $x^2 + (-y)^2 = 16$
$$x^2 + y^2 = 16$$
Since the equation remains unchanged, there is symmetry.

y-axis: Replace x by -x: $(-x)^2 + y^2 = 16$
$$x^2 + y^2 = 16$$
Since the equation remains unchanged, there is symmetry.

origin: Replace y by -y and x by -x: $(-x)^2 + (-y)^2 = 16$
$$x^2 + y^2 = 16$$
Since the equation remains unchanged, there is symmetry.

35. x-axis: Replace y by - y: $-y = x^2 + x^3$
$$y = -x^2 - x^3$$
Since the equation is changed, there is no symmetry.

y-axis: Replace x by -x: $y = (-x)^2 + (-x)^3$
$$y = x^2 - x^3$$
Since the equation is changed, there is no symmetry.

origin: Replace y by -y and x by -x: $-y = (-x)^2 + (-x)^3$
$$y = -x^2 + x^3$$
Since the equation is changed, there is no symmetry.

37. x-axis: Replace y by -y: $x + (-y) = 1$
$$x - y = 1$$
Since the equation is changed, there is no symmetry.

y-axis: Replace x by -x: $(-x) + y = 1$
$$-x + y = 1$$
Since the equation is changed, there is no symmetry.

origin: Replace y by -y and x by -x: $(-x) + (-y) = 1$
$$x + y = -1$$
Since the equation is changed, there is no symmetry.

39. $y = x^2$
x- and y-intercept: 0; symmetry: y-axis
We set up a table of values:

x	1	2	3	4
y	1	4	9	16

Now graph the curve:

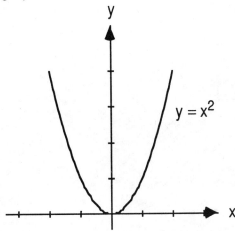

41. $y = \dfrac{1}{x}$

x- and y-intercepts: none; symmetry: origin
We set up a table of values:

x	1/5	1	2	3
y	5	1	1/2	1/3

Now graph the curve:

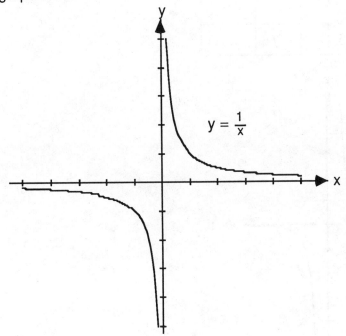

43. $y = -x^2$

x- and y-intercept: 0; symmetry: y-axis

We set up a table of values:

x	1	2	3	4
y	-1	-4	-9	-16

Now graph the curve:

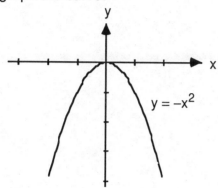

45. $y = -\dfrac{1}{x^3}$

x- and y-intercepts: none; symmetry: origin

We set up a table of values:

x	1/3	1/2	1	2	3
y	−27	−8	−1	−1/8	−1/27

Now graph the curve:

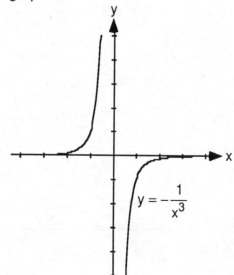

47. $y = \sqrt{x^2}$

x- and y-intercept: 0; symmetry: y-axis

We set up a table of values:

x	1	2	3	4
y	1	2	3	4

Now graph the curve:

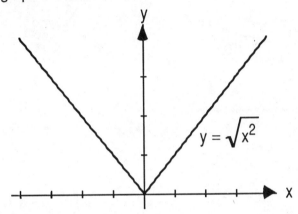

$y = \sqrt{x^2}$

49. $y = x^2 - 2x + 1$

x-intercept: 1; y-intercept: 1; symmetry: none

We set up a table of values:

x	-2	-1	2	3
y	9	4	1	4

Now graph the curve:

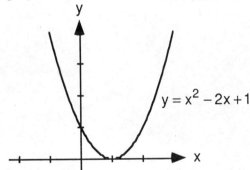

$y = x^2 - 2x + 1$

51. $y^2 = 2x - 4$

x-intercept: 2; y-intercept: none; symmetry: x-axis

We set up a table of values:

x	2	2.5	4	10
y	0	±1	±2	±4

Now graph the curve:

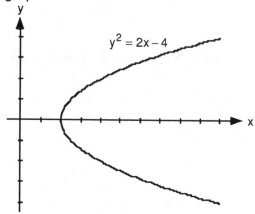

53. $y = 2x^2 + x - 4$

x-intercepts: $\dfrac{-1 \pm \sqrt{33}}{4}$; y-intercept: -4; symmetry: none

We set up a table of values:

x	-3	-2	-1	0	1	2
y	11	2	-3	-4	-1	6

Now graph the curve:

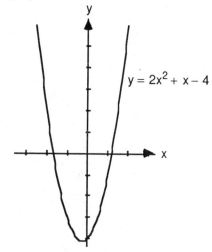

55. (a) $y = 3x - 6$
     x-intercept: 2; y-intercept: -6; symmetry: none
     We set up a table of values:

x	-3	-2	-1	1	3	4
y	-15	-12	-9	-3	3	6

Now graph the curve:

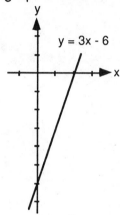

(b) $y = |3x - 6|$
     x-intercept: 2; y-intercept: 6; symmetry: none
     We set up a table of values:

x	-2	-1	1	3	4
y	12	9	3	3	6

Now graph the curve:

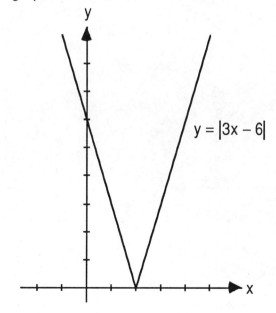

57. $y = \dfrac{x^2 + x - 20}{x - 4} = \dfrac{(x + 5)(x - 4)}{x - 4} = x + 5$ if $x \neq 4$

Domain: $x \neq 4$

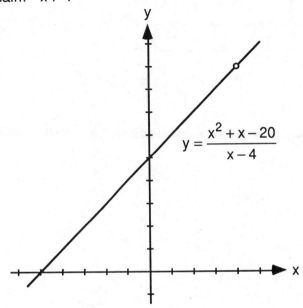

$$y = \dfrac{x^2 + x - 20}{x - 4}$$

59. $y = \dfrac{x^2 - 9}{x - 3} = \dfrac{(x - 3)(x + 3)}{x - 3} = x + 3$ if $x \neq 3$

Domain: $x \neq 3$

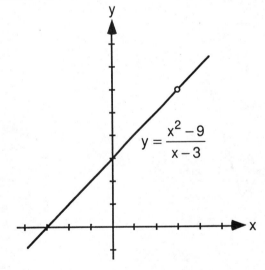

$$y = \dfrac{x^2 - 9}{x - 3}$$

61. (a)   We set up a table of values:

x	0	1	2	3
y	0	16	64	144

Now graph the curve:

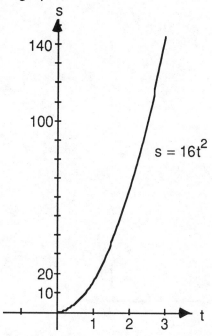

(b)   When $0 \le t \le 1$, we have $0 \le s \le 16$, from the graph:

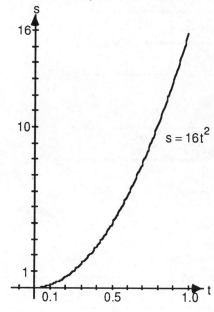

(c)   When $1 \le t \le 2$, we have $16 \le s \le 64$, from the graph:

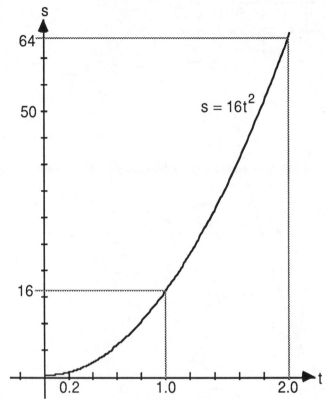

63.   (a) $y = x$
       We set up a table of values:

x	0	1/4	1/3	1/2	3/4	1
y	0	1/4	1/3	1/2	3/4	1

       (b) $y = x^2$
       We set up a table of values:

x	0	1/4	1/3	1/2	3/4	1
y	0	1/16	1/9	1/4	9/16	1

       (c) $y = x^3$
       We set up a table of values:

x	0	1/4	1/3	1/2	3/4	1
y	0	1/64	1/27	1/8	27/64	1

(d) $y = x^4$
We set up a table of values:

x	0	1/4	1/3	1/2	3/4	1
y	0	1/256	1/81	1/16	81/256	1

Now graph the four curves:

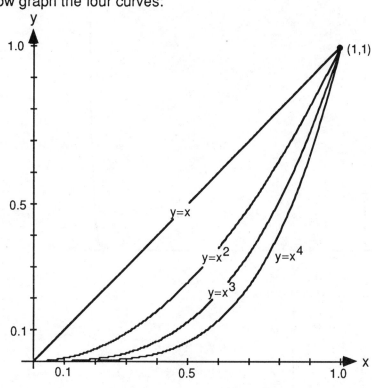

The pattern seems to be that as n gets larger the graph of $y = x^n$, flattens out more and more like in the figure. We could guess $y = x^{100}$ would look something like this:

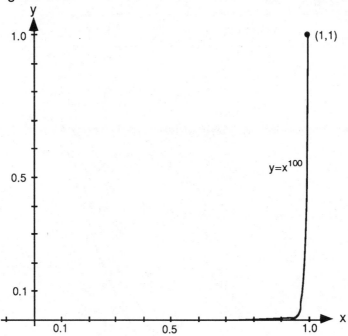

65.   (a)   We graph the given curves:

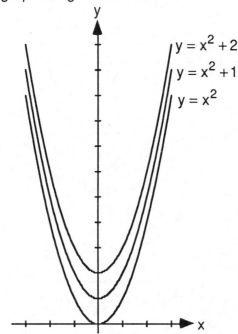

(b) $y = x^2 + K$ is a shift of $y = x^2$ $|K|$ units (up if K > 0, down if K < 0)

67. (a)   We graph the given curves:

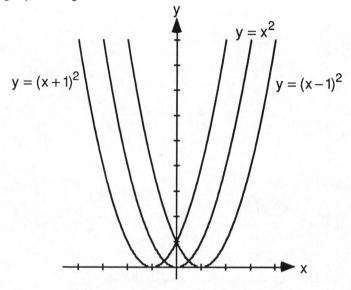

(b) $y = (x + 2)^2$ will be a shift of $y = x^2$ to the left 2 units. We have the graph:

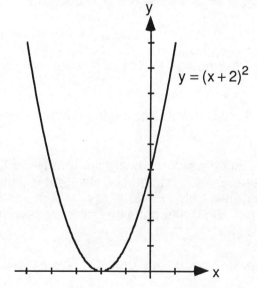

69. We re-draw the graph identifying points we are interested in:

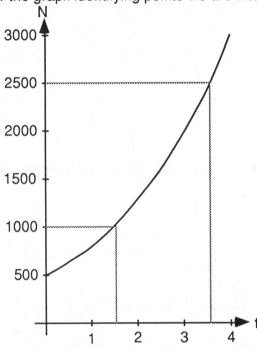

(a)   Tracing up to the curve from t = 0, we get N = 500 bacteria.

(b)   Since (0,500) lies on the curve, we find where (t , 1000) would be on the curve, since the population would now be double. Tracing down from N = 1000, we get t = 1.5 hours. So the population will double in 1.5 hours.

(c)   As in (b), we find where (t , 2500) would be on the curve. Tracing down from N = 2500, we get t = 3.5 hours.

(d)   Between t = 0 and t = 1, the population has grown from N = 500 to N = 800, so it has increased by 300 bacteria. Between t = 3 and t = 4, the population has grown from N = 2000 to N = 3000, so it has increased by 1000 bacteria. So the population has increased more rapidly between t = 3 and t = 4.

Note: This is the normal case with population growth. The world's population has grown as much during the last 35 years as it had from the beginning of time. The problem here is the shape of the curve (increasing at greater and greater rates), rather than with the fact that the population is merely increasing.

71. x-intercepts:
$$y = 0$$
$$x^3 - 27x = 0$$
$$x(x - 3\sqrt{3})(x + 3\sqrt{3}) = 0$$
$$x = 0, \pm 3\sqrt{3} \approx 0, \pm 5.2$$

y-intercept: 0; symmetry: origin

We set up a table of values:

x	0	0.5	1	1.5	2	2.5	3	3.5	4	4.5	5	5.5	6
y	0	-13.4	-26	-37.1	-46	-51.9	-54	-51.6	-44	-30.4	-10	17.9	54

Now graph the curve:

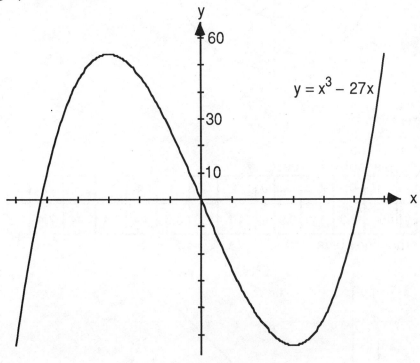

$$y = x^3 - 27x$$

73. Note that if $(x^2 + y^2 - 1)(x^2 + y^2 - 4) = 0$, then either $x^2 + y^2 - 1 = 0$ or $x^2 + y^2 - 4 = 0$, thus $x^2 + y^2 = 1$ or $x^2 + y^2 = 4$. Thus the graph is two circles:

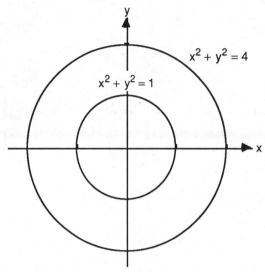

75. $y = x + \dfrac{1}{\sqrt{x+1}}$

symmetry: none
We set up a table of values:

x	-1	-0.9	-0.8	-0.5	0	1	2	3	4	5	6	7	8
y	none	2.3	1.4	0.9	1	1.7	2.6	3.5	4.4	5.4	6.4	7.4	8.3

Now graph the curve:

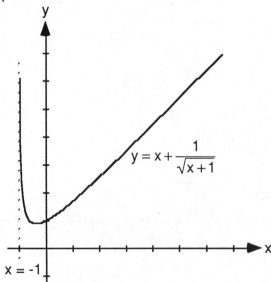

2.2 Equations of Lines

1. (a) Here $(x_1, y_1) = (-3, 2)$ and $(x_2, y_2) = (1, -6)$, so:
$$\text{slope} = \frac{-6 - 2}{1 - (-3)} = \frac{-8}{4} = -2$$

(b) Here $(x_1, y_1) = (2, -5)$ and $(x_2, y_2) = (4, 1)$, so:
$$\text{slope} = \frac{1 - (-5)}{4 - 2} = \frac{6}{2} = 3$$

(c) Here $(x_1, y_1) = (-2, 7)$ and $(x_2, y_2) = (1, 0)$, so:
$$\text{slope} = \frac{0 - 7}{1 - (-2)} = -\frac{7}{3}$$

(d) Here $(x_1, y_1) = (4, 5)$ and $(x_2, y_2) = (5, 8)$, so:
$$\text{slope} = \frac{8 - 5}{5 - 4} = \frac{3}{1} = 3$$

3. (a) Here $(x_1, y_1) = (1, 1)$ and $(x_2, y_2) = (-1, -1)$, so:
$$\text{slope} = \frac{-1 - 1}{-1 - 1} = \frac{-2}{-2} = 1$$

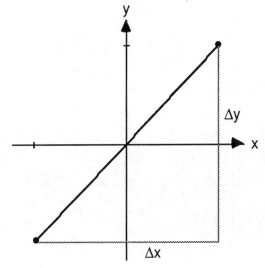

(b)   Here $(x_1, y_1) = (0, 5)$ and $(x_2, y_2) = (-8, 5)$, so:

$$\text{slope} = \frac{5 - 5}{-8 - 0} = \frac{0}{-8} = 0$$

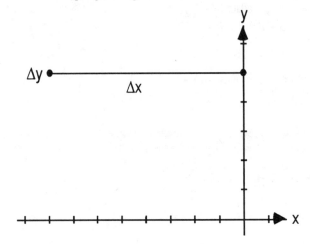

(c)   Here $(x_1, y_1) = (-1, 1)$ and $(x_2, y_2) = (1, -1)$, so:

$$\text{slope} = \frac{-1 - 1}{1 - (-1)} = \frac{-2}{2} = -1$$

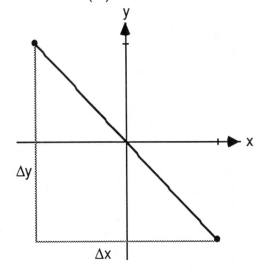

(d)   Here $(x_1, y_1) = (a, b)$ and $(x_2, y_2) = (b, a)$, so:

$$\text{slope} = \frac{a - b}{b - a} = -1$$

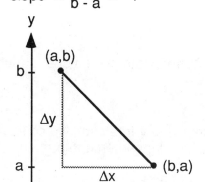

5. m_3 is smallest (since it is negative)
      m_2 is next (it appears to be zero)
      m_4 is next (it is not as steep as m_1)
      m_1 is largest (it is steeper than m_4)

7.   slope of AB $= \dfrac{1/2 - (-2)}{2 - (-8)} = \dfrac{5/2}{10} = \dfrac{1}{4}$

      slope of BC $= \dfrac{-1 - 1/2}{11 - 2} = \dfrac{-3/2}{9} = -\dfrac{1}{6}$

      Since these slopes are different, the three points cannot be collinear.

9.   slope of AB $= \dfrac{4 - (-5)}{3 - 0} = \dfrac{9}{3} = 3$

      slope of BC $= \dfrac{-8 - 4}{-1 - 3} = \dfrac{-12}{-4} = 3$

      Since these slopes are equal, the three points are collinear.

11.   (a)   Here $(x_1, y_1) = (-2, 1)$ and $m = -5$, so by the point-slope formula:

            $y - 1 = -5 [x - (-2)]$
            $y - 1 = -5 (x + 2)$
            $y - 1 = -5x - 10$
            $ y = -5x - 9$

      (b)   Here $(x_1, y_1) = (4, -4)$ and $m = 4$, so by the point-slope formula:

            $y - (-4) = 4 (x - 4)$
            $y + 4 = 4x - 16$
            $ y = 4x - 20$

(c)   Here $(x_1, y_1) = (-6, -2/3)$ and $m = 1/3$, so by the point-slope formula:

$$y - (-2/3) = (1/3) [x - (-6)]$$
$$y + 2/3 = (1/3)(x + 6)$$
$$y + 2/3 = 1/3x + 2$$
$$y = 1/3x + 4/3$$

(d)   Here $(x_1, y_1) = (0, 1)$ and $m = -1$, so by the point-slope formula:

$$y - 1 = -1(x - 0)$$
$$y - 1 = -x$$
$$y = -x + 1$$

Note in (d) that, since the given point is the y-intercept, we could have immediately written $y = -x + 1$ using the slope-intercept formula.

13.   (a)   First we find the slope: $m = \dfrac{-6 - 8}{-3 - 4} = \dfrac{-14}{-7} = 2$

Using $(x_1, y_1) = (4, 8)$ in the point-slope formula, we have:

$$y - 8 = 2(x - 4)$$
$$y - 8 = 2x - 8$$
$$y = 2x$$

(b)   First we find the slope: $m = \dfrac{-10 - 0}{3 - (-2)} = \dfrac{-10}{5} = -2$

Using $(x_1, y_1) = (-2, 0)$ in the point-slope formula, we have:

$$y - 0 = -2[x - (-2)]$$
$$y = -2(x + 2)$$
$$y = -2x - 4$$

(c)   First we find the slope: $m = \dfrac{-1 - (-2)}{4 - (-3)} = \dfrac{1}{7}$

Using $(x_1, y_1) = (4, -1)$ in the point-slope formula, we have:

$$y - (-1) = 1/7 (x - 4)$$
$$y + 1 = 1/7 x - 4/7$$
$$y = 1/7 x - 11/7$$

15.   Since vertical lines have the form x = constant, and $(-3, 4)$ is on the line, then the equation is $x = -3$.

17.   Since horizontal lines have the form y = constant, and $(-3, 4)$ is on the line, then the equation is $y = 4$.

19.   The y-axis is vertical, so its equation must have the form x = constant. Since $(0, 0)$ is on the y-axis, the equation is $x = 0$.

21. (a) Using the slope-intercept formula with m = -4 and b = 7, we have
          y = -4x + 7.
     (b) Using the slope-intercept formula with m = 2 and b = 3/2, we have
          $y = 2x + \dfrac{3}{2}$.
     (c) Using the slope-intercept formula with m = -4/3 and b = 14, we have
          $y = -\dfrac{4}{3}x + 14$.

23. (a) We use the point-slope formula:
$$y - (-1) = 4\,[\,x - (-3)\,]$$
$$y + 1 = 4\,(x + 3)$$
$$y + 1 = 4x + 12$$
$$y = 4x + 11$$
          We draw the graph:

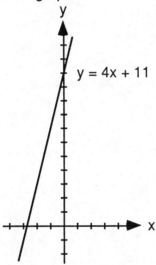

y = 4x + 11

     (b) We use the point-slope formula:
$$y - 0 = 1/2\,(x - 5/2)$$
$$y = 1/2x - 5/4$$
          We draw the graph:

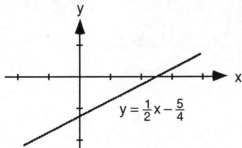

$y = \dfrac{1}{2}x - \dfrac{5}{4}$

(c)   We find the slope between the points $(6, 0)$ and $(0, 5)$:

$$m = \frac{5 - 0}{0 - 6} = -\frac{5}{6}$$

Since 5 is the y-intercept, then by the slope-intercept formula:

    $y = -5/6\ x + 5$.

We draw the graph:

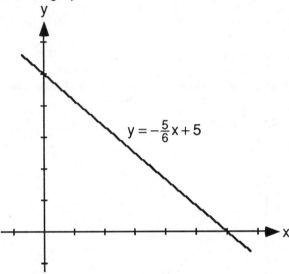

(d)   We use the point-slope formula with the point $(-2, 0)$:

$$y - 0 = 3/4\,[\,x - (-2)\,]$$
$$y = 3/4\,(x + 2)$$
$$y = 3/4\ x + 3/2$$

We draw the graph:

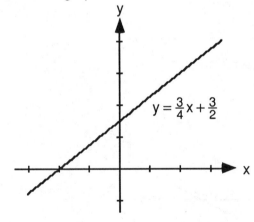

(e)   We first find the slope:
$$m = \frac{6 - 2}{2 - 1} = \frac{4}{1} = 4$$

Using the point $(1, 2)$ in the point-slope formula, we have:
$$y - 2 = 4(x - 1)$$
$$y - 2 = 4x - 4$$
$$y = 4x - 2$$

We draw the graph:

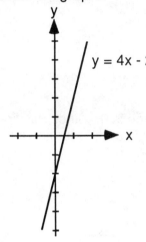

25.   We first find the x- and y-intercepts of the circle:

<u>x-intercepts:</u>   <u>y-intercepts:</u>
$$y = 0 \qquad\qquad\qquad\qquad x = 0$$
$$x^2 + 4x + 4 = 0 \qquad\qquad y^2 - 4y + 4 = 0$$
$$(x + 2)^2 = 0 \qquad\qquad\quad (y - 2)^2 = 0$$
$$x = -2 \qquad\qquad\qquad\quad y = 2$$

So the line passes through the points $(-2, 0)$ and $(0, 2)$. We find its slope:
$$m = \frac{2 - 0}{0 - (-2)} = \frac{2}{2} = 1$$

So $y = x + 2$ is the equation (in slope-intercept form) of the line.

We draw the graph:

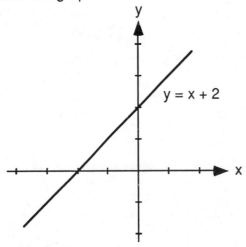

27.   If the line is parallel to the x-axis, then its slope is 0. Since this line is of the form y = constant, then for (-3, 4) to lie of the line the equation is y = 4, or y - 4 = 0 in the desired form. We draw the graph:

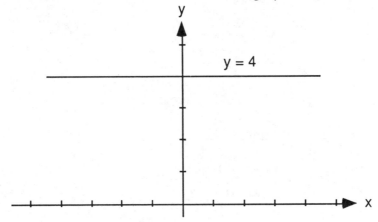

29.   (a) $3x + 5y = 15$

We divide by 15 to get $\frac{x}{5} + \frac{y}{3} = 1$.

So the x-intercept is 5 and the y-intercept is 3. Thus we have:

$$\text{area} = \frac{1}{2}(5)(3) = \frac{15}{2}$$

$$\text{perimeter} = 5 + 3 + \sqrt{5^2 + 3^2} = 8 + \sqrt{34}$$

(b) $3x - 5y = 15$

We divide by 15 to get $\frac{x}{5} - \frac{y}{3} = 1$.

So the x-intercept is 5 and the y-intercept is -3. Thus we have:

$$\text{area} = \frac{1}{2}(5)(3) = \frac{15}{2}$$

$$\text{perimeter} = 5 + 3 + \sqrt{5^2 + 3^2} = 8 + \sqrt{34}$$

31. (a)   We find the slopes of each:

$$
\begin{array}{ll}
3x - 4y = 12 & 4x - 3y = 12 \\
\quad -4y = -3x + 12 & \quad -3y = -4x + 12 \\
\quad\quad y = \frac{3}{4}x - 3 & \quad\quad y = \frac{4}{3}x - 4 \\
\quad\quad m = \frac{3}{4} & \quad\quad m = \frac{4}{3}
\end{array}
$$

The lines are not parallel (slopes aren't the same), the lines are not perpendicular ($3/4 \cdot 4/3 = 1$, not -1), so they are neither.

(b)   We find the slopes of each:

$$
\begin{array}{ll}
y = 5x - 16 & y = 5x + 2 \\
m = 5 & m = 5
\end{array}
$$

Since these slopes are the same, the lines are parallel.

(c)   We find the slopes of each:

$$
\begin{array}{ll}
5x - 6y = 25 & 6x + 5y = 0 \\
\quad -6y = -5x + 25 & \quad 5y = -6x \\
\quad\quad y = \frac{5}{6}x - \frac{25}{6} & \quad\quad y = -\frac{5}{6}x \\
\quad\quad m = \frac{5}{6} & \quad\quad m = -\frac{6}{5}
\end{array}
$$

Since $(5/6)(-6/5) = -1$, the lines are perpendicular.

(d)   We find the slopes of each:

$$
\begin{array}{ll}
y = -\frac{2}{3}x - 1 & y = \frac{3}{2}x - 1 \\
m = -\frac{2}{3} & m = \frac{3}{2}
\end{array}
$$

Since $(-2/3)(3/2) = -1$, the lines are perpendicular.

(e)   We find the slopes of each:

$$-2x - 5y = 1 \qquad\qquad y - \frac{2}{5}x - 4 = 0$$

$$-5y = 2x + 1 \qquad\qquad y = \frac{2}{5}x + 4$$

$$y = -\frac{2}{5}x - \frac{1}{5}$$

$$m = -\frac{2}{5} \qquad\qquad m = \frac{2}{5}$$

The lines are not parallel (slopes aren't the same); the lines are not perpendicular (-2/5 • 2/5 = -4/25, not -1), so they are neither.

(f)   We find the slopes of each:

$$x = 8y + 3 \qquad\qquad 4y - \frac{1}{2}x = 32$$

$$8y = x - 3 \qquad\qquad 4y = \frac{1}{2}x + 32$$

$$y = \frac{1}{8}x - \frac{3}{8} \qquad\qquad y = \frac{1}{8}x + 8$$

$$m = \frac{1}{8} \qquad\qquad m = \frac{1}{8}$$

Since these slopes are the same, the lines are parallel.

33.   We first find the slope:

$$2x - 5y = 10$$

$$-5y = -2x + 10$$

$$y = \frac{2}{5}x - 2$$

So the slope is 2/5. We use the point (-1, 2) in the point-slope formula:

$$y - 2 = \frac{2}{5}[x - (-1)]$$

$$y - 2 = \frac{2}{5}(x + 1)$$

$$y - 2 = \frac{2}{5}x + \frac{2}{5}$$

$$y = \frac{2}{5}x + \frac{12}{5} \quad \text{[form } y = mx + b]$$

$$5y = 2x + 12$$

$$2x - 5y + 12 = 0 \qquad\qquad \text{[form } Ax + By + C = 0]$$

This could also be written as -2x + 5y - 12 = 0

35. We first find the slope of 4y - 3x = 1:
$$4y = 3x + 1$$
$$y = \frac{3}{4}x + \frac{1}{4}$$
Since this slope is 3/4, the perpendicular line slope is -4/3. We now use the point (4, 0) in the point-slope formula:
$$y - 0 = -\frac{4}{3}(x - 4)$$
$$y = -\frac{4}{3}x + \frac{16}{3} \quad \text{[form } y = mx + b \text{]}$$
$$3y = -4x + 16$$
$$4x + 3y - 16 = 0 \quad \text{[form } Ax + By + C = 0 \text{]}$$

37. We first find the slope of 3x - 5y = 25:
$$-5y = -3x + 25$$
$$y = \frac{3}{5}x - 5$$
So the slope is 3/5. We now find the y-intercept of 6x - y + 11 = 0:
$$y = 6x + 11$$
So the y-intercept is 11. We write the equation:
$$y = \frac{3}{5}x + 11 \quad \text{[form } y = mx + b \text{]}$$
$$5y = 3x + 55$$
$$3x - 5y + 55 = 0 \quad \text{[form } Ax + By + C = 0 \text{]}$$
This could also be written as -3x + 5y - 55 = 0.

39. (a) Its center is (0, 0) and its radius is 5. We draw the graph:

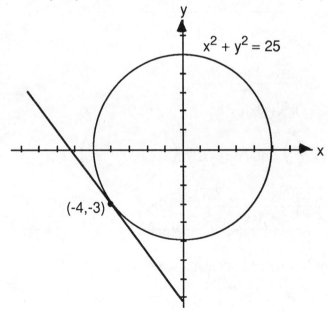

(b) The tangent line will be perpendicular to the radius drawn from the center $(0, 0)$ and the point $(-4, -3)$. We find the slope:

$$m = \frac{-3 - 0}{-4 - 0} = \frac{-3}{-4} = \frac{3}{4}$$

So the perpendicular line will have slope $= -4/3$. We use the point $(-4, -3)$ in the point-slope formula:

$$y - (-3) = -\frac{4}{3}[x - (-4)]$$

$$y + 3 = -\frac{4}{3}(x + 4)$$

$$y + 3 = -\frac{4}{3}x - \frac{16}{3}$$

$$y = -\frac{4}{3}x - \frac{25}{3}$$

41. Let $(x_1, y_1) = (3, 9)$ and $(x_2, y_2) = \left(3 + h, (3 + h)^2\right)$, so:

$$m = \frac{(3 + h)^2 - 9}{3 + h - 3} = \frac{9 + 6h + h^2 - 9}{h} = \frac{6h + h^2}{h} = 6 + h$$

43. Let $(x_1, y_1) = (x, x^3)$ and $(x_2, y_2) = \left(x + h, (x + h)^3\right)$

Since
$$\begin{aligned}(x + h)^3 &= (x + h)(x + h)^2 \\ &= (x + h)(x^2 + 2xh + h^2) \\ &= x^3 + 3x^2h + 3xh^2 + h^3,\end{aligned}$$

then
$$\begin{aligned}\text{slope} &= \frac{(x + h)^3 - x^3}{x + h - x} \\ &= \frac{x^3 + 3x^2h + 3xh^2 + h^3 - x^3}{h} \\ &= \frac{3x^2h + 3xh^2 + h^3}{h} \\ &= \frac{h(3x^2 + 3xh + h^2)}{h} \\ &= 3x^2 + 3xh + h^2\end{aligned}$$

45. Let $(x_1, y_1) = \left(x, \frac{1}{x}\right)$ and $(x_2, y_2) = \left(x + h, \frac{1}{x + h}\right)$, so:

$$\text{slope} = \frac{\frac{1}{x + h} - \frac{1}{x}}{x + h - x} = \frac{\frac{1}{x + h} - \frac{1}{x}}{h}$$

We multiply the numerator and denominator by $x(x + h)$ to get:

$$\text{slope} = \frac{x - x - h}{hx(x + h)} = \frac{-h}{hx(x + h)} = \frac{-1}{x(x + h)}$$

47. $y = x^2$
We draw the graph:

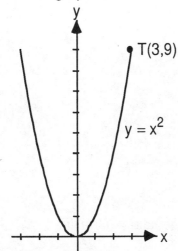

The completed table is:

x	2.5	2.9	2.99	2.999	2.9999
y	6.25	8.41	8.9401	8.994001	8.99940001
Δx	0.5	0.1	0.01	0.001	0.0001
Δy	2.75	0.59	0.0599	0.005999	0.00059999
m	5.5	5.9	5.99	5.999	5.9999

It would appear that as x approaches 3, the slope of these lines (called secant lines) approaches 6. So we would estimate that the slope of the tangent line to the curve $y = x^2$ at $T(3, 9)$ is 6.

49. Let the coordinate of P be (x, x^3). Since the slope of the line passing through P and $(1, 1)$ is 3/4, we have:

$$\frac{x^3 - 1}{x - 1} = \frac{3}{4}$$

$$\frac{(x - 1)(x^2 + x + 1)}{x - 1} = \frac{3}{4}$$

$$x^2 + x + 1 = \frac{3}{4}$$

$$4x^2 + 4x + 4 = 3$$

$$4x^2 + 4x + 1 = 0$$

$$(2x + 1)^2 = 0$$

$$2x + 1 = 0, \text{ so } x = -\frac{1}{2} \text{ and } y = \left(-\frac{1}{2}\right)^3 = -\frac{1}{8}$$

Thus the point P is $(-1/2, -1/8)$.

51.   Let the coordinates of P be (x, 1/x). Since the slope of the line through P and (2, 1/2) is -1/16, we have:

$$\frac{\dfrac{1}{x} - \dfrac{1}{2}}{x - 2} = \frac{-1}{16}$$

Multiply the left side by $\dfrac{2x}{2x}$:

$$\frac{2 - x}{2x(x - 2)} = \frac{-1}{16}$$

$$\frac{-1}{2x} = \frac{-1}{16}$$

$$2x = 16$$

$$x = 8$$

So the point P is (8, 1/8).

53.   We use the point-slope formula to find the equation of the line:

$$y - 6 = -5 (x - 3)$$
$$y - 6 = -5x + 15$$
$$y = -5x + 21$$

We now find the intercepts:

x-intercept: Let   y = 0

$$-5x + 21 = 0$$
$$5x = 21$$
$$x = \frac{21}{5}$$

y-intercept: Let x = 0, so y = 21

We draw the graph:

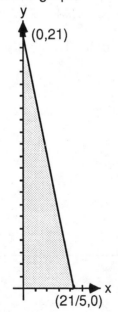

From the figure, we see that: A = (1/2)(base)(height)
           = (1/2)(21/5)(21)
           = 44.1 sq. units

55. (a) We draw the graph:

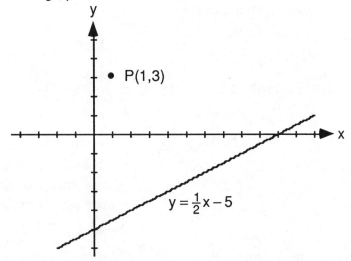

(b) Its slope must be -2, so we use (1, 3) in the point-slope formula:
$$y - 3 = -2(x - 1)$$
$$y - 3 = -2x + 2$$
$$y = -2x + 5$$

(c) We set the two equations equal:
$$-2x + 5 = \frac{1}{2}x - 5$$
$$-4x + 10 = x - 10$$
$$-5x = -20$$
$$x = 4$$
$$y = -2(4) + 5 = -3$$
The intersection point is (4, -3).

(d) We find the distance from (1, 3) to (4, -3):
$$d = \sqrt{(4 - 1)^2 + (-3 - 3)^2} = \sqrt{9 + 36} = \sqrt{45} = 3\sqrt{5}$$

57. (a) Since the slope is m and the point (2, 1) lies on the line, we use the point-slope formula to get $y - 1 = m(x - 2)$

(b)   For the x-intercept, let y = 0: $-1 = m(x - 2)$

$$-1 = mx - 2m$$
$$mx = 2m - 1$$
$$x = \frac{2m - 1}{m}$$

For the y-intercept, let x = 0: $y - 1 = m(-2)$

$$y - 1 = -2m$$
$$y = -2m + 1$$

(c)   Area = (1/2)(base)(height) = $\frac{1}{2}\left(\frac{2m - 1}{m}\right)(-2m + 1)$

(d)   Since the area is 4, we have: $\frac{1}{2}\left(\frac{2m - 1}{m}\right)(-2m + 1) = 4$

Multiply by 2m:

$$(2m - 1)(-2m + 1) = 8m$$
$$-4m^2 + 4m - 1 = 8m$$
$$-4m^2 - 4m - 1 = 0$$
$$4m^2 + 4m + 1 = 0$$

(e)   We solve for m: $(2m + 1)^2 = 0$

Taking roots:

$$2m + 1 = 0$$
$$2m = -1$$
$$m = -1/2$$

59.   (a)   Since $\frac{\Delta x}{\Delta P} = -\frac{2}{3}$, we have the equation:

$$x = 280 - \frac{2}{3}(P - 195) = 410 - \frac{2}{3}P$$

(b)   If P = 270, we have: $x = 280 - \frac{2}{3}(270 - 195)$

$$= 280 - \frac{2}{3}(75)$$
$$= 280 - 50$$
$$= 230$$

So 230 units can be sold in a month.

(c)   If x = 205, we have: $205 = 280 - \frac{2}{3}(P - 195)$

$$-75 = -\frac{2}{3}(P - 195)$$
$$112.5 = P - 195$$
$$307.5 = P$$

The price would be $307.50 per unit.

. 61. (a) Since A and C lie on the line $y = m_1 x + b_1$, and the x-coordinates of A and C are 0 and 1, respectively, then the y-coordinates will be b_1 and $m_1 + b_1$, so $A = (0, b_1)$ and $C = (1, m_1 + b_1)$. Similarly, the points B and D are $B = (0, b_2)$ and $D = (1, m_2 + b_2)$.

(b) $AB = \sqrt{(0 - 0)^2 + (b_1 - b_2)^2} = \sqrt{(b_1 - b_2)^2} = |b_1 - b_2|$,
which is $b_1 - b_2$ since $b_1 > b_2$

$CD = \sqrt{(1 - 1)^2 + [(m_1 + b_1) - (m_2 + b_2)]^2}$
$= \sqrt{[(m_1 + b_1) - (m_2 + b_2)]^2}$
$= |(m_1 + b_1) - (m_2 + b_2)|$
$= m_1 + b_1 - (m_2 + b_2)$ since $m_1 + b_1 > m_2 + b_2$

(c) Since $AB = CD$, we have:
$b_1 - b_2 = m_1 + b_1 - m_2 - b_2$
$0 = m_1 - m_2$
$m_1 = m_2$

63. (a) When $y = mx + b$ is reflected about the x-axis, its slope becomes $-m$ and its y-intercept becomes $-b$, so the new equation is $y = -mx - b$. Alternate approach: Use $(x, -y)$ to get $-y = mx + b$, or $y = -mx - b$.

(b) When $y = mx + b$ is reflected about the y-axis, its slope becomes $-m$ and its y-intercept remains b, so the new equation is $y = -mx + b$. Alternate approach: Use $(-x, y)$ to get $y = m(-x) + b$, or $y = -mx + b$.

(c) When $y = mx + b$ is reflected about the origin, its slope remains m and its y-intercept becomes $-b$, so the new equation is $y = mx - b$. Alternate approach: Use $(-x, -y)$ to get $-y = m(-x) + b$, or $y = mx - b$.

65. (a) We find the slope between $(a, 0)$ and $(0, b)$:
$$m = \frac{b - 0}{0 - a} = -\frac{b}{a}$$

(b) The equation $\left(\text{using the point } (0, b)\right)$ is:
$$y = -\frac{b}{a}x + b$$
$$ay = -bx + ab$$
$$bx + ay = ab$$
Dividing through by ab, we have:
$$\frac{bx}{ab} + \frac{ay}{ab} = \frac{ab}{ab}$$
$$\frac{x}{a} + \frac{y}{b} = 1$$

67. (a) Since the dotted lines are parallel to the coordinate axes, we can label points as shown in the figure:

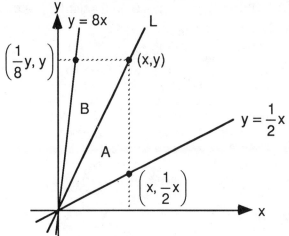

We have:

$$\text{Area of A} = \frac{1}{2}(x)(y) - \frac{1}{2}(x)\left(\frac{1}{2}x\right) = \frac{1}{2}xy - \frac{1}{4}x^2$$

$$\text{Area of B} = \frac{1}{2}(y)(x) - \frac{1}{2}(y)\left(\frac{1}{8}y\right) = \frac{1}{2}xy - \frac{1}{16}y^2$$

Setting these two areas equal, we have:

$$\frac{1}{2}xy - \frac{1}{4}x^2 = \frac{1}{2}xy - \frac{1}{16}y^2$$

$$-\frac{1}{4}x^2 = -\frac{1}{16}y^2$$

$$4x^2 = y^2$$

$$y = 2x$$

(b) Again, we label points as indicated in the figure:

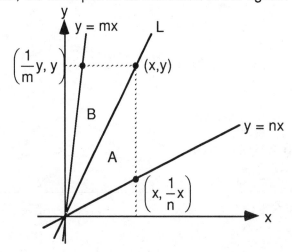

We have:

$$\text{Area of A} = \frac{1}{2}(x)(y) - \frac{1}{2}(x)\left(\frac{1}{n}x\right) = \frac{1}{2}xy - \frac{1}{2n}x^2$$

$$\text{Area of B} = \frac{1}{2}(y)(x) - \frac{1}{2}(y)\left(\frac{1}{m}y\right) = \frac{1}{2}xy - \frac{1}{2m}y^2$$

Setting these two areas equal, we have:

$$\frac{1}{2}xy - \frac{1}{2n}x^2 = \frac{1}{2}xy - \frac{1}{2m}y^2$$

$$-\frac{1}{2n}x^2 = -\frac{1}{2m}y^2$$

$$\frac{m}{n}x^2 = y^2$$

$$y = \sqrt{\frac{m}{n}}\,x$$

2.3 The Definition of a Function

1. (a) All real numbers, or $(-\infty,\infty)$

   (b) We must solve: $-5x + 1 \geq 0$
   $$-5x \geq -1$$
   $$x \leq \frac{1}{5}$$
   So the domain is $\left(-\infty, \frac{1}{5}\right]$.

   (c) We must solve: $|-5x + 1| > 0$
   Since $|-5x + 1| \geq 0$ already, we need to find when:
   $$-5x + 1 = 0$$
   $$-5x = -1$$
   $$x = \frac{1}{5}$$
   So the domain is all real numbers except 1/5, or $(-\infty, 1/5) \cup (1/5, \infty)$.

3. (a) We must exclude those values of x where: $x - 4 = 0$
   $$x = 4$$
   So the domain is all real numbers except 4, or $(-\infty, 4) \cup (4,\infty)$.

   (b) We must exclude those values of x where: $x^2 - 4 = 0$
   $$x^2 = 4$$
   $$x = \pm 2$$
   So the domain is all real numbers except ± 2, or $(-\infty,-2) \cup (-2,2) \cup (2,\infty)$.

(c)   We must solve: $\dfrac{x^2 + 4}{x^2 - 4} \geq 0$

$\dfrac{x^2 + 4}{(x - 2)(x + 2)} \geq 0$

Key numbers: ± 2

A sign chart results in the following information:

$(-\infty, -2)$:	positive
$(-2, 2)$:	negative
$(2, \infty)$:	positive

So the domain is $(-\infty, -2) \cup (2, \infty)$.

5.   (a)   We must solve: $x^2 - 4x - 5 \geq 0$

$(x - 5)(x + 1) \geq 0$

Key numbers: 5, -1

A sign chart results in the following information:

$(-\infty, -1)$:	positive
$(-1, 5)$:	negative
$(5, \infty)$:	positive

So the domain is $(-\infty, -1] \cup [5, \infty)$.

(b)   We must solve $x^2 - 4x - 5 > 0$, which has the same solutions as in (a) but excluding the endpoints. So the domain is $(-\infty, -1) \cup (5, \infty)$.

(c)   There are no restrictions on $\sqrt[3]{x^2 - 4x - 5}$, so the domain is all real numbers, or $(-\infty, \infty)$.

7.   (a)   We solve for x: $y = \dfrac{x + 3}{x - 5}$

$y(x - 5) = x + 3$

$yx - 5y = x + 3$

$yx - x = 5y + 3$

$x(y - 1) = 5y + 3$

$x = \dfrac{5y + 3}{y - 1}$

We see that $y = 1$ will be excluded from the range. So the range is all real numbers except 1, or $(-\infty, 1) \cup (1, \infty)$.

(b)   We solve for x: $y = \dfrac{x - 5}{x + 3}$

$$y(x + 3) = x - 5$$
$$yx + 3y = x - 5$$
$$yx - x = -3y - 5$$
$$x(y - 1) = -3y - 5$$
$$x = \dfrac{-3y - 5}{y - 1}$$
$$x = \dfrac{3y + 5}{1 - y}$$

We see that y = 1 will be excluded from the range. So the range is all real numbers except 1, or $(-\infty, 1) \cup (1, \infty)$.

9.   (a)   We solve for x: $y = x^2 + 4$

$$y - 4 = x^2$$
$$x = \pm \sqrt{y - 4}$$

We see that y - 4 ≥ 0, and thus y ≥ 4. So the range is $[4, \infty)$.

(b)   We solve for x: $y = x^3 + 4$

$$y - 4 = x^3$$
$$x = \sqrt[3]{y - 4}$$

Since $\sqrt[3]{y - 4}$ has no restrictions, then the range is all real numbers, or $(-\infty, \infty)$.

11.   f: YES; g: YES; F: YES; H: YES
h: NO, since h(x) = 1 and h(x) = 2, which violates the definition of a function.
G: NO, since G(y) has not been assigned a value.

13.   (a)   range of f = {1,2,3}; range of g = {2,3}
range of F = {1}; range of H = {1,2}

(b)   range of g = {i,j}; range of F = {i,j}; range of G = {k}

15.   (a) $y = (x - 3)^2$
(b) $y = x^2 - 3$
(c) $y = (3x)^2$
(d) $y = 3x^2$

17. (a) $f(1) = (1)^2 - 3(1) + 1 = 1 - 3 + 1 = -1$

(b) $f(0) = (0)^2 - 3(0) + 1 = 0 - 0 + 1 = 1$

(c) $f(-1) = (-1)^2 - 3(-1) + 1 = 1 + 3 + 1 = 5$

(d) $f(3/2) = (3/2)^2 - 3(3/2) + 1 = 9/4 - 9/2 + 1 = -5/4$

(e) $f(z) = (z)^2 - 3(z) + 1 = z^2 - 3z + 1$

(f) $f(x + 1)$ $= (x + 1)^2 - 3(x + 1) + 1$
$= x^2 + 2x + 1 - 3x - 3 + 1$
$= x^2 - x - 1$

(g) $f(a + 1)$ $= (a + 1)^2 - 3(a + 1) + 1$
$= a^2 + 2a + 1 - 3a - 3 + 1$
$= a^2 - a - 1$

(h) $f(-x) = (-x)^2 - 3(-x) + 1 = x^2 + 3x + 1$

(i) $|f(1)| = |-1| = 1$ from (a)

(j) $f(\sqrt{3}) = (\sqrt{3})^2 - 3(\sqrt{3}) + 1 = 3 - 3\sqrt{3} + 1 = 4 - 3\sqrt{3}$

(k) $f(1 + \sqrt{2})$ $= (1 + \sqrt{2})^2 - 3(1 + \sqrt{2}) + 1$
$= 1 + 2\sqrt{2} + 2 - 3 - 3\sqrt{2} + 1$
$= 1 - \sqrt{2}$

(l) $|1 - f(2)|$ $= \left| -[(2)^2 - 3(2) + 1] \right|$
$= \left| 1 - [4 - 6 + 1] \right|$
$= |1 - (-1)|$
$= |1 + 1|$
$= 2$

19. (a) $f(2x) = 3(2x)^2 = 3(4x^2) = 12x^2$
(b) $2f(x) = 2(3x^2) = 6x^2$
(c) $f(x^2) = 3(x^2)^2 = 3x^4$
(d) $[f(x)]^2 = (3x^2)^2 = 9x^4$
(e) $f(x/2) = 3(x/2)^2 - 3(x^2/4) = 3x^2/4$
(f) $f(x) / 2 = 3x^2/2$

21. (a) $H(0) = 1 - 2(0)^2 = 1 - 0 = 1$

(b) $H(2) = 1 - 2(2)^2 = 1 - 2(4) = 1 - 8 = -7$

(c) $H(\sqrt{2}) = 1 - 2(\sqrt{2})^2 = 1 - 2(2) = 1 - 4 = -3$

(d) $H(5/6) = 1 - 2(5/6)^2 = 1 - 2(25/36) = 1 - 25/18 = -7/18$

(e) $\begin{aligned} H(x + 1) &= 1 - 2(x + 1)^2 \\ &= 1 - 2(x^2 + 2x + 1) \\ &= 1 - 2x^2 - 4x - 2 \\ &= -2x^2 - 4x - 1 \end{aligned}$

(f) $H(x + h) = 1 - 2(x + h)^2 = 1 - 2(x^2 + 2xh + h^2) = 1 - 2x^2 - 4xh - 2h^2$

(g) $\begin{aligned} H(x + h) - H(x) &= (1 - 2x^2 - 4xh - 2h^2) - (1 - 2x^2) \qquad \text{from (f)} \\ &= 1 - 2x^2 - 4xh - 2h^2 - 1 + 2x^2 \\ &= -4xh - 2h^2 \end{aligned}$

(h) $\begin{aligned} \frac{H(x + h) - H(x)}{h} &= \frac{-4xh - 2h^2}{h} \qquad \text{from (g)} \\ &= \frac{h(-4x - 2h)}{h} \\ &= -4x - 2h \end{aligned}$

23. (a) For the domain, we must exclude those values which make $x - 2 = 0$, or $x = 2$. So the domain is all real numbers except 2, or $(-\infty, 2) \cup (2, \infty)$. For the range, we solve for x:

$$y = \frac{2x - 1}{x - 2}$$
$$y(x - 2) = 2x - 1$$
$$yx - 2y = 2x - 1$$
$$yx - 2x = 2y - 1$$
$$x(y - 2) = 2y - 1$$
$$x = \frac{2y - 1}{y - 2}$$

Since the denominator cannot be zero, $y = 2$ is excluded. So the range is all real numbers except 2, or $(-\infty, 2) \cup (2, \infty)$.

(b) $R(0) = \frac{2(0) - 1}{0 - 2} = \frac{-1}{-2} = \frac{1}{2}$

(c) $R(1/2) = \dfrac{2(1/2) - 1}{1/2 - 2} = \dfrac{1 - 1}{-3/2} = 0$

(d) $R(-1) = \dfrac{2(-1) - 1}{-1 - 2} = \dfrac{-2 - 1}{-3} = \dfrac{-3}{-3} = 1$

(e) $R(x^2) = \dfrac{2(x^2) - 1}{x^2 - 2} = \dfrac{2x^2 - 1}{x^2 - 2}$

(f) $R(1/x) = \dfrac{2(1/x) - 1}{1/x - 2} = \dfrac{2/x - 1}{1/x - 2} = \dfrac{2 - x}{1 - 2x}$ by multiplying by $\dfrac{x}{x}$

(g) $R(a) = \dfrac{2a - 1}{a - 2}$

(h) $R(x - 1) = \dfrac{2(x - 1) - 1}{(x - 1) - 2} = \dfrac{2x - 2 - 1}{x - 3} = \dfrac{2x - 3}{x - 3}$

25.   (a) $d(1) = -16 (1)^2 + 96 (1) = -16 + 96 = 80$

  $d(3/2) = -16 (3/2)^2 + 96 (3/2) = -16 (9/4) + 144 = 108$

  $d(2) = -16 (2)^2 + 96 (2) = -64 + 192 = 128$

  $d(t_0) = -16t_0^2 + 96t_0$

(b)   We set $d(t) = 0$

  $-16t^2 + 96t = 0$

  $-16t (t - 6) = 0$

  $t = 0 , 6$

(c)   We set $d(t) = 1$

  $-16t^2 + 96t = 1$

  $16t^2 - 96t + 1 = 0$

  $$t = \frac{96 \pm \sqrt{(-96)^2 - 4(16)(1)}}{2(16)}$$

  $$= \frac{96 \pm \sqrt{9216 - 64}}{32}$$

  $$= \frac{96 \pm \sqrt{9152}}{32}$$

  $$= \frac{96 \pm 8\sqrt{143}}{32}$$

  $$= \frac{12 \pm \sqrt{143}}{4}$$

27. $g(3) = |3 - 4| = |-1| = 1$

  $g(x + 4) = |x + 4 - 4| = |x|$

29. (a) $f(x + h) = (x + h)^2 = x^2 + 2xh + h^2$

So $\dfrac{f(x + h) - f(x)}{h} = \dfrac{(x^2 + 2xh + h^2) - (x^2)}{h}$

$= \dfrac{2xh + h^2}{h}$

$= \dfrac{h(2x + h)}{h}$

$= 2x + h$

(b) $f(x + h) = 2(x + h)^2 - 3(x + h) + 1$

$= 2(x^2 + 2xh + h^2) - 3x - 3h + 1$

$= 2x^2 + 4xh + 2h^2 - 3x - 3h + 1$

So $\dfrac{f(x + h) - f(x)}{h} = \dfrac{(2x^2 + 4xh + 2h^2 - 3x - 3h + 1) - (2x^2 - 3x + 1)}{h}$

$= \dfrac{2x^2 + 4xh + 2h^2 - 3x - 3h + 1 - 2x^2 + 3x - 1}{h}$

$= \dfrac{4xh + 2h^2 - 3h}{h}$

$= \dfrac{h(4x + 2h - 3)}{h}$

$= 4x + 2h - 3$

(c) $f(x + h) = (x + h)^3 = x^3 + 3x^2h + 3xh^2 + h^3$

So $\dfrac{f(x + h) - f(x)}{h} = \dfrac{(x^3 + 3x^2h + 3xh^2 + h^3) - (x^3)}{h}$

$= \dfrac{3x^2h + 3xh^2 + h^3}{h}$

$= \dfrac{h(3x^2 + 3xh + h^2)}{h}$

$= 3x^2 + 3xh + h^2$

31. (a) $\dfrac{f(x) - f(a)}{x - a} = \dfrac{\dfrac{x}{x - 1} - \dfrac{a}{a - 1}}{x - a} \bullet \dfrac{(x - 1)(a - 1)}{(x - 1)(a - 1)}$

$= \dfrac{x(a - 1) - a(x - 1)}{(x - a)(x - 1)(a - 1)}$

$= \dfrac{ax - x - ax + a}{(x - a)(x - 1)(a - 1)}$

$= \dfrac{-(x - a)}{(x - a)(x - 1)(a - 1)}$

$= \dfrac{-1}{(x - 1)(a - 1)}$

(b)   Using our result from (a) with a = 3, we have:

$$\frac{f(x) - f(3)}{x - 3} = \frac{-1}{(x - 1)(3 - 1)} = \frac{-1}{2(x - 1)}$$

(c)

$$\frac{f(x + h) - f(x)}{h} = \frac{\dfrac{x + h}{x + h - 1} - \dfrac{x}{x - 1}}{h} \cdot \frac{(x - 1)(x + h - 1)}{(x - 1)(x + h - 1)}$$

$$= \frac{(x + h)(x - 1) - x(x + h - 1)}{h(x - 1)(x + h - 1)}$$

$$= \frac{x^2 + hx - x - h - x^2 - xh + x}{h(x - 1)(x + h - 1)}$$

$$= \frac{-h}{h(x - 1)(x + h - 1)}$$

$$= \frac{-1}{(x - 1)(x + h - 1)}$$

(d)   Using our result from (c) with x = 3, we have:

$$\frac{f(3 + h) - f(3)}{h} = \frac{-1}{(3 - 1)(3 + h - 1)} = \frac{-1}{2(2 + h)}$$

33.   (a)   We set $f(x_0) = g(x_0)$: $4x_0 - 3 = 8 - x_0$

$$5x_0 = 11, \text{ so } x_0 = \frac{11}{5}$$

(b)   We set $f(x_0) = g(x_0)$: $x_0^2 - 4 = 4 - x_0^2$

$$2x_0^2 = 8$$

$$x_0^2 = 4$$

Taking roots: $x_0 = \pm 2$

$$x_0 = 2 \text{ or } x_0 = -2$$

(c)   We set $f(x_0) = g(x_0)$: $x_0^2 = x_0^3$

$$x_0^3 - x_0^2 = 0$$

$$x_0^2(x_0 - 1) = 0$$

$$x_0 = 0 \text{ or } x_0 = 1$$

(d)   We set $f(x_0) = g(x_0)$: $2x_0^2 - x_0 = 3$

$$2x_0^2 - x_0 - 3 = 0$$

$$(2x_0 - 3)(x_0 + 1) = 0$$

$$x_0 = \frac{3}{2} \text{ or } x_0 = -1$$

35. (a) $A(1) = 1000\left(1 + \dfrac{0.12}{4}\right)^{4(1)} = \$1125.51$

     $A(0) = 1000\left(1 + \dfrac{0.12}{4}\right)^{4(0)} = \$1000.00$

     So $A(1) - A(0) = 1125.51 - 1000.00 = \$125.51$

    (b) $A(10) = 1000\left(1 + \dfrac{0.12}{4}\right)^{4(10)} = \$3262.04$

     $A(9) = 1000\left(1 + \dfrac{0.12}{4}\right)^{4(9)} = \$2898.28$

     So $A(10) - A(9) = 3262.04 - 2898.28 = \$363.76$

37. (a) We fill in the table:

n	2	3	4	5	6	7	8
g(n)	1.4142	1.4422	1.4142	1.3797	1.3480	1.3205	1.2968

    (b) $g(15) = 1.19786$ and $g(14) = 1.20744$, so 15 is the smallest natural number n such that $g(n) < 1.2$

39. (a) $f(a) = \dfrac{a - a}{a + a} = \dfrac{0}{2a} = 0$

     $f(2a) = \dfrac{2a - a}{2a + a} = \dfrac{a}{3a} = \dfrac{1}{3}$

     $f(3a) = \dfrac{3a - a}{3a + a} = \dfrac{2a}{4a} = \dfrac{1}{2}$

     So $f(3a) \neq f(a) + f(2a)$, since $\dfrac{1}{2} \neq 0 + \dfrac{1}{3}$

    (b) $f(5a) = \dfrac{5a - a}{5a + a} = \dfrac{4a}{6a} = \dfrac{2}{3}$

     So $f(5a) = 2\left(\dfrac{1}{3}\right) = 2\,f(2a)$

41. $\phi(y^2) = 2(y^2) - 3 = 2y^2 - 3$

    $[\phi(y)]^2 = (2y - 3)^2 = 4y^2 - 12y + 9$

    So $\phi(y^2) \neq [\phi(y)]^2$

43. $f(ax + b) = 2(ax + b) + 3 = 2ax + 2b + 3$
We set $f(ax + b) = x$: $2ax + 2b + 3 = x$
Equating constants, we have $2ax = x$ and $2b + 3 = 0$
$$2a = 1 \qquad\qquad 2b = -3$$
$$a = \frac{1}{2} \qquad\qquad b = -\frac{3}{2}$$

So $a = \frac{1}{2}$ and $b = -\frac{3}{2}$

45. $f(x + y) = \dfrac{(x + y) - x}{(x + y) + y} = \dfrac{y}{x + 2y}$ and $f(x - y) = \dfrac{(x - y) - x}{(x - y) + y} = \dfrac{-y}{x}$

So $f(x + y) + f(x - y) = \dfrac{y}{x + 2y} - \dfrac{y}{x}$

$$= \frac{yx - y(x + 2y)}{x(x + 2y)}$$

$$= \frac{yx - yx - 2y^2}{x^2 + 2xy}$$

$$= \frac{-2y^2}{x^2 + 2xy}$$

47. $F\left(\dfrac{ax + b}{cx - a}\right) = \dfrac{a\left(\dfrac{ax + b}{cx - a}\right) + b}{c\left(\dfrac{ax + b}{cx - a}\right) - a}$

$$= \frac{a(ax + b) + b(cx - a)}{c(ax + b) - a(cx - a)} \quad \text{by multiplying by } \frac{cx - a}{cx - a}$$

$$= \frac{a^2x + ab + bcx - ab}{acx + bc - acx + a^2}$$

$$= \frac{a^2x + bcx}{a^2 + bc}$$

$$= \frac{x(a^2 + bc)}{a^2 + bc}$$

$$= x$$

49. $g(1) = (1)^2 - 3(1)k - 4 = 1 - 3k - 4 = -3k - 3$, so if $g(1) = -2$ we have:
$$-3k - 3 = -2$$
$$-3k = 1$$
$$k = -\frac{1}{3}$$

51. (a) $L(1) = 0$, since $2^0 = 1$
    (b) $L(2) = 1$, since $2^1 = 1$
    (c) $L(4) = 2$, since $2^2 = 4$
    (d) $L(64) = 6$, since $2^6 = 64$
    (e) $L(1/2) = -1$, since $2^{-1} = \dfrac{1}{2}$
    (f) $L(1/4) = -2$, since $2^{-2} = \dfrac{1}{4}$
    (g) $L(1/64) = -6$, since $2^{-6} = \dfrac{1}{64}$
    (h) $L(\sqrt{2}) = \dfrac{1}{2}$, since $2^{1/2} = \sqrt{2}$

53. Actually, we already know the answer to this question. Since $\dfrac{-b + \sqrt{b^2 - 4ac}}{2a}$ is one of the roots to the quadratic equation $q(x) = 0$, we know

$$q\left(\frac{-b + \sqrt{b^2 - 4ac}}{2a} \right) = 0.$$ Let's check our answer manually:

$$q\left(\frac{-b + \sqrt{b^2 - 4ac}}{2a} \right)$$

$$= a\left(\frac{-b + \sqrt{b^2 - 4ac}}{2a} \right)^2 + b\left(\frac{-b + \sqrt{b^2 - 4ac}}{2a} \right) + c$$

$$= a\left(\frac{b^2 - 2b\sqrt{b^2 - 4ac} + b^2 - 4ac}{4a^2} \right) + \left(\frac{-b^2 + b\sqrt{b^2 - 4ac}}{2a} \right) + c$$

$$= \frac{2b^2 - 4ac - 2b\sqrt{b^2 - 4ac}}{4a} + \frac{-b^2 + b\sqrt{b^2 - 4ac}}{2a} + c$$

$$= \frac{b^2 - 2ac - b\sqrt{b^2 - 4ac} - b^2 + b\sqrt{b^2 - 4ac}}{2a} + c$$

$$= \frac{-2ac}{2a} + c$$

$$= -c + c$$

$$= 0 \quad \text{It checks!}$$

55. (a) $f[f(x)] = f\left(\dfrac{3x-4}{x-3}\right)$

$$= \dfrac{3\left(\dfrac{3x-4}{x-3}\right) - 4}{\left(\dfrac{3x-4}{x-3}\right) - 3}$$

$$= \dfrac{3(3x-4) - 4(x-3)}{(3x-4) - 3(x-3)} \qquad \text{multiplying by } \dfrac{x-3}{x-3}$$

$$= \dfrac{9x - 12 - 4x + 12}{3x - 4 - 3x + 9}$$

$$= \dfrac{5x}{5}$$

$$= x$$

(b) Since $f[f(x)] = x$, then $f[f(22/7)] = \dfrac{22}{7}$

57. The problem here is the word "nearest." $G(4) = 3$, but also $G(4) = 5$, since both 3 and 5 are equally "near" 4. So G is not a function, since it assigns more than one value to $x = 4$. To alter the definition of G, one could define $G(x)$ to be the closest prime number less than or equal to x (or, for that matter, greater than or equal to x). This would provide G with a way of "deciding" between 3 and 5, in the previous example. Why do we need the "or equal to" portion of the definition? [Hint: How would you define $G(5)$ otherwise?]

59. $P(1) = (1)^2 - 1 + 41 = 41$
       $P(2) = (2)^2 - 2 + 41 = 43$
       $P(3) = (3)^2 - 3 + 41 = 47$
       $P(4) = (4)^2 - 4 + 41 = 53$
Yes, although one has to search quite a while:
    $P(41) = (41)^2 - (41) + 41$
           $= (41)(41 - 1 + 1)$
           $= (41)(41)$, which is not prime.
This is the first such number.

2.4 The Graph of a Function

1.   (a) positive
     (b) $f(-2) = 4$; $f(1) = 1$; $f(2) = 2$; $f(3) = 0$
     (c) $f(2)$, since $f(2) > 0$ and $f(4) < 0$
     (d) $f(4) - f(1) = -2 - 1 = -3$
     (e) $|f(4) - f(1)| = |-3| = 3$
     (f) domain $= [-2,4]$; range $= [-2,4]$

3.   (a)   f(-2) = 0 and g(-2) = 1, so g(-2) is larger.

      (b)   f(0) - g(0) = 2 - (-3) = 2 + 3 = 5

      (c)   f(1) - g(1) = 1 - (-1) = 2
             f(2) - g(2) =   1 - 0   = 1
             f(3) - g(3) =   4 - 1   = 3
             So f(2) - g(2) is the smallest.

      (d)   Since f(1) = 1, we see that g(x) = 1 when x = -2 or x = 3

      (e)   Since (3,4) is a point on the graph of f, then 4 is in the range of f.

5.   range of f = [0, 4]
      range of g = [-3, 3]

7.   The completed table is:

Function	Turning Point	Maximum Value	Minimum Value	Interval(s) Increasing	Interval(s) Decreasing
$|x|$	(0,0)	none	0	$(0, \infty)$	$(-\infty, 0)$
x^2	(0,0)	none	0	$(0, \infty)$	$(-\infty, 0)$
x^3	none	none	none	$(-\infty, \infty)$	none

9.   (a)   yes
      (b)   no
      (c)   no
      (d)   yes

11. The slope is:

$$m = \frac{f(4) - f(3)}{4 - 3} = \frac{4^2 - 3^2}{1} = \frac{16 - 9}{1} = 7$$

We draw the graph:

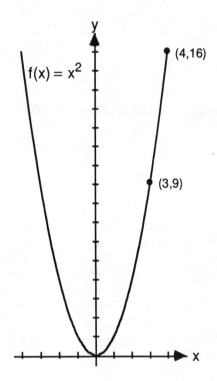

13. We find the two slopes:

$$m_1 = \frac{T(4) - T(1)}{4 - 1} \qquad\qquad m_2 = \frac{T(9) - T(4)}{9 - 4}$$

$$= \frac{\sqrt{4} - \sqrt{1}}{3} \qquad\qquad\quad = \frac{\sqrt{9} - \sqrt{4}}{5}$$

$$= \frac{2 - 1}{3} \qquad\qquad\qquad\; = \frac{3 - 2}{5}$$

$$= \frac{1}{3} \qquad\qquad\qquad\quad\; = \frac{1}{5}$$

Since $m_1 > m_2$, then the line between $\left(1, T(1)\right)$ and $\left(4, T(4)\right)$ has the larger slope.

15. (a) $k(x) = \sqrt{1 - x^2}$,   [0,1]

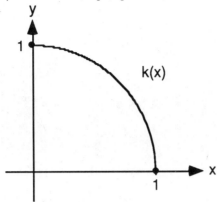

(b) $m(x) = \sqrt{1 - x^2}$,   (0,1)
This graph will be the same as in (a), except the points (0, 1) and (1, 0) will be excluded.

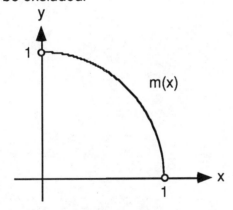

(c)   We graph n(x) on the required domain:

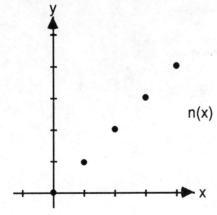

(d)   We graph z(x) on the required domain:

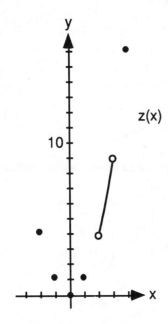

17.   We graph f(x):

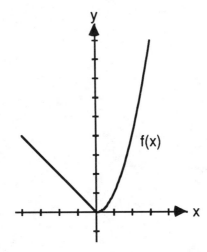

19. We graph A(x):

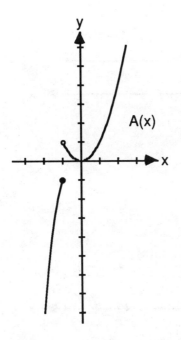

21. We graph C(x):

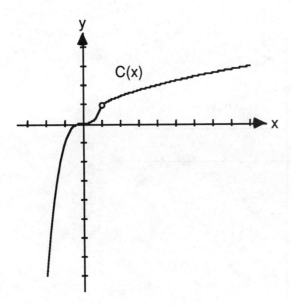

23. (a)   We graph g(x):

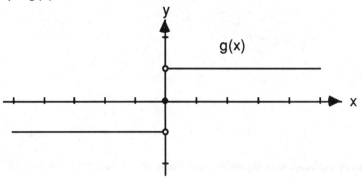

(b)   We graph G(x):

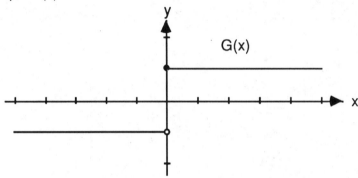

25.   We graph V(x):

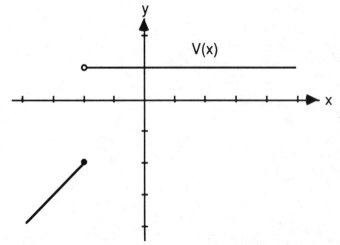

27. We graph f(x):

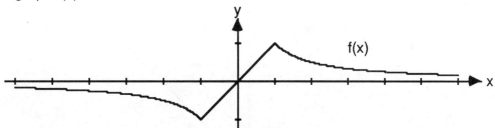

29. We graph y(x):

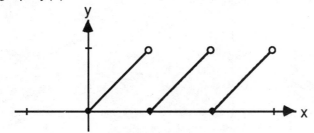

31. (a) Note that, for x ≠ -5, we have:
$$\frac{x^2 - 25}{x + 5} = \frac{(x + 5)(x - 5)}{x + 5} = x - 5$$
That makes it much easier to graph. The domain is all real numbers except -5, or $(-\infty, -5) \cup (-5, \infty)$:

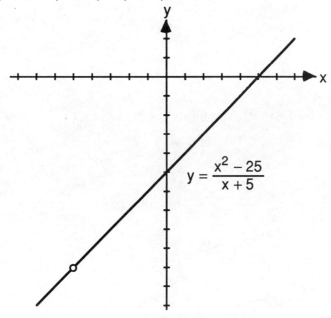

(b)   This just adds the point (-5, -10) to the graph:

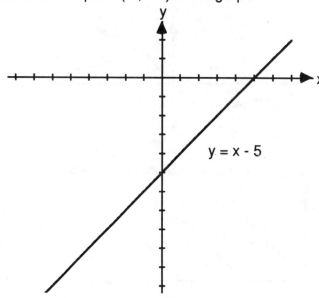

y = x - 5

33.   Let the coordinates of T be (t, 1/t). Then:

$$m = \frac{\frac{1}{t} - 1}{t - 1} = -\frac{1}{5}$$

Multiplying by $\frac{t}{t}$, we get:

$$\frac{1 - t}{t(t - 1)} = -\frac{1}{5}$$

$$\frac{-1}{t} = \frac{-1}{5}$$

$$-t = -5$$

$$t = 5$$

So the point T is (5, 1/5). We draw the sketch:

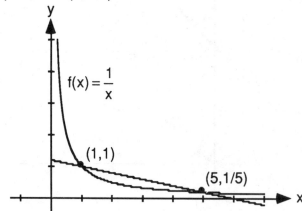

$f(x) = \dfrac{1}{x}$

(1,1)

(5,1/5)

35. B is the point $(x + h, f(x + h))$
     Since A is $(x, f(x))$, then the slope is:
     $$m = \frac{f(x + h) - f(x)}{h}$$

37. (a) We can see from the figure that the slope of the line segment joining $(a, f(a))$ and $(b, f(b))$ is $m = \frac{f(b) - f(a)}{b - a}$:

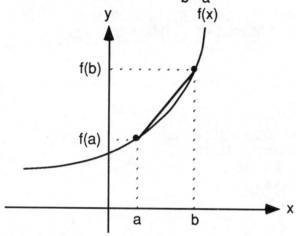

     (b) We compute the slope between $(0, 0)$ and $(1, 1)$:
          $$m = \frac{1 - 0}{1 - 0} = \frac{1}{1} = 1$$
          We compute the slope between $(10, 100)$ and $(11, 121)$:
          $$m = \frac{121 - 100}{11 - 10} = \frac{21}{1} = 21$$
          Clearly the average rate of change between 10 and 11 is larger.

     (c) We compute the average rate of change for each function:
          $f(x) = x^2$, the points are $(3, 9)$ and $(4, 16)$:
          $$m = \frac{16 - 9}{4 - 3} = \frac{7}{1} = 7$$
          $g(x) = x^3$, the points are $(3, 27)$ and $(4, 64)$:
          $$m = \frac{64 - 27}{4 - 3} = \frac{37}{1} = 37$$
          $h(x) = \frac{1}{x}$, the points are $(3, 1/3)$ and $(4, 1/4)$:
          $$m = \frac{1/4 - 1/3}{4 - 3} = \frac{-1/12}{1} = -\frac{1}{12}$$
          So $g(x) = x^3$ has the largest average rate of change between 3 and 4.

(d)   (i)   Points are (1, 1) and (1.1, 1.21):

$$m = \frac{1.21 - 1}{1.1 - 1} = \frac{0.21}{0.1} = 2.1$$

(ii)   Points are (1, 1) and (1.01, 1.0201):

$$m = \frac{1.0201 - 1}{1.01 - 1} = \frac{0.0201}{0.01} = 2.01$$

(iii)   Points are (1, 1) and (1.001, 1.002001):

$$m = \frac{1.002001 - 1}{1.001 - 1} = \frac{0.002001}{0.001} = 2.001$$

It appears that, as b approaches 1, the average rate of change is approaching 2.

39.   (a) $f(2) - f(1) = 16(2)^2 - 16(1)^2$
$$= 16(4) - 16(1)$$
$$= 64 - 16$$
$$= 48 \text{ ft}$$

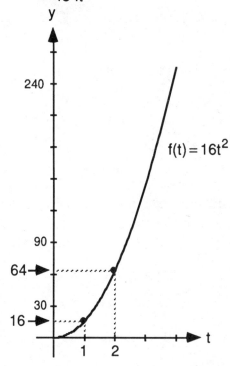

(b) $f(3) - f(2) = 16(3)^2 - 16(2)^2$
$= 16(9) - 16(4)$
$= 144 - 64$
$= 80$ ft

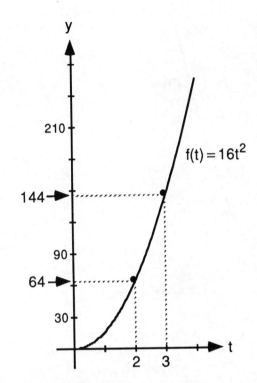

(c)   Avg. vel. $= \dfrac{f(3) - f(1)}{3 - 1}$

$= \dfrac{144 - 16}{3 - 1}$

$= \dfrac{128}{2}$

$= 64$ ft/sec

This is the same as the slope of the line joining the points $(1, f(1))$ and $(3, f(3))$.

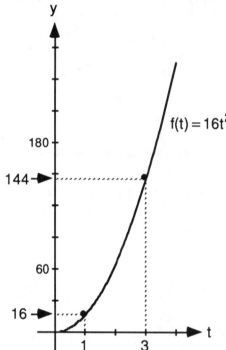

(d)   (i) $v_{avg} = \dfrac{f(1.1) - f(1)}{1.1 - 1} = \dfrac{19.36 - 16}{0.1} = \dfrac{3.36}{0.1} = 33.6$

(ii) $v_{avg} = \dfrac{f(1.001) - f(1)}{1.001 - 1} = \dfrac{16.032016 - 16}{0.001} = 32.016$

(iii) $v_{avg} = \dfrac{f(1.00001) - f(1)}{1.00001 - 1} = \dfrac{16.0003200016 - 16}{0.00001} = 32.00016$

As b approaches 1, the average velocity seems to be approaching 32 ft/sec. Case (iii) gives the clearest indication of what these values are approaching.

41.   (a)   We complete the table:

t	0	0.25	0.5	0.75	1	1.25	1.5	1.75	2	2.25	2.5	2.75	3
S(t)	0	0.25	0.5	0.75	1	1	1	1	1	1	1	1	1

Now graph the function S(t) on the interval $0 \le t \le 3$:

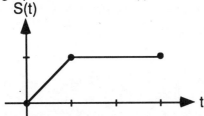

(b) We complete the table:

t	3	3.25	3.5	3.75	4	4.25	4.5	4.75	5
S(t)	1	0.75	0.5	0.25	0	−0.25	−0.5	−0.75	−1

Now graph the function S(t) on the interval $3 \le t \le 5$:

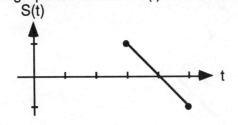

(c) We draw the graph:

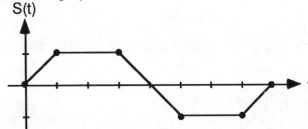

(d) We draw the graph:

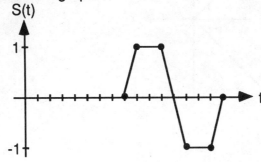

The graph is identical to that of part (c) except for the t-values. This is an example of a periodic function, that is, one which repeats its values over a specified period. In this example, the period is t = 8.

2.5 Techniques in Graphing

1.   (a) C;   (b) F;   (c) I;   (d) A;   (e) J;   (f) K
     (g) D;   (h) B;   (i) E;   (j) H;   (k) G

3.   (a) $|x - 2| + |y| = 2$
           This is $|x| + |y| = 2$ displaced 2 units to the right. See graph:

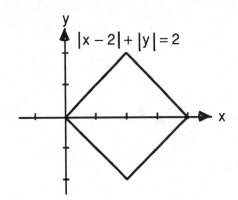

$|x - 2| + |y| = 2$

     (b) $|x + 2| + |y| = 2$
           This is $|x| + |y| = 2$ displaced 2 units to the left. See graph:

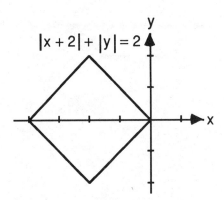

$|x + 2| + |y| = 2$

(c) $|x| + |y - 2| = 2$
This is $|x| + |y| = 2$ displaced 2 units up. See graph:

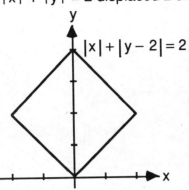

(d) $|x| + |y + 2| = 2$
This is $|x| + |y| = 2$ displaced 2 units down. See graph:

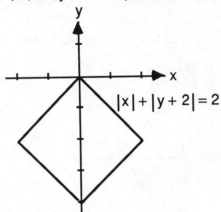

(e) $|x - 2| + |y + 2| = 2$
This is $|x| + |y| = 2$ displaced 2 units to the right and 2 units down.
See graph:

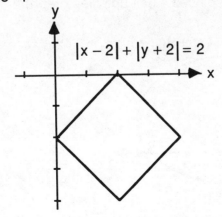

(f) $|x + 2| + |y + 2| = 2$
This is $|x| + |y| = 2$ displaced 2 units to the left and 2 units down.
See graph:

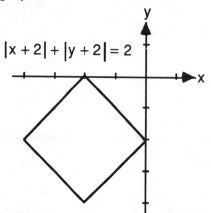

5.   (a) $4(x - 1)^2 + 9y^2 = 36$
This is $4x^2 + 9y^2 = 36$ displaced 1 unit to the right. See graph:

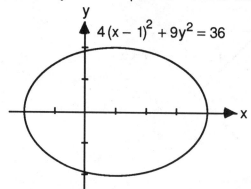

(b) $4x^2 + 9(y - 1)^2 = 36$
This is $4x^2 + 9y^2 = 36$ displaced 1 unit up. See graph:

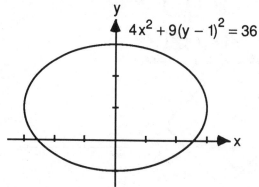

(c) $4(x + 1)^2 + 9(y + 1)^2 = 36$
This is $4x^2 + 9y^2 = 36$ displaced 1 unit to the left and 1 unit down.
See graph:

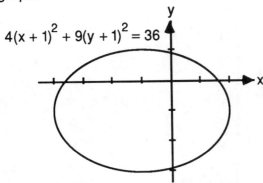

(d) $4(x - 1)^2 + 9(y - 1)^2 = 36$
This is $4x^2 + 9y^2 = 36$ displaced 1 unit to the right and 1 unit up. See graph:

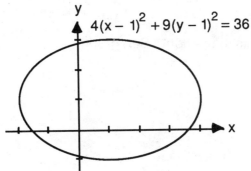

7. $y = x^2 - 3$
This is $y = x^2$ displaced down 3 units. See graph:

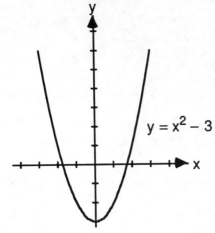

9. $y = (x + 4)^2$
     This is $y = x^2$ displaced 4 units to the left.   See graph:

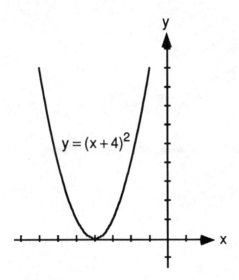

11. $y = (x - 4)^2$
     This is $y = x^2$ displaced 4 units to the right.   See graph:

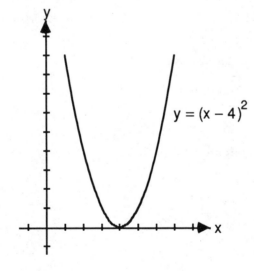

13. $y = -x^2$
This is $y = x^2$ reflected across the x-axis. See graph:

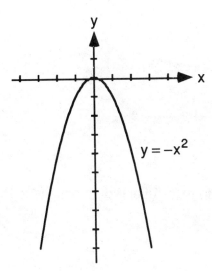

15. $y = -(x - 3)^2$
This is $y = x^2$ displaced 3 units to the right, then reflected across the x-axis.
See graph:

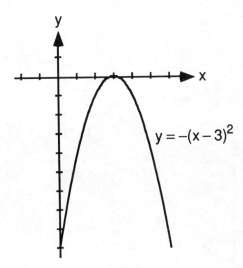

17. $y = \sqrt{x - 3}$

This is $y = \sqrt{x}$ displaced 3 units to the right. See graph:

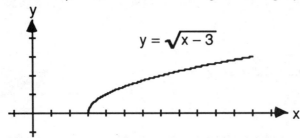

19. $y = -\sqrt{x + 1}$

This is $y = \sqrt{x}$ displaced 1 unit to the left, then reflected across the x-axis.
See graph:

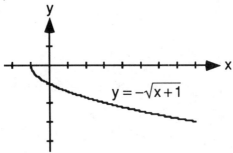

21. $y = \dfrac{1}{x + 2} + 2$

This is $y = \dfrac{1}{x}$ displaced 2 units to the left and 2 units up. See graph:

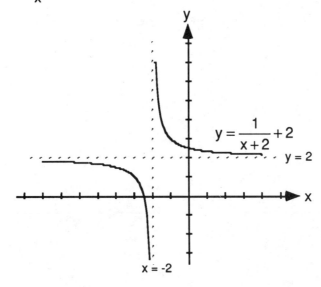

23. $y = (x - 2)^3$
     This is $y = x^3$ displaced 2 units to the right. See graph:

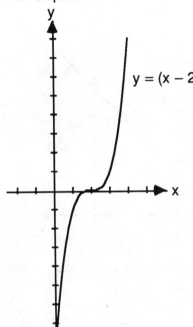

25. $y = -x^3 + 4$
     This is $y = x^3$ reflected across the x-axis, then displaced 4 units up. See graph:

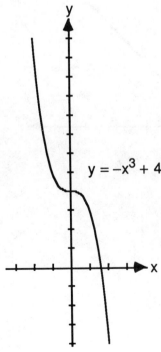

27.   (a) $y = |x + 4|$
This is $y = |x|$ displaced 4 units to the left. See graph:

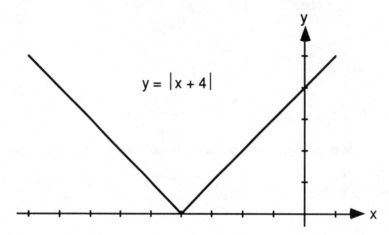

$y = |x + 4|$

(b) $y = |4 - x|$
This is $y = |x|$ reflected across the y-axis, then displaced 4 units to the right. See graph:

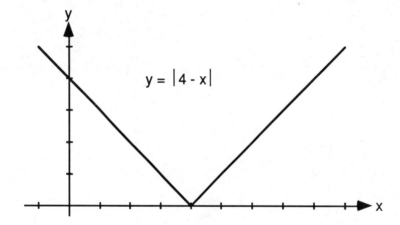

$y = |4 - x|$

(c) $y = -|4 - x| + 1$

This is $y = |x|$ reflected across the y-axis, displaced 4 units to the right, reflected across the x-axis, then displaced 1 unit up. See graph:

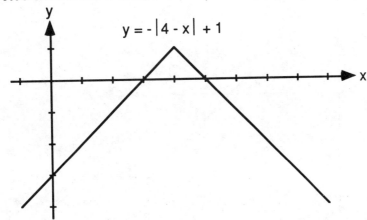

$y = -|4 - x| + 1$

29. $y = f(x - 5) = |x - 5|$

This is $y = |x|$ displaced 5 units to the right. See graph:

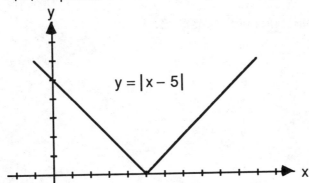

$y = |x - 5|$

31. $y = f(5 - x) = |5 - x|$

This is $y = |x|$ reflected across the y-axis, then displaced 5 units to the right. See graph:

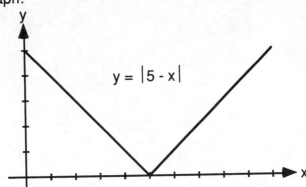

$y = |5 - x|$

33. $y = 1 - f(x - 5) = 1 - |x - 5|$
This is $y = |x|$ displaced 5 units to the right, then reflected across the x-axis, then displaced up 1 unit. See graph:

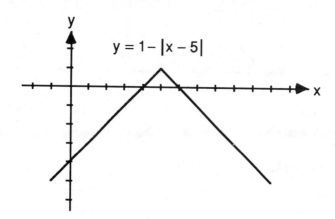

35. $y = F(x + 3) = \dfrac{1}{x + 3}$

This is $y = \dfrac{1}{x}$ displaced 3 units to the left. See graph:

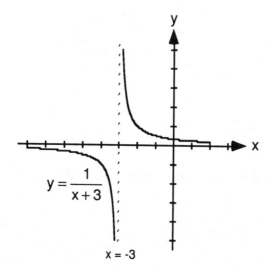

37. $y = -F(x + 3) = \dfrac{-1}{x + 3}$

This is $y = \dfrac{1}{x}$ displaced 3 units to the left and reflected across the x-axis.
See graph:

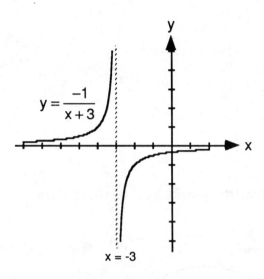

39. $y = g(x - 2) = \sqrt{1 - (x - 2)^2}$

This is $y = \sqrt{1 - x^2}$ displaced 2 units to the right. See graph:

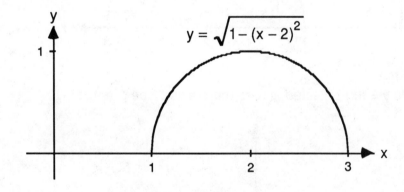

41. $y = 1 - g(x - 2) = 1 - \sqrt{1 - (x - 2)^2}$

This is $y = \sqrt{1 - x^2}$ displaced 2 units to the right, reflected across the x-axis, and displaced up 1 unit. See graph:

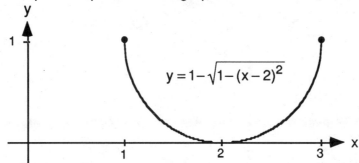

43. $y = g(2 - x) = \sqrt{1 - (2 - x)^2}$

This is $y = \sqrt{1 - x^2}$ reflected across the y-axis, then displaced 2 units to the right. See graph:

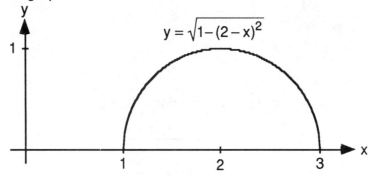

45. (a) $y = -f(x)$

This is $y = f(x)$ reflected across the x-axis. See graph:

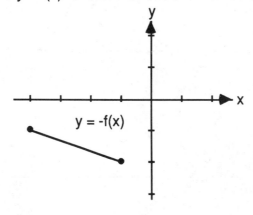

(b)   y = f(-x)
This is y = f(x) reflected across the y-axis. See graph:

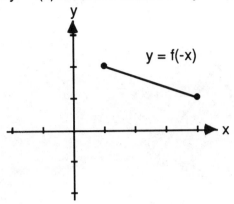

(c)   y = -f(-x)
This is y = f(x) reflected across the y-axis and reflected across the
x-axis. See graph:

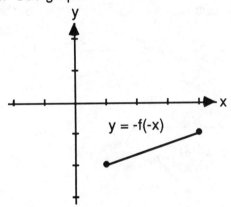

47.   (a)   y = g(-x)
This is y = g(x) reflected across the y-axis. See graph:

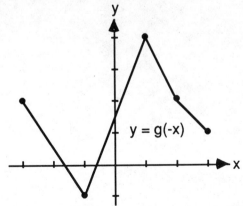

(b)   y = -g(x)
       This is y = g(x) reflected across the x-axis. See graph:

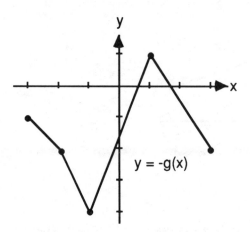

y = -g(x)

(c)   y = -g(-x)
       This is y = g(x) reflected across the y-axis and reflected across the
       x-axis. See graph:

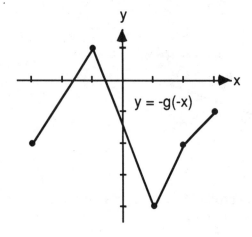

y = -g(-x)

49. (a) $y = 10^{-x}$
    This is $y = 10^x$ reflected across the y-axis. See graph:

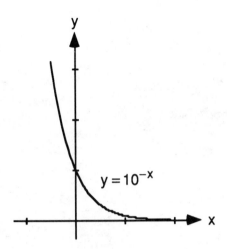

$$y = 10^{-x}$$

(b) $y = -10^x$
    This is $y = 10^x$ reflected across the x-axis. See graph:

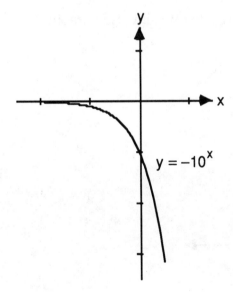

$$y = -10^x$$

(c) $y = -10^{-x}$

This is $y = 10^x$ reflected across the y-axis and reflected across the x-axis. See graph:

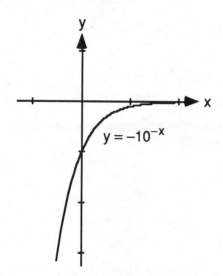

(d) $y = 10^{x-1}$

This is $y = 10^x$ displaced 1 unit to the right. See graph:

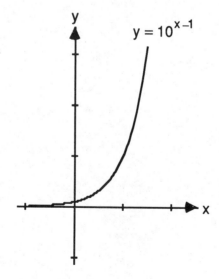

(e) $y = 10^x + 1$
This is $y = 10^x$ displaced up 1 unit. See graph:

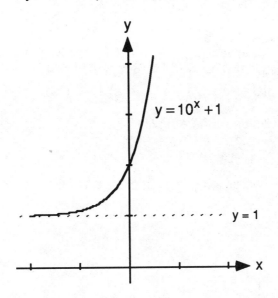

(f) $y = -10^{x-1} - 1$
This is $y = 10^x$ displaced to the right 1 unit, reflected across the x-axis, then displaced down 1 unit. See graph:

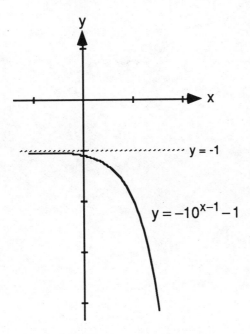

51. (a) $(a + 3, b)$, since $f(a + 3 - 3) = f(a) = b$
     (b) $(a, b - 3)$, since $f(a) - 3 = b - 3$
     (c) $(a + 3, b - 3)$, since $f(a + 3 - 3) - 3 = f(a) - 3 = b - 3$
     (d) $(a, -b)$, since $-f(a) = -b$
     (e) $(-a, b)$, since $f(-(-a)) = f(a) = b$
     (f) $(-a, -b)$, since $-f(-(a)) = -f(a) = -b$
     (g) $(-a + 3, b)$, since $f(3 - (-a + 3)) = f(3 + a - 3) = f(a) = b$
     (h) $(-a + 3, -b + 1)$, since $-f(3 - (-a + 3)) + 1 = -f(a) + 1 = -b + 1$

53. We work from the right-hand side of the equality:
$$\frac{1}{x - 1} + 1 = \frac{1 + x - 1}{x - 1} = \frac{x}{x - 1}$$
Since $g(x) = \dfrac{1}{x - 1} + 1$, then we graph $y = \dfrac{1}{x}$ displaced 1 unit to the right and 1 unit up. See graph:

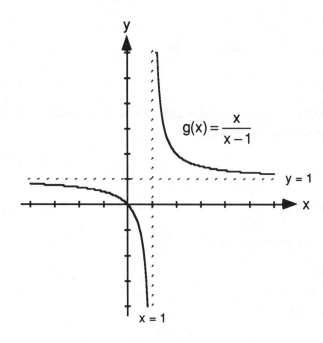

55. We work from the right-hand side of the equality:

$$(x - 2)^3 - 1 = x^3 - 6x^2 + 12x - 8 - 1 = x^3 - 6x^2 + 12x - 9$$

Since $y = (x - 2)^3 - 1$, then we graph $y = x^3$ displaced 2 units to the right and 1 unit down. See graph:

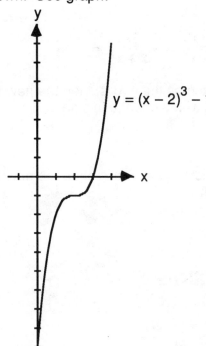

$$y = (x - 2)^3 - 1$$

57. We rationalize the denominator (which is valid for $0 < |x| \le 1$):

$$\frac{x^2}{1 - \sqrt{1 - x^2}} \cdot \frac{1 + \sqrt{1 - x^2}}{1 + \sqrt{1 - x^2}} = \frac{x^2\left(1 + \sqrt{1 - x^2}\right)}{1 - 1 + x^2}$$

$$= \frac{x^2\left(1 + \sqrt{1 - x^2}\right)}{x^2}$$

$$= 1 + \sqrt{1 - x^2}$$

Now, since $0 \le \sqrt{1 - x^2} < 1$, then $1 \le 1 + \sqrt{1 - x^2} < 2$. So the range is $[1, 2)$.

59. (a) Call $y = f(x)$. We replace x by $-x$ and y by $-y$:

$$-y = f(-x)$$
$$-y = -f(x) \qquad \text{since } f(-x) = -f(x)$$
$$y = f(x)$$

So the resulting equation is identical to the original equation, and thus the graph of $y = f(x)$ is symmetric about the origin.

(b)　(i)　$f(-x) = (-x)^3 = -x^3 = -f(x)$

　　(ii)　$f(-x) = -2(-x)^5 + 4(-x)^3 - (-x)$

　　　　　$= 2x^5 - 4x^3 + x$

　　　　　$= -(-2x^5 + 4x^3 - x)$

　　　　　$= -f(x)$

　　(iii)　$f(-x) = \dfrac{|-x|}{(-x) + (-x)^7} = \dfrac{|x|}{-x - x^7} = -\dfrac{|x|}{x + x^7} = -f(x)$

61.　(a)　Since $y = f(-x)$ is a reflection across the y-axis, then the new function will have these intervals reversed with a change in sign:

　　　　increasing:　$(-\infty, -4) \cup (-2, \infty)$

　　　　decreasing:　$(-4, -2)$

　　(b)　Since $y = -f(x)$ is a reflection across the x-axis, then the new function will have these intervals reversed:

　　　　increasing:　$(-\infty, 2) \cup (4, \infty)$

　　　　decreasing:　$(2, 4)$

2.6 Methods of Combining Functions

1.　(a)　$(f + g)(x) = f(x) + g(x)$

　　　　　　　　$= (2x - 1) + (x^2 - 3x - 6)$

　　　　　　　　$= x^2 - x - 7$

　　(b)　$(f - g)(x) = f(x) - g(x)$

　　　　　　　　$= (2x - 1) - (x^2 - 3x - 6)$

　　　　　　　　$= -x^2 + 5x + 5$

　　(c)　$(f - g)(0) = -(0)^2 + 5(0) + 5$

　　　　　　　　$= 0 + 0 + 5$

　　　　　　　　$= 5$

3.　(a)　$(m - f)(x) = m(x) - f(x)$

　　　　　　　　$= (x^2 - 9) - (2x - 1)$

　　　　　　　　$= x^2 - 9 - 2x + 1$

　　　　　　　　$= x^2 - 2x - 8$

　　(b)　$(f - m)(x) = f(x) - m(x)$

　　　　　　　　$= (2x - 1) - (x^2 - 9)$

　　　　　　　　$= 2x - 1 - x^2 + 9$

　　　　　　　　$= -x^2 + 2x + 8$

5. (a) $(fk)(x) = f(x)\,k(x) = (2x - 1)\,(2) = 4x - 2$
    (b) $(kf)(x) = k(x)\,f(x) = 2(2x - 1) = 4x - 2$
    (c) $(fk)(1) - (kf)(2) = [4(1) - 2] - [4(2) - 2] = 2 - 6 = -4$

7. (a) $\dfrac{f}{m}(x) - \dfrac{m}{f}(x) = \dfrac{f(x)}{m(x)} - \dfrac{m(x)}{f(x)}$

$$= \frac{[f(x)]^2 - [m(x)]^2}{f(x)m(x)}$$

$$= \frac{(2x - 1)^2 - (x^2 - 9)^2}{(x^2 - 9)(2x - 1)}$$

$$= \frac{(4x^2 - 4x + 1) - (x^4 - 18x^2 + 81)}{2x^3 - x^2 - 18x + 9}$$

$$= \frac{-x^4 + 22x^2 - 4x - 80}{2x^3 - x^2 - 18x + 9}$$

    (b) $\dfrac{f}{m}(0) - \dfrac{m}{f}(0) = \dfrac{-0^4 + 22(0)^2 - 4(0) - 80}{2(0)^3 - 0^2 - 18(0) + 9} = -\dfrac{80}{9}$

9. (a) $[m\,(k - h)]\,(x) = m(x)\,[\,k(x) - h(x)\,]$
            $= (x^2 - 9)\,(2 - x^3)$
            $= 2x^2 - 18 - x^5 + 9x^3$
            $= -x^5 + 9x^3 + 2x^2 - 18$

    (b) $(mk)(x) - (mh)(x) = m(x)\,k(x) - m(x)\,h(x)$
            $= (x^2 - 9)(2) - (x^2 - 9)(x^3)$
            $= 2x^2 - 18 - x^5 + 9x^3$
            $= -x^5 + 9x^3 + 2x^2 - 18$

    (c) $(mk)(-1) - (mh)(-1) = -(-1)^5 + 9(-1)^3 + 2(-1)^2 - 18$
            $= -(-1) + 9(-1) + 2(1) - 18$
            $= 1 - 9 + 2 - 18$
            $= -24$

11. (a) $(f \circ g)(x) = f\,[\,g(x)\,]$
            $= f\,(-2x - 5)$
            $= 3(-2x - 5) + 1$
            $= -6x - 15 + 1$
            $= -6x - 14$

    (b) $(f \circ g)(10) = -6(10) - 14 = -60 - 14 = -74$

(c) $(g \circ f)(x)$ $= g[f(x)]$
$= g(3x + 1)$
$= -2(3x + 1) - 5$
$= -6x - 2 - 5$
$= -6x - 7$

(d) $(g \circ f)(10) = -6(10) - 7 = -60 - 7 = -67$

13. (a) $(f \circ g)(x) = f[g(x)] = f(1 + x) = 1 - (1 + x) = 1 - 1 - x = -x$
$(f \circ g)(-2) = -(-2) = 2$
$(g \circ f)(x) = g[f(x)] = g(1 - x) = 1 + (1 - x) = 2 - x$
$(g \circ f)(-2) = 2 - (-2) = 2 + 2 = 4$

(b) $(f \circ g)(x)$ $= f[g(x)]$
$= f(2 - 3x)$
$= (2 - 3x)^2 - 3(2 - 3x) - 4$
$= 4 - 12x + 9x^2 - 6 + 9x - 4$
$= 9x^2 - 3x - 6$
$(f \circ g)(-2) = 9(-2)^2 - 3(-2) - 6 = 36 + 6 - 6 = 36$
$(g \circ f)(x)$ $= g[f(x)]$
$= g(x^2 - 3x - 4)$
$= 2 - 3(x^2 - 3x - 4)$
$= 2 - 3x^2 + 9x + 12$
$= -3x^2 + 9x + 14$
$(g \circ f)(-2)$ $= -3(-2)^2 + 9(-2) + 14 = -12 - 18 + 14 = -16$

(c) $(f \circ g)(x)$ $= f[g(x)] = f(1 - x^4) = \dfrac{1 - x^4}{3}$

$(f \circ g)(-2) = \dfrac{1 - (-2)^4}{3} = \dfrac{1 - 16}{3} = \dfrac{-15}{3} = -5$

$(g \circ f)(x)$ $= g[f(x)] = g\left(\dfrac{x}{3}\right) = 1 - \left(\dfrac{x}{3}\right)^4 = 1 - \dfrac{x^4}{81}$

$(g \circ f)(-2) = 1 - \dfrac{(-2)^4}{81} = 1 - \dfrac{16}{81} = \dfrac{65}{81}$

(d) $(f \circ g)(x)$ $= f[g(x)] = f(x^2 + 1) = 2^{x^2 + 1}$
$(f \circ g)(-2) = 2^{(-2)^2 + 1} = 2^{4+1} = 2^5 = 32$
$(g \circ f)(x) = g[f(x)] = g(2^x) = (2^x)^2 + 1 = 2^{2x} + 1$
$(g \circ f)(-2) = 2^{2(-2)} + 1 = 2^{-4} + 1 = \dfrac{1}{16} + 1 = \dfrac{17}{16}$

(e) $(f \circ g)(x) = f[g(x)] = f(3x^5 - 4x^2) = 3x^5 - 4x^2$
     $(f \circ g)(-2) = 3(-2)^5 - 4(-2)^2 = -96 - 16 = -112$
     $(g \circ f)(x) = g[f(x)] = g(x) = 3x^5 - 4x^2$
     $(g \circ f)(-2) = 3(-2)^5 - 4(-2)^2 = -96 - 16 = -112$

(f) $(f \circ g)(x) = f[g(x)] = f\left(\dfrac{x+4}{3}\right) = 3\left(\dfrac{x+4}{3}\right) - 4 = x + 4 - 4 = x$

     $(f \circ g)(-2) = -2$

     $(g \circ f)(x) = g[f(x)] = g(3x - 4) = \dfrac{3x - 4 + 4}{3} = \dfrac{3x}{3} = x$

     $(g \circ f)(-2) = -2$

15. (a) $(F \circ G)(x) = F[G(x)]$

     $= F\left(\dfrac{x+1}{x-1}\right)$

     $= \dfrac{3\left(\dfrac{x+1}{x-1}\right) - 4}{3\left(\dfrac{x+1}{x-1}\right) + 3}$

     Multiplying by $\dfrac{x-1}{x-1}$ yields:

     $= \dfrac{3(x+1) - 4(x-1)}{3(x+1) + 3(x-1)}$

     $= \dfrac{3x + 3 - 4x + 4}{3x + 3 + 3x - 3}$

     $= \dfrac{-x + 7}{6x}$

     (b) $F[G(t)] = \dfrac{-t + 7}{6t}$

     (c) $(F \circ G)(2) = F[G(2)] = \dfrac{-2 + 7}{6(2)} = \dfrac{5}{12}$

     (d) $(G \circ F)(x) = G[F(x)]$

     $= G\left(\dfrac{3x - 4}{3x + 3}\right)$

     $= \dfrac{\dfrac{3x - 4}{3x + 3} + 1}{\dfrac{3x - 4}{3x + 3} - 1}$

Multiplying by $\dfrac{3x + 3}{3x + 3}$ yields:

$$= \frac{(3x - 4) + 1(3x + 3)}{(3x - 4) - 1(3x + 3)}$$

$$= \frac{3x - 4 + 3x + 3}{3x - 4 - 3x - 3}$$

$$= \frac{6x - 1}{-7}$$

$$= \frac{1 - 6x}{7}$$

(e) $G[F(y)] = \dfrac{1 - 6y}{7}$

(f) $(G \circ F)(2) = G[F(2)] = \dfrac{1 - 6(2)}{7} = \dfrac{-11}{7}$

17. (a) $M(7) = \dfrac{2(7) - 1}{7 - 2} = \dfrac{14 - 1}{5} = \dfrac{13}{5}$

$$M[M(7)] = M\left(\frac{13}{5}\right) = \frac{2\left(\frac{13}{5}\right) - 1}{\frac{13}{5} - 2} = \frac{\frac{26}{5} - 1}{\frac{3}{5}} = \frac{\frac{21}{5}}{\frac{3}{5}} = 7$$

(b) $(M \circ M)(x) = M[M(x)]$

$$= M\left(\frac{2x - 1}{x - 2}\right)$$

$$= \frac{2\left(\frac{2x - 1}{x - 2}\right) - 1}{\left(\frac{2x - 1}{x - 2}\right) - 2}$$

Multiply by $\dfrac{x - 2}{x - 2}$:

$$= \frac{2(2x - 1) - 1(x - 2)}{(2x - 1) - 2(x - 2)}$$

$$= \frac{4x - 2 - x + 2}{2x - 1 - 2x + 4}$$

$$= \frac{3x}{3}$$

$$= x$$

(c) $(M \circ M)(7) = M[M(7)] = 7$. Yes, it agrees!

19. (a) f [g(3)] = f(0) = 1
     (b) g [f(3)] = g(4) = -3
     (c) f [h(3)] = f(2) = -1
     (d) (h ∘ g)(2) = h [g(2)] = h(1) = 2
     (e) h { f [g(3)] } = h [f(0)] = h(1) = 2
     (f) (g ∘ f ∘ h ∘ f)(2) = (g ∘ f ∘ h)(-1) = (g ∘ f)(3) = g(4) = -3

21. (a) (T ∘ I)(x) = T [I(x)] = T(x) = $4x^3 - 3x^2 + 6x - 1$
          (I ∘ T)(x) = I [T(x)] = I($4x^3 - 3x^2 + 6x - 1$) = $4x^3 - 3x^2 + 6x - 1$

     (b) (G ∘ I)(x) = G [I(x)] = G(x) = $ax^2 + bx + c$
          (I ∘ G)(x) = I [G(x)] = I($ax^2 + bx + c$) = $ax^2 + bx + c$

     (c) In general, given any function f(x) and I(x) = x, then:
          (f ∘ I)(x) = f(x) and (I ∘ f)(x) = f(x)
          Such a function, I(x) = x, is called the identity function.

23. (f ∘ g)(0) = f [g(0)] = f(3) = 1
     (f ∘ g)(1) = f [g(1)] = f(2) = 3
     (f ∘ g)(2) = f [g(2)] = f(0) = 2
     (f ∘ g)(3) = f [g(3)] = f(4) = undefined
     (f ∘ g)(4) = f [g(4)] = f(-1) = 2

     Thus we have the table:

x	0	1	2	3	4
(f ∘ g)(x)	1	3	2	und.	2

     (g ∘ f)(-1) = g [f(-1)] = g(2) = 0
     (g ∘ f)(0) = g [f(0)] = g(2) = 0
     (g ∘ f)(1) = g [f(1)] = g(0) = 3
     (g ∘ f)(2) = g [f(2)] = g(3) = 4
     (g ∘ f)(3) = g [f(3)] = g(1) = 2
     (g ∘ f)(4) = g [f(4)] = undefined

     Thus we have the table:

x	−1	0	1	2	3	4
(g ∘ f)(x)	0	0	3	4	2	und.

25. (a) $(f \circ g)(x) = f[g(x)] = f(3x - 4) = 2(3x - 4) + 1 = 6x - 8 + 1 = 6x - 7$
We draw the graph:

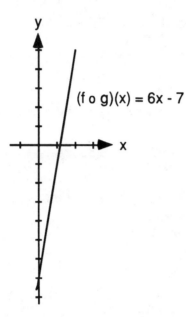

$(f \circ g)(x) = 6x - 7$

(b) $(g \circ f)(x) = g[f(x)] = g(2x + 1) = 3(2x + 1) - 4 = 6x + 3 - 4 = 6x - 1$
We draw the graph:

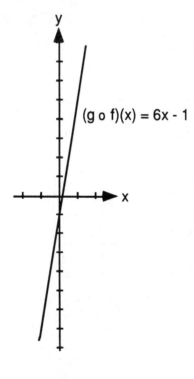

$(g \circ f)(x) = 6x - 1$

27. (a) $g(x) = \sqrt{x} - 3$
            domain: $[\,0, \infty)$; range: $[-3, \infty)$

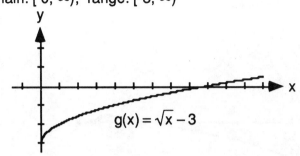

$$g(x) = \sqrt{x} - 3$$

(b) $f(x) = x - 1$
       domain: all real numbers; range: all real numbers

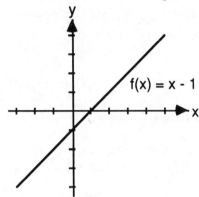

$$f(x) = x - 1$$

(c) $(f \circ g)(x) = f\,[\,g(x)\,]$
                     $= f(\sqrt{x} - 3)$
                     $= (\sqrt{x} - 3) - 1$
                     $= \sqrt{x} - 4$
       domain: $[0, \infty)$; range: $[-4, \infty)$

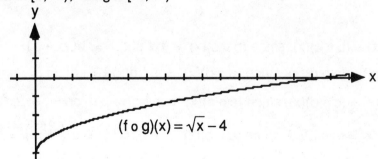

$$(f \circ g)(x) = \sqrt{x} - 4$$

(d) $g[f(x)] = g(x - 1) = \sqrt{x - 1} - 3$
       domain: $[1, \infty)$; range: $[-3, \infty)$

(e)   We draw the graph:

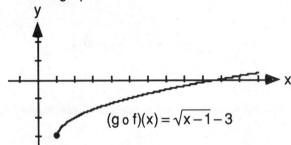

$(g \circ f)(x) = \sqrt{x - 1} - 3$

29.   Let $f(x) = x^4$ and $g(x) = 3x - 1$. Then $C(x) = (f \circ g)(x)$, since
       $(f \circ g)(x) = f[g(x)] = f(3x - 1) = (3x - 1)^4$.

31.   (a)   Let $f(x) = \sqrt[3]{x}$ and $g(x) = 3x + 4$. Then $F(x) = (f \circ g)(x)$,
              since $(f \circ g)(x) = f[g(x)] = f(3x + 4) = \sqrt[3]{3x + 4}$.

       (b)   Let $f(x) = |x|$ and $g(x) = 2x - 3$. Then $G(x) = (f \circ g)(x)$,
              since $(f \circ g)(x) = f[g(x)] = f(2x - 3) = |2x - 3|$.

       (c)   Let $f(x) = x^5$ and $g(x) = ax + b$. Then $H(x) = (f \circ g)(x)$,
              since $(f \circ g)(x) = f[g(x)] = f(ax + b) = (ax + b)^5$.

       (d)   Let $f(x) = \dfrac{1}{x}$ and $g(x) = \sqrt{x}$. Then $T(x) = (f \circ g)(x)$,
              since $(f \circ g)(x) = f[g(x)] = f(\sqrt{x}) = \dfrac{1}{\sqrt{x}}$.

33.   (a) $f(x) = (b \circ c)(x)$, since $(b \circ c)(x) = b[c(x)] = b(2x + 1) = \sqrt[3]{2x + 1}$

       (b) $g(x) = (a \circ d)(x)$, since $(a \circ d)(x) = a[d(x)] = a(x^2) = \dfrac{1}{x^2}$

       (c) $h(x) = (c \circ d)(x)$, since $(c \circ d)(x) = c[d(x)] = c(x^2) = 2x^2 + 1$

       (d) $K(x) = (c \circ b)(x)$, since $(c \circ b)(x) = c[b(x)] = c(\sqrt[3]{x}) = 2\sqrt[3]{x} + 1$

       (e) $l(x) = (c \circ a)(x)$, since $(c \circ a)(x) = c[a(x)] = c\left(\dfrac{1}{x}\right) = 2\left(\dfrac{1}{x}\right) + 1 = \dfrac{2}{x} + 1$

       (f) $m(x) = (a \circ c)(x)$, since $(a \circ c)(x) = a[c(x)] = a(2x + 1) = \dfrac{1}{2x + 1}$

(g) $n(x) = (b \circ d)(x)$, since $(b \circ d)(x) = b[d(x)] = b(x^2) = \sqrt[3]{x^2} = x^{2/3}$
Note that we could also use:

   $n(x) = (d \circ b)(x)$, since $(d \circ b)(x) = d[b(x)] = d\left(\sqrt[3]{x}\right) = \left(\sqrt[3]{x}\right)^2 = x^{2/3}$

35. $(C \circ f)(t) = C[f(t)] = C\left(\dfrac{1}{t^2+1}\right) = 2\pi\left(\dfrac{1}{t^2+1}\right) = \dfrac{2\pi}{t^2+1}$

When $t = 3$, $(C \circ f)(3) = \dfrac{2\pi}{3^2+1} = \dfrac{2\pi}{10} = \dfrac{\pi}{5}$ ft

37. (a) $(C \circ f)(t) = C[f(t)] = C(5t) = 100 + 90(5t) - (5t)^2 = 100 + 450t - 25t^2$

(b) When $t = 3$ hr., we have $C[f(3)] = 100 + 450(3) - 25(3)^2 = \$1225$

(c) When $t = 6$ hr., we have $C[f(6)] = 100 + 450(6) - 25(6)^2 = \$1900$
No, the cost is not twice as much for 6 hours.

39. Call $y = f(x)$. Since $(g \circ f)(x) = g[f(x)] = g(y)$, then:

$$g(y) = x + 5$$
$$4y - 1 = x + 5$$
$$4y = x + 6$$
$$y = \dfrac{x+6}{4}$$

So $f(x) = \dfrac{x+6}{4}$

41. We set $f[g(x)] = x$
$$f(ax + b) = x$$
$$-2(ax + b) + 1 = x$$
$$-2ax - 2b + 1 = x$$
Since a and b are constants, we can equate components:

$-2a = 1$ and $-2b + 1 = 0$

$a = -\dfrac{1}{2}$ $-2b = -1$

$b = \dfrac{1}{2}$

So $a = -1/2$ and $b = 1/2$.

43. (a) $\dfrac{f[g(x)] - f[g(a)]}{g(x) - g(a)}$ $= \dfrac{f(2x - 1) - f(2a - 1)}{(2x - 1) - (2a - 1)}$

$= \dfrac{(2x - 1)^2 - (2a - 1)^2}{2x - 1 - 2a + 1}$

$= \dfrac{[(2x - 1) + (2a - 1)][(2x - 1) - (2a - 1)]}{2x - 2a}$

$= \dfrac{(2x + 2a - 2)(2x - 2a)}{2x - 2a}$

$= 2x + 2a - 2$

(b) $\dfrac{f[g(x)] - f[g(a)]}{x - a}$ $= \dfrac{(2x + 2a - 2)(2x - 2a)}{x - a}$

$= \dfrac{4(x + a - 1)(x - a)}{x - a}$

$= 4x + 4a - 4$

45. (a) $(g \circ h \circ f)(x) = g\{h[f(x)]\} = g[h(x^2)] = g\left(\dfrac{x^2}{2}\right) = \dfrac{x^2}{2} + 1$

(b) $(h \circ f \circ g)(x) = h\{f[g(x)]\} = h[f(x + 1)] = h[(x + 1)^2] = \dfrac{(x + 1)^2}{2}$

(c) $(g \circ f \circ h)(x) = g\{f[h(x)]\}$

$= g\left[f\left(\dfrac{x}{2}\right)\right]$

$= g\left[\left(\dfrac{x}{2}\right)^2\right]$

$= g\left(\dfrac{x^2}{4}\right)$

$= \dfrac{x^2}{4} + 1$

(d) $(f \circ h \circ g)(x) = f\{h[g(x)]\}$
$= f[h(x + 1)]$

$= f\left(\dfrac{x + 1}{2}\right)$

$= \left(\dfrac{x + 1}{2}\right)^2$

$= \dfrac{(x + 1)^2}{4}$

(e) $(h \circ g \circ f)(x) = h\{g[f(x)]\} = h[g(x^2)] = h(x^2 + 1) = \dfrac{x^2 + 1}{2}$

47. (a) $p(x) = (g \circ f \circ h)(x)$, since $(g \circ f \circ h)(x) = g\{f[h(x)]\}$
$$= g[f(3x)]$$
$$= g[(3x)^2]$$
$$= g(9x^2)$$
$$= 1 - 9x^2$$

(b) $q(x) = (h \circ g \circ f)(x)$, since $(h \circ g \circ f)(x) = h\{g[f(x)]\}$
$$= h[g(x^2)]$$
$$= h(1 - x^2)$$
$$= 3(1 - x^2)$$
$$= 3 - 3x^2$$

(c) $r(x) = (f \circ g \circ h)(x)$, since $(f \circ g \circ h)(x) = f\{g[h(x)]\}$
$$= f[g(3x)]$$
$$= f(1 - 3x)$$
$$= (1 - 3x)^2$$
$$= 1 - 6x + 9x^2$$

(d) $s(x) = (h \circ f \circ g)(x)$, since $(h \circ f \circ g)(x) = h\{f[g(x)]\}$
$$= h[f(1 - x)]$$
$$= h[(1 - x)^2]$$
$$= h(1 - 2x + x^2)$$
$$= 3(1 - 2x + x^2)$$
$$= 3 - 6x + 3x^2$$

49. (a) $F'[G(x)] \bullet G'(x) = F'(x^2 + 2x + 2) \bullet (2x + 2)$
$$= \frac{1}{2\sqrt{x^2 + 2x + 2}} \bullet (2x + 2)$$
$$= \frac{x + 1}{\sqrt{x^2 + 2x + 2}}$$

(b) $F'[G(9)] \bullet G'(9) = \dfrac{9 + 1}{\sqrt{9^2 + 2(9) + 2}}$
$$= \frac{10}{\sqrt{81 + 18 + 2}}$$
$$= \frac{10}{\sqrt{101}}$$
$$= \frac{10\sqrt{101}}{101}$$

51. (a) We have the following compositions:

$(i \circ i)(x) = i(x) = x = i$ $(a \circ i)(x) = a(x) = -x = a$

$(i \circ a)(x) = i(-x) = -x = a$ $(a \circ a)(x) = a(-x) = x = i$

$(i \circ b)(x) = i\left(\dfrac{1}{x}\right) = \dfrac{1}{x} = b$ $(a \circ b)(x) = a\left(\dfrac{1}{x}\right) = -\dfrac{1}{x} = c$

$(i \circ c)(x) = i\left(-\dfrac{1}{x}\right) = -\dfrac{1}{x} = c$ $(a \circ c)(x) = a\left(-\dfrac{1}{x}\right) = \dfrac{1}{x} = b$

$(b \circ i)(x) = b(x) = \dfrac{1}{x} = b$ $(c \circ i)(x) = c(x) = -\dfrac{1}{x} = c$

$(b \circ a)(x) = b(-x) = -\dfrac{1}{x} = c$ $(c \circ a)(x) = c(-x) = \dfrac{1}{x} = b$

$(b \circ b)(x) = b\left(\dfrac{1}{x}\right) = x = i$ $(c \circ b)(x) = c\left(\dfrac{1}{x}\right) = -x = a$

$(b \circ c)(x) = b\left(-\dfrac{1}{x}\right) = -x = a$ $(c \circ c)(x) = c\left(-\dfrac{1}{x}\right) = x = i$

So we have the composition table:

$\circ$	i	a	b	c
i	i	a	b	c
a	a	i	c	b
b	b	c	i	a
c	c	b	a	i

(b) yes

(c) $a^2 = i$; $b^2 = i$; $c^2 = i$; $c^3 = c \circ c^2 = c \circ i = c$

(d) $(a \circ b) \circ c = (c) \circ c = i$ and $a \circ (b \circ c) = a \circ (a) = i$,
so $(a \circ b) \circ c = a \circ (b \circ c)$

(e) Since $i^2 = a^2 = b^2 = c^2 = i$, then the range of f is $\{\, i \,\}$.

(f) $f(a \circ b) = f(c) = c^2 = i$
$[\, f(a) \,] \circ [\, f(b) \,] = a^2 \circ b^2 = i \circ i = i$, so $f(a \circ b) = [\, f(a) \,] \circ [\, f(b) \,]$

(g) $f(a \circ b \circ c) = f(a \circ a) = f(i) = i^2 = i$
$[\, f(a) \,] \circ [\, f(b) \,] \circ [\, f(c) \,] = a^2 \circ b^2 \circ c^2 = i \circ (i \circ i) = i \circ i = i$,
so $f(a \circ b \circ c) = [\, f(a) \circ f(b) \circ f(c) \,]$

2.7 **Inverse Functions**

1. (a) We need to show that $(f \circ g)(x) = x$ and that $(g \circ f)(x) = x$:

$$(f \circ g)(x) = f[g(x)] = f\left(\frac{x}{3}\right) = 3\left(\frac{x}{3}\right) = x$$

$$(g \circ f)(x) = g[f(x)] = g(3x) = \frac{3x}{3} = x$$

So $f(x)$ and $g(x)$ are inverse functions.

(b) We need to show $(f \circ g)(x) = x$ and that $(g \circ f)(x) = x$:

$$(f \circ g)(x) = f[g(x)] = f\left(\frac{x+1}{4}\right) = 4\left(\frac{x+1}{4}\right) - 1 = x + 1 - 1 = x$$

$$(g \circ f)(x) = g[f(x)] = g(4x - 1) = \frac{(4x-1)+1}{4} = \frac{4x}{4} = x$$

So $f(x)$ and $g(x)$ are inverse functions.

(c) We need to show $(g \circ h)(x) = x$ and that $(h \circ g)(x) = x$:

$$(g \circ h)(x) = g[h(x)] = g(x^2) = \sqrt{x^2} = x, \quad \text{since } x \geq 0$$

$$(h \circ g)(x) = h[g(x)] = h(\sqrt{x}) = (\sqrt{x})^2 = x$$

So $g(x)$ and $h(x)$ are inverse functions.

3. (a) Since $f[f^{-1}(x)] = x$, then $f[f^{-1}(4)] = 4$
   (b) Since $f^{-1}[f(x)] = x$, then $f^{-1}[f(-1)] = -1$
   (c) Since $(f \circ f^{-1})(x) = x$, then $(f \circ f^{-1})(\sqrt{2}) = \sqrt{2}$
   (d) Since $f[f^{-1}(x)] = x$, then $f[f^{-1}(t+1)] = t + 1$
   (e) $f(0) = 0^3 + 2(0) + 1 = 1$, then $f^{-1}(1) = 0$
   (f) $f(-1) = (-1)^3 + 2(-1) + 1 = -1 - 2 + 1 = -2$, then $f^{-1}(2) = -1$

5. (a) Let $y = 3x - 1$
   We switch the roles of x and y and solve the resulting equation for y:

$$x = 3y - 1$$
$$3y = x + 1$$
$$y = \frac{x+1}{3}$$

So the inverse is $f^{-1}(x) = \frac{x+1}{3}$

(b) $f[f^{-1}(x)] = f\left(\frac{x+1}{3}\right) = 3\left(\frac{x+1}{3}\right) - 1 = x + 1 - 1 = x$

$f^{-1}[f(x)] = f^{-1}(3x - 1) = \frac{(3x-1)+1}{3} = \frac{3x}{3} = x$

We have $f[f^{-1}(x)] = x$ and $f^{-1}[f(x)] = x$, which verifies that $f(x)$ and $f^{-1}(x)$ are inverse funtions.

(c)   The graphs of each line are given below. Note the symmetry of each line about the line $y = x$:

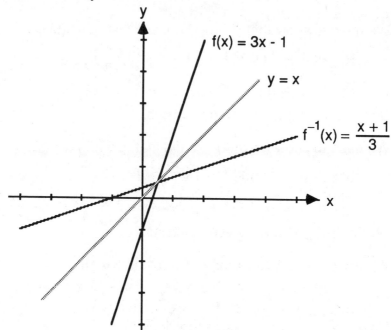

7.   (a)   Let $y = \sqrt{x - 1}$
We switch the roles of x and y and solve the resulting equation for y:
$$x = \sqrt{y - 1}$$
Squaring each side:
$$x^2 = y - 1$$
$$y = x^2 + 1$$
So the inverse is $f^{-1}(x) = x^2 + 1$.

(b) $f[\,f^{-1}(x)\,] = f(x^2 + 1) = \sqrt{(x^2 + 1) - 1} = \sqrt{x^2} = x$, since $x \geq 0$
$f^{-1}[\,f(x)\,] = f^{-1}(\sqrt{x - 1}) = (\sqrt{x - 1}\,)^2 + 1 = x - 1 + 1 = x$
We have $f[\,f^{-1}(x)\,] = x$ and $f^{-1}[\,f(x)\,] = x$, which verifies that f(x) and $f^{-1}(x)$ are inverse functions.

(c)   The graphs of each curve are given below. Note the symmetry of each curve about the line y = x:

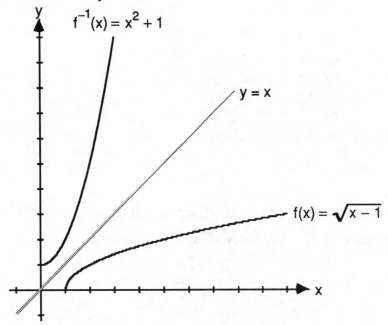

$f^{-1}(x) = x^2 + 1$

y = x

$f(x) = \sqrt{x - 1}$

9.   (a)   domain of f: all real numbers except 3, or $(-\infty, 3) \cup (3, \infty)$
        range of f: We solve for x:
        $$y = \frac{x + 2}{x - 3}$$
        $$y(x - 3) = x + 2$$
        $$yx - 3y = x + 2$$
        $$yx - x = 3y + 2$$
        $$x(y - 1) = 3y + 2$$
        $$x = \frac{3y + 2}{y - 1}$$
        So the range of f(x) is all real numbers except 1, or $(-\infty, 1) \cup (1, \infty)$

(b)   Let $y = \dfrac{x+2}{x-3}$

We switch the roles of x and y and solve the resulting equation for y:

$$x = \frac{y+2}{y-3}$$
$$x(y-3) = y+2$$
$$xy-3x = y+2$$
$$xy-y = 3x+2$$
$$y(x-1) = 3x+2$$
$$y = \frac{3x+2}{x-1}$$

So $f^{-1}(x) = \dfrac{3x+2}{x-1}$

(c)   domain of f^{-1}: all real numbers except 1, or $(-\infty, 1) \cup (1,\infty)$

range of f^{-1}:   We solve $y = \dfrac{3x+2}{x-1}$ for x:

$$y(x-1) = 3x+2$$
$$yx-y = 3x+2$$
$$yx-3x = y+2$$
$$x(y-3) = y+2$$
$$x = \frac{y+2}{y-3}$$

So the range of f^{-1} is all real numbers except 3, or $(-\infty, 3) \cup (3, \infty)$

Notice that: domain of f = range of f^{-1}

range of f = domain of f^{-1}

11.   Let $y = 2x^3 + 1$

We switch the roles of x and y and solve the resulting equation for y:

$$x = 2y^3 + 1$$
$$2y^3 = x-1$$
$$y^3 = \frac{x-1}{2}$$
$$y = \sqrt[3]{\frac{x-1}{2}}$$

So $f^{-1}(x) = \sqrt[3]{\dfrac{x-1}{2}}$

13. $f[f^{-1}(x)] = f\left(\frac{x+4}{3}\right) = 3\left(\frac{x+4}{3}\right) - 4 = x + 4 - 4 = x$

   $f^{-1}[f(x)] = f^{-1}(3x - 4) = \frac{(3x-4)+4}{3} = \frac{3x}{3} = x$

   This verfies that f and f^{-1} are inverse functions. We sketch the graph:

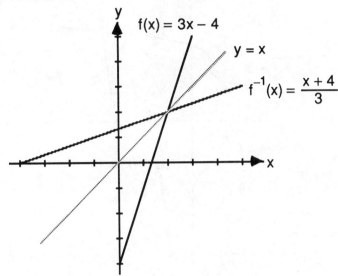

15.   (a)   Let $y = (x-3)^3 - 1$
      We switch the roles of x and y and solve the resulting equation for y:

      $$x = (y-3)^3 - 1$$
      $$(y-3)^3 = x + 1$$

      Taking the cube root:

      $$y - 3 = \sqrt[3]{x+1}$$
      $$y = \sqrt[3]{x+1} + 3$$

   So $f^{-1}(x) = \sqrt[3]{x+1} + 3$

(b)   The graph of each curve is given below:

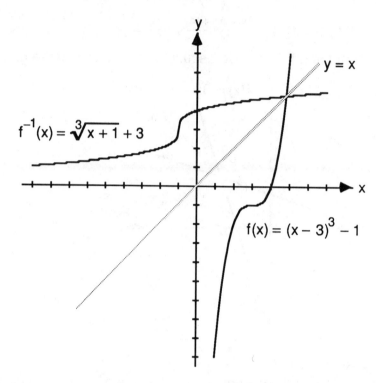

$$f^{-1}(x) = \sqrt[3]{x+1} + 3$$

$$y = x$$

$$f(x) = (x-3)^3 - 1$$

17.   (a) $y = g^{-1}(x)$

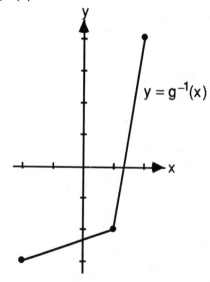

$$y = g^{-1}(x)$$

(b) $y = g^{-1}(x) - 1$

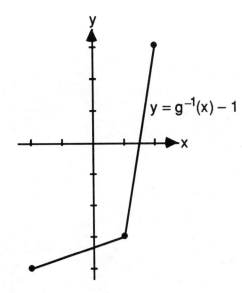

$y = g^{-1}(x) - 1$

(c) $y = g^{-1}(x - 1)$

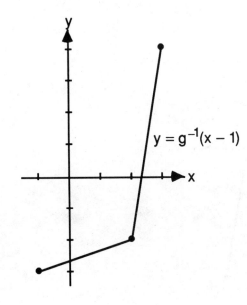

$y = g^{-1}(x - 1)$

(d) $y = g^{-1}(-x)$

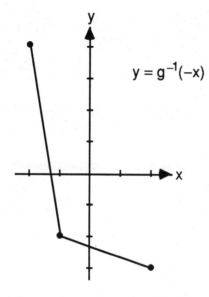

$y = g^{-1}(-x)$

(e) $y = -g^{-1}(x)$

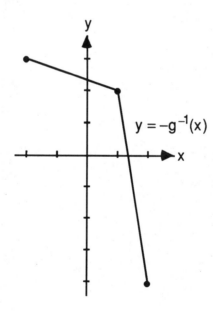

$y = -g^{-1}(x)$

(f) $y = -g^{-1}(-x)$

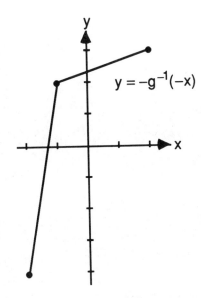

$y = -g^{-1}(-x)$

19.   The graph of $y = x^2 + 1$ is a parabola opening upward, which fails the horizontal line test, so it is not one-to-one.

21.   The graph of $f(x) = \dfrac{1}{x}$ passes the horizontal line test, so it is one-to-one.

23.   The graph of $y = x^3$ passes the horizintal line test, so it is one-to-one.

25.   The graph of $y = \sqrt{1 - x^2}$ is a semi-circle opening downward, which fails the horizontal line-test, so it is not one-to-one.

27.   The graph of $g(x) = 5$ is a horizontal line, which clearly fails the horizontal line test (it is a horizontal line), so the function is not one-to-one.

29.   The graph of $f(x)$ passes the horizontal line test (even at $y = 1$), so it is one-to-one.

31. $f[f(x)] = f\left(\dfrac{3x-2}{5x-3}\right)$

$$= \dfrac{3\left(\dfrac{3x-2}{5x-3}\right) - 2}{5\left(\dfrac{3x-2}{5x-3}\right) - 3}$$

We multiply by $\dfrac{5x-3}{5x-3}$:

$$= \dfrac{3(3x-2) - 2(5x-3)}{5(3x-2) - 3(5x-3)}$$

$$= \dfrac{9x-6-10x+6}{15x-10-15x+9}$$

$$= \dfrac{-x}{-1}$$

$$= x$$

Thus $f^{-1}(x) = f(x)$.

33.   (a) $7 + f^{-1}(x-1) = 9$

$f^{-1}(x-1) = 2$

$x - 1 = f(2)$

$x - 1 = 6$

$x = 7$

(b) $4 + f(x+3) = -3$

$f(x+3) = -7$

$x + 3 = f^{-1}(-7)$

$x + 3 = 0$

$x = -3$

35. $f^{-1}\left(\dfrac{t+1}{t-2}\right) = 12$

$\dfrac{t+1}{t-2} = f(12)$

$\dfrac{t+1}{t-2} = 13$

$t + 1 = 13t - 26$

$27 = 12t$

$t = 27/12 = 9/4$

37.   (a)   Let $y = \sqrt{x}$. We switch the roles of x and y and solve the resulting equation for y: $x = \sqrt{y}$

Squaring each side: $x^2 = y$

So $f^{-1}(x) = x^2$. Since $\sqrt{y} = x$, then $x \geq 0$. So the domain of $f^{-1}(x)$ is $[0, \infty)$.

(b) (i)   Since $2 = \sqrt{4}$, then $(4, 2)$ lies on the graph of f.

(ii) Since $4 = 2^2$, then $(2, 4)$ lies on the graph of f^{-1}.

(iii) Since $\sqrt{5} = \sqrt{5}$, then $(5, \sqrt{5})$ lies on the graph of f.

(iv) Since $5 = (\sqrt{5})^2$, then $(\sqrt{5}, 5)$ lies on the graph of f^{-1}.

(v)   Since $f(a) = f(a)$, then $(a, f(a))$ lies on the graph of f.

(vi) Since $a = f^{-1}[f(a)]$, then $(f(a), a)$ lies on the graph of f^{-1}.

(vii) Since $f^{-1}(b) = f^{-1}(b)$, then $(b, f^{-1}(b))$ lies on the graph of f^{-1}.

(viii) Since $b = f[(f^{-1}(b)]$, then $(f^{-1}(b), b)$ lies on the graph of f.

39. Let the points $P = (7, -1)$ and $Q = (-1, 7)$. We must first show that the line segment PQ is perpendicular to the line $y = x$:

$$m = \frac{7 - (-1)}{-1 - 7} = \frac{8}{-8} = -1$$

Since $y = x$ has a slope of 1, and $1(-1) = -1$, then the two lines are perpendicular. Next, we must show that P and Q are equidistant from $y = x$. Call the point $C = (c,c)$ on $y = x$. We use the distance formula:

$$PC = \sqrt{(-1 - c)^2 + (7 - c)^2}$$
$$QC = \sqrt{(7 - c)^2 + (-1 - c)^2}$$

So PC = QC. So, since PQ is perpendicular to $y = x$, and PC = QC, then by the definition of symmetry P and Q are symmetric about the line $y = x$.

41. Let the points $P = (a, b)$ and $Q = (b, a)$. We must first show that the line seqment PQ is perpendicular to the line $y = x$:

$$m = \frac{a - b}{b - a} = -1$$

Since $y = x$ has a slope of 1, and $1(-1) = -1$, then the two lines are perpendicular. Next, we must show that P and Q are equidistant from $y = x$. Call the point $C = (c,c)$ on $y = x$. We use the distance formula:

$$PC = \sqrt{(a - c)^2 + (b - c)^2}$$
$$QC = \sqrt{(b - c)^2 + (a - c)^2}$$

So PC = QC. So, since PQ is perpendicular to $y = x$, and PC = QC, then by the definition of symmetry P and Q are symmetric about the line $y = x$.

43. Let's pick the points $P(0, 3)$, $Q(2, 4)$, $R(4, 5)$. Then the reflected points will be $P'(3, 0)$, $Q'(4, 2)$, and $R'(5, 4)$. We will show that P', Q', and R' are collinear by computing the slopes:

$$m(P'Q') = \frac{2 - 0}{4 - 3} = \frac{2}{1} = 2$$
$$m(Q'R') = \frac{4 - 2}{5 - 4} = \frac{2}{1} = 2$$

So P', Q', and R' all are collinear (lie on the same line). There are two ways to find the equation of the line.

1st way: We use the point $(3, 0)$ and $m = 2$ in the point-slope formula:
$$y - 0 = 2(x - 3)$$
$$y = 2x - 6$$

2nd way: We realize that this line must be the inverse function of $y = \frac{1}{2}x + 3$.

Exchange x and y and solve for y:
$$x = \frac{1}{2}y + 3$$
$$x - 3 = \frac{1}{2}y$$
$$y = 2x - 6$$

In either case, we obtain the same equation.

45. $F[f^{-1}(x) + 1] = f[f^{-1}(x) + 1 - 1]$ by the definition $F(x) = f(x - 1)$
$$= f[f^{-1}(x)]$$
$$= x$$

An interesting note: This approach did not use our actual definition of $f(x)$!

47.   Let $P = (2, 1)$ and $Q = (a, b)$. Q is the point we are trying to find. Since PQ is perpendicular to $y = 3x$, which has a slope of 3, then we have:
$$\frac{b - 1}{a - 2} = -\frac{1}{3}$$
$$3b - 3 = -a + 2$$
$$a + 3b = 5$$
$$a = 5 - 3b$$

Now call $C = (c, 3c)$ a point on the line $y = 3x$:
$$\frac{3c - 1}{c - 2} = -\frac{1}{3}$$
$$9c - 3 = 2 - c$$
$$10c = 5$$
$$c = \frac{1}{2}$$

Since PC = QC, then by the distance formula, we have:
$$\sqrt{(c - 2)^2 + (3c - 1)^2} = \sqrt{(c - a)^2 + (3c - b)^2}$$

Squaring each side:
$$(c - 2)^2 + (3c - 1)^2 = (c - a)^2 + (3c - b)^2$$
$$c^2 - 4c + 4 + 9c^2 - 6c + 1 = c^2 - 2ac + a^2 + 9c^2 - 6bc + b^2$$
$$-4c + 4 - 6c + 1 = -2ac - 6bc + a^2 + b^2$$

$c = \frac{1}{2}$:
$$-2 + 4 - 3 + 1 = -a - 3b + a^2 + b^2$$
$$0 = a^2 + b^2 - a - 3b$$

Substituting $a = 5 - 3ab$:

$$0 = (5 - 3b)^2 + b^2 - (5 - 3b) - 3b$$
$$0 = 25 - 30b + 9b^2 + b^2 - 5 + 3b - 3b$$
$$0 = 10b^2 - 30b + 20$$
$$b^2 - 3b + 2 = 0$$
$$(b - 2)(b - 1) = 0$$
$$b = 1, 2$$

Since $a = 5 - 3b$, we have the points $(2, 1)$ and $(-1, 2)$. But $(2, 1)$ was our original point P, which clearly is <u>not</u> the desired solution. So the point symmetric to $(2, 1)$ about the line $y = 3x$ is $(-1, 2)$.

49. (a) By drawing a graph, it is easy to see that the reflected point is $(-b, -a)$.

   (b) Q has coordinates $Q(a, -b)$. Reflecting this in the y-axis results in $R(-a, -b)$. Reflecting R in the line $y = x$ reverses the coordinates to yield $(-b, -a)$, which is the reflection found in part (a).

Chapter 2 Review Exercises

1. (a) We must guarantee that the quantity within the radical is non-negative:
$$15 - 5x \geq 0$$
$$-5x \geq -15$$
$$x \leq 3$$
So the domain is $(-\infty, 3]$.

   (b) We solve $y = \dfrac{3 + x}{2x - 5}$ for x:
$$y(2x - 5) = 3 + x$$
$$2xy - 5y = 3 + x$$
$$2xy - x = 5y + 3$$
$$x(2y - 1) = 5y + 3$$
$$x = \frac{5y + 3}{2y - 1}$$
So the range is all real numbers except 1/2, or $(-\infty, 1/2) \cup (1/2, \infty)$.

2. (a) $(f - g)(x) = f(x) - g(x)$
$$= (3x^2 - 4x) - (2x + 1)$$
$$= 3x^2 - 4x - 2x - 1$$
$$= 3x^2 - 6x - 1$$

(b) $(f \circ g)(x)$ $= f[g(x)]$
$= f(2x + 1)$
$= 3(2x + 1)^2 - 4(2x + 1)$
$= 3(4x^2 + 4x + 1) - 8x - 4$
$= 12x^2 + 12x + 3 - 8x - 4$
$= 12x^2 + 4x - 1$

(c) $f[g(-1)]$ $= (f \circ g)(-1)$
$= 12(-1)^2 + 4(-1) - 1$
$= 12 - 4 - 1$
$= 7$

3.   We first complete the square to find the center of the circle:
$$(x^2 + 4x) + (y^2 - 2y) = 8$$
$$(x^2 + 4x + 4) + (y^2 - 2y + 1) = 8 + 4 + 1$$
$$(x + 2)^2 + (y - 1)^2 = 13$$
So the center is $(-2, 1)$. The slope from the center to the point $(1, 3)$ is:
$$m = \frac{3 - 1}{1 - (-2)} = \frac{2}{3}$$
So the tangent line (which is perpendicular) has a slope of -3/2. Using the point-slope formula with the point $(1, 3)$:
$$y - 3 = -\frac{3}{2}(x - 1)$$
$$y - 3 = -\frac{3}{2}x + \frac{3}{2}$$
$$y = -\frac{3}{2}x + \frac{9}{2}$$

4. $y = 2x^3 - x^5$
x-axis: Replace (x, y) with $(x, -y)$
$$-y = 2x^3 - x^5$$
Since the equation is changed, there is no symmetry.
y-axis: Replace (x, y) with $(-x, y)$
$$y = 2(-x)^3 - (-x)^5$$
$$y = -2x^3 + x^5$$
Since the equation is changed, there is no symmetry.
origin: Replace (x, y) with $(-x, -y)$
$$-y = 2(-x)^3 - (-x)^5$$
$$-y = -2x^3 + x^5$$
$$y = 2x^3 - x^5$$
Since the equation remains unchanged, there is symmetry.

5.   (a) $\dfrac{F(x) - F(a)}{x - a} = \dfrac{\frac{1}{x} - \frac{1}{a}}{x - a} \bullet \dfrac{ax}{ax} = \dfrac{a - x}{ax(x - a)} = -\dfrac{1}{ax}$

(b) $g(x + h) = (x + h) - 2(x + h)^2 = x + h - 2x^2 - 4xh - 2h^2$
So we have:

$$\dfrac{g(x + h) - g(x)}{h} = \dfrac{(x + h - 2x^2 - 4xh - 2h^2) - (x - 2x^2)}{h}$$

$$= \dfrac{x + h - 2x^2 - 4xh - 2h^2 - x + 2x^2}{h}$$

$$= \dfrac{h - 4xh - 2h^2}{h}$$

$$= 1 - 4x - 2h$$

6.   We convert the line to slope-intercept form:

$$3x - 5y = 15$$
$$-5y = -3x + 15$$
$$y = \dfrac{3}{5}x - 3$$

So the slope is 3/5 and the y-intercept is -3. We graph the line:

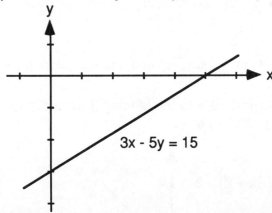

7.   (a)   We switch the roles of x and y and solve the resulting equation for y:

$$y = \dfrac{1 - 5x}{3x}$$
$$3xy = 1 - 5x$$
$$3xy + 5x = 1$$
$$x(3y + 5) = 1$$
$$x = \dfrac{1}{3y + 5}$$

So $g^{-1}(x) = \dfrac{1}{3x + 5}$.

(b)   We graph f^{-1}:

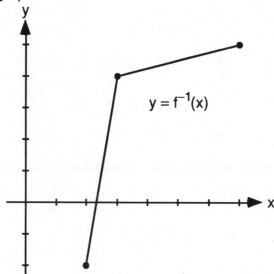

8.   We find the slope:

$$5x - 6y = 30$$
$$-6y = -5x + 30$$
$$y = \frac{5}{6}x - 5$$

So the slope is 5/6. Since the y-intercept is 0, the equation is $y = \frac{5}{6}x$.

9.   (a)   We displace $y = |x|$ two units to the left and 3 units down.
         x-intercepts: -5,1; y-intercept: -1

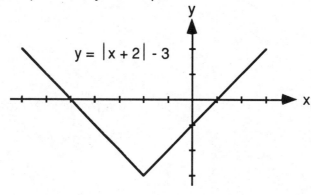

(b)   We displace $y = \dfrac{1}{x}$ two units to the left and 1 unit down.

x-intercept: -1; y-intercept: -1/2

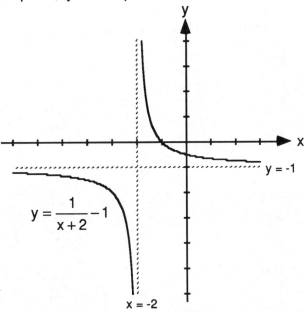

$$y = \frac{1}{x+2} - 1$$

y = -1

x = -2

10.   (a)   (-3, 3), (-2, -1)
       (b)   3
       (c)   x = -1
       (d)   (-5, -3) ∪ (-2, 2)

11.   (a) $f(-1) = 3(-1)^2 - 2(-1) = 3 + 2 = 5$
       (b) $f(1 - \sqrt{2}) = 3(1 - \sqrt{2})^2 - 2(1 - \sqrt{2})$
                           $= 3(1 - 2\sqrt{2} + 2) - 2 + 2\sqrt{2}$
                           $= 9 - 6\sqrt{2} - 2 + 2\sqrt{2}$
                           $= 7 - 4\sqrt{2}$

12.   We graph G(x):

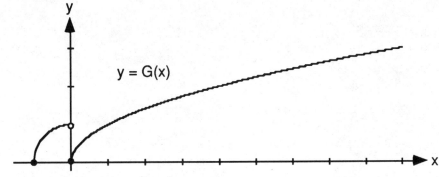

y = G(x)

13. The slope is given by:

$$m = \frac{(5+h)^2 - 25}{5+h-5} = \frac{25 + 10h + h^2 - 25}{h} = \frac{10h + h^2}{h} = 10 + h$$

14. x-intercepts: -3, 3; y-intercept: 9; symmetry: y-axis

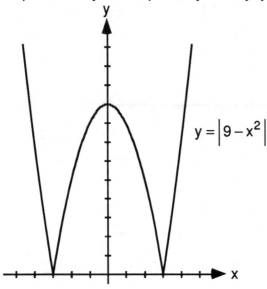

$$y = \left| 9 - x^2 \right|$$

15. y = f(-x) will result in a reflection across the y-axis:

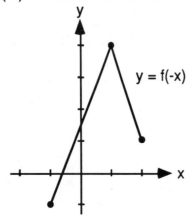

y = f(-x)

16. $2 + f(3t + 5) = 3$
    $f(3t + 5) = 1$
    $3t + 5 = f^{-1}(1)$
    $3t + 5 = -4$
    $3t = -9$
    $t = -3$

17. We find the slope: $m = \dfrac{6 - 2}{-6 - (-4)} = \dfrac{4}{-2} = -2$

   Using the point $(-4, 2)$ in the point-slope formula:
   $$y - 2 = -2\,[\,x - (-4)\,]$$
   $$y - 2 = -2\,(x + 4)$$
   $$y - 2 = -2x - 8$$
   $$y = -2x - 6$$

19. Using the point-slope formula: $y - (-3) = \dfrac{1}{4}\,[\,x - (-2)\,]$

   $$y + 3 = \dfrac{1}{4}\,(x + 2)$$
   $$y + 3 = \dfrac{1}{4}\,x + \dfrac{1}{2}$$
   $$y = \dfrac{1}{4}\,x - \dfrac{5}{2}$$

21. We find the slope between the points $(-4, 0)$ and $(0, 8)$:
   $$m = \dfrac{8 - 0}{0 - (-4)} = \dfrac{8}{4} = 2$$
   Using the slope-intercept formula: $y = 2x + 8$

23. Since it is parallel to the x-axis, its equation will be of the form $y = $ constant (horizontal line). Since $(0, -2)$ is on the line, its equation is $y = -2$.

25. We find the slope of $x + y + 1 = 0$ by putting it in slope-intercept form, and get $y = -x - 1$. So its slope is -1, and thus a perpendicular slope would be 1. We use the point $(1, 2)$ in the point-slope formula:
   $$y - 2 = 1(x - 1)$$
   $$y - 2 = x - 1$$
   $$y = x + 1$$

27. We find the center of each circle by completing the square:
   $$x^2 + 4x + y^2 + 2y = 0$$
   $$(x^2 + 4x + 4) + (y^2 + 2y + 1) = 0 + 4 + 1$$
   $$(x + 2)^2 + (y + 1)^2 = 5$$
   center: $(-2, -1)$

   $$x^2 - 4x + y^2 - 16y = 0$$
   $$(x^2 - 4x + 4) + (y^2 - 16y + 64) = 0 + 4 + 64$$
   $$(x - 2)^2 + (y - 8)^2 = 68$$
   center: $(2, 8)$

   We find the slope between $(-2, -1)$ and $(2, 8)$:
   $$m = \dfrac{8 - (-1)}{2 - (-2)} = \dfrac{9}{4}$$

We use the point $(2, 8)$ in the point-slope formula:

$$y - 8 = \frac{9}{4}(x - 2)$$

$$y - 8 = \frac{9}{4}x - \frac{9}{2}$$

$$y = \frac{9}{4}x + \frac{7}{2}$$

29. We find the midpoint of the line segment joining $(-2, -3)$ and $(6, -5)$:

$$M = \left(\frac{-2 + 6}{2}, \frac{-3 - 5}{2}\right) = \left(\frac{4}{2}, -\frac{8}{2}\right) = (2, -4)$$

Now we find the slope between $(0, 0)$ and $(2, -4)$:

$$m = \frac{-4 - 0}{2 - 0} = \frac{-4}{2} = -2$$

We use the slope-intercept formula to get $y = -2x + 0$, or $y = -2x$.

31. We first find the center of the circle by completing the square:

$$x^2 - 6x + y^2 + 8y = 0$$

$$(x^2 - 6x + 9) + (y^2 + 8y + 16) = 0 + 9 + 16$$

$$(x - 3)^2 + (y + 4)^2 = 25$$

So the center is $(3, -4)$. We now find the slope of the radius drawn from $(3, -4)$ to $(0, 0)$:

$$m = \frac{0 - (-4)}{0 - 3} = \frac{4}{-3} = -\frac{4}{3}$$

So the slope of the perpendicular tangent line is 3/4. We use the slope-intercept formula:

$$y = \frac{3}{4}x + 0$$

$$y = \frac{3}{4}x$$

33. Call the x-intercept a. Then the y-intercept is 2 - a, and we find the slope from each to $(2, -1)$:

$$m = \frac{-1 - 0}{2 - a} = \frac{-1}{2 - a}$$

$$m = \frac{-1 - (2 - a)}{2 - 0} = \frac{-1 - 2 + a}{2} = \frac{a - 3}{2}$$

Since these two slopes must be equal, we have:

$$\frac{-1}{2-a} = \frac{a-3}{2}$$

Cross-multiply:

$$-2 = (2-a)(a-3)$$
$$-2 = -a^2 + 5a - 6$$
$$0 = a^2 - 5a + 4$$
$$0 = (a-4)(a-1)$$
$$a = 1 \quad \text{or} \quad a = 4$$

When a = 1, we have $m = \dfrac{1-3}{2} = \dfrac{-2}{2} = -1$

When a = 4, we have $m = \dfrac{-1}{2-4} = \dfrac{-1}{-2} = \dfrac{1}{2}$

We use the point (2, -1), and each of these slopes, in the point-slope formula:

$$y - (-1) = -1(x-2) \qquad\qquad y - (-1) = \frac{1}{2}(x-2)$$

$$y + 1 = -x + 2 \qquad\qquad y + 1 = \frac{1}{2}x - 1$$

$$y = -x + 1 \qquad\qquad y = \frac{1}{2}x - 2$$

Both of these lines satisfy the given conditions.

35. (a) $y = f(x) + 1$
   E, since $f(a) + 1 = b + 1$

   (b) $y = f(x + 1)$
   C, since $f(a - 1 + 1) = f(a) = b$

   (c) $y = f(x - 1) + 1$
   L, since $f(a + 1 - 1) + 1 = f(a) + 1 = b + 1$

   (d) $y = f(-x)$
   A, since $f\left(-(-a)\right) = f(a) = b$

   (e) $y = -f(x)$
   J, since $-f(a) = -b$

   (f) $y = -f(-x)$
   G, since $-f\left(-(-a)\right) = -f(a) = -b$

   (g) $y = f^{-1}(x)$
   B, since $f^{-1}(b) = a$

   (h) $y = f^{-1}(x) + 1$
   M, since $f^{-1}(b) + 1 = a + 1$

   (i) $y = f^{-1}(x - 1)$
   K, since $f^{-1}(b + 1 - 1) = f^{-1}(b) = a$

   (j) $y = f^{-1}(-x) + 1$
   D, since $f^{-1}\left(-(-b)\right) + 1 = f^{-1}(b) + 1 = a + 1$

   (k) $y = -f^{-1}(x)$
   I, since $-f^{-1}(b) = -a$

(l) $y = -f^{-1}(-x) + 1$

H, since $-f^{-1}\big(-(-b)\big) + 1 = -f^{-1}(b) + 1 = -a + 1 = 1 - a$

(m) $y = 1 - f^{-1}(x)$

N, since $1 - f^{-1}(b) = 1 - a$

(n) $y = f(1 - x)$

F, since $f\big(1 - (1 - a)\big) = f(1 - 1 + a) = f(a) = b$

37.   x-intercepts: $1 \pm \sqrt{2}$; y-intercept: 1

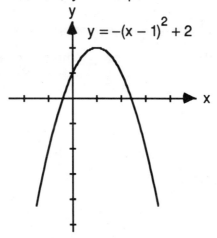

$$y = -(x - 1)^2 + 2$$

39.   x-intercept: none; y-intercept: 1

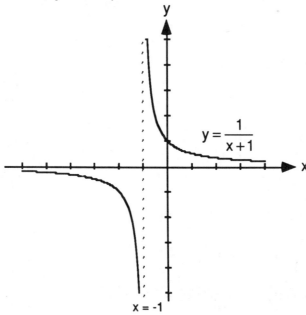

$$y = \frac{1}{x + 1}$$

$x = -1$

41.   x-intercept: -3; y-intercept: 3

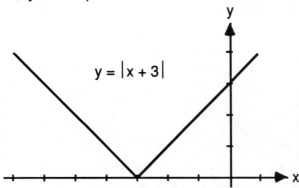

$$y = |x + 3|$$

43.   x-intercepts: ±1; y-intercept: 1

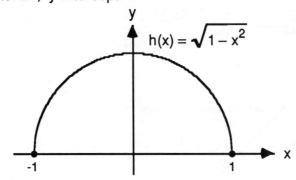

$$h(x) = \sqrt{1 - x^2}$$

45.   x-intercept: 0; y-intercept: 0

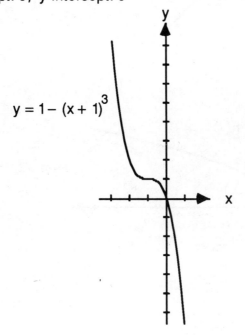

$$y = 1 - (x + 1)^3$$

47.   x-intercept: 0; y-intercept: 0

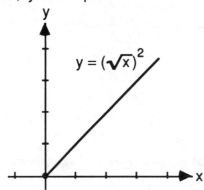

$$y = (\sqrt{x})^2$$

49. $(f \circ g)(x) = f(\sqrt{x-1}) = -(\sqrt{x-1})^2$
       x-intercept: 1; y-intercept: none

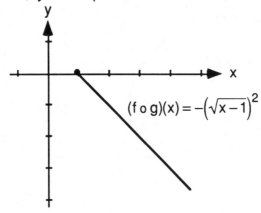

$$(f \circ g)(x) = -\left(\sqrt{x-1}\right)^2$$

51.   x-intercepts: -1, 0; y-intercept: 0

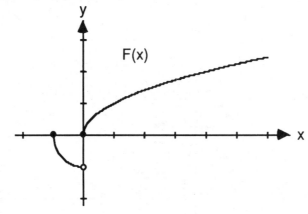

F(x)

53. x-intercept: none; y-intercept: none

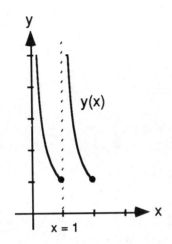

55. $x = \dfrac{y + 1}{2}$

$2x = y + 1$

$y = 2x - 1 = f^{-1}(x)$

x-intercept: 1/2; y-intercept: -1

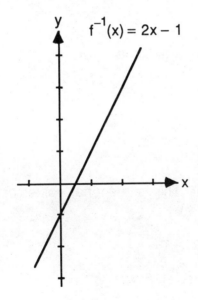

57. $(f \circ f^{-1})(x) = x$, with domain $x \geq 0$ for $f^{-1}(x)$:
x-intercept: 0; y-intercept: 0

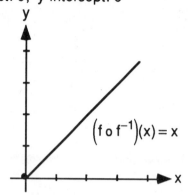

$$\left(f \circ f^{-1}\right)(x) = x$$

59.   x-axis: no; y-axis: yes; origin: no

61.   x-axis: no; y-axis: no; origin: no

63.   x-axis: no; y-axis: no; origin: yes

65.   We must make sure that $x^2 - 9 \neq 0$. We find the points to exclude:
$$x^2 - 9 = 0$$
$$x^2 = 9$$
$$x = \pm 3$$
So the domain is all real numbers except 3 and -3, or
$(-\infty, -3) \cup (-3, 3) \cup (3, \infty)$

67.   We must be sure that $8 - 2x \geq 0$
$$8 \geq 2x$$
$$4 \geq x$$
So the domain is $x \leq 4$, or $(-\infty, 4]$

69.   We must be sure that $|2 - 5x| \geq 0$. This is true for all values of x, so the
domain is all real numbers, or $(-\infty, \infty)$.

71.   We must be sure that $x^2 - 2x - 3 \geq 0$
$$(x - 3)(x + 1) \geq 0$$
key numbers: -1, 3
We find the signs of each interval:
$(-\infty, -1)$:   positive
$(-1, 3)$:   negative
$(3, \infty)$:   positive
So $(x - 3)(x + 1) \geq 0$ when $x \leq -1$ or $x \geq 3$.
So the domain is $(-\infty, -1] \cup [3, \infty)$.

73. We must be sure that $x \neq 0$. So the domain is all real numbers except 0, or $(-\infty, 0) \cup (0, \infty)$.

75. We solve for x: $y = \dfrac{x + 4}{3x - 1}$

$$y(3x - 1) = x + 4$$
$$3xy - y = x + 4$$
$$3xy - x = y + 4$$
$$x(3y - 1) = y + 4$$
$$x = \dfrac{y + 4}{3y - 1}$$

Now $3y - 1 = 0$ when $y = 1/3$, so the range is all real numbers except 1/3, or $(-\infty, 1/3) \cup (1/3, \infty)$.

77. $(f \circ g)(x) = f(3x + 4) = \dfrac{1}{3x + 4}$. We solve $y = \dfrac{1}{3x + 4}$ for x:

$$y = \dfrac{1}{3x + 4}$$
$$y(3x + 4) = 1$$
$$3xy + 4y = 1$$
$$3xy = 1 - 4y$$
$$x = \dfrac{1 - 4y}{3y}$$

Now $3y = 0$ when $y = 0$, so the range is all real numbers except 0, or $(-\infty, 0) \cup (0, \infty)$.

79. Since the range of f^{-1} is the domain of f, we must exclude the values of x where $3x - 6 = 0$, or $x = 2$. So the range is all real numbers except 2, or $(-\infty, 2) \cup (2, \infty)$.

81. $a(x) = (f \circ g)(x)$, since $(f \circ g)(x) = f[g(x)] = f(x - 1) = \dfrac{1}{x - 1}$

83. $c(x) = (G \circ g)(x)$, since $(G \circ g)(x) = G[g(x)] = G(x - 1) = \sqrt{x - 1}$

85. $A(x) = (g \circ f \circ G)(x)$, since $(g \circ f \circ G)(x) = (g \circ f)(\sqrt{x}) = g\left(\dfrac{1}{\sqrt{x}}\right) = \dfrac{1}{\sqrt{x}} - 1$

87. $C(x) = (g \circ G \circ G)(x)$, since $(g \circ G \circ G)(x) = (g \circ G)(\sqrt{x})$

$$= g(\sqrt{\sqrt{x}})$$
$$= g(\sqrt[4]{x})$$
$$= \sqrt[4]{x} - 1$$

89.　$f(-3) = (-3)^2 - (-3) = 9 + 3 = 12$

91.　$F\left(\dfrac{3}{4}\right) = \dfrac{\dfrac{3}{4} - 3}{\dfrac{3}{4} + 4} \cdot \dfrac{4}{4} = \dfrac{3 - 3(4)}{3 + 4(4)} = \dfrac{3 - 12}{3 + 16} = -\dfrac{9}{19}$

93.　$f(-t) = (-t)^2 - (-t) = t^2 + t$

95.　$f(x - 2) = (x - 2)^2 - (x - 2) = x^2 - 4x + 4 - x + 2 = x^2 - 5x + 6$

97.　$g(2) = 1 - 2(2) = 1 - 4 = -3$
　　$g(0) = 1 - 2(0) = 1 - 0 = 1$
　　So $g(2) - g(0) = -3 - 1 = -4$

99.　$f(1) = (1)^2 - 1 = 1 - 1 = 0$
　　$f(3) = (3)^2 - 3 = 9 - 3 = 6$
　　So $|f(1) - f(3)| = |0 - 6| = |-6| = 6$

101.　$f(x^2) = (x^2)^2 - x^2 = x^4 - x^2$

103.　$[f(x)]\,[g(x)] = (x^2 - x)(1 - 2x) = x^2 - 2x^3 - x + 2x^2 = -2x^3 + 3x^2 - x$

105.　$\begin{aligned} f[g(x)] &= f(1 - 2x) \\ &= (1 - 2x)^2 - (1 - 2x) \\ &= 1 - 4x + 4x^2 - 1 + 2x \\ &= 4x^2 - 2x \end{aligned}$

107.　$\begin{aligned} (g \circ f)(x) &= g[f(x)] \\ &= g(x^2 - x) \\ &= 1 - 2(x^2 - x) \\ &= 2 - 2x^2 + 2x \\ &= -2x^2 + 2x + 1 \end{aligned}$

109.　$\begin{aligned} (F \circ g)(x) &= F[g(x)] \\ &= F(1 - 2x) \\ &= \dfrac{(1 - 2x) - 3}{(1 - 2x) + 4} \\ &= \dfrac{-2x - 2}{-2x + 5} \text{ or } \dfrac{2x + 2}{2x - 5} \end{aligned}$

111.　$\dfrac{f(x + h) - f(x)}{h} = \dfrac{2xh + h^2 - h}{h} = \dfrac{h(2x + h - 1)}{h} = 2x + h - 1$

113.   Let $y = \dfrac{x-3}{x+4}$. We switch the roles of x and y and solve the resulting equation for y:

$$x = \frac{y-3}{y+4}$$
$$x(y+4) = y-3$$
$$xy + 4x = y-3$$
$$xy - y = -4x-3$$
$$y(x-1) = -4x-3$$
$$y = \frac{-4x-3}{x-1}$$

So $F^{-1}(x) = \dfrac{-4x-3}{x-1} = \dfrac{4x+3}{1-x}$

115. $F^{-1}[F(x)] = x$, by definition of $F^{-1}(x)$

117. $(g \circ g^{-1})(x) = x$, by the definition of $g^{-1}(x)$

119. $g^{-1}(x) = \dfrac{1-x}{2}$, so $g^{-1}(-x) = \dfrac{1-(-x)}{2} = \dfrac{1+x}{2}$

121. $F^{-1}[F(x)] = x$ by the definition of $F^{-1}(x)$, so $F^{-1}[F(22/7)] = 22/7$

123. $f(0) = -2$, so $f(0)$ is negative

125. $f(-3) = -1$

127. $f(0) = -2$ and $f(8) = -1$, so $f(0) - f(8) = -2 - (-1) = -1$

129. $(0, -2)$ and $(5, 1)$

131. $(-6, 0) \cup (5, 8)$

133.   On the interval $-2 \le x \le 2$, the largest value of f(x) is 0, at x = 2.

135.   No. Since f is not a one-to-one function, then it cannot possess an inverse function.

137. $f(x) = g(x)$ when x = 4

139.   (a)   When x = 10, since $f(10) = 0$
       (b)   When x = 0, since $g(0) = 0$

141.   (a) $(f + g)(8) = f(8) + g(8) = 1 + 4 = 5$
       (b) $(f - g)(8) = f(8) - g(8) = 1 - 4 = -3$

(c) $(fg)(8) = f(8) \cdot g(8) = 1(4) = 4$

(d) $\left(\dfrac{f}{g}\right)(8) = \dfrac{f(8)}{g(8)} = \dfrac{1}{4}$

143. $f(10) = 0$, so $(f \circ f)(10) = f[f(10)] = f(0) = 5$
$g(10) = 3$, so $(g \circ g)(10) = g[g(10)] = g(3) = 1$
So $(f \circ f)(10)$ is larger.

145. $f(x) \geq 3$ whenever $0 \leq x \leq 4$, or $[0, 4]$

147. $g(6) = 5$, the highest point on the curve $y = g(x)$, so 5 is the largest number in the range of g.

149. $(1, 3) \cup (6, 10)$

151. We consider two cases:
If $4 < x < 5$, then $f(x) > f(5)$ and $x < 5$, thus $f(x) - f(5) > 0$ while $x - 5 < 0$.
Thus $\dfrac{f(x) - f(5)}{x - 5} < 0$.
If $5 < x < 7$, then $f(x) < f(5)$ and $x > 5$, thus $f(x) - f(5) < 0$ while $x - 5 > 0$.
Thus $\dfrac{f(x) - f(5)}{x - 5} < 0$.
Therefore, the quantity is negative for all x-values in the interval $(4, 7)$.

153. (a) We find the slope of P_1Q:
$$m = \dfrac{\frac{1}{3}y_1 + \frac{2}{3}y_2 - y_1}{\frac{1}{3}x_1 + \frac{2}{3}x_2 - x_1}$$
Multiply by $\dfrac{3}{3}$ to get:
$$m = \dfrac{y_1 + 2y_2 - 3y_1}{x_1 + 2x_2 - 3x_1} = \dfrac{2y_2 - 2y_1}{2x_2 - 2x_1} = \dfrac{y_2 - y_1}{x_2 - x_1}$$
We find the slope of P_2Q:
$$m = \dfrac{\frac{1}{3}y_1 + \frac{2}{3}y_2 - y_2}{\frac{1}{3}x_1 + \frac{2}{3}x_2 - x_2}$$
Multiply by $\dfrac{3}{3}$ to get:
$$m = \dfrac{y_1 + 2y_2 - 3y_2}{x_1 + 2x_2 - 3x_2} = \dfrac{y_1 - y_2}{x_1 - x_2}$$
Since the two slopes are the same, P_1, P_2, and Q are collinear.

(b)   We use the distance formula:

$$P_1Q = \sqrt{\left(\tfrac{1}{3}x_1 + \tfrac{2}{3}x_2 - x_1\right)^2 + \left(\tfrac{1}{3}y_1 + \tfrac{2}{3}y_2 - y_1\right)^2}$$

$$= \sqrt{\left(\tfrac{2}{3}x_2 - \tfrac{2}{3}x_1\right)^2 + \left(\tfrac{2}{3}y_2 - \tfrac{2}{3}y_2\right)^2}$$

$$= \sqrt{\tfrac{4}{9}(x_2 - x_1)^2 + \tfrac{4}{9}(y_2 - y_1)^2}$$

$$= \tfrac{2}{3}\sqrt{(x_2 - x_1)^2 + (y_2 - y_1)^2}$$

$$P_1P_2 = \sqrt{(x_2 - x_1)^2 + (y_2 - y_1)^2}$$

So $P_1Q = \tfrac{2}{3}P_1P_2$

155.   (a)   The two triangles have a parallel side, so the opposite interior angles cut
by the transversal $y = mx + b$ are equal. Since the two triangles are
both right triangles, they must be similar. So we set up the proportion:

$$\frac{d}{1} = \frac{AB}{\sqrt{1 + m^2}}$$

$$d = \frac{AB}{\sqrt{1 + m^2}}$$

(b)   Since the coordinates of A are (x_0, y_0) and those of B are $(x, mx_0 + b)$,
then:

$$AB = \sqrt{(x_0 - x_0)^2 + (y_0 - mx_0 - b)^2} = |y_0 - mx_0 - b|$$

In our case $y_0 > mx_0 + b$, so $AB = y_0 - mx_0 - b$

(c)   Substituting the above result into our equation from (a) yields:

$$d = \frac{AB}{\sqrt{1 + m^2}} = \frac{y_0 - mx_0 - b}{\sqrt{1 + m^2}}$$

157.   (a)   If the center is (h, k) and the circle is tangent to the coordinate axes,
then the points of tangency are $(h, 0)$ and $(0, k)$. Since the distances
from the center to the coordinate axes are the same, $h = k = r$ (the
radius) and the center must be (r, r). We write the line in slope-intercept
form:

$$3x + 4y = 12$$

$$4y = -3x + 12$$

$$y = -\tfrac{3}{4}x + 3$$

We find the distance from (r, r) to this line, using the fact that this distance is also r:

$$r = \frac{\left| r + \frac{3}{4}r - 3 \right|}{\sqrt{1 + (3/4)^2}} = \frac{\left| \frac{7}{4}r - 3 \right|}{5/4}$$

So we have the equation:

$$\frac{5}{4}r = \left| \frac{7}{4}r - 3 \right|$$

Thus we have:

$$\frac{5}{4}r = \frac{7}{4}r - 3 \qquad \text{or} \qquad -\frac{5}{4}r = \frac{7}{4}r - 3$$

$$5r = 7r - 12 \qquad \text{or} \qquad -5r = 7r - 12$$

$$-2r = -12 \qquad \text{or} \qquad -12r = -12$$

$$r = 6 \qquad \text{or} \qquad r = 1$$

Clearly r = 6 corresponds to a circle above the line, so r = 1. Thus the equation of the circle is $(x - 1)^2 + (y - 1)^2 = 1$.

(b)   We have the coordinates S(1, 0) and U(0, 1). We must find the coordinates of T. We know the slope of the center to 3x + 4y = 12 is 4/3, so we use the point (1, 1) in the point-slope formula:

$$y - 1 = \frac{4}{3}(x - 1)$$

$$y - 1 = \frac{4}{3}x - \frac{4}{3}$$

$$y = \frac{4}{3}x - \frac{1}{3}$$

We now find the intersection point of this line with our given line:

$$\frac{4}{3}x - \frac{1}{3} = -\frac{3}{4}x + 3$$

$$16x - 4 = -9x + 36$$

$$25x = 40$$

$$x = 8/5$$

Substituting, we find y = 9/5, so we have the point T(8/5, 9/5). We now can find the required equations.

$$\overline{AT}: \quad m = \frac{9/5 - 0}{8/5 - 0} = \frac{9}{8}$$

$$\text{point} = (0, 0)$$

$$y - 0 = \frac{9}{8}(x - 0)$$

$$y = \frac{9}{8}x$$

$\overline{BU}$: $m = \dfrac{0 - 1}{4 - 0} = -\dfrac{1}{4}$

point $= (0, 1)$

$y - 1 = -\dfrac{1}{4}(x - 0)$

$y = -\dfrac{1}{4}x + 1$

$\overline{CS}$: $m = \dfrac{3 - 0}{0 - 1} = -3$

point $= (1, 0)$

$y - 0 = -3(x - 1)$

$y = -3x + 3$

(c)   To find the required intersection points, we set the equations equal.

$\overline{AT}$ and $\overline{CS}$: $\dfrac{9}{8}x = -3x + 3$

$\dfrac{33}{8}x = 3$

$x = \dfrac{24}{33} = \dfrac{8}{11}$

$y = \dfrac{9}{11}$

intersection: $(8/11, 9/11)$

$\overline{AT}$ and $\overline{BU}$: $\dfrac{9}{8}x = -\dfrac{1}{4}x + 1$

$9x = -2x + 8$

$11x = 8$

$x = \dfrac{8}{11}$

$y = \dfrac{9}{11}$

intersection: $(8/11, 9/11)$

Notice that the point of intersection is the same in both cases.

CHAPTER THREE
POLYNOMIAL AND RATIONAL FUNCTIONS.
APPLICATIONS TO OPTIMIZATION

3.1 Linear Functions

1. We first find the slope between the points (-1, 0) and (5, 4):
$$m = \frac{4 - 0}{5 - (-1)} = \frac{4}{6} = \frac{2}{3}$$
Now we use the point (-1, 0) in the point-slope formula:
$$y - 0 = \frac{2}{3}[x - (-1)]$$
$$y = \frac{2}{3}(x + 1)$$
$$y = \frac{2}{3}x + \frac{2}{3}$$
Using functional notation, we have $f(x) = \frac{2}{3}x + \frac{2}{3}$.

3. We first find the slope between the points (0, 0) and (1, $\sqrt{2}$):
$$m = \frac{\sqrt{2} - 0}{1 - 0} = \sqrt{2}$$
Now, since (0, 0) is the y-intercept, we use the slope-intercept formula to write
$y = \sqrt{2}\,x$.
Using functional notation, we have $g(x) = \sqrt{2}\,x$.

225

5.   We find the slope of $x - y = 1$:

$$-y = -x + 1$$
$$y = x - 1$$

So the parallel slope is 1. We use the point (1/2, -3) in the point-slope formula:

$$y - (-3) = 1 \left(x - \frac{1}{2} \right)$$

$$y + 3 = x - \frac{1}{2}$$

$$y = x - \frac{7}{2}$$

Using functional notation, we have $f(x) = x - \frac{7}{2}$.

7.   We set $x = 0$ to find the y-intercepts of the circle:

$$0 - 0 + y^2 - 3 = 0$$
$$y^2 = 3$$
$$y = \pm \sqrt{3}$$

So a horizontal line passing through $(0, \sqrt{3})$ is $y = \sqrt{3}$.

Using functional notation, we have $f(x) = \sqrt{3}$.

9.   Since the points (-1, 2) and (0, 4) lie on the graph of the inverse function, then (2, -1) and (4, 0) must lie on the graph of the function. We find the slope:

$$m = \frac{0 - (-1)}{4 - 2} = \frac{1}{2}$$

We use the point (4, 0) in the point-slope formula:

$$y - 0 = \frac{1}{2} (x - 4)$$

$$y = \frac{1}{2} x - 2$$

Using functional notation, we have $f(x) = \frac{1}{2} x - 2$.

11. $(f \circ g)(x) = f[g(x)]$
            $= f(1 - 2x)$
            $= 3(1 - 2x) - 4$
            $= 3 - 6x - 4$
            $= -6x - 1$

So $f \circ g$ is a linear function (it is in standard form).

13.   Call V(t) the value of the machine after t years. When $t = 0$ we have $V = 20,000$ and when $t = 8$ we have $V = 1,000$. We find the slope of the line between the points (0, 20000) and (8, 1000):

$$m = \frac{1000 - 20000}{8 - 0} = \frac{-19000}{8} = -2375$$

Now, since $(0, 20000)$ is the y-intercept, we use the slope-intercept formula to write $V = -2375\,t + 20,000$.
Using functional notation, we have $V(t) = -2375\,t + 20,000$.

15. (a) Call $V(t)$ the value of the machine after t years. Now $V = 60,000$ when $t = 0$ and $V = 0$ when $t = 5$. We find the slope of the line between $(0, 60000)$ and $(5, 0)$:

$$m = \frac{0 - 60000}{5 - 0} = \frac{-60000}{5} = -12,000$$

Now, since $(0, 60000)$ is the y-intercept, we use the slope-intercept formula to get $V = -12,000\,t + 60,000$.
Using functional notation, we have $V(t) = -12,000\,t + 60,000$.

(b) The completed schedule is:

End of Year	Yearly Depreciation	Accumulated Depreciation	Value V
0	0	0	60,000
1	12,000	12,000	48,000
2	12,000	24,000	36,000
3	12,000	36,000	24,000
4	12,000	48,000	12,000
5	12,000	60,000	0

17. (a) We let $x = 10$, so $C(10) = 450 + 8x = 450 + 8(10) = \$530$.

(b) We let $x = 11$, so $C(11) = 450 + 8(11) = \$538$.

(c) There are two ways to find the marginal cost. One way is to recognize that the marginal cost will be the slope of the line, which is \$8/fan. Another way would be to use the definition of the marginal cost: the cost of producing the next unit. Since $C(10)$ is the cost of producing 10 fans and $C(11)$ is the cost of producing 11 fans, then the marginal cost would be $C(11) - C(10) = 538 - 530 = \$8$/fan. We get the same answer using either approach.

19. (a) $C(n + 1) = 400 + 50(n + 1) = 400 + 50n + 50 = 450 + 50n$
          So:
$$C(n + 1) - C(n) = (450 + 50n) - (400 + 50n)$$
$$= 450 + 50n - 400 - 50n$$
$$= 50$$

     (b)   The marginal cost, which represents the cost to produce the next unit, is
          the slope of the line. So the marginal cost is $50/player.

     (c)   The answers are the same. Notice that (a) directly computed marginal
          cost from its definition.

21. Since the velocity will be the slope of the distance line, we compute the slope
     of each line.

     (a)   Let $(x_1, y_1) = (1, 4)$ and $(x_2, y_2) = (6, 8)$. Then:
$$m = \frac{8 - 4}{6 - 1} = \frac{4}{5}$$
          So the velocity is 4/5 ft/sec.

     (b)   Let $(x_1, y_1) = (2, 4)$ and $(x_2, y_2) = (5, 4)$. Then:
$$m = \frac{4 - 4}{5 - 2} = \frac{0}{3} = 0$$
          So the velocity is 0 cm/sec.

     (c)   Let $(x_1, y_1) = (0, 0)$ and $(x_2, y_2) = (2, 16)$. Then:
$$m = \frac{16 - 0}{2 - 0} = \frac{16}{2} = 8$$
          So the velocity is 8 mph.

23. (a)   Since the velocity of A is 3 units/sec and the velocity of B is 20 units/sec,
          then B is traveling faster.

     (b)   When $t = 0$, A is at $x = 100$ and B is at $x = -36$. So A is farther to the
          right.

     (c)   We set the two x's equal: $3t + 100 = 20t - 36$
$$136 = 17t$$
$$8 = t$$
          When $t = 8$ sec , A and B have the same x-coordinate.

25.   (a)   We plot the points:

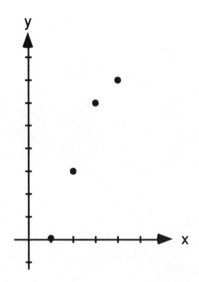

(b)   The slope appears to be approximately 2.5 and the y-intercept is -2:

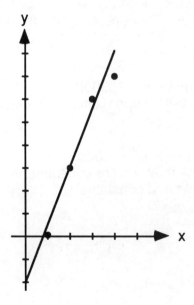

(c)   We graph the regression line y = 2.4x - 2:

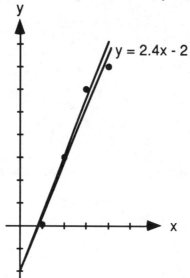

y = 2.4x - 2

27.   (a)   We let x = 2000:
y = 37025(2000) - 70226566 = 3823434
It would appear that Los Angeles will not reach a population of 4 million by the year 2000.

(b)   We let x = 2010:
y = 37025(2010) - 70226566 ≈ 4195000
The population in Los Angeles will be approximately 4195000 in the year 2010.

29. $(f \circ f)(x) = f(mx + b) = m(mx + b) + b = m^2 x + (mb + b)$
So, since $(f \circ f)(x) = 9x + 4$, and since m and b are constants, we must have the two equations (equating x-coefficients and constants):
$m^2 = 9$ and $mb + b = 4$
Since m > 0, then m = 3 and:
$3b + b = 4$
$4b = 4$
$b = 1$
So f(x) = 3x + 1.

31.   (a)   Since f is a linear function, then f(x) = mx + b. We compute each side of the equality:
$$f\left(\frac{x_1 + x_2}{2}\right) = m\left(\frac{x_1 + x_2}{2}\right) + b$$
$$= \frac{m}{2}x_1 + \frac{m}{2}x_2 + b$$

$$\frac{f(x_1) + f(x_2)}{2} = \frac{(mx_1 + b) + (mx_2 + b)}{2}$$

$$= \frac{mx_1 + mx_2 + 2b}{2}$$

$$= \frac{m}{2}x_1 + \frac{m}{2}x_2 + b$$

Since each quantity is equal, we have shown the desired result.

(b)   We compute each side of the equality:

$$f\left(\frac{x_1 + x_2}{2}\right) = \left(\frac{x_1 + x_2}{2}\right)^2$$

$$= \frac{x_1^2 + 2x_1x_2 + x_2^2}{4}$$

$$= \frac{1}{4}x_1^2 + \frac{1}{2}x_1x_2 + \frac{1}{4}x_2^2$$

$$\frac{f(x_1) + f(x_2)}{2} = \frac{x_1^2 + x_2^2}{2}$$

$$= \frac{1}{2}x_1^2 + \frac{1}{2}x_2^2$$

Clearly the two quantities are not equal.

33. (a) $\sum x = 1 + 2 + 3 + 4 = 10$

$\sum y = 0 + 3 + 6 + 7 = 16$

(b) $\sum x^2 = 1 + 4 + 9 + 16 = 30$

$\sum xy = 0 + 6 + 18 + 28 = 52$

(c) We multiply the first equation by -3:

$$-12b - 30m = -48$$
$$10b + 30m = 52$$

Adding, we get:

$$-2b = 4$$
$$b = -2$$

Substituting into the first equation:

$$4b + 10m = 16$$
$$-8 + 10m = 16$$
$$10m = 24$$
$$m = 2.4$$

So the regression line is $y = 2.4x - 2$.

35.   We first do the computations:

$$\Sigma x = 1 + 2 + 3 + 4 + 5 = 15$$

$$\Sigma y = 2 + 3 + 9 + 9 + 11 = 34$$

$$\Sigma x^2 = 1 + 4 + 9 + 16 + 25 = 55$$

$$\Sigma xy = 2 + 6 + 27 + 36 + 55 = 126$$

So the system of equations becomes:

$$5b + 15m = 34$$
$$15b + 55m = 126$$

We multiply the first equation by -3:

$$-15b - 45m = -102$$
$$15b + 55m = 126$$

Adding, we get:

$$10m = 24$$
$$m = 2.4$$

Substituting into the first equation:

$$5b + 36 = 34$$
$$5b = -2$$
$$b = -0.4$$

So the regression line is $y = 2.4x - 0.4$.

37.   We first do the computations:

$$\Sigma x = 520 + 740 + 560 + 610 + 650 = 3080$$

$$\Sigma y = 81 + 98 + 83 + 88 + 95 = 445$$

$$\Sigma x^2 = 270400 + 547600 + 313600 + 372100 + 422500 = 1926200$$

$$\Sigma xy = 42120 + 72520 + 46480 + 53680 + 61750 = 276550$$

So the system of equations becomes:

$$5b + 3080m = 445$$
$$3080b + 1926200m = 276550$$

Divide the first equation by 5 and the second equation by 10:

$$b + 616m = 89$$
$$308b + 192620m = 27655$$

We multiply the first equation by -308:

$$-308b - 189728m = -27412$$
$$308b + 192620m = 27655$$

Adding, we get:

$$2892m = 243$$
$$m \approx 0.084$$

Substituting into the first equation:

$$5b + 258.8 = 445$$
$$5b = 186.2$$
$$b \approx 37.241$$

So the regression line is $y = 0.084x + 37.241$.

3.2 Quadratic Functions

1. $y = (x + 2)^2$
    vertex: (-2, 0); axis: x = -2; minimum: 0
    x-intercept: -2; y-intercept: 4

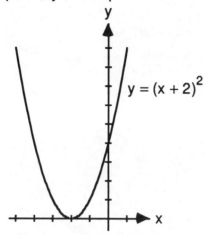

$$y = (x + 2)^2$$

3. $y = 2(x + 2)^2$
    vertex: (-2, 0); axis: x = -2; minimum: 0
    x-intercept: -2; y-intercept: 8

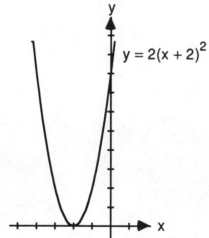

$$y = 2(x + 2)^2$$

5. $y = -2(x + 2)^2 + 4$
vertex: $(-2, 4)$; axis: $x = -2$; maximum: 4
x-intercepts: $-2 \pm \sqrt{2}$; y-intercept: -4

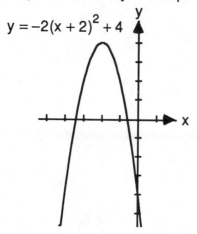

$y = -2(x + 2)^2 + 4$

7. $f(x) = x^2 - 4x$
Complete the square:
$$f(x) = x^2 - 4x = (x^2 - 4x + 4) - 4 = (x - 2)^2 - 4$$
vertex: $(2, -4)$; axis: $x = 2$; minimum: -4
x-intercepts: 0, 4; y-intercept: 0

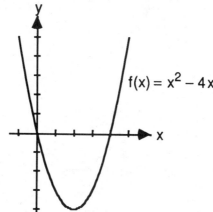

$f(x) = x^2 - 4x$

9. $g(x) = 1 - x^2$
    vertex: $(0, 1)$; axis: $x = 0$; maximum: 1
    x-intercepts: ± 1; y-intercept: 1

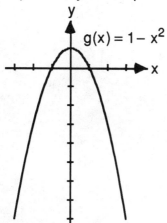

11. $y = x^2 - 2x - 3$
    Complete the square:
    $$y = x^2 - 2x - 3 = (x^2 - 2x + 1) - 3 - 1 = (x - 1)^2 - 4$$
    vertex: $(1, -4)$; axis: $x = 1$; minimum: -4
    x-intercepts: 3, -1; y-intercept: -3

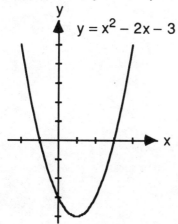

13. $y = -x^2 + 6x + 2$
Complete the square:
$$y = -x^2 + 6x + 2 = -(x^2 - 6x) + 2 = -(x^2 - 6x + 9) + 2 + 9 = -(x - 3)^2 + 11$$
vertex: $(3, 11)$; axis: $x = 3$; maximum: 11

x-intercepts: $3 \pm \sqrt{11}$; y-intercept: 2

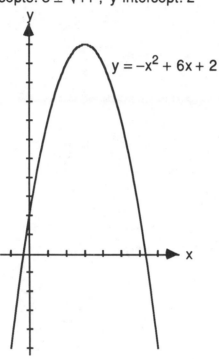

15. $s = 16t^2$
vertex: $(0, 0)$; axis: $t = 0$; minimum: 0
t-intercept: 0; s-intercept: 0

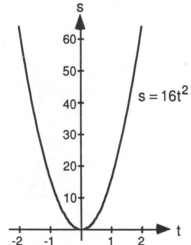

17. $s = 2 + 3t - 9t^2$
Complete the square:

$$s = -9\left(t^2 - \frac{1}{3}t\right) + 2 = -9\left(t^2 - \frac{1}{3}t + \frac{1}{36}\right) + 2 + \frac{1}{4} = -9\left(t - \frac{1}{6}\right)^2 + \frac{9}{4}$$

vertex: $(1/6, 9/4)$; axis: $t = 1/6$; maximum: $9/4$
t-intercepts: $-1/3, 2/3$; s-intercept: 2

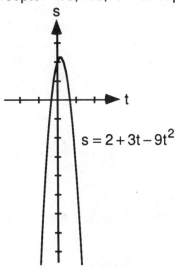

$s = 2 + 3t - 9t^2$

19. We complete the square:

$$y = 2x^2 - 4x + 11$$
$$y = 2(x^2 - 2x) + 11$$
$$y = 2(x^2 - 2x + 1) + 11 - 2$$
$$y = 2(x - 1)^2 + 9$$

Since the vertex is $(1, 9)$ and the parabola will be pointed up, then $x = 1$ will yield a minimum output value.

21. We complete the square:

$$g(x) = -6x^2 + 18x$$
$$g(x) = -6(x^2 - 3x)$$
$$g(x) = -6(x^2 - 3x + 9/4) + 27/2$$
$$g(x) = -6(x - 3/2)^2 + 27/2$$

Since the vertex is $(3/2, 27/2)$ and the parabola will be pointed down, then $x = 3/2$ will yield a maximum output value.

23. Since the vertex is $(0, -10)$ and the parabola will be pointed up, then $x = 0$ will yield a minimum output value.

25. We complete the square:
$$y = x^2 - 8x + 3$$
$$y = (x^2 - 8x + 16) + 3 - 16$$
$$y = (x - 4)^2 - 13$$
Since the vertex is $(4, -13)$ and the parabola will be pointed up, then the function has a minimum value of -13.

27. We complete the square:
$$y = -2x^2 - 3x + 2$$
$$y = -2\left(x^2 + \frac{3}{2}x\right) + 2$$
$$y = -2\left(x^2 + \frac{3}{2}x + \frac{9}{16}\right) + 2 + \frac{9}{8}$$
$$y = -2(x + 3/4)^2 + 25/8$$
Since the vertex is $(-3/4, 25/8)$ and the parabola will be pointed down, then the function has a maximum value of $25/8$.

29. We do not need to complete the square, since the vertex is $(0, 1000)$ and the parabola will be pointed down. So the function has a maximum value of 1000.

31. We find the vertex of the parabola by completing the square:
$$y = x^2 - 6x + 13$$
$$y = (x^2 - 6x + 9) + 13 - 9$$
$$y = (x - 3)^2 + 4$$
So the vertex is $(3, 4)$. We now use the distance formula with the points $(0, 0)$ and $(3, 4)$:
$$d = \sqrt{(3 - 0)^2 + (4 - 0)^2} = \sqrt{9 + 16} = \sqrt{25} = 5$$
So the vertex is 5 units from the origin.

33. $(f \circ g)(x) = 2(x^2 + 4x + 1) - 3$
$$= 2x^2 + 8x + 2 - 3$$
$$= 2x^2 + 8x - 1$$
So $f \circ g$ is a quadratic function.

35. $(g \circ h)(x) = \left(1 - 2x^2\right)^2 + 4(1 - 2x^2) + 1$
$$= 1 - 4x^2 + 4x^4 + 4 - 8x^2 + 1$$
$$= 4x^4 - 12x^2 + 6$$
So $g \circ h$ is neither linear nor quadratic.

37. $(f \circ f)(x) = 2(2x - 3) - 3 = 4x - 6 - 3 = 4x - 9$
So $f \circ f$ is a linear function.

39. (a) We first complete the square on $x^2 - 6x + 73$:
$$x^2 - 6x + 73 = (x^2 - 6x + 9) + 73 - 9 = (x - 3)^2 + 64$$
So $f(x) = \sqrt{(x - 3)^2 + 64}$
This would achieve a minimum value at $(3, \sqrt{64}) = (3, 8)$.

   (b) Here $g(x) = \sqrt[3]{(x - 3)^2 + 64}$, which would achieve a minimum
value at $(3, \sqrt[3]{64}) = (3, 4)$.

   (c) We complete the square on $x^4 - 6x^2 + 73$:
$$x^4 - 6x^2 + 73 = (x^4 - 6x^2 + 9) + 73 - 9 = (x^2 - 3)^2 + 64$$
So $h(x) = (x^2 - 3)^2 + 64$, which would achieve a minimum value at
$(\pm\sqrt{3}, 64)$.

41. (a) We complete the square on $-x^2 + 4x + 12$:
$$-x^2 + 4x + 12 = -(x^2 - 4x) + 12$$
$$= -(x^2 - 4x + 4) + 12 + 4$$
$$= -(x - 2)^2 + 16$$
So $f(x) = \sqrt{-(x - 2)^2 + 16}$, which has a maximum value at
$(2, \sqrt{16}) = (2, 4)$

   (b) Now $g(x) = \sqrt[3]{-(x - 2)^2 + 16}$, which has a maximum value at
$(2, \sqrt[3]{16}) = (2, 2\sqrt[3]{2})$

   (c) Here $h(x) = -(x^2 - 2)^2 + 16$, which has a maximum value at $(\pm\sqrt{2}, 16)$

43. Since the vertex is $(2, 2)$, we know its equation will be $y = A(x - 2)^2 + 2$. Since
$(0, 0)$ must lie on this parabola, we plug the points in to find A:
$$y = A(x - 2)^2 + 2$$
$$0 = A(0 - 2)^2 + 2$$
$$0 = 4A + 2$$
$$-2 = 4A$$
$$A = -\frac{1}{2}$$
So the parabola is $y = -\frac{1}{2}(x - 2)^2 + 2$.

45.   Since the vertex is (3, -1), we know its equation will be $y = A(x - 3)^2 - 1$. Since (1, 0) must lie on this parabola, we plug the points in to find A:

$$y = A(x - 3)^2 - 1$$
$$0 = A(1 - 3)^2 - 1$$
$$0 = 4A - 1$$
$$1 = 4A$$
$$A = \frac{1}{4}$$

So the parabola is $y = \frac{1}{4}(x - 3)^2 - 1$.

47.   We complete the square:

$$y = ax^2 + bx + c$$
$$y = a\left(x^2 + \frac{b}{a}x\right) + c$$
$$y = a\left(x^2 + \frac{b}{a}x + \frac{b^2}{4a^2}\right) + c - \frac{ab^2}{4a^2}$$
$$y = a\left(x + \frac{b}{2a}\right)^2 + \frac{4ac - b^2}{4a}$$

So the vertex is $\left(-\frac{b}{2a}, \frac{4ac - b^2}{4a}\right)$.

49.   We complete the square:

$$y = x^2 + 2x + c$$
$$y = (x^2 + 2x + 1) + c - 1$$
$$y = (x + 1)^2 + c - 1$$

So the minimum value is $c - 1 = \sqrt{2}$, thus $c = 1 + \sqrt{2}$.

51.   Since a and b will be the x-intercepts of the parabola, and all points with the same y-coordinate will be symmetric about the axis of symmetry, it follows that the midpoint $\left(\frac{a + b}{2}, 0\right)$ must lie on the axis of symmetry. Thus the x-coordinate of the vertex (which also lies on this axis) is $\frac{a + b}{2}$.

53.   (a)   We first complete the square to find the vertex:

$$y = p(x^2 + x) + r = p\left(x^2 + x + \frac{1}{4}\right) + r - \frac{p}{4} = p\left(x + \frac{1}{2}\right)^2 + \frac{4r - p}{4}$$

Now, if the vertex lies on the x-axis, then $\frac{4r - p}{4} = 0$, so $4r - p = 0$, so $p = 4r$.

(b)   If $p = 4r$, then $y = 4rx^2 + 4rx + r$. We complete the square:

$$y = 4r(x^2 + x) + r = 4r\left(x^2 + x + \frac{1}{4}\right) + r - r = 4r\left(x + \frac{1}{2}\right)^2$$

But then the vertex is $\left(-\frac{1}{2}, 0\right)$, and thus it lies on the x-axis.

55.   If $a + bi$ and $a - bi$ are roots of the equation, then we can write the equation in factored form as:

$$[x - (a + bi)] [x - (a - bi)] = 0$$
$$x^2 - (a + bi)x - (a - bi)x + (a + bi)(a - bi) = 0$$
$$x^2 - 2ax + (a^2 + b^2) = 0$$

We complete the square:

$$\begin{aligned} f(x) &= (x^2 - 2ax) + (a^2 + b^2) \\ &= (x^2 - 2ax + a^2) + (a^2 + b^2 - a^2) \\ &= (x - a)^2 + b^2 \end{aligned}$$

So the vertex is (a, b^2).

3.3 Applied Functions: Setting Up Equations

1.   (a)   We first draw the figure:

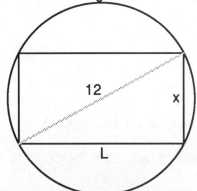

Call P the perimeter. We are asked to come up with a formula for P in terms of x. Since the diameter forms a right triangle, we use the Pythagorean Theorem to get:

$$L^2 + x^2 = 12^2$$
$$L^2 = 144 - x^2$$
$$L = \sqrt{144 - x^2}$$

Now $P = 2x + 2L = 2x + 2\sqrt{144 - x^2}$

Using functional notation, we have $P(x) = 2x + 2\sqrt{144 - x^2}$

(b)   Let A denote the area of the rectangle. Then $A = xL = x\sqrt{144 - x^2}$
Using functional notation, we have $A(x) = x\sqrt{144 - x^2}$

3.   (a)   We first draw the figure:

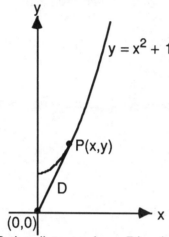

Call D the distance from P(x, y) to the origin. We are asked to come up
with a formula for D in terms of x. By the distance formula, we have:
$$D = \sqrt{(x - 0)^2 + (y - 0)^2} = \sqrt{x^2 + y^2}$$
Since P(x, y) lies on the curve, then $y = x^2 + 1$. Substituting this for y in
our equation for D, we have:
$$D = \sqrt{x^2 + y^2}$$
$$= \sqrt{x^2 + (x^2 + 1)^2}$$
$$= \sqrt{x^2 + x^4 + 2x^2 + 1}$$
$$= \sqrt{x^4 + 3x^2 + 1}$$

Using functional notation, we have $D(x) = \sqrt{x^4 + 3x^2 + 1}$

(b)   Let M denote the slope of the line segment from the origin to P(x, y).
Then:
$$M = \frac{y - 0}{x - 0} = \frac{y}{x}$$
Substituting $y = x^2 + 1$ in for y in this equation, we have:
$$M = \frac{y}{x} = \frac{x^2 + 1}{x}$$

Using functional notation, we have $M(x) = \frac{x^2 + 1}{x}$

5.   (a)   We first draw the figure:

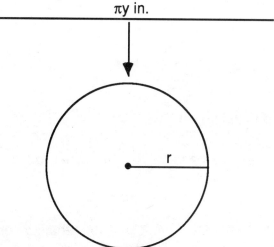

πy in.

Call A the area of the circle and r its radius. We are asked to come up with a formula for A in terms of y. SInce πy is the circumference (C) of the circle, and C = 2πr, we have:

$$2\pi r = \pi y$$

$$r = \frac{y}{2}$$

Now $A = \pi r^2 = \pi\left(\frac{y}{2}\right)^2 = \frac{\pi y^2}{4}$

Using functional notation, we have $A(y) = \frac{\pi y^2}{4}$

(b)   We draw the figure:

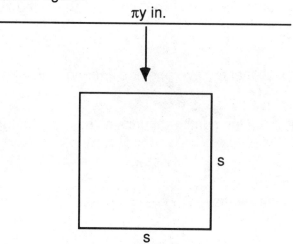

πy in.

Let A denote the area of the square, and s the length of the side.
Since the perimeter (P) is πy and P = 4s, we have:

$$4s = \pi y$$
$$s = \frac{\pi y}{4}$$

Now $A = s^2 = \left(\frac{\pi y}{4}\right)^2 = \frac{\pi^2 y^2}{16}$

Using functional notation, we have $A(y) = \frac{\pi^2 y^2}{16}$

7.   (a)   Let the two numbers be x and 16 - x. Then the product P would be:
$$P = x(16 - x) = 16x - x^2$$
Using functional notation, we have $P(x) = 16x - x^2$

(b)   Since the two numbers are x and 16 - x, then the sum of squares S
would be:
$$S = (x)^2 + (16 - x)^2$$
$$= x^2 + 256 - 32x + x^2$$
$$= 2x^2 - 32x + 256$$
Using functional notation, we have $S(x) = 2x^2 - 32x + 256$

(c)   There are two ways to set this up. SInce the two numbers are x and
16 - x, then the difference of the cubes D could be:
$$D = (x)^3 - (16 - x)^3 \quad \text{or} \quad D = (16 - x)^3 - x^3$$
Using functional notation, we have:
$$D(x) = x^3 - (16 - x)^3 \quad \text{or} \quad D(x) = (16 - x)^3 - x^3$$

(d)   Let A denote the average of the two numbers. SInce the two numbers
are x and 16 - x, we have:
$$A = \frac{x + 16 - x}{2} = \frac{16}{2} = 8$$
So A(x) = 8. Notice that the average does not depend what the two
numbers are!

9.   Let R be the revenue, x be the number of units sold, and p be the demand
(price). Then:
$$R = xp = x\left(-\frac{1}{4}x + 8\right) = -\frac{1}{4}x^2 + 8x$$

Using functional notation, we have $R(x) = -\frac{1}{4}x^2 + 8x$

11. (a)   We complete the table:

x	1	2	3	4	5	6	7
P(x)	17.88	19.49	20.83	21.86	22.49	22.58	21.75

(b)   The largest value for P(x) is 22.58, corresponding to x = 6.

(c) $P(4\sqrt{2}) = 2(4\sqrt{2}) + 2\sqrt{64 - (4\sqrt{2})^2}$

$= 8\sqrt{2} + 2\sqrt{64 - 32}$

$= 8\sqrt{2} + 2\sqrt{32}$

$= 8\sqrt{2} + 8\sqrt{2}$

$= 16\sqrt{2}$

≈ 22.63

This is indeed larger than any of our table values.

13. (a)   We first draw the figure:

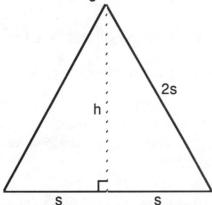

Let h denote the height and 2s denote the sides. Note that the height (called the altitude) bisects the base into the lengths of s and s. We are asked to find h in terms of s, so we use the Pytrhagorean Theorem on the right triangle:

$$h^2 + s^2 = (2s)^2$$
$$h^2 + s^2 = 4s^2$$
$$h^2 = 3s^2$$
$$h = \sqrt{3s^2}$$
$$h = \sqrt{3}\,s$$

Using functional notation we have $h(s) = \sqrt{3}\,s$.

(b)   Let A denote the area of the triangle. Then:
$$A = \frac{1}{2}\text{(base)(height)} = \frac{1}{2}(2s)(\sqrt{3}\,s) = \sqrt{3}\,s^2$$
Using functional notation, we have $A(s) = \sqrt{3}\,s^2$.

(c)   If each side is 8 cm, then:
$$2s = 8$$
$$s = 4$$
Using the function from (a), we have:
$$h(4) = \sqrt{3} \cdot 4 = 4\sqrt{3}\text{ cm.}$$

(d)   If each side is 5 in., then:
$$2s = 5$$
$$s = \frac{5}{2}$$
Using the function from (b), we have:
$$A\left(\frac{5}{2}\right) = \sqrt{3}\left(\frac{5}{2}\right)^2 = \frac{25\sqrt{3}}{4}\text{ in}^2$$

15.   Let h be the height, r be the radius, and V be the volume. We know that:
$$V = \pi r^2 h$$
We are also given that h = 2r, so we plug into the formula for V:
$$V = \pi r^2(2r) = 2\pi r^3$$
Using functional notation, we have $V(r) = 2\pi\,r^3$.

17.   (a)   Let h be the height, r be the radius, and V be the volume. We know
that $V = 12\pi$ and $V = \pi r^2 h$, so:
$$\pi r^2 h = 12\pi$$
$$h = \frac{12\pi}{\pi r^2}$$
$$h = \frac{12}{r^2}$$

Using functional notation, we have $h(r) = \frac{12}{r^2}$

(b)   Let S be the total surface area. Then:
$$S = 2\pi r^2 + 2\pi rh$$
$$= 2\pi r^2 + 2\pi r\left(\frac{12}{r^2}\right)\quad\text{by (a)}$$
$$= 2\pi r^2 + \frac{24\pi}{r}$$
Using functional notation, we have $S(r) = 2\pi r^2 + \frac{24\pi}{r}$

19. We solve $S = 4\pi r^2$ for r:

$$4\pi r^2 = S$$

$$r^2 = \frac{S}{4\pi}$$

$$r = \sqrt{\frac{S}{4\pi}}$$

Now $V = \frac{4}{3}\pi r^3$

$$= \frac{4}{3}\pi \left(\sqrt{\frac{S}{4\pi}}\right)^3$$

$$= \frac{4\pi S\sqrt{S}}{3(4\pi)\sqrt{4\pi}}$$

$$= \frac{S\sqrt{S}}{3\sqrt{4\pi}} \quad \text{or} \quad \frac{S\sqrt{4\pi S}}{12\pi}$$

Using functional notation, we have $V(S) = \dfrac{S\sqrt{4\pi S}}{12\pi} = \dfrac{S\sqrt{S\pi}}{6\pi}$

21. We draw a figure:

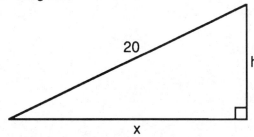

Let A be the area of the triangle, and let x and h be its two legs. By the Pythagorean Theorem, we have:

$$x^2 + h^2 = 20^2$$

$$h^2 = 400 - x^2$$

$$h = \sqrt{400 - x^2}$$

Now $A = \frac{1}{2}$ (base)(height) $= \frac{1}{2}(x)(h) = \frac{1}{2}x\sqrt{400 - x^2}$

Using functional notation, we have $A(x) = \frac{1}{2}x\sqrt{400 - x^2}$

23.   We draw the figure:

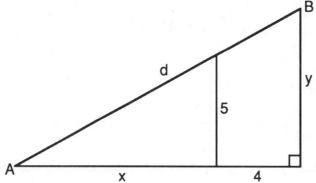

Let d = AB.
Using similar triangles, we have:

$$\frac{x}{5} = \frac{x + 4}{y}$$

$$xy = 5(x + 4)$$

$$y = \frac{5(x + 4)}{x}$$

Now:

$$d^2 = (x + 4)^2 + y^2$$

$$= (x + 4)^2 + \left(\frac{5(x + 4)}{x}\right)^2$$

$$= (x + 4)^2 + \frac{25(x + 4)^2}{x^2}$$

$$= \frac{x^2(x + 4)^2 + 25(x + 4)^2}{x^2}$$

$$= \frac{(x + 4)^2(x^2 + 25)}{x^2}$$

So: $d = \dfrac{(x + 4)\sqrt{x^2 + 25}}{x}$

Using functional notation, we have: $d(x) = \dfrac{(x + 4)\sqrt{x^2 + 25}}{x}$

25.   We plug into $A(x) = 50x - x^2$:

x	5	10	20	24	24.8	24.9	25	25.1	25.2	45
A(x)	225	400	600	624	624.96	624.99	625	624.99	624.96	225

x = 25 yields the largest area. Since L = 50 - x = 50 - 25 = 25, then L = 25 is
the corresponding value.

27. (a) We plug into $A(x) = 8x - \frac{1}{2}x^3$:

Table 1:

x	1	2	3	4
A	7.5	12	10.5	0

x = 2 yields the largest area

Table 2:

x	1.75	2.00	2.25	2.50	2.75
A	11.3203	12.0000	12.3047	12.1875	11.6016

x = 2.25 yields the largest area.

Table 3:

x	2.15	2.20	2.25	2.30	2.35
A	12.2308	12.2760	12.3047	12.3165	12.3111

x = 2.30 yields the largest area.

(b) Since $x = \frac{4\sqrt{3}}{3} = 2.309$ to four significant places, then x = 2.30 is the closest x-value. This yields an area of 12.3168. Notice that x = 2.30 agrees with this to five significant digits.

29. (a) Since $V = \frac{1}{3}\pi r^2 h$ and $h = \sqrt{3}\,r$, we have:

$$V = \frac{1}{3}\pi r^2 (\sqrt{3}\,r) = \frac{\sqrt{3}}{3}\pi r^3$$

Using functional notation, we have $V(r) = \frac{\sqrt{3}}{3}\pi r^3$

(b) Since $S = \pi r \sqrt{r^2 + h^2}$ and $h = \sqrt{3}\,r$, we have:

$$S = \pi r \sqrt{r^2 + h^2}$$
$$= \pi r \sqrt{r^2 + (\sqrt{3}r)^2}$$
$$= \pi r \sqrt{r^2 + 3r^2}$$
$$= \pi r \sqrt{4r^2}$$
$$= \pi r(2r)$$
$$= 2\pi r^2$$

Using functional notation, we have $S(r) = 2\pi r^2$

31. (a)   Since $V = \frac{1}{3}\pi r^2 h$ and $S = \pi r \sqrt{r^2 + h^2}$, and $V = S$, we have:

$$\frac{1}{3}\pi r^2 h = \pi r \sqrt{r^2 + h^2}$$

$$rh = 3\sqrt{r^2 + h^2}$$

Squaring:

$$r^2 h^2 = 9(r^2 + h^2)$$
$$r^2 h^2 = 9r^2 + 9h^2$$
$$r^2 h^2 - 9r^2 = 9h^2$$
$$r^2(h^2 - 9) = 9h^2$$
$$r^2 = \frac{9h^2}{h^2 - 9}$$

Taking roots:

$$r = \sqrt{\frac{9h^2}{h^2 - 9}}$$

$$r = \frac{3h}{\sqrt{h^2 - 9}}$$

Using functional notation, we have $r(h) = \dfrac{3h}{\sqrt{h^2 - 9}}$

(b)   After squaring in (a), we had:

$$r^2 h^2 = 9r^2 + 9h^2$$
$$r^2 h^2 - 9h^2 = 9r^2$$
$$h^2(r^2 - 9) = 9r^2$$
$$h^2 = \frac{9r^2}{r^2 - 9}$$

Taking roots:

$$h = \sqrt{\frac{9r^2}{r^2 - 9}} = \frac{3r}{\sqrt{r^2 - 9}}$$

Using functional notation, we have $h(r) = \dfrac{3r}{\sqrt{r^2 - 9}}$

33. Let x be the length of wire used for the circle. Then 14 - x is the length of wire used for the square. We have:

Circle   Square
Circum $= 2\pi r = x$ Perim $= 4S = 14 - x$

$$r = \frac{x}{2\pi}$$ $$S = \frac{14 - x}{4}$$

$$\text{Area} = \pi r^2 = \pi \left(\frac{x}{2\pi}\right)^2 \qquad \text{Area} = S^2 = \left(\frac{14 - x}{4}\right)^2$$

$$= \frac{\pi x^2}{4\pi^2} \qquad\qquad\qquad = \frac{(14 - x)^2}{16}$$

$$= \frac{x^2}{4\pi}$$

So the total combined area is $A = \dfrac{x^2}{4\pi} + \dfrac{(14 - x)^2}{16} = \dfrac{4x^2 + \pi(14 - x)^2}{16\pi}$

Using functional notation, we have:

$$A(x) = \frac{4x^2 + \pi(14 - x)^2}{16\pi}$$

35. The perimeter of each semi-circle is $\dfrac{1}{2}(2\pi r) = \pi r$, so the total perimeter P is given by:

$$P = \pi r + \pi r + l + l = 2\pi r + 2l$$

Since $P = \dfrac{1}{4}$, we have:

$$2\pi r + 2l = \frac{1}{4}$$

$$2l = \frac{1}{4} - 2\pi r$$

$$2l = \frac{1 - 8\pi r}{4}$$

$$l = \frac{1 - 8\pi r}{8}$$

We now find the area A. The area of each semicircle is $\dfrac{1}{2}(\pi r^2)$, and the area of the rectangle is length • width:

$$A = \frac{1}{2}\pi r^2 + \frac{1}{2}\pi r^2 + lw, \quad \text{but } w = 2r$$

$$= \pi r^2 + \left(\frac{1 - 8\pi r}{8}\right)(2r)$$

$$= \pi r^2 + \frac{r - 8\pi r^2}{4}$$

$$= \frac{4\pi r^2 + r - 8\pi r^2}{4}$$

$$= \frac{r - 4\pi r^2}{4}$$

Using functional notation, we have $A(r) = \dfrac{r(1 - 4\pi r)}{4}$

37. We draw the figure:

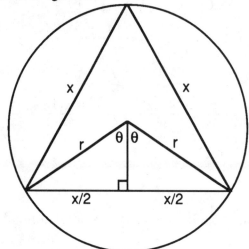

Using geometry, we see that:

$$2\theta = \frac{1}{3}(360°)$$

$$2\theta = 120°$$

$$\theta = 60°$$

Since $\theta = 60°$, then:

$$\frac{x}{2} = \frac{\sqrt{3}}{2}\,r$$

$$x = \sqrt{3}\,r$$

$$r = \frac{x}{\sqrt{3}}$$

So the area of the circle A is:

$$A = \pi r^2 = \pi\left(\frac{x}{\sqrt{3}}\right)^2 = \frac{\pi x^2}{3}$$

Using functional notation, we have $A(x) = \dfrac{\pi x^2}{3}$

39. We draw the figure:

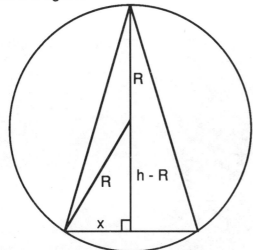

We first find x by the Pythagorean Theorem:

$$x^2 + (h - R)^2 = R^2$$
$$x^2 = R^2 - (h - R)^2$$
$$x^2 = R^2 - (h^2 - 2hR + R^2)$$
$$x^2 = -h^2 + 2hR$$

Taking roots:

$$x = \sqrt{2Rh - h^2}$$

Now the area of the triangle is given by:

$$A_\Delta = \frac{1}{2}\,(\text{base})\,(\text{height})$$

$$= \frac{1}{2}\,(2x)\,(h)$$

$$= \frac{1}{2}\,(2\sqrt{2Rh - h^2})\,(h)$$

$$= h\sqrt{2Rh - h^2}$$

The area of the circle is:

$$A_0 = \pi R^2$$

So the desired area A is given by:

$$A = A_0 - A_\Delta = \pi R^2 - h\sqrt{2Rh - h^2}$$

Since R is a constant, we use functional notation to write:

$$A(h) = \pi R^2 - h\sqrt{2Rh - h^2}$$

41. Since $V = l \bullet w \bullet h$ and $l = 8 - 2x$, $w = 6 - 2x$, $h = x$, we have:

$$V = (8 - 2x)(6 - 2x)(x) = (48 - 28x + 4x^2)(x) = 4x^3 - 28x^2 + 48x$$

Using functional notation, we have $V(x) = 4x^3 - 28x^2 + 48x$

43. (a) The area of the window would be:

$$A = \frac{1}{2}(\pi r^2) + lw$$

It remains to find l and w in terms of r. We see that $w = 2r$, and the perimeter $P = 32$ and:

$$P = \frac{1}{2}(2\pi r) + 2l + w$$

So:

$$\frac{1}{2}(2\pi r) + 2l + w = 32$$

$$\pi r + 2l + 2r = 32$$

$$2l = 32 - \pi r - 2r$$

$$l = \frac{32 - \pi r - 2r}{2}$$

We now find the area:

$$A = \frac{1}{2}(\pi r^2) + lw$$

$$= \frac{1}{2}(\pi r^2) + \left(\frac{32 - \pi r - 2r}{2}\right)(2r)$$

$$= \frac{\pi r^2}{2} + 32r - \pi r^2 - 2r^2$$

$$= 32r - 2r^2 - \frac{\pi r^2}{2}$$

Using functional notation, we write $A(r) = 32r - 2r^2 - \frac{\pi r^2}{2}$

(b) $A(r) = -\left(\frac{4 + \pi}{2}\right)r^2 + 32r$, which will open downward. Since $A(0) = 0$,

it does pass through the origin. We complete the square:

$$A(r) = -\left(\frac{4 + \pi}{2}\right)\left(r^2 - \frac{64}{4 + \pi}r\right)$$

$$= -\left(\frac{4 + \pi}{2}\right)\left(r^2 - \frac{64}{4 + \pi}r + \left(\frac{32}{4 + \pi}\right)^2\right) + \left(\frac{4 + \pi}{2}\right)\left(\frac{32}{4 + \pi}\right)^2$$

$$= -\left(\frac{4 + \pi}{2}\right)\left(r - \frac{32}{4 + \pi}\right)^2 + \frac{512}{4 + \pi}$$

So the vertex is $\left(\frac{32}{4 + \pi}, \frac{512}{4 + \pi}\right)$.

45. (a) We use the Pythagorean Theorem:
$$3^2 + y^2 = z^2$$
Taking roots:
$$z = \sqrt{y^2 + 9}$$
Now $s = \dfrac{y}{z} = \dfrac{y}{\sqrt{y^2 + 9}}$, so $s\sqrt{y^2 + 9} = y$

Squaring, we get:
$$s^2(y^2 + 9) = y^2$$
$$s^2 y^2 + 9s^2 = y^2$$
$$y^2 - s^2 y^2 = 9s^2$$
$$y^2(1 - s^2) = 9s^2$$
$$y^2 = \frac{9s^2}{1 - s^2}$$

Taking roots:
$$y = \frac{3s}{\sqrt{1 - s^2}}$$

Using functional notation, we have $y(s) = \dfrac{3s}{\sqrt{1 - s^2}}$

(b) This was done in (a); we had $s(y) = \dfrac{y}{\sqrt{y^2 + 9}}$

(c) Since $s = \dfrac{y}{z}$, then $z = \dfrac{y}{s}$. Using our result from (a), we have:
$$z = \frac{y}{s} = \frac{\dfrac{3s}{\sqrt{1 - s^2}}}{s} = \frac{3}{\sqrt{1 - s^2}}$$

Using functional notation, we have $z(s) = \dfrac{3}{\sqrt{1 - s^2}}$

(d) Using our answer from (c), we have:
$$z = \frac{3}{\sqrt{1 - s^2}}$$
$$z\sqrt{1 - s^2} = 3$$
Squaring each side, we get:
$$z^2(1 - s^2) = 9$$
$$z^2 - z^2 s^2 = 9$$
$$-z^2 s^2 = 9 - z^2$$
$$s^2 = \frac{z^2 - 9}{z^2}$$

Taking roots:

$$s = \frac{\sqrt{z^2 - 9}}{z}$$

Using functional notation, we have $s(z) = \frac{\sqrt{z^2 - 9}}{z}$

47. (a) $m(a) = \frac{a^2 - (-1)}{a - 0} = \frac{a^2 + 1}{a}$

(b)   The area of the triangle, A, is:

$$A = \frac{1}{2}\text{(base)(height)} = \frac{1}{2}(a - x_0)(a^2)$$

where x_0 is the x-intercept. To find the x-intercept, we must find the

equation of the line. We use $m = \frac{a^2 + 1}{a}$ (from (a) above) and $(0, -1)$

in the slope-intercept formula to get:

$$y = \frac{a^2 + 1}{a} x - 1$$

We find x_0 by letting $y = 0$:

$$0 = \frac{a^2 + 1}{a} x_0 - 1$$

$$\frac{a^2 + 1}{a} x_0 = 1$$

$$x_0 = \frac{a}{a^2 + 1}$$

So $A = \frac{1}{2}(a - x_0) a^2$

$$= \frac{1}{2}\left(a - \frac{a}{a^2 + 1}\right) a^2$$

$$= \frac{a^2}{2}\left(\frac{a(a^2 + 1) - a}{a^2 + 1}\right)$$

$$= \frac{a^2(a^3 + a - a)}{2(a^2 + 1)}$$

$$= \frac{a^2(a^3)}{2(a^2 + 1)}$$

$$= \frac{a^5}{2(a^2 + 1)}$$

49. We re-draw the figure (differently):

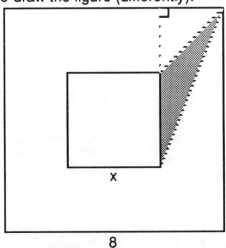

We extend the triangle to form a right triangle as pictured. We find the areas of the large and small right triangles:

$$A_{large} = \frac{1}{2}\,(\text{base})(\text{height})$$

$$= \frac{1}{2}\left(x + \frac{8 - x}{2}\right)\left(\frac{8 - x}{2}\right)$$

$$= \frac{1}{2}\left(\frac{2x + 8 - x}{2}\right)\left(\frac{8 - x}{2}\right)$$

$$= \frac{(x + 8)(8 - x)}{8}$$

$$= \frac{64 - x^2}{8}$$

$$A_{small} = \frac{1}{2}\,(\text{base})(\text{height}) = \frac{1}{2}\left(\frac{8 - x}{2}\right)\left(\frac{8 - x}{2}\right) = \frac{64 - 16x + x^2}{8}$$

So $A = A_{large} - A_{small}$

$$= \frac{64 - x^2}{8} - \frac{64 - 16x + x^2}{8}$$

$$= \frac{64 - x^2 - 64 + 16x - x^2}{8}$$

$$= \frac{16x - 2x^2}{8}$$

$$= \frac{8x - x^2}{4}$$

Using functional notation, we write $A(x) = \dfrac{8x - x^2}{4}$

<u>Note:</u>   A slightly easier approach is to realize that the altitude of the triangle need not lie on the triangle. That is:

$$\text{Area } = \frac{1}{2}\text{ (base)(altitude)} = \frac{1}{2}(x)\left(\frac{8-x}{2}\right) = \frac{8x - x^2}{4}$$

Both approaches are correct.

51. We draw the diagram:

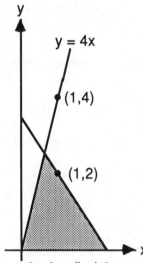

We are asked to find the area **A** of the shaded triangle. Since the line has slope m and passes through (1, 2), then by the point-slope formula, we have:

$$y - 2 = m(x - 1)$$
$$y - 2 = mx - m$$
$$y = mx + (2 - m)$$

Its x-intercept is where y = 0:

$$0 = mx + (2 - m)$$
$$mx = m - 2$$
$$x = \frac{m - 2}{m}$$

This is the base of a triangle. To find its height, we must find the value of y where this line and y = 4x intersect. We set the two y-values equal:

$$mx + 2 - m = 4x$$
$$mx - 4x = m - 2$$
$$x(m - 4) = m - 2$$
$$x = \frac{m - 2}{m - 4}$$

Since this point lies on y = 4x, its y-coordinate is:

$$y = 4x = 4\left(\frac{m - 2}{m - 4}\right)$$

Finally, we find the area:

$$A = \frac{1}{2}(\text{base})(\text{height})$$

$$= \frac{1}{2}\left(\frac{m-2}{m}\right)(4)\left(\frac{m-2}{m-4}\right)$$

$$= 2\,\frac{(m-2)^2}{m(m-4)}$$

$$= \frac{2(m^2 - 4m + 4)}{m^2 - 4m}$$

$$= \frac{2m^2 - 8m + 8}{m^2 - 4m}$$

Using functional notation, we have $A(m) = \dfrac{2m^2 - 8m + 8}{m^2 - 4m}$

53. We draw a figure:

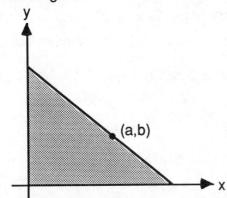

The line has the equation $y - b = m(x - a)$. Since the base and height are the x- and y-intercepts, respectively, we find each intercept:

base:
$$y = 0$$
$$-b = m(x - a)$$
$$-b = mx - ma$$
$$mx = ma - b$$
$$x = \frac{ma - b}{m}$$

height:
$$x = 0$$
$$y - b = m(-a)$$
$$y = b - ma$$

So the area of the triangle is $A = \dfrac{1}{2}\left(\dfrac{ma - b}{m}\right)(b - ma) = \dfrac{(ma - b)^2}{-2m}$

3.4 Maximum and Minimum Problems

1. Call the two numbers x and y. Then $x + y = 5$, so $y = 5 - x$. So the product can be written as:
$$P = xy = x(5 - x) = 5x - x^2$$
We now complete the square:
$$P = -(x^2 - 5x) = -\left(x^2 - 5x + \frac{25}{4}\right) + \frac{25}{4} = -\left(x - \frac{5}{2}\right)^2 + \frac{25}{4}$$
Since this is a parabola opening downward, it will have a maximum value of 25/4.

3. Call the two numbers x and y. Then $y - x = 1$, so $y = x + 1$. The sum of their squares can be written as:
$$S = x^2 + y^2 = x^2 + (x + 1)^2 = x^2 + x^2 + 2x + 1 = 2x^2 + 2x + 1$$
We now complete the square:
$$S = 2(x^2 + x) + 1 = 2\left(x^2 + x + \frac{1}{4}\right) + 1 - \frac{1}{2} = 2\left(x + \frac{1}{2}\right)^2 + \frac{1}{2}$$
Since this is a parabola opening upward, it will have a minimum value of 1/2.

5. Let w and l be the width and length, respectively. Since $P = 2w + 2l$, then:
$$2w + 2l = 25$$
$$2l = 25 - 2w$$
$$l = \frac{25 - 2w}{2}$$
So the area is given by:
$$A = wl = w\left(\frac{25 - 2w}{2}\right) = \frac{1}{2}(-2w^2 + 25)$$
We now complete the square:
$$A = -\left(w^2 - \frac{25}{2}w\right) = -\left(w^2 - \frac{25}{2}w + \frac{625}{16}\right) = -\left(w - \frac{25}{4}\right)^2 + \frac{625}{16}$$
This is a parabola opening downward, so it will achieve a maximum value when $w = 25/4$. We find l:
$$l = \frac{25 - 2\left(\frac{25}{4}\right)}{2} = \frac{25 - \frac{25}{2}}{2} = \frac{25}{4}$$
So the largest such rectangle is a square of dimensions 25/4 m by 25/4m.

7. Let x and y be the lengths of the two shorter sides, so $x + y = 100$, and $y = 100 - x$. Then the area is given by:
$$A = \frac{1}{2}xy = \frac{1}{2}x(100 - x) = \frac{1}{2}(-x^2 + 100x)$$

We now complete the square:

$$A = -\frac{1}{2}(x^2 - 100x)$$

$$= -\frac{1}{2}(x^2 - 100x + 2500) + 1250$$

$$= -\frac{1}{2}(x - 50)^2 + 1250$$

This is a parabola opening downward, so it will achieve a maximum value of 1250 in^2.

9.   Let x and y be the two numbers, so $x + y = 6$ and thus $y = 6 - x$.

(a) $T = x^2 + y^2$

$$= x^2 + (6 - x)^2$$

$$= x^2 + 36 - 12x + x^2$$

$$= 2x^2 - 12x + 36$$

We now complete the square:

$$T = 2(x^2 - 6x) + 36$$

$$= 2(x^2 - 6x + 9) + 36 - 18$$

$$= 2(x - 3)^2 + 18$$

This is a parabola opening upward, so it will have a minimum value of 18.

(b) $S = x + y^2$

$$= x + (6 - x)^2$$

$$= x + 36 - 12x + x^2$$

$$= x^2 - 11x + 36$$

We now complete the square:

$$S = (x^2 - 11x) + 36$$

$$= \left(x^2 - 11x + \frac{121}{4}\right) + 36 - \frac{121}{4}$$

$$= \left(x - \frac{11}{2}\right)^2 + \frac{23}{4}$$

This is a parabola opening upward, so it will have a minimum value of 23/4.

(c) $U = x + 2y^2$

$$= x + 2(6 - x)^2$$

$$= x + 72 - 24x + 2x^2$$

$$= 2x^2 - 23x + 72$$

We now complete the square:

$$U = 2\left(x^2 - \frac{23}{2}x\right) + 72$$

$$= 2\left(x^2 - \frac{23}{2}x + \frac{529}{16}\right) + 72 - \frac{529}{8}$$

$$= 2\left(x - \frac{23}{4}\right)^2 + \frac{47}{8}$$

This is a parabola opening upward, so it will have a minimum value of 47/8.

(d) $V = x + (2y)^2$

$= x + 4y^2$

$= x + 4(6 - x)^2$

$= x + 144 - 48x + 4x^2$

$= 4x^2 - 47x + 144$

We now complete the square:

$$V = 4\left(x^2 - \frac{47}{4}x\right) + 144$$

$$= 4\left(x^2 - \frac{47}{4}x + \frac{2209}{64}\right) + 144 - \frac{2209}{16}$$

$$= 4\left(x - \frac{47}{8}\right)^2 + \frac{95}{16}$$

This is a parabola opening upward, so it will have a minimum value of 95/16.

11. (a) $h(1) = -16(1)^2 + 32(1) = -16 + 32 = 16$ ft

$$h\left(\frac{3}{2}\right) = -16\left(\frac{3}{2}\right)^2 + 32\left(\frac{3}{2}\right) = -16\left(\frac{9}{4}\right) + 48 = -36 + 48 = 12 \text{ ft}$$

(b)   We complete the square:

$h = -16t^2 + 32t$

$= -16(t^2 - 2t)$

$= -16(t^2 - 2t + 1) + 16$

$= -16(t - 1)^2 + 16$

This is a parabola opening downward, so it will have a maximum height of 16 ft, attained after 1 second.

(c) We set $h = 7$:

$$7 = -16t^2 + 32t$$
$$16t^2 - 32t + 7 = 0$$
$$(4t - 7)(4t - 1) = 0$$
$$t = \frac{7}{4}, \frac{1}{4}$$

So $h = 7$ ft when $t = 7/4$ sec or $t = 1/4$ sec.

13. Every point on the given curve has coordinates of the form $(x, \sqrt{x - 2} + 1)$, and using the distance formula gives:

$$d = \sqrt{(4 - x)^2 + (1 - \sqrt{x - 2} - 1)^2}$$
$$= \sqrt{16 - 8x + x^2 + x - 2}$$
$$= \sqrt{x^2 - 7x + 14}$$

and we look for a minimum value of the radicand.
We complete the square:

$$(x^2 - 7x) + 14 = \left(x^2 - 7x + \frac{49}{4}\right) + 14 - \frac{49}{4} = \left(x - \frac{7}{2}\right)^2 + \frac{7}{4}$$

This is a parabola opening upward which will achieve a minimum value of

$$\sqrt{\frac{7}{4}} = \frac{\sqrt{7}}{2} \text{ at } x = \frac{7}{2}. \text{ Then:}$$

$$y = \sqrt{\frac{7}{2} - 2} + 1 = \sqrt{\frac{3}{2}} + 1 = \frac{2 + \sqrt{6}}{2}$$

So the point is $\left(\frac{7}{2}, \frac{2 + \sqrt{6}}{2}\right)$ and the distance is $\frac{\sqrt{7}}{2}$.

15. (a) We must find the value of x such that $x - x^2$ is as large as possible.
Call $f(x) = -x^2 + x$. We complete the square:

$$f(x) = -(x^2 - x)$$
$$= -\left(x^2 - x + \frac{1}{4}\right) + \frac{1}{4}$$
$$= -\left(x - \frac{1}{2}\right)^2 + \frac{1}{4}$$

This is a parabola opening downward, so it will achieve a maximum value when $x = 1/2$. So the number is $1/2$.

(b)   We must find the value of x such that $x - 2x^2$ is as large as possible.
       Call $f(x) = -2x^2 + x$. We complete the square:

$$f(x) = -2\left(x^2 - \frac{1}{2}x\right)$$

$$= -2\left(x^2 - \frac{1}{2}x + \frac{1}{16}\right) + \frac{1}{8}$$

$$= -2\left(x - \frac{1}{4}\right)^2 + \frac{1}{8}$$

This is a parabola opening downward, so it will achieve a maximum
value when $x = 1/4$. So the number is 1/4.

17.   If we choose x for the depth of the pasture, then 500 - 2x is the length
       paralleling the river. The area of the pasture will then be given by:

$$A = x(500 - 2x) = -2x^2 + 500x$$

We complete the square:

$$A = -2(x^2 - 250x)$$

$$= -2(x^2 - 250x + 125^2) + 2(125)^2$$

$$= -2(x - 125)^2 + 31,250$$

This is a parabola opening downward, so it will achieve a maximum value at
$x = 125$. Then the length $= 500 - 2(125) = 500 - 250 = 250$. So the
dimensions are 125 ft by 250 ft.

19. $$R - C = (0.4x^2 + 10x + 5) - (0.5x^2 + 2x + 101)$$

$$= 0.4x^2 + 10x + 5 - 0.5x^2 - 2x - 101$$

$$= -0.1x^2 + 8x - 96$$

We now complete the square:

$$R - C = -0.1(x^2 - 80x) - 96$$

$$= -0.1(x^2 - 80x + 1600) - 96 + 160$$

$$= -0.1(x - 40)^2 + 64$$

This is a parabola opening downward, so it will achieve a maximum value
when $x = 40$.

21. Recall that revenue, R, is x • p. So:

$$R = x\left(-\frac{1}{4}x + 30\right) = -\frac{1}{4}x^2 + 30x$$

We complete the square:

$$R = -\frac{1}{4}x^2 + 30x$$

$$= -\frac{1}{4}(x^2 - 120x)$$

$$= -\frac{1}{4}(x^2 - 120x + 3600) + 900$$

$$= -\frac{1}{4}(x - 60)^2 + 900$$

This is a parabola opening downward, so it will achieve a maximum value at x = 60. The maximum revenue is $900. The corresponding unit price, p, is

$$p = -\frac{1}{4}(60) + 30 = -15 + 30 = \$15.$$

23. (a) To use max/min methods, we need to substitute in the quantity $x^2 + y^2$ and write it strictly in terms of x or y. So take 2x + 3y = 6 and solve for y:

$$3y = 6 - 2x$$

$$y = \frac{6 - 2x}{3}$$

Then substitute, and the quantity $x^2 + y^2$ becomes:

$$Q = x^2 + \left(\frac{6 - 2x}{3}\right)^2 = x^2 + \frac{36 - 24x + 4x^2}{9} = \frac{13}{9}x^2 - \frac{8}{3}x + 4$$

We now complete the square:

$$Q = \frac{13}{9}\left(x^2 - \frac{24}{13}x\right) + 4$$

$$= \frac{13}{9}\left(x^2 - \frac{24}{13}x + \frac{144}{169}\right) + 4 - \frac{13}{9}\left(\frac{144}{169}\right)$$

$$= \frac{13}{9}\left(x - \frac{12}{13}\right)^2 + \frac{36}{13}$$

This is a parabola opening up, so it will achieve a minimum value of 36/13.

(b) The equation of a circle with its center at the origin is $x^2 + y^2 = r^2$ where r is the radius. The line 2x + 3y = 6 will intersect the circle in two points whenever r is sufficiently large. As we reduce r, we gradually reach a position where the circle and line are tangent and this is the minimum value of r or $\sqrt{x^2 + y^2}$. In this case, it is

$$\sqrt{\frac{36}{13}} = \frac{6\sqrt{13}}{13}.$$ This is the square root of the answer from (a).

25.   (a)   We plug $y = 15 - x$ into $Q = x^2 + y^2$
$$= x^2 + (15 - x)^2$$
$$= x^2 + 225 - 30x + x^2$$
$$= 2x^2 - 30x + 225$$

We now complete the square:
$$Q = 2x^2 - 30x + 225$$
$$= 2(x^2 - 15x) + 225$$
$$= 2\left(x^2 - 15x + \frac{225}{4}\right) + 225 - \frac{225}{2}$$
$$= 2\left(x - \frac{15}{2}\right)^2 + \frac{225}{2}$$

This is a parabola opening upward, so it will achieve a minimum value of 225/2.

(b)   We plug $y = C - x$ into $Q = x^2 + y^2$
$$= x^2 + (C - x)^2$$
$$= x^2 + C^2 - 2Cx + x^2$$
$$= 2x^2 - 2Cx + C^2$$

We now complete the square:
$$Q = 2x^2 - 2Cx + C^2$$
$$= 2(x^2 - Cx) + C^2$$
$$= 2\left(x^2 - Cx + \frac{C^2}{4}\right) + C^2 - \frac{C^2}{2}$$
$$= 2\left(x - \frac{C}{2}\right)^2 + \frac{C^2}{2}$$

This is a parabola opening upward, so it will achieve a minimum value of $\frac{C^2}{2}$.   When C = 15, the result from (a) is verified.

27.   Let the other two sides of each of the four triangles be t and 1 - t, respectively. Then the area of the square will be a minimum when the area of these triangles is a maximum. Let's write an expression for the total area of the four triangles.

$$A = 4\left(\frac{1}{2}\right)(t)(1 - t) = 2t - 2t^2 = -2t^2 + 2t$$

We complete the square:

$$A = -2t^2 + 2t = -2(t^2 - t) = -2\left(t^2 - t + \frac{1}{4}\right) + \frac{1}{2} = -2\left(t - \frac{1}{2}\right)^2 + \frac{1}{2}$$

This is a parabola opening downward, so it will achieve a maximum area of 1/2 when t = 1/2. Since the large square has area = 1, then the minimum area

is $\frac{1}{2}$ when $x = \frac{1}{\sqrt{2}} = \frac{\sqrt{2}}{2}$.

29. We draw the figure:

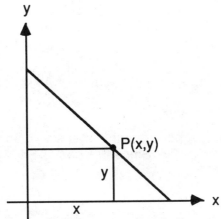

$A = xy = x(7 - 3x) = -3x^2 + 7x$
We complete the square:
$$A = -3\left(x^2 - \frac{7}{3}x\right) = -3\left(x^2 - \frac{7}{3}x + \frac{49}{36}\right) + \frac{49}{12} = -3\left(x - \frac{7}{6}\right)^2 + \frac{49}{12}$$
Since this parabola opens downward, the largest possible area is 49/12.

31. See the figure:

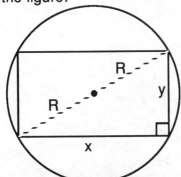

Using the Pythagorean Theorem, we obtain $y = \sqrt{4R^2 - x^2}$. The area A of the rectangle, then, is:
$$A = xy = x\sqrt{4R^2 - x^2}$$
Then:
$$A^2 = x^2(4R^2 - x^2) = 4R^2x^2 - x^4$$
In order to maximize the expression $4R^2x^2 - x^4$, first let $t = x^2$, so that the expression becomes $4R^2t - t^2$.

We complete the square:
$$A^2 = -t^2 + 4R^2t$$
$$= -(t^2 - 4R^2t)$$
$$= -(t^2 - 4R^2t + 4R^4) + 4R^4$$
$$= -(t - 2R^2)^2 + 4R^4$$

This parabola opens downward, so the maximum value of A^2 is $4R^4$, Then the maximum area is $\sqrt{4R^4} = 2R^2$.

33. Let x = east-west dimension, and y = north-south dimension. So the cost is given by $C = 12(2x) + 8(2y) = 24x + 16y$. Since this cost is \$4,800, we have $24x + 16y = 4800$, so:
$$y = \frac{4800 - 24x}{16} = \frac{600 - 3x}{2}$$

Now the area is $A = xy = x\left(\dfrac{600 - 3x}{2}\right) = \dfrac{-3}{2}x^2 + 300x$.

So $A(x) = -\dfrac{3}{2}x^2 + 300x$

This will be a parabola opening downward, so it will have a maximum value. We complete the square:
$$A(x) = -\frac{3}{2}x^2 + 300x$$
$$= -\frac{3}{2}(x^2 - 200x)$$
$$= -\frac{3}{2}(x^2 - 200x + 100^2) + 15,000$$
$$= -\frac{3}{2}(x - 100)^2 + 15,000$$

So $x = 100$ will maximize area, which is 15,000 yd^2. We find y:
$$y = \frac{600 - 3(100)}{2} = \frac{600 - 300}{2} = 150 \text{ yd}$$

So the dimensions are 100 yd by 150 yd.

35. The given function can be rewritten:
$$y = (a_1 + a_2)x^2 - 2(a_1x_1 + a_2x_2)x + (a_1x_1^2 + a_2x_2^2)$$
We complete the square:
$$y = (a_1 + a_2)\left(x^2 - \frac{2(a_1x_1 + a_2x_2)}{a_1 + a_2}x\right) + (a_1x_1^2 + a_2x_2^2)$$
$$= (a_1 + a_2)\left(x - \frac{a_1x_1 + a_2x_2}{a_1 + a_2}\right)^2 + (a_1x_1^2 + a_2x_2^2) - \frac{(a_1x_1 + a_2x_2)^2}{a_1 + a_2}$$

Since a_1 and a_2 are both positive, then $a_1 + a_2 > 0$ and thus this parabola opens upward. So the minimum must occur where $x = \dfrac{a_1 x_1 + a_2 x_2}{a_1 + a_2}$.

37. (a) We have $\dfrac{\Delta p}{\Delta x} = \dfrac{10}{-5} = -2$. Also $p = 200$ when $x = 150$. We use the point-slope formula with the point $(150, 200)$:
$$p - 200 = -2(x - 150)$$
$$p - 200 = -2x + 300$$
$$p = -2x + 500$$
Using functional notation, we have $p(x) = -2x + 500$.

(b) Since $R = xp$, we have $R = x(-2x + 500) = -2x^2 + 500x$.
We complete the square:
$$R = -2x^2 + 500x$$
$$R = -2(x^2 - 250x)$$
$$R = -2(x^2 - 250x + 15625) + 31{,}250$$
$$R = -2(x - 125)^2 + 31{,}250$$
Using functional notation, we have $R(x) = -2(x - 125)^2 + 31{,}250$. This simplifies to $R(x) = -2x^2 + 500x$. Since this parabola opens downward, we have a maximum revenue of $\$31{,}250$ when $x = 125$. We find
$$p = -2(125) + 500 = \$250.$$

39. Let $x = t^2$, so $f(x) = x - x^2 = -x^2 + x$. We complete the square:
$$f(x) = -(x^2 - x) = -\left(x^2 - x + \frac{1}{4}\right) + \frac{1}{4} = -\left(x - \frac{1}{2}\right)^2 + \frac{1}{4}$$
So $f(x)$ has a maximum value when $x = \frac{1}{2}$. Then $t^2 = \frac{1}{2}$, so $t = \pm \dfrac{\sqrt{2}}{2}$

41. Let $x = t^2$. Then $y = -t^4 + 6t^2 - 6 = -x^2 + 6x - 6$. We complete the square:
$$y = -x^2 + 6x - 6$$
$$= -(x^2 - 6x) - 6$$
$$= -(x^2 - 6x + 9) - 6 + 9$$
$$= -(x - 3)^2 + 3$$
So $x = 3$ will yield the largest output. Since $x = t^2$, we have:
$$t^2 = 3$$
$$t = \pm \sqrt{3}$$
So $t = \sqrt{3}$ or $t = -\sqrt{3}$ will yield the largest output.

43. (a)   Circle   Square
            Circumference = x   Perimeter = 16 - x
            $2\pi r = x$ $4s = 16 - x$
            $r = \dfrac{x}{2\pi}$ $s = \dfrac{16 - x}{4}$
            $A = \pi r^2$ $A = s^2$
            $A = \pi \left(\dfrac{x}{2\pi}\right)^2$ $A = \left(\dfrac{16 - x}{4}\right)^2$
            $A = \dfrac{x^2}{4\pi}$ $A = \dfrac{256 - 32x + x^2}{16} = 16 - 2x + \dfrac{1}{16}x^2$

So the total combined area is given by $A(x) = \dfrac{x^2}{4\pi} + 16 - 2x + \dfrac{1}{16}x^2$, or

$$A(x) = \left(\dfrac{1}{4\pi} + \dfrac{1}{16}\right)x^2 - 2x + 16$$

   (b)   We complete the square:

$$A(x) = \left(\dfrac{4 + \pi}{16\pi}\right)x^2 - 2x + 16$$

$$= \dfrac{4 + \pi}{16\pi}\left(x^2 - \dfrac{32\pi}{4 + \pi}x\right) + 16$$

$$= \dfrac{4 + \pi}{16\pi}\left(x - \dfrac{16\pi}{4 + \pi}\right)^2 + 16 - \dfrac{4 + \pi}{16\pi}\left(\dfrac{16\pi}{4 + \pi}\right)^2$$

This is a parabola opening upward, so it will have a minimum value at
$x = \dfrac{16\pi}{4 + \pi}$

   (c)   This ratio is $\dfrac{\dfrac{16\pi}{4 + \pi}}{16 - \dfrac{16\pi}{4 + \pi}} \bullet \dfrac{4 + \pi}{4 + \pi} = \dfrac{16\pi}{64 + 16\pi - 16\pi} = \dfrac{16\pi}{64} = \dfrac{\pi}{4}$

45. (a)   Circle: $2\pi r = x$, so $r = \dfrac{x}{2\pi}$

$$A = \pi\left(\dfrac{x}{2\pi}\right)^2 = \dfrac{x^2}{4\pi}$$

           Square: $s = \dfrac{L - x}{4}$

$$A = \left(\dfrac{L - x}{4}\right)^2 = \dfrac{L^2 - 2Lx + x^2}{16} = \dfrac{1}{16}x^2 - \dfrac{L}{8}x + \dfrac{L^2}{16}$$

So the total combined area is given by:

$$A(x) = \left(\dfrac{1}{4\pi} + \dfrac{1}{16}\right)x^2 - \dfrac{L}{8}x + \dfrac{L^2}{16} = \dfrac{4 + \pi}{16\pi}x^2 - \dfrac{L}{8}x + \dfrac{L^2}{16}$$

(b)   This will have a minimum value when $x = -\dfrac{b}{2a}$, so:

$$x = \dfrac{L/8}{\dfrac{4+\pi}{8\pi}} \cdot \dfrac{8\pi}{8\pi} = \dfrac{\pi L}{4+\pi}$$

(c)   This ratio is:

$$\dfrac{\dfrac{\pi L}{4+\pi}}{L - \dfrac{\pi L}{4+\pi}} \cdot \dfrac{4+\pi}{4+\pi} = \dfrac{\pi L}{4L + \pi L - \pi L} = \dfrac{\pi L}{4L} = \dfrac{\pi}{4}$$

It is interesting to note that this ratio does not depend on L, the length of the wire.

47.   We re-draw the figure and label additional sides:

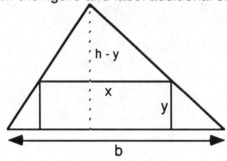

By similar triangles:
$$\dfrac{h-y}{h} = \dfrac{x}{b}$$
$$bh - by = xh$$
$$by = bh - xh$$
$$y = h - \dfrac{h}{b}x$$

So the area of the rectangle is given by:
$$A = xy$$
$$A = x\left(h - \dfrac{h}{b}x\right)$$
$$A = -\dfrac{h}{b}x^2 + hx$$

We complete the square:
$$A(x) = -\dfrac{h}{b}(x^2 - bx) = -\dfrac{h}{b}\left(x^2 - bx + \dfrac{b^2}{4}\right) + \dfrac{hb}{4} = -\dfrac{h}{b}\left(x - \dfrac{b}{2}\right)^2 + \dfrac{hb}{4}$$

So the maximum rectangle will have an area of $\frac{hb}{4}$. Since the triangle has an area of $\frac{hb}{2}$, then the desired ratio is:

$$\frac{\dfrac{hb}{2}}{\dfrac{hb}{4}} = \frac{4}{2} = 2$$

49.   Call h the height of the triangle (see figure), and call y the indicated value:

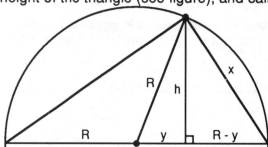

The key is to find h in terms of x. By the Pythagorean Theorem, we have the following relationships:

$$y^2 + h^2 = R^2 \qquad \text{and} \qquad (R - y)^2 + h^2 = x^2$$
$$y^2 = R^2 - h^2$$
$$y = \sqrt{R^2 - h^2}$$

Substituting, we have:

$$\left(R - \sqrt{R^2 - h^2}\right)^2 + h^2 = x^2$$
$$R^2 - 2R\sqrt{R^2 - h^2} + R^2 - h^2 + h^2 = x^2$$
$$2R^2 - 2R\sqrt{R^2 - h^2} = x^2$$

We solve for h:

$$-2R\sqrt{R^2 - h^2} = x^2 - 2R^2$$
$$\sqrt{R^2 - h^2} = R - \frac{x^2}{2R}$$
$$R^2 - h^2 = R^2 - x^2 + \frac{x^4}{4R^2}$$
$$-h^2 = \frac{x^4}{4R^2} - x^2$$
$$h^2 = -\frac{x^4}{4R^2} + x^2$$

We now use the hint. Since the area of the triangle is given by

$$A = \frac{1}{2}(2R)(h) = Rh, \text{ we maximize } A^2 = R^2h^2 = R^2\left(\frac{-x^4}{4R^2} + x^2\right) = -\frac{1}{4}x^4 + R^2x^2$$

We complete the square:

$$A^2 = -\frac{1}{4}(x^4 - 4R^2x^2) = -\frac{1}{4}(x^2 - 2R^2)^2 + R^4$$

So the maximum value is $A^2 = R^4$, or $A = R^2$. Thus, the shaded area is:

$$\frac{1}{2}(\pi R^2) - R^2 = \frac{\pi R^2}{2} - R^2 = R^2\left(\frac{\pi - 2}{2}\right)$$

51.   We wish to minimize the sum $x + \frac{1}{x}$. Now:

$$x + \frac{1}{x} = \left(\sqrt{x} - \sqrt{\frac{1}{x}}\right)^2 + 2$$

So the smallest possible value of 2 occurs if:

$$\sqrt{x} = \sqrt{\frac{1}{x}}$$

$$x = \frac{1}{x}$$

$$x^2 = 1$$

$$x = 1$$

So if both numbers are 1, the minimum sum of 2 occurs.

53. $G(x) = \dfrac{(a + x)(b + x)}{x}$

$$= \frac{ab + (a + b)x + x^2}{x}$$

$$= \frac{ab}{x} + (a + b) + x$$

$$= (a + b) + \left(\frac{ab}{x} + x\right)$$

Using the hint, we can rewrite $G(x)$ as:

$$G(x) = \left(\sqrt{x} - \sqrt{\frac{ab}{x}}\right)^2 + (a + b - 2\sqrt{ab})$$

$$= \left(\sqrt{x} - \sqrt{\frac{ab}{x}}\right)^2 + (\sqrt{a} - \sqrt{b})^2$$

Since $G(x)$ is the sum of two squares, we have $G(x) \geq 0$. Thus the minimum value occurs when:

$$\sqrt{x} - \sqrt{\frac{ab}{x}} = 0$$

$$\sqrt{x} = \frac{\sqrt{ab}}{\sqrt{x}}$$

$$x = \sqrt{ab}$$

So the minimum value is:

$$G(\sqrt{ab}) = (a + b) + \left(\frac{ab}{\sqrt{ab}} + \sqrt{ab} \right) = a + b + 2\sqrt{ab} = (\sqrt{a} + \sqrt{b})^2$$

This proves the desired result.

55.   Note that $2x^2 - x + 1 = 2\left(x^2 - \frac{1}{2}x \right) + 1$

$$= 2\left(x^2 - \frac{1}{2}x + \frac{1}{16} \right) + 1 - \frac{7}{8}$$

$$= 2(x - 1/4)^2 + 7/8$$

So the minimum value of this quantity is 7/8, thus:

$$2x^2 - x + 1 \geq 7/8$$

$$\frac{1}{2x^2 - x + 7} \leq 8/7$$

3.5 Polynomial Functions

1.   This graph has 4 turning points, but a polynomial function of degree 3 can have
      at most 2 turning points.

3.   As $|x|$ gets very large, our function should be similar to $f(x) = a_3 x^3$. But $f(x)$
      does not have a parabolic shape like the given graph.

5.   As $|x|$ gets very large with x negative, the graph should resemble $2x^5$. But the
      y-values of $2x^5$ are always negative when x is negative, contrary to the
      given graph.

7.   This graph has a corner, which cannot occur in the graph of a polynomial
      function.

9. $y = (x - 2)^2 + 1$
     This is $y = x^2$ shifted 2 units to the right and 1 unit up. See graph:

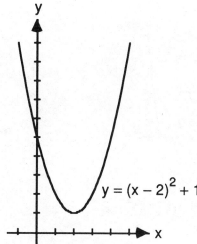

$$y = (x - 2)^2 + 1$$

x-intercept: none; y-intercept: 5

11. $y = -(x - 1)^4$
      This is $y = x^4$ reflected about the x-axis and shifted 1 unit to the right. See graph:

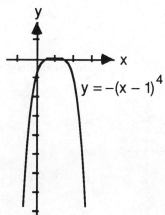

$$y = -(x - 1)^4$$

x-intercept: 1; y-intercept: -1

13. $y = (x - 4)^3 - 2$
This is $y = x^3$ shifted 4 units to the right and 2 units down. See graph:

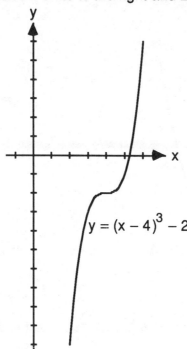

$$y = (x - 4)^3 - 2$$

x-intercept: $4 + \sqrt[3]{2}$; y-intercept: -66

15. $y = -2(x + 5)^4$
This is $y = 2x^4$ shifted 5 units to the left and reflected about the x-axis. See graph:

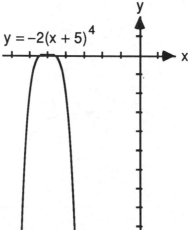

$$y = -2(x + 5)^4$$

x-intercept: -5; y-intercept: -1250

17. $y = \dfrac{1}{2}(x + 1)^5$

This is $y = \dfrac{1}{2}x^5$ shifted 1 unit to the left. See graph:

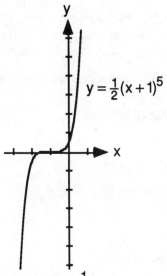

$y = \frac{1}{2}(x+1)^5$

x-intercept: -1; y-intercept: $\dfrac{1}{2}$

19. $y = -(x - 1)^3 - 1$

This is $y = x^3$ shifted 1 unit to the right, 1 unit down, and reflected about the x-axis. See graph:

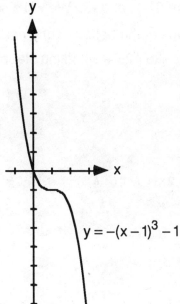

$y = -(x-1)^3 - 1$

x-intercept: 0; y-intercept: 0

21. $y = (x - 2)(x - 1)(x + 1)$
The roots can be found by inspection. If $x = 2$, then the $(x - 2)$ factor is zero. The roots of -1 and 1 can be found the same way. Near $x = -1$, y is near $(-1 - 2)(-1 - 1)(x + 1)$ or $6x + 6$. It rises fairly steeply to the right. At $x = 1$ the curve is like the line $y = -2x + 2$ and near $x = 2$ it approximates $y = 3x - 6$. To complete the sketch we need to pick points between the roots and get an idea how high turning points may be. Incidentally, such turning points are not necessarily halfway between the roots, but they are usually in the general area. Here we might choose to find $f(0)$ (always a good choice) and $f\left(\frac{3}{2}\right)$.

$f(0) = 2$ and $f\left(\frac{3}{2}\right) = -\frac{5}{8}$. We sketch the graph:

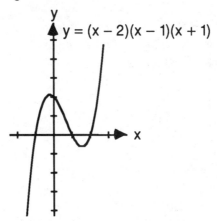

23. $y = 2x(x + 1)(x + 3)$
The roots of $y = 2x(x + 1)(x + 3)$ are 0, -1, and -3. We will also want to know when $x = -2$ and $-\frac{1}{2}$. Again, we look at the behavior of y near the roots. For example, when x is close to -3, y is like $12x + 36$, rising steeply to the right. We sketch the graph:

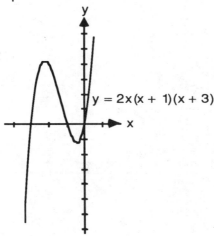

25. $y = x^3(x + 2)$

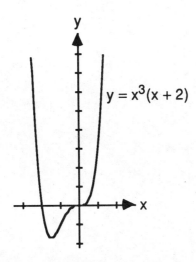

27. $y = 2(x - 1)(x - 4)^3$
The roots are 1 and 4. Look at f(0). Its enormous!
$f(0) = 2(0 - 1)(0 - 4)^3 = 128$. The graph must be very steep between x = 0 and
x = 1. Let's find f(2) and f(3) to help. We discover that the curve passes
through (2,-16) and (3,-4). Near x = 4 it behaves like $y = 6(x - 4)^3$, a tall, thin
version of $y = x^3$. Put it together and you have a sketch like:

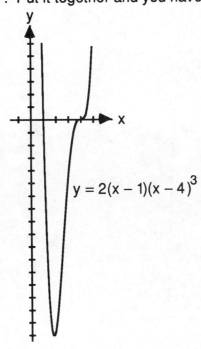

29. $y = (x + 1)^2(x - 1)(x - 3)$

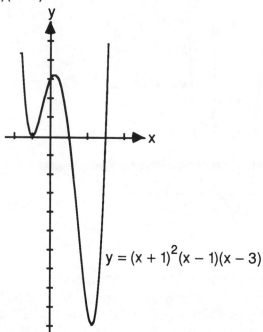

$$y = (x + 1)^2(x - 1)(x - 3)$$

31. $y = -x^3(x - 4)(x + 2)$

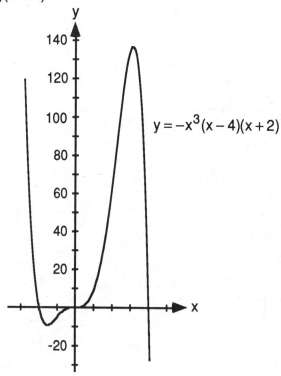

$$y = -x^3(x - 4)(x + 2)$$

33. $y = -4x(x - 2)^2(x + 2)^3$

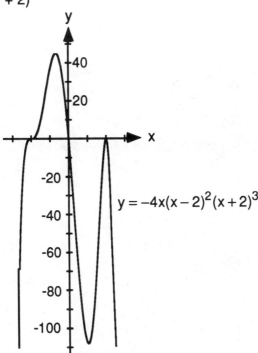

$$y = -4x(x-2)^2(x+2)^3$$

35. From left to right, they are: $f(x) = x$, $g(x) = x^2$, $h(x) = x^3$, $F(x) = x^4$, $G(x) = x^5$, $H(x) = x^6$.

37. We must find where $0 \leq H(x) < 0.1$
$$0 \leq x^6 < 0.1$$
Taking roots: $0 \leq x < 0.68$
So, when x lies in the interval $[0,0.68)$, then $H(x)$ will lie in the interval $[0,0.1)$.

39. We must find where:
$$g(t) - F(t) = 0.26$$
$$t^2 - t^4 = 0.26$$
$$t^4 - t^2 + 0.26 = 0$$
Using the quadratic formula:
$$t^2 = \frac{1 \pm \sqrt{1 - 4(0.26)}}{2} = \frac{1 \pm \sqrt{1 - 1.04}}{2} = \frac{1 \pm \sqrt{-0.04}}{2}$$
Since this equation has no real solutions, there is no such value of t.

41. We set them equal:

$$x = \frac{1}{100} x^2$$

$$0 = \frac{1}{100} x^2 - x$$

$$0 = \frac{1}{100} (x^2 - 100x)$$

$$0 = \frac{1}{100} \cdot x (x - 100)$$

The graph intersects at the origin but also at the point (100, 100).

43. $y = 2x^3 - x^4 = x^3(2 - x)$

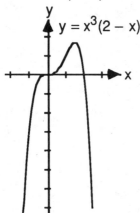

45. $y = x^3 + x^2 - 2x = x(x^2 + x - 2) = x(x + 2)(x - 1)$

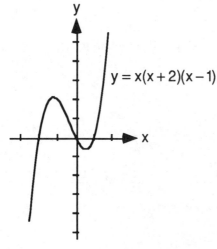

47. $y = 4x^2 - x^4 = x^2(4 - x^2) = x^2(2 + x)(2 - x)$

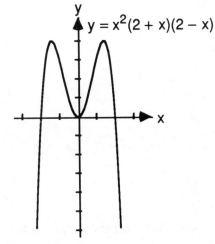

$y = x^2(2 + x)(2 - x)$

49. (a)   We graph the function:

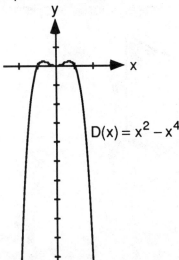

$D(x) = x^2 - x^4$

(b)   We complete the square:

$$D(x) = x^2 - x^4$$
$$= -(x^4 - x^2)$$
$$= -(x^4 - x^2 + 1/4) + 1/4$$
$$= -(x^2 - 1/2)^2 + 1/4$$

So the turning points are at $\left(\pm\dfrac{1}{\sqrt{2}}, \dfrac{1}{4}\right) = \left(\pm\dfrac{\sqrt{2}}{2}, \dfrac{1}{4}\right)$, which yield

maximum values. Note that the graph also has a turning point at $(0, 0)$, which is a minimum value.

(c)   We graph the two functions:

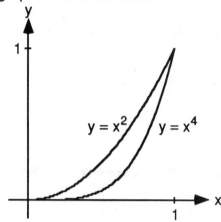

From part (a), we know that the maximum vertical distance between the
two curves is 1/4.

51.   (a)   Drawing a diagonal between two corners where the cylinder touches the
circle yields the right triangle:

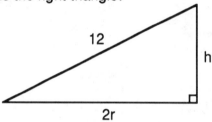

Using the Pythagorean Theorem:

$$(2r)^2 + h^2 = 12^2$$
$$4r^2 + h^2 = 144$$
$$h^2 = 144 - 4r^2$$
$$h = \sqrt{144 - 4r^2}$$
$$h = 2\sqrt{36 - r^2}$$

(b) $V = \pi r^2 h = \pi r^2 \left(2\sqrt{36 - r^2}\right) = 2\pi r^2 \sqrt{36 - r^2}$

(c)   We must have $36 - r^2 > 0$, so $0 < r < 6$. So the domain is $(0, 6)$.

(d)   We complete the table:

r	f(r)
0.0	0
0.5	88
1.0	1382
1.5	6745
2.0	20213
2.5	45878
3.0	86339
3.5	140700
4.0	202129
4.5	254971
5.0	271414
5.5	207720
6.0	0

We graph $f(r) = 4\pi^2 r^4(36 - r^2)$:

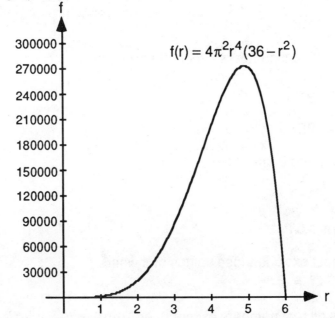

Using a graphics program such as GraphToolz™, we find the maximum value to be approximately 272,875. Thus, the maximum possible volume for the cylinder is approximately $\sqrt{272875} \approx 522$ cm^3.

3.6 Graphs of Rational Functions

1.   Domain: We must exclude those values of x where:
$$4x - 12 = 0$$
$$4x = 12$$
$$x = 3$$
So the domain is all real numbers except 3, or $(-\infty, 3) \cup (3, \infty)$.
x-intercepts: We must find where:
$$3x + 15 = 0$$
$$3x = -15$$
$$x = -5$$
So the x-intercept is -5.
y-intercepts: Let x = 0
$$y = \frac{0 + 15}{0 - 12} = -\frac{5}{4}$$
So the y-intercept is -5/4.

3.   Domain: We must exclude those values of x where:
$$x^2 - x - 6 = 0$$
$$(x - 3)(x + 2) = 0$$
$$x = 3, -2$$
So the domain is all real numbers except 3 and -2, or
$(-\infty, -2) \cup (-2, 3) \cup (3, \infty)$.
x-intercepts: We must find where:
$$x^2 - 8x - 9 = 0$$
$$(x - 9)(x + 1) = 0$$
$$x = 9, -1$$
So the x-intercepts are 9 and -1.
y-intercepts: Let x = 0
$$y = \frac{-9}{-6} = \frac{3}{2}$$
So the y-intercept is 3/2.

5.   Domain: We must exclude those values of x where:
$$x^6 = 0$$
Taking roots: $x = 0$
So the domain is all real numbers except 0, or $(-\infty, 0) \cup (0, \infty)$.
x-intercepts: We must find where:
$$(x^2 - 4)(x^3 - 1) = 0$$
$$x^2 - 4 = 0 \quad \text{or} \quad x^3 - 1 = 0$$
$$x^2 = 4 \qquad\qquad x^3 = 1$$

Taking roots:
$$x = \pm 2 \qquad\qquad x = 1$$
So the x-intercepts are -2, 2, and 1.
y-intercepts: Let x = 0
$$y = \frac{(-4)(-1)}{0}, \text{ which is undefined.}$$
So there are no y-intercepts.

7. $y = \dfrac{1}{x + 4}$

x-intercept: none
y-intercept: 1/4
horizontal asymptote: y = 0 (x-axis)
vertical asymptote: x = -4

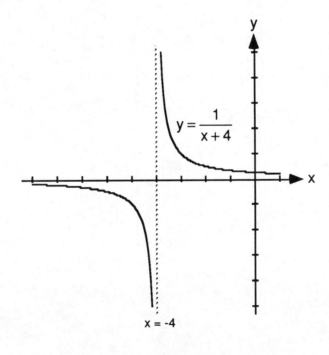

9. $y = \dfrac{3}{x+2}$

x-intercept: none
y-intercept: 3/2
horizontal asymptote: y = 0 (x-axis)
vertical asymptote: x = -2

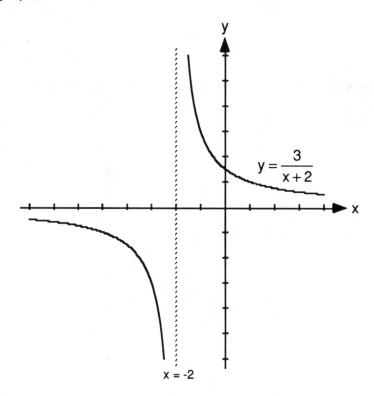

11. $y = \dfrac{-2}{x-3}$

    x-intercept: none
    y-intercept: 2/3
    horizontal asymptote: y = 0 (x-axis)
    vertical asymptote: x = 3

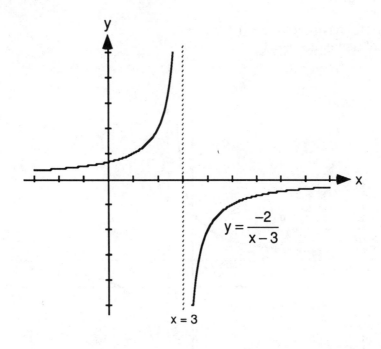

$y = \dfrac{-2}{x-3}$

x = 3

13. $y = \dfrac{x - 3}{x - 1}$

Using long division, we have:

$$\dfrac{x - 3}{x - 1} = 1 - \dfrac{2}{x - 1}$$

x-intercept: 3
y-intercept: 3
horizontal asymptote: y = 1
vertical asymtote: x = 1

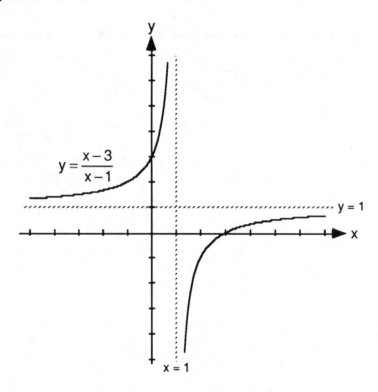

15. $y = \dfrac{4x - 2}{2x + 1}$

Using long division, we have:

$$\dfrac{4x - 2}{2x + 1} = 2 - \dfrac{4}{2x + 1}$$

x-intercept: 1/2
y-intercept: -2
horizontal asymptote: y = 2
vertical asymptote: x = -1/2

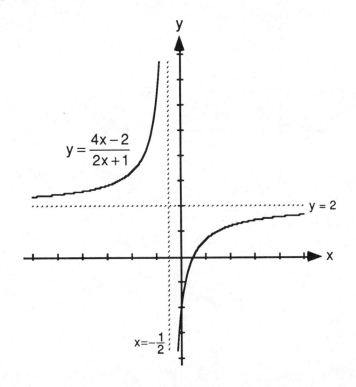

17. $y = \dfrac{1}{(x-2)^2}$

  x-intercept: none; y-intercept: 1/4

  horizontal asymptote: y = 0 (x-axis); vertical asymptote: x = 2

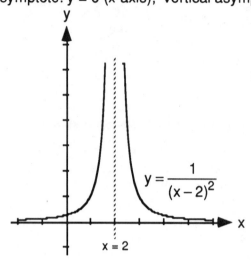

$$y = \frac{1}{(x-2)^2}$$

x = 2

19. $y = \dfrac{3}{(x+1)^2}$

  x-intercept: none; y-intercept: 3

  horizontal asymptote: y = 0 (x-axis); vertical asymptote: x = -1

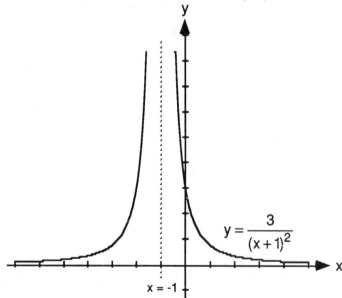

$$y = \frac{3}{(x+1)^2}$$

x = -1

21. $y = \dfrac{1}{(x+2)^3}$

x-intercept: none
y-intercept: 1/8
horizontal asymptote: y = 0 (x-axis)
vertical asymptote: x = -2

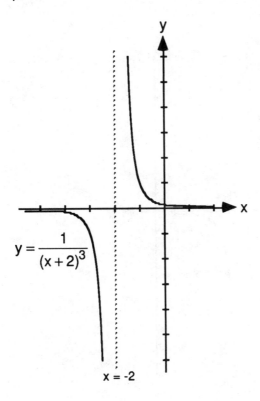

$y = \dfrac{1}{(x+2)^3}$

x = -2

23. $y = \dfrac{-4}{(x+5)^3}$

x-intercept: none
y-intercept: -4/125
horizontal asymptote: y = 0 (x-axis)
vertical asymptote: x = -5

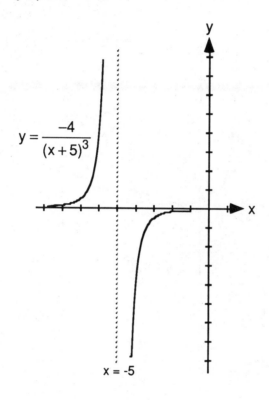

25. $y = \dfrac{-x}{(x + 2)(x - 2)}$
x-intercept: 0
y-intercept: 0
horizontal asymptote: y = 0 (x-axis)
vertical asymptotes: x = -2 , x = 2

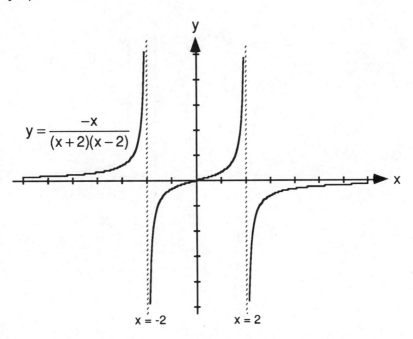

27. $y = \dfrac{x}{(x - 1)(x + 3)}$
x-intercept: 0
y-intercept: 0
horizontal asymptote: y = 0 (x-axis)
vertical asymptotes: x = -3 , x = 1

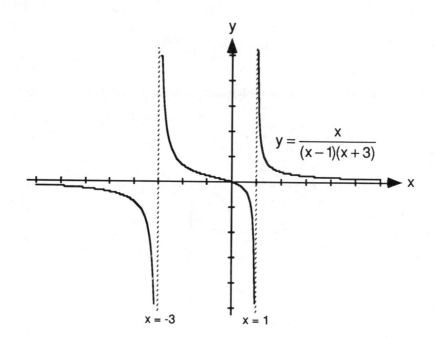

29. (a) $f(x) = \dfrac{(x-2)(x-4)}{x(x-1)}$

x-intercepts: 2, 4; y-intercept: none
horizontal asymptote: y = 1; vertical asymptotes: x = 0, x = 1

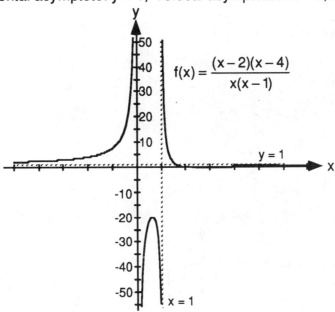

$$f(x) = \frac{(x-2)(x-4)}{x(x-1)}$$

(b) $g(x) = \dfrac{(x-2)(x-4)}{x(x-3)}$

x-intercepts: 2, 4; y-intercept: none
horizontal asymptote: y = 1; vertical asymptotes: x = 0, x = 3

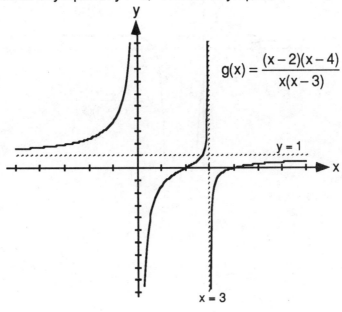

$$g(x) = \frac{(x-2)(x-4)}{x(x-3)}$$

31. $y = \dfrac{(x - 4)(x + 2)}{(x - 1)(x - 3)}$

x-intercepts: -2, 4
y-intercept: -8/3
horizontal asymptote: y = 1
vertical asymptotes: x = 1, x = 3

We find where the curve crosses the horizontal asymptote:

$$\frac{(x - 4)(x + 2)}{(x - 1)(x - 3)} = 1$$

$$(x - 4)(x + 2) = (x - 1)(x - 3)$$

$$x^2 - 2x - 8 = x^2 - 4x + 3$$

$$-2x - 8 = -4x + 3$$

$$2x = 11$$

$$x = \frac{11}{2}$$

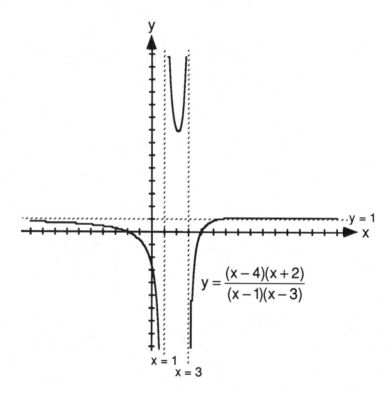

$$y = \frac{(x - 4)(x + 2)}{(x - 1)(x - 3)}$$

y = 1

x = 1

x = 3

33. $y = \dfrac{(x + 1)^2}{(x - 1)(x - 3)}$

x-intercept: -1; y-intercept: 1/3

horizontal asymptote: y = 1; vertical asymptotes: x = 1, x = 3

We find where the curve crosses the horizontal asymptote:

$$\dfrac{(x + 1)^2}{(x - 1)(x - 3)} = 1$$

$$(x + 1)^2 = (x - 1)(x - 3)$$

$$x^2 + 2x + 1 = x^2 - 4x + 3$$

$$2x + 1 = -4x + 3$$

$$6x = 2$$

$$x = \dfrac{1}{3}$$

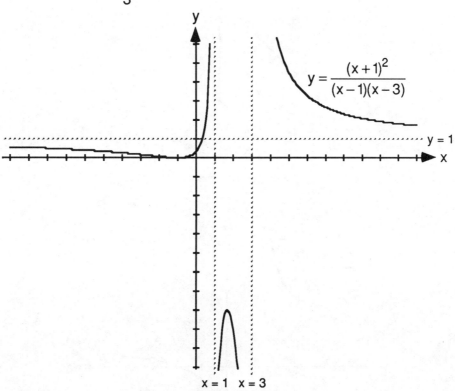

35. (a) x near -2: $y \approx \dfrac{(-5)(x + 2)}{(-1)(-4)} = -\dfrac{5}{4}(x + 2) = -\dfrac{5}{4}x - \dfrac{5}{2}$

(b) x near -1: $y \approx \dfrac{(-4)(1)}{(x + 1)(-3)} = \dfrac{4/3}{x + 1}$

(c) x near 2: $y \approx \dfrac{(-1)(4)}{(3)(x - 2)} = \dfrac{-4/3}{x - 2}$

37. (a) For $x \neq 3$, $y = \dfrac{x^2 - 9}{x + 3} = \dfrac{(x + 3)(x - 3)}{x + 3} = x - 3$. So this is the graph

of $y = x - 3$, without the point at $(-3, -6)$:

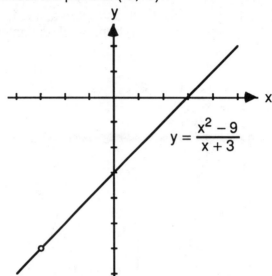

(b) $y = \dfrac{x^2 - 5x + 6}{x^2 - 2x - 3} = \dfrac{(x - 2)(x - 3)}{(x + 1)(x - 3)} = \dfrac{x - 2}{x + 1}$ if $x \neq 3$. So this is the

graph of $y = \dfrac{x - 2}{x + 1}$, without the point at $(3, 1/4)$:

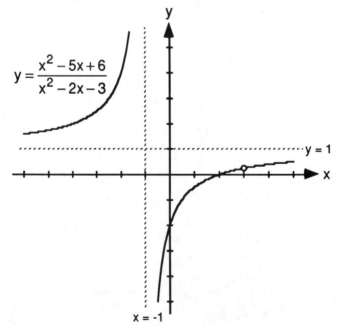

(c)   For $x \neq 1, 2, 3$, $y = \dfrac{(x-1)(x-2)(x-3)}{(x-1)(x-2)(x-3)(x-4)} = \dfrac{1}{x-4}$. So this is

the graph of $y = \dfrac{1}{x-4}$, without the points at $(1, -1/3)$, $(2, -1/2)$, $(3, -1)$:

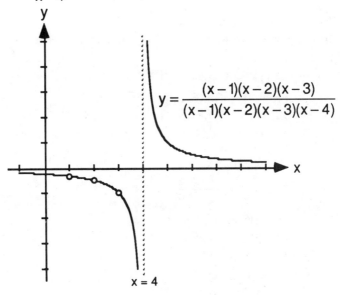

$$y = \frac{(x-1)(x-2)(x-3)}{(x-1)(x-2)(x-3)(x-4)}$$

$x = 4$

39. $y = \dfrac{x}{(x-3)^2}$
     horizontal asymptote: $y = 0$; vertical asymptote: $x = 3$

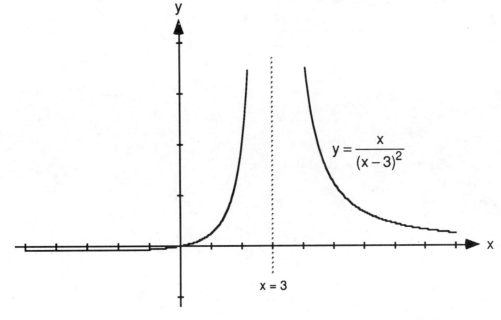

$$y = \frac{x}{(x-3)^2}$$

$x = 3$

We find the value of k where $k = \dfrac{x}{(x-3)^2}$

$$k(x-3)^2 = x$$
$$kx^2 - 6kx + 9k = x$$
$$kx^2 - (6k+1)x + 9k = 0$$

Since this equation must have only one solution, we set the discriminant equal to zero:

$$\left(-(6k+1)\right)^2 - 4k(9k) = 0$$
$$(6k+1)^2 - 36k^2 = 0$$
$$(6k+1+6k)(6k+1-6k) = 0$$
$$(12k+1)(1) = 0$$

So $12k + 1 = 0$, thus $k = -1/12$

Thus $y = -1/12$. We find x:

$$-\frac{1}{12} = \frac{x}{(x-3)^2}$$
$$-(x-3)^2 = 12x$$
$$(x-3)^2 = -12x$$
$$x^2 - 6x + 9 = -12x$$
$$x^2 + 6x + 9 = 0$$
$$(x+3)^2 = 0$$
$$x = -3$$

So the low point is $(-3, -1/12)$.

41. (a)   We use long division:

$$
\begin{array}{r}
x + 4 \\
x - 3 \enclose{longdiv}{x^2 + x - 6} \\
\underline{x^2 - 3x} \\
4x - 6 \\
\underline{4x - 12} \\
6
\end{array}
$$

So $\dfrac{x^2 + x - 6}{x - 3} = (x+4) + \dfrac{6}{x-3}$

(b) We complete the tables:

x	$x + 4$	$\dfrac{x^2 + x - 6}{x - 3}$
10	14	14.8571
100	104	104.0619
1000	1004	1004.0060

x	$x + 4$	$\dfrac{x^2 + x - 6}{x - 3}$
−10	−6	−6.4615
−100	−96	−96.0583
−1000	−996	−996.060

(c) vertical asymptote: $x = 3$

x-intercepts:
$$x^2 + x - 6 = 0$$
$$(x + 3)(x - 2) = 0$$
$$x = -3, 2$$

y-intercept: $F(0) = \dfrac{-6}{-3} = 2$

(d) We graph F(x):

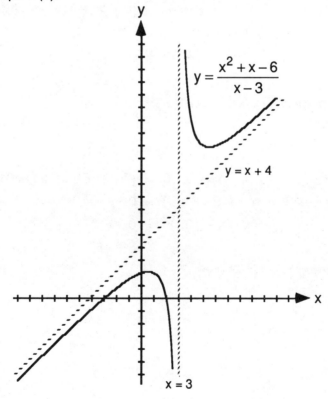

(e)   We find where

$$\frac{x^2 + x - 6}{x - 3} = k$$

$$x^2 + x - 6 = kx - 3k$$

$$x^2 + (1 - k)x + (3k - 6) = 0$$

Set the discriminant equal to 0:

$$(1 - k)^2 - 4(1)(3k - 6) = 0$$

$$1 - 2k + k^2 - 12k + 24 = 0$$

$$k^2 - 14k + 25 = 0$$

$$(k - 7)^2 = -25 + 49$$

$$(k - 7)^2 = 24$$

$$k - 7 = \pm \sqrt{24}$$

$$k = 7 \pm 2\sqrt{6}$$

So either $y = 7 + 2\sqrt{6}$ or $y = 7 - 2\sqrt{6}$

For each of these values, we find x:

$$\frac{x^2 + x - 6}{x - 3} = 7 + 2\sqrt{6}$$

$$x^2 + x - 6 = (7 + 2\sqrt{6})x - 21 - 6\sqrt{6}$$

$$x^2 + (-6 - 2\sqrt{6})x + (15 + 6\sqrt{6}) = 0$$

$$(x - (3 + \sqrt{6}))^2 = 0$$

$$x = 3 + \sqrt{6}$$

So one point is $(3 + \sqrt{6}, 7 + 2\sqrt{6})$

$$\frac{x^2 + x - 6}{x - 3} = 7 - 2\sqrt{6}$$

$$x^2 + x - 6 = (7 - 2\sqrt{6})x - 21 + 6\sqrt{6}$$

$$x^2 + (-6 + 2\sqrt{6})x + (15 - 6\sqrt{6}) = 0$$

$$(x - (3 - \sqrt{6}))^2 = 0$$

$$x = 3 - \sqrt{6}$$

So the other point is $(3 - \sqrt{6}, 7 - 2\sqrt{6})$.

43. Using long division, we find that:
$$\frac{-x^2 + 1}{x} = -x + \frac{1}{x},$$
and thus $y = -x$ is a slant asymptote. We sketch the graph:

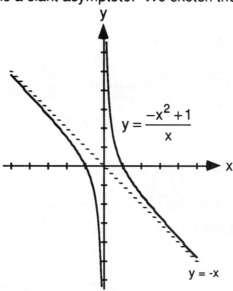

Chapter 3 Review Exercises

1. We find the slope between the points $(1, -2)$ and $(-2, -11)$:
$$m = \frac{-11 - (-2)}{-2 - 1} = \frac{-9}{-3} = 3$$
Now use the point-slope formula:
$$y - (-2) = 3(x - 1)$$
$$y + 2 = 3x - 3$$
$$y = 3x - 5$$
So $G(x) = 3x - 5$, and thus $G(0) = -5$.

2. (a) We complete the square:
$$G(x) = 3x^2 + 6x - 10$$
$$= 3(x^2 + 2x) - 10$$
$$= 3(x^2 + 2x + 1) - 10 - 3$$
$$= 3(x + 1)^2 - 13$$
So the function will have a minimum value of -13 when $x = -1$.

(b)   We complete the square:

$$g(t) = 6t^2 - t^4$$
$$= -(t^4 - 6t^2)$$
$$= -(t^4 - 6t^2 + 9) + 9$$
$$= -(t^2 - 3)^2 + 9$$

So the function will have a maximum value of 9 when $t = \pm\sqrt{3}$.

3. $R(x) = xp = x\left(-\dfrac{1}{8}x + 100\right) = -\dfrac{1}{8}x^2 + 100x$

We complete the square:

$$R(x) = -\frac{1}{8}(x^2 - 800x)$$

$$= -\frac{1}{8}(x^2 - 800x + 160000) + 20000$$

$$= -\frac{1}{8}(x - 400)^2 + 20000$$

So the maximum possible revenue is $20,000.

4.   We graph the function:

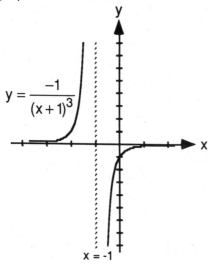

$$y = \frac{-1}{(x+1)^3}$$

$$x = -1$$

5.   We graph the function:

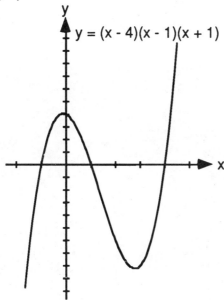

$y = (x - 4)(x - 1)(x + 1)$

6.   We complete the square:

$$f(x) = x^2 + 4x - 5 = (x^2 + 4x + 4) - 5 - 4 = (x + 2)^2 - 9$$

vertex: $(-2,-9)$; x-intercepts: $-5, 1$; y-intercept: -5; axis of symmetry: $x = -2$

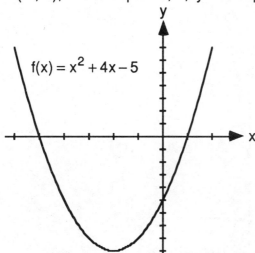

$f(x) = x^2 + 4x - 5$

7.   We have the points $(0, 1000)$ and $(5, 100)$. We find the slope:

$$m = \frac{100 - 1000}{5 - 0} = \frac{-900}{5} = -180$$

So $V(t) = -180t + 1000$.

8.   We graph the function:

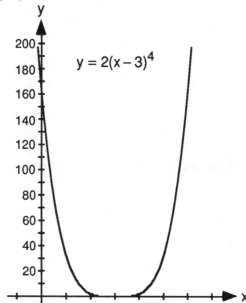

$$y = 2(x-3)^4$$

The graph crosses the y-axis when x = 0, so y = 162. Thus the point is (0, 162).

9. $y = \dfrac{3x + 5}{x + 2}$

x-intercept: -5/3; y-intercept: 5/2
horizontal asymptote: y = 3; vertical asymptote: x = -2

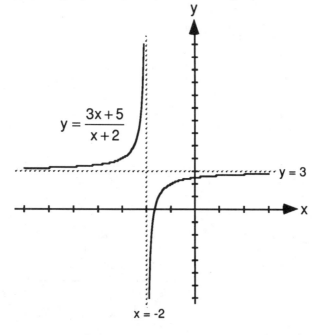

$$y = \frac{3x+5}{x+2}$$

y = 3

x = -2

10. We draw the triangle:

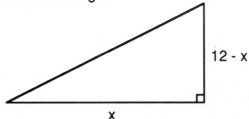

So $A(x) = \frac{1}{2}x(12 - x) = 6x - \frac{1}{2}x^2$. We complete the square:

$$\begin{aligned}
A(x) &= -1/2\, x^2 + 6x \\
&= -1/2\,(x^2 - 12x) \\
&= -1/2\,(x^2 - 12x + 36) + 18 \\
&= -1/2\,(x - 6)^2 + 18
\end{aligned}$$

So the largest possible area is 18 cm^2.

11. We graph the function:

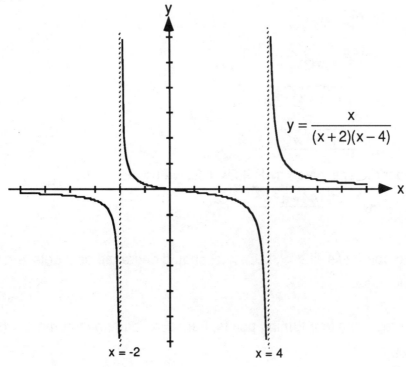

$$y = \frac{x}{(x + 2)(x - 4)}$$

x = -2   x = 4

12. Call $P(x, x^3)$. We find the slope:

$$m = \frac{x^3 - (-1)}{x - (-1)} = \frac{x^3 + 1}{x + 1} = \frac{(x + 1)(x^2 - x + 1)}{x + 1} = x^2 - x + 1$$

Using functional notation, we have $m(x) = x^2 - x + 1$.

13.   We draw the figure:

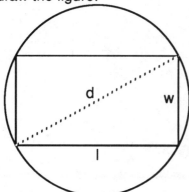

We can find r, since the circumference of the circle is 12 cm:

$$2\pi r = 12, \text{ so } r = \frac{6}{\pi} \text{ and thus } d = \frac{12}{\pi}$$

Using the Pythagorean Theorem:

$$w^2 + l^2 = \left(\frac{12}{\pi}\right)^2$$

$$w^2 + l^2 = \frac{144}{\pi^2}$$

$$l^2 = \frac{144}{\pi^2} - w^2$$

$$l = \sqrt{\frac{144 - \pi^2 w^2}{\pi^2}}$$

$$l = \frac{\sqrt{144 - \pi^2 w^2}}{\pi}$$

Since the perimeter is given by P = 2w + 2l, we have:

$$P(w) = 2w + \frac{2\sqrt{144 - \pi^2 w^2}}{\pi}$$

14.   (a)   This graph *looks* like x^3, but $-\frac{1}{3} x^3$ should decrease as x gets large, not increase.

(b)   This graph has four turning points, but $-\frac{1}{3} x^3$ can have at most two turning points.

15. We find the slope between the points $(3, 5)$ and $(-2, 0)$:

$$m = \frac{0-5}{-2-3} = \frac{-5}{-5} = 1$$

We use the point $(3, 5)$ in the point-slope formula:

$$y - 5 = 1(x - 3)$$
$$y - 5 = x - 3$$
$$y = x + 2$$

Using functional notation, we have $f(x) = x + 2$.

17. We find the slope of the line $3x - 8y = 16$

$$-8y = -3x + 16$$
$$y = \frac{3}{8}x - 2$$

We use $m = \frac{3}{8}$ and the point $(4, -1)$ in the point-slope formula:

$$y - (-1) = \frac{3}{8}(x - 4)$$
$$y + 1 = \frac{3}{8}x - \frac{3}{2}$$
$$y = \frac{3}{8}x - \frac{5}{2}$$

Using functional notation, we have $f(x) = \frac{3}{8}x - \frac{5}{2}$

19. If the graph of the inverse function passes through $(2, 1)$, then $(1, 2)$ must lie on the graph of the function. We find the slope between the points $(1, 2)$ and $(-3, 5)$:

$$m = \frac{5-2}{-3-1} = \frac{3}{-4} = -\frac{3}{4}$$

We use the point $(1, 2)$ in the point-slope formula:

$$y - 2 = -\frac{3}{4}(x - 1)$$
$$y - 2 = -\frac{3}{4}x + \frac{3}{4}$$
$$y = -\frac{3}{4}x + \frac{11}{4}$$

Using functional notation, we have $f(x) = -\frac{3}{4}x + \frac{11}{4}$

21. $y = x^2 + 2x - 3$

     $y + 3 = x^2 + 2x$

$y + 3 + 1 = x^2 + 2x + 1$

   $y + 4 = (x + 1)^2$

vertex: $(-1, -4)$; x-intercepts: $1, -3$; y-intercept: -3

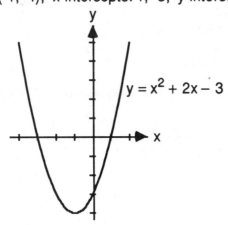

$y = x^2 + 2x - 3$

23. $y = -x^2 + 2\sqrt{3}\,x + 3$

   $y - 3 = -(x^2 - 2\sqrt{3}\,x)$

$y - 3 - 3 = -(x^2 - 2\sqrt{3}\,x + 3)$

   $y - 6 = -(x - \sqrt{3}\,)^2$

vertex: $(\sqrt{3}, 6)$; x-intercepts: $\sqrt{3} + \sqrt{6},\ \sqrt{3} - \sqrt{6}$; y-intercept: 3

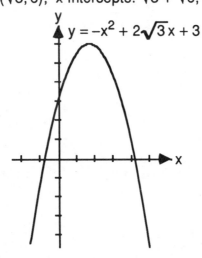

$y = -x^2 + 2\sqrt{3}\,x + 3$

25. $y = -3x^2 + 12x$
          $y = -3(x^2 - 4x)$
   $y - 12 = -3(x^2 - 4x + 4)$
   $y - 12 = -3(x - 2)^2$
   vertex: (2, 12); x-intercepts: 0, 4; y-intercept: 0

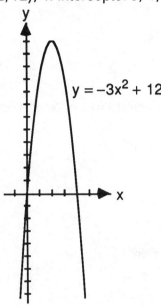

27. We find the two vertices:

   $y = x^2 - 4x + 6$ $y = -x^2 - 4x - 5$
   $y - 6 = x^2 - 4x$ $y + 5 = -(x^2 + 4x)$
   $y - 6 + 4 = x^2 - 4x + 4$ $y + 5 - 4 = -(x^2 + 4x + 4)$
   $y - 2 = (x - 2)^2$ $y + 1 = -(x + 2)^2$
   vertex: (2, 2)   vertex: (-2, -1)

   We now find the distance between (2, 2) and (-2, -1):

   $$d = \sqrt{(-2 - 2)^2 + (-1 - 2)^2} = \sqrt{16 + 9} = \sqrt{25} = 5$$

29. Call x and y the two numbers, so $x + y = \sqrt{3}$, and thus $y = \sqrt{3} - x$.
   We find their product:

   $$P = xy = x(\sqrt{3} - x) = -x^2 + \sqrt{3}\,x$$

   We now complete the square:

   $$P = -(x^2 - \sqrt{3}\,x) = -\left(x^2 - \sqrt{3}\,x + \frac{3}{4}\right) + \frac{3}{4} = -\left(x - \frac{\sqrt{3}}{2}\right)^2 + \frac{3}{4}$$

   The maximum product is 3/4.

31. (a) $h(t) = v_0t - 16t^2$
          We complete the square:
          $$h = -16t^2 + v_0t$$
          $$= -16\left(t^2 - \frac{v_0}{16}t\right)$$
          $$= -16\left(t^2 - \frac{v_0}{16}t + \frac{v_0^2}{1024}\right) + \frac{v_0^2}{64}$$
          $$= -16\left(t - \frac{v_0}{32}\right)^2 + \frac{v_0^2}{64}$$

          So the maximum height of $\frac{v_0^2}{64}$ ft. is obtained when $t = \frac{v_0}{32}$ sec.

     (b) The object will strike the ground when $h(t) = 0$:
          $$-16t^2 + v_0t = 0$$
          $$t(-16t + v_0) = 0$$
          $$t = 0 \quad \text{or} \quad t = \frac{v_0}{16}$$

          So the object will strike the ground when $t = \frac{v_0}{16}$ sec.

33. (a) We find the distance between $(0, 2)$ and (x, x^2):
          $$d = \sqrt{(x - 0)^2 + (x^2 - 2)^2}$$
          $$= \sqrt{x^2 + x^4 - 4x^2 + 4}$$
          $$= \sqrt{x^4 - 3x^2 + 4}$$

     (b) We want to minimize d. This will occur at the same x-coordinate as the
          minimum of d^2. We complete the square:
          $$d^2 = x^4 - 3x^2 + 4$$
          $$= \left(x^4 - 3x^2 + \frac{9}{4}\right) + 4 - \frac{9}{4}$$
          $$= \left(x^2 - \frac{3}{2}\right)^2 + \frac{7}{4}$$

          So the minimum occurs where $x^2 = \frac{3}{2}$, so $x = \pm\sqrt{\frac{3}{2}} = \frac{\pm\sqrt{6}}{2}$. Since
          the point is in the second quadrant, we know $x < 0$, and thus the point

          on the parabola is $\left(\frac{-\sqrt{6}}{2}, \frac{3}{2}\right)$.

35. We find the distance from $(2, 0)$ and $(x, \frac{4}{3}x + b)$:

$$d = \sqrt{(x-2)^2 + \left(\frac{4}{3}x + b\right)^2}$$

$$= \sqrt{x^2 - 4x + 4 + \frac{16}{9}x^2 + \frac{8b}{3}x + b^2}$$

$$= \sqrt{\frac{25}{9}x^2 + \left(\frac{8b}{3} - 4\right)x + (4 + b^2)}$$

We complete the square on d^2:

$$d^2 = \frac{25}{9}\left(x^2 + \frac{9}{25}\left(\frac{8b}{3} - 4\right)x\right) + (4 + b^2)$$

$$= \frac{25}{9}\left(x^2 + \frac{12}{25}(2b - 3)x\right) + (4 + b^2)$$

$$= \frac{25}{9}\left(x^2 + \frac{12}{25}(2b - 3)x + \frac{36}{625}(2b - 3)^2\right) + (4 + b^2) - \frac{4}{25}(2b - 3)^2$$

$$= \frac{25}{9}\left(x + \frac{6}{25}(2b - 3)\right)^2 + \frac{25(4 + b^2) - 4(4b^2 - 12b + 9)}{25}$$

$$= \frac{25}{9}\left(x + \frac{6}{25}(2b - 3)\right)^2 + \frac{(3b + 8)^2}{25}$$

Since the minimum distance is 5, then $5 = \left| \dfrac{3b + 8}{5} \right|$. We now solve for b:

$$|\, 3b + 8 \,| = 25$$

$$3b + 8 = 25 \quad \text{or} \quad 3b + 8 = -25$$

$$3b = 17 \qquad\qquad\quad 3b = -33$$

$$b = \frac{17}{3} \qquad\qquad\quad b = -11$$

37. Since $x + y = \sqrt{2}$, then $y = \sqrt{2} - x$. Then:

$$s = x^2 + y^2$$

$$= x^2 + (\sqrt{2} - x)^2$$

$$= x^2 + 2 - 2\sqrt{2}\,x + x^2$$

$$= 2x^2 - 2\sqrt{2}\,x + 2$$

We complete the square:

$$s = 2(x^2 - \sqrt{2}\,x) + 2$$

$$= 2\left(x^2 - \sqrt{2}\,x + \frac{1}{2}\right) + 2 - 1$$

$$= 2\left(x - \frac{\sqrt{2}}{2}\right)^2 + 1$$

So the minimum value of s is 1.

39. Let x and h be the two legs. We have:
$$x^2 + h^2 = 15^2$$
$$h^2 = 225 - x^2$$
$$h = \sqrt{225 - x^2}$$

So $A = \frac{1}{2}$ (base)(height) $= \frac{1}{2} x \sqrt{225 - x^2}$

We find $A^2 = \frac{1}{4} x^2 (225 - x^2) = -\frac{1}{4} x^4 + \frac{225}{4} x^2$

We now complete the square on A^2:

$$A^2 = -\frac{1}{4} (x^4 - 225x^2)$$

$$= -\frac{1}{4} \left[x^4 - 225x^2 + \left(\frac{225}{2}\right)^2 \right] + \left(\frac{225}{4}\right)^2$$

$$= -\frac{1}{4} \left(x^2 - \frac{225}{2} \right)^2 + \left(\frac{225}{4}\right)^2$$

So the maximum of $A^2 = \left(\frac{225}{4}\right)^2$, thus $A = \frac{225}{4}$ cm^2.

41. $f(x) = x^2 - (a^2 + 2a) x + 2a^3 = (x - a^2)(x - 2a)$

So the x-intercepts are a^2 and $2a$. Since $2a > a^2$ when $0 < a < 2$, then the distance between $(a^2, 0)$ and $(2a, 0)$ will be $D = 2a - a^2 = -a^2 + 2a$

We now complete the square:

$$D = -(a^2 - 2a) = -(a^2 - 2a + 1) + 1 = -(a - 1)^2 + 1$$

So D is maximum when $a = 1$.

43. $R = xp = x(160 - \frac{1}{5} x) = -\frac{1}{5} x^2 + 160 x$

We now complete the square:

$$R = -\frac{1}{5} (x^2 - 800x)$$

$$= -\frac{1}{5} (x^2 - 800x + 160{,}000) + 32{,}000$$

$$= -\frac{1}{5} (x - 400)^2 + 32{,}000$$

So x = 400 units will maximize the revenue. Then $p = 160 - \frac{1}{5} (400) = \$80$.

45. $y = (x + 4)(x - 2)$
x-intercepts: -4, 2; y-intercept: -8; vertex: (-1, -9)

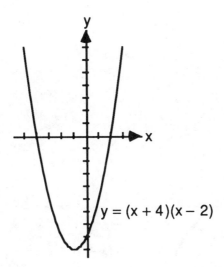

47. $y = -(x + 5)^3$
x-intercept: -5; y-intercept: -125

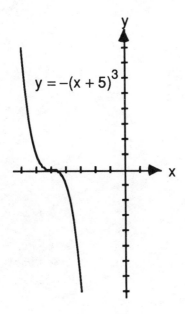

49. $y = -x^2(x + 1)$
      x-intercepts: -1, 0; y-intercept: 0

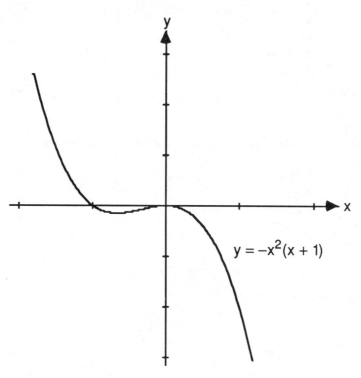

$$y = -x^2(x + 1)$$

51. $y = x(x - 2)(x + 2)$
      x-intercepts: 0, 2, -2; y-intercept: 0

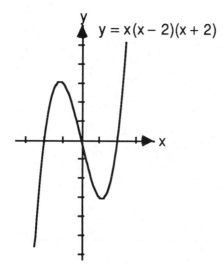

$$y = x(x - 2)(x + 2)$$

53. $y = \dfrac{3x + 1}{x}$

x-intercept: -1/3; y-intercept: none
horizontal asymptote: y = 3; vertical asymptote: x = 0

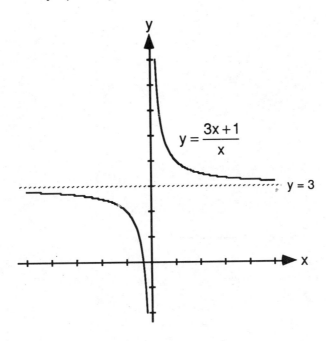

55. $y = \dfrac{-1}{(x - 1)^2}$

x-intercept: none; y-intercept: -1
horizontal asymptote: y = 0; vertical asymptote: x = 1

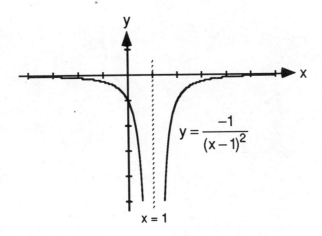

57. $y = \dfrac{x - 2}{x - 3}$

x-intercept: 2
y-intercept: 2/3
horizontal asymptote: y = 1
vertical asymptote: x = 3

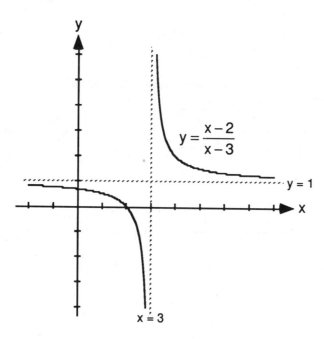

59. $y = \dfrac{(x-1)^2}{(x-2)^2}$

x-intercept: 1; y-intercept: 1/4
horizontal asymptote: y = 1; vertical asymptote: x = 2

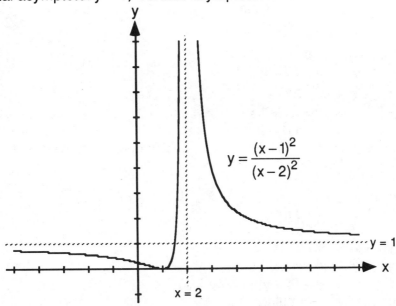

61. (a) If b = 1, then f(x) = $x^2 + 2x + 1$ = $(x+1)^2$, so the vertex is (-1, 0). By the distance formula :

$$d = \sqrt{(-1-0)^2 + (0-0)^2} = 1$$

(b) If b = 2, then f(x) = $x^2 + 4x + 1$. We complete the square:

$$f(x) = (x^2 + 4x + 4) + 1 - 4 = (x+2)^2 - 3$$

So the vertex is (-2, -3). By the distance formula:

$$d = \sqrt{(-2-0)^2 + (-3-0)^2} = \sqrt{4+9} = \sqrt{13}$$

(c) We complete the square:

$$f(x) = x^2 + 2bx + 1$$
$$= (x^2 + 2bx + b^2) + 1 - b^2$$
$$= (x+b)^2 + 1 - b^2$$

So the vertex is (-b, 1 - b^2). By the distance formula:

$$d = \sqrt{(-b)^2 + (1-b^2)^2} = \sqrt{b^2 + 1 - 2b^2 + b^4} = \sqrt{b^4 - b^2 + 1}$$

We now complete the square on d^2:

$$d^2 = b^4 - b^2 + 1 = \left(b^4 - b^2 + \frac{1}{4}\right) + 1 - \frac{1}{4} = \left(b^2 - \frac{1}{2}\right)^2 + \frac{3}{4}$$

So d^2 (and thus d) is minimized when $b^2 = \frac{1}{2}$, thus $b = \pm\frac{1}{\sqrt{2}} = \frac{\pm\sqrt{2}}{2}$.

63. We complete the square:

$$y = x^2 - 2x + k$$
$$y - k = x^2 - 2x$$
$$y - k + 1 = x^2 - 2x + 1$$
$$y = (x - 1)^2 + (k - 1)$$

Since the vertex is $(1, k-1)$ and the parabola is opening upward, then
$k - 1 = 5$, so $k = 6$.

65. We solve for x:

$$y = \frac{(x - 1)(x - 3)}{x - 4}$$
$$y(x - 4) = (x - 1)(x - 3)$$
$$yx - 4y = x^2 - 4x + 3$$
$$0 = x^2 - (4 + y)x + (4y + 3)$$

Using the quadratic formula:

$$x = \frac{4 + y \pm \sqrt{(4 + y)^2 - 4(4y + 3)}}{2}$$
$$= \frac{4 + y \pm \sqrt{16 + 8y + y^2 - 16y - 12}}{2}$$
$$= \frac{4 + y \pm \sqrt{y^2 - 8y + 4}}{2}$$

So we must make sure that $y^2 - 8y + 4 \geq 0$.
We find the key numbers by using the quadratic formula:

$$y = \frac{8 \pm \sqrt{64 - 16}}{2} = \frac{8 \pm 4\sqrt{3}}{2} = 4 \pm 2\sqrt{3}$$

From a sign chart, we see that the range is $y \leq 4 - 2\sqrt{3}$ or $y \geq 4 + 2\sqrt{3}$.
We write this as $(-\infty, 4 - 2\sqrt{3}] \cup [4 + 2\sqrt{3}, \infty)$.

67. We first draw a figure:

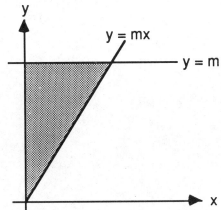

We find the intersection point of these two lines:

$$mx = m$$
$$x = 1$$
$$y = m$$

So the point is $(1, m)$. Since these are the base and height, respectively, of the triangle, we have:

$$A = \frac{1}{2}(1)(m) = \frac{m}{2}$$

Using functional notation, $A(m) = \frac{m}{2}$

69. We re-draw the figure and label essential parts:

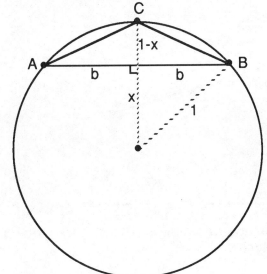

By the labeled parts of the figure, we have:

$$x^2 + b^2 = 1^2, \text{ so } b = \sqrt{1 - x^2}$$

Thus the base of the triangle is $2b = 2\sqrt{1 - x^2}$ and the height is $1 - x$, thus the area is given by:

$$A = \frac{1}{2} \cdot 2\sqrt{1 - x^2} \cdot (1 - x) = (1 - x)\sqrt{1 - x^2}$$

Using functional notation, $A(x) = (1 - x)\sqrt{1 - x^2}$

71. (a) We draw the scatter diagram (not to scale):

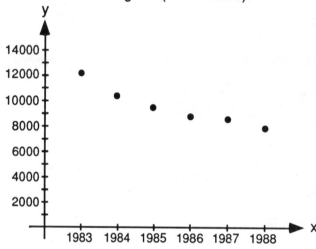

(b) We draw the best-fit line (not to scale):

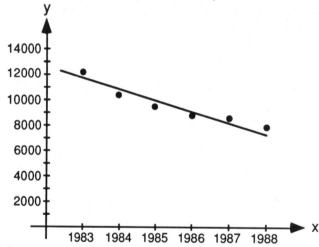

The slope appears to be approximately -770 and the y-intercept appears to be approximately 1.5 million.

(c) We let x = 1995:

$f(1995) = (-771.4)(1995) + 1,541,090 = 2147$

We would estimate that approximately 2100 refugees would arrive in 1995.

(d)   We switch the roles of x and y, and solve the resulting equation for y:
$$x = -771.4y + 1{,}541{,}090$$
$$771.4y = 1{,}541{,}090 - x$$
$$y = \frac{1541090 - x}{771.4}$$

So $f^{-1}(x) = \dfrac{1541090 - x}{771.4}$

(e)   We find $f^{-1}(1000) = \dfrac{1541090 - 1000}{771.4} \approx 1996$. The number of refugees should dip below 1000 in the year 1996.

73. (a)   The graphs are reflections of each other about the y-axis:

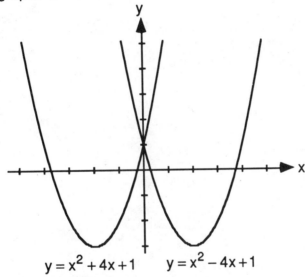

$$y = x^2 + 4x + 1 \qquad y = x^2 - 4x + 1$$

(b) $f(-x) = a(-x)^2 + b(-x) + c = ax^2 - bx + c$

(c)   Reversing the sign of b will reflect the graph of $f(x) = ax^2 + bx + c$ across the y-axis.

CHAPTER FOUR
EXPONENTIAL AND LOGARITHMIC FUNCTIONS

4.1 Exponential Functions

1.   (a)   Since $2^{10} \approx 10^3$, then $2^{30} = (2^{10})^3 \approx (10^3)^3 = 10^9$

       (b)   Since $2^{10} \approx 10^3$, then $2^{50} = (2^{10})^5 \approx (10^3)^5 = 10^{15}$

3.   (a) $3^x = 27$
$$3^x = 3^3$$
$$x = 3$$

       (b) $9^t = 27$
$$(3^2)^t = 3^3$$
$$3^{2t} = 3^3$$
$$2t = 3$$
$$t = 3/2$$

       (c) $3^{1-2y} = \sqrt{3}$
$$3^{1-2y} = 3^{1/2}$$
$$1 - 2y = 1/2$$
$$-2y = -1/2$$
$$y = 1/4$$

(d) $3^z = 9\sqrt{3}$
      $3^z = 3^2 \cdot 3^{1/2}$
      $3^z = 3^{5/2}$
      $z = 5/2$

5.   All real numbers, or $(-\infty, \infty)$

7.   Since $2^{x-1} \neq 0$ (even if $x = 1$), then domain is all real numbers, or $(-\infty, \infty)$.

9.   We graph $y = 2^x$ and $y = 2^{-x}$:

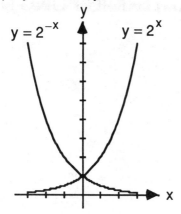

11.   We graph $y = 3^x$ and $y = -3^x$ (note that $y = -3^x$ is a reflection about the x-axis):

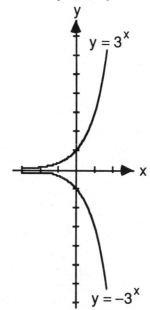

13. We graph $y = 2^x$ and $y = 3^x$:

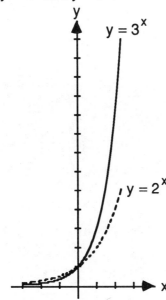

15. We graph $y = \left(\frac{1}{2}\right)^x = 2^{-x}$ and $y = \left(\frac{1}{3}\right)^x = 3^{-x}$:

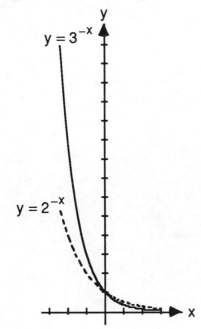

17. $y = -2^x + 1$
     domain: $(-\infty, \infty)$; range: $(-\infty, 1)$
     x-intercept: 0; y-intercept: 0; asymptote: $y = 1$

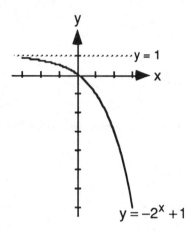

19. $y = 3^{-x} + 1$
     domain: $(-\infty, \infty)$; range: $(1, \infty)$
     x-intercept: none; y-intercept: 2; asymptote: $y = 1$

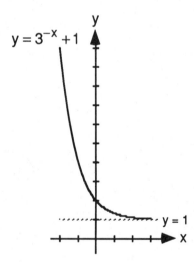

21. $y = 2^{x-1}$

domain: $(-\infty, \infty)$; range: $(0, \infty)$
x-intercept: none; y-intercept: 1/2; asymptote: $y = 0$

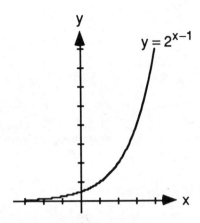

23. $y = 3^{x+1} + 1$

domain: $(-\infty, \infty)$; range: $(1, \infty)$
x-intercept: none; y-intercept: 4; asymptote: $y = 1$

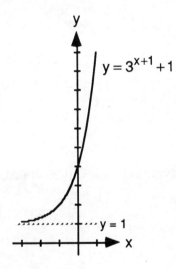

25. $3x(10^x) + 10^x = 0$

$10^x(3x + 1) = 0$

$3x + 1 = 0$ or $10^x = 0$

$x = -1/3$, since $10^x \neq 0$

27. $3(3^x) - 5x(3^x) + 2x^2(3^x) = 0$
       $3^x(3 - 5x + 2x^2) = 0$
       $3^x(3 - 2x)(1 - x) = 0$
       $3^x = 0$ or $3 - 2x = 0$ or $1 - x = 0$
       $x = 3/2$ or $x = 1$, since $3^x \neq 0$

29. $\dfrac{f(x + h) - f(x)}{h} = \dfrac{2^{x+h} - 2^x}{h} = \dfrac{2^x 2^h - 2^x}{h} = \dfrac{2^x(2^h - 1)}{h} = 2^x \left(\dfrac{2^h - 1}{h} \right)$

31. (a)   We know the graph of $y = 2^x$ and the graph of g, the inverse of f,
            should contain these points with the x and y coordinates interchanged.
            g(x) will be reflected across the line $y = x$:

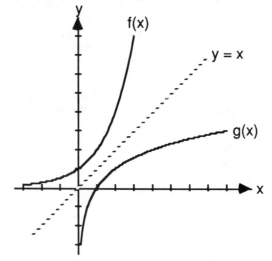

     (b)   domain: $(0, \infty)$; range: $(-\infty, \infty)$
            intercept: $x = 1$ (no y-intercept); asymptote: $x = 0$ (the negative y-axis)

33. (a) $\sqrt{2} = 2^{1/2} = 2^{0.5} \approx 1.4$

     (b) $\sqrt[5]{2} = 2^{1/5} = 2^{.2} \approx 1.15$

     (c) $\sqrt[5]{8} = 8^{1/5} = (2^3)^{1/5} = 2^{3/5} = 2^{.6} \approx 1.5$

35. (a)   Since $10^0 = 1$, the entry in the table corresponding to $x = 1$ is 0. Since
            $10^1 = 10$, the entry corresponding to $x = 10$ is 1.

     (b)   Since $10^{.3} \approx 2$, we have $(10^{.3})^2 \approx 2^2$. That is, $10^{.6} \approx 4$. Therefore,
            the entry in the table corresponding to $x = 4$ is 0.6. Similarly, by
            cubing both sides of the approximation $10^{.3} \approx 2$, we obtain $10^{.9} \approx 8$.
            Thus, the entry in the table corresponding to $x = 8$ is 0.9.

(c) Using the hint that is given, we have $5 \approx \frac{10}{10^{.3}} = 10^{.7}$. Thus, the entry in the table corresponding to $x = 5$ is 0.7.

(d) We have $7^2 \approx (5)(10) \approx (10^{.7})(10^1) = 10^{1.7}$. Therefore, $(7^2)^{1/2} \approx (10^{1.7})^{1/2}$, or $7 \approx 10^{.85}$. Thus the power to which 10 must be raised to yield 7 is approximately 0.85.

(e) We have $3^4 \approx (8)(10) \approx (10^{.9})(10^1) = 10^{1.9}$. Therefore, $(3^4)^{1/4} \approx (10^{1.9})^{1/4} \approx 10^{.475}$. Thus, the power to which 10 must be raised to yield 3 is approximately 0.48.

(f) We have $6 = (2)(3) \approx (10^{.3})(10^{.48}) = 10^{.78}$. Thus, the power to which 10 must be raised to yield 6 is approximately 0.78. We also have $9 = (3)(3) \approx (10^{.475})(10^{.475}) = 10^{.95}$. Thus, the power to which 10 must be raised to yield 9 is approximately 0.95. We complete the table:

x	$\log_{10} x$
1	0.00
2	0.30
3	0.48
4	0.60
5	0.70
6	0.78
7	0.85
8	0.90
9	0.95
10	1.00

4.2 The Exponential Function $y = e^x$

1. $y = e^x$
    domain: $(-\infty, \infty)$; range: $(0, \infty)$
    x-intercept: none; y-intercept: 1; asymptote: $y = 0$

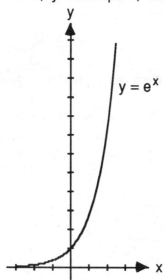

3. $y = -e^x$
    domain: $(-\infty, \infty)$; range: $(-\infty, 0)$
    x-intercept: none; y-intercept: -1; asymptote: $y = 0$

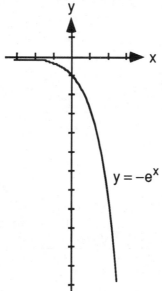

5. $y = e^x + 1$
     domain: $(-\infty, \infty)$;   range: $(1, \infty)$
     x-intercept: none;   y-intercept: 2;   asymptote: $y = 1$

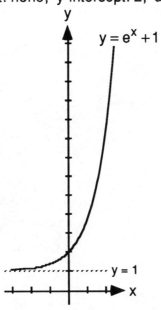

7. $y = e^{x+1} + 1$
     domain: $(-\infty, \infty)$;   range: $(1, \infty)$
     x-intercept: none;   y-intercept: $e + 1$;   asymptote: $y = 1$

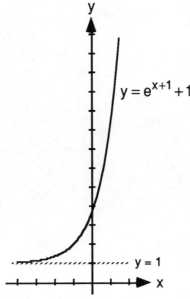

9. $y = -e^{x-2}$

    domain: $(-\infty, \infty)$; range: $(-\infty, 0)$

    x-intercept: none; y-intercept: $-\dfrac{1}{e^2}$; asymptote: $y = 0$

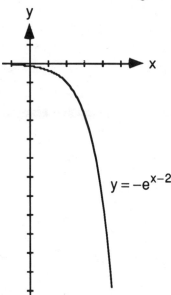

11. $y = e - e^x$

    domain: $(-\infty, \infty)$; range: $(-\infty, e)$

    x-intercept: 1; y-intercept: $e - 1$; asymptote: $y = e$

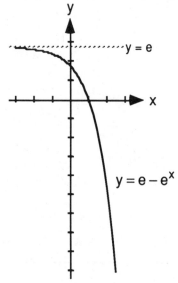

13. We graph the three functions:

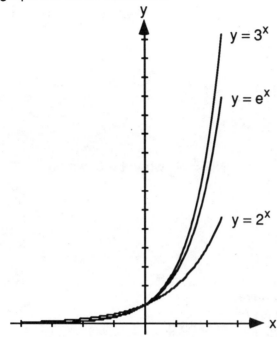

$y = 3^x$

$y = e^x$

$y = 2^x$

15. $e^{5k} = (e^k)^5$, so:

$$(e^k)^5 = 32$$
$$e^k = 32^{1/5}$$
$$e^k = 2$$

17. $e^{3t} = (e^t)^3$, so:

$$(e^t)^3 = 4$$
$$e^t = \sqrt[3]{4}$$

19. (a) Given the growth law $N = N_0 e^{kt}$, and $N_0 = 2000$, $N = 6000$, $t = 2$,
        we have:

$$6000 = 2000\, e^{k(2)}$$
$$3 = e^{2k}$$
$$\sqrt{3} = 3^k$$

     (b) When $t = 10$, we have $N = 2000\, e^{10k}$
                                    $= 2000\, (e^k)^{10}$
                                    $= 2000\, (\sqrt{3}\,)^{10}$
                                    $= 2000\, (243)$
                                    $= 486{,}000$

21. Given the growth law $N = N_0 e^{kt}$, and $N_0 = 3200$, $e^k = \sqrt[5]{2}$, $t = 5$, we have:

$$N = 3200\, e^{5k}$$
$$= 3200\, (e^k)^5$$
$$= 3200\, (\sqrt[5]{2}\,)^5$$
$$= 3200\, (2)$$
$$= 6400 \text{ bacteria}$$

23. Given the decay law $N = N_0 e^{kt}$, and $N = \frac{1}{2} N_0$ when $t = 8$, we have:

$$\frac{1}{2} N_0 = N_0 e^{8k}$$
$$\frac{1}{2} = e^{8k}$$
$$\left(\frac{1}{2}\right)^{1/8} = e^k$$

So when $t = 7$ and $N_0 = 1$, we have:

$$N = 1 e^{7k} = (3^k)^7 = \left(\frac{1}{2}\right)^{7/8} \approx 0.55 \text{ g}$$

25. Given the decay law $N = N_0 e^{kt}$, and $N = \frac{1}{2} N_0$ when $t = 24000$, we have:

$$\frac{1}{2} N_0 = N_0 e^{24000k}$$
$$\frac{1}{2} = e^{24000k}$$
$$\left(\frac{1}{2}\right)^{1/24000} = e^k$$

So when $t = 1000$, we have:

$$N = N_0 e^{1000k} = N_0 \left(\frac{1}{2}\right)^{1/24} \approx 0.9715 N_0$$

So about 97.15 % will still be remaining.

27. $\dfrac{E(x + h) - E(x)}{h} = \dfrac{e^{x+h} - e^x}{h} = \dfrac{e^x e^h - e^x}{h} = \dfrac{e^x(e^h - 1)}{h} = e^x \left(\dfrac{e^h - 1}{h}\right)$

29. $C(x) = \dfrac{e^x + e^{-x}}{2}$

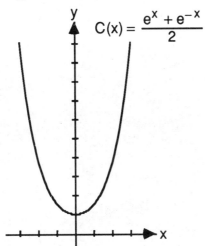

$$C(x) = \dfrac{e^x + e^{-x}}{2}$$

31. We complete the table:

n	$1 + \dfrac{1}{n}$	$\left(1 + \dfrac{1}{n}\right)^n$
1	2	2.0000
10	1.1	2.5937
100	1.01	2.7048
1000	1.001	2.7169
10000	1.0001	2.7181
100000	1.00001	2.7183

33. (a) Since $N = N_0 e^{kt}$

$N = 1 e^{kt}$ using $N_0 = 1$ billion

$2 = e^{k \cdot 80}$

$e^k = 2^{1/80}$

So N in 1985 should be given by:

$N = (2^{1/80})^{135}$

$N = 2^{27/16}$ or about 3.22 billion

(b) It's too low, by about 1.6 billion people!

35. (a)   We draw the graphs:

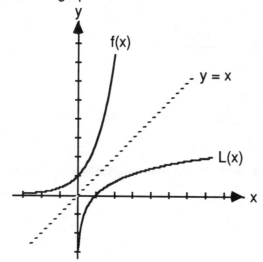

(b)   domain: $(0, \infty)$; range: $(-\infty, \infty)$
x-intercept: 1; asymptote: $x = 0$

(c)   (i) $y = -L(x)$
x-intercept: 1; asymptote: $x = 0$

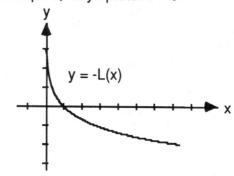

(ii) $y = L(-x)$
x-intercept: -1; asymptote: $x = 0$

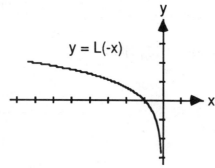

(iii) $y = L(x - 1)$
         x-intercept: 2; asymptote: $x = 1$

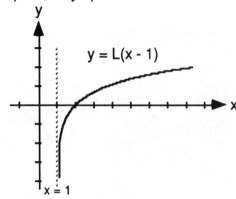

4.3 Logarithmic Functions

1.   (a)   No, because a horizontal line can intersect the parabola twice.
      (b)   Yes, because any horizontal line intersects the line only once.
      (c)   Yes, because any horizontal line intersects the curve only once.

3.   (a)   Let $y = \dfrac{2x - 1}{3x + 4}$. We switch the roles of x and y and solve the resulting equation for y:

$$x = \frac{2y - 1}{3y + 4}$$
$$x(3y + 4) = 2y - 1$$
$$3xy + 4x = 2y - 1$$
$$3xy - 2y = -1 - 4x$$
$$y(3x - 2) = -1 - 4x$$
$$y = \frac{-1 - 4x}{3x - 2}$$
$$y = \frac{4x + 1}{2 - 3x}$$

So $f^{-1}(x) = \dfrac{4x + 1}{2 - 3x}$

      (b) $\dfrac{1}{f(x)} = \dfrac{3x + 4}{2x - 1}$

      (c) $f^{-1}(0) = \dfrac{4(0) + 1}{2 - 3(0)} = \dfrac{1}{2}$

(d) $\dfrac{1}{f(0)} = \dfrac{3(0) + 4}{2(0) - 1} = \dfrac{4}{-1} = -4$

5. $y = f^{-1}(x)$ would join the points $(-2, 3)$ and $(5, -1)$, so $y = f^{-1}(x - 1)$ will join the points $(-1, 3)$ and $(6, -1)$.

7.   (a) $\log_3 9 = 2$
      (b) $\log_{10} 1000 = 3$
      (c) $\log_7 343 = 3$
      (d) $\log_2 \sqrt{2} = 1/2$

9.   (a) $2^5 = 32$
      (b) $10^0 = 1$
      (c) $e^{1/2} = \sqrt{e}$
      (d) $3^{-4} = 1/81$
      (e) $t^v = u$

11. $\log_5 30$ represents the power to which 5 must be raised to get 30. It is clearly greater than 2, since $5^2 = 25$. $\log_8 60$ is less than 2 since $8^2 = 64$. Hence, $\log_5 30$ is larger.

13.   (a) $\log_9 27$ is the power to which 9 must be raised to get 27. We can see it's between 1 and 2 since $9^1 = 9$ while $9^2 = 81$. To find it let $\log_9 27 = n$ then $9^n = 27$ in exponential form and $3^{2n} = 3^3$. So, $2n = 3$ and $n = 3/2$.

      (b) If $\log_4 \dfrac{1}{32} = n$ then $4^n = \dfrac{1}{32}$ or $2^{2n} = 2^{-5}$. So $2n = -5$, and $n = -\dfrac{5}{2}$.
           So $\log_4 \dfrac{1}{32} = -\dfrac{5}{2}$.

      (c) Follow the same steps. If $\log_5 5\sqrt{5} = n$, then:
           $$5^n = 5\sqrt{5}$$
           $$5^n = 5^{3/2}$$
           $$n = \dfrac{3}{2}$$

15.   (a) $\log_x 256 = 8$
           $$x^8 = 256 = 2^8$$
           So $x = 2$

(b) $\log_5 x = -1$

$5^{-1} = x$

So $x = 1/5$

The solution to problems of this type frequently depends on our ability to move back and forth between the logarithmic and exponential form.

17. (a)   We must have $5x > 0$, so $x > 0$. So the domain is $(0, \infty)$.

(b)   We must have $3 - 4x > 0$, so $3 > 4x$ and $x < \dfrac{3}{4}$. So the domain is

$(-\infty, 3/4)$.

(c)   We must have $x^2 > 0$, so $x \neq 0$. So the domain is all real numbers except 0, or $(-\infty, 0) \cup (0, \infty)$.

(d)   We must have $x > 0$. So the domain is $(0, \infty)$.

(e)   We must have $x^2 - 25 > 0$

$(x - 5)(x + 5) > 0$

Key numbers: ± 5

From a sign chart, we see that $x < -5$ or $x > 5$. So the domain is $(-\infty, -5) \cup (5, \infty)$.

19. We must make sure that $1 - \ln x \neq 0$. We find where $1 - \ln x = 0$:

$1 - \ln x = 0$

$1 = \ln x$

$e^1 = x$

So $x = e$ must be excluded from the domain. For the logarithm to be defined, however, we must also make sure that $x > 0$. So the domain is $(0, e) \cup (e, \infty)$. For the range, we switch the roles of x and y and solve the resulting equation for y:

$$x = \frac{1}{1 - \ln y}$$

$$1 - \ln y = \frac{1}{x}$$

$$\ln y = 1 - \frac{1}{x}$$

$$y = e^{1 - 1/x}$$

So $x \neq 0$. So the range is all real numbers except 0, or $(-\infty, 0) \cup (0, \infty)$.

21.   (a) $y = \log_{10}(x + 1)$

domain: $(-1, \infty)$; range: $(-\infty, \infty)$
x-intercept: 0; y-intercept: 0; asymptote: $x = -1$

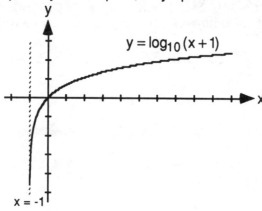

(b) $y = -\log_{10}(x + 1)$

domain: $(-1, \infty)$; range: $(-\infty, \infty)$
x-intercept: 0; y-intercept: 0; asymptote: $x = -1$

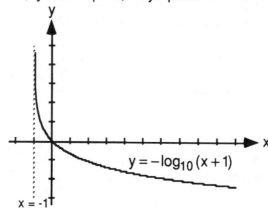

23.   (a) $y = \ln x$

domain: $(0, \infty)$; range: $(-\infty, \infty)$
x-intercept: 1; y-intercept: none; asymptote: $x = 0$

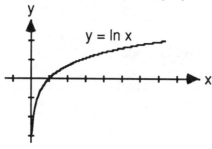

(b) $y = \ln(-x)$
domain: $(-\infty, 0)$; range: $(-\infty, \infty)$
x-intercept: -1; y-intercept: none; asymptote: $x = 0$

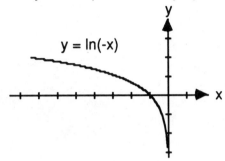

(c) $y = -1 + \ln(-x)$
domain: $(-\infty, 0)$; range: $(-\infty, \infty)$
x-intercept: -e; y-intercept: none; asymptote: $x = 0$

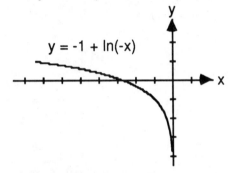

25.   (a)   Let $x = \ln e^4$
$$e^x = e^4$$
$$x = 4$$

(b)   Let $x = \ln \dfrac{1}{e}$
$$e^x = \dfrac{1}{e}$$
$$e^x = e^{-1}$$
$$x = -1$$

(c)   Let $x = \ln \sqrt{e}$
$$e^x = \sqrt{e}$$
$$e^x = e^{1/2}$$
$$x = \dfrac{1}{2}$$

27. $10^x = 25$

$\qquad x = \log_{10} 25$

$\qquad x \approx 1.40$

29. $10^{(x^2)} = 40$

$\qquad x^2 = \log_{10} 40$

$\qquad x = \pm\sqrt{\log_{10} 40}$

$\qquad x = \pm\sqrt{1 + \log_{10} 4}$

$\qquad x \approx \pm 1.27$

31. $e^{2t+3} = 10$

$\qquad 2t + 3 = \ln 10$

$\qquad 2t = -3 + \ln 10$

$\qquad t = \dfrac{-3 + \ln 10}{2}$

$\qquad t \approx -0.35$

33. $e^{1-4t} = 12.405$

$\qquad 1 - 4t = \ln 12.405$

$\qquad -4t = -1 + \ln 12.405$

$\qquad t = \dfrac{1 - \ln 12.405}{4}$

$\qquad t \approx -0.38$

35. (a) Use the decay equation $N = N_0 e^{kt}$, when $N = \frac{1}{2} N_0$ when $t = 4.5 \times 10^9$:

$$\frac{1}{2} N_0 = N_0\, e^{(4.5 \times 10^9)\,k}$$

$$\frac{1}{2} = e^{(4.5 \times 10^9)\,k}$$

$$\ln \frac{1}{2} = (4.5 \times 10^9)\,k$$

$$k = \frac{\ln 0.5}{4.5 \times 10^9} \approx -1.54 \times 10^{-10}$$

(b) Use $t = 1000$:

$$N = N_0 e^{1000(-1.54 \times 10^{-10})} = 0.999999846 N_0$$

So 99.9999846 % is still remaining.

37. (a) Starting with $N = N_0 e^{kt}$, we have:

$$\frac{1}{2} N_0 = N_0 e^{k \cdot 1}$$

$$e^k = \frac{1}{2}$$

$$k = \ln \frac{1}{2}$$

(b) If 90% is gone, the amount remaining will be 10%, or .4 g, and we have:

$$.4 = 4 e^{(\ln .5)t}$$
$$.1 = e^{(\ln .5)t}$$
$$\ln .1 = \ln (e^{(\ln .5)t})$$
$$\ln .1 = (\ln .5)t$$
$$t = \frac{\ln .1}{\ln .5} \approx 3.32 \text{ years}$$

39. (a) We start with:

$$3 \times 10^8 = (2 \times 10^7) e^{k \cdot 2}$$
$$e^{2k} = 15$$
$$2k = \ln 15$$
$$k = \frac{\ln 15}{2}$$
$$2N_0 = N_0 e^{[(\ln 15)/2]t}$$
$$2 = e^{[(\ln 15)/2]t}$$
$$\ln 2 = \frac{\ln 15}{2} \cdot t$$
$$t = \frac{2 \ln 2}{\ln 15} \approx 0.51 \text{ hrs}$$

(b) Since 1 billion $= 10^9$, we want:

$$10^9 = 2 \times 10^7 e^{[(\ln 15)/2]t}$$
$$t = \frac{2 \ln 50}{\ln 15} \approx 2.89 \text{ hrs}$$

41. Our rule for finding inverses is to interchange x and y and then solve for y, so:

$$f(x) = e^{x+1}$$
$$y = e^{x+1}$$

becomes

$$x = e^{y+1}$$
$$\ln x = \ln (e^{y+1})$$
$$\ln x = y + 1$$
$$y = -1 + \ln x$$
$$f^{-1}(x) = -1 + \ln x$$

A word of caution here. Be careful about writing an answer like this as ln x - 1. It can be incorrectly read as ln (x - 1) instead of (ln x) - 1. The form of our answer avoids this problem. The x-intercept will be e and x = 0 is the asymptote:

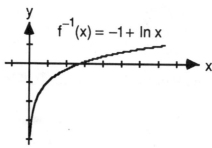

43.   We graph the region:

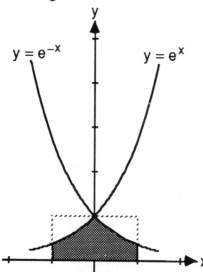

The area is less than the rectangle (shown dotted on the graph), which has an area of two square units.

45. $e^{2x} - 5e^x - 6 = 0$ has the form of a quadratic in e^x. To see this let $e^x = n$, then the equation becomes $n^2 - 5n - 6 = 0$ and we factor:

$$(e^x - 6)(e^x + 1) = 0$$

If $e^x - 6 = 0$, then $e^x = 6$ and $x = \ln 6$, but e^x can never equal -1, so there is no root corresponding to this factor, thus $x = \ln 6$ is the only solution.

47.   If $\log_2 x = 100$, then $x = 2^{100} = (2^{10})^{10} \approx (10^3)^{10} = 10^{30}$

49. We set A = B:

$$A_0 e^{k_1 t} = B_0 e^{k_2 t}$$

$$\frac{A_0}{B_0} = \frac{e^{k_2 t}}{e^{k_1 t}}$$

$$\frac{A_0}{B_0} = e^{(k_2 - k_1) t}$$

$$\ln\left(\frac{A_0}{B_0}\right) = (k_2 - k_1) t$$

$$t = \frac{\ln\left(\frac{A_0}{B_0}\right)}{k_2 - k_1}$$

This represents the amount of time it takes for two radioactive substances to decay to the same mass.

51. (a) $P(10) = 4$, since 2, 3, 5, 7 do not exceed 10.
       $P(18) = 7$, since 2, 3, 5, 7, 11, 13, 17, do not exceed 18.
       $P(19) = 8$, since 2, 3, 5, 7, 11, 13, 17, 19, do not exceed 19.

   (b)   We complete the table:

x	$P(x)$	$\dfrac{x}{\ln x}$	$\dfrac{P(x)}{x / \ln x}$
10^2	25	22	1.151
10^4	1229	1086	1.132
10^6	78498	72382	1.084
10^8	5761455	5428681	1.061
10^9	50847534	48254942	1.054
10^{10}	455052512	434294482	1.048

(c)   We complete the table:

x	$P(x)$	$\dfrac{x}{\ln x - 1.08366}$	$\dfrac{P(x)}{x\,/\,(\ln x - 1.08366)}$
10^2	25	28	0.8804
10^4	1229	1231	0.9988
10^6	78498	78543	0.9994
10^8	5761455	5768004	0.9989
10^9	50847534	50917519	0.9986
10^{10}	455052512	455743004	0.9985

53.   The easiest approach to use is to convert the equation to exponential form:
$\ln y = x$, so $y = e^x$
Thus the graph is identical to $y = e^x$:

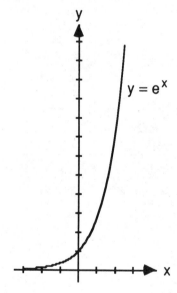

4.4 Properties of Logarithms

1. $\log_{10} 70 - \log_{10} 7 = \log_{10} \dfrac{70}{7} = \log_{10} 10 = 1$

3. $\log_7 \sqrt{7} = \log_7 (7^{1/2}) = 1/2$

5. $\log_3 108 + \log_3 \dfrac{3}{4} = \log_3 \left(\dfrac{108 \cdot 3}{4} \right)$
$= \log_3 81$
$= \log_3 3^4$
$= 4$

7. $-\dfrac{1}{2} + \ln \sqrt{e} = -\dfrac{1}{2} + \ln e^{1/2} = -\dfrac{1}{2} + \dfrac{1}{2} = 0$

9. $2^{\log_2 5} - 3 \log_5 \sqrt[3]{5} = 5 - 3 \log_5 5^{1/3}$
$= 5 - 3\left(\dfrac{1}{3}\right)$
$= 5 - 1$
$= 4$

11. $\log_{10} 30 + \log_{10} 2 = \log_{10} (30 \cdot 2) = \log_{10} 60$

13. $\log_5 6 + \log_5 \dfrac{1}{3} + \log_5 10 = \log_5 \left(6 \cdot \dfrac{1}{3} \cdot 10 \right) = \log_5 20$

15. (a) $\ln 3 - 2 \ln 4 + \ln 32 = \ln 3 - \ln (4^2) + \ln 32$
$= \ln \left(\dfrac{3 \cdot 32}{4^2} \right)$
$= \ln 6$

(b) $\ln 3 - 2 (\ln 4 + \ln 32) = \ln 3 - 2 [\ln (4 \cdot 32)]$
$= \ln 3 - 2 \ln 128$
$= \ln 3 - \ln (128^2)$
$= \ln \left(\dfrac{3}{128^2} \right)$
$= \ln \left(\dfrac{3}{16384} \right)$

17. $\log_b 4 + 3 [\log_b (1 + x) - \frac{1}{2} \log_b (1 - x)]$

$\qquad = \log_b 4 + 3 \left(\log_b (1 + x) - \log_b \sqrt{1 - x} \right)$

$\qquad = \log_b 4 + \log_b (1 + x)^3 - \log_b (1 - x)^{3/2}$

$\qquad = \log_b \left(\dfrac{4(1 + x)^3}{(1 - x)^{3/2}} \right)$

19. $4 \log_{10} 3 - 6 \log_{10} (x^2 + 1) + \frac{1}{2} [\log_{10} (x + 1) - 2 \log_{10} 3]$

$\qquad = \log_{10} 3^4 - \log_{10} (x^2 + 1)^6 + \frac{1}{2} [\log_{10} (x + 1) - \log_{10} 3^2]$

$\qquad = \log_{10} 81 - \log_{10} (x^2 + 1)^6 + \frac{1}{2} \log_{10} \left(\dfrac{x + 1}{9} \right)$

$\qquad = \log_{10} 81 - \log_{10} (x^2 + 1)^6 + \log_{10} \left(\dfrac{x + 1}{9} \right)^{1/2}$

$\qquad = \log_{10} \left(\dfrac{81 \dfrac{\sqrt{x + 1}}{3}}{(x^2 + 1)^6} \right)$

$\qquad = \log_{10} \left(\dfrac{27 \sqrt{x + 1}}{(x^2 + 1)^6} \right)$

21. (a) $\log_{10} \left(\dfrac{x^2}{1 + x^2} \right) = \log_{10} x^2 - \log_{10} (1 + x^2) = 2 \log_{10} x - \log_{10} (1 + x^2)$

$\quad$ (b) $\ln \left(\dfrac{x^2}{\sqrt{1 + x^2}} \right) = \ln x^2 - \ln \sqrt{1 + x^2} = 2 \ln x - \frac{1}{2} \ln (1 + x^2)$

23. (a) $\log_{10} \sqrt{9 - x^2} = \frac{1}{2} \log_{10} (9 - x^2)$

$\qquad\qquad\qquad\quad = \frac{1}{2} \log_{10} [(3 + x)(3 - x)]$

$\qquad\qquad\qquad\quad = \frac{1}{2} \log_{10} (3 + x) + \frac{1}{2} \log_{10} (3 - x)$

$\quad$ (b) $\ln \left(\dfrac{\sqrt{4 - x^2}}{(x - 1)(x + 1)^{3/2}} \right) = \frac{1}{2} \ln (4 - x^2) - \ln (x - 1) - \ln (x + 1)^{3/2}$

$\qquad\qquad\qquad\qquad\qquad\quad = \frac{1}{2} \ln [(2 + x)(2 - x)] - \ln (x - 1) - \frac{3}{2} \ln (x + 1)$

$\qquad\qquad\qquad\qquad\qquad\quad = \frac{1}{2} \ln (2 + x) + \frac{1}{2} \ln (2 - x) - \ln (x - 1) - \frac{3}{2} \ln (x + 1)$

25. (a) $\log_b \sqrt{\dfrac{x}{b}} = \dfrac{1}{2} \log_b \dfrac{x}{b}$

$= \dfrac{1}{2} \log_b x - \dfrac{1}{2} \log_b b$

$= \dfrac{1}{2} \log_b x - \dfrac{1}{2}$

(b) $2 \ln \sqrt{(1 + x^2)(1 + x^4)(1 + x^6)} = \ln [\, (1 + x^2)(1 + x^4)(1 + x^6) \,]$

$= \ln (1 + x^2) + \ln (1 + x^4) + \ln (1 + x^6)$

27. (a) $\log_{10} (AB^2C^3) = \log_{10} A + \log_{10} B^2 + \log_{10} C^3$

$= \log_{10} A + 2 \log_{10} B + 3 \log_{10} C$

$= a + 2b + 3c$

(b) $\log_{10} \sqrt{10ABC} = \dfrac{1}{2} \log_{10} (10ABC)$

$= \dfrac{1}{2} \log_{10} 10 + \dfrac{1}{2} \log_{10} A + \dfrac{1}{2} \log_{10} B + \dfrac{1}{2} \log_{10} C$

$= \dfrac{1}{2} (1) + \dfrac{1}{2} a + \dfrac{1}{2} b + \dfrac{1}{2} c$

$= \dfrac{1}{2} (1 + a + b + c)$

(c) $\log_{10} \left(\dfrac{10A}{\sqrt{BC}} \right) = \log_{10} (10A) - \dfrac{1}{2} \log_{10} (BC)$

$= \log_{10} 10 + \log_{10} A - \dfrac{1}{2} \log_{10} B - \dfrac{1}{2} \log_{10} C$

$= 1 + a - \dfrac{1}{2} b - \dfrac{1}{2} c$

(d) $\log_{10} \left(\dfrac{100A^2}{B^4 \sqrt[3]{C}} \right) = \log_{10} 10^2 + \log_{10} A^2 - \log_{10} B^4 - \log_{10} C^{1/3}$

$= 2 \log_{10} 10 + 2 \log_{10} A - 4 \log_{10} B - \dfrac{1}{3} \log_{10} C$

$= 2(1) + 2a - 4b - \dfrac{1}{3} c$

$= 2 + 2a - 4b - \dfrac{1}{3} c$

(e) $\log_{10}\left(\dfrac{(AB)^5}{C}\right)$ $= \log_{10} A^5 + \log_{10} B^5 - \log_{10} C$

$= 5 \log_{10} A + 5 \log_{10} B - \log_{10} C$

$= 5a + 5b - c$

29. $5 = 2e^{2x-1}$

Taking the natural log of each side, we have:

$$\ln 5 = \ln 2 + \ln e^{2x-1}$$
$$\ln 5 = \ln 2 + (2x - 1)$$
$$\ln 5 = \ln 2 + 2x - 1$$
$$2x = \ln 5 - \ln 2 + 1$$
$$x = \frac{\ln 5 - \ln 2 + 1}{2}$$

31. $$3e^{1+t} = 2$$
$$\ln 3 + \ln e^{1+t} = \ln 2$$
$$\ln 3 + 1 + t = \ln 2$$
$$t = \ln 2 - \ln 3 - 1$$

33. $$2^x = 9$$
$$\ln 2^x = \ln 9$$
$$x \ln 2 = \ln 9$$
$$x = \frac{\ln 9}{\ln 2}$$

35. $$10 \bullet 2^x = 5^x$$
$$\ln 10 + \ln 2^x = \ln 5^x$$
$$\ln 10 + x \ln 2 = x \ln 5$$
$$\ln 10 = x \ln 5 - x \ln 2$$
$$\ln 10 = x (\ln 5 - \ln 2)$$
$$x = \frac{\ln 10}{\ln 5 - \ln 2}$$
$$x = \frac{\ln 5 + \ln 2}{\ln 5 - \ln 2}$$

37.
$$\log_9 (x + 1) = \frac{1}{2} + \log_9 x$$

$$\log_9 (x + 1) - \log_9 x = \frac{1}{2}$$

$$\log_9 \left(\frac{x + 1}{x} \right) = \frac{1}{2}$$

$$9^{1/2} = \frac{x + 1}{x}$$

$$3 = \frac{x + 1}{x}$$

$$3x = x + 1$$

$$2x = 1$$

$$x = \frac{1}{2}$$

39.
$$\log_{10} (2x + 4) + \log_{10} (x - 2) = 1$$

$$\log_{10} [\, (2x + 4)(x - 2) \,] = 1$$

$$(2x + 4)(x - 2) = 10^1$$

$$2x^2 - 8 = 10$$

$$2x^2 = 18$$

$$x^2 = 9$$

$$x = \pm 3$$

But $x = -3$ is an extraneous root ($\log_{10} -2$ is undefined), so $x = 3$.

41.
$$\log_{10} (x + 3) - \log_{10} (x - 2) = 2$$

$$\log_{10} \left(\frac{x + 3}{x - 2} \right) = 2$$

$$10^2 = \frac{x + 3}{x - 2}$$

$$100(x - 2) = x + 3$$

$$100x - 200 = x + 3$$

$$99x = 203$$

$$x = \frac{203}{99}$$

43. $\log_b (x + 1) = 2 \log_b (x - 1)$
$$\log_b (x + 1) = \log_b (x - 1)^2$$
$$x + 1 = (x - 1)^2$$
$$x + 1 = x^2 - 2x + 1$$
$$x^2 - 3x = 0$$
$$x(x - 3) = 0$$
$$x = 0, 3$$
But $x = 0$ is an extraneous root ($\log_b (-1)$ is undefined), so $x = 3$.

45. $\log_{10} (x - 6) + \log_{10} (x + 3) = 1$
$$\log_{10} [(x - 6)(x + 3)] = 1$$
$$10^1 = (x - 6)(x + 3)$$
$$x^2 - 3x - 18 = 10$$
$$x^2 - 3x - 28 = 0$$
$$(x - 7)(x + 4) = 0$$
$x = 7$ and $x = -4$ are roots of this equation.
However, we must check to make sure both roots work in the original equation. 7 does, but when we try -4 we have $\log_{10} -10$ and $\log_{10} -1$, neither of which are defined.

47.   (a) $\log_{10} x - y = \log_{10} (3x - 1)$
$$\log_{10} x - \log_{10} (3x - 1) = y$$
$$\log_{10} \left(\frac{x}{3x - 1} \right) = y$$
$$10^y = \frac{x}{3x - 1}$$
$$10^y (3x - 1) = x$$
$$3(10^y)x - 10^y = x$$
$$3(10^y)x - x = 10^y$$
$$x[3(10^y) - 1] = 10^y$$
$$x = \frac{10^y}{3(10^y) - 1}$$

(b) $\log_{10} (x - y) = \log_{10} (3x - 1)$ is easier to solve, for we can conclude directly that:
$$x - y = 3x - 1$$
$$-2x = y - 1$$
$$x = \frac{y - 1}{-2} \text{ or } \frac{1 - y}{2}$$

49. There is a formula which shows us how to convert to logs in any base, but let's do one the longer way and review how the formula is derived.
Given $\log_2 5$, we are asked to write it as a base 10 log:

$$\log_2 5 = N$$
$$2^N = 5$$
$$\log_{10} 2^N = \log_{10} 5$$
$$N \cdot \log_{10} 2 = \log_{10} 5$$
$$N = \frac{\log_{10} 5}{\log_{10} 2}$$
$$\log_2 5 = \frac{\log_{10} 5}{\log_{10} 2}$$

51. $\ln 3 = \log_e 3 = \dfrac{\log_{10} 3}{\log_{10} e}$

53. $\log_b 2 = \dfrac{\log_{10} 2}{\log_{10} b}$

55. $\log_{10} 6 = \dfrac{\ln 6}{\ln 10}$

57. $\log_{10} e = \dfrac{\ln e}{\ln 10} = \dfrac{1}{\ln 10}$

59. $\log_{10} (\log_{10} x) = \log_{10}\left(\dfrac{\ln x}{\ln 10}\right) = \dfrac{\ln\left(\dfrac{\ln x}{\ln 10}\right)}{\ln 10} = \dfrac{\ln (\ln x) - \ln (\ln 10)}{\ln 10}$

61. (a) true
    (b) true
    (c) true
    (d) false -- $\ln x^3 = 3 \ln x$, not $\ln 3x$
    (e) true
    (f) false -- $\ln (2x)^3 = 3 \ln 2x$, but $\ln 2x^3 = \ln 2 + 3 \ln x$
    (g) true
    (h) false -- $\log_5 24$ is between 1 and 2, not 5^1 and 5^2
    (i) true
    (j) false -- $\log_5 24$ is close to 2 $(2 = \log_5 25)$
    (k) false -- it is $x > 0$
    (l) true
    (m) true

63. $\ln (P + Q) = \ln (3 + 4) = \ln 7 \approx 1.94591$
    $\ln P + \ln Q = \ln 3 + \ln 4 \approx 1.09861 + 1.38629 \approx 2.48490$
    So $\ln (3 + 4) \neq \ln 3 + \ln 4$

65. $\ln (PQ) = \ln (10\cdot20) = \ln 200 \approx 5.29832$
    $(\ln P)(\ln Q) = (\ln 10)(\ln 20) \approx (2.30259)(2.99573) \approx 6.89794$
    So $\ln (10\cdot20) \neq (\ln 10)(\ln 20)$

67. $\dfrac{\log_{10} 19}{\log_{10} 89} \approx \dfrac{1.27875}{1.94939} \approx 0.65598$

    $\log_{10} 19 - \log_{10} 89 \approx 1.27875 - 1.94939 = -0.67064$

    So $\dfrac{\log_{10} 19}{\log_{10} 89} \neq \log_{10} 19 - \log_{10} 89$

69. $\log_{10} \pi^7 \approx 3.48005$
    $7 \log_{10} \pi \approx 7(0.49715) = 3.48005$
    So $\log_{10} \pi^7 = 7 \log_{10} \pi$

71. $b^{\log_b P} = 10^{\log_{10} 1776} = 10^{3.24944} = 1776$
    $10^{\log_{10} 1776} = 1776$

73. $\log_{10} A + \log_{10} B + \log_{10} C = \log_{10} 11 + \log_{10} 12 + \log_{10} 13$
    $$\approx 1.04139 + 1.07918 + 1.11394$$
    $$= 3.23451$$
    $\log_{10} (ABC) = \log_{10} (11\cdot12\cdot13) = \log_{10} 1716 \approx 3.23451$
    So $\log_{10} A + \log_{10} B + \log_{10} C = \log_{10} (ABC)$

75. $g\big(f(0.123456)\big) = g(10^{0.123456})$
    $$\approx g(1.3287889)$$
    $$\approx \log_{10} 1.3287889$$
    $$\approx 0.123456$$

77. (a) We substitute for x:
    $$3e^{1 - (\ln 0.3 + 1)} = 3e^{-\ln 0.3}$$
    $$= 3e^{\ln (0.3)^{-1}}$$
    $$= 3(0.3)^{-1}$$
    $$= 3\left(\frac{10}{3}\right)$$
    $$= 10$$

(b) $\dfrac{\ln 0.3 + 1}{2} = \dfrac{1}{2} \ln 0.3 + \dfrac{1}{2} = \ln (0.3)^{1/2} + \dfrac{1}{2} = \dfrac{1}{2} + \ln \sqrt{0.3}$

(c) Since $\ln e = 1$, then $\dfrac{1}{2} = \dfrac{1}{2} \ln e = \ln \sqrt{e}$. So:

$$\dfrac{1}{2} + \ln \sqrt{0.3} = \ln \sqrt{e} + \ln \sqrt{0.3} = \ln \sqrt{\dfrac{3e}{10}}$$

79. $\log_b \left(\dfrac{\sqrt{3} + \sqrt{2}}{\sqrt{3} - \sqrt{2}} \right) = \log_b \left(\dfrac{\sqrt{3} + \sqrt{2}}{\sqrt{3} - \sqrt{2}} \cdot \dfrac{\sqrt{3} + \sqrt{2}}{\sqrt{3} + \sqrt{2}} \right)$

$\qquad\qquad\qquad = \log_b \left(\dfrac{(\sqrt{3} + \sqrt{2})^2}{3 - 2} \right)$

$\qquad\qquad\qquad = \log_b (\sqrt{3} + \sqrt{2})^2$

$\qquad\qquad\qquad = 2 \log_b (\sqrt{3} + \sqrt{2})$

81. $b^{3 \log_b x} = b^{\log_b x^3} = x^3$

83. $\log_2 \sqrt[5]{4\sqrt{2}} = \dfrac{1}{5} \log_2 4\sqrt{2}$

$\qquad\qquad\quad = \dfrac{1}{5} \log_2 (2^2 \cdot 2^{1/2})$

$\qquad\qquad\quad = \dfrac{1}{5} \log_2 (2^{5/2})$

$\qquad\qquad\quad = \dfrac{1}{5} \cdot \dfrac{5}{2}$

$\qquad\qquad\quad = \dfrac{1}{2}$

85. $\qquad\qquad 3 \ln x = \alpha + 3 \ln \beta$

$\qquad 3\ln x - 3\ln \beta = \alpha$

$\qquad 3(\ln x - \ln \beta) = \alpha$

$\qquad\qquad 3 \ln \dfrac{x}{\beta} = \alpha$

$\qquad\qquad\quad \ln \dfrac{x}{\beta} = \dfrac{\alpha}{3}$

$\qquad\qquad\qquad \dfrac{x}{\beta} = e^{\alpha/3}$

$\qquad\qquad\qquad\quad x = \beta e^{\alpha/3}$

87. Using the change of base formula, we have:

$$\log_b a = \frac{\log_a a}{\log_a b} = \frac{1}{\log_a b}$$

89. Using the change of base formula, we have:

$$\log_{ab} x = \frac{\log_a x}{\log_a ab} = \frac{\log_a x}{\log_a a + \log_a b} = \frac{\log_a x}{1 + \log_a b}$$

So $\quad \dfrac{\log_a x}{\log_{ab} x} = \dfrac{\log_a x}{\dfrac{\log_a x}{1 + \log_a b}} = 1 + \log_a b$

This proves the desired result.

91. We work from the right-hand side:

$$\frac{1}{2}(\log a + \log b) = \frac{1}{2}\log(ab) = \log\sqrt{ab}$$

So, proving the desired equality is equivalent to proving:

$$\frac{1}{3}(a + b) = \sqrt{ab}\,, \text{ since log is a 1-1 function.}$$

If a and b are both positive, we can square each side:

$$\frac{1}{9}(a^2 + 2ab + b^2) = ab$$

We now work with the left-hand side:

$$\frac{1}{9}(a^2 + 2ab + b^2) = \frac{1}{9}(7ab + 2ab) \text{ by our assumption } a^2 + b^2 = 7ab$$

$$= \frac{1}{9}(9ab)$$

$$= ab$$

This proves the result.

93. Let $y = \ln(x + \sqrt{x^2 + 1}\,)$. We interchange the roles of x and y, then solve for y:

$$x = \ln(y + \sqrt{y^2 + 1}\,)$$
$$e^x = y + \sqrt{y^2 + 1}$$
$$e^x - y = \sqrt{y^2 + 1}$$

Squaring each side:

$$e^{2x} - 2ye^x + y^2 = y^2 + 1$$
$$e^{2x} - 2ye^x = 1$$
$$e^{2x} - 1 = 2ye^x$$
$$\frac{e^{2x} - 1}{2e^x} = y$$

So $f^{-1}(x) = \dfrac{e^{2x} - 1}{2e^x}$

95. We complete the table:

x	10^2	10^3	10^6	10^{20}	10^{50}	10^{99}
y	0.4234	0.6589	0.9654	1.3428	1.5573	1.6918

As x approaches infinity, so does ln x, and thus ln (ln x), and finally ln [ln(ln x)]. The table is misleading -- it only indicates that y approaches infinity much slower! An actual proof of the result is more complicated: Assume that y does <u>not</u> approach infinity, so there is some number N such that $y < N$, then ln [ln(ln x)] $< N$, so ln (ln x) $< e^N$.

But since ln (ln x) $< e^N$, then ln x $< e^{(e^N)}$, and finally $x < e^{e^{(e^N)}}$. But clearly this is false, since x approaches infinity and thus cannot be bounded. Thus y must approach infinity.

4.5 Applications

1. For annual compounding of money we use the formula $A = P(1 + r)^t$. We want A when P = \$800, r = 0.06 and t = 4 yrs:
$$A = 800(1 + 0.06)^4 = 800(1.06)^4 \approx \$1009.98$$

3. For annual compounding of money we use the formula $A = P(1 + r)^t$. We want r when A = \$6000, P = \$4000 and t = 5:
$$6000 = 4000 (1 + r)^5$$
$$1.5 = (1 + r)^5$$
$$(1.5)^{1/5} = 1 + r$$
$$r = (1.5)^{1/5} - 1$$
$$r \approx 0.0845$$
So the interest rate is 8.45%.

5. In the first bank, we have P = \$500, r = 0.05, and t = 4:
$$A = 500 (1 + 0.05)^4 = 500 (1.05)^4 \approx 607.75$$
We now deposit P = \$607.75, r = 0.06, and t = 4:
$$A = 607.75 (1 + 0.06)^4 = 607.75 (1.06)^4 \approx 767.27$$
So the new balance will be \$767.27.

7. (a) We use $A = P(1 + r)^t$ with P = 1000, r = 0.07, and t = 20:
$$A = 1000(1 + 0.07)^{20} = 1000(1.07)^{20} \approx 3869.69$$
The new balance is \$3869.68.

(b)　We use $A = P\left(1 + \dfrac{r}{N}\right)^{Nt}$ with P = 1000, r = 0.07, N = 4, t = 20:

$$A = 1000\left(1 + \frac{0.07}{4}\right)^{4(20)} = 1000\,(1.0175)^{80} \approx 4006.39$$

The new balance is $4006.39.

9.　For compounding quarterly we use the formula:

$$A = P\left(1 + \frac{r}{N}\right)^{Nt}$$

So here P = $100, r = 6% and we have N = 4 compoundings per year.
We want the value of t for which A ≥ $120:

$$120 \leq 100\left(1 + \frac{0.06}{4}\right)^{4t}$$

$$1.2 \leq (1.015)^{4t}$$

$$\ln 1.2 \leq 4t \ln 1.015$$

$$4t \geq \frac{\ln 1.2}{\ln 1.015}$$

$$t \geq \frac{\ln 1.2}{4 \ln 1.015}$$

$$t \geq 3.06$$

This is slightly over 3 years, and so 13 quarters will be required.

11.　We use $A = P\left(1 + \dfrac{r}{N}\right)^{Nt}$ where r = 0.055, N = 2, A = 6000, t = 10:

$$6000 = P\left(1 + \frac{0.55}{2}\right)^{2(10)}$$

$$6000 = P\,(1.0275)^{20}$$

$$P = \frac{6000}{(1.0275)^{20}}$$

$$P \approx 3487.50$$

You must deposit a principal of $3487.50.

13.　We use $A = Pe^{rt}$ where A = 5000, t = 10, and r = 0.065:

$$5000 = Pe^{(0.065)(10)}$$

$$5000 = Pe^{0.65}$$

$$P = \frac{5000}{e^{0.65}}$$

$$P \approx 2610.23$$

A principal of $2610.23 will grow to $5000 in 10 yrs.

15.   Since the effective rate is $r = 0.06$, we have:
$$A = P (1 + 0.06)^1 = 1.06\, P$$
The nominal rate r would yield a balance of:
$$A = Pe^{r(1)} = Pe^r$$
Setting these equal:
$$Pe^r = P (1.06)$$
$$e^r = 1.06$$
$$r = \ln 1.06$$
$$r \approx 0.0583$$
So the nominal rate is 5.83%.

17.   Let's take the 6% investment first:
$$A = 10{,}000(1 + 0.06)^5 = 10{,}000(1.3382) \approx \$13382.26$$
The second choice will be:
$$A = 10{,}000e^{0.05\,(5)} = 10{,}000e^{.25} \approx \$12840.25, \text{ considerably less.}$$

19.   (a) $T_2 \approx \dfrac{0.7}{r} = \dfrac{0.7}{0.05} = 14$ yrs

      (b) $T_2 = \dfrac{\ln 2}{r} = \dfrac{\ln 2}{0.05} = 13.86$ yrs

      (c)   Here $d_1 = 13.86$, $d_2 = 14$, so $d = |13.86 - 14| = 0.14$

             This represents $\dfrac{0.14}{13.86}$ (100) $\approx 1.01\%$ of the actual doubling time.

21.   Here: $A = 1000e^{(.08)\,300} = 1000e^{24} = 1000(2.65 \times 10^{10}) = \$2.65 \times 10^{13}$
      That's $26.5 trillion, a nice inheritance.

23. (a) $T_2 \approx \dfrac{0.7}{0.05} = 14$ yrs

(b)   We sketch the graph:

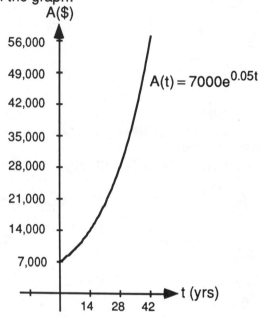

25. The growth problems are solved by assuming an exponential growth rate:
$$N = N_0 e^{kt}$$
First we find the percent distribution by dividing the total population into each of the two regions:
$$\frac{1.131}{4.090} \approx 27.7\% \text{ for more developed regions}$$
Applying the growth formula to the total world population, we have:
$$N = N_0 e^{kt} = 4.090 e^{0.18\,(25)} = 4.090\, e^{.45} \approx 6.414 \text{ billion}$$
The other calculations are similar to these two. The completed table is:

	1975 Population (billions)	% Population in 1975	Growth Rate (% per year)	Year 2000 Population (billions)	% of World Population in 2000
World	4.090	100	1.8	6.414	100
More Dev.	1.131	27.7	0.6	1.314	20.5
Less Dev.	2.959	72.3	2.1	5.002	78.0

27. We complete the table:

	1975 Population (billions)	Growth Rate (% per year)	Year 2000 Population (billions)	% Increase in Population
Low	4.043	1.5	5.883	45.5
Medium	4.090	1.8	6.414	56.8
High	4.134	2.0	6.816	64.9

29. (a) Use $N = N_0 e^{kt}$:

$$62{,}947{,}714 = 23{,}191{,}876\, e^{k\,(50)}$$
$$2.7142 = e^{50k}$$
$$\ln 2.7142 = 50k$$
$$k = \frac{\ln 2.7142}{50}$$
$$k \approx 0.0200$$

(b) In 1950, we have:
$$N = (62{,}947{,}714)\, e^{(0.02)\,(50)} \approx 170{,}853{,}155$$
(Your answer may differ slightly due to round-off error)

(c) The actual growth over that period was slower than that predicted from (b) with a constant growth rate.

31. (a) $k \approx 0.0068$, or 0.68%

(b) $k \approx 0.0096$, or 0.96%

(c) It would be 19,751,512

(d) Our prediction is higher than the actual population.

33.   (a)   We draw the graph:

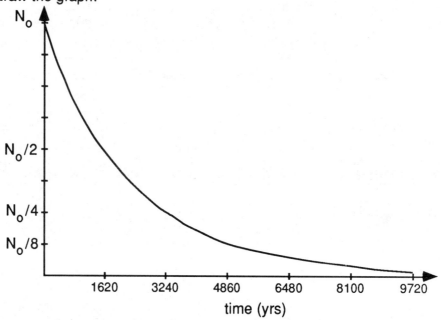

(b)   We draw the graph:

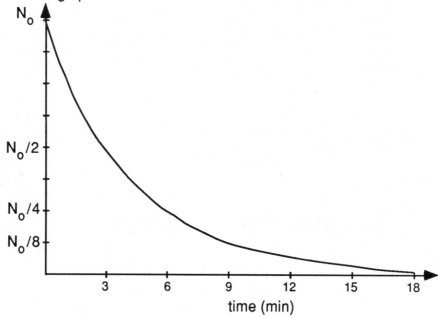

35. (a) $N = N_0 e^{kt}$

$\frac{1}{2} N_0 = N_0 e^{k \cdot 13}$ because after 13 years, N will be one-half of the original amount. So, dividing by N_0, we get:

$$e^{13k} = .5$$
$$13k = \ln .5$$
$$k = \frac{\ln .5}{13} \approx -0.0533$$

Once you understand this, it will be convenient for you to remember that k always equals ln .5 divided by the length of a half-life for decay problems.

(b) $N = N_0 e^{(-.0533)(10)}$

$N \approx .587 N_0$ or about 58.7% of N_0 after 10 years.

If t = 100, $N \approx .5$% of N_0.

37. (a) $k = \frac{\ln 0.5}{28} \approx -0.0248$

(b) We set $\frac{N_0}{1000} = N_0 e^{kt}$

$$0.001 = e^{-0.0248\,t}$$
$$\ln 0.001 = -0.0248\,t$$
$$t = \frac{\ln 0.001}{-0.0248} \approx 279 \text{ yrs}$$

(c) Since $2^{10} \approx 1000$, then after 10 half-lives, it should be reduced to $\frac{N_0}{1000}$. Since each half-life is 28 years, this is approximately 280 years. Note that this is close to our answer from (b).

39. (a) We use $N = N_0 e^{kt}$ with $N = 10 \times 10^9$, $N_0 = 3.6 \times 10^9$, and $k = 0.02$:

$$10 \times 10^9 = (3.6 \times 10^9) e^{0.02\,t}$$
$$\frac{10}{3.6} = e^{0.02\,t}$$
$$\ln \frac{10}{3.6} = 0.02\,t$$
$$t = \frac{\ln \frac{10}{3.6}}{0.02}$$
$$t \approx 51 \text{ years}$$

So 51 years after 1969, or 2020, the carrying capacity will be reached.

(b)   We use $N = N_0 e^{kt}$ with $N = 10 \times 10^9$, $N_0 = 4.043 \times 10^9$, and $k = 0.015$:

$$10 \times 10^9 = (4.043 \times 10^9)\, e^{0.015\,t}$$

$$\frac{10}{4.043} = e^{0.015\,t}$$

$$\ln \frac{10}{4.043} = 0.015\,t$$

$$t = \frac{\ln \dfrac{10}{4.043}}{0.015}$$

$$t \approx 60 \text{ years}$$

So 60 years after 1975, or 2035, the carrying capacity will be reached.

(c)   We use $N = N_0 e^{kt}$ with $N = 10 \times 10^9$, $N_0 = 4.134 \times 10^9$, and $k = 0.02$:

$$10 \times 10^9 = (4.134 \times 10^9)\, e^{0.02\,t}$$

$$\frac{10}{4.134} = e^{0.02\,t}$$

$$\ln \frac{10}{4.134} = 0.02\,t$$

$$t = \frac{\ln \dfrac{10}{4.134}}{0.02}$$

$$t \approx 44 \text{ years}$$

So 44 years after 1975, or 2019, the carrying capacity will be reached.

41.   (a) $T = \dfrac{\ln \left(\dfrac{Ak}{A_0} + 1 \right)}{k} = \dfrac{\ln \left(\dfrac{161241(0.01)}{250} + 1 \right)}{0.01} \approx 201 \text{ yrs}$

(b) $T = \dfrac{\ln \left(\dfrac{Ak}{A_0} + 1 \right)}{k} = \dfrac{\ln \left(\dfrac{161241(0.02)}{250} + 1 \right)}{0.02} \approx 132 \text{ yrs}$

43.   (a) $\log_{10} E = 11.4 + 1.5M$

$$E = 10^{11.4 + 1.5M}$$

$$E = 10^{11.4} \cdot 10^{1.5M}$$

(b) $\dfrac{E_2}{E_1} = \dfrac{10^{11.4} \cdot 10^{1.5M_2}}{10^{11.4} \cdot 10^{1.5M_1}}$

$$= 10^{1.5\,(M_2 - M_1)}$$

$$= 10^{1.5\,(7.8 - 6.8)}$$

$$= 10^{1.5\,(1.0)}$$

$$\approx 31.6$$

45. $k = \dfrac{\ln 0.5}{4.7 \times 10^{10}} \approx -1.4748 \times 10^{-11}$

47. $T = \dfrac{\ln \left(\dfrac{N_s}{N_r} + 1 \right)}{-k} = \dfrac{\ln (0.0636 + 1)}{-(-1.4748 \times 10^{-11})} \approx 4.181 \times 10^9 \text{ yrs}$

The rock is approximately 4.181 billion years old.

49. $T = \dfrac{5730 \ln \dfrac{N}{920}}{\ln \dfrac{1}{2}} = \dfrac{5730 \ln \dfrac{141}{920}}{\ln \dfrac{1}{2}} \approx 15505 \text{ yrs}$

The two paintings are 15,505 years old.

51. $T = \dfrac{5730 \ln \dfrac{N}{920}}{\ln \dfrac{1}{2}} = \dfrac{5730 \ln \dfrac{226}{920}}{\ln \dfrac{1}{2}} \approx 11{,}605 \text{ yrs}$

This is 11,500 years (to the nearest 500 years).

Chapter 4 Review Exercises

1.   If $x = \log_5 126$, then $5^x = 126$. Since $5^3 = 125$, then $x > 3$.
     If $y = \log_{10} 999$, then $10^y = 999$. Since $10^3 = 1000$, then $y < 3$.
     So $\log_5 126$ is larger.

2. $y = 3^{-x} - 3$
      This is $y = 3^x$ reflected across the y-axis, then displaced down 3 units:

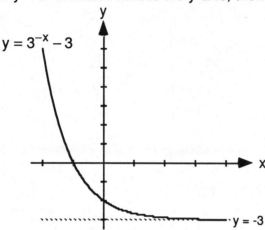

domain: $(-\infty, \infty)$; range: $(-3, \infty)$
x-intercept: -1; y-intercept: -2; asymptote: $y = -3$

3.   Since $N(t) = N_0 e^{kt}$ and $N_0 = 8000$, then $N(t) = 8000 e^{kt}$. Since $N(4) = 10000$,
      we can find k:
$$N(4) = 10000$$
$$8000 e^{4k} = 10000$$
$$e^{4k} = 1.25$$
$$4k = \ln 1.25$$
$$k = \frac{\ln 1.25}{4}$$
      We now find t such that $N(t) = 12000$:
$$N(t) = 12000$$
$$8000 e^{kt} = 12000$$
$$e^{kt} = 1.5$$
$$kt = \ln 1.5$$
$$t = \frac{\ln 1.5}{k} = \frac{\ln 1.5}{\frac{\ln 1.25}{4}} = \frac{4 \ln 1.5}{\ln 1.25}$$

4. $\log_{10} 2 = \dfrac{\ln 2}{\ln 10}$

5.   We graph f(x):

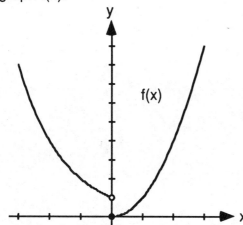

f is not one-to-one since it does not pass the horizontal line test.

6.   Since $2^{10} \approx 10^3$, then $2^{60} = (2^{10})^6 \approx (10^3)^6 = 10^{18}$.

7.
$$\ln(x + 1) - 1 = \ln(x - 1)$$
$$\ln(x + 1) - \ln(x - 1) = 1$$
$$\ln \frac{x + 1}{x - 1} = 1$$
$$\frac{x + 1}{x - 1} = e$$
$$x + 1 = ex - e$$
$$e + 1 = ex - x$$
$$e + 1 = x(e - 1)$$
$$x = \frac{e + 1}{e - 1}$$

8.   Actually the doubling time does not depend upon the principal ($5000), so we solve the equation:
$$2P = P(1 + .08)^t$$
$$2 = (1.08)^t$$
$$\ln 2 = t \ln 1.08$$
$$t = \frac{\ln 2}{\ln 1.08} \approx 9 \text{ yrs}$$

9.   We graph each function:

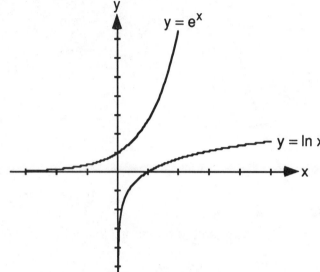

$y = e^x$:   domain: $(-\infty, \infty)$; range: $(0, \infty)$
$y = \ln x$:   domain: $(0, \infty)$; range: $(-\infty, \infty)$

10. $xe^x - 2e^x = 0$
$e^x(x - 2) = 0$
$e^x \neq 0$, so $x = 2$

11. $\log_9 \dfrac{1}{27} = \log_9 (3^{-3}) = \log_9 (9^{1/2})^{-3} = \log_9 9^{-3/2} = -3/2$

12. $\ln \dfrac{A^2\sqrt{B}}{C^3} = \ln A^2 + \ln \sqrt{B} - \ln C^3$

$= 2 \ln A + \dfrac{1}{2} \ln B - 3 \ln C$

$= 2a + \dfrac{b}{2} - 3c$ or $\dfrac{4a + b - 6c}{2}$

13. Using the decay equation $N = N_0 e^{kt}$, we find k when t = 13 and $N = \frac{1}{2} N_0$:

$$\frac{1}{2} N_0 = N_0 e^{13k}$$

$$\frac{1}{2} = e^{13k}$$

$$\ln \frac{1}{2} = 13k$$

$$k = \frac{\ln \frac{1}{2}}{13} \approx -0.05$$

14. $3 \log_{10} x - \log_{10} (1 - x) = \log_{10} x^3 - \log_{10} (1 - x) = \log_{10} \frac{x^3}{1 - x}$

15. $5e^{2 - x} = 12$

$e^{2 - x} = 12/5$

$2 - x = \ln \frac{12}{5}$

$-x = -2 + \ln \frac{12}{5}$

$x = 2 - \ln \frac{12}{5}$

16. We interchange the roles of x and y and solve the resulting equation for y:

$$x = e^{y + 1}$$
$$\ln x = y + 1$$
$$y = \ln x - 1$$

So $f^{-1}(x) = \ln x - 1$
Domain: $(0, \infty)$

17. We use $N = N_0 e^{kt}$ where $N_0 = 2$ and k = 0.02, so $N(t) = 2e^{0.02t}$.
We find when N = 3:

$$3 = 2e^{0.02t}$$
$$1.5 = e^{0.02t}$$
$$\ln 1.5 = 0.02t$$
$$t = \frac{\ln 1.5}{0.02} \approx 20 \text{ yrs}$$

We would expect the population to reach 3 million in the year 2000.

18. $\ln e + \ln \sqrt{e} + \ln 1 + \ln e^{\ln 10} = 1 + 1/2 + 0 + \ln 10 = 3/2 + \ln 10$

19. We use $A = Pe^{rt}$ where $P = \$1000$ and $r = 0.10$, so $A(t) = 1000e^{0.1t}$. The doubling time is approximately $\frac{70}{10} = 7$ years. We sketch the graph:

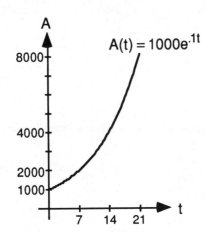

20. $\log_8 56 - \log_8 7 = \log_8 \frac{56}{7} = \log_8 8 = 1$, so:

$\ln(\log_8 56 - \log_8 7) = \ln 1 = 0$

21. $y = e^x$
horizontal asymptote: $y = 0$; vertical asymptote: none
x-intercept: none; y-intercept: 1

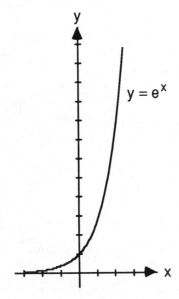

23. $y = \ln x$
horizontal asymptote: none; vertical asymptote: $x = 0$
x-intercept: 1; y-intercept: none

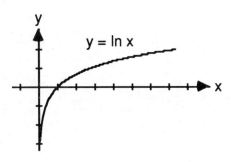

25. $y = 2^{x+1} + 1$
horizontal asymptote: $y = 1$; vertical asymptote: none
x-intercept: none; y-intercept: 3

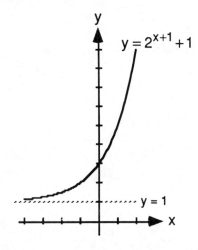

27. $y = \left(\dfrac{1}{e}\right)^x$

horizontal asymptote: y = 0; vertical asymptote: none
x-intercept: none; y-intercept: 1

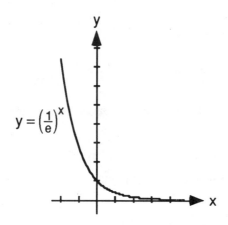

29. $y = e^{x+1} + 1$

horizontal asymptote: y = 1; vertical asymptote: none
x-intercept: none; y-intercept: e + 1

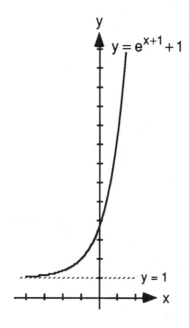

31. $y = \ln(e^x) = x$ for all real x
     horizontal asymptote: none; vertical asymptote: none
     x-intercept: 0; y-intercept: 0

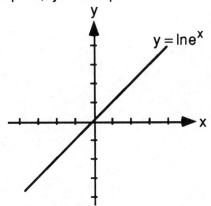

$y = \ln e^x$

33. $\log_4 x + \log_4 (x - 3) = 1$

$\log_4 [x(x - 3)] = 1$

$x(x - 3) = 4^1$

$x^2 - 3x = 4$

$x^2 - 3x - 4 = 0$

$(x - 4)(x + 1) = 0$

$x = 4, -1$

But x = -1 is an extraneous root [$\log_4 (-1)$ is undefined], so x = 4.

35. $\ln x + \ln (x + 2) = \ln 15$

$\ln [x(x + 2)] = \ln 15$

$x(x + 2) = 15$

$x^2 + 2x = 15$

$x^2 + 2x - 15 = 0$

$(x + 5)(x - 3) = 0$

$x = -5, 3$

But x = -5 is an extraneous root [$\ln (-5)$ is undefined], so x = 3.

37. $\log_2 x + \log_2 (3x + 10) - 3 = 0$

$\log_2 [x(3x + 10)] = 3$

$x(3x + 10) = 2^3$

$3x^2 + 10x = 8$

$3x^2 + 10x - 8 = 0$

$(3x - 2)(x + 4) = 0$

$x = 2/3, -4$

But x = -4 is an extraneous root [$\log_2 (-4)$ is undefined], so x = 2/3.

39. $3 \log_9 x = \dfrac{1}{2}$

$\log_9 x = \dfrac{1}{6}$

$x = 9^{1/6}$

$x = \sqrt[6]{9} = \sqrt[3]{3}$

41. $e^{1-5x} = 3\sqrt{e}$

$1 - 5x = \ln 3\sqrt{e}$

$1 - 5x = \ln 3 + \dfrac{1}{2} \ln e$

$1 - 5x = \ln 3 + \dfrac{1}{2}$

$-5x = \ln 3 - \dfrac{1}{2}$

$x = \dfrac{1 - 2 \ln 3}{10}$

43. $\log_{10} x - 2 = \log_{10} (x - 2)$

$\log_{10} x - \log_{10} (x - 2) = 2$

$\log_{10} \dfrac{x}{x - 2} = 2$

$\dfrac{x}{x - 2} = 100$

$x = 100(x - 2)$

$x = 100x - 200$

$200 = 99x$

$x = \dfrac{200}{99}$

45. $\ln (x + 2) = \ln x + \ln 2$

$\ln (x + 2) = \ln 2x$

$x + 2 = 2x$

$2 = x$

47. $\ln (x^4) = 4 \ln x$

This is an identity, so the solution is all real numbers $x > 0$, or $(0, \infty)$.

49.
$$\log_{10} x = \ln x$$
$$\frac{\ln x}{\ln 10} = \ln x$$
$$\ln x = (\ln 10)(\ln x)$$
$$\ln x - (\ln 10)(\ln x) = 0$$
$$\ln x (1 - \ln 10) = 0$$
$$\ln x = 0, \text{ so } x = 1$$

51. $\log_{10} \sqrt{10} = \log_{10} (10^{1/2}) = 1/2$

53. $\ln (\sqrt[5]{e}) = \ln (e^{1/5}) = 1/5$

55. $\log_{10} \pi - \log_{10} 10\pi = \log_{10} \pi - (\log_{10} 10 + \log_{10} \pi)$
$$= \log_{10} \pi - \log_{10} 10 - \log_{10} \pi$$
$$= - \log_{10} 10$$
$$= -1$$

57. $10^{\log_{10} 16} = 16$

59. $\ln (e^4) = 4$

61. $\log_{12} 2 + \log_{12} 18 + \log_{12} 4 = \log_{12} (2 \bullet 18 \bullet 4) = \log_{12} 144 = \log_{12} (12^2) = 2$

63. $\dfrac{\ln 100}{\ln 10} = \dfrac{\ln (10^2)}{\ln 10} = \dfrac{2 \ln 10}{\ln 10} = 2$

65. $\log_2 \sqrt[7]{16 \sqrt[3]{2\sqrt{2}}} = \frac{1}{7} \log_2 16 \sqrt[3]{2\sqrt{2}}$

$$= \frac{1}{7} \left(\log_2 16 + \log_2 \sqrt[3]{2\sqrt{2}} \right)$$

$$= \frac{1}{7} \left[\log_2 (2^4) + \frac{1}{3} \log_2 2\sqrt{2} \right]$$

$$= \frac{1}{7} \left[4 + \frac{1}{3} \left(\log_2 2 + \log_2 \sqrt{2} \right) \right]$$

$$= \frac{1}{7} \left[4 + \frac{1}{3} \left(1 + \log_2 (2^{1/2}) \right) \right]$$

$$= \frac{1}{7} \left(4 + \frac{1}{3} \cdot \frac{3}{2} \right)$$

$$= \frac{1}{7} \left(4 + \frac{1}{2} \right)$$

$$= \frac{1}{7} \cdot \frac{9}{2}$$

$$= \frac{9}{14}$$

67. $\log_{10} (A^2 B^3 \sqrt{C}) = \log_{10} A^2 + \log_{10} B^3 + \log_{10} \sqrt{C}$

$$= 2 \log_{10} A + 3 \log_{10} B + \frac{1}{2} \log_{10} C$$

$$= 2a + 3b + \frac{c}{2}$$

69. $16 \log_{10} \sqrt{A} \sqrt[4]{B} = 16 \left(\log_{10} \sqrt{A} + \log_{10} \sqrt[4]{B} \right)$

$$= 16 \left(\frac{1}{2} \log_{10} A + \frac{1}{4} \log_{10} B \right)$$

$$= 8 \log_{10} A + 4 \log_{10} B$$

$$= 8a + 4b$$

71. $\log_{10} 100 = 2$ and $\log_{10} 1000 = 3$, so $\log_{10} 209$ lies between 2 and 3.

73. $\log_6 36 = 2$ and $\log_6 216 = 3$, so $\log_6 100$ lies between 2 and 3.

75. $\log_{10} 0.010 = -2$ and $\log_{10} 0.001 = -3$, so $\log_{10} 0.003$ lies between -2 and -3.

77. (a)   We graph $y = \ln(x + 2)$ and $y = \ln(-x) - 1$:

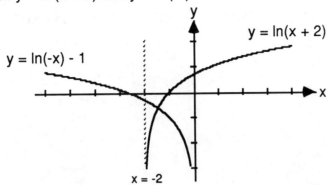

The graph shows these two curves intersect in the third quadrant.

(b)   We set:
$$\ln(x + 2) = \ln(-x) - 1$$
$$\ln(x + 2) - \ln(-x) = -1$$
$$\ln \frac{x + 2}{-x} = -1$$
$$\frac{x + 2}{-x} = e^{-1}$$
$$e(x + 2) = -x$$
$$ex + 2e = -x$$
$$ex + x = -2e$$
$$x(e + 1) = -2e$$
$$x = \frac{-2e}{e + 1} \approx -1.46$$

79.   We know $N = N_0 e^{kt}$, and $N = \frac{1}{2} N_0$ when $t = T$:

$$\frac{1}{2} N_0 = N_0 e^{kT}$$
$$\frac{1}{2} = e^{kT}$$
$$\ln \frac{1}{2} = kT$$
$$k = \frac{\ln \frac{1}{2}}{T}$$

81.   Since 4 half-lives have passed, we will have
$$\frac{1}{2} \left(\frac{1}{2} \left(\frac{1}{2} \left(\frac{1}{2} N_0 \right) \right) \right) = \frac{1}{16} N_0$$ of the subtance left, or 6.25% remaining.

83. $k = \dfrac{\ln \frac{1}{2}}{d}$, and $N_0 = b$. We want to find the value of t when $N = c$:

$$N = N_0 e^{kt},$$

$$c = b e^{kt}$$

$$\frac{c}{b} = e^{kt}$$

$$\ln \frac{c}{b} = kt$$

$$\ln \frac{c}{b} = \frac{\ln \frac{1}{2}}{d} \cdot t$$

$$t = \frac{d \ln \frac{c}{b}}{\ln \frac{1}{2}}$$

85. $\log_{10} 8 + \log_{10} 3 - \log_{10} 12 = \log_{10} \left(\dfrac{8 \cdot 3}{12} \right) = \log_{10} 2$

87. $\ln 5 - 3 \ln 2 + \ln 16$ $= \ln 5 - \ln 2^3 + \ln 16$

$\qquad\qquad\qquad\qquad = \ln 5 - \ln 8 + \ln 16$

$\qquad\qquad\qquad\qquad = \ln \left(\dfrac{5 \cdot 16}{8} \right)$

$\qquad\qquad\qquad\qquad = \ln 10$

89. $a \ln x + b \ln y = \ln x^a + \ln y^b = \ln x^a y^b$

91. $\ln \sqrt{(x - 3)(x + 4)} = \dfrac{1}{2} \ln \big((x - 3)(x + 4) \big) = \dfrac{1}{2} \ln (x - 3) + \dfrac{1}{2} (x + 4)$

93. $\log_{10} \dfrac{x^3}{\sqrt{1 + x}}$ $= \log_{10} x^3 - \log_{10} \sqrt{1 + x}$

$\qquad\qquad\qquad = \log_{10} x^3 - \log_{10} (1 + x)^{1/2}$

$\qquad\qquad\qquad = 3 \log_{10} x - \dfrac{1}{2} \log_{10} (1 + x)$

95. $\log_{10} \sqrt[3]{\dfrac{x}{100}} = \log_{10} \left(\dfrac{x}{100}\right)^{1/3}$

$= \dfrac{1}{3} \log_{10} \dfrac{x}{100}$

$= \dfrac{1}{3} \log_{10} x - \dfrac{1}{3} \log_{10} 100$

$= \dfrac{1}{3} \log_{10} x - \dfrac{1}{3} \log_{10} 100$

$= \dfrac{1}{3} \log_{10} x - \dfrac{2}{3}$

97. $\ln \left(\dfrac{1 + 2e}{1 - 2e}\right)^3 = 3 \ln \dfrac{1 + 2e}{1 - 2e} = 3 \ln (1 + 2e) - 3 \ln (1 - 2e)$

99.   We use $B = P(1 + r)^t$ where $P = A$, $B = 2A$, $r = \dfrac{R}{100}$:

$2A = A \left(1 + \dfrac{R}{100}\right)^t$

$2 = \left(1 + \dfrac{R}{100}\right)^t$

$\ln 2 = t \ln \left(1 + \dfrac{R}{100}\right)$

$t = \dfrac{\ln 2}{\ln \left(1 + \dfrac{R}{100}\right)}$

101.   The balance after 1 year will be $A = P\left(1 + \dfrac{0.095}{12}\right)^{12}$. We must find the effective interest rate r where $A = P(1 + r)^1$. We set these equal:

$P(1 + r) = P \left(1 + \dfrac{0.095}{12}\right)^{12}$

$1 + r = \left(1 + \dfrac{0.095}{12}\right)^{12}$

$r = \left(1 + \dfrac{0.095}{12}\right)^{12} - 1$

$r \approx 0.0992$

So the effective interest rate is 9.92%.

384 Chapter 4 Exponential and Logarithmic Functions

103. We use $A = Pe^{rt}$ where $P = D$, $A = 2D$, and $r = \dfrac{R}{100}$:

$$2D = De^{(R/100)t}$$
$$2 = e^{(R/100)t}$$
$$\ln 2 = \dfrac{R}{100}(t)$$
$$t = \dfrac{100\ln 2}{R}$$

105. (a) We use $A = P\left(1 + \dfrac{r}{N}\right)^{Nt}$ where $P = \$660$, $r = .055$, $N = 4$, and $A = \$1000$:

$$1000 = 660\left(1 + \dfrac{.055}{4}\right)^{4t}$$
$$\dfrac{50}{33} = (1.01375)^{4t}$$
$$\ln\dfrac{50}{33} = 4t\ln 1.01375$$
$$t = \dfrac{\ln\dfrac{50}{33}}{4\ln 1.01375} \approx 7.61 \text{ yrs}$$

So the balance will reach $1000 after $7\dfrac{3}{4}$ yrs.

(b) We use $A = P\left(1 + \dfrac{r}{N}\right)^{Nt}$ where $P = D$, $r = \dfrac{R}{100}$, $N = 4$, and $A = nD$:

$$nD = D\left(1 + \dfrac{R}{400}\right)^{t}$$
$$n = \left(1 + \dfrac{R}{400}\right)^{t}$$
$$\ln n = t\ln\left(1 + \dfrac{R}{400}\right)$$
$$t = \dfrac{\ln n}{\ln\left(1 + \dfrac{R}{400}\right)}$$

107. (a) Domain is $x > 0$, or $(0, \infty)$

(b) We must make sure $\log_{10} x \geq 0$, so $x \geq 1$
So the domain is $x \geq 1$, or $[1, \infty)$

109.   (a)   We must make sure $x^2 - 2x - 15 \neq 0$
$(x - 5)(x + 3) \neq 0$
$x \neq 5, -3$
So the domain is all real numbers except 5 and -3, or
$(-\infty, -3) \cup (-3, 5) \cup (5, \infty)$.

(b)   We must make sure $x^2 - 2x - 15 > 0$
$(x - 5)(x + 3) > 0$
Key numbers: -3,5
From a sign chart, we find the domain is $x < -3$ or $x > 5$, or
$(-\infty, -3) \cup (5, \infty)$.

111.   We solve for x:

$$y = \frac{e^x + 1}{e^x - 1}$$

$$y(e^x - 1) = e^x + 1$$

$$ye^x - y = e^x + 1$$

$$ye^x - e^x = y + 1$$

$$e^x(y - 1) = y + 1$$

$$e^x = \frac{y + 1}{y - 1}$$

$$x = \ln \frac{y + 1}{y - 1}$$

So we must make sure $\frac{y + 1}{y - 1} > 0$:

Key numbers: 1, -1

Using a sign chart, the intervals are $y < -1$ or $y > 1$. So the range is
$(-\infty, -1) \cup (1, \infty)$.

113. $\ln 0.5 = \ln (2^{-1}) = -\ln 2 \approx -0.7$

115. $\ln \frac{1}{9} = \ln (3^{-2}) = -2 \ln 3 \approx -2(1.1) = -2.2$

117. $\ln 72 = \ln (3^2 \bullet 2^3)$
$= \ln (3^2) + \ln (2^3)$
$= 2 \ln 3 + 3 \ln 2$
$\approx 2(1.1) + 3(0.7)$
$= 2.2 + 2.1$
$= 4.3$

119.   Let $x = e$, then $\ln x = 1$. From the graph, we see $x \approx 2.7$.

121.　$\log_2 3 = \dfrac{\ln 3}{\ln 2} \approx \dfrac{1.1}{0.7} \approx 1.6$

123.　(a)　We complete the table:

Region	1990 Population (millions)	Growth Rate (%)	2025 Population
North America	275.2	0.7	351.6
Soviet Union	291.3	0.7	372.2
Europe	499.5	0.2	535.7
Nigeria	113.3	3.1	335.3

(b)　It will be 335.3 mil - 113.3 mil = 222.0 million

(c)　North America:　351.6 mil - 275.2 mil = 76.4 mil
　　Soviet Union:　372.2 mil - 291.3 mil = 80.9 mil
　　Europe:　535.7 mil - 499.5 mil = 36.2 mil
　　combined:　193.5 million

(d)　For Nigeria, our results support his projection.

125.　(a)　The corresponding x-coordinate when y = 3.000 is $x \approx 1.0986$

(b)　% error $= \dfrac{|1.0986 - \ln 3|}{\ln 3} \cdot 100 = 0.00112\,\%$

(c)　$\ln \sqrt{3} = \dfrac{1}{2} \ln 3 \approx \dfrac{1}{2}(1.0986) \approx 0.5493$

　　$\ln 9 = \ln(3^2) = 2 \ln 3 \approx 2(1.0986) \approx 2.1972$

　　$\ln \dfrac{1}{3} = \ln(3^{-1}) = -\ln 3 \approx -1.0986$

CHAPTER FIVE
TRIGONOMETRIC FUNCTIONS OF ANGLES

5.1 Trigonometric Functions of Acute Angles

1. (a) $8^2 + 15^2 = 17^2$
        $64 + 225 = 289$ √

    (b) $\sin \theta = \dfrac{\text{opposite}}{\text{hypotenuse}} = \dfrac{15}{17}$

         $\cos \beta = \dfrac{\text{adjacent}}{\text{hypotenuse}} = \dfrac{15}{17}$

    (c) $\cos \theta = \dfrac{\text{adjacent}}{\text{hypotenuse}} = \dfrac{8}{17}$

         $\sin \beta = \dfrac{\text{opposite}}{\text{hypotenuse}} = \dfrac{8}{17}$

    (d) $\tan \theta = \dfrac{\text{opposite}}{\text{adjacent}} = \dfrac{15}{8}$

         $\csc \theta = \dfrac{\text{hypotenuse}}{\text{opposite}} = \dfrac{17}{15}$

         $\sec \theta = \dfrac{\text{hypotenuse}}{\text{adjacent}} = \dfrac{17}{8}$

         $\cot \theta = \dfrac{\text{adjacent}}{\text{opposite}} = \dfrac{8}{15}$

(e) $\tan \beta = \dfrac{\text{opposite}}{\text{adjacent}} = \dfrac{8}{15}$

$\csc \beta = \dfrac{\text{hypotenuse}}{\text{opposite}} = \dfrac{17}{8}$

$\sec \beta = \dfrac{\text{hypotenuse}}{\text{adjacent}} = \dfrac{17}{15}$

$\cot \beta = \dfrac{\text{adjacent}}{\text{opposite}} = \dfrac{15}{8}$

3.   We draw the figure:

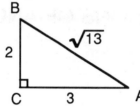

(a) $\sin A = \dfrac{2}{\sqrt{13}} = \dfrac{2\sqrt{13}}{13} \;;\; \cos A = \dfrac{3}{\sqrt{13}} = \dfrac{3\sqrt{13}}{13} \;;\; \tan A = \dfrac{2}{3}$

(b) $\sin^2 A + \cos^2 A = \left(\dfrac{2}{\sqrt{13}}\right)^2 + \left(\dfrac{3}{\sqrt{13}}\right)^2 = \dfrac{4}{13} + \dfrac{9}{13} = 1$

$\dfrac{\sin A}{\cos A} = \dfrac{2/\sqrt{13}}{3/\sqrt{13}} = \dfrac{2}{3} = \tan A$

(c) $\cos B = \dfrac{2}{\sqrt{13}} = \dfrac{2\sqrt{13}}{13}$

$\sin^2 A + \cos^2 B = \left(\dfrac{2}{\sqrt{13}}\right)^2 + \left(\dfrac{2}{\sqrt{13}}\right)^2 = \dfrac{4}{13} + \dfrac{4}{13} = \dfrac{8}{13} \neq 1$

5.   We draw the figure:

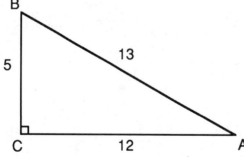

$\sin A = \dfrac{5}{13} \;;\; \cos A = \dfrac{12}{13} \;;\; \tan A = \dfrac{5}{12} \;;\; \sec A = \dfrac{13}{12} \;;\; \csc A = \dfrac{13}{5} \;;\; \cot A = \dfrac{12}{5}$

7.   We draw the figure:

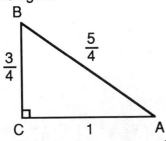

(a) $\sin B = \dfrac{1}{5/4} = \dfrac{4}{5}$; $\cos A = \dfrac{1}{5/4} = \dfrac{4}{5}$

(b) $\cos B = \dfrac{3/4}{5/4} = \dfrac{3}{5}$; $\sin A = \dfrac{3/4}{5/4} = \dfrac{3}{5}$

(c) $\tan A = \dfrac{3/4}{1} = \dfrac{3}{4}$ and $\tan B = \dfrac{1}{3/4} = \dfrac{4}{3}$, so:

$$(\tan A)(\tan B) = \left(\dfrac{3}{4}\right)\left(\dfrac{4}{3}\right) = 1$$

9.   We draw the figure:

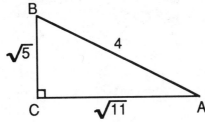

(a) $\sin A = \dfrac{\sqrt{5}}{4}$; $\cos A = \dfrac{\sqrt{11}}{4}$

$$\sin^2 A + \cos^2 A = \left(\dfrac{\sqrt{5}}{4}\right)^2 + \left(\dfrac{\sqrt{11}}{4}\right)^2 = \dfrac{5}{16} + \dfrac{11}{16} = 1$$

(b) $\tan B = \dfrac{\sqrt{11}}{\sqrt{5}} = \dfrac{\sqrt{55}}{5}$; $\sin B = \dfrac{\sqrt{11}}{4}$; $\cos B = \dfrac{\sqrt{5}}{4}$

$$\dfrac{\sin B}{\cos B} = \dfrac{\sqrt{11}/4}{\sqrt{5}/4} = \dfrac{\sqrt{11}}{\sqrt{5}} = \dfrac{\sqrt{55}}{5} = \tan B$$

11. $\cos 60° = \dfrac{1}{2}$

$\cos^2 30° - \sin^2 30° = \left(\dfrac{\sqrt{3}}{2}\right)^2 - \left(\dfrac{1}{2}\right)^2 = \dfrac{3}{4} - \dfrac{1}{4} = \dfrac{1}{2}$

So $\cos 60° = \cos^2 30° - \sin^2 30°$.

13. $\sin^2 30° + \sin^2 45° + \sin^2 60° = \left(\dfrac{1}{2}\right)^2 + \left(\dfrac{\sqrt{2}}{2}\right)^2 + \left(\dfrac{\sqrt{3}}{2}\right)^2$

$= \dfrac{1}{4} + \dfrac{1}{2} + \dfrac{3}{4}$

$= \dfrac{6}{4}$

$= \dfrac{3}{2}$

15. $2 \sin 30° \cos 30° = 2 \left(\dfrac{1}{2}\right)\left(\dfrac{\sqrt{3}}{2}\right) = \dfrac{\sqrt{3}}{2}$

$\sin 60° = \dfrac{\sqrt{3}}{2}$

So $2 \sin 30° \cos 30° = \sin 60°$

17. $\sqrt{\dfrac{1 - \cos 60°}{2}} = \sqrt{\dfrac{1 - \dfrac{1}{2}}{2}} = \sqrt{\dfrac{1}{4}} = \dfrac{1}{2} = \sin 30°$

19. $\dfrac{\sin 60°}{1 + \cos 60°} = \dfrac{\dfrac{\sqrt{3}}{2}}{1 + \dfrac{1}{2}} = \dfrac{\sqrt{3}/2}{3/2} = \dfrac{\sqrt{3}}{3} = \tan 30°$

21. $1 + \tan^2 45° = 1 + (1)^2 = 2$

$\sec^2 45° = \left(\dfrac{2}{\sqrt{2}}\right)^2 = \dfrac{4}{2} = 2$

So $1 + \tan^2 45° = \sec^2 45°$

23. We draw the figure:

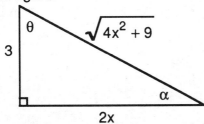

(a) $\sin \theta = \dfrac{2x}{\sqrt{4x^2 + 9}} = \dfrac{2x\sqrt{4x^2 + 9}}{4x^2 + 9}$

$\cos \theta = \dfrac{3}{\sqrt{4x^2 + 9}} = \dfrac{3\sqrt{4x^2 + 9}}{4x^2 + 9}$

$\tan \theta = \dfrac{2x}{3}$

(b) $\sin^2 \theta = \dfrac{4x^2}{4x^2 + 9}$; $\cos^2 \theta = \dfrac{9}{4x^2 + 9}$; $\tan^2 \theta = \dfrac{4x^2}{9}$

(c) $\sin (90° - \theta) = \sin \alpha = \dfrac{3}{\sqrt{4x^2 + 9}} = \dfrac{3\sqrt{4x^2 + 9}}{4x^2 + 9}$

$\cos (90° - \theta) = \cos \alpha = \dfrac{2x}{\sqrt{4x^2 + 9}} = \dfrac{2x\sqrt{4x^2 + 9}}{4x^2 + 9}$

$\tan (90° - \theta) = \tan \alpha = \dfrac{3}{2x}$

25. We draw the figure:

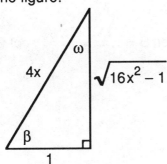

(a) $\sin \beta = \dfrac{\sqrt{16x^2 - 1}}{4x}$; $\cos \beta = \dfrac{1}{4x}$; $\tan \beta = \dfrac{\sqrt{16x^2 - 1}}{1} = \sqrt{16x^2 - 1}$

(b) $\csc \beta = \dfrac{4x}{\sqrt{16x^2 - 1}} = \dfrac{4x\sqrt{16x^2 - 1}}{16x^2 - 1}$

   $\sec \beta = \dfrac{4x}{1} = 4x$

   $\cot \beta = \dfrac{1}{\sqrt{16x^2 - 1}} = \dfrac{\sqrt{16x^2 - 1}}{16x^2 - 1}$

(c) $\sin(90° - \beta) = \sin \omega = \dfrac{1}{4x}$

   $\cos(90° - \beta) = \cos \omega = \dfrac{\sqrt{16x^2 - 1}}{4x}$

   $\tan(90° - \beta) = \tan \omega = \dfrac{1}{\sqrt{16x^2 - 1}} = \dfrac{\sqrt{16x^2 - 1}}{16x^2 - 1}$

27.   We draw the figure:

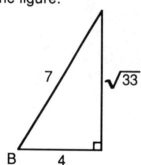

$\sin B = \dfrac{\sqrt{33}}{7}$; $\tan B = \dfrac{\sqrt{33}}{4}$; $\sec B = \dfrac{7}{4}$; $\csc B = \dfrac{7}{\sqrt{33}} = \dfrac{7\sqrt{33}}{33}$; $\cot B = \dfrac{4}{\sqrt{33}} = \dfrac{4\sqrt{33}}{33}$

29.   We draw the figure:

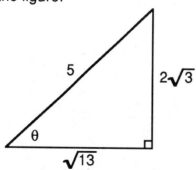

$$\cos \theta = \frac{\sqrt{13}}{5} \; ; \tan \theta = \frac{2\sqrt{3}}{\sqrt{13}} = \frac{2\sqrt{39}}{13} \; ; \sec \theta = \frac{5}{\sqrt{13}} = \frac{5\sqrt{13}}{13} \; ;$$

$$\csc \theta = \frac{5}{2\sqrt{3}} = \frac{5\sqrt{3}}{6} \; ; \cot \theta = \frac{\sqrt{13}}{2\sqrt{3}} = \frac{\sqrt{39}}{6}$$

31. We draw the figure:

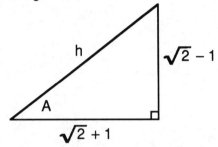

We find side h:

$$(\sqrt{2} + 1)^2 + (\sqrt{2} - 1)^2 = h^2$$
$$3 + 2\sqrt{2} + 3 - 2\sqrt{2} = h^2$$
$$6 = h^2$$
$$h = \sqrt{6}$$

$$\sin A = \frac{\sqrt{2} - 1}{\sqrt{6}} = \frac{2\sqrt{3} - \sqrt{6}}{6} \; ; \cos A = \frac{\sqrt{2} + 1}{\sqrt{6}} = \frac{2\sqrt{3} + \sqrt{6}}{6} \; ;$$

$$\sec A = \frac{\sqrt{6}}{\sqrt{2} + 1} = 2\sqrt{3} - \sqrt{6} \; ; \csc A = \frac{\sqrt{6}}{\sqrt{2} - 1} = 2\sqrt{3} + \sqrt{6} \; ;$$

$$\cot A = \frac{\sqrt{2} + 1}{\sqrt{2} - 1} = 3 + 2\sqrt{2}$$

33. We draw the figure:

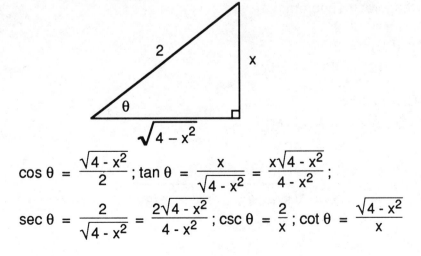

$$\cos \theta = \frac{\sqrt{4 - x^2}}{2} \; ; \tan \theta = \frac{x}{\sqrt{4 - x^2}} = \frac{x\sqrt{4 - x^2}}{4 - x^2} \; ;$$

$$\sec \theta = \frac{2}{\sqrt{4 - x^2}} = \frac{2\sqrt{4 - x^2}}{4 - x^2} \; ; \csc \theta = \frac{2}{x} \; ; \cot \theta = \frac{\sqrt{4 - x^2}}{x}$$

35.   We draw the figure:

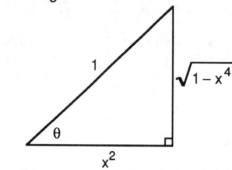

$$\sin \theta = \frac{\sqrt{1 - x^4}}{1} = \sqrt{1 - x^4}; \ \tan \theta = \frac{\sqrt{1 - x^4}}{x^2}; \ \sec \theta = \frac{1}{x^2};$$

$$\csc \theta = \frac{1}{\sqrt{1 - x^4}} = \frac{\sqrt{1 - x^4}}{1 - x^4}; \ \cot \theta = \frac{x^2}{\sqrt{1 - x^4}} = \frac{x^2 \sqrt{1 - x^4}}{1 - x^4}$$

37.   (a) $\cos 30° \approx .86603$; $\cos 45° \approx .70711$; $\sin 60° \approx .86603$

(b) $\cos 30° = \sin 60° = \dfrac{\sqrt{3}}{2} \approx .86603$; $\cos 45° = \dfrac{\sqrt{2}}{2} \approx .70711$

39. $\csc 25° \approx 2.36620$; $\sec 25° \approx 1.10338$; $\cot 25° \approx 2.14451$

41.   (a) $\sin \beta$ is larger

(b) $\csc \theta = \dfrac{1}{\sin \theta}$ and $\csc \beta = \dfrac{1}{\sin \beta}$. Since $\sin \beta > \sin \theta$, then $\csc \theta$ is larger.

(c) $\cos \theta$ is larger

43.   Extending AB to D an equal distance to AB guarantees $\triangle DBC$ congruent to $\triangle ABC$. Now $\triangle ADC$ is equilateral as each angle is 60°. By construction AD = 2AB and since the triangle is equilateral, AC = AD, hence AC = 2AB.

45.   (a)   By the Pythagorean Theorem:
$$(BC)^2 + (1)^2 = 2^2$$
$$(BC)^2 = 3$$
$$BC = \sqrt{3}$$

(b)   Using $\triangle ACD$, we have:
$$(2 + \sqrt{3})^2 + (1)^2 = (AD)^2$$
$$4 + 4\sqrt{3} + 4 = (AD)^2$$
$$8 + 4\sqrt{3} = (AD)^2$$
$$AD = \sqrt{8 + 4\sqrt{3}} = 2\sqrt{2 + \sqrt{3}}$$

(c) Using the hint:

$$(AD)^2 = 8 + 4\sqrt{3}$$
$$(\sqrt{6} + \sqrt{2})^2 = 6 + 2\sqrt{12} + 2 = 8 + 4\sqrt{3}$$

So $AD = \sqrt{6} + \sqrt{2}$

(d) $\angle BAD = \angle BDA$ because they are the base angles of an isoceles triangle ($\triangle ABD$)

(e) By the theorem, $\angle BAD + \angle BDA = 30°$, and since part (d) shows that these angles are equal, then:

$$2\,(\angle BAD) = 30°$$
$$\angle BAD = 15°$$

(f) $\sin 15° = \dfrac{1}{\sqrt{6} + \sqrt{2}}$ and $\cos 15° = \dfrac{2 + \sqrt{3}}{\sqrt{6} + \sqrt{2}}$

(g) Rationalizing denominators:

$$\sin 15° = \frac{\sqrt{6} - \sqrt{2}}{6 - 2} = \frac{\sqrt{6} - \sqrt{2}}{4}$$

$$\cos 15° = \frac{(2 + \sqrt{3})(\sqrt{6} - \sqrt{2})}{6 - 2}$$

$$= \frac{2\sqrt{6} + \sqrt{18} - 2\sqrt{2} - \sqrt{6}}{4}$$

$$= \frac{\sqrt{6} + \sqrt{2}}{4}$$

(h) $\sin 15° \approx 0.25882$ and $\cos 15° \approx 0.96593$, which agree with the radical calculations

47. (a) $\angle ADC = 180° - 36° - 36° = 108°$
$\angle BDC = 180° - 108° = 72°$
$\angle B = 180° - 72° - 72° = 36°$

(b) $\angle A = \angle B$ because both are 36°. Therefore $\triangle ACB$ is isosceles with $AC = BC$. Also, $\angle BDC = \angle BCD = 72°$, and therefore $\triangle BDC$ is isosceles with $BC = BD$. Thus we have $AC = BC = BD$.

(c) $\angle DAC = \angle DCA = 36°$. So $\triangle DAC$ is isosceles with $AD = CD$. Therefore $CD = 1$ because $AD = 1$.

(d) ΔDAC is similar to ΔCAB (because both are isosceles triangles with base angles of 30°). Therefore, $\dfrac{AC}{AB} = \dfrac{AD}{AC}$. That is:

$$\frac{x}{1+x} = \frac{1}{x}$$
$$x^2 = 1+x$$
$$x^2 - x - 1 = 0$$

This last equation can be solved by means of the quadratic formula.

The result is $x = \dfrac{1 \pm \sqrt{5}}{2}$. We want the positive root here, because the

length x is positive. Thus $x = \dfrac{1 + \sqrt{5}}{2}$.

(e) In right triangle BFC we have:

$$\sin 18° = \frac{FC}{BC} = \frac{1/2}{x} = \frac{1/2}{\left(\dfrac{1+\sqrt{5}}{2}\right)} = \frac{1}{1+\sqrt{5}}$$

(f) Rationalizing the denominator, we have:

$$\frac{1}{1+\sqrt{5}} \bullet \frac{1-\sqrt{5}}{1-\sqrt{5}} = \frac{1-\sqrt{5}}{1-5} = \frac{1-\sqrt{5}}{-4} = \frac{\sqrt{5}-1}{4}$$

Thus, $\sin 18° = \dfrac{\sqrt{5}-1}{4}$

(g)
$$\cos 18° = \sqrt{1 - \sin^2 18°}$$
$$= \sqrt{1 - \left(\frac{\sqrt{5}-1}{4}\right)^2}$$
$$= \sqrt{\frac{16}{16} - \frac{5 - 2\sqrt{5} + 1}{16}}$$
$$= \sqrt{\frac{10 + 2\sqrt{5}}{16}}$$
$$= \frac{\sqrt{10 + 2\sqrt{5}}}{4}$$

5.2 <u>Right Triangle Applications</u>

1. We draw the figure:

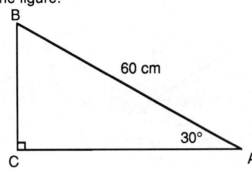

$\sin 30° = \dfrac{BC}{60}$, so BC $= 60 \sin 30° = 60 \left(\dfrac{1}{2}\right) = 30$ cm

$\cos 30° = \dfrac{AC}{60}$, so AC $= 60 \cos 30° = 60 \left(\dfrac{\sqrt{3}}{2}\right) = 30\sqrt{3}$ cm

3. We draw the figure:

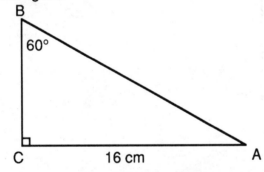

$\sin 60° = \dfrac{16}{AB}$, so AB $= \dfrac{16}{\sin 60°} = \dfrac{16}{\sqrt{3}/2} = \dfrac{32}{\sqrt{3}} = \dfrac{32\sqrt{3}}{3}$ cm

$\tan 60° = \dfrac{16}{BC}$, so BC $= \dfrac{16}{\tan 60°} = \dfrac{16}{\sqrt{3}} = \dfrac{16\sqrt{3}}{3}$ cm

5.   We draw the figure:

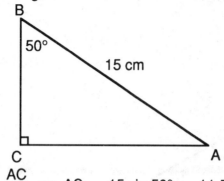

$\sin 50° = \dfrac{AC}{15}$, so $AC = 15 \sin 50° \approx 11.5$ cm

$\cos 50° = \dfrac{BC}{15}$, so $BC = 15 \cos 50° \approx 9.6$ cm

7.   We draw a figure:

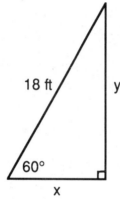

(a)   We are asked to find y:

$$\sin 60° = \dfrac{y}{18}$$
$$y = 18 \sin 60°$$
$$y = 18 \left(\dfrac{\sqrt{3}}{2} \right)$$
$$y = 9\sqrt{3} \text{ ft}$$

Using a calculator, this is approximately 15.59 ft

(b)   We are asked to find x:

$$\cos 60° = \dfrac{x}{18}$$
$$x = 18 \cos 60°$$
$$x = 18 \left(\dfrac{1}{2} \right)$$
$$x = 9 \text{ ft}$$

9. Using the sine function we have that sin ∠SEM = $\frac{MS}{SE}$, so:

$$\sin 21.16° = \frac{MS}{93000000}$$

Thus MS is about 34 million miles.

11. (a) The height is 3 sin 30°, so:
$$\text{Area} = \frac{1}{2}(2 \text{ in.})(3 \sin 30° \text{ in.}) = 1.5 \text{ in.}^2$$

(b) The height is 6 sin 70°, so:
$$\text{Area} = \frac{1}{2}(4 \text{ cm})(6 \sin 70° \text{ cm}) \approx 11.28 \text{ cm}^2$$

13. We form 10 triangles, each with a central angle of 36°. Then:
$$\begin{aligned}\text{Area of decagon} &= 10 \text{ (area of triangle)}\\ &= 10\left(\frac{1}{2}\right)(20)(20 \sin 36°)\\ &= 2000 \sin 36° \text{ cm}^2\\ &\approx 1175.6 \text{ cm}^2\end{aligned}$$

15. We draw the figure:

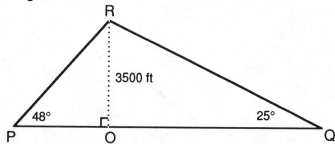

$$\tan 48° = \frac{3500}{PO} \text{ and } \tan 25° = \frac{3500}{OQ}$$

So $PO = \dfrac{3500}{\tan 48°}$ and $OQ = \dfrac{3500}{\tan 25°}$

Thus $PQ = \dfrac{3500}{\tan 48°} + \dfrac{3500}{\tan 25°} \approx 10{,}660 \text{ ft}$

17. We draw a figure:

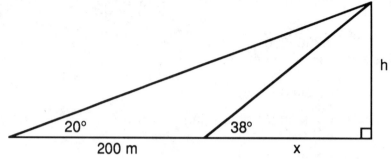

Now tan 38° $= \dfrac{h}{x}$, so x $= \dfrac{h}{\tan 38°}$

Also tan 20° $= \dfrac{h}{200 + x}$, so h $= (200 + x) \tan 20°$

Substituting, we have:

$$h = \left(200 + \dfrac{h}{\tan 38°} \right) \tan 20°$$

$$h \tan 38° = 200 \tan 38° \tan 20° + h \tan 20°$$

$$h (\tan 38° - \tan 20°) = 200 \tan 38° \tan 20°$$

$$h = \dfrac{200 \tan 38° \tan 20°}{\tan 38° - \tan 20°}$$

$$h \approx 136 \text{ m}$$

19. We draw the figure:

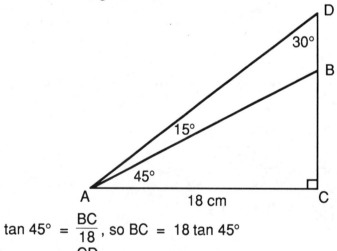

$$\tan 45° = \dfrac{BC}{18} \text{, so } BC = 18 \tan 45°$$

$$\tan 60° = \dfrac{CD}{18} \text{, so } CD = 18 \tan 60°$$

So   BD $= CD - BC$
$= 18(\tan 60° - \tan 45°)$
$= 18(\sqrt{3} - 1)$ cm

21. (a) $\angle BOA = 90° - \theta$
$\angle OAB = \theta$, since both angles are complementary to the same angle ($\angle AOB$).
$\angle BAP = 90° - \theta$
$\angle BPA = \theta$, since $\angle BPA$ and $\angle OAB$ are both complementary to the same angle ($\angle BAP$)

(b) Using $\triangle AOP$, we have:
$$\sin \theta = \frac{AO}{OP} = \frac{AO}{1}, \text{ so } AO = \sin \theta$$
$$\cos \theta = \frac{AP}{OP} = \frac{AP}{1}, \text{ so } AP = \cos \theta$$
Using $\triangle AOB$, we have:
$$\sin \theta = \frac{OB}{OA} = \frac{OB}{\sin \theta}, \text{ so } OB = \sin^2 \theta$$
Using $\triangle ABP$, we have:
$$\cos \theta = \frac{BP}{AP} = \frac{BP}{\cos \theta}, \text{ so } BP = \cos^2 \theta$$

23. (a) $\sin \theta = \frac{4}{5} = 0.8$, so $\theta \approx 53.1°$

(b) $\tan \theta = \frac{12}{5} = 2.4$, so $\theta \approx 67.4°$

(c) $\sin \theta = \frac{6}{8} = 0.75$, so $\theta \approx 48.6°$

25. Examine the similar triangles having AB and BC as hypotenuses, and notice that θ is also the angle at B in the smaller triangle. We will write trigonometric relationships for each triangle, solve for AB and BC, and then add to get AC:
$$\sin \theta = \frac{5}{BC}, \text{ so } BC = \frac{5}{\sin \theta}$$
$$\cos \theta = \frac{4}{AB}, \text{ so } AB = \frac{4}{\cos \theta}$$

Now AC = AB + BC and therefore:
$$AC = \frac{4}{\cos \theta} + \frac{5}{\sin \theta} = \frac{4 \sin \theta + 5 \cos \theta}{\sin \theta \cos \theta} = 4 \sec \theta + 5 \csc \theta$$

27. First observe that the figure $x^2 + y^2 = 1$ is a circle with a radius of one. Then any segment which is a radius can be replaced by one. In each case, we will look for a trigonometric relationship involving the required segment:

(a) $\sin \theta = \dfrac{DE}{OD}$, so $DE = \sin \theta$

(b) $\cos \theta = \dfrac{OE}{OD}$, so $OE = \cos \theta$

(c) $\tan \theta = \dfrac{CF}{OF}$, so $CF = \tan \theta$

(d) $\sec \theta = \dfrac{OC}{OF}$, so $OC = \sec \theta$

Going to $\triangle OAB$, $\angle B = \theta$, and

(e) $\cot \theta = \dfrac{AB}{OA}$, so $AB = \cot \theta$

(f) $\csc \theta = \dfrac{OB}{OA}$, so $OB = \csc \theta$

These segments are sometimes called the line values of the six trigonometric functions.

29. Since $\sin \theta = \dfrac{r}{PS + r}$ then:

(a) $(r + PS) \sin \theta = r$ and $r (1 - \sin \theta) = PS \sin \theta$

So $r = PS \left(\dfrac{\sin \theta}{1 - \sin \theta} \right)$

(b) $r = (238,857) \left(\dfrac{\sin (0.257°)}{1 - \sin (0.257°)} \right) \approx 1080$ miles

31. (a) We draw the figure:

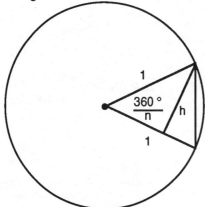

Since $h = \sin\dfrac{360°}{n}$, then the area of this triangle is $\dfrac{1}{2}\left(\sin\dfrac{360°}{n}\right)$. Since there are n congruent triangles in an n-gon, then the area is $\dfrac{n}{2}\sin\left(\dfrac{360°}{n}\right)$.

(b) We complete the table:

n	5	10	50	100	1,000	5,000	10,000
A_n	2.38	2.94	3.1333	3.1395	3.141572	3.1415918	3.1415924

(c) As n gets larger, A_n becomes closer to the area of the circle, which is π.

33. We draw the figure:

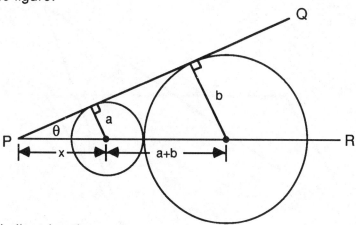

Using the similar triangles:

$$\sin\theta = \frac{a}{x} \quad\text{and}\quad \sin\theta = \frac{b}{x + a + b}$$

So $\sin\theta = \dfrac{b}{\dfrac{a}{\sin\theta} + a + b} = \dfrac{b\sin\theta}{a + (a+b)\sin\theta}$

$a\sin\theta + (a+b)\sin^2\theta = b\sin\theta$

$a + (a+b)\sin\theta = b$ and $\sin\theta = \dfrac{b-a}{a+b}$ (assuming $\theta \neq 0$, which will always occur).

Since $\cos^2\theta + \sin^2\theta = 1$, then:

$$\begin{aligned}
\cos\theta &= \sqrt{1 - \sin^2\theta} \\
&= \sqrt{1 - \frac{(b-a)^2}{(a+b)^2}} \\
&= \sqrt{\frac{a^2 + 2ab + b^2 - b^2 + 2ab - a^2}{(a+b)^2}} \\
&= \sqrt{\frac{4ab}{(a+b)^2}} \\
&= \frac{2\sqrt{ab}}{a+b}
\end{aligned}$$

35.   We draw the figure:

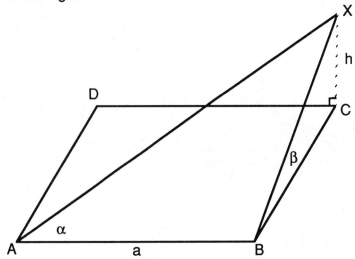

We are asked to find h. Using $\triangle ABX$ (which is a right triangle), we have:

$$\tan\alpha = \frac{BX}{a}, \quad BX = a\tan\alpha$$

Now, using $\triangle BCX$, we have:

$$\sin\beta = \frac{CX}{BX} = \frac{h}{a\tan\alpha}, \text{ so } h = a\tan\alpha\sin\beta \text{ ft}$$

5.3 Trigonometric Functions of General Angles

1. (a) reference angle: 70°

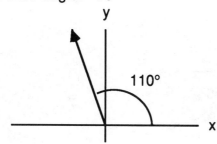

    (b) reference angle: 60°

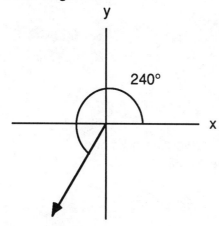

    (c) reference angle: 60°

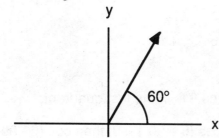

(d)   reference angle: 60°

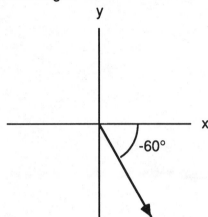

3.   (a) $\cos 0° = 1$
      (b) $\sin 450° = \sin 90° = 1$
      (c) $\sin 270° = -\sin 90° = -1$
      (d) $\sin (-630°) = \sin 90° = 1$

5.   (a) $\csc (-90°) = \dfrac{1}{\sin (-90°)} = \dfrac{1}{-1} = -1$

      (b) $\cot 720° = \cot 0° = \dfrac{\cos 0°}{\sin 0°}$ which is undefined

      (c) $\cos (-540) = \cos 180° = -1$
      (d) $\sin 810° = \sin 90° = 1$

7.   (a) $\cos \theta = \dfrac{3}{4}$

      (b) $\sin \theta = \sqrt{1 - \left(\dfrac{3}{4}\right)^2} = \sqrt{\dfrac{7}{16}} = \dfrac{\sqrt{7}}{4}$

            $\tan \theta = \dfrac{\sqrt{7}/4}{3/4} = \dfrac{\sqrt{7}}{3}$
            Both values are positive, since θ is in the first quadrant.

      (c)   Since $\cos (\beta - 90°) > 0$ and $\cos (\theta + 90°) < 0$, then $\cos (\beta - 90°)$ is larger.

9.   In each case we will follow a three-step procedure: find the reference angle, recall the value of the trigonometric function for that angle, and then apply a positive or negative value depending on the quadrant.

(a) $\sin 315°$: reference angle is $45°$

$$\sin 45° = \frac{\sqrt{2}}{2}$$

4th quadrant therefore negative

So $\sin 315° = -\dfrac{\sqrt{2}}{2}$

(b) $\cos 300°$: reference angle is $60°$

$$\cos 60° = \frac{1}{2}$$

4th quadrant, so it's positive

So $\cos 300° = \dfrac{1}{2}$

(c) Using a similar process, we find:

$$\tan 330° = -\tan 30° = -\frac{\sqrt{3}}{3}$$

(d) $\sin(-315°) = \sin 45° = \dfrac{\sqrt{2}}{2}$

11. (a) $\tan 135° = -\tan 45° = -1$

(b) $\cot 120° = -\cot 60° = -\dfrac{\sqrt{3}}{3}$

(c) $\cot 480° = -\cot 60° = -\dfrac{\sqrt{3}}{3}$

(d) $\tan(-135°) = \tan 45° = 1$

13. $\sin(-30°) = -\dfrac{1}{2}$; $\csc(-30°) = -2$; $\cos(-30°) = \dfrac{\sqrt{3}}{2}$

$\sec(-30°) = \dfrac{2}{\sqrt{3}} = \dfrac{2\sqrt{3}}{3}$; $\cot(-30°) = -\dfrac{3}{\sqrt{3}} = -\sqrt{3}$; $\tan(-30°) = -\dfrac{\sqrt{3}}{3}$

15. (a) We draw the chart:

θ	0°	90°	180°	270°	360°	450°	540°	630°	720°
$\sin\theta$	0	1	0	−1	0	1	0	−1	0
$\cos\theta$	1	0	−1	0	1	0	−1	0	1

(b)   We draw the chart:

θ	30°	60°	90°	120°	150°	180°	210°	240°	270°	300°	330°	360°
sin θ	$\frac{1}{2}$	$\frac{\sqrt{3}}{2}$	1	$\frac{\sqrt{3}}{2}$	$\frac{1}{2}$	0	$-\frac{1}{2}$	$-\frac{\sqrt{3}}{2}$	−1	$-\frac{\sqrt{3}}{2}$	$-\frac{1}{2}$	0

17.   We draw the angle:

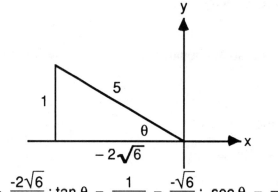

$$\cos \theta = \frac{-2\sqrt{6}}{5} \; ; \tan \theta = \frac{1}{-2\sqrt{6}} = \frac{-\sqrt{6}}{12} \; ; \; \sec \theta = \frac{-5}{2\sqrt{6}} = \frac{-5\sqrt{6}}{12} \; ;$$

$$\csc \theta = \frac{5}{1} = 5; \; \cot \theta = \frac{-2\sqrt{6}}{1} = -2\sqrt{6}$$

19.   We draw the angle:

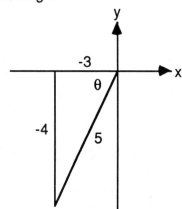

$$\sin \theta = \frac{-4}{5} \; ; \; \tan \theta = \frac{4}{3} \; ; \sec \theta = \frac{-5}{3} \; ; \; \csc \theta = \frac{-5}{4} \; ; \; \cot \theta = \frac{3}{4}$$

21. We draw the figure:

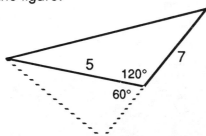

Area $= \frac{1}{2} (7)(5 \sin 60°) = \left(\frac{35}{2}\right)\left(\frac{\sqrt{3}}{2}\right) = \frac{35\sqrt{3}}{4}$ cm^2

23. We draw the figure:

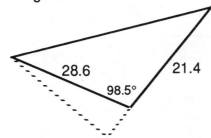

Area $= \frac{1}{2}$ (21.4)(28.6 sin 98.5°) $\approx$ 302.7 cm^2

25. sin 90° = 1, sin 450° = 1, sin (-270°) = 1 (other answers possible)

27. (a)   sin 10° ≈ 0.17; cos 10° ≈ 0.99
     (b)   sin 20° ≈ 0.34; cos 20° ≈ 0.94
     (c)   sin 30° ≈ 0.50; cos 30° ≈ 0.87
     (d)   sin 40° ≈ 0.64; cos 40° ≈ 0.77
     (e)   sin 50° ≈ 0.77; cos 50° ≈ 0.64
     (f)   sin 70° ≈ 0.94; cos 70° ≈ 0.34
     (g)   sin 80° ≈ 0.99; cos 80° ≈ 0.17
     (h)   sin 100° ≈ 0.99 , since sin 100° = sin 80°
           cos 100° ≈ -0.17 , since cos 100° = - cos 80°
     (i)   sin 130° ≈ 0.77 , since sin 130° = sin 50°
           cos 130° ≈ -0.64 , since cos 130° = - cos 50°

29. (a) $\sin 195° = -\sin 15° = \frac{1}{4}(\sqrt{2} - \sqrt{6})$

(b) $\cos 162° = -\cos 18° = -\frac{1}{4}\sqrt{10 + 2\sqrt{5}}$

(c) $\tan 345° = -\dfrac{\sin 15°}{\cos 15°}$

$$= \frac{\frac{1}{4}(\sqrt{2} - \sqrt{6})}{\sqrt{1 - \left(\frac{1}{4}(\sqrt{6} - \sqrt{2})\right)^2}}$$

$$= \frac{\frac{1}{4}(\sqrt{2} - \sqrt{6})}{\sqrt{1 - \frac{1}{16}(6 - 4\sqrt{3} + 2)}}$$

$$= \frac{\frac{1}{4}(\sqrt{2} - \sqrt{6})}{\sqrt{1 - \frac{1}{2} + \frac{\sqrt{3}}{4}}}$$

$$= \frac{\frac{1}{4}(\sqrt{2} - \sqrt{6})}{\sqrt{\frac{1}{2} + \frac{\sqrt{3}}{4}}}$$

$$= \frac{1}{2}\left(\frac{\sqrt{2} - \sqrt{6}}{\sqrt{2 + \sqrt{3}}}\right)$$

(d) $\sin(-15°) = -\sin 15° = \frac{1}{4}(\sqrt{2} - \sqrt{6})$

(e) $\cos(-18°) = \cos 18° = \frac{1}{4}\sqrt{10 + 2\sqrt{5}}$

(f) $\cos(918°) = -\cos 18° = -\frac{1}{4}\sqrt{10 + 2\sqrt{5}}$

31. (a)   P(cos θ, sin θ); Q(cos φ, sin φ)

(b)   Using the distance formula:

$$PQ = \sqrt{(\cos\theta - \cos\phi)^2 + (\sin\theta - \sin\phi)^2}$$
$$= \sqrt{\cos^2\theta - 2\cos\theta\cos\phi + \cos^2\phi + \sin^2\theta - 2\sin\theta\sin\phi + \sin^2\phi}$$
$$= \sqrt{2 - 2\cos\theta\cos\phi - 2\sin\theta\sin\phi}$$
$$= \sqrt{2}\sqrt{1 - \cos\theta\cos\phi - \sin\theta\sin\phi}$$

33. $2\log_{10}\sin\theta = \log_{10}\sin^2\theta$
$$= \log_{10}(1 - \cos^2\theta)$$
$$= \log_{10}[(1 - \cos\theta)(1 + \cos\theta)]$$
$$= \log_{10}(1 - \cos\theta) + \log_{10}(1 + \cos\theta)$$

The expression $2\log_{10}\sin^2\theta$ is valid only if $\sin\theta$ is positive. The restriction $0° < \theta < 180°$ guarantees that $\sin\theta$ will be positive, and thus $\log_{10}\sin\theta$ is defined.

35. (a)   Since OP and OQ are both radii of the same circle then they are equal. So ΔOPQ is isosceles and the base angles PQO and QPO are equal, and thus ∠PQO = 30°.

(b)   They are opposite interior angles and thus equal.

(c)   Since ∠QCO and ∠PCO are 90°, then ∠QOC and ∠POC are each 60°, thus we have side-angle-side equality and thus the two triangles are congruent.

(d)   CQ = CP as they are corresponding parts of congruent triangles, and hence the x-coordinate are equal but of opposite sign.

37. For θ = 0°:
cos (180° - 0°) = cos 180° = -1 and -cos 0° = -1, so:
    cos (180° - 0°) = -cos 0°
sin (180° - 0°) = sin 180° = 0 and sin 0° = 0, so:
    sin (180° - 0°) = sin 0°
For θ = 90°:
cos (180° - 90°) = cos 90° = 0 and -cos 90° = 0, so:
    cos (180° - 90°) = -cos 90°
sin (180° - 90°) = sin 90° = 1 and sin 90° = 1, so:
    sin (180° - 90°) = sin 90°

For $\theta = 180°$:
$$\cos(180° - 180°) = \cos 0° = 1 \text{ and } -\cos 180° = 1, \text{ so:}$$
$$\cos(180° - 180°) = -\cos 180°$$
$$\sin(180° - 180°) = \sin 0° = 0 \text{ and } \sin 180° = 0, \text{ so:}$$
$$\sin(180° - 180°) = \sin 180°$$

5.4   Algebra and the Trigonometric Functions

1. (a) $(1 - \cos \theta)^2 = 1 - 2\cos\theta + \cos^2\theta$

(b) $(\sin\theta + \cos\theta)^2 = \sin^2\theta + 2\sin\theta\cos\theta + \cos^2\theta = 1 + 2\sin\theta\cos\theta$

(c) $\cos\theta + \dfrac{1}{\sin\theta} = \dfrac{\cos\theta\sin\theta + 1}{\sin\theta}$

3. (a) $\tan^2\theta - 5\tan\theta - 6 = (\tan\theta - 6)(\tan\theta + 1)$

(b) $\sin^2 B - \cos^2 B = (\sin B + \cos B)(\sin B - \cos B)$

(c) $\cos^2 A + 2\cos A + 1 = (\cos A + 1)^2$

5. $\dfrac{\dfrac{\cos\theta + 1}{\cos\theta} + 1}{\dfrac{\cos\theta - 1}{\cos\theta} - 1} = \dfrac{\cos\theta + 1 + \cos\theta}{\cos\theta - 1 - \cos\theta} = \dfrac{2\cos\theta + 1}{-1} = -2\cos\theta - 1$

7. $\dfrac{1 - \tan\theta}{\dfrac{\sin\theta}{\cos\theta} - 1} = \dfrac{1 - \tan\theta}{\tan\theta - 1} = -1$

9. $\dfrac{\sin^2 A - \cos^2 A}{\sin A - \cos A} = \dfrac{(\sin A - \cos A)(\sin A + \cos A)}{\sin A - \cos A} = \sin A + \cos A$

11. $\sin^2\theta\cos\theta\csc^3\theta\sec\theta = \dfrac{\sin^2\theta\cos\theta}{\sin^3\theta\cos\theta} = \dfrac{1}{\sin\theta} = \csc\theta$

13. $\cot B\sin^2 B\cot B = \dfrac{\cos B\sin^2 B\cos B}{\sin B\sin B} = \cos^2 B$

15. $\dfrac{\cos^2 A + \cos A - 12}{\cos A - 3} = \dfrac{(\cos A - 3)(\cos A + 4)}{\cos A - 3} = \cos A + 4$

17. $\dfrac{\cos A - 2\sin A \cos A}{\cos^2 A - \sin^2 A + \sin A - 1}$ $= \dfrac{\cos A\,(1 - 2\sin A)}{1 - \sin^2 A - \sin^2 A + \sin A - 1}$

$= \dfrac{\cos A\,(1 - 2\sin A)}{\sin A - 2\sin^2 A}$

$= \dfrac{\cos A\,(1 - 2\sin A)}{\sin A\,(1 - 2\sin A)}$

$= \dfrac{\cos A}{\sin A}$

$= \cot A$

19. $\cot\theta + \dfrac{1 - 2\cos^2\theta}{\sin\theta\cos\theta}$ $= \dfrac{\cos\theta}{\sin\theta} + \dfrac{1 - 2\cos^2\theta}{\sin\theta\cos\theta}$

$= \dfrac{\cos^2\theta + 1 - 2\cos^2\theta}{\sin\theta\cos\theta}$

$= \dfrac{1 - \cos^2\theta}{\sin\theta\cos\theta}$

$= \dfrac{\sin^2\theta}{\sin\theta\cos\theta}$

$= \dfrac{\sin\theta}{\cos\theta}$

$= \tan\theta$

21. $\dfrac{\sec\theta - 1}{\sec\theta + 1} - \dfrac{\tan\theta - \sin\theta}{\tan\theta + \sin\theta}$ $= \dfrac{\dfrac{1}{\cos\theta} - 1}{\dfrac{1}{\cos\theta} + 1} - \dfrac{\dfrac{\sin\theta}{\cos\theta} - \sin\theta}{\dfrac{\sin\theta}{\cos\theta} + \sin\theta}$

$= \dfrac{1 - \cos\theta}{1 + \cos\theta} - \dfrac{\sin\theta - \sin\theta\cos\theta}{\sin\theta\,(1 + \cos\theta)}$

$= \dfrac{\sin\theta\,(1 - \cos\theta) - \sin\theta + \sin\theta\cos\theta}{\sin\theta\,(1 + \cos\theta)}$

$= \dfrac{\sin\theta - \sin\theta\cos\theta - \sin\theta + \sin\theta\cos\theta}{\sin\theta\,(1 + \cos\theta)}$

$= 0$

23. $\dfrac{\cot^2\theta}{\csc^2\theta} + \dfrac{\tan^2\theta}{\sec^2\theta}$ $= \dfrac{\dfrac{\cos^2\theta}{\sin^2\theta}}{\dfrac{1}{\sin^2\theta}} + \dfrac{\dfrac{\sin^2\theta}{\cos^2\theta}}{\dfrac{1}{\cos^2\theta}} = \cos^2\theta + \sin^2\theta = 1$

25. $\sin\theta\cos\theta\sec\theta\csc\theta = \dfrac{\sin\theta\cos\theta}{\sin\theta\cos\theta} = 1$

27. $\dfrac{\sin\theta\sec\theta}{\tan\theta} = \dfrac{\sin\theta\left(\dfrac{1}{\cos\theta}\right)}{\dfrac{\sin\theta}{\cos\theta}} = \dfrac{\sin\theta\cos\theta}{\sin\theta\cos\theta} = 1$

29. $\sec x - 5\tan x = \dfrac{1}{\cos x} - \dfrac{5\sin x}{\cos x} = \dfrac{1 - 5\sin x}{\cos x}$

31. $\cos A\,(\sec A - \cos A) = \cos A\left(\dfrac{1}{\cos A} - \cos A\right) = 1 - \cos^2 A = \sin^2 A$

33. $(1 - \sin\theta)(\sec\theta + \tan\theta)$
$$= \sec\theta + \tan\theta - \sin\theta\sec\theta - \sin\theta\tan\theta$$
$$= \sec\theta + \tan\theta - \tan\theta - \dfrac{\sin^2\theta}{\cos\theta}$$
$$= \dfrac{1}{\cos\theta} - \dfrac{\sin^2\theta}{\cos\theta}$$
$$= \dfrac{\cos^2\theta}{\cos\theta}$$
$$= \cos\theta$$

35. $(\sec\alpha - \tan\alpha)^2 = \sec^2\alpha - 2\tan\alpha\sec\alpha + \tan^2\alpha$
$$= \dfrac{1}{\cos^2\alpha} - \dfrac{2\sin\alpha}{\cos^2\alpha} + \dfrac{\sin^2\alpha}{\cos^2\alpha}$$
$$= \dfrac{1 - 2\sin\alpha + \sin^2\alpha}{\cos^2\alpha}$$
$$= \dfrac{(1 - \sin\alpha)^2}{1 - \sin^2\alpha}$$
$$= \dfrac{(1 - \sin\alpha)^2}{(1 - \sin\alpha)(1 + \sin\alpha)}$$
$$= \dfrac{1 - \sin\alpha}{1 + \sin\alpha}$$

37. $\dfrac{\sin A}{1 - \cot A} - \dfrac{\cos A}{\tan A - 1} = \dfrac{\sin A}{1 - \dfrac{\cos A}{\sin A}} - \dfrac{\cos A}{\dfrac{\sin A}{\cos A} - 1}$
$$= \dfrac{\sin^2 A}{\sin A - \cos A} - \dfrac{\cos^2 A}{\sin A - \cos A}$$
$$= \dfrac{(\sin A - \cos A)(\sin A + \cos A)}{\sin A - \cos A}$$
$$= \sin A + \cos A$$

39. $\csc^2 \theta + \sec^2 \theta$ $= \dfrac{1}{\sin^2 \theta} + \dfrac{1}{\cos^2 \theta}$

$= \dfrac{\cos^2 \theta + \sin^2 \theta}{\sin^2 \theta \cos^2 \theta}$

$= \dfrac{1}{\sin^2 \theta \cos^2 \theta}$

$= \left(\dfrac{1}{\sin^2 \theta}\right)\left(\dfrac{1}{\cos^2 \theta}\right)$

$= \csc^2 \theta \sec^2 \theta$

41. $\dfrac{2 \sin^3 \beta}{1 - \cos \beta}$ $= \dfrac{2 \sin \beta (\sin^2 \beta)}{1 - \cos \beta}$

$= \dfrac{2 \sin \beta (1 - \cos^2 \beta)}{1 - \cos \beta}$

$= \dfrac{2 \sin \beta (1 - \cos \beta)(1 + \cos \beta)}{1 - \cos \beta}$

$= 2 \sin \beta (1 + \cos \beta)$

$= 2 \sin \beta + 2 \sin \beta \cos \beta$

43. $\dfrac{\sin^3 \theta + \cos^3 \theta}{\sin \theta + \cos \theta}$ $= \dfrac{(\sin \theta + \cos \theta)(\sin^2 \theta - \sin \theta \cos \theta + \cos^2 \theta)}{\sin \theta + \cos \theta}$

$= \sin^2 \theta + \cos^2 \theta - \sin \theta \cos \theta$

$= 1 - \sin \theta \cos \theta$

45. $\dfrac{\sec \theta - \csc \theta}{\sec \theta + \csc \theta}$ $= \dfrac{\dfrac{1}{\cos \theta} - \dfrac{1}{\sin \theta}}{\dfrac{1}{\cos \theta} + \dfrac{1}{\sin \theta}}$

$= \dfrac{\dfrac{\sin \theta}{\cos \theta} - \dfrac{\sin \theta}{\sin \theta}}{\dfrac{\sin \theta}{\cos \theta} + \dfrac{\sin \theta}{\sin \theta}}$

$= \dfrac{\tan \theta - 1}{\tan \theta + 1}$

47. $(r \sin \theta \cos \phi)^2 + (r \sin \theta \sin \phi)^2 + (r \cos \theta)^2$

$= r^2 (\sin^2 \theta \cos^2 \phi + \sin^2 \theta \sin^2 \phi + \cos^2 \theta)$

$= r^2 \left(\sin^2 \theta (\cos^2 \phi + \sin^2 \phi) + \cos^2 \theta\right)$

$= r^2 (\sin^2 \theta + \cos^2 \theta)$

$= r^2$

49. Using the hint, we first solve each equation for A and B, respectively:

$$A \sin \theta + \cos \theta = 1$$
$$A \sin \theta = 1 - \cos \theta$$
$$A = \frac{1 - \cos \theta}{\sin \theta}$$
$$B \sin \theta - \cos \theta = 1$$
$$B \sin \theta = 1 + \cos \theta$$
$$B = \frac{1 + \cos \theta}{\sin \theta}$$

So $$AB = \left(\frac{1 - \cos \theta}{\sin \theta}\right)\left(\frac{1 + \cos \theta}{\sin \theta}\right) = \frac{1 - \cos^2 \theta}{\sin^2 \theta} = \frac{\sin^2 \theta}{\sin^2 \theta} = 1$$

51. Let x_0, y_0 be the x,y intercepts respectively. Then:

$$\cos \theta = \frac{d}{x_0} \text{ and } \cos (90° - \theta) = \frac{d}{y_0}$$
$$x_0 = \frac{d}{\cos \theta} \text{ and } y_0 = \frac{d}{\cos (90° - \theta)} = \frac{d}{\sin \theta}$$

Hence, the two points on line L are:

$$\left(\frac{d}{\cos \theta}, 0\right) \text{ and } \left(0, \frac{d}{\sin \theta}\right)$$

So the slope of the line is:

$$\frac{\frac{d}{\sin \theta} - 0}{0 - \frac{d}{\cos \theta}} = -\frac{\cos \theta}{\sin \theta}$$

Thus, by the slope-intercept formula, we have:

$$y = -\frac{\cos \theta}{\sin \theta} x + \frac{d}{\sin \theta}$$
$$y \sin \theta = -(\cos \theta) x + d$$
$$x \cos \theta + y \sin \theta = d$$

53. $a + b = (\sin \alpha + \cos \alpha) + (\sin \alpha - \cos \alpha) = 2 \sin \alpha$
     $a - b = (\sin \alpha + \cos \alpha) - (\sin \alpha - \cos \alpha) = 2 \cos \alpha$

So $\dfrac{a + b}{a - b} = \dfrac{2 \sin \alpha}{2 \cos \alpha} = \tan \alpha$

55. We label point P as $P(x, mx)$. We draw the triangle:

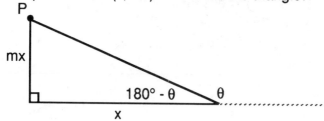

$$\tan\theta = \frac{mx}{x} = m$$

Using functional notation, we have $m(\theta) = \tan\theta$.

57. $\dfrac{\tan\theta + \sec\theta - 1}{\tan\theta - \sec\theta + 1}$

$$= \frac{\dfrac{\sin\theta}{\cos\theta} + \dfrac{1}{\cos\theta} - 1}{\dfrac{\sin\theta}{\cos\theta} - \dfrac{1}{\cos\theta} + 1}$$

$$= \frac{\sin\theta + 1 - \cos\theta}{\sin\theta - 1 + \cos\theta}$$

$$= \frac{(\sin\theta + 1) - \cos\theta}{(\sin\theta - 1) + \cos\theta} \bullet \frac{(\sin\theta + 1) - \cos\theta}{(\sin\theta + 1) - \cos\theta}$$

$$= \frac{(\sin\theta + 1)^2 - 2\cos\theta(\sin\theta + 1) + \cos^2\theta}{(\sin^2\theta - 1) + \cos\theta(\sin\theta + 1) - \cos\theta(\sin\theta - 1) - \cos^2\theta}$$

$$= \frac{\sin^2\theta + 2\sin\theta + 1 - 2\sin\theta\cos\theta - 2\cos\theta + \cos^2\theta}{\sin^2\theta - 1 + \sin\theta\cos\theta + \cos\theta - \sin\theta\cos\theta + \cos\theta - \cos^2\theta}$$

$$= \frac{2 + 2\sin\theta - 2\sin\theta\cos\theta - 2\cos\theta}{\sin^2\theta - \cos^2\theta - 1 + 2\cos\theta}$$

$$= \frac{2(1 - \cos\theta) + 2\sin\theta(1 - \cos\theta)}{1 - \cos^2\theta - \cos^2\theta - 1 + 2\cos\theta}$$

$$= \frac{2(1 - \cos\theta)(1 + \sin\theta)}{-2\cos^2\theta + 2\cos\theta}$$

$$= \frac{(1 - \cos\theta)(1 + \sin\theta)}{\cos\theta(1 - \cos\theta)}$$

$$= \frac{1 + \sin\theta}{\cos\theta}$$

5.5 The Law of Sines and The Law of Cosines

1. We draw the triangle (SAA case):

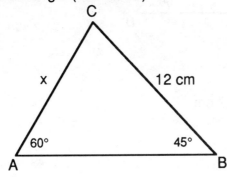

$$\frac{\sin 45°}{x} = \frac{\sin 60°}{12}$$

Thus:

$$x = 12 \cdot \frac{\sin 45°}{\sin 60°} = 12 \cdot \frac{\sqrt{2}}{2} \cdot \frac{2}{\sqrt{3}} = \frac{12\sqrt{2}}{\sqrt{3}} = 4\sqrt{6} \text{ cm}$$

3.   We draw the triangle (SAA case):

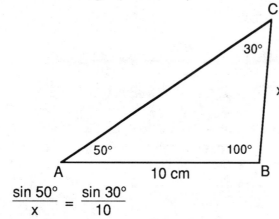

$$\frac{\sin 50°}{x} = \frac{\sin 30°}{10}$$

Thus:

$$x = \frac{10 \sin 50°}{\sin 30°} = \frac{10 \sin 50°}{\frac{1}{2}} = 20 \sin 50° \text{ cm}$$

5.   We draw a triangle (SAA case):

$$\frac{\sin 36°}{a} = \frac{\sin 50°}{12.61}$$

Thus:

$$a = \frac{12.61 \sin 36°}{\sin 50°} \approx 9.7 \text{ cm}$$

$$\frac{\sin 94°}{c} = \frac{\sin 50°}{12.61}$$

Thus:

$$c = \frac{12.61 \sin 94°}{\sin 50°} \approx 16.4 \text{ cm}$$

7.   We draw a triangle (SSA case):

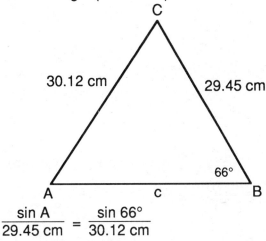

$$\frac{\sin A}{29.45 \text{ cm}} = \frac{\sin 66°}{30.12 \text{ cm}}$$

Thus:

$$\sin A = \frac{29.45 \sin 66°}{30.12} \approx 0.8932, \text{ so } A \approx 63.3°$$

Then $C = 180° - 66° - 63.3° \approx 50.7°$

$$\frac{\sin 50.7°}{c} = \frac{\sin 66°}{30.12}$$

Thus:

$$c = \frac{30.12 \sin 50.7°}{\sin 66°} \approx 25.5 \text{ cm}$$

9.   (a)   Since the reference angle is 45° and the angle belongs to a triangle,
               then: $\angle B = 45°$ or $135°$
       (b)   Reference: 30°, quadrant: II; hence: $\angle A = 150°$
       (c)   Quadrants: I or II, reference: $\approx 14.5°$, so $\angle D = 14.5°$ or $165.5°$

11.   (a) $\dfrac{\sin A}{\sqrt{2}} = \dfrac{\sin 30°}{1}$ hence $\sin A = \sqrt{2} \sin 30° = \dfrac{\sqrt{2}}{2}$

       (b)   Hence A has a reference angle 45°, and so A = 45° or 135°

       (c)   If $A = 45°$, $B = 30°$, $a = \sqrt{2}$, $b = 1$, then:

               $$C = 105° \text{ and } \frac{\sin 45°}{\sqrt{2}} = \frac{\sin 105°}{c}$$

               Hence $c = \dfrac{\sqrt{2} \sin 105°}{\sin 45°} = \dfrac{\sqrt{2} \sin 75°}{\sin 45°} \approx 1.93$

(d)   If $A = 135°$, $B = 30°$, $a = \sqrt{2}$, $b = 1$, then:

$$C = 15° \text{ and } \frac{\sin 30°}{1} = \frac{\sin 15°}{c}$$

Hence $c = \dfrac{\sin 15°}{\sin 30°} \approx 0.52$

13. $\dfrac{\sin 20°}{2} = \dfrac{\sin 100°}{a} = \dfrac{\sin 50°}{b}$

$\dfrac{\sin 70°}{c} = \dfrac{\sin 95°}{b} = \dfrac{\sin 15°}{d}$

Hence:

$a = \dfrac{2 \sin 110°}{\sin 20°} = \dfrac{2 \sin 70°}{\sin 20°} \text{ cm}$

$b = \dfrac{2 \sin 50°}{\sin 20°} \text{ cm}$

$c = \dfrac{b \sin 70°}{\sin 95°} = \dfrac{2 \sin 50° \sin 70°}{\sin 20° \sin 85°} \text{ cm}$

$d = \dfrac{b \sin 15°}{\sin 95°} = \dfrac{2 \sin 50° \sin 15°}{\sin 20° \sin 85°} \text{ cm}$

15.   (a) $x^2 = (15)^2 + (9)^2 - 2(9)(15) \cos 120° \text{ cm}^2$

$= 306 - 270\left(-\dfrac{1}{2}\right)$

$= 441 \text{ cm}^2$

$x = \sqrt{441 \text{ cm}^2} = 21 \text{ cm}$

(b) $x^2 = 4^2 + 4^2 - 2(4)(4) \cos 85° \text{ in.}^2 \approx 29.2 \text{ in.}^2$, so $x \approx 5.4$ in.

17. $a = 6$, $b = 7$, $c = 10$, so:

$6^2 = 7^2 + 10^2 - 2(7)(10) \cos A$, so $\cos A = \dfrac{113}{140}$

$7^2 = 6^2 + 10^2 - 2(6)(10) \cos B$, so $\cos B = \dfrac{87}{120} = \dfrac{29}{40}$

$10^2 = 6^2 + 7^2 - 2(6)(7) \cos C$, so $\cos C = -\dfrac{15}{84} = -\dfrac{5}{28}$

19. We first draw the figure:

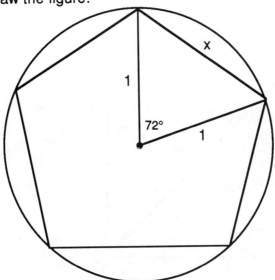

We apply the law of cosines to find x:

$$x^2 = 1^2 + 1^2 - 2(1)(1) \cos 72°$$
$$= 2 - 2 \cos 72°$$
$$\approx 2 - .6180$$
$$\approx 1.382$$

$x \approx \sqrt{1.38} \approx 1.18$ and 5x, the perimeter of the pentagon, is 5.9 units.

21. (a) $a = \sqrt{(6.1)^2 + (3.2)^2 - 2(6.1)(3.2) \cos 40°}$ cm $\approx$ 4.2 cm

(b) $\dfrac{\sin C}{3.2} = \dfrac{\sin 40°}{4.2}$ so $\sin C = \dfrac{3.2}{4.2} \sin 40° \approx .49$, then $C \approx 29.3°$

(c) Hence $\angle B = 180° - 40° - 29.3° \approx 110.7°$

23.   We draw the figure:

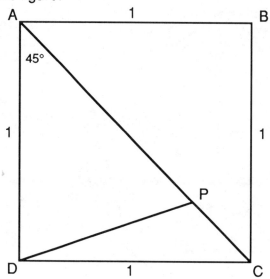

AP = 1, so applying the law of cosines to △APD:

$$(PD)^2 = 1^2 + 1^2 - 2(1)(1) \cos 45° = 2 - 2 \cdot \frac{\sqrt{2}}{2} = 2 - \sqrt{2}$$

Hence $PD = \sqrt{2 - \sqrt{2}}$

25.   (a)   Using the law of cosines, we have:

$$(m^2 + n^2 + mn)^2 = (2mn + n^2)^2 + (m^2 - n^2)^2 - 2(2mn + n^2)(m^2 - n^2)\cos C$$

After carrying out the indicated squaring operations, and then combining like terms, the equation becomes:

$$2m^3n - 2mn^3 + m^2n^2 - n^4 = -2(2mn + n^2)(m^2 - n^2) \cos C$$
$$2mn(m^2 - n^2) + n^2(m^2 - n^2) = -2(2mn + n^2)(m^2 - n^2) \cos C$$
$$(m^2 - n^2)(2mn + n^2) = -2(2mn + n^2)(m^2 - n^2) \cos C$$

Therefore $\cos C = -\frac{1}{2}$, and consequently C = 120°

(b)   Let m = 2 and n = 1. Then by means of the expressions in part (a), we obtain a = 5, b = 3, c = 7.

27. We draw the figure:

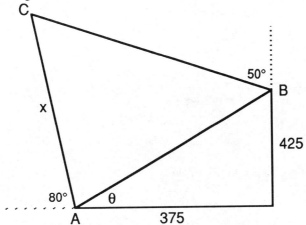

$AB = \sqrt{(375)^2 + (425)^2} \approx 566.8$ ft

$\tan\theta = \dfrac{425}{375}$, so $\theta = 48.6°$

$\angle CAB = 180° - 80° - 48.6° = 51.4°$

$\angle ABC = 180° - 50° - (90° - 48.6°) = 88.6°$

$\angle ACB = 180° - 51.4° - 88.6° = 40°$

Hence:

$$\dfrac{\sin 40°}{566.8} = \dfrac{\sin 88.6°}{x}$$

So:

$$x = \dfrac{566.8 \sin 88.6°}{\sin 40°} \approx 881.5 \text{ ft}$$

29. (a)   We use the law of cosines:

$a^2 = b^2 + c^2 - 2bc \cos A$

$$= \left(\frac{1}{\sqrt{6}-\sqrt{2}}\right)^2 + \left(\frac{1}{\sqrt{6}+\sqrt{2}}\right)^2 - 2\left(\frac{1}{\sqrt{6}-\sqrt{2}}\right)\left(\frac{1}{\sqrt{6}+\sqrt{2}}\right)\cos 60°$$

$$= \frac{1}{6-2\sqrt{12}+2} + \frac{1}{6+2\sqrt{12}+2} - \frac{2}{6-2}\cdot\frac{1}{2}$$

$$= \frac{1}{8-4\sqrt{3}} + \frac{1}{8+4\sqrt{3}} - \frac{1}{4}$$

$$= \frac{1}{4(2-\sqrt{3})} + \frac{1}{4(2+\sqrt{3})} - \frac{1}{4}$$

$$= \frac{(2+\sqrt{3}) + (2-\sqrt{3}) - (2+\sqrt{3})(2-\sqrt{3})}{4(2+\sqrt{3})(2-\sqrt{3})}$$

$$= \frac{4 - (4-3)}{4(4-3)}$$

$$= \frac{3}{4}$$

So $a = \sqrt{3/4} = \dfrac{\sqrt{3}}{2}$

(b)   Using the law of sines to find sin B:

$$\frac{\sin B}{b} = \frac{\sin A}{a}$$

$$\frac{\sin B}{\dfrac{1}{\sqrt{6}-\sqrt{2}}} = \frac{\sin 60°}{\dfrac{\sqrt{3}}{2}}$$

$$(\sqrt{6}-\sqrt{2}) \sin B = \frac{2}{\sqrt{3}} \cdot \frac{\sqrt{3}}{2}$$

$$(\sqrt{6}-\sqrt{2}) \sin B = 1$$

$$\sin B = \frac{1}{\sqrt{6}-\sqrt{2}}$$

Using the law of sines to find sin C:

$$\frac{\sin C}{c} = \frac{\sin A}{a}$$

$$\frac{\sin C}{\dfrac{1}{\sqrt{6}+\sqrt{2}}} = \frac{\sin 60°}{\dfrac{\sqrt{3}}{2}}$$

$$(\sqrt{6}+\sqrt{2}) \sin C = \frac{2}{\sqrt{3}} \cdot \frac{\sqrt{3}}{2}$$

$$(\sqrt{6}+\sqrt{2}) \sin C = 1$$

$$\sin C = \frac{1}{\sqrt{6}+\sqrt{2}}$$

31. We draw the figure:

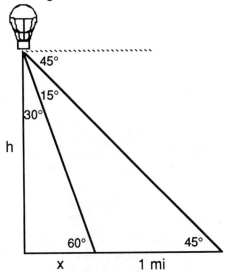

Using right triangles, we have:

$$\tan 60° = \frac{h}{x}, \text{ so } x = \frac{h}{\tan 60°}$$

$$\tan 45° = \frac{h}{x + 1}, \text{ so } h = x + 1$$

Substituting for x, we have:

$$h = \frac{h}{\tan 60°} + 1$$

$$h = \frac{h}{\sqrt{3}} + 1$$

$$\sqrt{3}\, h = h + \sqrt{3}$$

$$h(\sqrt{3} - 1) = \sqrt{3}$$

$$h = \frac{\sqrt{3}}{\sqrt{3} - 1} \approx 2.366 \text{ mi} \approx 12,495 \text{ ft}$$

33.   We draw the figure:

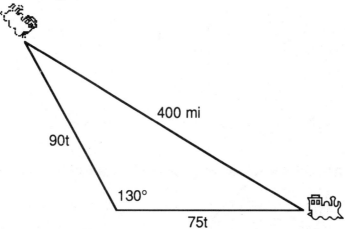

If t is the time of travel, then the trains have traveled 75t mi and 90t mi, as indicated in the figure. We use the law of cosines:

$$(400)^2 = (90t)^2 + (75t)^2 - 2(90t)(75t) \cos 130°$$
$$160000 = 8100t^2 + 5625t^2 - 13500 \cos 130° \; t^2$$
$$t^2 = \frac{160000}{13725 - 13500 \cos 130°} \approx 7.142$$
$$t \approx 2.672 \text{ hr} \approx 160 \text{ minutes}$$

The trains are 400 mi apart after 160 minutes, which occurs at 2:40 P.M.

35.   Using P to denote the plane, we have the following figure:

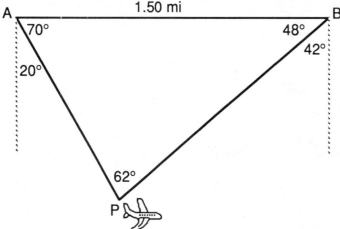

We use the law of sines to find AP:

$$\frac{AP}{\sin 48°} = \frac{1.5}{\sin 62°}$$
$$AP = \frac{1.5 \sin 48°}{\sin 62°} \approx 1.26 \text{ mi}$$

We use the law of sines to find BP:

$$\frac{BP}{\sin 70°} = \frac{1.5}{\sin 62°}$$

$$BP = \frac{1.5 \sin 70°}{\sin 62°} \approx 1.60 \text{ mi}$$

So the distance from the plane to each lighthouse is: A: 1.26 mi; B: 1.60 mi

37. $\dfrac{\sin (\angle BAD)}{n} = \dfrac{\sin \theta}{c}$ while $\dfrac{\sin (\angle DAC)}{m} = \dfrac{\sin (180° - \theta)}{b}$

But $\angle BAD = \angle DAC$ and $\sin \theta = \sin (180° - \theta)$, so:

$$\frac{n}{c} = \frac{\sin (\angle BAD)}{\sin \theta} = \frac{\sin (\angle DAC)}{\sin (180° - \theta)} = \frac{m}{b}$$

Hence:

$$\frac{n}{m} = \frac{c}{b}$$

39. (a)
$$c^2 = a^2 + b^2 - 2ab \cos C$$
$$c^2 - a^2 - b^2 = -2ab \cos C$$
$$\cos C = \frac{c^2 - a^2 - b^2}{-2ab} = \frac{a^2 + b^2 - c^2}{2ab}$$

(b)
$$\begin{aligned}
1 - \cos C &= \frac{2ab - (a^2 + b^2 - c^2)}{2ab} \\
&= \frac{2ab - a^2 - b^2 + c^2}{2ab} \\
&= \frac{c^2 - (a^2 - 2ab + b^2)}{2ab} \\
&= \frac{c^2 - (a - b)^2}{2ab} \\
&= \frac{\big(c - (a - b)\big)\big(c + (a - b)\big)}{2ab} \\
&= \frac{(c + a - b)(c - a + b)}{2ab}
\end{aligned}$$

(c)
$$\begin{aligned}
1 + \cos C &= \frac{2ab + a^2 + b^2 - c^2}{2ab} \\
&= \frac{(a^2 + 2ab + b^2) - c^2}{2ab} \\
&= \frac{(a + b)^2 - c^2}{2ab} \\
&= \frac{(a + b + c)(a + b - c)}{2ab}
\end{aligned}$$

(d)   Since $\sin^2 C = 1 - \cos^2 C = (1 - \cos C)(1 + \cos C)$ then:

$$\sin^2 C = \frac{(c + a - b)(c - a + b)}{2ab} \cdot \frac{(a + b + c)(a + b - c)}{2ab}$$

$$= \frac{(a + b + c)(-a + b + c)(a - b + c)(a + b - c)}{4a^2b^2}$$

(e)   area $\triangle ABC = \frac{1}{2} ab \sin C$

$$= \frac{1}{2} ab \sqrt{\frac{(a + b + c)(-a + b + c)(a - b + c)(a + b - c)}{4a^2b^2}}$$

$$= \frac{1}{4} \sqrt{(a + b + c)(-a + b + c)(a - b + c)(a + b - c)}$$

(f)   Letting $\frac{1}{2}(a + b + c) = s$, then:

   (i) $a + b + c = 2s$
   (ii) $-a + b + c = a + b + c - 2a = 2s - 2a = 2(s - a)$
   (iii) $a - b + c = a + b + c - 2b = 2s - 2b = 2(s - b)$
   (iv) $a + b - c = a + b + c - 2c = 2s - 2c = 2(s - c)$

Hence from (e):

$$\text{area } \triangle ABC = \frac{1}{4} \sqrt{2s\big(2(s - a)\big)\big(2(s - b)\big)\big(2(s - c)\big)}$$

$$= \frac{1}{4} \sqrt{16s(s - a)(s - b)(s - c)}$$

$$= \sqrt{s(s - a)(s - b)(s - c)}$$

41.   (a)   From the geometry theorem $\angle C = \frac{1}{2} \angle AOB$

Since $\angle A = \angle B$ (base angles of an isosceles triangle)

then $\angle AOD = \angle BOD = \frac{1}{2} \angle AOB$, thus $\angle C = \angle AOD$.

(b)   Since $AD = \frac{1}{2} AB = \frac{c}{2}$, then:

$$\frac{\sin C}{c} = \frac{\sin \angle AOD}{2\,AD}$$

From the law of sines:

$$\frac{\sin \angle AOD}{AD} = \frac{\sin 90°}{r}$$

Hence:

$$\frac{1}{r} = \frac{2 \sin C}{c}$$

$$r = \frac{c}{2 \sin C}$$

(c)   We draw the figure:

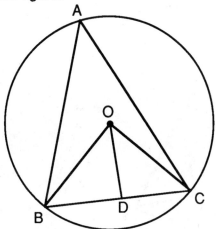

And also the figure:

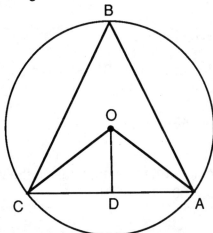

Using the same reasoning as (a) and (b), we have:

$$r = \frac{a}{2 \sin A} \quad \text{and} \quad r = \frac{b}{2 \sin B}$$

So $\quad \frac{1}{2} r = \frac{\sin C}{c}, \quad \frac{1}{2} r = \frac{\sin A}{a}, \quad \frac{1}{2} r = \frac{\sin B}{b}$

Hence:

$$\frac{\sin A}{a} = \frac{\sin B}{b} = \frac{\sin C}{c}$$

(d)   We draw the figure:

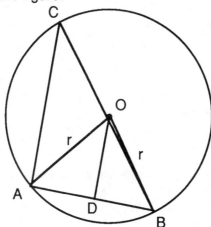

Using this figure and the reasoning from (a) and (b), we get:

$$r = \frac{c}{2 \sin C}$$

43.   The area of the triangle is given by:

$$A = \frac{1}{2}(base)(height) = \frac{1}{2}(a)(b \sin 60°) = \frac{\sqrt{3}}{4}ab$$

Since the area is $10\sqrt{3}$ cm^2, we have:

$$\frac{\sqrt{3}}{4}ab = 10\sqrt{3}$$
$$ab = 40$$

We can find the third side (d) in terms of a and b using the law of cosines:

$$d^2 = a^2 + b^2 - 2ab \cos 60°$$
$$d^2 = a^2 + b^2 - 2(40)(1/2)$$
$$d = \sqrt{a^2 + b^2 - 40}$$

Since the perimeter of the triangle is 20 cm, we have:

$$a + b + \sqrt{a^2 + b^2 - 40} = 20$$
$$\sqrt{a^2 + b^2 - 40} = 20 - (a + b)$$

Squaring each side, we have:

$$a^2 + b^2 - 40 = 400 - 40(a + b) + (a + b)^2$$
$$a^2 + b^2 - 40 = 400 - 40a - 40b + a^2 + 2ab + b^2$$
$$-440 = -40a - 40b + 2(40)$$
$$-520 = -40a - 40b$$
$$13 = a + b$$

So, we have the system of equations:

$$a + b = 13$$
$$ab = 40$$

Solving the first equation for b yields b = 13 - a, now substitute:

$$a(13 - a) = 40$$
$$13a - a^2 = 40$$
$$a^2 - 13a + 40 = 0$$
$$(a - 8)(a - 5) = 0$$
$$a = 8, 5$$

Since a is the smaller of the two numbers, we have a = 5 and b = 8.

45.   We work from the right-hand side:

$$\frac{1}{(b + a)^2} + \frac{1}{(b - a)^2} = \frac{(b - a)^2 + (b + a)^2}{(b + a)^2(b - a)^2}$$

$$= \frac{b^2 - 2ab + a^2 + b^2 + 2ab + a^2}{(b^2 - a^2)^2}$$

$$= \frac{2(a^2 + b^2)}{(a^2 - b^2)^2}$$

$$= \frac{2}{c^2} \qquad \text{using our result from the above problem.}$$

Chapter 5 Review Exercises

1. $\cos 30° = \dfrac{\sqrt{3}}{2}$

$\tan 60° = \dfrac{\sin 60°}{\cos 60°} = \dfrac{\sqrt{3}/2}{1/2} = \sqrt{3}$

$\sin^2 7° + \cos^2 7° = 1$

2.   (a) $\sin (-270°) = \sin 90° = 1$
     (b) $\cos 540° = \cos 180° = -1$
     (c) $\cot 450° = \cot 90° = \dfrac{\cos 90°}{\sin 90°} = \dfrac{0}{1} = 0$

3. $2 \cos^2 \theta + 11 \cos \theta + 12 = (2 \cos \theta + 3)(\cos \theta + 4)$

4. $\text{Area} = \dfrac{1}{2} (\text{base})(\text{height}) = \dfrac{1}{2} (5)(6 \sin 135°) = \dfrac{15\sqrt{2}}{2} \text{ cm}^2$

5.   We draw the triangle:

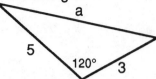

Using the law of cosines:
$$a^2 = 3^2 + 5^2 - 2(3)(5)\cos 120° = 9 + 25 - 30(-1/2) = 49$$
So a = 7 cm.

6.   We draw the triangle:

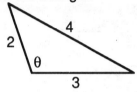

We use the law of cosines:
$$4^2 = 2^2 + 3^2 - 2(2)(3)\cos \theta$$
$$16 = 4 + 9 - 12 \cos \theta$$
$$3 = -12 \cos \theta$$
$$\cos \theta = -1/4$$
The angle opposite the 4 cm side must be obtuse (not acute), since its cosine is negative.

7.   (a) $\cos 330° = \cos (-30°) = \dfrac{\sqrt{3}}{2}$

       (b) $\tan (-135°) = \dfrac{\sin (-135°)}{\cos (-135°)} = \dfrac{-\sqrt{2}/2}{-\sqrt{2}/2} = 1$

8.   Since 270° < θ < 360° is the fourth quadrant, we know cos θ > 0. So:

$$\cos \theta = \sqrt{1 - \sin^2 \theta} = \sqrt{1 - 1/9} = \sqrt{8/9} = \dfrac{2\sqrt{2}}{3}$$

$$\cot \theta = \dfrac{\cos \theta}{\sin \theta} = \dfrac{2\sqrt{2}/3}{-1/3} = -2\sqrt{2}$$

9.   The missing side (adjacent) is $\sqrt{5^2 - 3^2} = \sqrt{25 - 9} = 4$, so $\tan \theta = \dfrac{3}{4}$.

10. $\dfrac{\dfrac{\tan \theta + 1}{\tan \theta} + 1}{\dfrac{\tan \theta - 1}{\tan \theta} - 1} \bullet \dfrac{\tan \theta}{\tan \theta} = \dfrac{\tan \theta + 1 + \tan \theta}{\tan \theta - 1 - \tan \theta} = \dfrac{2 \tan \theta + 1}{-1} = -2 \tan \theta - 1$

11. We use the law of sines:

$$\frac{\sin 45°}{20\sqrt{2}} = \frac{\sin 30°}{x}$$

$$x = \frac{20\sqrt{2}\,\sin 30°}{\sin 45°} = \frac{(20\sqrt{2})(1/2)}{\sqrt{2}/2} = 20 \text{ cm}$$

12. Call h the vertical height we are trying to find. Then:

$$\sin 60° = \frac{h}{10}, \text{ so } h = 10\sin 60° = 10(\sqrt{3}/2) = 5\sqrt{3} \text{ ft}$$

13.
$$\frac{\cos\theta + 1}{\csc\theta + \cot\theta} = \frac{\cos\theta + 1}{\dfrac{1}{\sin\theta} + \dfrac{\cos\theta}{\sin\theta}} \bullet \frac{\sin\theta}{\sin\theta}$$

$$= \frac{\sin\theta\,(\cos\theta + 1)}{1 + \cos\theta}$$

$$= \sin\theta$$

14. We label $\triangle ABP$ as follows:

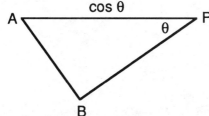

AP = cos θ, since it represents the x-coordinate of point P, which lies on the unit circle. Therefore:

$$\cos\theta = \frac{BP}{\cos\theta}, \text{ so } BP = \cos^2\theta$$

$$\sin\theta = \frac{AB}{\cos\theta}, \text{ so } AB = \cos\theta\,\sin\theta$$

15. Since cos (180° - θ) = - cos θ and sin (180° - θ) = sin θ, we have:

$$\frac{\sin\theta}{1 + \cos(180° - \theta)} = \frac{\sin\theta}{1 - \cos\theta} \bullet \frac{1 + \cos\theta}{1 + \cos\theta}$$

$$= \frac{\sin\theta\,(1 + \cos\theta)}{1 - \cos^2\theta}$$

$$= \frac{\sin\theta\,(1 + \cos\theta)}{\sin^2\theta}$$

$$= \frac{1 + \cos\theta}{\sin\theta}$$

$$= \frac{1 + \cos\theta}{\sin(180° - \theta)}$$

16. $\dfrac{(\cos\theta + \sin\theta)^2}{1 + 2\sin\theta\cos\theta}$ = $\dfrac{\cos^2\theta + 2\sin\theta\cos\theta + \sin^2\theta}{1 + 2\sin\theta\cos\theta}$

$\qquad\qquad\qquad\quad = \dfrac{1 + 2\sin\theta\cos\theta}{1 + 2\sin\theta\cos\theta}$

$\qquad\qquad\qquad\quad = 1$

17.   Since 15° is in the first quadrant, then sin 15° is positive. Thus:

$$\sin 15° = \sqrt{1 - \cos^2 15°}$$

$$= \sqrt{1 - \tfrac{1}{16}\left(6 + 2\sqrt{12} + 2\right)}$$

$$= \sqrt{1 - \tfrac{1}{16}\left(8 + 4\sqrt{3}\right)}$$

$$= \dfrac{\sqrt{16 - 8 - 4\sqrt{3}}}{4}$$

$$= \dfrac{\sqrt{8 - 4\sqrt{3}}}{4}$$

$$= \dfrac{2\sqrt{2 - \sqrt{3}}}{4}$$

$$= \dfrac{\sqrt{2 - \sqrt{3}}}{2}$$

18.   We draw the figure:

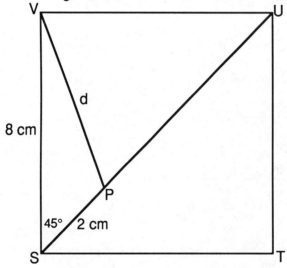

Note that the diagonals of a square bisect the vertex angles. We use the law of cosines with $\triangle SPV$:

$$d^2 = 8^2 + 2^2 - 2(8)(2)\cos 45° = 64 + 4 - 32(\sqrt{2}/2) = 68 - 16\sqrt{2}$$

$$d = \sqrt{68 - 16\sqrt{2}} = 2\sqrt{17 - 4\sqrt{2}}$$

So $PV = 2\sqrt{17 - 4\sqrt{2}}$ cm.

19. We draw the figure, labeling angles and sides:

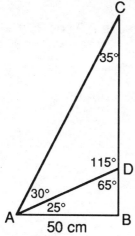

We first find AD:

$$\cos 25° = \frac{50}{AD}, \text{ so } AD = \frac{50}{\cos 25°}$$

Now use the law of sines with $\triangle ADC$:

$$\frac{\sin 35°}{AD} = \frac{\sin 30°}{CD}$$

$$\frac{\sin 35°}{\dfrac{50}{\cos 25°}} = \frac{1/2}{CD}$$

$$CD \sin 35° = \frac{25}{\cos 25°}$$

$$CD = \frac{25}{\cos 25° \sin 35°} \text{ cm}$$

20. The central angle of the polygon is $\frac{360°}{9}$ = 40°, so we have nine triangles each which look like:

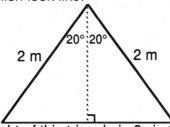

The height of this triangle is 2 sin 20°, and the base is 2(2 cos 20°) = 4 cos 20°. So the area is:

$$A = \frac{1}{2}\text{(base)(height)} = \frac{1}{2}(4 \cos 20°)(2 \sin 20°) = 4 \sin 20° \cos 20°$$

Since there are nine such triangles, the area of the polygon is 36 sin 20° cos 20° m² or 18 sin 40° m².

21. We draw a triangle:

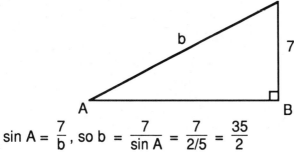

$$\sin A = \frac{7}{b}, \text{ so } b = \frac{7}{\sin A} = \frac{7}{2/5} = \frac{35}{2}$$

23. We draw a triangle:

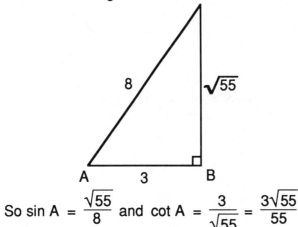

So $\sin A = \frac{\sqrt{55}}{8}$ and $\cot A = \frac{3}{\sqrt{55}} = \frac{3\sqrt{55}}{55}$

25.   We draw a triangle:

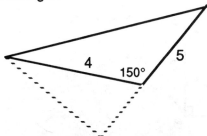

Using the law of cosines, we have:

$$a^2 = 4^2 + 5^2 - 2(4)(5)\cos 150° = 16 + 25 - 40(-\sqrt{3}/2) = 41 + 20\sqrt{3}$$

$$a = \sqrt{41 + 20\sqrt{3}}$$

$$\text{Area} = \frac{1}{2}(5)(4\sin 150°) = \frac{1}{2}(10) = 5$$

27.   We draw the triangle:

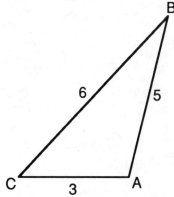

We use the law of cosines:

$$6^2 = 3^2 + 5^2 - 2(3)(5)\cos A$$
$$36 = 9 + 25 - 30\cos A$$
$$2 = -30\cos A$$
$$\cos A = -1/15$$

Now we find sin A:

$$\sin A = \sqrt{1 - \cos^2 A} = \sqrt{1 - 1/225} = \sqrt{224/225} = \frac{4\sqrt{14}}{15}$$

So $\cos A = -\dfrac{1}{15}$ and $\sin A = \dfrac{4\sqrt{14}}{15}$.

29. We draw a triangle:

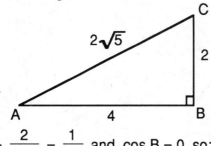

$$\sin A \ = \ \frac{2}{2\sqrt{5}} \ = \ \frac{1}{\sqrt{5}} \ \text{and} \ \cos B = 0, \text{so:}$$

$$\sin^2 A + \cos^2 B \ = \ \frac{1}{5} + 0 \ = \ \frac{1}{5}$$

31. We draw the triangle:

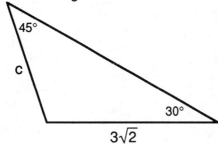

We use the law of sines:

$$\frac{\sin 30°}{c} = \frac{\sin 45°}{3\sqrt{2}}$$

$$\frac{1/2}{c} = \frac{\sqrt{2}/2}{3\sqrt{2}}$$

$$\frac{3\sqrt{2}}{2} = \frac{\sqrt{2}}{2}c$$

$$c = 3$$

33. We draw the triangle:

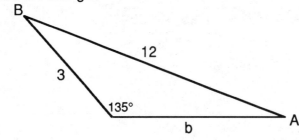

We use the law of sines to find sin A:

$$\frac{\sin A}{3} = \frac{\sin 135°}{12}$$

$$\sin A = \frac{3(\sqrt{2}/2)}{12} = \frac{\sqrt{2}}{8}$$

We use the Pythagorean Identity $\sin^2 A + \cos^2 A = 1$ to find cos A:

$$\cos A = \sqrt{1 - \sin^2 A} = \sqrt{1 - 1/32} = \sqrt{31/32} = \frac{\sqrt{62}}{8}$$

Using a calculator we find $A \approx 10.18°$, so:

$$B = 180° - C - A \approx 180° - 135° - 10.18° \approx 34.82°$$

Thus $\sin A = \frac{\sqrt{2}}{8}$, $\cos A = \frac{\sqrt{62}}{8}$, and $B \approx 34.82°$.

35. We draw the triangle:

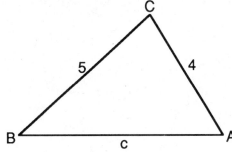

We use the law of cosines:

$$c^2 = 5^2 + 4^2 - 2(5)(4) \cos C = 25 + 16 - 40(1/8) = 36$$

So $c = 6$.

37. $\sin 135° = \sin 45° = \dfrac{\sqrt{2}}{2}$

39. $\tan(-240°) = \tan 120° = -\tan 60° = -\sqrt{3}$

41. $\csc 210° = \dfrac{1}{\sin 210°} = -\dfrac{1}{\sin 30°} = -\dfrac{1}{1/2} = -2$

43. $\sin 270° = -1$

45. $\cos(-315°) = \cos 45° = \dfrac{\sqrt{2}}{2}$

47. $\cos 1800° = \cos 0° = 1$

49. $\csc 240° = \dfrac{1}{\sin 240°} = \dfrac{1}{-\sqrt{3}/2} = -\dfrac{2}{\sqrt{3}} = -\dfrac{2\sqrt{3}}{3}$

51. $\sec 780° = \sec 60° = \dfrac{1}{\cos 60°} = \dfrac{1}{1/2} = 2$

53.   Letting z be the side opposite β, we have:

$$\tan(\alpha + \beta) = \frac{y+z}{x}, \quad \tan \beta = \frac{z}{x}$$

So $\tan(\alpha + \beta) - \tan \beta = \dfrac{y+z}{x} - \dfrac{z}{x} = \dfrac{y}{x}$, thus:

$$y = x\left(\tan(\alpha + \beta) - \tan \beta\right)$$

55.   Letting c be the side opposite $(90° - \alpha)$, we have:

$$\cot \theta = \frac{a+c}{b}; \quad \cot \alpha = \frac{c}{b}$$

$$\cot \theta - \cot \alpha = \frac{a}{b}$$

So $\cot \theta = \dfrac{a}{b} + \cot \alpha$

57.   Since $\sin^2 \theta + \cos^2 \theta = 1$, we have:

$$\left(\frac{2p^2q^2}{p^4 + q^4}\right)^2 + \cos^2 \theta = 1$$

$$\frac{4p^4q^4}{(p^4 + q^4)^2} + \cos^2 \theta = 1$$

$$\cos^2 \theta = \frac{(p^4 + q^4)^2 - 4p^4q^4}{(p^4 + q^4)^2}$$

$$\cos^2 \theta = \frac{p^8 - 2p^4q^4 + q^4}{(p^4 + q^4)^2}$$

$$\cos^2 \theta = \frac{(p^4 - q^4)^2}{(p^4 + q^4)^2}$$

$$\cos \theta = \frac{p^4 - q^4}{p^4 + q^4}$$

Now find $\tan \theta$:

$$\tan \theta = \frac{\sin \theta}{\cos \theta} = \frac{2p^2q^2}{p^4 - q^4}$$

59. Since $\dfrac{\tan \alpha}{\tan \beta} = \sqrt{3}$, then:

$$\dfrac{\sin \alpha}{\sin \beta} = \sqrt{3} \cdot \dfrac{\cos \alpha}{\cos \beta}$$

$$\sqrt{2} = \sqrt{3} \cdot \dfrac{\cos \alpha}{\cos \beta}$$

$$\sqrt{2}\cos \beta = \sqrt{3}\cos \alpha$$

$$2\cos^2 \beta = 3\cos^2 \alpha$$

$$\dfrac{2}{3}\cos^2 \beta = \cos^2 \alpha$$

Now $\sin \alpha = \sqrt{2}\sin \beta$, so $\sin^2 \alpha = 2\sin^2 \alpha$. Thus:

$$\sin^2 \alpha + \cos^2 \alpha = 1$$

$$2\sin^2 \beta + \dfrac{2}{3}\cos^2 \beta = 1$$

$$2\sin^2 \beta + \dfrac{2}{3}(1 - \sin^2 \beta) = 1$$

$$\dfrac{4}{3}\sin^2 \beta = \dfrac{1}{3}$$

$$\sin^2 \beta = \dfrac{1}{4}$$

$$\sin \beta = \dfrac{1}{2}$$

$$\beta = 30°$$

Thus $\sin \alpha = \sqrt{2}\left(\dfrac{1}{2}\right) = \dfrac{\sqrt{2}}{2}$, and so $\alpha = 45°$

61. We draw a triangle:

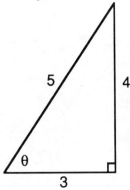

$\sin \theta = \dfrac{4}{5}$ and $\tan \theta = \dfrac{4}{3}$

63.   We draw a triangle:

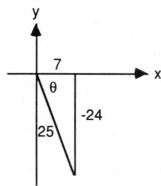

$$\tan \theta = \frac{-24}{7}$$

65.   We draw a triangle:

$$\cot \theta = \frac{5}{12}$$

67.   We draw a triangle:

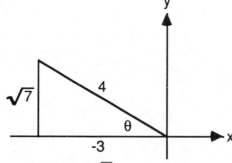

$$\tan (90° - \theta) = \frac{-3}{\sqrt{7}} = \frac{-3\sqrt{7}}{7}$$

69.   Since $\cos(180° - \theta) = -\cos\theta$ for $0° < \theta < 90°$, then $\cos(180° - \theta) = \dfrac{-7}{9}$

71.
$$\tan\theta + \cot\theta = 2$$
$$\frac{\sin\theta}{\cos\theta} + \frac{\cos\theta}{\sin\theta} = 2$$
$$\frac{\sin^2\theta + \cos^2\theta}{\sin\theta\cos\theta} = 2$$
$$1 = 2\sin\theta\cos\theta$$

Now $(\sin\theta + \cos\theta)^2 = \sin^2\theta + 2\sin\theta\cos\theta + \cos^2\theta = 1 + 1 = 2$, so
$\sin\theta + \cos\theta = \sqrt{2}$ since $0° < \theta < 90°$

73.   We draw the figure:

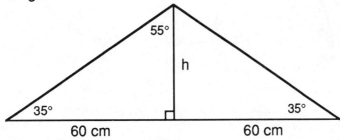

Now $\tan 35° = \dfrac{h}{60}$, so $h = 60\tan 35°$

Thus Area $= \dfrac{1}{2}(120)(60\tan 35°) = 3600\tan 35°\ \text{cm}^2 \approx 2521\ \text{cm}^2$

75.   We draw the figure:

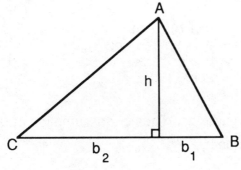

Now:

$$\cot B = \frac{b_1}{h}, \text{ so } b_1 = h\cot B$$
$$\cot C = \frac{b_2}{h}, \text{ so } b_2 = h\cot C$$

So we have:

$$b_1 + b_2 = a$$
$$h \cot B + h \cot C = a$$
$$h(\cot B + \cot C) = a$$
$$h = \frac{a}{\cot B + \cot C}$$

77.   We draw the figure:

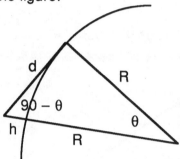

We have:

$$d^2 + R^2 = (R + h)^2$$
$$d^2 = h^2 + 2Rh$$
$$d = \sqrt{2Rh + h^2}$$

So:

$$\cot \theta = \frac{R}{d} = \frac{R}{\sqrt{2Rh + h^2}}$$

79.   (a)   Assume $\dfrac{a - b}{a + b} \neq \dfrac{c - d}{c + d}$

Now cross-multiply:

$$(a - b)(c + d) \neq (a + b)(c - d)$$
$$ac - bc + ad - bd \neq ac + bc - ad - bd$$
$$-bc + ad \neq bc - ad$$
$$2ad \neq 2bc$$
$$ad \neq bc$$

But since $\dfrac{a}{b} = \dfrac{c}{d}$, then $ad = bc$. Thus our assumption must be false, verifying the original equality.

   (b)   Since $\dfrac{a}{b} = \dfrac{\sin A}{\sin B}$, then using $c = \sin A$ and $d = \sin B$, we have:

$$\frac{a - b}{a + b} = \frac{\sin A - \sin B}{\sin A + \sin B}$$

81. (a)   PN $= \sin \theta$

(b)   ON $= \cos \theta$

(c)   Since $\cos \theta = \dfrac{PN}{PT}$ (note $\theta = \angle TPN$), then $\cos \theta = \dfrac{\sin \theta}{PT}$

Hence, PT $= \tan \theta$

(d)   Here $\cos \theta = \dfrac{1}{OT}$ (using $\triangle OPT$), so OT $= \dfrac{1}{\cos \theta} = \sec \theta$

(e)   NA $= 1 - ON = 1 - \cos \theta$

(f)   NT $= OT - ON$

$= \sec \theta - \cos \theta$

$= \dfrac{1}{\cos \theta} - \cos \theta$

$= \dfrac{1 - \cos^2 \theta}{\cos \theta}$

$= \dfrac{\sin^2 \theta}{\cos \theta}$

$= \sin \theta \left(\dfrac{\sin \theta}{\cos \theta} \right)$

$= \sin \theta \tan \theta$

83. $\sin^2 (90° - \theta) \csc \theta - \tan^2 (90° - \theta) \sin \theta = \cos^2 \theta \cdot \dfrac{1}{\sin \theta} - \cot^2 \theta \sin \theta$

$= \dfrac{\cos^2 \theta}{\sin \theta} - \dfrac{\cos^2 \theta}{\sin^2 \theta} \cdot \sin \theta$

$= \dfrac{\cos^2 \theta}{\sin \theta} - \dfrac{\cos^2 \theta}{\sin \theta}$

$= 0$

85. $\cos^2 \theta - \sin^2 \theta = \cos^2 \theta - (1 - \cos^2 \theta) = 2\cos^2 \theta - 1$

87. $\sin A \tan A = \dfrac{\sin^2 A}{\cos A} = \dfrac{1 - \cos^2 A}{\cos A}$

89. $-\cot^4 A + \csc^4 A$ $= \dfrac{-\cos^4 A}{\sin^4 A} + \dfrac{1}{\sin^4 A}$

$= \dfrac{(1 - \cos^2 A)(1 + \cos^2 A)}{\sin^4 A}$

$= \dfrac{\sin^2 A\,(1 + \cos^2 A)}{\sin^4 A}$

$= \dfrac{1 + \cos^2 A}{\sin^2 A}$

$= \dfrac{1}{\sin^2 A} + \dfrac{\cos^2 A}{\sin^2 A}$

$= \cot^2 A + \csc^2 A$

91. $\dfrac{\cot^2 A - \tan^2 A}{(\cot A + \tan A)^2}$ $= \dfrac{\cot A - \tan A}{\cot A + \tan A}$

$= \dfrac{\dfrac{\cos A}{\sin A} - \dfrac{\sin A}{\cos A}}{\dfrac{\cos A}{\sin A} + \dfrac{\sin A}{\cos A}}$

$= \dfrac{\cos^2 A - \sin^2 A}{\cos^2 A + \sin^2 A}$

$= \cos^2 A - (1 - \cos^2 A)$

$= 2\cos^2 A - 1$

93. $\dfrac{\cos A - \sin A}{\cos A + \sin A} = \dfrac{1 - \dfrac{\sin A}{\cos A}}{1 + \dfrac{\sin A}{\cos A}} = \dfrac{1 - \tan A}{1 + \tan A}$

95. $\dfrac{1}{\sec A + \tan A}$ $= \dfrac{1}{\dfrac{1}{\cos A} + \dfrac{\sin A}{\cos A}}$

$= \dfrac{\cos A}{1 + \sin A}$

$= \dfrac{(1 - \sin A)\cos A}{1 - \sin^2 A}$

$= \dfrac{(1 - \sin A)\cos A}{\cos^2 A}$

$= \dfrac{1 - \sin A}{\cos A}$

Thus: $\dfrac{1 - \sin A}{\cos A} - \dfrac{1}{\sec A + \tan A} = 0$

97. $\dfrac{\tan A + \tan B}{\cot A + \cot B} = \dfrac{\dfrac{\sin A}{\cos A} + \dfrac{\sin B}{\cos B}}{\dfrac{\cos A}{\sin A} + \dfrac{\cos B}{\sin B}}$

$= \dfrac{(\sin A \sin B)(\cos A \sin B + \sin A \cos B)}{(\cos A \cos B)(\sin A \cos B + \cos A \sin B)}$

$= \left(\dfrac{\sin A}{\cos A}\right)\left(\dfrac{\sin B}{\cos B}\right)$

$= \tan A \tan B$

99. $\tan A - \dfrac{\sec A \sin^3 A}{1 + \cos A} = \dfrac{\sin A}{\cos A} - \dfrac{\sin^3 A}{\cos A\,(1 + \cos A)}$

$= \dfrac{(\sin A)(1 + \cos A) - \sin^3 A}{\cos A\,(1 + \cos A)}$

$= \dfrac{\sin A\,(1 + \cos A) - \sin A\,(1 - \cos^2 A)}{\cos A\,(1 + \cos A)}$

$= \dfrac{\sin A - \sin A\,(1 - \cos A)}{\cos A}$

$= \dfrac{\sin A \cos A}{\cos A}$

$= \sin A$

101. $\dfrac{1}{\csc A - \cot A} - \dfrac{1}{\csc A + \cot A} = \dfrac{2 \cot A}{\csc^2 A - \cot^2 A} = \dfrac{2 \cot A}{\dfrac{1 - \cos^2 A}{\sin^2 A}} = 2 \cot A$

103. Since $\dfrac{1}{1 + \sec^2 A} = \dfrac{\cos^2 A}{\cos^2 A + 1}$ and $\dfrac{1}{1 + \csc^2 A} = \dfrac{\sin^2 A}{\sin^2 A + 1}$

The left-hand side becomes:

$\dfrac{1}{1 + \sin^2 A} + \dfrac{1}{1 + \cos^2 A} + \dfrac{\cos^2 A}{1 + \cos^2 A} + \dfrac{\sin^2 A}{1 + \sin^2 A}$

$= \dfrac{1 + \sin^2 A}{1 + \sin^2 A} + \dfrac{1 + \cos^2 A}{1 + \cos^2 A}$

$= 2$

105. $\dfrac{\sec A - \csc A}{\sec A + \csc A} = \dfrac{1 - \dfrac{\cos A}{\sin A}}{1 + \dfrac{\cos A}{\sin A}} = \dfrac{\sin A - \cos A}{\sin A + \cos A}$

107. $\dfrac{\tan A}{1 + \tan^2 A} = \dfrac{\sin A}{\cos A + \dfrac{\sin^2 A}{\cos A}} = \dfrac{\sin A \cos A}{\cos^2 A + \sin^2 A} = \sin A \cos A$

109.   (a)   For AB, we use the law of cosines with $\triangle OAB$:

$$AB^2 = 1^2 + 1^2 - 2(1)(1) \cos 108°$$
$$= 2 - 2 \cos 108°$$
$$= 2 - 2(-\cos 72°)$$
$$= 2 + 2 \cos 72°$$

So $AB = \sqrt{2 + 2 \cos 72°}$.
Since $\angle COB = 60°$ and $OC = OB$, then $\triangle OBC$ is an
equilateral triangle, and thus all sides are equal. Thus $BC = 1$.
For CD, we use the law of cosines with $\triangle OCD$:

$$CD^2 = 1^2 + 1^2 - 2(1)(1) \cos 36° = 2 - 2 \cos 36°$$

So $CD = \sqrt{2 - 2 \cos 36°}$.

(b)   Both sides are 1.618034, accurate to six decimal places.

111. $$\frac{\csc A \sec A}{\sec^2 A + \csc^2 A} = \frac{\left(\dfrac{1}{\sin A}\right)\left(\dfrac{1}{\cos A}\right)}{\dfrac{1}{\cos^2 A} + \dfrac{1}{\sin^2 A}} = \frac{\sin A \cos A}{\sin^2 A + \cos^2 A} = \sin A \cos A$$

113. $$\cos A + \tan A \sin A = \cos A + \frac{\sin^2 A}{\cos A} = \frac{\cos^2 A + \sin^2 A}{\cos A} = \frac{1}{\cos A}$$

115. $$\frac{1}{\sec A - 1} \div \frac{1}{\sec A + 1} = \frac{\sec A + 1}{\sec A - 1} = \frac{1 + \cos A}{1 - \cos A}$$

117. $$\frac{\dfrac{\tan^2 A - 1}{\tan^3 A + \tan A}}{\dfrac{\tan A + 1}{\tan^2 A + 1}} = \frac{(\tan^2 A - 1)(\tan^2 A + 1)}{\tan A \, (\tan^2 A + 1)(\tan A + 1)}$$

$$= \frac{(\tan A - 1)(\tan A + 1)}{\tan A \, (\tan A + 1)}$$

$$= \frac{\tan A - 1}{\tan A}$$

$$= 1 - \cot A$$

$$= 1 - \frac{\cos A}{\sin A}$$

$$= \frac{\sin A - \cos A}{\sin A}$$

119. $\dfrac{\sin A \tan A - \cos A \cot A}{\sec A - \csc A} = \dfrac{\dfrac{\sin^2 A}{\cos A} - \dfrac{\cos^2 A}{\sin A}}{\dfrac{1}{\cos A} - \dfrac{1}{\sin A}}$

$= \dfrac{\dfrac{\sin^3 A - \cos^3 A}{\sin A - \cos A}}{}$

$= 1 + \sin A \cos A$

121.   Following the suggestion, we have:

$b^2 = a^2 + c^2 - 2ac \cos B$

$c^2 = a^2 + b^2 - 2ab \cos C$

Adding, we have:

$b^2 + c^2 = 2a^2 + b^2 + c^2 - (2c \cos B + 2b \cos C)a$

$-2a^2 = -2a(c \cos B + b \cos C)$

$a = c \cos B + b \cos C$

(We can divide each side by -2a since a ≠ 0)

Similarly, we use:

$a^2 = b^2 + c^2 - 2bc \cos A$

$b^2 = a^2 + c^2 - 2ac \cos B$

Adding:

$a^2 + b^2 = a^2 + b^2 + 2c^2 - 2c(b \cos A + a \cos B)$

$-2c^2 = -2c(b \cos A + a \cos B)$

$c = b \cos A + a \cos B$

The third projection law is proved in a similar fashion.

123.   For the triangle, note the following figure:

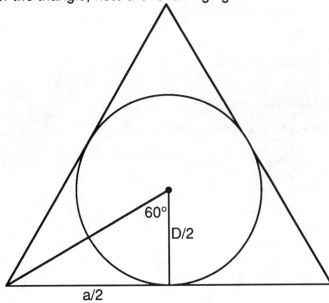

So $\tan 60° = \dfrac{a/2}{D/2}$, or $\sqrt{3} = \dfrac{a}{D}$, thus $a = D\sqrt{3}$.

For the hexagon, note the following figure:

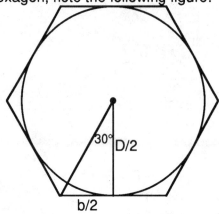

So $\tan 30° = \dfrac{b/2}{D/2}$, or $\dfrac{1}{\sqrt{3}} = \dfrac{b}{D}$, thus $b = \dfrac{D}{\sqrt{3}}$.

Thus we have:

$$ab = \left(D\sqrt{3}\right)\left(\dfrac{D}{\sqrt{3}}\right) = D^2$$

125.   (a)   The area is $\dfrac{1}{2}$ cr since the base is c and the height is r.

(b)   For $\triangle AOC$, we have:

$$\text{Area} = \dfrac{1}{2}\,(\text{base})(\text{height}) = \dfrac{1}{2}\,br$$

For $\triangle BOC$, we have:

$$\text{Area} = \dfrac{1}{2}\,(\text{base})(\text{height}) = \dfrac{1}{2}\,ar$$

(c)   Setting the areas equal, we have:

$$S = \dfrac{1}{2}\,cr + \dfrac{1}{2}\,br + \dfrac{1}{2}\,ar = \dfrac{1}{2}\,r(a + b + c)$$

Thus:

$$r = \dfrac{2S}{a + b + c}$$

CHAPTER SIX
TRIGONOMETRIC FUNCTIONS OF REAL NUMBERS

6.1 **Radian Measure**

1. Remember, to convert from degrees to radians, we must multiply by $\dfrac{\pi}{180°}$:

(a) $60° \left(\dfrac{\pi}{180°} \right) = \dfrac{\pi}{3}$ radians

(b) $225° \left(\dfrac{\pi}{180°} \right) = \dfrac{5\pi}{4}$ radians

(c) $36° \left(\dfrac{\pi}{180°} \right) = \dfrac{\pi}{5}$ radians

(d) $450° \left(\dfrac{\pi}{180°} \right) = \dfrac{5\pi}{2}$ radians

(e) $0° \left(\dfrac{\pi}{180°} \right) = 0$ radians

3.   To convert from radians to degrees, we multiply by $\frac{180°}{\pi}$:

(a) $\left(\frac{\pi}{12}\right)\left(\frac{180°}{\pi}\right) = 15°$

(b) $\left(\frac{3\pi}{2}\right)\left(\frac{180°}{\pi}\right) = 270°$

(c) $(6\pi)\left(\frac{180°}{\pi}\right) = 1080°$

(d) $\left(\frac{\pi}{10}\right)\left(\frac{180°}{\pi}\right) = 18°$

(e) $\left(\frac{\pi}{2}\right)\left(\frac{180°}{\pi}\right) = 90°$

(f) $(3)\left(\frac{180°}{\pi}\right) = \frac{540°}{\pi}$

5.   Since $90° = \frac{\pi}{2}$, which is about $\frac{3.14}{2}$ radians, then $\frac{3}{2}$ radians is smaller than a right angle.

7.   We complete the table:

θ	0	$\pi/2$	π	$3\pi/2$	2π
$\cos\theta$	1	0	-1	0	1

9. $30° = \frac{\pi}{6}$ radians, $45° = \frac{\pi}{4}$ radians, $60° = \frac{\pi}{3}$ radians

$120° = \frac{2\pi}{3}$ radians, $135° = \frac{3\pi}{4}$ radians, $150° = \frac{5\pi}{6}$ radians

11.   (a)   sin 2 is positive, since $\frac{\pi}{2} < 2 < \pi$

(b)   sin 3 is positive, since $\frac{\pi}{2} < 3 < \pi$

13.   (a)   sin 3.16 is negative, since $\pi < 3.16 < \frac{3\pi}{2}$

(b)   tan 3.16 is positive, since $\pi < 3.16 < \frac{3\pi}{2}$

15. $s = r\theta = 3\left(\frac{4\pi}{3}\right) = 4\pi$ ft

17. $s = r\theta = 2\left(\dfrac{45\pi}{180}\right) = \dfrac{\pi}{2}$ cm

19. Since $s = r\theta$, and $s = 1$ cm while $r = 6$ cm, we have:

$$1 = 6\theta$$

$$\theta = \dfrac{1}{6}$$

The radian measure of θ is $\dfrac{1}{6}$.

21. (a) Each revolution of the wheel is 2π radians, so in 6 revolutions there are $\theta = 6(2\pi) = 12\pi$ radians.
Consequently, we have:

$$\omega = \dfrac{\theta}{t} = \dfrac{12\pi \text{ radians}}{1 \text{ sec}} = 12\pi \text{ radians/sec}$$

(b) Using the formula $s = r\theta$, where $r = 12$ cm and $\theta = 12\pi$ radians, we have $s = (12 \text{ cm})(12\pi \text{ radians}) = 122\pi$ cm.
The linear speed, therefore, is:

$$v = \dfrac{d}{t} = \dfrac{144\pi \text{ cm}}{1 \text{ sec}} = 144\pi \text{ cm/sec}$$

(c) Using the formula $s = r\theta$, where $r = 6$ cm and $\theta = 12\pi$ radians, we have $s = (6 \text{ cm})(12\pi \text{ rad}) = 72\pi$ cm.
Thus, we have:

$$v = \dfrac{d}{t} = \dfrac{72\pi \text{ cm}}{1 \text{ sec}} = 72\pi \text{ cm/sec}$$

23. (a) In 1 second, the wheel has rotated $1080° \cdot \dfrac{\pi \text{ rad}}{180°} = 6\pi$ radians.
Consequently, we have:

$$\omega = \dfrac{\theta}{t} = \dfrac{6\pi \text{ rad}}{1 \text{ sec}} = 6\pi \text{ rad/sec}$$

(b) Using $\theta = 6\pi$ radians and $r = 25$ cm, then:

$$s = r\theta = (25 \text{ cm})(6\pi \text{ rad}) = 150\pi \text{ cm}$$

Thus, we have:

$$v = \dfrac{150\pi \text{ cm}}{1 \text{ sec}} = 150\pi \text{ cm/sec}$$

(c)   Using $\theta = 6\pi$ radians and $r = \dfrac{25}{2}$ cm, then:

$$s = r\theta = \left(\dfrac{25}{2}\,\text{cm}\right)(6\pi\ \text{rad}) = 75\pi\ \text{cm}$$

Thus, we have:

$$v = \dfrac{75\pi\ \text{cm}}{1\ \text{sec}} = 75\pi\ \text{cm/sec}$$

25.   (a)   In 1 minute, the wheel has rotated 500 rev. Since each revolution is equal to 2π radians, then we have:

$$\theta = (500)(2\pi) = 1000\pi\ \text{radians}$$

Consequently, we have:

$$\omega = \dfrac{\theta}{t} = \dfrac{1000\pi\ \text{rad}}{60\ \text{sec}} = \dfrac{50\pi}{3}\ \text{rad/sec}$$

(b)   Using $\theta = 1000\pi$ radians and $r = 45$ cm, then:

$$s = r\theta = (45\ \text{cm})(1000\pi\ \text{rad}) = 45000\pi\ \text{cm}$$

Thus, we have:

$$v = \dfrac{45000\pi\ \text{cm}}{60\ \text{sec}} = 750\pi\ \text{cm/sec}$$

(c)   Using $\theta = 1000\pi$ radians and $r = \dfrac{45}{2}$ cm, then:

$$s = r\theta = \left(\dfrac{45}{2}\,\text{cm}\right)(1000\pi\ \text{rad}) = 22500\pi\ \text{cm}$$

Thus, we have:

$$v = \dfrac{22500\pi\ \text{cm}}{60\ \text{sec}} = 375\pi\ \text{cm/sec}$$

27.   (a)   Here $r = 5$ cm and $\theta = 210° \bullet \dfrac{\pi\ \text{rad}}{180°} = \dfrac{7\pi}{6}$ radians, so:

$$A = \dfrac{1}{2}r^2\theta = \dfrac{1}{2}(5\ \text{cm})^2\left(\dfrac{7\pi}{6}\right) = \dfrac{175\pi}{12}\ \text{cm}^2$$

(b)   Here $r = 2$ in. and $\theta = 15° \bullet \dfrac{\pi\ \text{rad}}{180°} = \dfrac{\pi}{12}$ radians, so:

$$A = \dfrac{1}{2}r^2\theta = \dfrac{1}{2}(2\ \text{in.})^2\left(\dfrac{\pi}{12}\right) = \dfrac{\pi}{6}\ \text{in.}^2$$

29.   area of the shaded region = area of sector - area of triangle

$$= \frac{1}{2}(10 \text{ cm})^2 \left(\frac{\pi}{3}\right) - \frac{1}{2}(10 \text{ cm})(10 \text{ cm})\sin\frac{\pi}{3}$$

$$= \left[\frac{50\pi}{3} - 50\left(\frac{\sqrt{3}}{2}\right)\right]\text{cm}^2$$

$$= \frac{50\pi}{3} - 25\sqrt{3} \ \text{cm}^2$$

31.   With arc length 1 ft and radius 1 ft, then angle A = 1 radian, which is approximately 57.3°, slightly less than 60°.

33.   Since each revolution results in a distance traveled of $(2\pi)\left(\frac{3}{2}\text{ ft}\right) = 3\pi$ ft, then in x revolutions the point on the circumference has traveled $3\pi x$ ft. Thus:

$$3\pi x = 22619$$
$$x = \frac{22619}{3\pi} \text{ rev}$$
$$x \approx 600 \text{ rev}$$

35.   (a)   Each revolution is 2π radians, and 24 hr = 86400 sec, so:

$$w = \frac{\theta}{t} = \frac{2\pi \text{ rad}}{86400 \text{ sec}} \approx 0.000073 \text{ rad/sec}$$

(b)   Using $\theta = 2\pi$ rad and r = 3960 mi, then:
$$s = r\theta = (3960 \text{ mi})(2\pi \text{ rad}) = 7920\pi \text{ mi}$$
Thus, we have:
$$v = \frac{s}{t} = \frac{7920\pi \text{ mi}}{24 \text{ hr}} = 330\pi \text{ mi/hr} \approx 1040 \text{ mph}$$

37.   (a) $Area_1 = \frac{1^2(\pi - \theta)}{2}$, $Area_2 = \frac{1^2(\theta)}{2}$, hence:

$$P = \frac{\pi - \theta}{2} \bullet \frac{\theta}{2} = \frac{\pi\theta - \theta^2}{4}$$

This is a quadratic function.

(b)   We complete the square:

$$P = \frac{-\theta^2}{4} + \frac{\pi}{4}\theta$$

$$= -\frac{1}{4}(\theta^2 - \pi\theta)$$

$$= -\frac{1}{4}\left(\theta^2 - \pi\theta + \frac{\pi^2}{4}\right) + \frac{\pi^2}{16}$$

$$= -\frac{1}{4}\left(\theta - \frac{\pi}{2}\right)^2 + \frac{\pi^2}{16}$$

Thus P has a maximum value of $\frac{\pi^2}{16}$ when $\theta = \frac{\pi}{2}$.

39.   We draw the sketch:

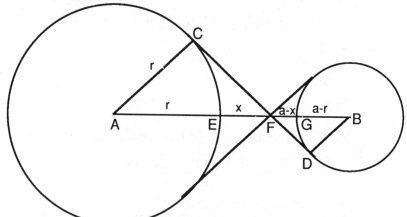

Let the radii be r and a - r, respectively, as indicated in the figure. Using the fact that the distance between the centers is 2a, we find FG = a - x. Since △ACF is similar to △BDF (they both have a right angle and a vertical angle at F), we have:

$$\frac{AF}{FB} = \frac{AC}{BD}$$

$$\frac{r + x}{(a - x) + (a - r)} = \frac{r}{a - r}$$

$$ra + xa - r^2 - xr = 2ar - xr - r^2$$

$$a(x + r) = 2ar$$

$$x + r = 2r$$

$$x = r$$

Then AF = r + r = 2r. But then:

$$\sin(CFA) = \frac{r}{2r} = 1/2, \text{ thus } CFA = \frac{\pi}{6} \text{ and thus } CAF = FBD = \frac{\pi}{3}$$

We can now compute the length of string. Using △ACF, we have:

$$\sin\frac{\pi}{3} = \frac{CF}{2r}, \text{ thus } CF = r\sqrt{3}$$

Similarly, using ΔBDF:

$$\sin \frac{\pi}{3} = \frac{DF}{a-r}, \text{ thus } DF = (a-r)\sqrt{3}$$

Therefore:

$$CD = CF + DF = r\sqrt{3} + (a-r)\sqrt{3} = a\sqrt{3}$$

So the amount of string required for the straight lines is $2a\sqrt{3}$.

For the curves pieces, each has a central angle of $\frac{4\pi}{3}$, and thus the lengths required are:

$$\frac{4\pi r}{3} + \frac{4\pi(a-r)}{3} = \frac{4\pi a}{3}$$

So, the total length of string needed is:

$$2a\sqrt{3} + \frac{4\pi a}{3} = \left(\frac{4\pi}{3} + 2\sqrt{3} \right)a$$

6.2 Trigonometric Functions of Real Numbers

1. We complete the table:

θ	$\sin \theta$	$\cos \theta$	$\tan \theta$	$\csc \theta$	$\sec \theta$	$\cot \theta$
0	0	1	0	undef.	1	undef.
$\frac{\pi}{6}$	$\frac{1}{2}$	$\frac{\sqrt{3}}{2}$	$\frac{\sqrt{3}}{3}$	2	$\frac{2\sqrt{3}}{3}$	$\sqrt{3}$
$\frac{\pi}{4}$	$\frac{\sqrt{2}}{2}$	$\frac{\sqrt{2}}{2}$	1	$\sqrt{2}$	$\sqrt{2}$	1
$\frac{\pi}{3}$	$\frac{\sqrt{3}}{2}$	$\frac{1}{2}$	$\sqrt{3}$	$\frac{2\sqrt{3}}{3}$	2	$\frac{\sqrt{3}}{3}$
$\frac{\pi}{2}$	1	0	undef.	1	undef.	0
$\frac{2\pi}{3}$	$\frac{\sqrt{3}}{2}$	$-\frac{1}{2}$	$-\sqrt{3}$	$\frac{2\sqrt{3}}{3}$	-2	$-\frac{\sqrt{3}}{3}$
$\frac{3\pi}{4}$	$\frac{\sqrt{2}}{2}$	$-\frac{\sqrt{2}}{2}$	-1	$\sqrt{2}$	$-\sqrt{2}$	-1
$\frac{5\pi}{6}$	$\frac{1}{2}$	$-\frac{\sqrt{3}}{2}$	$-\frac{\sqrt{3}}{3}$	2	$-\frac{2\sqrt{3}}{3}$	$-\sqrt{3}$
π	0	-1	0	undef.	1	undef.

3. $\cos \theta = \pm \sqrt{1 - \sin^2\theta} = \pm \sqrt{1 - \dfrac{9}{25}} = \pm \dfrac{4}{5}$. Now, since $\pi < \theta < \dfrac{3\pi}{2}$,

then $\cos \theta = -\dfrac{4}{5}$, and thus $\tan \theta = \dfrac{\sin \theta}{\cos \theta} = \dfrac{3}{4}$

5.   With $\sin t = \dfrac{\sqrt{3}}{4}$ and $\dfrac{\pi}{2} < t < \pi$, so $\cos t = -\sqrt{1 - \dfrac{3}{16}}$, which is equal to

$-\sqrt{\dfrac{13}{16}} = -\dfrac{\sqrt{13}}{4}$, thus $\tan t = -\dfrac{\sqrt{3}}{\sqrt{13}} = -\dfrac{\sqrt{39}}{13}$.

7. $\tan \alpha = \dfrac{12}{5}$, so: $1 + \left(\dfrac{12}{5}\right)^2 = \sec^2 \alpha$

$$1 + \dfrac{144}{25} = \sec^2 \alpha$$

$$\dfrac{169}{25} = \sec^2 \alpha$$

$$\pm \dfrac{13}{5} = \sec \alpha$$

Since $\cos \alpha > 0$, so is $\sec \alpha$ and thus we pick $\sec \alpha = \dfrac{13}{5}$. Thus

$\cos \alpha = \dfrac{5}{13}$, and we use $\sin^2 \alpha + \cos^2 \alpha = 1$ to get:

$$\sin^2 \alpha = 1 - \left(\dfrac{5}{13}\right)^2 = \dfrac{144}{169}, \text{ thus } \sin \alpha = \pm \dfrac{12}{13}$$

We pick the positive value since, if both the tangent and cosine are positive,

then so is the sine. Thus $\sin \alpha = \dfrac{12}{13}$.

9.   For $0 < \theta < \dfrac{\pi}{2}$, we have:

$$\sqrt{9 - x^2} = \sqrt{9 - (3 \sin \theta)^2} = \sqrt{9(1 - \sin^2 \theta)} = \sqrt{9 \cos^2 \theta} = 3 \cos \theta$$

11. $\dfrac{1}{(u^2 - 25)^{3/2}} = \dfrac{1}{(25 \sec^2 \theta - 25)^{3/2}} = \dfrac{1}{125 \tan^3 \theta}$

Since $0 < \theta < \dfrac{\pi}{2}$, then $\tan \theta > 0$. This can also be written as $\dfrac{\cot^3 \theta}{125}$.

13. Since $\sec \theta > 0$, we have:

$$\dfrac{1}{\sqrt{u^2 + 7}} = \dfrac{1}{\sqrt{7 \tan^2 \theta + 7}} = \dfrac{1}{\sqrt{7} \sec \theta}$$

This can also be written as $\dfrac{\cos \theta}{\sqrt{7}} = \dfrac{\sqrt{7} \cos \theta}{7}$

15. (a) $\sin(-\theta) = -\sin\theta = -2/3$
    (b) $\sin(-\phi) = -\sin\phi = 1/4$
    (c) $\cos(-\alpha) = \cos\alpha = 1/5$
    (d) $\cos(-\beta) = \cos\beta = -1/5$

17. (a) Since $\cos\theta = -\dfrac{1}{3}$ then, since $\dfrac{\pi}{2} < \theta < \pi$, we have $\sin\theta > 0$ and

$$\sin\theta = \sqrt{1 - \frac{1}{9}} = \sqrt{\frac{8}{9}} = \frac{2\sqrt{2}}{3}. \text{ Hence } \sin(-\theta) = -\frac{2\sqrt{2}}{3} \text{ and}$$

$$\cos(-\theta) = -\frac{1}{3}, \text{ thus } \sin(-\theta) + \cos(-\theta) = -\frac{2\sqrt{2}}{3} - \frac{1}{3}, \text{ which is}$$

$$-\frac{1 + 2\sqrt{2}}{3}.$$

(b) This is 1, regardless of θ.

19. (a) $\cos\left(\dfrac{\pi}{4} + 2\pi\right) = \cos\dfrac{\pi}{4} = \dfrac{\sqrt{2}}{2}$

    (b) $\sin\left(\dfrac{\pi}{3} + 2\pi\right) = \sin\dfrac{\pi}{3} = \dfrac{\sqrt{3}}{2}$

    (c) $\sin\left(\dfrac{\pi}{2} - 6\pi\right) = \sin\dfrac{\pi}{2} = 1$

21. $\dfrac{\sin^2\theta + \cos^2\theta}{\tan^2\theta + 1} = \dfrac{1}{\sec^2\theta} = \cos^2\theta$

23. $\dfrac{\sec^2\theta - \tan^2\theta}{1 + \cot^2\theta} = \dfrac{\tan^2\theta + 1 - \tan^2\theta}{\csc^2\theta} = \dfrac{1}{\csc^2\theta} = \sin^2\theta$

25. $\sin\theta + \cot\theta\cos\theta = \sin\theta + \dfrac{\cos\theta}{\sin\theta}(\cos\theta)$

$$= \frac{\sin^2\theta}{\sin\theta} + \frac{\cos^2\theta}{\sin\theta}$$

$$= \frac{\sin^2\theta + \cos^2\theta}{\sin\theta}$$

$$= \frac{1}{\sin\theta}$$

$$= \csc\theta$$

27. $\dfrac{1}{1 + \sec\theta} + \dfrac{1}{1 - \sec\theta}$

$= \dfrac{(1 - \sec\theta) + (1 + \sec\theta)}{(1 - \sec\theta)(1 + \sec\theta)}$

$= \dfrac{2}{1 - \sec^2\theta}$

$= \dfrac{-2}{\tan^2\theta}$

$= -2\cot^2\theta$

29.   Denoting $\sin\theta$ by S and $\cos\theta$ by C, we have:

$$\frac{\cot\theta}{1 - \tan\theta} + \frac{\tan\theta}{1 - \cot\theta} = \frac{\frac{C}{S}}{1 - \frac{S}{C}} + \frac{\frac{S}{C}}{1 - \frac{C}{S}} = \frac{C^2}{S(C - S)} - \frac{S^2}{C(C - S)} = \frac{1}{SC} + 1$$

Now we replace C with $\cos\theta$ and S with $\sin\theta$:

$$\frac{1}{SC} + 1 = \frac{\cos^2\theta + \sin^2\theta}{\sin\theta\cos\theta} + 1 = \frac{\cos\theta}{\sin\theta} + \frac{\sin\theta}{\cos\theta} + 1 = \cot\theta + \tan\theta + 1$$

31.   The expression on the left-hand side becomes:

$\tan\theta - (\tan\theta\cot\theta)(\cot\theta) + \cot\theta - (\cot\theta\tan\theta)(\tan\theta)$,

which multiplies out to become $\tan\theta - \cot\theta + \cot\theta - \tan\theta$, which is 0.

33.   If $\sec t = \dfrac{13}{5}$, then $\cos t = \dfrac{5}{13}$. Given $\dfrac{3\pi}{2} < t < 2\pi$, then $\sin t < 0$ (fourth quadrant), thus:

$\sin t = -\sqrt{1 - \cos^2 t} = -\sqrt{1 - 25/169} = -\sqrt{144/169} = -12/13$

So we have:

$\dfrac{2\sin t - 3\cos t}{4\sin t - 9\cos t} = \dfrac{2(-12/13) - 5(5/13)}{4(-12/13) - 9(5/13)} \cdot \dfrac{13}{13}$

$= \dfrac{-24 - 15}{-48 - 45}$

$= \dfrac{-39}{-93}$

$= \dfrac{13}{31}$

35.   We have:

$\sin t = \dfrac{y}{\sqrt{x^2 + y^2}}$ and $\cos t = \dfrac{x}{\sqrt{x^2 + y^2}}$

Similarly:

$\sin(t + \pi) = \dfrac{-y}{\sqrt{x^2 + y^2}}$ and $\cos(t + \pi) = \dfrac{-x}{\sqrt{x^2 + y^2}}$

And:

$$\sin(t - \pi) = \frac{-y}{\sqrt{x^2 + y^2}} \quad \text{and} \quad \cos(t - \pi) = \frac{-x}{\sqrt{x^2 + y^2}}$$

Thus we have the results:

$$\sin(t + \pi) = -\sin t$$
$$\sin(t - \pi) = -\sin t$$
$$\cos(t + \pi) = -\cos t$$
$$\cos(t - \pi) = -\cos t$$

37. The substitutions are $x = \frac{\sqrt{2}}{2}(X - Y)$ and $y = \frac{\sqrt{2}}{2}(X + Y)$. Thus we have:

$$x^2 = \frac{1}{2}(X^2 - 2XY + Y^2) \quad \text{and} \quad y^2 = \frac{1}{2}(X^2 + 2XY + Y^2)$$

and thus:

$$x^4 = \frac{1}{4}(X^4 - 4X^3Y + 6X^2Y^2 - 4XY^3 + Y^4)$$

$$y^4 = \frac{1}{4}(X^4 + 4X^3Y + 6X^2Y^2 + 4XY^3 + Y^4)$$

We also find $x^2y^2 = \frac{1}{4}(X^2 - Y^2)^2 = \frac{1}{4}(X^4 - 2X^2Y^2 + Y^4)$

Now we use the expressions that have been found for x^2, y^2, x^4, and y^4 to substitute in the expression $x^4 + 6x^2y^2 + y^4$ to get:

$$\frac{X^4}{4} - X^3Y + \frac{3}{2}X^2Y^2 - XY^3 + \frac{Y^4}{4} + \frac{3}{2}X^4 - 3X^2Y^2 + \frac{3}{2}Y^4 + \frac{X^4}{4} + X^3Y + \frac{3}{2}X^2Y^2 + XY^3 + \frac{Y^4}{4}$$

which is $2X^4 + 2Y^4$. In light of this result, the equation $x^4 + 6x^2y^2 + y^4 = 32$ is equivalent to $2X^4 + 2Y^4 = 32$, or $X^4 + Y^4 = 16$, as required.

39. We complete the chart:

θ	$1 - \dfrac{\theta^2}{2}$	$\cos\theta$
0.1	0.995	0.995004...
0.2	0.980	0.980066...
0.3	0.955	0.955336...

41. $a + b - c = (\sin^2\theta + \csc^2\theta) + (\cos^2\theta + \sec^2\theta) - (\tan^2\theta + \cot^2\theta)$
$= (\sin^2\theta + \cos^2\theta) + (\csc^2\theta - \cot^2\theta) + (\sec^2\theta - \tan^2\theta)$
$= 1 + 1 + 1$
$= 3$

43. (a) $0, \pi, 2\pi, 3\pi$

     (b)   The domain of $f(\theta)$ are those real numbers for which $\sin \theta \neq 0$, that is all reals except $0, \pm\pi, \pm2\pi, \ldots$ This can be written as all real numbers except $k\pi$, where k is any integer.

     (c)   all reals except the integers

45. (a)   We complete the table:

t	0.2	0.4	0.6	0.8	1.0	1.2	1.4
f(t)	219.07	50.53	19.70	9.55	6.14	7.98	33.88

     (b)   The smallest output is 6.14, which occurs at t = 1.0.

     (c)   We work from the right-hand side:
$$(\tan t - 3 \cot t)^2 + 6 = \tan^2 t - 6 \tan t \cot t + 9 \cot^2 t + 6$$
$$= \tan^2 t - 6 + 9 \cot^2 t + 6$$
$$= \tan^2 t + 9 \cot^2 t$$

     (d)   Since $(\tan t - 3 \cot t)^2 \geq 0$, then:
$$\tan^2 t + 9\cot^2 t = (\tan t - 3 \cot t)^2 + 6 \geq 0 + 6 \geq 6$$

     (e)   The minimum will occur when:
$$\tan t - 3 \cot t = 0$$
$$\tan t = 3 \cot t$$
$$\tan t = \frac{3}{\tan t}$$
$$\tan^2 t = 3$$
$$\tan t = \sqrt{3} \quad \text{(since } 0 < t < \pi/2, \text{ then } \tan t > 0\text{)}$$
$$t = \frac{\pi}{3}$$

Since $\frac{\pi}{3} \approx 1.05$, our answer from part (b) is consistent with this result.

6.3 Graphs of the Sine and Cosine Functions

1.   period: 2; amplitude: 1

3.   period: 4; amplitude: 6

5.   period: 4; amplitude: 2

7.   period: 6; amplitude: 3/2

9.   (a)   y = 2 sin x
        amplitude: 2; period: 2π; x-intercepts: 0, π, 2π
        increasing: (0, π/2) ∪ (3π/2, 2π)

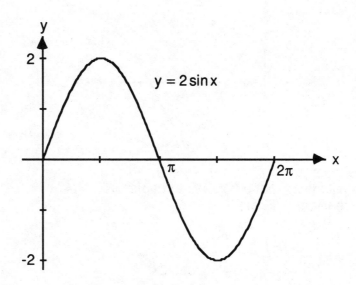

       (b)   y = - sin 2x
        amplitude: 1; period: π; x-intercepts: 0, π/2, π
        increasing: (π/4, 3π/4)

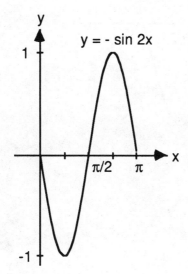

11. (a) $y = \cos 2x$
        amplitude: 1; period: π; x-intercepts: $\pi/4$, $3\pi/4$
        increasing: $(\pi/2, \pi)$

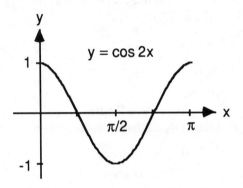

(b) $y = 2 \cos 2x$
        amplitude: 2; period: π; x-intercepts: $\pi/4$, $3\pi/4$
        increasing: $(\pi/2, \pi)$

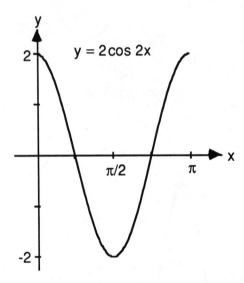

13.   (a) $y = 3 \sin \dfrac{\pi x}{2}$

amplitude: 3; period: 4; x-intercepts: 0, 2, 4; increasing: $(0, 1) \cup (3, 4)$

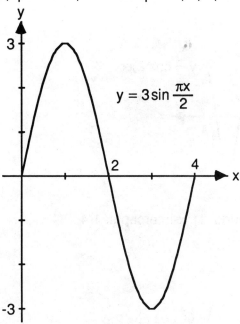

$y = 3 \sin \dfrac{\pi x}{2}$

(b) $y = -3 \sin \dfrac{\pi x}{2}$

amplitude: 3; period: 4; x-intercepts: 0, 2, 4; increasing: $(1, 3)$

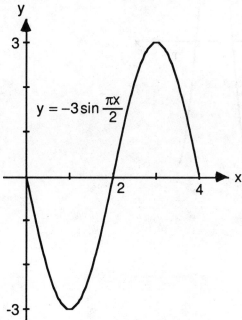

$y = -3 \sin \dfrac{\pi x}{2}$

15. (a) $y = \cos 2\pi x$
          amplitude: 1; period: 1; x-intercepts: 1/4, 3/4
          increasing: (1/2, 1)

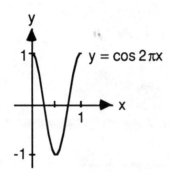

     (b) $y = -4 \cos 2\pi x$
          amplitude: 4; period: 1; x-intercepts: 1/4, 3/4
          increasing: (0, 1/2)

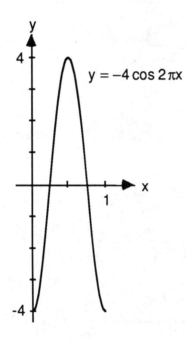

17. $y = 1 + \sin 2x$
     amplitude: 1; period: π; x-intercept: $3\pi/4$
     increasing: $(0, \pi/4) \cup (3\pi/4, \pi)$

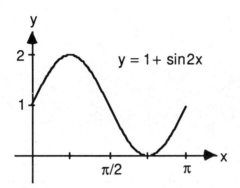

19. $y = 1 - \cos \dfrac{\pi x}{3}$

     amplitude: 1; period: 6; x-intercepts: 0, 6
     increasing: $(0, 3)$

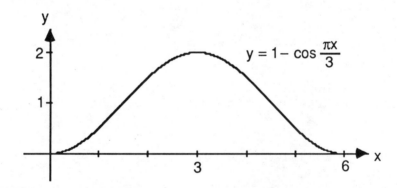

21. $f(x) = \sin\left(x - \dfrac{\pi}{6}\right)$

amplitude: 1; period: 2π; phase shift: $\pi/6$
x-intercepts: $\pi/6$, $7\pi/6$, $13\pi/6$; high point: $(2\pi/3, 1)$; low point: $(5\pi/3, -1)$

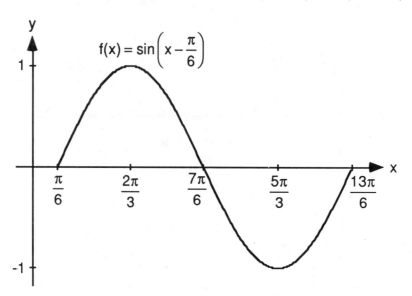

23. $F(x) = -\cos\left(x + \dfrac{\pi}{4}\right)$

amplitude: 1; period: 2π; phase shift: $-\pi/4$
x-intercepts: $\pi/4$, $5\pi/4$; high point: $(3\pi/4, 1)$; low points: $(-\pi/4, -1)$, $(7\pi/4, -1)$

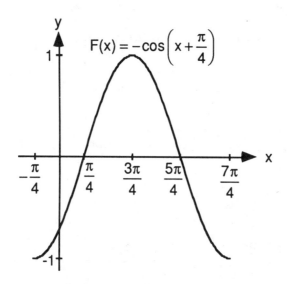

25. $y = \sin\left(2x - \dfrac{\pi}{2}\right)$

amplitude: 1; period: π; phase shift: $\pi/4$; x-intercepts: $\pi/4$, $3\pi/4$, $5\pi/4$
high point: $(\pi/2, 1)$; low point: $(\pi, -1)$

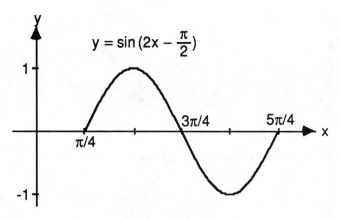

27. $y = \cos(2x - \pi)$

amplitude: 1; period: π; phase shift: $\pi/2$; x-intercepts: $3\pi/4$, $5\pi/4$
high points: $(\pi/2, 1)$, $(3\pi/2, 1)$; low point: $(\pi, -1)$

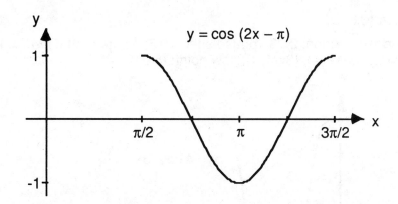

29. $y = 3 \sin \left(\frac{1}{2} x + \frac{\pi}{6} \right)$

amplitude: 3; period: 4π; phase shift: -π/3; x-intercepts: -π/3, 5π/3, 11π/3
high point: (2π/3, 3); low point: (8π/3, -3)

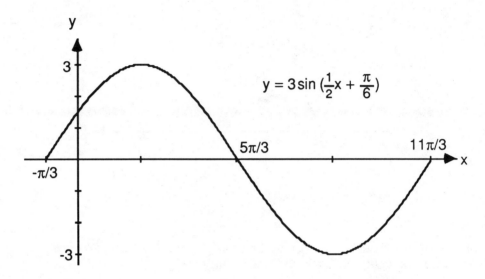

31. $y = 4 \cos \left(3x - \frac{\pi}{4} \right)$

amplitude: 4; period: 2π/3; phase shift: π/12; x-intercepts: π/4, 7π/12
high points: (π/12, 4), (3π/4, 4); low point: (5π/12, -4)

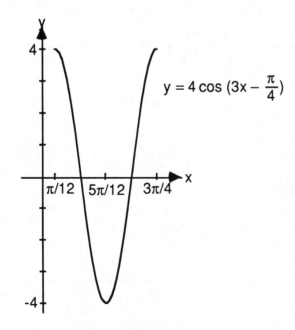

33. $y = \frac{1}{2} \sin \left(\frac{\pi x}{2} - \pi^2 \right)$

amplitude: 1/2; period: 4; phase shift: 2π; x-intercepts: 2π, $2\pi + 2$, $2\pi + 4$
high point: $(2\pi + 1, 1/2)$; low point: $(2\pi + 3, -1/2)$

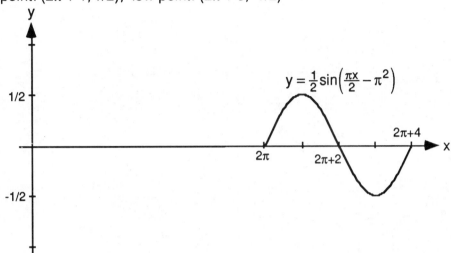

35. $y = 1 - \cos \left(2x - \frac{\pi}{3} \right)$

amplitude: 1; period: π; phase shift: $\pi/6$; x-intercepts: $\pi/6$, $7\pi/6$
high point: $(2\pi/3, 2)$; low points: $(\pi/6, 0)$, $(7\pi/6, 0)$

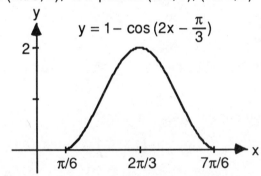

37. This is a sine function where the amplitude is 2 and the period is 4π.
So A = 2, B = 1/2.

39. This is a sine function (reflected across the x-axis) where the amplitude is
3 and the period is 2. So A = -3, B = π.

41. This is a cosine function (reflected across the x-axis) where the amplitude is
4 and the period is 10π. So A = -4, B = 1/5.

43.   amplitude: 1/2; period: π

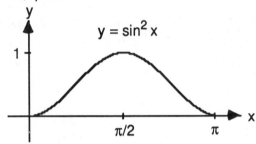

45. $y = \sin x \cos x = \dfrac{1}{2} \sin 2x$

amplitude: 1/2; period: π

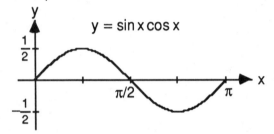

47.   (a)   Since C lies on the unit circle, its coordinates are C(cos θ, sin θ).

(b)   Since ∠AOB = θ = ∠COD, and AO = CO, then the two triangles are congruent.

(c)   Since AB = CD and OB = OD, then the coordinates of B are B(- sin θ, cos θ).

(d)   Matching up x- and y-coordinates, we have:

$$\cos\left(\theta + \frac{\pi}{2}\right) = -\sin\theta \ \text{ and } \ \sin\left(\theta + \frac{\pi}{2}\right) = \cos\theta$$

49.   At P, we find the first positive value of x where sin x = 1:
$$y = e^{\sin x} = e^1 = e \approx 2.71$$
$$x = \frac{\pi}{2} \approx 1.57$$
So P = (π/2, e) ≈ (1.57, 2.71).
At Q, we find the first positive value of x where sin x = -1:
$$y = e^{\sin x} = e^{-1} = \frac{1}{e} \approx 0.37$$
$$x = \frac{3\pi}{2} \approx 4.71$$
So Q = (3π/2, 1/e) ≈ (4.71, 0.37).

51. (a)   Clearly the amplitude is 3. The period is $\frac{2\pi}{\pi/3} = 6$. For $0 \le t \le 12$, we get two cycles:

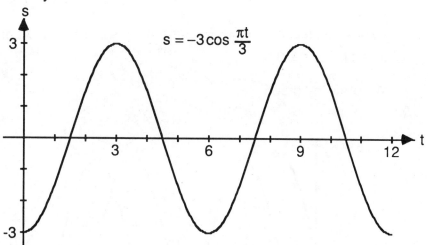

$$s = -3\cos\frac{\pi t}{3}$$

(b)   The weight is farthest from the origin when $|s| = 3$. This occurs when $t = 0, 3, 6, 9, 12$ sec.

(c)   The weight is positioned at the origin when $s = 0$. This occurs when $t = \frac{3}{2}, \frac{9}{2}, \frac{15}{2}, \frac{21}{2}$ sec.

(d)   The amplitude here is π, slightly more than 3.   The period is 6. For $0 \le t \le 12$, we get two cycles:

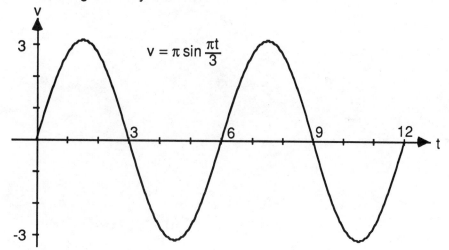

$$v = \pi \sin\frac{\pi t}{3}$$

(e)   The velocity is 0 when $t = 0, 3, 6, 9, 12$ sec. At those values, s is alternately -3, 3, -3, 3, and -3.

(f) $v < 0$ when $3 < t < 6$ and $9 < t < 12$

(g)   The velocity is greatest at $t = \dfrac{3}{2}, \dfrac{15}{2}$, where $v \approx 3.14$ ft/sec. The velocity is least at $t = \dfrac{9}{2}, \dfrac{21}{2}$, where $v \approx -3.14$ ft/sec. At each of these times $s = 0$.

(h)   We draw the graph:

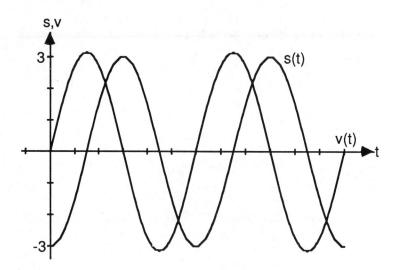

6.4 Graphs of the Tangent and the Reciprocal Functions

1. (a) $y = \tan\left(x + \frac{\pi}{4}\right)$

x-intercept: -π/4
y-intercept: 1
asymptotes: x = -3π/4, x = π/4

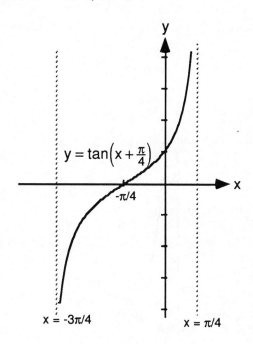

(b) $y = -\tan\left(x + \dfrac{\pi}{4}\right)$

x-intercept: -π/4
y-intercept: -1
asymptotes: x = -3π/4, x = π/4

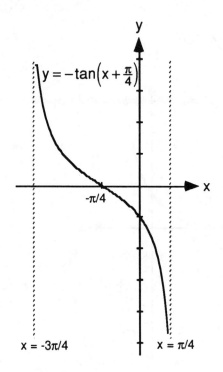

3.   (a) $y = \tan \dfrac{x}{3}$

x-intercept: 0
y-intercept: 0
asymptotes: $x = -3\pi/2$, $x = 3\pi/2$

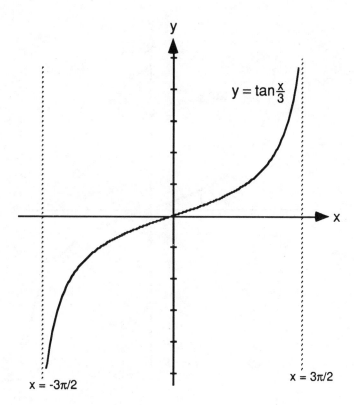

(b) $y = -\tan\dfrac{x}{3}$

   x-intercept: 0
   y-intercept: 0
   asymptotes: $x = -3\pi/2$, $x = 3\pi/2$

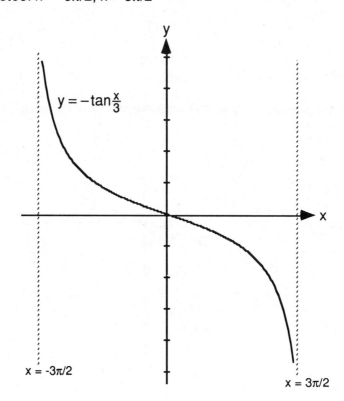

5. $y = \dfrac{1}{2}\tan\dfrac{\pi x}{2}$

x-intercept: 0; y-intercept: 0; asymptotes: x = -1, x = 1

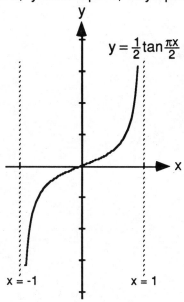

7. $y = \cot\dfrac{\pi x}{2}$

x-intercept: 1; y-intercept: none; asymptotes: x = 0, x = 2

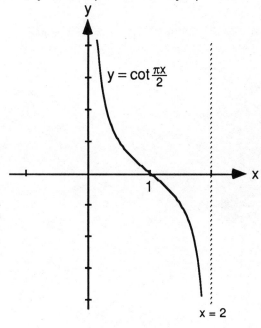

9. $y = -\cot\left(x - \dfrac{\pi}{4}\right)$

x-intercept: $3\pi/4$; y-intercept: 1; asymptotes: $x = \pi/4$, $x = 5\pi/4$

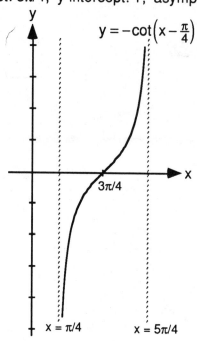

11. $y = \dfrac{1}{2}\cot 2x$

x-intercept: $\pi/4$; y-intercept: none; asymptotes: $x = 0$, $x = \pi/2$

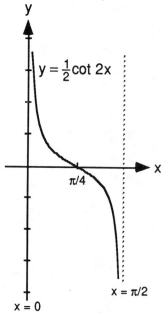

13. $y = \csc\left(x - \dfrac{\pi}{4}\right)$

x-intercept: none

y-intercept: $-\sqrt{2}$
asymptotes: $x = -3\pi/4$, $x = \pi/4$, $x = 5\pi/4$

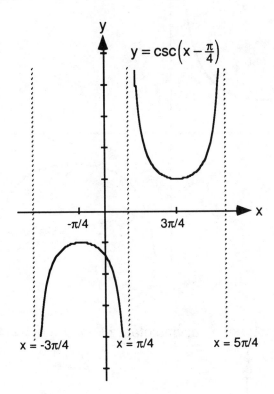

15. $y = -\csc \dfrac{x}{2}$

x-intercept: none; y-intercept: none; asymptotes: $x = -2\pi$, $x = 0$, $x = 2\pi$

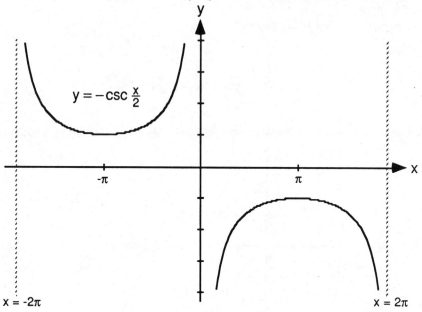

17. $y = \dfrac{1}{3} \csc \pi x$

x-intercept: none; y-intercept: none; asymptotes: $x = -1$, $x = 0$, $x = 1$

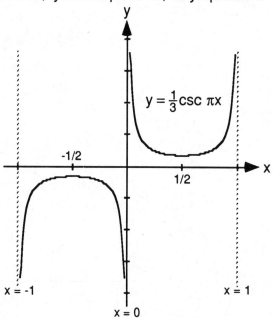

19. y = - sec x
     x-intercept: none; y-intercept: -1; asymptotes: x = -π/2, x = π/2, x = 3π/2

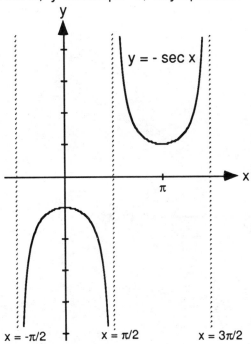

21. y = sec (x - π)
     x-intercept: none; y-intercept: -1; asymptotes: x = π/2, x = 3π/2, x = 5π/2

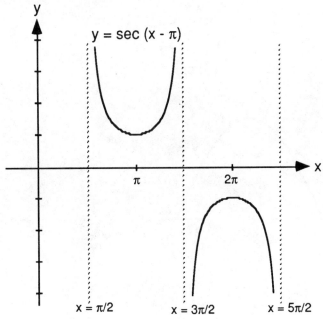

23. $y = 3 \sec \dfrac{\pi x}{2}$

x-intercept: none; y-intercept: 3; asymptotes: x = -1, x = 1, x = 3

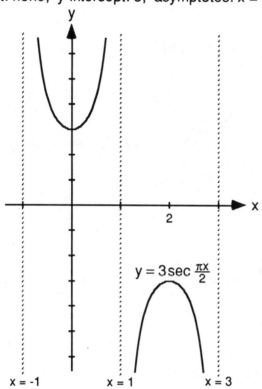

25. (a) $(f \circ h)(x) = f\left(\pi x - \dfrac{\pi}{6}\right) = \sin\left(\pi x - \dfrac{\pi}{6}\right)$

period: 2; amplitude: 1; phase shift: 1/6

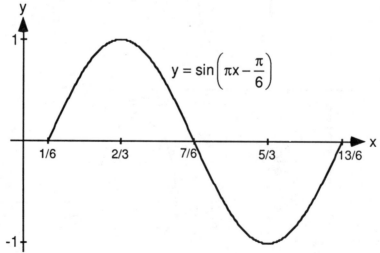

(b) $(g \circ h)(x) = g\left(\pi x - \dfrac{\pi}{6}\right) = \csc\left(\pi x - \dfrac{\pi}{6}\right)$

period: 2; phase shift: 1/6; asymptotes: x = 1/6, x = 7/6, x = 11/6

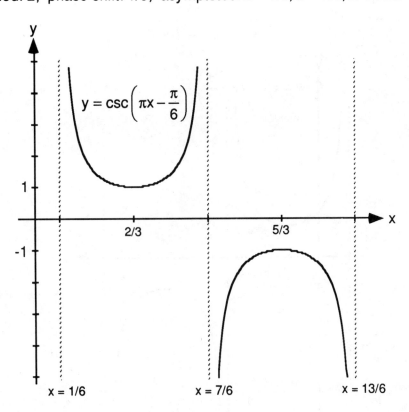

27.   (a) $(f \circ H)(x) = f\left(\pi x + \dfrac{\pi}{4}\right) = \sin\left(\pi x + \dfrac{\pi}{4}\right)$

period: 2; amplitude: 1; phase shift: -1/4

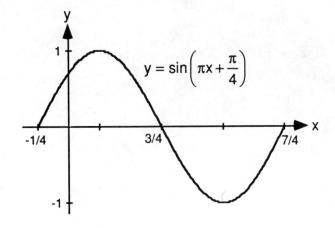

(b) $(g \circ H)(x) = g\left(\pi x + \dfrac{\pi}{4}\right) = \csc\left(\pi x + \dfrac{\pi}{4}\right)$

period: 2
phase shift: -1/4
asymptotes: x = -1/4, x = 3/4, x = 7/4

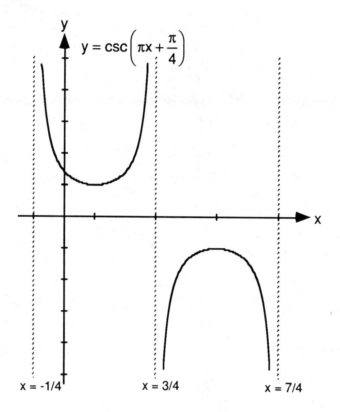

29. $(A \circ T)(x) = A(\tan x) = |\tan x|$

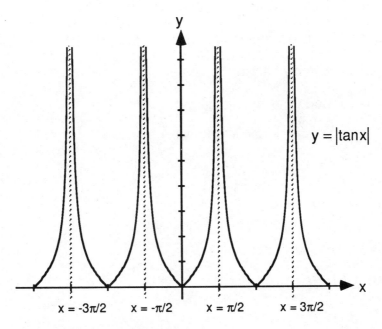

$y = |\tan x|$

$x = -3\pi/2$ $x = -\pi/2$ $x = \pi/2$ $x = 3\pi/2$

31. $(A \circ f)(x) = A(\csc x) = |\csc x|$

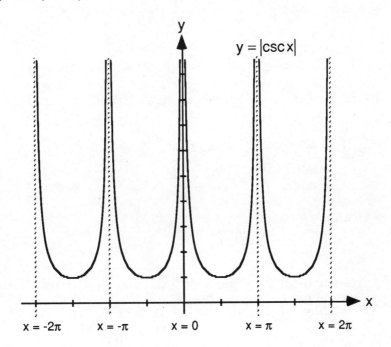

$y = |\csc x|$

$x = -2\pi$ $x = -\pi$ $x = 0$ $x = \pi$ $x = 2\pi$

33. (a) P and Q are both points on the unit circle, and thus the coordinates
are P(cos s, sin s) and $Q\left(\cos(s - \pi/2), \sin(s - \pi/2)\right)$.

(b) Since △OAP is congruent to △OBQ (labeling the third vertex B), then
OA = OB and AP = BQ. Because the y-coordinate at Q is negative, we
have concluded what was required.

(c) Restating part (b), we have shown:

$$\cos\left(s - \frac{\pi}{2}\right) = \sin s \quad \text{and} \quad \sin\left(s - \frac{\pi}{2}\right) = -\cos s$$

(d) $\cot s = \dfrac{\cos s}{\sin s} = \dfrac{-\sin\left(s - \frac{\pi}{2}\right)}{\cos\left(s - \frac{\pi}{2}\right)} = -\tan\left(s - \frac{\pi}{2}\right)$

6.5 The Addition Formulas

1. (a) $\sin\theta\cos2\theta + \cos\theta\sin2\theta = \sin(\theta + 2\theta) = \sin3\theta$

(b) $\sin\dfrac{\pi}{6}\cos\dfrac{\pi}{3} + \cos\dfrac{\pi}{6}\sin\dfrac{\pi}{3} = \sin\left(\dfrac{\pi}{6} + \dfrac{\pi}{3}\right) = \sin\dfrac{\pi}{2} = 1$

3. (a) $\cos2u\cos3u - \sin2u\sin3u = \cos(2u + 3u) = \cos5u$

(b) $\cos2u\cos3u + \sin2u\sin3u = \cos(2u - 3u) = \cos(-u) = \cos u$

5. $\sin(A + B)\cos A - \cos(A + B)\sin A = \sin(A + B - A) = \sin B$

7. $\sin\left(\theta - \dfrac{3\pi}{2}\right) = \sin\theta\cos\dfrac{3\pi}{2} - \cos\theta\sin\dfrac{3\pi}{2}$

$$= \sin\theta \cdot 0 - \cos\theta \cdot (-1)$$
$$= \cos\theta$$

9. $\cos(\theta + \pi) = \cos\theta\cos\pi - \sin\theta\sin\pi$

$$= \cos\theta \cdot (-1) - \sin\theta \cdot 0$$
$$= -\cos\theta$$

11. $\sin(\theta + 2\pi) = \sin\theta\cos2\pi + \cos\theta\sin2\pi$

$$= \sin\theta \cdot 1 + \cos\theta \cdot 0$$
$$= \sin\theta$$

13. $\cos (75°) = \cos (45° + 30°)$

$= (\cos 45°)(\cos 30°) - (\sin 45°)(\sin 30°)$

$= \dfrac{\sqrt{2}}{2} \cdot \dfrac{\sqrt{3}}{2} - \dfrac{\sqrt{2}}{2} \cdot \dfrac{1}{2}$

$= \dfrac{\sqrt{6} - \sqrt{2}}{4}$

15. $\sin \dfrac{7\pi}{12} = \sin \left(\dfrac{\pi}{3} + \dfrac{\pi}{4} \right)$

$= \sin \dfrac{\pi}{3} \cos \dfrac{\pi}{4} + \sin \dfrac{\pi}{4} \cos \dfrac{\pi}{3}$

$= \dfrac{\sqrt{3}}{2} \cdot \dfrac{\sqrt{2}}{2} + \dfrac{\sqrt{2}}{2} \cdot \dfrac{1}{2}$

$= \dfrac{\sqrt{6} + \sqrt{2}}{4}$

17. $\sin\left(\dfrac{\pi}{4} + s\right) - \sin\left(\dfrac{\pi}{4} - s\right) = \left(\sin \dfrac{\pi}{4} \cos s + \cos \dfrac{\pi}{4} \sin s \right) - \left(\sin \dfrac{\pi}{4} \cos s - \cos \dfrac{\pi}{4} \sin s \right)$

$= \dfrac{\sqrt{2}}{2} \cos s + \dfrac{\sqrt{2}}{2} \sin s - \dfrac{\sqrt{2}}{2} \cos s + \dfrac{\sqrt{2}}{2} \sin s$

$= \sqrt{2} \sin s$

19. $\cos\left(\dfrac{\pi}{3} - \theta\right) - \cos\left(\dfrac{\pi}{3} + \theta\right) = \left(\cos \dfrac{\pi}{3} \cos\theta + \sin \dfrac{\pi}{3} \sin\theta \right) - \left(\cos \dfrac{\pi}{3} \cos\theta - \sin \dfrac{\pi}{3} \sin\theta \right)$

$= \dfrac{1}{2} \cos \theta + \dfrac{\sqrt{3}}{2} \sin \theta - \dfrac{1}{2} \cos \theta + \dfrac{\sqrt{3}}{2} \sin \theta$

$= \sqrt{3} \sin \theta$

21. (a) First we need to compute $\cos \alpha$ and $\sin \beta$. Since the terminal side of α lies in the second quadrant, $\cos \alpha$ is negative and we have:

$$\cos \alpha = -\sqrt{1 - \sin^2 \alpha} = -\sqrt{1 - \dfrac{144}{169}} = -\sqrt{\dfrac{25}{169}} = -\dfrac{5}{13}$$

Since the terminal side of β lies in the fourth quadrant, $\sin \beta$ is negative and we have:

$$\sin \beta = -\sqrt{1 - \cos^2 \beta} = -\sqrt{1 - \dfrac{9}{25}} = -\sqrt{\dfrac{16}{25}} = -\dfrac{4}{5}$$

Thus:

$$\sin(\alpha + \beta) = \sin\alpha\cos\beta + \cos\alpha\sin\beta$$

$$= \frac{12}{13} \cdot \frac{3}{5} - \frac{-5}{13} \cdot \frac{-4}{5}$$

$$= \frac{36}{65} + \frac{20}{65}$$

$$= \frac{56}{65}$$

(b) $\sin(\alpha - \beta) = \sin\alpha\cos\beta - \cos\alpha\sin\beta$

$$= \frac{12}{13} \cdot \frac{3}{5} - \frac{-5}{13} \cdot \frac{-4}{5}$$

$$= \frac{36}{65} - \frac{20}{65}$$

$$= \frac{16}{65}$$

(c) $\cos(\alpha + \beta) = \cos\alpha\cos\beta - \sin\alpha\sin\beta$

$$= -\frac{5}{13} \cdot \frac{3}{5} - \frac{12}{13} \cdot \frac{-4}{5}$$

$$= \frac{-15}{65} + \frac{48}{65}$$

$$= \frac{33}{65}$$

(d) $\cos(\alpha - \beta) = \cos\alpha\cos\beta + \sin\alpha\sin\beta$

$$= -\frac{5}{13} \cdot \frac{3}{5} + \frac{12}{13} \cdot \frac{-4}{5}$$

$$= -\frac{15}{65} - \frac{48}{65}$$

$$= -\frac{63}{65}$$

23. (a)   For $\dfrac{3\pi}{2} < \theta < 2\pi$, we have:

$$\sin\theta = -\sqrt{1 - \cos^2\theta} = -\sqrt{1 - \frac{144}{169}} = -\frac{5}{13}$$

(b) $\cos 2\theta = \cos(\theta + \theta)$
$= \cos\theta\cos\theta - \sin\theta\sin\theta$
$= \cos^2\theta - \sin^2\theta$
$= \dfrac{144}{169} - \dfrac{25}{169}$
$= \dfrac{119}{169}$

25. $\sec s = \dfrac{5}{4}$ so $\cos s = \dfrac{4}{5}$ and $\sin s = -\sqrt{1 - \dfrac{16}{25}} = -\dfrac{3}{5}$

$\cot t = -1$ so $\cos t = -\dfrac{\sqrt{2}}{2}$ and $\sin t = \dfrac{\sqrt{2}}{2}$

Thus, we have:
$\sin(s - t) = \sin s\cos t - \sin t\cos s$
$= -\dfrac{3}{5}\bullet\dfrac{-\sqrt{2}}{2} - \dfrac{\sqrt{2}}{2}\bullet\dfrac{4}{5}$
$= \dfrac{3\sqrt{2} - 4\sqrt{2}}{10}$
$= -\dfrac{\sqrt{2}}{10}$

$\cos(s + t) = \cos s\cos t - \sin s\sin t$
$= \dfrac{4}{5}\bullet\dfrac{-\sqrt{2}}{2} - \dfrac{-3}{5}\bullet\dfrac{\sqrt{2}}{2}$
$= \dfrac{-4\sqrt{2} + 3\sqrt{2}}{10}$
$= -\dfrac{\sqrt{2}}{10}$

27. $\dfrac{\sin(s + t)}{\cos s\cos t} = \dfrac{\sin s\cos t + \cos s\sin t}{\cos s\cos t} = \dfrac{\sin s}{\cos s} + \dfrac{\sin t}{\cos t} = \tan s + \tan t$

29. $\cos(A - B) - \cos(A + B)$
$= (\cos A\cos B + \sin A\sin B) - (\cos A\cos B - \sin A\sin B)$
$= \cos A\cos B + \sin A\sin B - \cos A\cos B + \sin A\sin B$
$= 2\sin A\sin B$

31. $\cos(A + B)\cos(A - B) = (\cos A\cos B - \sin A\sin B)(\cos A\cos B + \sin A\sin B)$
$= (\cos A\cos B)^2 - (\sin A\sin B)^2$
$= \cos^2 A\cos^2 B - \sin^2 A\sin^2 B$
$= \cos^2 A(1 - \sin^2 B) - (1 - \cos^2 A)\sin^2 B$
$= \cos^2 A - \cos^2 A\sin^2 B - \sin^2 B + \cos^2 A\sin^2 B$
$= \cos^2 A - \sin^2 B$

33. $\cos(\alpha + \beta)\cos\beta + \sin(\alpha + \beta)\sin\beta$
$$= (\cos\alpha\cos\beta - \sin\alpha\sin\beta)\cos\beta + (\sin\alpha\cos\beta + \cos\alpha\sin\beta)\sin\beta$$
$$= \cos\alpha\cos^2\beta - \sin\alpha\sin\beta\cos\beta + \sin\alpha\sin\beta\cos\beta + \cos\alpha\sin^2\beta$$
$$= \cos\alpha\cos^2\beta + \cos\alpha\sin^2\beta$$
$$= \cos\alpha\,(\cos^2\beta + \sin^2\beta)$$
$$= \cos\alpha$$

35.   (a)   We complete the table:

t	1	2	3	4
f(t)	1.5	1.5	1.5	1.5

(b)   Conjecture: $f(t) = 1.5$
To prove this, we first simplify the expressions:
$$\cos\left(t + \frac{2\pi}{3}\right) = \cos t \cos\frac{2\pi}{3} - \sin t \sin\frac{2\pi}{3} = -\frac{1}{2}\cos t - \frac{\sqrt{3}}{2}\sin t$$
$$\cos\left(t - \frac{2\pi}{3}\right) = \cos t \cos\frac{2\pi}{3} + \sin t \sin\frac{2\pi}{3} = -\frac{1}{2}\cos t + \frac{\sqrt{3}}{2}\sin t$$

So:
$$\cos^2\left(t + \frac{2\pi}{3}\right) = \left(-\frac{1}{2}\cos t - \frac{\sqrt{3}}{2}\sin t\right)^2$$
$$= \frac{1}{4}\cos^2 t + \frac{\sqrt{3}}{2}\sin t \cos t + \frac{3}{4}\sin^2 t$$
$$\cos^2\left(t - \frac{2\pi}{3}\right) = \left(-\frac{1}{2}\cos t + \frac{\sqrt{3}}{2}\sin t\right)^2$$
$$= \frac{1}{4}\cos^2 t - \frac{\sqrt{3}}{2}\sin t \cos t + \frac{3}{4}\sin^2 t$$

Thus:
$$f(t) = \cos^2 t + \left(\frac{1}{4}\cos^2 t + \frac{\sqrt{3}}{2}\sin t \cos t + \frac{3}{4}\sin^2 t\right)$$
$$+ \left(\frac{1}{4}\cos^2 t - \frac{\sqrt{3}}{2}\sin t \cos t + \frac{3}{4}\sin^2 t\right)$$
$$= \frac{3}{2}\cos^2 t + \frac{3}{2}\sin^2 t$$
$$= \frac{3}{2}(\cos^2 t + \sin^2 t)$$
$$= \frac{3}{2}$$

37.   When $f(\theta) = \sin\theta$, then $f(\theta + h) = \sin(\theta + h) = \sin\theta\cos h + \cos\theta\sin h$
So $f(\theta + h) - f(\theta) = \sin\theta\,(\cos h - 1) + \cos\theta\sin h$
Thus $\dfrac{f(\theta + h) - f(\theta)}{h} = \sin\theta \bullet \dfrac{\cos h - 1}{h} + \cos\theta \bullet \dfrac{\sin h}{h}$

39.   Consider $\dfrac{\sin (A - B)}{\cos A \cos B} = \dfrac{\sin A \cos B - \sin B \cos A}{\cos A \cos B} = \tan A - \tan B$

Hence the given expression is equivalent to:

$\tan \alpha - \tan \beta + \tan \beta - \tan \gamma + \tan \gamma - \tan \alpha = 0$

41.   Since $a^2 + b^2 = 1$ and $c^2 + d^2 = 1$, then $-1 \le a \le 1$ and $-1 \le c \le 1$.
So, choosing θ and ϕ such that $a = \cos \theta$, $c = \cos \phi$, we have:

$b^2 = 1 - a^2 = 1 - \cos^2 \theta = \sin^2 \theta$

$d^2 = 1 - c^2 = 1 - \cos^2 \phi = \sin^2 \phi$

and thus $b = \sin \theta$ and $d = \sin \phi$. Thus:

$\left| ac + bd \right| = \left| \cos \theta \cos \phi + \sin \theta \sin \phi \right| = \left| \cos (\theta - \phi) \right| \le 1$

43.   (a)   Using $\triangle ABH$, $\cos (\alpha + \beta) = \dfrac{AB}{1}$, so $\cos (\alpha + \beta) = AB$

(b)   Using $\triangle ACF$, $\cos \alpha = \dfrac{AC}{AF} = \dfrac{AC}{\cos \beta}$ using #42(e),

so $AC = \cos \alpha \cos \beta$

(c)   Using $\triangle EFH$, $\sin (\angle EHF) = \dfrac{EF}{HF}$. But $\angle EHF = \alpha$ from #42(c), and

$HF = \sin \beta$ from #42(b), so $\sin \alpha = \dfrac{EF}{\sin \beta}$, and thus $EF = \sin \alpha \sin \beta$

(d) $AB = AC - BC$
$\cos (\alpha + \beta) = \cos \alpha \cos \beta - \sin \alpha \sin \beta$ from the above three steps

45.   (a) $\tan A + \tan B + \tan C = \tan 20° + \tan 50° + \tan 110° \approx -1.1918$
$\tan A \tan B \tan C = \tan 20° \tan 50° \tan 110° \approx -1.1918$
It appears that they both equal each other.

(b) $\tan \alpha + \tan \beta + \tan \gamma = \tan \dfrac{\pi}{10} + \tan \dfrac{3\pi}{10} + \tan \dfrac{3\pi}{5} \approx -1.3764$

$\tan \alpha \tan \beta \tan \gamma = \tan \dfrac{\pi}{10} \tan \dfrac{3\pi}{10} \tan \dfrac{3\pi}{5} \approx -1.3764$

Again, they appear to be equal.

(c)   Since:

$\dfrac{\tan A + \tan B}{1 - \tan A \tan B} = \tan (A + B)$

And:

$\tan (A + B) = - \tan [\pi - (A + B)] = - \tan C \quad (\text{recall } A + B + C = \pi)$

So:

$$\frac{\tan A + \tan B}{1 - \tan A \tan B} = -\tan C$$

$$\tan A + \tan B = -\tan C + \tan A \tan B \tan C$$

$$\tan A + \tan B + \tan C = \tan A \tan B \tan C$$

6.6 Further Identities

1. (a) $\tan \theta = \frac{3}{4}$ and $\tan t = \frac{7}{24}$, so:

$$\tan (\theta + t) = \frac{\tan \theta + \tan t}{1 - \tan \theta \tan t} = \frac{\frac{3}{4} + \frac{7}{24}}{1 - \frac{3}{4} \cdot \frac{7}{24}} = \frac{\frac{25}{24}}{\frac{25}{32}} = \frac{4}{3}$$

(b) $\tan (\theta - t) = \frac{\tan \theta - \tan t}{1 + \tan \theta \tan t} = \frac{\frac{3}{4} - \frac{7}{24}}{1 + \frac{3}{4} \cdot \frac{7}{24}} = \frac{\frac{11}{24}}{\frac{39}{32}} = \frac{44}{117}$

3. (a) $\tan \theta = \frac{3}{4}$ and $\tan \frac{\pi}{4} = 1$, so:

$$\tan \left(\theta + \frac{\pi}{4}\right) = \frac{\tan \theta + \tan \frac{\pi}{4}}{1 - \tan \theta \tan \frac{\pi}{4}} = \frac{\frac{3}{4} + 1}{1 - \frac{3}{4} \cdot 1} = \frac{\frac{7}{4}}{\frac{1}{4}} = 7$$

(b) $\tan \left(\theta - \frac{\pi}{4}\right) = \frac{\tan \theta - \tan \frac{\pi}{4}}{1 + \tan \theta \tan \frac{\pi}{4}} = \frac{\frac{3}{4} - 1}{1 + \frac{3}{4} \cdot 1} = \frac{-\frac{1}{4}}{\frac{7}{4}} = -\frac{1}{7}$

5. (a) $\sin \theta = \frac{3}{5}$ and $\cos \theta = \frac{4}{5}$, so:

$$\sin 2\theta = 2 \sin \theta \cos \theta = 2 \cdot \frac{3}{5} \cdot \frac{4}{5} = \frac{24}{25}$$

(b) $\cos 2\theta = \cos^2 \theta - \sin^2 \theta = \left(\frac{4}{5}\right)^2 - \left(\frac{3}{5}\right)^2 = \frac{16}{25} - \frac{9}{25} = \frac{7}{25}$

(c) $\tan \theta = \dfrac{3}{4}$, so:

$$\tan 2\theta \;=\; \frac{2\tan\theta}{1-\tan^2\theta} \;=\; \frac{2\cdot\dfrac{3}{4}}{1-\left(\dfrac{3}{4}\right)^2} \;=\; \frac{\dfrac{3}{2}}{\dfrac{7}{16}} \;=\; \frac{24}{7}$$

Note: An easier approach, after doing (a) and (b), would be to say:

$$\tan 2\theta \;=\; \frac{\sin 2\theta}{\cos 2\theta} \;=\; \frac{\dfrac{24}{25}}{\dfrac{7}{25}} \;=\; \frac{24}{7}$$

7.   (a) $\sin \beta = \dfrac{4}{5}$ and $\cos \beta = \dfrac{3}{5}$, so:

$$\sin 2\beta \;=\; 2\sin\beta\cos\beta \;=\; 2\cdot\frac{4}{5}\cdot\frac{3}{5} \;=\; \frac{24}{25}$$

(b) $\cos 2\beta \;=\; \cos^2\beta - \sin^2\beta \;=\; \left(\dfrac{3}{5}\right)^2 - \left(\dfrac{4}{5}\right)^2 \;=\; \dfrac{9}{25} - \dfrac{16}{25} \;=\; -\dfrac{7}{25}$

(c) $\tan 2\beta \;=\; \dfrac{\sin 2\beta}{\cos 2\beta} \;=\; \dfrac{\dfrac{24}{25}}{-\dfrac{7}{25}} \;=\; \dfrac{-24}{7}$

Note: We could also have used the double-angle formula.

9.   (a) $\sin \dfrac{\theta}{2}$ is positive and $\cos \theta = \dfrac{4}{5}$, so:

$$\sin \frac{\theta}{2} \;=\; \sqrt{\frac{1-\cos\theta}{2}} \;=\; \sqrt{\frac{1-\dfrac{4}{5}}{2}} \;=\; \sqrt{\frac{1}{10}} \;=\; \frac{\sqrt{10}}{10}$$

(b) $\cos \dfrac{\theta}{2}$ is positive and $\cos \theta = \dfrac{4}{5}$, so:

$$\cos \frac{\theta}{2} \;=\; \sqrt{\frac{1+\cos\theta}{2}} \;=\; \sqrt{\frac{1+\dfrac{4}{5}}{2}} \;=\; \sqrt{\frac{9}{10}} \;=\; \frac{3\sqrt{10}}{10}$$

(c) $\sin \theta = \dfrac{3}{5}$ and $\cos \theta = \dfrac{4}{5}$, so:

$$\tan \frac{\theta}{2} = \frac{\sin \theta}{1 + \cos \theta} = \frac{\dfrac{3}{5}}{1 + \dfrac{4}{5}} = \frac{3}{9} = \frac{1}{3}$$

Note: We could also have computed this directly after parts (a) and (b), as:

$$\tan \frac{\theta}{2} = \frac{\sin \dfrac{\theta}{2}}{\cos \dfrac{\theta}{2}} = \frac{\dfrac{\sqrt{10}}{10}}{\dfrac{3\sqrt{10}}{10}} = \frac{1}{3}$$

11.   (a) $\sin \dfrac{\beta}{2}$ is positive and $\cos \beta = \dfrac{3}{5}$, so:

$$\sin \frac{\beta}{2} = \sqrt{\frac{1 - \cos \beta}{2}} = \sqrt{\frac{1 - \dfrac{3}{5}}{2}} = \sqrt{\frac{1}{5}} = \frac{\sqrt{5}}{5}$$

(b) $\cos \dfrac{\beta}{2}$ is positive and $\cos \beta = \dfrac{3}{5}$, so:

$$\cos \frac{\beta}{2} = \sqrt{\frac{1 + \cos \beta}{2}} = \sqrt{\frac{1 + \dfrac{3}{5}}{2}} = \sqrt{\frac{4}{5}} = \frac{2\sqrt{5}}{5}$$

(c) $\tan \dfrac{\beta}{2} = \dfrac{\sin \dfrac{\beta}{2}}{\cos \dfrac{\beta}{2}} = \dfrac{\dfrac{\sqrt{5}}{5}}{\dfrac{2\sqrt{5}}{5}} = \dfrac{1}{2}$

13.   We first draw a reference triangle in the second quadrant:

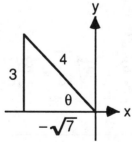

(a) $\sin 2\theta = 2 \sin \theta \cos \theta = 2 \cdot \dfrac{3}{4} \cdot \dfrac{-\sqrt{7}}{4} = -\dfrac{3\sqrt{7}}{8}$

(b) $\cos 2\theta = \cos^2\theta - \sin^2\theta = \left(-\dfrac{\sqrt{7}}{4}\right)^2 - \left(\dfrac{3}{4}\right)^2 = \dfrac{7}{16} - \dfrac{9}{16} = -\dfrac{1}{8}$

(c)   Since $\dfrac{\pi}{4} < \dfrac{\theta}{2} < \dfrac{\pi}{2}$, then $\sin\dfrac{\theta}{2}$ is positive:

$$\sin\dfrac{\theta}{2} = \sqrt{\dfrac{1 - \cos\theta}{2}} = \sqrt{\dfrac{1 - \left(-\dfrac{\sqrt{7}}{4}\right)}{2}} = \sqrt{\dfrac{4 + \sqrt{7}}{8}} = \dfrac{\sqrt{8 + 2\sqrt{7}}}{4}$$

(d)   Since $\dfrac{\pi}{4} < \dfrac{\theta}{2} < \dfrac{\pi}{2}$, then $\cos\dfrac{\theta}{2}$ is positive:

$$\cos\dfrac{\theta}{2} = \sqrt{\dfrac{1 + \cos\theta}{2}} = \sqrt{\dfrac{1 - \dfrac{\sqrt{7}}{4}}{2}} = \sqrt{\dfrac{4 - \sqrt{7}}{8}} = \dfrac{\sqrt{8 - 2\sqrt{7}}}{4}$$

15.   We first draw a reference triangle in the third quadrant:

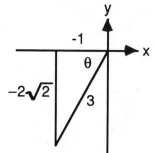

(a) $\sin 2\theta = 2\sin\theta\cos\theta = 2 \bullet \dfrac{-2\sqrt{2}}{3} \bullet \dfrac{-1}{3} = \dfrac{4\sqrt{2}}{9}$

(b) $\cos 2\theta = \cos^2\theta - \sin^2\theta = \left(-\dfrac{1}{3}\right)^2 - \left(-\dfrac{2\sqrt{2}}{3}\right)^2 = \dfrac{1}{9} - \dfrac{8}{9} = -\dfrac{7}{9}$

(c)   Since $\dfrac{\pi}{2} < \dfrac{\theta}{2} < \dfrac{3\pi}{4}$, then $\sin\dfrac{\theta}{2}$ is positive:

$$\sin\dfrac{\theta}{2} = \sqrt{\dfrac{1 - \cos\theta}{2}} = \sqrt{\dfrac{1 - \left(-\dfrac{1}{3}\right)}{2}} = \sqrt{\dfrac{2}{3}} = \dfrac{\sqrt{6}}{3}$$

(d)   Since $\dfrac{\pi}{2} < \dfrac{\theta}{2} < \dfrac{3\pi}{4}$, then $\cos\dfrac{\theta}{2}$ is negative:

$$\cos\dfrac{\theta}{2} = -\sqrt{\dfrac{1 + \cos\theta}{2}} = -\sqrt{\dfrac{1 - \dfrac{1}{3}}{2}} = -\sqrt{\dfrac{1}{3}} = -\dfrac{\sqrt{3}}{3}$$

17. (a) Since $0 < \dfrac{\pi}{12} < \dfrac{\pi}{2}$, then:

$$\sin \frac{\pi}{12} = \sqrt{\frac{1 - \cos \frac{\pi}{6}}{2}} = \sqrt{\frac{1 - \frac{\sqrt{3}}{2}}{2}} = \frac{\sqrt{2 - \sqrt{3}}}{2}$$

(b) Since $0 < \dfrac{\pi}{12} < \dfrac{\pi}{2}$, then:

$$\cos \frac{\pi}{12} = \sqrt{\frac{1 + \cos \frac{\pi}{6}}{2}} = \sqrt{\frac{1 + \frac{\sqrt{3}}{2}}{2}} = \frac{\sqrt{2 + \sqrt{3}}}{2}$$

(c) $\tan \dfrac{\pi}{12} = \dfrac{\sin \frac{\pi}{6}}{1 + \cos \frac{\pi}{6}}$

$$= \frac{\frac{1}{2}}{1 + \frac{\sqrt{3}}{2}}$$

$$= \frac{1}{2 + \sqrt{3}} \cdot \frac{2 - \sqrt{3}}{2 - \sqrt{3}}$$

$$= \frac{2 - \sqrt{3}}{4 - 3}$$

$$= 2 - \sqrt{3}$$

Note: We could also use (a) and (b), as follows:

$$\tan \frac{\pi}{12} = \frac{\sin \frac{\pi}{12}}{\cos \frac{\pi}{12}}$$

$$= \frac{\dfrac{\sqrt{2-\sqrt{3}}}{2}}{\dfrac{\sqrt{2+\sqrt{3}}}{2}}$$

$$= \frac{\sqrt{2-\sqrt{3}}}{\sqrt{2+\sqrt{3}}} \cdot \frac{\sqrt{2+\sqrt{3}}}{\sqrt{2+\sqrt{3}}}$$

$$= \frac{\sqrt{4-3}}{2+\sqrt{3}} \cdot \frac{2-\sqrt{3}}{2-\sqrt{3}}$$

$$= \frac{2-\sqrt{3}}{4-3}$$

$$= 2-\sqrt{3}$$

Since using the identity results in less algebraic simplification, we will use that approach.

19. (a) Since $90° < 105° < 180°$, then:

$$\sin 105° = \sqrt{\frac{1-\cos 210°}{2}} = \sqrt{\frac{1-\left(-\frac{\sqrt{3}}{2}\right)}{2}} = \frac{\sqrt{2+\sqrt{3}}}{2}$$

(b) Since $90° < 105° < 180°$, then:

$$\cos 105° = -\sqrt{\frac{1+\cos 210°}{2}} = -\sqrt{\frac{1-\frac{\sqrt{3}}{2}}{2}} = -\frac{\sqrt{2-\sqrt{3}}}{2}$$

(c) $\tan 105° = \dfrac{\sin 210°}{1 + \cos 210°}$

$= \dfrac{-\dfrac{1}{2}}{1 - \dfrac{\sqrt{3}}{2}}$

$= -\dfrac{1}{2 - \sqrt{3}} \cdot \dfrac{2 + \sqrt{3}}{2 + \sqrt{3}}$

$= -\dfrac{2 + \sqrt{3}}{4 - 3}$

$= -2 - \sqrt{3}$

21.   We draw a triangle in the first quadrant:

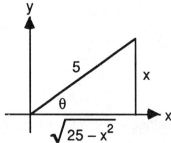

We now apply the double angle formulas:

$\sin 2\theta = 2 \sin \theta \cos \theta$

$= 2 \left(\dfrac{x}{5}\right) \left(\dfrac{\sqrt{25 - x^2}}{5}\right)$

$= \dfrac{2x\sqrt{25 - x^2}}{25}$

$\cos 2\theta = \cos^2 \theta - \sin^2 \theta$

$= \left(\dfrac{\sqrt{25 - x^2}}{5}\right)^2 - \left(\dfrac{x}{5}\right)^2$

$= \dfrac{25 - x^2}{5} - \dfrac{x^2}{25}$

$= \dfrac{25 - 2x^2}{25}$

23.   We draw a triangle in the first quadrant:

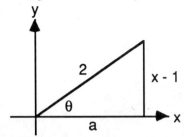

First, we find side a:
$$a^2 + (x - 1)^2 = 4$$
$$a^2 + x^2 - 2x + 1 = 4$$
$$a^2 = 3 + 2x - x^2$$
$$a = \sqrt{3 + 2x - x^2}$$

We now apply the double-angle formulas:
$$\sin 2\theta = 2 \sin \theta \cos \theta$$
$$= 2 \left(\frac{x - 1}{2}\right)\left(\frac{\sqrt{3 + 2x - x^2}}{2}\right)$$
$$= \frac{(x - 1)\sqrt{3 + 2x - x^2}}{2}$$
$$\cos 2\theta = \cos^2\theta - \sin^2\theta$$
$$= \left(\frac{\sqrt{3 + 2x - x^2}}{2}\right)^2 - \left(\frac{x - 1}{2}\right)^2$$
$$= \frac{3 + 3x - x^2}{4} - \frac{x^2 - 2x + 1}{4}$$
$$= \frac{2 + 4x - 2x^2}{4}$$
$$= \frac{1 + 2x - x^2}{2}$$

25. $\sin^4\theta = (\sin^2\theta)^2$
$$= \left(\frac{1 - \cos 2\theta}{2}\right)^2$$
$$= \frac{1 - 2\cos 2\theta + (\cos 2\theta)^2}{4}$$
$$= \frac{1 - 2\cos 2\theta + \dfrac{1 + \cos 4\theta}{2}}{4}$$
$$= \frac{2 - 4\cos 2\theta + 1 + \cos 4\theta}{8}$$
$$= \frac{3 - 4\cos 2\theta + \cos 4\theta}{8}$$

27. $\sin^4 \dfrac{\theta}{2} = \left(\sin^2 \dfrac{\theta}{2}\right)^2$

$\qquad = \left(\dfrac{1 - \cos\theta}{2}\right)^2$

$\qquad = \dfrac{1 - 2\cos\theta + \cos^2\theta}{4}$

$\qquad = \dfrac{1 - 2\cos\theta + \dfrac{1 + \cos 2\theta}{2}}{4}$

$\qquad = \dfrac{2 - 4\cos\theta + 1 + \cos 2\theta}{8}$

$\qquad = \dfrac{3 - 4\cos\theta + \cos 2\theta}{8}$

29. (a) $\cos 2\theta = \cos(\theta + \theta) = \cos\theta \cos\theta - \sin\theta \sin\theta = \cos^2\theta - \sin^2\theta$

(b) $\tan 2\theta = \tan(\theta + \theta) = \dfrac{\tan\theta + \tan\theta}{1 - \tan\theta \tan\theta} = \dfrac{2\tan\theta}{1 - \tan^2\theta}$

31. $\dfrac{1 - \tan^2 s}{1 + \tan^2 s} \cdot \dfrac{\cos^2 s}{\cos^2 s} = \dfrac{\cos^2 s - \sin^2 s}{\cos^2 s + \sin^2 s} = \cos^2 s - \sin^2 s = \cos 2s$

33. $\cos\theta = \cos\left[2\left(\dfrac{\theta}{2}\right)\right]$

$\qquad = \cos^2 \dfrac{\theta}{2} - \sin^2 \dfrac{\theta}{2}$

$\qquad = \cos^2 \dfrac{\theta}{2} - \left(1 - \cos^2 \dfrac{\theta}{2}\right)$

$\qquad = 2\cos^2 \dfrac{\theta}{2} - 1$

35. $\frac{1}{8}(3 - 4\cos 2\theta + \cos 4\theta)$ $= \frac{1}{8}(3 - 4\cos 2\theta + \cos^2 2\theta - \sin^2 2\theta)$

$= \frac{1}{8}(3 - 4\cos 2\theta + 2\cos^2 2\theta - 1)$

$= \frac{1}{8}(2 - 4\cos 2\theta + 2\cos^2 2\theta)$

$= \frac{1}{4}(\cos^2 2\theta - 2\cos 2\theta + 1)$

$= \frac{1}{4}(\cos 2\theta - 1)^2$

$= \frac{1}{4}(\cos^2\theta - \sin^2\theta - 1)^2$

$= \frac{1}{4}(\cos^2\theta - \sin^2\theta - \sin^2\theta - \cos^2\theta)^2$

$= \frac{1}{4}(-2\sin^2\theta)^2$

$= \sin^4\theta$

37. $\dfrac{2\tan\theta}{1 + \tan^2\theta}$ $= \dfrac{2\sin\theta}{\cos\theta\left(1 + \dfrac{\sin^2\theta}{\cos^2\theta}\right)}$

$= \dfrac{2\sin\theta\cos\theta}{\cos^2\theta + \sin^2\theta}$

$= 2\sin\theta\cos\theta$

$= \sin 2\theta$

39. $\sin 2\theta$ $= 2\sin\theta\cos\theta$

$= 2\sin\theta\cos\theta(\sin^2\theta + \cos^2\theta)$

$= 2\sin^3\theta\cos\theta + 2\sin\theta\cos^3\theta$

41. $\dfrac{1 + \tan \frac{\theta}{2}}{1 - \tan \frac{\theta}{2}} = \dfrac{1 + \dfrac{\sin \frac{\theta}{2}}{\cos \frac{\theta}{2}}}{1 - \dfrac{\sin \frac{\theta}{2}}{\cos \frac{\theta}{2}}}$

$= \dfrac{\cos \frac{\theta}{2} + \sin \frac{\theta}{2}}{\cos \frac{\theta}{2} - \sin \frac{\theta}{2}}$

$= \dfrac{\left[\cos \frac{\theta}{2} + \sin \frac{\theta}{2}\right]^2}{\cos^2 \frac{\theta}{2} - \sin^2 \frac{\theta}{2}}$

$= \dfrac{1 + 2 \cos \frac{\theta}{2} \sin \frac{\theta}{2}}{\cos \theta}$

$= \dfrac{1 + \sin \theta}{\cos \theta}$

$= \tan \theta + \sec \theta$

43. $2 \sin^2 (45° - \theta) = 2 [\sin 45° \cos \theta - \cos 45° \sin \theta]^2$

$= 2 \left(\dfrac{\cos \theta - \sin \theta}{\sqrt{2}}\right)^2$

$= 1 - 2 \cos \theta \sin \theta$

$= 1 - \sin 2\theta$

45. $\tan 2\theta (\cot \theta - \tan \theta) = (\tan 2\theta) \left(\dfrac{\cos \theta}{\sin \theta} - \dfrac{\sin \theta}{\cos \theta}\right)$

$= (\tan 2\theta) \left(\dfrac{\cos^2 \theta - \sin^2 \theta}{\sin \theta \cos \theta}\right)$

$= (2 \tan 2\theta) \left(\dfrac{\cos 2\theta}{\sin 2\theta}\right)$

$= 2$

Hence $\tan 2\theta \cot \theta - 1 = \tan 2\theta \tan \theta + 1$

47. (a) $\sin 2A = 2 \sin A \cos A$

$= 2 \sin (90° - B) \cos (90° - B)$

$= 2 \cos B \sin B$

$= \sin 2B$

(b) $\cos 2A = \cos^2 A - \sin^2 A$
$= [\cos (90° - B)]^2 - [\sin (90° - B)]^2$
$= (\sin B)^2 - (\cos B)^2$
$= -(\cos^2 B - \sin^2 B)$
$= -\cos 2B$

Hence $\cos 2A + \cos 2B = 0$

(c) $\sin 3A = \sin (2A + A)$
$= \sin 2A \cos A + \cos 2A \sin A$
$= 2 \sin A \cos^2 A + \cos^2 A \sin A - \sin^3 A$
$= 3 \sin A \cos^2 A - \sin^3 A$
$= 3 \left(\dfrac{a}{c}\right)\left(\dfrac{b}{c}\right)^2 - \left(\dfrac{a}{c}\right)^3$
$= \dfrac{3ab^2 - a^3}{c^3}$

49. $\sin (\alpha + 2\beta) = \sin [(\alpha + \beta) + \beta]$
$= \sin (\alpha + \beta) \cos \beta + \sin \beta \cos (\alpha + \beta)$
$= [\sin \alpha \cos \beta + \sin \beta \cos \alpha] \cos \beta$
$= \sin \alpha \cos^2 \beta + \cos \alpha \sin \beta \cos \beta$
$= (\sin \alpha)(1 - \sin^2 \beta) + \cos \alpha \sin \beta \cos \beta$
$= \sin \alpha + \sin \beta (\cos \alpha \cos \beta - \sin \alpha \sin \beta)$
$= \sin \alpha + \sin \beta \cos (\alpha + \beta)$
$= \sin \alpha$

51. Because $\sin \theta = \dfrac{a^2 - b^2}{a^2 + b^2}$, $\cos \theta = \sqrt{1 - \left(\dfrac{a^2 - b^2}{a^2 + b^2}\right)^2}$
$= \sqrt{\dfrac{(a^2 + b^2)^2 - (a^2 - b^2)^2}{(a^2 + b^2)^2}}$
$= \sqrt{\dfrac{4a^2 b^2}{(a^2 + b^2)^2}}$
$= \dfrac{2ab}{a^2 + b^2}$

Thus $\tan \dfrac{\theta}{2} = \dfrac{\sin \theta}{1 + \cos \theta} = \dfrac{a^2 - b^2}{a^2 + b^2 + 2ab} = \dfrac{a^2 - b^2}{(a + b)^2} = \dfrac{a - b}{a + b}$

53. (a)   Since:
$$\cos (A - B) = \cos A \cos B + \sin A \sin B$$
$$\cos (A + B) = \cos A \cos B - \sin A \sin B$$
Then:
$$\cos (A - B) - \cos (A + B) = 2 \sin A \sin B$$
Thus $\sin A \sin B = \frac{1}{2} [\cos (A - B) - \cos (A + B)]$

(b)   Since:
$$\sin (A + B) = \sin A \cos B + \sin B \cos A$$
$$\sin (A - B) = \sin A \cos B - \sin B \cos A$$
Then:
$$\sin (A + B) + \sin (A - B) = 2 \sin A \cos B$$
Thus $\sin A \cos B = \frac{1}{2} [\sin (A + B) + \sin (A - B)]$

(c)   It follows from (a) that $\cos (A + B) + \cos (A - B) = 2 \cos A \cos B$, thus
$\cos A \cos B = \frac{1}{2} [\cos (A + B) + \cos (A - B)]$

55. (a) $\sin \dfrac{\pi}{4} \cos \dfrac{\pi}{12} = \dfrac{1}{2} \left[\sin \dfrac{4\pi}{12} + \sin \dfrac{2\pi}{12} \right]$

$= \dfrac{1}{2} \left[\sin \dfrac{\pi}{3} + \sin \dfrac{\pi}{6} \right]$

$= \dfrac{1}{2} \left[\dfrac{\sqrt{3}}{2} + \dfrac{1}{2} \right]$

$= \dfrac{1}{4} (\sqrt{3} + 1)$

(b) $2 \sin 82.5° \cos 37.5° = \sin 120° + \sin 45°$

$= \dfrac{\sqrt{3}}{2} + \dfrac{\sqrt{2}}{2}$

$= \dfrac{\sqrt{3} + \sqrt{2}}{2}$

57. If $A + B = \alpha$ and $A - B = \beta$, then $2A = \alpha + \beta$ and $2B = \alpha - \beta$, so:
$A = \dfrac{1}{2} (\alpha + \beta)$ and $B = \dfrac{1}{2} (\alpha - \beta)$
Therefore:
$$\sin A \cos B = \sin \left(\dfrac{\alpha + \beta}{2} \right) \cos \left(\dfrac{\alpha - \beta}{2} \right)$$
$$\sin (A + B) + \sin (A - B) = \sin \alpha + \sin \beta$$
Hence #53(b) implies: $\sin \alpha + \sin \beta = 2 \sin \left(\dfrac{\alpha + \beta}{2} \right) \cos \left(\dfrac{\alpha - \beta}{2} \right)$

59. (a) From #58(b): $\cos \frac{2\pi}{9} + \cos \frac{\pi}{9} = 2 \cos \frac{\pi}{6} \cos \frac{\pi}{18}$

$$= 2 \left(\frac{\sqrt{3}}{2}\right) \cos \frac{\pi}{18}$$

$$= \sqrt{3} \cos \frac{\pi}{18}$$

(b) From #57: $\sin 105° + \sin 15° = 2 \sin 60° \cos 45°$

$$= 2 \left(\frac{\sqrt{3}}{2}\right)\left(\frac{\sqrt{2}}{2}\right)$$

$$= \frac{\sqrt{6}}{2}$$

61. $\dfrac{\sin 7\theta - \sin 5\theta}{\cos 7\theta + \cos 5\theta} = \dfrac{2 \cos \frac{12\theta}{2} \sin \frac{2\theta}{2}}{2 \cos \frac{12\theta}{2} \cos \frac{2\theta}{2}} = \dfrac{\cos 6\theta \sin \theta}{\cos 6\theta \cos \theta} = \tan \theta$

63. (a) Using $\triangle ODC$, $OD = \cos \theta$ and $DC = \sin \theta$ (recall that $OC = 1$).
    Thus, using $\triangle ADC$, $\tan \frac{\theta}{2} = \dfrac{CD}{AD} = \dfrac{\sin \theta}{1 + \cos \theta}$, since $AO = 1$.

(b) $\tan 15° = \dfrac{\sin 30°}{1 + \cos 30°}$

$$= \dfrac{\frac{1}{2}}{1 + \frac{\sqrt{3}}{2}}$$

$$= \dfrac{1}{2 + \sqrt{3}} \cdot \dfrac{2 - \sqrt{3}}{2 - \sqrt{3}}$$

$$= \dfrac{2 - \sqrt{3}}{4 - 3}$$

$$= 2 - \sqrt{3}$$

$$\tan \frac{\pi}{8} = \frac{\sin \frac{\pi}{4}}{1 + \cos \frac{\pi}{4}}$$

$$= \frac{\frac{\sqrt{2}}{2}}{1 + \frac{\sqrt{2}}{2}}$$

$$= \frac{\sqrt{2}}{2 + \sqrt{2}} \cdot \frac{2 - \sqrt{2}}{2 - \sqrt{2}}$$

$$= \frac{2\sqrt{2} - 2}{4 - 2}$$

$$= \sqrt{2} - 1$$

65. (a)   We have:

$$\tan (60° - \theta) = \frac{\tan 60° - \tan \theta}{1 + \tan 60° \tan \theta} = \frac{\sqrt{3} - \tan \theta}{1 + \sqrt{3} \tan \theta}$$

$$\tan (60° + \theta) = \frac{\tan 60° + \tan \theta}{1 - \tan 60° \tan \theta} = \frac{\sqrt{3} + \tan \theta}{1 - \sqrt{3} \tan \theta}$$

So:

$$\tan \theta \tan (60° - \theta) \tan (60° + \theta) = \frac{(3 - \tan^2 \theta) \tan \theta}{1 - 3 \tan^2 \theta}$$

Meanwhile:

$$\tan 3\theta = \tan (2\theta + \theta)$$

$$= \frac{\tan 2\theta + \tan \theta}{1 - \tan \theta \tan 2\theta}$$

$$= \frac{\frac{2 \tan \theta}{1 - \tan^2 \theta} + \tan \theta}{1 - \tan \theta \left(\frac{2 \tan \theta}{1 - \tan^2 \theta} \right)}$$

$$= \frac{2 \tan \theta + \tan \theta - \tan^3 \theta}{1 - \tan^2 \theta - 2 \tan^2 \theta}$$

$$= \frac{(3 - \tan^2 \theta) \tan \theta}{1 - 3 \tan^2 \theta}$$

Hence: $\tan \theta \tan (60° - \theta) \tan (60° + \theta) = \tan 3\theta$

(b)   Since $\tan 60° = \sqrt{3}$, then letting $\theta = 20°$ in part (a) implies

$\tan 20° \tan 40° \tan 80° = \sqrt{3}$

67. (a) Computing areas of each triangle:

Left: area $= \frac{1}{2}$ (base)(height) $= \frac{1}{2}$ af $\sin\frac{C}{2}$

Right: area $= \frac{1}{2}$ (base)(height) $= \frac{1}{2}$ bf $\sin\frac{C}{2}$

Entire: area $= \frac{1}{2}$ (base)(height) $= \frac{1}{2}$ ab $\sin C$

Adding the left and right triangles, we have:

$$\frac{1}{2} \text{af} \sin\frac{C}{2} + \frac{1}{2} \text{bf} \sin\frac{C}{2} = \frac{1}{2} \text{ab} \sin C$$

(b) Since $\sin C = 2\sin\frac{C}{2}\cos\frac{C}{2}$, we have:

$$\frac{1}{2}\text{af}\sin\frac{C}{2} + \frac{1}{2}\text{bf}\sin\frac{C}{2} = \text{ab}\sin\frac{C}{2}\cos\frac{C}{2}$$

Multiplying by $\dfrac{2}{\sin\frac{C}{2}}$, we have:

$$\text{af} + \text{bf} = 2\text{ab}\cos\frac{C}{2}$$

$$\text{f(a + b)} = 2\text{ab}\cos\frac{C}{2}$$

$$\text{f} = \frac{2\text{ab}\cos\frac{C}{2}}{\text{a} + \text{b}}$$

(c) Using the half-angle formula, we have:

$$\cos\frac{C}{2} = \sqrt{\frac{1 + \cos C}{2}}$$

$$= \sqrt{\frac{1 + \frac{a^2 + b^2 - c^2}{2ab}}{2}}$$

$$= \sqrt{\frac{a^2 + 2ab + b^2 - c^2}{4ab}}$$

$$= \frac{1}{2}\sqrt{\frac{(a + b)^2 - c^2}{ab}}$$

$$= \frac{1}{2}\sqrt{\frac{(a + b - c)(a + b + c)}{ab}}$$

(d)   Combining our results from (b) and (c), we have:

$$f = \frac{2ab}{a+b} \cos \frac{C}{2}$$

$$= \frac{ab}{a+b} \sqrt{\frac{(a+b-c)(a+b+c)}{ab}}$$

$$= \frac{\sqrt{ab}}{a+b} \sqrt{(a+b-c)(a+b+c)}$$

6.7 Trigonometric Equations

1.   For $\theta = \frac{\pi}{2}$, $2\cos^2\theta - 3\cos\theta = 2(0)^2 - 3(0) = 0$, so $\theta = \frac{\pi}{2}$ is a solution.

3.   For $x = \frac{3\pi}{4}$, $\tan^2 x - 3\tan x + 2 = (-1)^2 + 3 + 2 = 6$, so $x = \frac{3\pi}{4}$ is not a solution.

5. $\sin\theta = \frac{\sqrt{3}}{2}$, so $\theta = \frac{\pi}{3}$ and $\theta = \frac{2\pi}{3}$ are the primary solutions. All solutions will be of the form $\theta = \frac{\pi}{3} + 2\pi k$ or $\theta = \frac{2\pi}{3} + 2\pi k$, where k is any integer.

7. $\sin\theta = -\frac{1}{2}$, so $\theta = \frac{7\pi}{6}$ and $\theta = \frac{11\pi}{6}$ are the primary solutions. All solutions will be of the form $\theta = \frac{7\pi}{6} + 2\pi k$ or $\theta = \frac{11\pi}{6} + 2\pi k$, where k is any integer.

9. $\cos\theta = -1$, so $\theta = \pi$ is the primary solution. All solutions will be of the form $\theta = \pi + 2\pi k$, where k is any integer.

11. $\tan\theta = \sqrt{3}$, so $\theta = \frac{\pi}{3}$ is the primary solution. All solutions will be of the form $\theta = \frac{\pi}{3} + \pi k$, where k is any integer.

13. $\tan x = 0$, so $x = 0$ is the primary solution. All solutions will be of the form $x = 0 + \pi k$, or $x = \pi k$, where k is any integer.

15. $2 \cos^2 \theta + \cos \theta = \cos \theta \, (2 \cos \theta + 1) = 0$, so the primary solutions are the solutions of $\cos \theta = 0$ or $\cos \theta = -\frac{1}{2}$, which are $\theta = \frac{\pi}{2}$, $\theta = \frac{3\pi}{2}$, $\theta = \frac{2\pi}{3}$ or $\theta = \frac{4\pi}{3}$. All solutions will be of the form $\theta = \frac{\pi}{2} + \pi k$, $\theta = \frac{2\pi}{3} + 2\pi k$ or $\theta = \frac{4\pi}{3} + 2\pi k$, where k is any integer.

17. $\cos^2 t \sin t - \sin t = \sin t \, (\cos^2 t - 1) = 0$, thus $\sin t = 0$ or $\cos t = \pm 1$, thus the primary solutions are $t = 0$ or $t = \pi$. All solutions are of the form $t = \pi k$, where k is any integer.

19. $2 \cos^2 x - \sin x - 1 = 2\,(1 - \sin^2 x) - \sin x - 1$
$$= -2 \sin^2 x - \sin x + 1$$
$$= (-2 \sin x + 1)(\sin x + 1)$$
So $\sin x = \frac{1}{2}$ or $\sin x = -1$. Thus the primary solutions are $x = \frac{\pi}{6}$, $x = \frac{5\pi}{6}$ or $x = \frac{3\pi}{2}$. All solutions are of the form $x = \frac{\pi}{6} + 2\pi k$, $x = \frac{5\pi}{6} + 2\pi k$ or $x = \frac{3\pi}{2} + 2\pi k$, where k is any integer.

21. $\sqrt{3} \sin t - \sqrt{1 + \sin^2 t} = 0$ is equivalent to $3 \sin^2 t = 1 + \sin^2 t$, so $2 \sin^2 t = 1$ and thus $\sin^2 t = \frac{1}{2}$ and $\sin t = \pm \frac{\sqrt{2}}{2}$. This would have primary solutions of $\frac{\pi}{4}, \frac{3\pi}{4}, \frac{5\pi}{4}$, or $\frac{7\pi}{4}$, but $\frac{5\pi}{4}$ and $\frac{7\pi}{4}$ do not work in the original equation. So the primary solutions are $t = \frac{\pi}{4}$ or $t = \frac{3\pi}{4}$. All solutions are of the form $t = \frac{\pi}{4} + 2\pi k$ or $t = \frac{3\pi}{4} + 2\pi k$, where k is any integer.

23. If $\cos 3\theta = 1$, then $3\theta = 2\pi k$ for any integer k. So $\theta = \frac{2\pi k}{3}$. Thus the values of θ in the interval $[0°, 360°)$ are $0°$, $120°$, and $240°$.

25. $\sin 3\theta = -\frac{\sqrt{2}}{2}$, so $3\theta = \frac{5\pi}{4} + 2\pi k$ or $\frac{7\pi}{4} + 2\pi k$. Thus $\theta = \frac{5\pi}{12} + \frac{2\pi k}{3}$ or $\frac{7\pi}{12} + \frac{2\pi k}{3}$. So the primary solutions are $75°$, $105°$, $195°$, $225°$, $315°$, or $345°$.

27. $\sin \theta = \cos \dfrac{\theta}{2}$, and using the hint $2 \sin \dfrac{\theta}{2} \cos \dfrac{\theta}{2} = \cos \dfrac{\theta}{2}$, so

$\left(\cos \dfrac{\theta}{2}\right)\left(2 \sin \dfrac{\theta}{2} - 1\right) = 0$, and $\cos \dfrac{\theta}{2} = 0$ or $\sin \dfrac{\theta}{2} = \dfrac{1}{2}$. We have

60° or 300° as solutions, also when $\cos \dfrac{\theta}{2} = 0$ we have $\dfrac{\theta}{2} = 90° + 360°k$ or

$270° + 360°k$, so $\theta = 180°$. Combining we have $\theta = 60°, 180°,$ or $300°$.

29. $\sin 2\theta = \sqrt{3} \cos 2\theta$, hence $\tan 2\theta = \sqrt{3}$ and $2\theta = 60° + 180°k$, so
     $\theta = 30° + 90°k$. Thus $\theta = 30°, 120°, 210°,$ or $300°$.

31. $\sin \theta = \dfrac{1}{4}$, hence $\theta = 14.5°$ or $165.5°$

33. $2 \tan \theta = -4$, so $\tan \theta = -2$, and thus $\theta = 116.6° + 180°k$, hence $\theta = 116.6°$
     or $296.6°$

35. $\cos^2 x - \cos x - 1 = 0$, so $\cos x = \dfrac{1 \pm \sqrt{5}}{2}$. Since $\dfrac{1 + \sqrt{5}}{2} > 1$, the only

     solutions are those for which $\cos x = \dfrac{1 - \sqrt{5}}{2}$, and thus $x = 128.2°$ or $231.8°$.

37. $\cos x = 0.184$, so $x \approx 1.39$ or $x \approx 4.90$

39. $\sin x = \dfrac{1}{\sqrt{5}}$, so $x \approx 0.46$ or $x \approx 2.68$

41. $\sin t = 5 \cos t$, so $\tan t = 5$. Thus $t \approx 1.37$ or $t \approx 4.51$

43. Since $\tan 3x = \tan(2x + x) = \dfrac{\tan 2x + \tan x}{1 - \tan x \tan 2x} = \dfrac{3 \tan x - \tan^3 x}{1 - 3 \tan^2 x}$

     So $\tan 3x - \tan x = \dfrac{2 \tan x + 2 \tan^3 x}{1 - 3 \tan^2 x} = 0$

     So $2 \tan x (1 + \tan^2 x) = 0$, thus $\tan x = 0$ since $\tan^2 x + 1 \neq 0$. Thus $x = 0, \pi$.

45. $\cos\dfrac{x}{2} = \pm\sqrt{\dfrac{1+\cos x}{2}} = 1 + \cos x$. Squaring each side, we get

$\dfrac{1+\cos x}{2} = 1 + 2\cos x + \cos^2 x$, thus $1 + \cos x = 2 + 4\cos x + 2\cos^2 x$.

So $2\cos^2 x + 3\cos x + 1 = 0$, or $(2\cos x + 1)(\cos x + 1) = 0$, thus

$\cos x = -\dfrac{1}{2}$ or $\cos x = -1$, and thus $x = \dfrac{2\pi}{3}, \dfrac{4\pi}{3}$, or π. When checking we find

that $x = \dfrac{4\pi}{3}$ is not a solution, and thus the solutions are $x = \dfrac{2\pi}{3}$ or $x = \pi$.

47. $\sec 4\theta + 2\sin 4\theta = 0$, so $\dfrac{1}{\cos 4\theta} = -2\sin 4\theta$, or $2\sin 4\theta \cos 4\theta = -1$ thus

$\sin 8\theta = -1$ and thus $8\theta = \dfrac{3\pi}{2} + 2\pi k$, so $\theta = \dfrac{3\pi}{16} + \dfrac{k\pi}{4}$, where k is any integer.

49. $\sin 5x - \sin 3x = 0$

$2\cos\dfrac{5x + 3x}{2}\ \sin\dfrac{5x - 3x}{2} = 0$

$2\cos 4x \sin x = 0$

$\cos 4x \sin x = 0$

$\cos 4x = 0$ or $\sin x = 0$

So $4x = \dfrac{\pi}{2}, \dfrac{3\pi}{2}, \dfrac{5\pi}{2}, \dfrac{7\pi}{2}, \dfrac{9\pi}{2}, \dfrac{11\pi}{2}, \dfrac{13\pi}{2}, \dfrac{15\pi}{2}$, or $x = 0, \pi, 2\pi$. So the

solutions are $x = \dfrac{\pi}{8}, \dfrac{3\pi}{8}, \dfrac{5\pi}{8}, \dfrac{7\pi}{8}, \dfrac{9\pi}{8}, \dfrac{11\pi}{8}, \dfrac{13\pi}{8}, \dfrac{15\pi}{8}, 0, \pi, 2\pi$.

51. $\sin 3x = \cos 2x = \sin\left(\dfrac{\pi}{2} - 2x\right)$, so:

$\sin 3x - \sin\left(\dfrac{\pi}{2} - 2x\right) = 2\cos\left(\dfrac{x}{2} + \dfrac{\pi}{4}\right)\sin\left(\dfrac{5x}{2} - \dfrac{\pi}{4}\right) = 0$

Hence $\dfrac{x}{2} + \dfrac{\pi}{4} = \dfrac{\pi}{2}, \dfrac{3\pi}{2}$, or $\dfrac{5x}{2} - \dfrac{\pi}{4} = 0, \pi, 2\pi, 3\pi, 4\pi, 5\pi$. So $\dfrac{x}{2} = \dfrac{\pi}{4}, \dfrac{5\pi}{4}$ and

thus $x = \dfrac{\pi}{2}, \dfrac{5\pi}{2}$. Or $\dfrac{5x}{2} = \dfrac{\pi}{4}, \dfrac{5\pi}{4}, \dfrac{9\pi}{4}, \dfrac{13\pi}{4}, \dfrac{17\pi}{4}, \dfrac{21\pi}{4}$ and thus

$x = \dfrac{\pi}{10}, \dfrac{\pi}{2}, \dfrac{9\pi}{10}, \dfrac{13\pi}{10}, \dfrac{17\pi}{10}, \dfrac{21\pi}{10}$. Now $\dfrac{5\pi}{2}$ and $\dfrac{21\pi}{10}$ are not in the interval, so

the solutions are $x = \dfrac{\pi}{10}, \dfrac{\pi}{2}, \dfrac{9\pi}{10}, \dfrac{13\pi}{10}$, or $\dfrac{17\pi}{10}$.

53. Since $\cos\left(x - \frac{2\pi}{9}\right) = \sin\left[\frac{\pi}{2} - \left(x - \frac{2\pi}{9}\right)\right] = \sin\left(\frac{13\pi}{18} - x\right)$, then:

$$\sin\left(x + \frac{\pi}{18}\right) - \cos\left(x - \frac{2\pi}{9}\right) = \sin\left(x + \frac{\pi}{18}\right) - \sin\left(\frac{13\pi}{18} - x\right)$$

$$= 2\cos\frac{7\pi}{18}\sin\left(x - \frac{\pi}{3}\right)$$

$$= 0$$

Thus $\sin\left(x - \frac{\pi}{3}\right) = 0$, and $x - \frac{\pi}{3} = 0$, π and thus $x = \frac{\pi}{3}$ or $x = \frac{4\pi}{3}$.

55.
$$4\sin\theta - 3\cos\theta = 2$$
$$4\sin\theta = 3\cos\theta + 2$$
$$16\sin^2\theta = 9\cos^2\theta + 12\cos\theta + 4$$
$$16(1 - \cos^2\theta) = 9\cos^2\theta + 12\cos\theta + 4$$
$$16 - 16\cos^2\theta = 9\cos^2\theta + 12\cos\theta + 4$$
$$25\cos^2\theta + 12\cos\theta - 12 = 0$$

This will not factor, so we use the quadratic formula:

$$\cos\theta = \frac{-12 \pm \sqrt{(12)^2 - 4(25)(-12)}}{2(25)}$$

$$= \frac{-12 \pm \sqrt{1344}}{50}$$

$$= \frac{-12 \pm 8\sqrt{21}}{50}$$

$$= \frac{-6 \pm 4\sqrt{21}}{25}$$

So $\cos\theta = .4932$ or $\cos\theta = -.9732$, and thus $\theta = 60.45°$ (the other solution is not in the required interval.)

57. (a) If $\sin x \cos x = 1$, then $\sin^2 x \cos^2 x = 1$, and thus $\sin^2 x\,(1 - \sin^2 x) = 1$ thus $\sin^2 x - \sin^4 x = 1$, so $\sin^4 x - \sin^2 x + 1 = 0$.

(b) Using the quadratic formula:

$$\sin^2 x = \frac{1 \pm \sqrt{1 - 4}}{2}$$, which has no solutions

Alternately, double both sides of the equation to get
$2\sin x \cos x = \sin 2x = 2$, which is impossible.

59. (a) $\cos x = 0.412$, so $x \approx 1.146$ or $x \approx -1.146$. We must now add multiples of 2π on to these values until we reach an x-value greater than 1000. The first such value is at $x \approx 1000.173$.

(b) cos x = -0.412, so x ≈ 1.995 or x ≈ -1.995. Again, we add multiples of
2π on to these values until we reach an x-value greater than 1000.
The first such value is at x ≈ 1001.022.

6.8 The Inverse Trigonometric Functions

1. $\pi/3$

3. $\pi/3$

5. $-\pi/6$

7. $\pi/4$

9. undefined

11. $1/4$

13. $3/4$

15. $-\pi/7$

17. $\pi/2$

19. 0

21. If $\theta = \sin^{-1}\dfrac{4}{5}$, then $\sin\theta = \dfrac{4}{5}$ and we have the triangle:

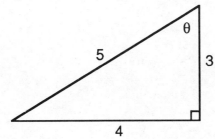

So $\tan\left(\sin^{-1}\dfrac{4}{5}\right) = \tan\theta = \dfrac{4}{3}$

23. $\sin(\tan^{-1} 1) = \sin\dfrac{\pi}{4} = \dfrac{\sqrt{2}}{2}$

25.   We have the triangle:

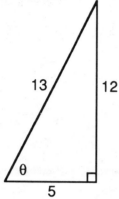

So $\tan\left(\arccos\dfrac{5}{13}\right) = \tan\theta = \dfrac{12}{5}$

27. $\cos\left(\arctan\sqrt{3}\right) = \cos 60° = \dfrac{1}{2}$

29.   We have the triangle:

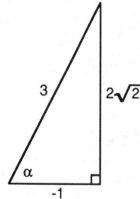

So $\sin\left(\cos^{-1}\left(-\dfrac{1}{3}\right)\right) = \sin\alpha = \dfrac{2\sqrt{2}}{3}$

31.   (a)   0.84 radians or 48.59°
      (b)   0.84 radians or 48.59°
      (c)   1.26 radians or 72.34°
      (d)   0.90 radians or 51.57°

33. $\sec\left(\cos^{-1}\left(\frac{\sqrt{2}}{2}\right) + \sin^{-1}(-1)\right) = \sec\left(\frac{\pi}{4} - \frac{\pi}{2}\right)$

$$= \sec\left(-\frac{\pi}{4}\right)$$

$$= \frac{1}{\cos\left(-\frac{\pi}{4}\right)}$$

$$= \frac{1}{\frac{\sqrt{2}}{2}}$$

$$= \frac{2}{\sqrt{2}}$$

$$= \sqrt{2}$$

35. Let $\theta = \sin^{-1} x$, so we have the triangle:

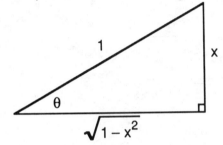

So $\cos(\sin^{-1} x) = \cos\theta = \sqrt{1 - x^2}$

37. Given $\sin\theta = \frac{3x}{2}$, we draw the triangle:

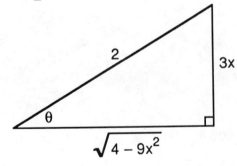

So $\dfrac{\theta}{4} - \sin 2\theta = \dfrac{\sin^{-1}\left(\dfrac{3x}{2}\right)}{4} - 2\sin\theta\cos\theta$

$= \dfrac{1}{4}\sin^{-1}\left(\dfrac{3x}{2}\right) - 2\left(\dfrac{3x}{2}\right)\cdot\dfrac{\sqrt{4-9x^2}}{2}$

$= \dfrac{1}{4}\sin^{-1}\left(\dfrac{3x}{2}\right) - \dfrac{3x\sqrt{4-9x^2}}{2}$

39. Given $\tan\theta = \dfrac{x-1}{2}$, we draw the triangle:

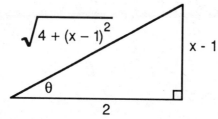

So $\theta - \cos\theta = \tan^{-1}\left(\dfrac{x-1}{2}\right) - \dfrac{2}{\sqrt{4+(x-1)^2}}$

$= \tan^{-1}\left(\dfrac{x-1}{2}\right) - \dfrac{2}{\sqrt{5-2x+x^2}}$

41. Let $\theta = \tan^{-1}4$, so we have the triangle:

So $\sin(2\tan^{-1}4) = \sin 2\theta$

$= 2\sin\theta\cos\theta$

$= 4\cdot\dfrac{4}{\sqrt{17}}\cdot\dfrac{1}{\sqrt{17}}$

$= \dfrac{8}{17}$

43.   Let α = arccos $\frac{3}{5}$, so we have the triangle:

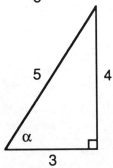

Let β = arctan $\frac{7}{13}$, so we have the triangle:

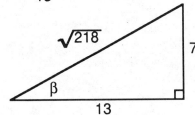

So $\sin\left(\arccos\frac{3}{5} - \arctan\frac{7}{13}\right)$ = $\sin(\alpha - \beta)$

= $\sin\alpha\cos\beta - \sin\beta\cos\alpha$

= $\frac{4}{5} \cdot \frac{13}{\sqrt{218}} - \frac{7}{\sqrt{218}} \cdot \frac{3}{5}$

= $\frac{31}{5\sqrt{218}}$

= $\frac{31\sqrt{218}}{1090}$

45.   Let A = $\tan^{-1} 2$, so we have the triangle:

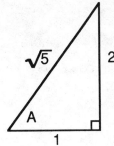

Let B = tan^{-1} 3, so we have the triangle:

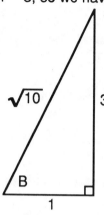

So   cos (tan^{-1} 2 + tan^{-1} 3)   = cos (A + B)

$$= \cos A \cos B - \sin A \sin B$$

$$= \frac{1}{\sqrt{5}} \cdot \frac{1}{\sqrt{10}} - \frac{2}{\sqrt{5}} \cdot \frac{3}{\sqrt{10}}$$

$$= -\frac{1}{\sqrt{2}}$$

$$= -\frac{\sqrt{2}}{2}$$

47.   Let θ = tan$^{-1} \frac{4}{3}$ and β = tan$^{-1} \frac{1}{7}$. Then we have:

$$\tan (\theta - \beta) = \frac{\tan \theta - \tan \beta}{1 + \tan \theta \tan \beta} = \frac{\frac{4}{3} - \frac{1}{7}}{1 + \frac{4}{3} \cdot \frac{1}{7}} = \frac{\frac{25}{21}}{\frac{25}{21}} = 1$$

Thus tan $(\theta - \beta)$ = 1. Also, by reasoning that is similar to that used in the solution to #46 we find that $0 < \theta - \beta < \frac{\pi}{2}$, and therefore $\theta - \beta = \frac{\pi}{4}$, as required.

49.   Let θ = sin^{-1} x, with -1 < x < 1. Then we have sin θ = x, where $-\frac{\pi}{2} < \theta < \frac{\pi}{2}$. From the equation sin θ = x we obtain cos θ = $\pm\sqrt{1 - x^2}$, and since cos θ is positive $\left(-\frac{\pi}{2} < \theta < \frac{\pi}{2}\right)$ we have cos θ = $\sqrt{1 - x^2}$.

Thus we have tan θ = $\frac{\sin \theta}{\cos \theta}$ = $\frac{x}{\sqrt{1 - x^2}}$, and thus θ = tan$^{-1} \frac{x}{\sqrt{1 - x^2}}$.

Therefore, sin^{-1} x = tan$^{-1} \frac{x}{\sqrt{1 - x^2}}$, as required.

51. Let $\beta = \tan^{-1} \frac{1}{7}$ and $\theta = \tan^{-1} \frac{1}{3}$. By means of the double-angle formula for tangent, we obtain $\tan 2\theta = \frac{3}{4}$. Now we compute:

$$\tan(\beta + 2\theta) = \frac{\tan\beta + \tan 2\theta}{1 - \tan\beta \tan 2\theta} = \frac{\frac{1}{7} + \frac{3}{4}}{1 - \frac{1}{7} \cdot \frac{3}{4}} = 1$$

That is, $\tan(\beta + 2\theta) = 1$. We can conclude from this that $\beta + 2\theta = \frac{\pi}{4}$ if we know $0 < \beta + 2\theta < \frac{\pi}{2}$. Now since $\tan\beta = \frac{1}{7}$ which is less than $\frac{1}{\sqrt{3}}$, we know that $\beta < \frac{\pi}{6}$. Similarly, since $\tan 2\theta = \frac{3}{4} < \frac{\sqrt{3}}{2}$, we know that $2\theta < \frac{\pi}{3}$. Therefore, $\beta + 2\theta$ is less than $\frac{\pi}{6} + \frac{\pi}{3} = \frac{\pi}{2}$. Clearly they are also both positive. In summary, we have $\tan(\beta + 2\theta) = 1$ and $0 < \beta + 2\theta < \frac{\pi}{2}$, which implies that $\beta + 2\theta = \frac{\pi}{4}$. Thus $\tan^{-1} \frac{1}{7} + 2\tan^{-1}\frac{1}{3} = \frac{\pi}{4}$, as required.

53. Let $\theta = \sin^{-1} x$. Notice that this implies that $-\frac{\pi}{2} < \theta < \frac{\pi}{2}$. Using the equation $\sin\theta = x$, we have $\cos\theta = \pm\sqrt{1 - x^2}$. Since $\cos\theta$ is positive in this interval, then $\cos\theta = \sqrt{1 - x^2}$. Thus:
$$\sin(2\sin^{-1} x) = \sin 2\theta = 2\sin\theta\cos\theta = 2x\sqrt{1 - x^2}$$

55. (a) The domain of f is $[-1, 1]$.

(b) $f(0.1) = \sin^{-1} 0.1 + \cos^{-1} 0.1 \approx 1.57 = \pi/2$
$f(0.2) = \sin^{-1} 0.2 + \cos^{-1} 0.2 \approx 1.57 = \pi/2$
$f(0.3) = \sin^{-1} 0.3 + \cos^{-1} 0.3 \approx 1.57 = \pi/2$

(c) $f(1/2) = \sin^{-1}\frac{1}{2} + \cos^{-1}\frac{1}{2} = \frac{\pi}{6} + \frac{\pi}{3} = \frac{\pi}{2}$

$f(\sqrt{2}/2) = \sin^{-1}\frac{\sqrt{2}}{2} + \cos^{-1}\frac{\sqrt{2}}{2} = \frac{\pi}{4} + \frac{\pi}{4} = \frac{\pi}{2}$

$f(\sqrt{3}/2) = \sin^{-1}\frac{\sqrt{3}}{2} + \cos^{-1}\frac{\sqrt{3}}{2} = \frac{\pi}{3} + \frac{\pi}{6} = \frac{\pi}{2}$

(d)   It appears that $f(x) = \sin^{-1}x + \cos^{-1}x = \frac{\pi}{2}$.

To prove this, first make the following variable substitutions:

$u = \sin^{-1}x$, so $\sin u = x$ and $\cos u = \sqrt{1 - x^2}$

$v = \cos^{-1}x$, so $\cos v = x$ and $\sin v = \sqrt{1 - x^2}$

Note that we can choose the positive square roots for cos u and sin v

since $-\frac{\pi}{2} \le u \le \frac{\pi}{2}$ and thus cos u ≥ 0, while $0 \le v \le \pi$ so sin v ≥ 0.

From these inequalities, we also see that $-\frac{\pi}{2} \le u + v \le \frac{3\pi}{2}$. It

remains to show that $u + v = \frac{\pi}{2}$. Note that, in the u + v interval,

$\sin(u + v) = 1$ only when $u + v = \frac{\pi}{2}$. Thus, we will show that:

$$\sin(u + v) = \sin u \cos v + \cos u \sin v$$
$$= x \bullet x + \sqrt{1 - x^2}\, \sqrt{1 - x^2}$$
$$= x^2 + 1 - x^2$$
$$= 1$$

This proves the result.

57.   (a)   Let $u = \sec^{-1}\frac{4}{3}$, so $\sec u = \frac{4}{3}$, and thus $\cos u = \frac{3}{4}$.

Thus $\cos\left(\sec^{-1}\frac{4}{3}\right) = \frac{3}{4}$.

(b)   Let $u = \sec^{-1} 4$, so $\sec u = 4$, and thus $\cos u = \frac{1}{4}$.

Thus $\sin\left(\sec^{-1} 4\right) = \sin u = \sqrt{1 - 1/16} = \frac{\sqrt{15}}{4}$.

(c)   Let $u = \sec^{-1}(-3)$, so $\sec u = -3$, and thus $\cos u = -\frac{1}{3}$ $\left(\text{and } \pi \le u \le \frac{3\pi}{2}\right)$.

Thus $\tan\left[\sec^{-1}(-3)\right] = \tan u = \frac{\sin u}{\cos u} = \frac{-\sqrt{1 - 1/9}}{-1/3} = \frac{-2\sqrt{2}/3}{-1/3} = 2\sqrt{2}$.

(d)   Let $u = \sec^{-1}\frac{13}{12}$, so $\sec u = \frac{13}{12}$, and thus $\cos u = \frac{12}{13}$.

Thus $\cot\left[\sec^{-1}\frac{13}{12}\right] = \cot u = \frac{\cos u}{\sin u} = \frac{12/13}{\sqrt{1 - 144/169}} = \frac{12/13}{5/13} = \frac{12}{5}$.

59. We take the sine of each side to get:

$$\sin\left(\sin^{-1}(3t-2)\right) = \sin\left(\sin^{-1}t - \cos^{-1}t\right)$$
$$3t-2 = \sin\left(\sin^{-1}t - \cos^{-1}t\right)$$

Let $u = \sin^{-1}t$, so $\sin u = t$ and $\cos u = \sqrt{1-t^2}$. Also, let $v = \cos^{-1}t$, so $\cos v = t$ and $\sin v = \sqrt{1-t^2}$. Thus:

$$\sin\left(\sin^{-1}t - \cos^{-1}t\right) = \sin(u-v)$$
$$= \sin u \cos v - \cos u \sin v$$
$$= t \cdot t - \sqrt{1-t^2}\,\sqrt{1-t^2}$$
$$= t^2 - 1 + t^2$$
$$= 2t^2 - 1$$

Thus, we have the equation:

$$3t-2 = 2t^2 - 1$$
$$0 = 2t^2 - 3t + 1$$
$$0 = (2t-1)(t-1)$$
$$t = 1/2,\ 1$$

61. $\tan(\tan^{-1}1 + \tan^{-1}2) = \dfrac{1+2}{1-1(2)} = -3$, and

$\tan(\pi - \tan^{-1}3) = \dfrac{\tan\pi - 3}{1 + 3\tan\pi} = -3$. So we have:

$$\tan^{-1}1 + \tan^{-1}2 + \tan^{-1}3 = \pi + k\pi \text{ for some } k$$

However we know that all three angles lie in $\left(0, \dfrac{\pi}{2}\right)$, and so their sum must lie in

$\left(0, \dfrac{3\pi}{2}\right)$, and thus $k = 0$. Hence $\tan^{-1}1 + \tan^{-1}2 + \tan^{-1}3 = \pi$.

63. (a) Letting $y = \tan^{-1}x$, then $\tan 2y = \dfrac{2\tan y}{1 - \tan^2 y}$, so:

$$\tan^{-1}[\tan 2y] = \tan^{-1}\left[\frac{2\tan y}{1-\tan^2 y}\right] = \tan^{-1}\left[\frac{2x}{1-x^2}\right]$$
$$2y = 2\tan^{-1}x = \tan^{-1}\left[\frac{2x}{1-x^2}\right]$$

(b)   From (a):

$$2 \tan^{-1} \frac{1}{5} = \tan^{-1} \left[\frac{\frac{2}{5}}{1 - \frac{1}{25}} \right] = \tan^{-1} \frac{5}{12}$$

Again applying the formula from (a):

$$4 \tan^{-1} \frac{1}{5} = 2 \tan^{-1} \frac{5}{12}$$

$$= \tan^{-1} \left[\frac{2 \cdot \frac{5}{12}}{1 - \left(\frac{5}{12}\right)^2} \right]$$

$$= \tan^{-1} \frac{120}{119}$$

(c) $4 \tan^{-1} \frac{1}{5} - \tan^{-1} \frac{1}{239} = \tan^{-1} \frac{120}{119} - \tan^{-1} \frac{1}{239}$

Using the formula $\tan^{-1} x - \tan^{-1} y = \tan^{-1} \left[\frac{x - y}{1 + xy} \right]$, we have the expression becoming:

$$\tan^{-1} \left[\frac{\frac{120}{119} - \frac{1}{239}}{1 + \frac{120}{119} \cdot \frac{1}{239}} \right] = \tan^{-1} 1 = \frac{\pi}{4}$$

Chapter 6 Review Exercises

1.   (a) $\sin \frac{5\pi}{3} = -\frac{\sqrt{3}}{2}$

(b) $\cot \frac{11\pi}{6} = \frac{\cos \frac{11\pi}{6}}{\sin \frac{11\pi}{6}} = \frac{\frac{\sqrt{3}}{2}}{-\frac{1}{2}} = -\sqrt{3}$

2. $y = 3 \cos 3\pi x$
     x-intercepts: -1/6, 1/6; high point: (0,3)

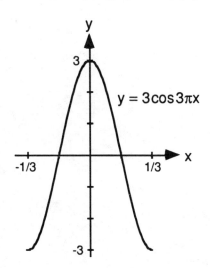

$y = 3\cos 3\pi x$

3. $\sin\left(\theta + \dfrac{3\pi}{2}\right) = \sin\theta \cos\dfrac{3\pi}{2} + \cos\theta \sin\dfrac{3\pi}{2}$

$= \sin\theta \bullet 0 + \cos\theta \bullet (-1)$

$= -\cos\theta$

4.   (a)   First, note that the third side is given by:

$\sqrt{(2\sqrt{5})^2 - 4^2} = \sqrt{20 - 16} = \sqrt{4} = 2$

$\cos 2\beta = \cos^2\beta - \sin^2\beta$

$= \left(\dfrac{2}{2\sqrt{5}}\right)^2 - \left(\dfrac{4}{2\sqrt{5}}\right)^2$

$= \dfrac{1}{5} - \dfrac{4}{5}$

$= -\dfrac{3}{5}$

(b) $\tan\dfrac{\alpha}{2} = \dfrac{\sin\alpha}{1+\cos\alpha}$

$= \dfrac{\dfrac{2}{2\sqrt{5}}}{1+\dfrac{4}{2\sqrt{5}}} \cdot \dfrac{2\sqrt{5}}{2\sqrt{5}}$

$= \dfrac{2}{2\sqrt{5}+4}$

$= \dfrac{1}{\sqrt{5}+2} \cdot \dfrac{\sqrt{5}-2}{\sqrt{5}-2}$

$= \dfrac{\sqrt{5}-2}{5-4}$

$= \sqrt{5}-2$

5. (a) $\angle BAC = 75° \cdot \dfrac{\pi}{180°} = \dfrac{5\pi}{12}$ radians, so:

$s = r\theta = \sqrt{5} \cdot \dfrac{5\pi}{12} = \dfrac{5\sqrt{5}\,\pi}{12}$ cm

(b) $A = \dfrac{1}{2}r^2\theta = \dfrac{1}{2}\left(\sqrt{5}\right)^2 \cdot \dfrac{5\pi}{12} = \dfrac{25\pi}{24}$ cm^2

6. $\dfrac{1}{\sqrt{4-t^2}} = \dfrac{1}{\sqrt{4-4\cos^2 x}}$

$= \dfrac{1}{\sqrt{4(1-\cos^2 x)}}$

$= \dfrac{1}{\sqrt{4\sin^2 x}}$

$= \dfrac{1}{2\sin x}$ (since sin x > 0 on the interval 0 < x < π)

$= \dfrac{1}{2}\csc x$

7. We convert 3° to radians:

$3° \cdot \dfrac{\pi}{180°} = \dfrac{3\pi}{180}$ radians $< \dfrac{\pi^2}{180}$ radians   (since 3 < π)

So $\dfrac{\pi^2}{180}$ radians is larger than 3°.

8. $2 \sin^2 x + 7 \sin x + 3 = 0$
      $(2 \sin x + 1)(\sin x + 3) = 0$

$$\sin x = -\frac{1}{2} \quad \text{or} \quad \sin x = -3 \quad \text{(impossible)}$$

So $x = \dfrac{7\pi}{6}, \dfrac{11\pi}{6}$.

9.   Since $\cos \alpha = \dfrac{2}{\sqrt{5}}$ and $\dfrac{3\pi}{2} < \alpha < 2\pi$ (fourth quadrant), then:

$$\sin \alpha = -\sqrt{1 - \cos^2 \alpha} = -\sqrt{1 - \frac{4}{5}} = -\frac{1}{\sqrt{5}}$$

Similarly, since $\sin \beta = \dfrac{4}{5}$ and $\dfrac{\pi}{2} < \beta < \pi$ (second quadrant), then:

$$\cos \beta = -\sqrt{1 - \sin^2 \beta} = -\sqrt{1 - \frac{16}{25}} = -\sqrt{\frac{9}{25}} = -\frac{3}{5}$$

Thus, we have:

$$\begin{aligned}
\sin(\beta - \alpha) &= \sin \beta \cos \alpha - \cos \beta \sin \alpha \\
&= \frac{4}{5} \cdot \frac{2}{\sqrt{5}} - \left(-\frac{3}{5}\right)\left(-\frac{1}{\sqrt{5}}\right) \\
&= \frac{8}{5\sqrt{5}} - \frac{3}{5\sqrt{5}} \\
&= \frac{5}{5\sqrt{5}} \\
&= \frac{\sqrt{5}}{5}
\end{aligned}$$

10.   Using the double-angle identity for cosine (twice), we have:

$$\begin{aligned}
\cos 4\theta &= \cos^2 2\theta - \sin^2 2\theta \\
&= (\cos^2 \theta - \sin^2 \theta)^2 - (2 \sin \theta \cos \theta)^2 \\
&= \cos^4 \theta - 2\sin^2 \theta \cos^2 \theta + \sin^4 \theta - 4 \sin^2 \theta \cos^2 \theta \\
&= \cos^4 \theta - 2(1 - \cos^2 \theta)\cos^2 \theta + (1 - \cos^2 \theta)^2 - 4(1 - \cos^2 \theta)\cos^2 \theta \\
&= \cos^4 \theta - 2\cos^2 \theta + 2\cos^4 \theta + 1 - 2\cos^2 \theta + \cos^4 \theta - 4\cos^2 \theta + 4\cos^4 \theta \\
&= 8\cos^4 \theta - 8\cos^2 \theta + 1
\end{aligned}$$

11.   Given $\sec t = -\dfrac{5}{3}$, then $\cos t = -\dfrac{3}{5}$. Since $\pi < t < \dfrac{3\pi}{2}$ (third quadrant), then:

$$\sin t = -\sqrt{1 - \cos^2 t} = -\sqrt{1 - \frac{9}{25}} = -\sqrt{\frac{16}{25}} = -\frac{4}{5}$$

So $\cot t = \dfrac{\cos t}{\sin t} = \dfrac{-3/5}{-4/5} = \dfrac{3}{4}$.

12. First, we simplify the left-hand side:

$$\sin (x + 30°) = \sin x \cos 30° + \cos x \sin 30° = \frac{\sqrt{3}}{2} \sin x + \frac{1}{2} \cos x$$

Thus, we have the equation:

$$\frac{\sqrt{3}}{2} \sin x + \frac{1}{2} \cos x = \sqrt{3} \sin x$$

$$\sqrt{3} \sin x + \cos x = 2\sqrt{3} \sin x$$

$$\cos x = \sqrt{3} \sin x$$

$$\tan x = \frac{1}{\sqrt{3}}$$

$$x = 30°$$

13. $y = - \sin (2x - \pi)$
amplitude: 1;　period: π;　phase shift: $\pi/2$

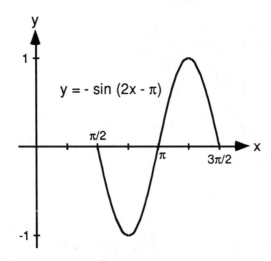

14. If $\csc \theta = -3$, then $\sin \theta = -\frac{1}{3}$. Since $\pi < \theta < \frac{3\pi}{2}$ (third quadrant), we have:

$$\cos \theta = - \sqrt{1 - \sin^2\theta} = - \sqrt{1 - \frac{1}{9}} = - \sqrt{\frac{8}{9}} = - \frac{2\sqrt{2}}{3}$$

Now $\frac{\pi}{2} < \frac{\theta}{2} < \frac{3\pi}{4}$ (second quadrant), so:

$$\sin \frac{\theta}{2} = \sqrt{\frac{1 - \cos \theta}{2}} = \sqrt{\frac{1 + \frac{2\sqrt{2}}{3}}{2}} = \sqrt{\frac{3 + 2\sqrt{2}}{6}} = \frac{\sqrt{18 + 12\sqrt{2}}}{6}$$

15. We graph the function for one period:

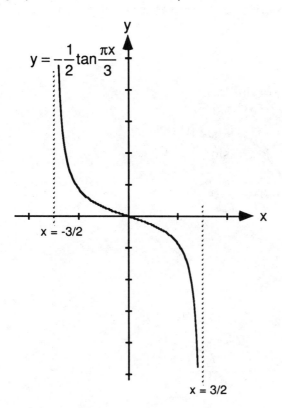

$$y = -\frac{1}{2}\tan\frac{\pi x}{3}$$

$x = -3/2$

$x = 3/2$

16. Since $\angle BPA = \theta$, then $\angle APC = \pi - \theta$, and the area of the sector formed by APC is:

$$\frac{1}{2}r^2\theta = \frac{1}{2}(\sqrt{2})^2(\pi - \theta) = \pi - \theta$$

Now $\triangle APC$ has a base of $\sqrt{2}$ and a height of $\sqrt{2}\sin\theta$, so its area is:

$$\frac{1}{2}(\text{base})(\text{height}) = \frac{1}{2}\sqrt{2}\bullet\sqrt{2}\sin\theta = \sin\theta$$

Thus, the area of the shaded region is given by:

$$A(\theta) = \pi - \theta - \sin\theta$$

17. We graph $y = \sin x$ for $-\dfrac{\pi}{2} \le x \le \dfrac{\pi}{2}$, and the corresponding $y = \sin^{-1} x$:

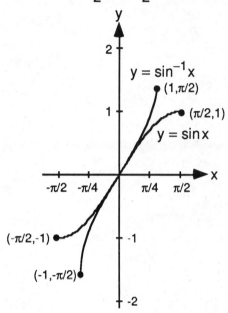

18. (a) $\sin^{-1}\left(\sin \dfrac{\pi}{10}\right) = \dfrac{\pi}{10}$ since $-\dfrac{\pi}{2} \le \dfrac{\pi}{10} \le \dfrac{\pi}{2}$.

(b) $\sin^{-1}(\sin 2\pi) = \sin^{-1} 0 = 0$

Note that $\sin^{-1}(\sin 2\pi) \ne 2\pi$, since 2π does not lie in the restricted domain of $\sin x$.

19. Call $u = \arcsin \dfrac{3}{4}$, so $\sin u = \dfrac{3}{4}$ and:

$$\cos u = \sqrt{1 - \dfrac{9}{16}} = \sqrt{\dfrac{7}{16}} = \dfrac{\sqrt{7}}{4}$$

Then $\cos\left(\arcsin \dfrac{3}{4}\right) = \cos u = \dfrac{\sqrt{7}}{4}$.

20. Using the sum formula for tangent, we have:

$$\tan\left(\dfrac{\pi}{4} + \dfrac{\theta}{2}\right) = \dfrac{\tan \dfrac{\pi}{4} + \tan \dfrac{\theta}{2}}{1 - \tan \dfrac{\pi}{4}\tan \dfrac{\theta}{2}}$$

$$= \dfrac{1 + \tan \dfrac{\theta}{2}}{1 - \tan \dfrac{\theta}{2}}$$

Now, using the half-angle formula for tangent, we have:

$$= \frac{1 + \dfrac{\sin \theta}{1 + \cos \theta}}{1 - \dfrac{\sin \theta}{1 + \cos \theta}} \cdot \frac{1 + \cos \theta}{1 + \cos \theta}$$

$$= \frac{1 + \cos \theta + \sin \theta}{1 + \cos \theta - \sin \theta}$$

This proves the identity.

21. $\dfrac{3\pi}{4} \cdot \dfrac{360°}{2\pi} = 135°$

23. $5\pi \cdot \dfrac{360°}{2\pi} = 900°$

25. $\dfrac{5\pi}{6} \cdot \dfrac{360°}{2\pi} = 150°$

27. $2 \cdot \dfrac{360°}{2\pi} = \dfrac{360°}{\pi}$

29. $360° \cdot \dfrac{2\pi \text{ radians}}{360°} = 2\pi \text{ radians}$

31. $1° \cdot \dfrac{2\pi \text{ radians}}{360°} = \dfrac{\pi}{180} \text{ radians}$

33. $7.5° \cdot \dfrac{2\pi \text{ radians}}{360°} = \dfrac{\pi}{24} \text{ radians}$

35. $\dfrac{1}{\pi}{}^{°} \cdot \dfrac{2\pi \text{ radians}}{360°} = \dfrac{1}{180} \text{ radians}$

37. $\cos \pi = -1$

39. $\csc \dfrac{2\pi}{3} = \dfrac{1}{\sin \dfrac{2\pi}{3}} = \dfrac{1}{\dfrac{\sqrt{3}}{2}} = \dfrac{2}{\sqrt{3}} = \dfrac{2\sqrt{3}}{3}$

41. $\cot \dfrac{11\pi}{6} = \dfrac{\cos \dfrac{11\pi}{6}}{\sin \dfrac{11\pi}{6}} = \dfrac{\dfrac{\sqrt{3}}{2}}{-\dfrac{1}{2}} = -\sqrt{3}$

43. $\sin \dfrac{\pi}{6} = \dfrac{1}{2}$

45. $\cot \dfrac{5\pi}{4} = 1$

47. $\csc \left(-\dfrac{5\pi}{6}\right) = \dfrac{1}{\sin \left(-\dfrac{5\pi}{6}\right)} = \dfrac{1}{-\dfrac{1}{2}} = -2$

49. $s = r\theta = 16 \cdot \dfrac{\pi}{8}$ cm $= 2\pi$ cm

    $A = \dfrac{1}{2} r^2\theta = \dfrac{1}{2} (16)^2 \cdot \dfrac{\pi}{8}$ cm^2 $= 16\pi$ cm^2

51. $\theta = \dfrac{s}{r} = 1$, so $A = \dfrac{1}{2} r^2\theta = \dfrac{1}{2} (1)^2(1)$ cm^2 $= \dfrac{1}{2}$ cm^2

53. $r = \dfrac{s}{\theta} = \dfrac{4 \text{ cm}}{\dfrac{\pi}{5}} = \dfrac{20}{\pi}$ cm

    $A = \dfrac{1}{2} r^2\theta = \dfrac{1}{2} \left(\dfrac{20}{\pi} \text{ cm}\right)^2 \left(\dfrac{\pi}{5}\right) = \dfrac{1}{2} \left(\dfrac{400}{\pi^2} \text{ cm}^2\right) \left(\dfrac{\pi}{5}\right) = \dfrac{40}{\pi}$ cm^2

55. $s = r\theta$, so $12 = r\theta = r(r + 1)$, hence:

    $r^2 + r - 12 = 0$

    $(r + 4)(r - 3) = 0$

    So $r = 3$ cm (since r cannot be negative), and $\theta = 4$ radians.

57. $180° - (40° + 70°) = 70°$, but $70° \cdot \dfrac{\pi}{180°} = \dfrac{7\pi}{18}$ radians

59. $\sin 1 \approx 0.841$

61. $\sin \dfrac{3\pi}{2} = -1.000$

63. $\sin \left(\sin (0.0123)\right) \approx 0.012$

65. $\sin^2 1986 + \cos^2 1986 \approx 0.241 + 0.759 = 1.000$

67. $\cos 0.5 \approx 0.878$ while $\cos^2 0.25 \approx 0.939$ and $\sin^2 0.25 \approx 0.061$, so:

    $\cos^2 0.25 - \sin^2 0.25 \approx 0.878 \approx \cos 0.5$

69. $\sqrt{25 - x^2}$ $= \sqrt{25 - 25 \sin^2 \theta}$
$= 5\sqrt{1 - \sin^2 \theta}$
$= 5\sqrt{\cos^2 \theta}$
$= 5\cos \theta$

71. $(x^2 - 100)^{1/2}$ $= (100 \sec^2 \theta - 100)^{1/2}$
$= 10 (\sec^2 \theta - 1)^{1/2}$
$= 10 (\tan^2 \theta)^{1/2}$
$= 10 \tan \theta$

73. $(x^2 + 5)^{-1/2} = (5 \tan^2 \theta + 5)^{-1/2} = \dfrac{\sqrt{5}}{5} (\sec^2 \theta)^{-1/2} = \dfrac{\sqrt{5}}{5} \cos \theta$

75. $\sin \theta = \dfrac{3}{5}$, so $\cos \theta = \sqrt{1 - \left(\dfrac{3}{5}\right)^2} = \sqrt{\dfrac{16}{25}} = \dfrac{4}{5}$. Thus:

$$\sin \dfrac{\theta}{2} = \sqrt{\dfrac{1 - \cos \theta}{2}} = \sqrt{\dfrac{1 - \dfrac{4}{5}}{2}} = \sqrt{\dfrac{1}{10}} = \dfrac{\sqrt{10}}{10}$$

77. If $\tan \theta = \dfrac{7}{24}$, then $\cos \theta = \dfrac{24}{25}$ and $\sin \theta = \dfrac{7}{25}$. So:

$\cos 2\theta = \cos^2 \theta - \sin^2 \theta$
$= \left(\dfrac{24}{25}\right)^2 - \left(\dfrac{7}{25}\right)^2$
$= \dfrac{576 - 49}{625}$
$= \dfrac{527}{625}$

79. $\csc \theta = \dfrac{29}{20}$, so $\sin \theta = \dfrac{20}{29}$ and:

$$\cos \theta = -\sqrt{1 - \left(\dfrac{20}{29}\right)^2} = -\sqrt{1 - \dfrac{400}{841}} = -\dfrac{441}{841} = -\dfrac{21}{29}$$

So $\dfrac{\pi}{2} < \theta < \pi$ and $\cos \dfrac{\theta}{2} = \sqrt{\dfrac{1 + \left(-\dfrac{21}{29}\right)}{2}} = \sqrt{\dfrac{8}{58}} = \dfrac{2\sqrt{29}}{29}$

81. $\sec^2 2\theta = 1 + \tan^2 2\theta = 1 + \left(\dfrac{7}{24}\right)^2 = \dfrac{625}{576}$, hence $\cos^2 2\theta = \dfrac{576}{625}$ and thus

$\cos 2\theta = -\dfrac{24}{25}$ (note that $\pi < 2\theta < \dfrac{3\pi}{2}$). Thus:

$$1 - 2\sin^2\theta = -\dfrac{24}{25}$$

$$\sin^2\theta = \dfrac{49}{50}$$

$$\sin\theta = \dfrac{7}{5\sqrt{2}} = \dfrac{7\sqrt{2}}{10}$$

83. Using the hint, we have two congruent shaded regions each with $r = 1$ cm and

$\theta = \dfrac{\pi}{2}$, and thus the total area is:

$$2 \bullet \dfrac{1}{2}\ \text{cm}^2 \left(\dfrac{\pi}{2} - 1\right) = \dfrac{\pi - 2}{2}\ \text{cm}^2$$

85. (a) $\cos 37° + \cos 35° \approx 1.62$ while $\cos 1° + \sin 19° + \sin 17° \approx 1.618$

(b) $\cos 40° + \cos 32° \approx 1.61$ while $\cos 4° + \sin 22° + \sin 14° \approx 1.614$

(c) $\cos 42° + \cos 30° \approx 1.61$ while $\cos 6° + \sin 24° + \sin 12° \approx 1.609$

87. $(\sin x + \cos x)^2 + (\sin x - \cos x)^2$
$\qquad = (\sin^2 x + 2\sin x \cos x + \cos^2 x) + (\sin^2 x - 2\sin x \cos x + \cos^2 x)$
$\qquad = 2(\sin^2 x + \cos^2 x)$
$\qquad = 2$

89. $(\cos x + \sin x - 1)(\cos x + \sin x + 1)$
$\qquad = (\cos x + \sin x)^2 - 1$
$\qquad = \cos^2 x + 2\sin x \cos x + \sin^2 x - 1$
$\qquad = 2\sin x \cos x$

91. $(9 - 4\sin x - \cos^2 x)(9 + 4\sin x - \cos^2 x)$
$\qquad = (9 - \cos^2 x)^2 - (4\sin x)^2$
$\qquad = 81 - 18\cos^2 x + \cos^4 x - 16\sin^2 x$
$\qquad = 81 + \cos^4 x - 16 - 2\cos^2 x$
$\qquad = 65 + (1 - \sin^2 x)^2 - 2(1 - \sin^2 x)$
$\qquad = 65 + 1 - 2\sin^2 x + \sin^4 x - 2 + 2\sin^2 x$
$\qquad = 64 + \sin^4 x$

93. $(a \sin x - b \cos x)^2 + (a \cos x + b \sin x)^2$
$= a^2 \sin^2 x - 2ab \cos x \sin x + b^2 \cos^2 x + a^2 \cos^2 x + 2ab \cos x \sin x + b^2 \sin^2 x$
$= (a^2 + b^2) \sin^2 x + (a^2 + b^2) \cos^2 x$
$= a^2 + b^2$

95. $\tan A = \dfrac{12}{5}$ implies that $\sin A = \dfrac{12}{13}$ and $\cos A = \dfrac{5}{13}$

$\tan B = \dfrac{3}{4}$ implies that $\sin B = \dfrac{3}{5}$ and $\cos B = \dfrac{4}{5}$

So $\cos (A + B) = \cos A \cos B - \sin A \sin B$

$\qquad\qquad\quad = \dfrac{5}{13} \cdot \dfrac{4}{5} - \dfrac{12}{13} \cdot \dfrac{3}{5}$

$\qquad\qquad\quad = \dfrac{20}{65} - \dfrac{36}{65}$

$\qquad\qquad\quad = -\dfrac{16}{65}$

97. $\sin (\pi - x) = \sin \pi \cos x - \cos \pi \sin x = 0 (\cos x) - (-1) \sin x = \sin x$

99. $\sin (10° + 80°) = \sin (90°) = 1$

101. $\cos \left(\dfrac{2\pi}{5} + \dfrac{\pi}{10} \right) = \cos \dfrac{5\pi}{10} = \cos \dfrac{\pi}{2} = 0$

103. $2 \sin \dfrac{\pi}{6} \cos x = 2 \cdot \dfrac{1}{2} \cdot \cos x = \cos x$

105. $\tan y = \tan (x + 60°) = \dfrac{\tan x + \sqrt{3}}{1 - \sqrt{3} \tan x}$

$\tan z = \tan (x - 60°) = \dfrac{\tan x - \sqrt{3}}{1 + \sqrt{3} \tan x}$

We will first simplify each of the quantities:

$\tan x \tan y = \dfrac{(\tan x)(\tan x + \sqrt{3})}{1 - \sqrt{3} \tan x}$

$\qquad\qquad = \dfrac{(\tan x)(\tan x + \sqrt{3})(1 + \sqrt{3} \tan x)}{1 - 3 \tan^2 x}$

$\qquad\qquad = \dfrac{\sqrt{3} \tan^3 x + 4 \tan^2 x + \sqrt{3} \tan x}{1 - 3 \tan^2 x}$

$$\tan y \tan z = \frac{\tan x + \sqrt{3}}{1 - \sqrt{3} \tan x} \cdot \frac{\tan x - \sqrt{3}}{1 + \sqrt{3} \tan x}$$

$$= \frac{\tan^2 x - 3}{1 - 3 \tan^2 x}$$

$$\tan x \tan z = \frac{(\tan x)(\tan x - \sqrt{3})}{1 + \sqrt{3} \tan x}$$

$$= \frac{(\tan x)(\tan x - \sqrt{3})(1 - \sqrt{3} \tan x)}{1 - 3 \tan^2 x}$$

$$= \frac{-\sqrt{3} \tan^3 x + 4 \tan^2 x - \sqrt{3} \tan x}{1 - 3 \tan^2 x}$$

Adding these three quantities and combining like terms, we get:

$$\frac{8 \tan^2 x + \tan^2 x - 3}{1 - 3 \tan^2 x} = \frac{9 \tan^2 x - 3}{1 - 3 \tan^2 x} = \frac{3(3 \tan^2 x - 1)}{-1(3 \tan^2 x - 1)} = -3$$

107. $\sin (x + y + z)$

$= \sin (x + y) \cos z + \sin z \cos (x + y)$

$= \cos z (\sin x \cos y + \sin y \cos x) + \sin z (\cos x \cos y - \sin x \sin y)$

$= \dfrac{15}{17} \cdot \dfrac{3}{5} \cdot \dfrac{12}{13} + \dfrac{15}{17} \cdot \dfrac{5}{13} \cdot \dfrac{4}{5} + \dfrac{8}{17} \cdot \dfrac{4}{5} \cdot \dfrac{12}{13} - \dfrac{8}{17} \cdot \dfrac{3}{5} \cdot \dfrac{5}{13}$

$= \dfrac{540 + 300 + 384 - 120}{1105}$

$= \dfrac{1104}{1105}$

109.   A = 4 and B = 1, so the equation is y = 4 sin x

111.   A = -2 and $\dfrac{2\pi}{B} = \dfrac{\pi}{2}$, so B = 4. So the equation is y = -2 cos 4x.

113.   Since $\sqrt{2} = A \sin \left(\dfrac{3\pi}{2} - \pi \right) = A \sin \dfrac{\pi}{2} = A$, then the amplitude is $\sqrt{2}$.

115.   y = -3 cos 4x
x-intercepts: π/8, 3π/8
high point: (π/4, 3)
low points: (0, -3), (π/2, -3)

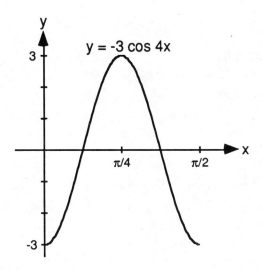

117. $y = 2 \sin\left(\dfrac{\pi x}{2} - \dfrac{\pi}{4}\right)$
x-intercepts: 1/2, 5/2, 9/2
high point: (3/2, 2)
low point: (7/2, -2)

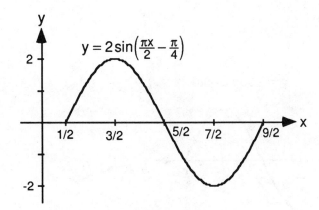

119. $y = 3 \cos \left(\dfrac{\pi x}{3} - \dfrac{\pi}{3} \right)$

x-intercepts: 5/2, 11/2
high points: (1, 3), (7, 3)
low point: (4, -3)

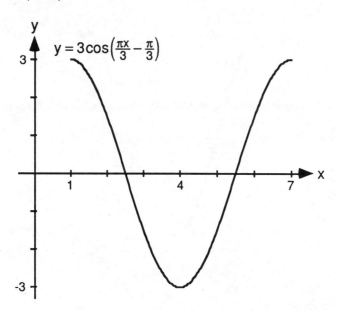

121. $y = -\cos 2x \sin 2x = -\dfrac{1}{2} \sin 4x$ by the double angle identity

x-intercepts: 0, $\pi/4$, $\pi/2$
high point: $(3\pi/8, 1/2)$
low point: $(\pi/8, -1/2)$

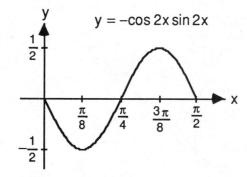

123.   (a) $y = \tan \dfrac{\pi x}{4}$

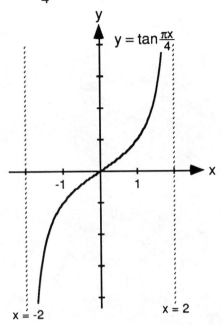

(b) $y = \cot \dfrac{\pi x}{4}$

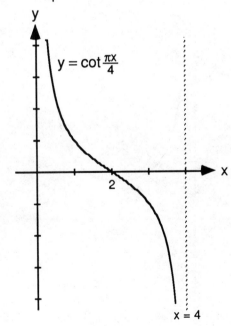

125.   (a) $y = 3 \sec \dfrac{x}{4}$

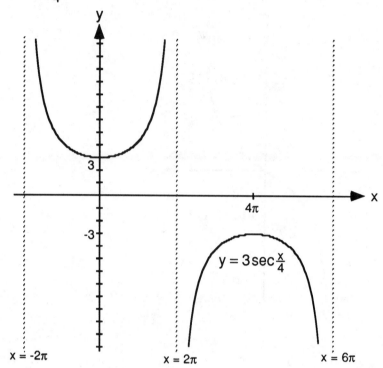

(b) $y = 3 \csc \dfrac{x}{4}$

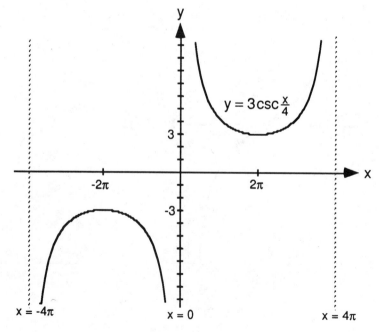

127. $y = \tan(x - 2)$

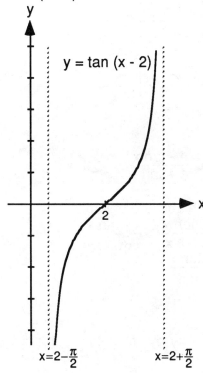

$x = 2 - \frac{\pi}{2}$ $x = 2 + \frac{\pi}{2}$

129. $\cot(x + y) = \dfrac{1}{\tan(x + y)}$

$= \dfrac{1 - \tan x \tan y}{\tan x + \tan y} \bullet \dfrac{\cot x \cot y}{\cot x \cot y}$

$= \dfrac{\cot x \cot y - 1}{\cot y + \cot x}$

131. $\dfrac{2 \tan x}{1 + \tan^2 x} \bullet \dfrac{\cos^2 x}{\cos^2 x} = \dfrac{2 \sin x \cos x}{\cos^2 x + \sin^2 x} = 2 \sin x \cos x = \sin 2x$

133.   Using the result from the above problem, we have:

$\dfrac{\sin(x + y) \sin(x - y)}{\cos^2 x \cos^2 y} = \dfrac{\sin^2 x \cos^2 y - \cos^2 x \sin^2 y}{\cos^2 x \cos^2 y}$

$= \dfrac{\sin^2 x}{\cos^2 x} - \dfrac{\sin^2 y}{\cos^2 y}$

$= \tan^2 x - \tan^2 y$

135. $\sin x \left(\tan \dfrac{x}{2} + \cot \dfrac{x}{2}\right) = \sin x \left[\dfrac{\sin x}{1 + \cos x} + \dfrac{1 + \cos x}{\sin x}\right]$

$= \sin x \left[\dfrac{\sin^2 x + 1 + 2 \cos x + \cos^2 x}{(\sin x)(1 + \cos x)}\right]$

$= \sin x \left[\dfrac{2 + 2 \cos x}{\sin x (1 + \cos x)}\right]$

$= 2$

137.   Since $\tan \left(\dfrac{\pi}{4} - x\right) = \dfrac{\tan \dfrac{\pi}{4} - \tan x}{1 + \tan x \tan \dfrac{\pi}{4}} = \dfrac{1 - \tan x}{1 + \tan x}$

Then combined with the result from the above problem:

$\tan \left(\dfrac{\pi}{4} + x\right) - \tan \left(\dfrac{\pi}{4} - x\right) = \dfrac{1 + \tan x}{1 - \tan x} - \dfrac{1 - \tan x}{1 + \tan x}$

$= \dfrac{4 \tan x}{1 - \tan^2 x}$

$= 2 \tan 2x$

139. $2 \sin \left(\dfrac{\pi}{4} - \dfrac{x}{2}\right) \cos \left(\dfrac{\pi}{4} - \dfrac{x}{2}\right) = \sin \left(\dfrac{\pi}{2} - x\right)$ by using the double-angle identity for sine, and this is equal to $\cos x$.

141. $\dfrac{\cos x + \sin x}{\cos x - \sin x} = \dfrac{(\cos x + \sin x)^2}{\cos^2 x - \sin^2 x}$

$= \dfrac{\cos^2 x + 2 \sin x \cos x + \sin^2 x}{\cos 2x}$

$= \dfrac{1 + \sin 2x}{\cos 2x}$

$= \dfrac{1}{\cos 2x} + \dfrac{\sin 2x}{\cos 2x}$

$= \tan 2x + \sec 2x$

143. $2 \sin x + \sin 2x = 2 \sin x + 2 \sin x \cos x$

$= 2 \sin x (1 + \cos x)$

$= \dfrac{2 \sin x (1 - \cos^2 x)}{1 - \cos x}$

$= \dfrac{2 \sin^3 x}{1 - \cos x}$

145. $\dfrac{1 - \cos x + \sin x}{1 + \cos x + \sin x}$

$= \dfrac{(1 + \sin x)^2 - \cos^2 x}{[(1 + \sin x) + \cos x]^2}$

$= \dfrac{1 + 2 \sin x + \sin^2 x - \cos^2 x}{(1 + 2 \sin x + \sin^2 x) + 2 \cos x \, (1 + \sin x) + \cos^2 x}$

$= \dfrac{2 \sin x + 2 \sin^2 x}{2 + 2 \sin x + 2 \cos x \, (1 + \sin x)}$

$= \dfrac{2 \sin x \, (1 + \sin x)}{2 \, (1 + \sin x) + 2 \cos x \, (1 + \sin x)}$

$= \dfrac{\sin x}{1 + \cos x}$

$= \tan \dfrac{x}{2}$

147. $\sin (x + y) \cos y - \cos (x + y) \sin y \; = \; \sin [(x + y) - y)] \; = \; \sin x$

149. $\dfrac{1 - \tan^2 \frac{x}{2}}{1 + \tan^2 \frac{x}{2}} \; = \; \dfrac{\cos^2 \frac{x}{2} - \sin^2 \frac{x}{2}}{\cos^2 \frac{x}{2} + \sin^2 \frac{x}{2}} \; = \; \cos^2 \dfrac{x}{2} - \sin^2 \dfrac{x}{2} \; = \; \cos 2 \bullet \dfrac{x}{2} \; = \; \cos x$

151. $\sin 4x \; = \; 2 \sin 2x \cos 2x$

$= 2(2 \sin x \cos x)(\cos^2 x - \sin^2 x)$

$= 4 \sin x \cos x \, (1 - 2 \sin^2 x)$

$= 4 \sin x \cos x - 8 \sin^3 x \cos x$

153. $\sin 5x$

$= \sin 4x \cos x + \cos 4x \sin x$

$= (4 \sin x \cos^2 x - 8 \sin^3 x \cos^2 x) + (8 \sin x \cos^4 x - 8 \sin x \cos^2 x + \sin x)$

$= -4 \sin x \cos^2 x - 8 \sin^3 x \cos^2 x + 8 \sin x \cos^4 x + \sin x$

$= -4 \sin x \, (1 - \sin^2 x) - 8 \sin^3 x \, (1 - \sin^2 x) + 8 \sin x \, (1 - \sin^2 x)^2 + \sin x$

$= -4 \sin x + 4 \sin^3 x - 8 \sin^3 x + 8 \sin^5 x + 8 \sin x - 16 \sin^3 x + 8 \sin^5 x + \sin x$

$= 16 \sin^5 x - 20 \sin^3 x + 5 \sin x$

155.   Following the hint, we apply the law of sines:

$$\frac{\sin \theta}{x} = \frac{\sin 2\theta}{2x}$$

$$\frac{\sin \theta}{x} = \frac{2 \sin \theta \cos \theta}{2x}$$

$$\frac{\sin \theta}{x} = \frac{\sin \theta \cos \theta}{x}$$

$$1 = \cos \theta$$

$$\theta = 90°$$

But if $\theta = 90°$, then $2\theta = 180°$, which is impossible.

157. $\sin 80° - \sin 20° = 2 \cos 50° \sin 30° = 2 (\cos 50°)\dfrac{1}{2} = \cos 50°$

159. $\dfrac{\cos x - \cos 3x}{\sin x + \sin 3x} = \dfrac{-2 \sin 2x \sin (-x)}{2 \sin 2x \cos x} = \dfrac{2 \sin 2x \sin x}{2 \sin 2x \cos x} = \tan x$

161. $\sin \dfrac{5\pi}{12} + \sin \dfrac{\pi}{12} = 2 \sin \dfrac{\pi}{4} \cos \dfrac{\pi}{6} = 2 \cdot \dfrac{\sqrt{2}}{2} \cdot \dfrac{\sqrt{3}}{2} = \dfrac{\sqrt{6}}{2}$

163. $\dfrac{\cos 3y + \cos (2x - 3y)}{\sin 3y + \sin (2x - 3y)} = \dfrac{2 \cos x \cos (3y - x)}{2 \sin x \cos (3y - x)} = \cot x$

165. $\dfrac{\sin 40° - \sin 20°}{\cos 20° - \cos 40°} = \dfrac{2 \cos 30° \sin 10°}{2 \sin 30° \sin 10°} = \cot 30° = \sqrt{3}$

While $\dfrac{\sin 10° - \sin 50°}{\cos 50° - \cos 10°} = \dfrac{2 \cos 30° \sin (-20°)}{-2 \sin 30° \sin 20°} = \cot 30° = \sqrt{3}$

Hence $\dfrac{\sin 40° - \sin 20°}{\cos 20° - \cos 40°} = \dfrac{\sin 10° - \sin 50°}{\cos 50° - \cos 10°}$

167.   (a)   We complete the table (using six decimal place accuracy for comparison). On a calculator, note that $\cos A + \cos B = \dfrac{a+b}{c}$:

a	b	c	$\cos A + \cos B$
3	4	5	1.400000
5	12	13	1.307692
20	21	29	1.413793
8	15	17	1.352941
1	$\sqrt{3}$	2	1.366025
1	1	$\sqrt{2}$	1.414214
$\sqrt{2}$	$\sqrt{3}$	$\sqrt{5}$	1.407052
696	697	985	1.414213

The triangle where $a = 1$, $b = 1$, $c = \sqrt{2}$ yields the largest value.

(b) $\cos A + \cos B = 2 \cos \dfrac{A+B}{2} \cos \dfrac{A-B}{2}$

$= 2 \cos \dfrac{90°}{2} \cos \dfrac{A-B}{2}$

$= 2 \cdot \dfrac{\sqrt{2}}{2} \cos \dfrac{A-B}{2}$

$= \sqrt{2} \cos \dfrac{A-B}{2}$

(c)   Since $\cos \dfrac{A-B}{2} \leq 1$, then $\cos A + \cos B \leq \sqrt{2}$. Equality will occur when $\cos \dfrac{A-B}{2} = 1$, so $\dfrac{A-B}{2} = 0$, thus $A = B = \dfrac{\pi}{4}$.

169.　　$\cot^2 x - \cot x = 0$

　　　　$\cot x (\cot x - 1) = 0$

So $\cot x = 0$, thus $x = \dfrac{\pi}{2}$ or $\dfrac{3\pi}{2}$ or $\cot x = 1$, thus $x = \dfrac{\pi}{4}$ or $\dfrac{5\pi}{4}$. So the

solutions are $x = \dfrac{\pi}{4}, \dfrac{\pi}{2}, \dfrac{5\pi}{4}$, or $\dfrac{3\pi}{2}$.

171.　$2 \sin 3x - \sqrt{3} = 0$, so $\sin 3x = \dfrac{\sqrt{3}}{2}$ and thus

　　　$3x = \dfrac{\pi}{3}, \dfrac{2\pi}{3}, \dfrac{7\pi}{3}, \dfrac{8\pi}{3}, \dfrac{13\pi}{3}$, or $\dfrac{14\pi}{3}$, and thus $x = \dfrac{\pi}{9}, \dfrac{2\pi}{9}, \dfrac{7\pi}{9}, \dfrac{8\pi}{9}, \dfrac{13\pi}{9}$, or $\dfrac{14\pi}{9}$.

173.　　　　$\sin x + \sin 2x = 0$

　　　$\sin x + 2 \sin x \cos x = 0$

　　　$\sin x (1 + 2 \cos x) = 0$

So $\sin x = 0$ or $\cos x = -\dfrac{1}{2}$, and therefore the solutions are

　　　$x = 0, \dfrac{2\pi}{3}, \pi$, or $\dfrac{4\pi}{3}$

175.　　　$2 \sin^2 x + \sin x - 1 = 0$

　　　$(2 \sin x - 1)(\sin x + 1) = 0$

　　　　　　　$\sin x = \dfrac{1}{2}$ or $\sin x = -1$

So the solutions are $x = \dfrac{\pi}{6}, \dfrac{5\pi}{6}$, or $\dfrac{3\pi}{2}$.

177.　　　$\sec^2 x - \sec x - 2 = 0$

　　　$(\sec x + 1)(\sec x - 2) = 0$

　　　　　　$\sec x = -1$ or $\sec x = 2$

So the solutions are $x = \dfrac{\pi}{3}, \pi$, or $\dfrac{5\pi}{3}$

179.　　　$4 \sin^2 2x + \cos 2x - 2 \cos^2 x - 2 = 0$

　　　　　$4 \sin^2 2x - \cos^2 x - \sin^2 x - 2 = 0$

　　　　　　　　　$4 \sin^2 2x - 3 = 0$

　　　　　　　　　　$\sin^2 2x = \dfrac{3}{4}$

　　　　　　　　　　$\sin 2x = \pm \dfrac{\sqrt{3}}{2}$

$2x = \dfrac{\pi}{3}, \dfrac{2\pi}{3}, \dfrac{4\pi}{3}, \dfrac{5\pi}{3}, \dfrac{7\pi}{3}, \dfrac{8\pi}{3}, \dfrac{10\pi}{3}$, or $\dfrac{11\pi}{3}$

So the solutions are $x = \dfrac{\pi}{6}, \dfrac{\pi}{3}, \dfrac{2\pi}{3}, \dfrac{5\pi}{6}, \dfrac{7\pi}{6}, \dfrac{4\pi}{3}, \dfrac{5\pi}{3}$, or $\dfrac{11\pi}{6}$.

181.   We have $a \cos A + b \sin A = c$ and $a \cos B + b \sin B = c$. Subtracting these two, we have $a(\cos A - \cos B) + b(\sin A - \sin B) = 0$.
Consequently:

$$\frac{\cos A - \cos B}{\sin A - \sin B} = -\frac{b}{a}$$

Using the sum-to-product formulas:

$$\frac{\cos A - \cos B}{\sin A - \sin B} = \frac{-2 \sin \frac{A+B}{2} \sin \frac{A-B}{2}}{2 \cos \frac{A+B}{2} \sin \frac{A-B}{2}} = -\tan \frac{A+B}{2}$$

Thus $\tan \dfrac{A+B}{2} = \dfrac{b}{a}$

183.   Using the triangle:

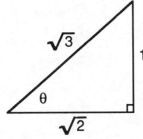

Then $\tan \theta = \dfrac{1}{\sqrt{2}} = \dfrac{\sqrt{2}}{2}$

So $\cos \left(\tan^{-1} \left(\sin \left(\tan^{-1} \frac{\sqrt{2}}{2} \right) \right) \right) = \cos (\tan^{-1} (\sin \theta))$

$$= \cos \left(\tan^{-1} \frac{1}{\sqrt{3}} \right)$$

$$= \cos \frac{\pi}{6}$$

$$= \frac{\sqrt{3}}{2}$$

185. $\arctan \dfrac{\sqrt{3}}{3} = \dfrac{\pi}{6}$

187. $\arcsin \dfrac{1}{2} = \dfrac{\pi}{6}$

189. $\cos^{-1} \dfrac{1}{2} = \dfrac{\pi}{3}$

191. $\cos^{-1}\left(-\dfrac{1}{2}\right) = \dfrac{2\pi}{3}$

193. $\cos\left(\cos^{-1}\dfrac{2}{7}\right) = \dfrac{2}{7}$

195. $\sin\left[\tan^{-1}(-1)\right] = \sin\left(-\dfrac{\pi}{4}\right) = -\dfrac{\sqrt{2}}{2}$

197. $\sec\left(\cos^{-1}\dfrac{\sqrt{2}}{3}\right) = \dfrac{1}{\cos\left(\cos^{-1}\dfrac{\sqrt{2}}{3}\right)} = \dfrac{1}{\dfrac{\sqrt{2}}{3}} = \dfrac{3}{\sqrt{2}} = \dfrac{3\sqrt{2}}{2}$

199. $\tan\left(\dfrac{\pi}{4} + \sin^{-1}\dfrac{5}{13}\right) = \dfrac{1 + \tan\left(\sin^{-1}\dfrac{5}{13}\right)}{1 - \tan\left(\sin^{-1}\dfrac{5}{13}\right)} = \dfrac{1 + \dfrac{5}{12}}{1 - \dfrac{5}{12}} = \dfrac{17}{7}$

201. $\tan(2\tan^{-1}2) = \dfrac{2\tan(\tan^{-1}2)}{1 - \tan^2(\tan^{-1}2)} = \dfrac{2(2)}{1 - (2)^2} = -\dfrac{4}{3}$

203. $\cos\left(\dfrac{1}{2}\cos^{-1}\dfrac{4}{5}\right) = \sqrt{\dfrac{1 + \cos\left(\cos^{-1}\dfrac{4}{5}\right)}{2}}$

$$= \sqrt{\dfrac{1 + \dfrac{4}{5}}{2}}$$

$$= \sqrt{\dfrac{9}{10}}$$

$$= \dfrac{3\sqrt{10}}{10}$$

205. $\tan\left[\dfrac{1}{2}\left(\arcsin\dfrac{1}{3}+\arccos\dfrac{1}{2}\right)\right]$

$$= \frac{\sin\left[\sin^{-1}\dfrac{1}{3}+\cos^{-1}\dfrac{1}{2}\right]}{1+\cos\left[\sin^{-1}\dfrac{1}{3}+\cos^{-1}\dfrac{1}{2}\right]}$$

$$= \frac{\sin\left(\sin^{-1}\dfrac{1}{3}\right)\cos\left(\cos^{-1}\dfrac{1}{2}\right)+\cos\left(\sin^{-1}\dfrac{1}{3}\right)\sin\left(\cos^{-1}\dfrac{1}{2}\right)}{1+\cos\left(\sin^{-1}\dfrac{1}{3}\right)\cos\left(\cos^{-1}\dfrac{1}{2}\right)-\sin\left(\sin^{-1}\dfrac{1}{3}\right)\sin\left(\cos^{-1}\dfrac{1}{2}\right)}$$

$$= \frac{\dfrac{1}{3}\bullet\dfrac{1}{2}+\dfrac{2\sqrt{2}}{3}\bullet\dfrac{\sqrt{3}}{2}}{1+\dfrac{2\sqrt{2}}{3}\bullet\dfrac{1}{2}-\dfrac{1}{3}\bullet\dfrac{\sqrt{3}}{2}}$$

$$= \frac{1+2\sqrt{6}}{6+2\sqrt{2}-\sqrt{3}}$$

207.   Let $\theta = \sin^{-1} x$:

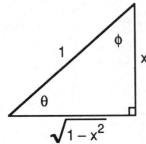

Since $\tan\theta = \dfrac{x}{\sqrt{1-x^2}}$, then $\tan^{-1}\dfrac{x}{\sqrt{1-x^2}} = \sin^{-1} x$

209.   Using the figure from the preceeding exercise, we have:

$$\begin{aligned}
\cos(2\cos^{-1} x) &= \cos 2\phi \\
&= \cos^2\phi - \sin^2\phi \\
&= x^2 - (\sqrt{1-x^2})^2 \\
&= x^2 - 1 + x^2 \\
&= 2x^2 - 1
\end{aligned}$$

211.   Since $\tan\left[\tan^{-1}\frac{1}{3} + \tan^{-1}\frac{1}{5}\right] = \dfrac{\tan\left(\tan^{-1}\frac{1}{3}\right) + \tan\left(\tan^{-1}\frac{1}{5}\right)}{1 - \tan\left(\tan^{-1}\frac{1}{3}\right)\tan\left(\tan^{-1}\frac{1}{5}\right)}$

$$= \dfrac{\frac{1}{3} + \frac{1}{5}}{1 - \frac{1}{3}\cdot\frac{1}{5}}$$

$$= \dfrac{\frac{8}{15}}{\frac{14}{15}}$$

$$= \frac{4}{7}$$

Then $\tan^{-1}\frac{1}{3} + \tan^{-1}\frac{1}{5} = \tan^{-1}\frac{4}{7}$

213.   If $\sin A = \frac{1}{3}$ then $\cos A = \frac{2\sqrt{2}}{3}$, and if $\cos B = \frac{1}{2}$ then $\sin B = \frac{\sqrt{3}}{2}$, so:

$$\tan\left(\sin^{-1}\frac{1}{3} + \cos^{-1}\frac{1}{2}\right) = \tan(A + B)$$

$$= \frac{\tan A + \tan B}{1 - \tan A \tan B}$$

$$= \dfrac{\frac{1}{2\sqrt{2}} + \sqrt{3}}{1 - \frac{\sqrt{3}}{2\sqrt{2}}}$$

$$= \frac{1 + 2\sqrt{6}}{2\sqrt{2} - \sqrt{3}}$$

$$= \frac{8\sqrt{2} + 9\sqrt{3}}{5}$$

CHAPTER SEVEN
SYSTEMS OF EQUATIONS

7.1 Systems of Two Linear Equations in Two Unknowns

1. (a) yes
   (b) no -- the xy term makes it non-linear
   (c) yes
   (d) yes

3. Yes. We simply test (5, 1) in the two equations and see if it produces true statements:

$$2(5) - 8(1) = 2$$
$$10 - 8 = 2 \quad \sqrt{}$$
$$3(5) + 7(1) = 22$$
$$15 + 7 = 22 \quad \sqrt{}$$

5. No. We test (0, -4) in the two equations and see if it produces true statements:

$$\frac{1}{6}(0) + \frac{1}{2}(-4) = -2$$
$$0 - 2 = -2 \quad \sqrt{}$$
$$\frac{2}{3}(0) + \frac{3}{4}(-4) = 2$$
$$0 - 3 = 2 \quad \text{false}$$

So (0, -4) is not a solution to the given system.

7.   Yes. We test (3, -2) in the two equations and see if it produces true statements:

$$\frac{2}{7}(3) - \frac{1}{5}(-2) = \frac{44}{35}$$

$$\frac{6}{7} + \frac{2}{5} = \frac{44}{35}$$

$$\frac{30}{35} + \frac{14}{35} = \frac{44}{35} \quad \sqrt{}$$

$$\frac{1}{3}(3) - \frac{5}{4}(-2) = \frac{7}{2}$$

$$1 + \frac{5}{2} = \frac{7}{2}$$

$$\frac{2}{2} + \frac{5}{2} = \frac{7}{2} \quad \sqrt{}$$

So (3, -2) is a solution to the given system.

9.   We solve the second equation for x:

$$x + 4y = -4$$

$$x = -4 - 4y$$

Now substitute $x = -4 - 4y$ for x in the first equation, and solve for y:

$$3x - 2y = -19$$

$$3(-4 - 4y) - 2y = -19$$

$$-12 - 12y - 2y = -19$$

$$-14y - 12 = -19$$

$$-14y = -7$$

$$y = \frac{1}{2}$$

We substitute this back into the second equation:

$$x = -4 - 4y = -4 - (4)\frac{1}{2} = -4 - 2 = -6$$

So the solution is (-6, 1/2).

11.   We solve the first equation for y:

$$4x + 2y = 3$$

$$2y = 3 - 4x$$

$$y = \frac{3 - 4x}{2}$$

Now substitute $y = \dfrac{3 - 4x}{2}$ for y in the second equation, and solve for x:

$$10x + 4y = 1$$

$$10x + 4\left(\dfrac{3 - 4x}{2}\right) = 1$$

$$10x + 2(3 - 4x) = 1$$

$$10x + 6 - 8x = 1$$

$$2x + 6 = 1$$

$$2x = -5, \quad \text{so} \quad x = -\dfrac{5}{2}$$

We substitute this back into the first equation:

$$y = \dfrac{3 - 4x}{2} = \dfrac{3 - 4\left(-\dfrac{5}{2}\right)}{2} = \dfrac{3 + 10}{2} = \dfrac{13}{2}$$

The solution is (-5/2, 13/2).

13. We solve the second equation for y:

$$-7x + 2y = 0$$

$$2y = 7x$$

$$y = \dfrac{7x}{2}$$

Now substitute $y = \dfrac{7x}{2}$ for y in the first equation, and solve for x:

$$13x - 8y = -3$$

$$13x - (8)\dfrac{7x}{2} = -3$$

$$13x - 28x = -3$$

$$-15x = -3$$

$$x = \dfrac{1}{5}$$

We substitute this back into the second equation:

$$y = \dfrac{7x}{2} = \dfrac{(7)\dfrac{1}{5}}{2} = \dfrac{7}{10}$$

The solution is (1/5, 7/10).

15. First we multiply each equation by 20 to clear fractions:

$$20\left(-\dfrac{2}{5}x + \dfrac{1}{4}y\right) = 20(3)$$

$$20\left(\dfrac{1}{4}x - \dfrac{2}{5}y\right) = 20(-3)$$

So:

$$-8x + 5y = 60$$

$$5x - 8y = -60$$

We solve the first equation for y:

$$-8x + 5y = 60$$
$$5y = 8x + 60$$
$$y = \frac{8x + 60}{5}$$

Now substitute $y = \frac{8x + 60}{5}$ for y in the second equation and solve for x:

$$5x - 8y = -60$$
$$5x - 8\left(\frac{8x + 60}{5}\right) = -60$$

Multiply by 5 to clear fractions:

$$25x - 8(8x + 60) = -300$$
$$25x - 64x - 480 = -300$$
$$-39x = 180$$
$$x = -\frac{180}{39} = -\frac{60}{13}$$

We substitute this back into the first equation:

$$y = \frac{8x + 60}{5} = \frac{8\left(-\frac{60}{13}\right) + 60}{5} = \frac{-480 + 780}{65} = \frac{300}{65} = \frac{60}{13}$$

The solution is $\left(-\frac{60}{13}, \frac{60}{13}\right)$.

17.   We solve the first equation for x:

$$\sqrt{2}\,x - \sqrt{3}\,y = \sqrt{3}$$
$$\sqrt{2}\,x = \sqrt{3}\,y + \sqrt{3}$$
$$x = \frac{\sqrt{3}\,y + \sqrt{3}}{\sqrt{2}}$$

Now substitute $x = \frac{\sqrt{3}\,y + \sqrt{3}}{\sqrt{2}}$ for x in the second equation and solve for y:

$$\sqrt{3}\,x - \sqrt{8}\,y = \sqrt{2}$$
$$\sqrt{3}\left(\frac{\sqrt{3}\,y + \sqrt{3}}{\sqrt{2}}\right) - \sqrt{8}\,y = \sqrt{2}$$
$$\frac{3y + 3}{\sqrt{2}} - \sqrt{8}\,y = \sqrt{2}$$

Multiply by $\sqrt{2}$ to clear the fractions:

$$3y + 3 - 4y = 2$$
$$3 - y = 2$$
$$-y = -1$$
$$y = 1$$

We substitute this back into the first equation:

$$x = \frac{\sqrt{3}\,y + \sqrt{3}}{\sqrt{2}} = \frac{\sqrt{3} + \sqrt{3}}{\sqrt{2}} = \frac{2\sqrt{3}}{\sqrt{2}} = \frac{2\sqrt{6}}{2} = \sqrt{6}$$

The solution is $(\sqrt{6}, 1)$.

19. We multiply the second equation by 2:

$$5x + 6y = 4$$
$$4x - 6y = -6$$

Adding, we get:

$$9x = -2$$
$$x = -\frac{2}{9}$$

We substitute $x = -\frac{2}{9}$ into the first equation:

$$5x + 6y = 4$$
$$5\left(-\frac{2}{9}\right) + 6y = 4$$
$$-\frac{10}{9} + 6y = 4$$
$$6y = \frac{46}{9}$$
$$y = \frac{46}{54} = \frac{23}{27}$$

The solution is $(-2/9, 23/27)$.

21. We multiply the second equation by -2:

$$4x + 13y = -5$$
$$-4x + 108y = 2$$

Adding, we get:

$$121y = -3$$
$$y = -\frac{3}{121}$$

We substitute $y = -\frac{3}{121}$ into the first equation:

$$4x + 13y = -5$$
$$4x + 13\left(-\frac{3}{121}\right) = -5$$
$$4x - \frac{39}{121} = -5$$
$$4x = -\frac{566}{121}$$
$$x = -\frac{283}{242}$$

The solution is $(-283/242, -3/121)$.

23. We multiply the first equation by 12 and the second equation by 70 to clear fractions:

$$12 \left(\frac{1}{4}x - \frac{1}{3}y \right) = 12 \, (4)$$

$$70 \left(\frac{2}{7}x - \frac{1}{7}y \right) = 70 \left(\frac{1}{10} \right)$$

So:

$$3x - 4y = 48$$
$$20x - 10y = 7$$

We multiply the first equation by -5 and the second equation by 2:

$$-15x + 20y = -240$$
$$40x - 20y = 14$$

Adding, we get:

$$25x = -226$$
$$x = -\frac{226}{25}$$

We substitute $x = -\frac{226}{25}$ into the second equation:

$$20x - 10y = 7$$

$$20 \left(-\frac{226}{25} \right) - 10y = 7$$

$$-\frac{904}{5} - 10y = 7$$

$$-10y = \frac{939}{5}$$

$$y = -\frac{939}{50}$$

The solution is $\left(-\frac{226}{25}, -\frac{939}{50} \right)$.

25. We multiply the second equation by -4:

$$8x + 16y = 5$$
$$-8x - 20y = -5$$

Adding, we get:

$$-4y = 0, \text{ so } y = 0$$

We substitute $y = 0$ into the first equation:

$$8x + 16y = 5$$
$$8x = 5$$
$$x = \frac{5}{8}$$

The solution is $(5/8, 0)$.

27. We divide the first equation by 5 and multiply the second equation by 10 to get:
$$25x - 8y = 9$$
$$x + y = 3$$
Multiply the second equation by 8:
$$25x - 8y = 9$$
$$8x + 8y = 24$$
Adding, we get:
$$33x = 33$$
$$x = 1$$
Now substititute $x = 1$ into the second equation:
$$x + y = 3$$
$$1 + y = 3$$
$$y = 2$$
The solution is $(1, 2)$.

29. The given points must satisfy the equation, so we get:
$$4 = 0^2 + b \bullet 0 + c$$
$$4 = c$$
and
$$14 = 2^2 + b \bullet 2 + c$$
$$10 = 2b + c$$
This system, $c = 4$ and $2b + c = 10$, is easily solved by substitution:
$$2b + c = 10$$
$$2b + 4 = 10$$
$$2b = 6$$
$$b = 3$$
$$y = x^2 + 3x + 4$$
So the equation of the parabola is $y = x^2 + 3x + 4$, as required.

31. Again, the points satisfy the equation.
$$Ax + By = 2$$
$$A(-4) + B(5) = 2$$
$$A(7) + B(-9) = 2$$
So, we have:
$$-4A + 5B = 2$$
$$7A - 9B = 2$$
Multiply the first equation by 7 and the second equation by 4:
$$-28A + 35B = 14$$
$$28A - 36B = 8$$
$$-B = 22$$
$$B = -22$$

Substituting for B:

$$7A - 9(-22) = 2$$
$$7A + 198 = 2$$
$$7A = -196$$
$$A = -28 \text{ as required.}$$

33. First we graph the region:

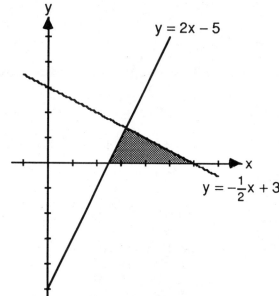

The base of the triangle is the difference between the x-intercepts, so:

$$\text{base} = 6 - \frac{5}{2} = \frac{7}{2}$$

The height is the y-coordinate of the intersection of the two lines $y = -\frac{1}{2}x + 3$
and $y = 2x - 5$, so:

$$-\frac{1}{2}x + 3 = 2x - 5$$
$$8 = \frac{5}{2}x$$
$$\frac{16}{5} = x$$

So $y = 2\left(\frac{16}{5}\right) - 5 = \frac{32}{5} - 5 = \frac{7}{5}$. So the area is:

$$\frac{1}{2}(\text{base})(\text{height}) = \frac{1}{2}\left(\frac{7}{2}\right)\left(\frac{7}{5}\right) = \frac{49}{20} \text{ square units.}$$

35. If we follow the example in this section, we let x = the amount of 10% solution and y = the amount of the 35% solution. Then x + y = 200 cc. Also, we know that the amount of acid in each separate solution, 10% of x and 35% of y must sum to equal the acid in the mixture, 25% of x + y. This second equation is usually in need of simplifying:

$$.10x + .35y = .25(x + y)$$
$$10x + 35y = 25(x + y)$$
$$2x + 7y = 5x + 5y$$
$$-3x + 2y = 0$$

This system is now solved by either method:

$$x + y = 200$$
$$-3x + 2y = 0$$

Multiply the first equation by 3:

$$3x + 3y = 600$$
$$-3x + 2y = 0$$

Adding, we get:

$$5y = 600$$
$$y = 120$$

So x = 80, and we need 80 cc of the 10% solution and 120 cc of the 35% solution.

Take a minute to consider what is a simpler solution. Using x + y = 200, substitute in the other equation:

$$10x + 35y = 25(x + y)$$
$$10x + 35(200 - x) = 25(200)$$
$$10x + 70000 - 35x = 5000$$
$$-25x = -2000$$
$$x = 80, \text{ so } y = 120$$

We get the same results with less work.

37. Let x = amount of $5.20 coffee and y = amount of $5.80 coffee. Then x + y = 16 pounds. The total value of each bean is 5.20x and 5.80y, respectively, and that of the mixture is 5.50(x + y), so we have:

$$5.20x + 5.80y = 5.50(x + y)$$
$$52x + 58y = 55(x + y)$$
$$52x + 58y = 55x + 55y$$
$$-3x + 3y = 0$$
$$-x + y = 0$$

We solve the system:

$$x + y = 16$$
$$-x + y = 0$$

Adding, we get:

$$2y = 16$$
$$y = 8$$

Since x = 16 - y, then x = 16 - 8 = 8.

So we mix 8 pounds of $5.20 coffee and 8 pounds of $5.80 coffee.

39. Eliminating fractions, we get:

$$bx + ay = ab$$
$$ax + by = ab$$

So:

$$abx + a^2y = a^2b$$
$$-abx - b^2y = -ab^2 \quad \text{adding gives}$$
$$(a^2 - b^2)y = a^2b - ab^2$$
$$y = \frac{ab(a - b)}{a^2 - b^2}$$

If we factor and reduce, we have $y = \dfrac{ab}{a + b}$. Now substitute to get x:

$$\frac{x}{a} + \frac{\frac{ab}{a + b}}{b} = 1$$
$$\frac{x}{a} + \frac{a}{a + b} = 1$$
$$(a + b)x + a^2 = a(a + b)$$
$$(a + b)x = a^2 + ab - a^2$$
$$x = \frac{ab}{a + b}$$

The solution is $\left(\dfrac{ab}{a + b}, \dfrac{ab}{a + b} \right)$. Note that we cannot have a = ±b for this solution.

41. We multiply the first equation by b and the second equation by -a:

$$abx + a^2by = b$$
$$-abx - ab^2y = -a$$

Adding, we get:

$$(a^2b - ab^2)y = b - a$$
$$y = \frac{b - a}{a^2b - ab^2} = \frac{-1}{ab}$$

We substitute $y = \dfrac{-1}{ab}$ into the first equation:

$$ax + a^2y = 1$$
$$ax - \frac{a}{b} = 1$$
$$ax = \frac{a + b}{b}$$
$$x = \frac{a + b}{ab}$$

So the solution is $\left(\dfrac{a + b}{ab}, \dfrac{-1}{ab} \right)$. Note that we cannot have ab = 0, so a ≠ 0 and b ≠ 0.

43. Let $x = \dfrac{1}{s}$ and $y = \dfrac{1}{t}$. Then we get:

$$\frac{1}{2}x - \frac{1}{2}y = -10$$
$$2x + 3y = 5$$

Multiply the first equation by -4:

$$-2x + 2y = 40$$
$$2x + 3y = 5$$

Adding, we get:

$$5y = 45$$
$$y = 9$$

We substitute $y = 9$ into the second equation, and solve for x:

$$2x + 3y = 5$$
$$2x + 3(9) = 5$$
$$2x + 27 = 5$$
$$2x = -22$$
$$x = -11$$

Since $s = \dfrac{1}{x}$ and $t = \dfrac{1}{y}$, then $s = -\dfrac{1}{11}$ and $t = \dfrac{1}{9}$. So the solution is (-1/11, 1/9).

45. First let's clear of fractions and put into a standard form:

$$\frac{2w - 1}{3} + \frac{z + 2}{4} = 4$$

Multiplying by 12 we get:

$$4(2w - 1) + 3(z + 2) = 12 \bullet 4$$
$$8w - 4 + 3z + 6 = 48$$
$$8w + 3z = 46$$

The second equation will be $w + 2z = 9$.

$$8w + 3z = 46$$
$$w + 2z = 9$$

Multiply the second equation by -8:

$$8w + 3z = 46$$
$$-8w - 16z = -72$$

Adding, we get:

$$-13z = -26$$
$$z = 2$$
$$w = 9 - 2(2) = 5$$

So the solution is $(w, z) = (5, 2)$.

47. Using substitution, we'll solve the first equation for x:

$$1.03x - 2.54y = 5.47$$
$$1.03x = 2.54y + 5.47$$
$$x = 2.4660y + 5.3107$$

Now substitute into the second equation:
$$3.85x + 4.29y = -1.84$$
$$3.85(2.466y + 5.3107) + 4.29y = -1.84$$
$$13.7841y = -22.2862$$
$$y \approx -1.62$$
Substituting back for x:
$$x = 2.4660(-1.62) + 5.3107 \approx 1.32$$
So the solution is (1.32, -1.62).

49. We'll use the addition-subtraction method. We eliminate y by multiplying the first equation by 3 and the second equation by 4:
$$3\sqrt{5}\,x - 12\sqrt{3}\,y = 18$$
$$4\sqrt{2}\,x + 12\sqrt{3}\,y = 32$$
Adding, we get:
$$(3\sqrt{5} + 4\sqrt{2})\,x = 50$$
$$x = \frac{50}{3\sqrt{5} + 4\sqrt{2}}$$
$$x \approx 4.04$$
We substitute into the first equation:
$$3\sqrt{5}\,(4.0437) - 12\sqrt{3}\,y = 18$$
$$y = \frac{18 - 3\sqrt{5}(4.0437)}{-12\sqrt{3}}$$
$$y \approx 0.44$$
So the solution is (4.04, 0.44)

51. If we take tu as our number, then it is important to distinguish between its value, $10t + u$, and the sum of its digits $t + u$. Here we are told that $t + u = 14$ and that $2t = u + 1$. We solve this system:
$$t + u = 14$$
$$2t - u = 1$$
Adding, we get:
$$3t = 15, \text{ so } t = 5$$
Thus $u = 9$ and our original two-digit number was 59.

53. Let l and w be the length and width, respectively, of the rectangle. Since the perimeter is 34 in., then $2l + 2w = 34$, or $l + w = 17$. We are also given that $l = 2 + 2w$, so we substitute:
$$l + w = 17$$
$$(2 + 2w) + w = 17$$
$$2 + 3w = 17$$
$$3w = 15, \text{ so } w = 5$$
Thus $l = 17 - w = 17 - 5 = 12$. Thus the length is 12 in. and the width is 5 in.

55. (a)   We solve the first equation for y:
$$x + y = 100$$
$$y = 100 - x$$
Now substituting into the second equation:
$$-2x + 3y = 0$$
$$-2x + 3(100 - x) = 0$$
$$-2x + 300 - 3x = 0$$
$$300 - 5x = 0$$
$$300 = 5x, \quad \text{so} \quad x = 60$$
So y = 100 - 60 = 40. Thus the solution is (60, 40).

(b)   We multiply the first equation by 2:
$$2x + 2y = 200$$
$$-2x + 3y = 0$$
Adding, we get:
$$5y = 200, \quad \text{so} \quad y = 40$$
Substituting back into the first equation:
$$x + y = 100$$
$$x + 40 = 100$$
$$x = 60$$
Again, the solution is (60, 40)

57.   We solve each equation for x:
$$x = by - ab$$
$$x = cy - ac$$
Setting these equal:
$$by - ab = cy - ac$$
$$by - cy = ab - ac$$
$$y(b - c) = a(b - c)$$
$$y = a, \quad \text{as long as } b \neq c$$
Plugging into the second equation, we get:
$$x = cy - ac = ac - ac = 0$$
So the solution is (0, a).

59.   Making the substitutions x = ln s and y = ln t, we have:
$$3x + 4y = 1$$
$$5x + 3y = 9$$
Multiply the first equation by -5 and the second equation by 3:
$$-15x - 20y = -5$$
$$15x + 9y = 27$$
Adding, we have:
$$-11y = 22$$
$$y = -2$$

Substitute into the first equation:
$$3x - 8 = 1$$
$$3x = 9$$
$$x = 3$$
So $x = 3$ and $y = -2$:
$$\ln s = 3, \text{ so } s = e^3 \approx 20.09$$
$$\ln t = -2, \text{ so } t = e^{-2} \approx 0.14$$
So the solution is $(e^3, e^{-2}) \approx (20.09, 0.14)$.

61.   Let $u = \dfrac{1}{x}$ and $v = \dfrac{1}{y}$. Then we have:
$$\frac{a}{b} u + \frac{b}{a} v = a + b$$
$$bu + av = a^2 + b^2$$
Multiply the first equation by ab to clear the fractions:
$$a^2 u + b^2 v = a^2 b + ab^2$$
$$bu + av = a^2 + b^2$$
We multiply the first equation by $-b$ and the second equation by a^2:
$$-a^2 bu - b^3 v = -a^2 b^2 - ab^3$$
$$a^2 bu + a^3 v = a^4 + a^2 b^2$$
Adding, we get:
$$(a^3 - b^3)v = a^4 - ab^3$$
$$(a^3 - b^3)v = a(a^3 - b^3)$$
$$v = a$$
Substituting $v = a$ into the second equation, we get:
$$bu + av = a^2 + b^2$$
$$bu + a^2 = a^2 + b^2$$
$$bu = b^2$$
$$u = b$$
Since $x = \dfrac{1}{u}$ and $y = \dfrac{1}{v}$, then $x = \dfrac{1}{b}$ and $y = \dfrac{1}{a}$.

So the solution is $\left(\dfrac{1}{b}, \dfrac{1}{a}\right)$.

63.   Since the lines are concurrent, the following two systems must possess the same solution:

I. $7x + 5y = 4$ II. $x + ky = 3$
      $x + ky = 3$ $5x + y = -k$

Using either method of this section, we find that the solution of system I is $\left(\dfrac{4k - 15}{7k - 5}, \dfrac{17}{7k - 5}\right)$. Also the solution of system II is found to be $\left(\dfrac{-3 - k^2}{5k - 1}, \dfrac{k + 15}{5k - 1}\right)$. Since the two solutions are the same, the corresponding x and y coordinates must be equal. Equating the y-coordinates gives us:

$$\frac{17}{7k - 5} = \frac{k + 15}{5k - 1}$$

After clearing the fractions and simplifying, this equation becomes $7k^2 + 15k - 58 = 0$. We factor to get $(7k + 29)(k - 2) = 0$ and therefore $k = -\dfrac{29}{7}$ or $k = 2$. These are the required values of k. If we equate the x-coordinates rather than the y-coordinates we obtain the equation $7k^3 + 15k^2 - 58k = 0$. We factor to get $k(7k + 29)(k - 2) = 0$, which has solutions $k = 0, -\dfrac{29}{7}$, and 2. The root $k = 0$ is extraneous, for in that case the two y-coordinates are not equal.

65. (a) We first draw the triangle:

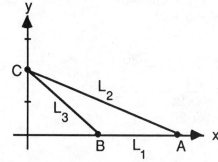

We find the equations for each side:

L_1: $y = 0$

L_2: $m = \dfrac{0 - 2}{2a - 0} = -\dfrac{1}{a}$

So $y = -\dfrac{1}{a}x + 2$

$ay = -x + 2a$

$x + ay = 2a$

L_3: $m = \dfrac{0 - 2}{2b - 0} = -\dfrac{1}{b}$

So $y = -\dfrac{1}{b}x + 2$

$by = -x + 2b$

$x + by = 2b$

(b)   We first find the midpoints of each side:

$$L_1: \quad \text{mid} = \left(\frac{2b + 2a}{2}, \frac{0}{2} \right) = (a + b, 0)$$

$$L_2: \quad \text{mid} = \left(\frac{0 + 2a}{2}, \frac{2 + 0}{2} \right) = (a, 1)$$

$$L_3: \quad \text{mid} = \left(\frac{0 + 2b}{2}, \frac{2 + 0}{2} \right) = (b, 1)$$

Now we find the slopes from each vertex to the adjacent midpoint:

$$CL_1: \quad m = \frac{0 - 2}{a + b - 0} = \frac{-2}{a + b}$$

$$BL_2: \quad m = \frac{1 - 0}{a - 2b} = \frac{1}{a - 2b}$$

$$AL_3: \quad m = \frac{1 - 0}{b - 2a} = \frac{1}{b - 2a}$$

Finally, we use these slopes and vertices in the point-slope formula:

$$CL_1: \qquad y - 2 = \frac{-2}{a + b}(x - 0)$$

$$y = \frac{-2}{a + b}x + 2$$

$$(a + b)y = -2x + 2(a + b)$$

$$2x + (a + b)y = 2(a + b)$$

$$BL_2: \qquad y - 0 = \frac{1}{a - 2b}(x - 2b)$$

$$y = \frac{1}{a - 2b}x - \frac{2b}{a - 2b}$$

$$(a - 2b)y = x - 2b$$

$$-x + (a - 2b)y = -2b$$

$$x + (2b - a)y = 2b$$

$$AL_3: \qquad y - 0 = \frac{1}{b - 2a}(x - 2a)$$

$$y = \frac{1}{b - 2a}x - \frac{2a}{b - 2a}$$

$$(b - 2a)y = x - 2a$$

$$-x + (b - 2a)y = -2a$$

$$x + (2a - b)y = 2a$$

(c)   We find the intersection of the three lines:

$$2x + (a + b)y = 2(a + b)$$
$$x + (2b - a)y = 2b$$
$$x + (2a - b)y = 2a$$

We will solve the second and third equations for x:

$$x = 2b - (2b - a)y$$
$$x = 2a - (2a - b)y$$

Setting these equal:

$$2b - (2b - a)y = 2a - (2a - b)y$$
$$(2a - b)y - (2b - a)y = 2a - 2b$$
$$(2a - b - 2b + a)y = 2a - 2b$$
$$(3a - 3b)y = 2a - 2b$$
$$y = \frac{2a - 2b}{3a - 3b} = \frac{2(a - b)}{3(a - b)} = \frac{2}{3}$$

We substitute $y = \frac{2}{3}$ into the second equation:

$$x = 2b - (2b - a)\frac{2}{3}$$
$$= \frac{6b - 4b + 2a}{3}$$
$$= \frac{2b + 2a}{3}$$
$$= \frac{2(a + b)}{3}$$

We must <u>still</u> show that this point $\left(\frac{2(a + b)}{3}, \frac{2}{3}\right)$ lies on the first line:

$$2x + (a + b)y = 2(a + b)$$
$$4\left(\frac{a + b}{3}\right) + (a + b)\frac{2}{3} = 2(a + b)$$
$$6\frac{(a + b)}{3} = 2(a + b) \quad \surd$$

Thus the point $\left(\frac{2(a + b)}{3}, \frac{2}{3}\right)$ is the intersection of all three medians:

(d)   The altitudes will be perpendicular to the slopes of each side, which we found in (a). So:

$$BL_2: \quad m = a$$
$$y - 0 = a(x - 2b)$$
$$y = ax - 2ab$$
$$-ax + y = -2ab$$
$$ax - y = 2ab$$

$$CL_1: \quad m = \text{undefined}$$
$$x = 0$$

$$AL_3: \quad m = b$$
$$y - 0 = b(x - 2a)$$
$$y = bx - 2ab$$
$$-bx + y = -2ab$$
$$bx - y = 2ab$$

(e)   We find the intersection of the three lines:
$$ax - y = 2ab$$
$$bx - y = 2ab$$
$$x = 0$$
Since $x = 0$, substituting into the first equation yields:
$$-y = 2ab$$
$$y = -2ab$$
We must still show that this point $(0, -2ab)$ lies on the second line:
$$bx - y = 2ab$$
$$b(0) - (-2ab) = 2ab$$
$$2ab = 2ab \quad \sqrt{}$$
Thus, the point $(0, -2ab)$ is the intersection of all three altitudes.

(f)   Recall that the perpendicular bisectors must be perpendicular and pass through the midpoints $\big($which we found in (b)$\big)$:

L_1:   mid $= (a + b, 0)$
$m =$ undefined
$x = a + b$

L_2:   mid $= (a, 1)$
$m = a$
$y - 1 = a(x - a)$
$y - 1 = ax - a^2$
$-ax + y = 1 - a^2$
$ax - y = a^2 - 1$

L_3:   mid $= (b, 1)$
$m = b$
$y - 1 = b(x - b)$
$y - 1 = bx - b^2$
$-bx + y = 1 - b^2$
$bx - y = b^2 - 1$

(g)   We find the intersection of the three lines:
$$ax - y = a^2 - 1$$
$$bx - y = b^2 - 1$$
$$x = a + b$$
Substituting into the first equation yields:
$$a(a + b) - y = a^2 - 1$$
$$a^2 + ab - y = a^2 - 1$$
$$-y = -ab - 1$$
$$y = ab + 1$$

We must still show that the point $(a + b, ab + 1)$ lies on the second line:
$$bx - y = b^2 - 1$$
$$b(a + b) - (ab + 1) = b^2 - 1$$
$$ab + b^2 - ab - 1 = b^2 - 1$$
$$b^2 - 1 = b^2 - 1 \quad \sqrt{}$$
Thus the point $(a + b, ab + 1)$ is the intersection of all three perpendicular bisectors.

(h) We find the line that passes through $\left(\dfrac{2(a + b)}{3}, \dfrac{2}{3}\right)$, $(0, -2ab)$, and $(a + b, ab + 1)$. We work with the last two points:
$$m = \frac{ab + 1 - (-2ab)}{a + b - 0} = \frac{3ab + 1}{a + b}$$
Since $(0, -2ab)$ is the y-intercept, then the line should be:
$$y = \frac{3ab + 1}{a + b} x - 2ab$$

We must still show that the point $\left(\dfrac{2(a + b)}{3}, \dfrac{2}{3}\right)$ lies on this line:
$$\frac{2}{3} = \left(\frac{3ab + 1}{a + b}\right)\left(\frac{2(a + b)}{3}\right) - 2ab$$
$$\frac{2}{3} = \frac{2(3ab + 1)}{3} - 2ab$$
$$\frac{2}{3} = \frac{6ab + 2 - 6ab}{3}$$
$$\frac{2}{3} = \frac{2}{3} \quad \sqrt{}$$
Thus, $y = \dfrac{3ab + 1}{a + b} x - 2ab$ is the Euler line.

7.2 Gaussian Elimination

1. Given:
$$2x + y + z = -9$$
$$3y - 2z = -4$$
$$8z = -8$$
We solve for z in the third equation:
$$8z = -8$$
$$z = -1$$

Substitute into the second equation:

$$3y - 2z = -4$$
$$3y - 2(-1) = -4$$
$$3y + 2 = -4$$
$$3y = -6$$
$$y = -2$$

Substitute into the first equation:

$$2x + y + z = -9$$
$$2x + (-2) + (-1) = -9$$
$$2x - 3 = 9$$
$$2x = -6$$
$$x = -3$$

So the solution is (-3, -2, -1).

3. Given:

$$8x + 5y + 3z = 1$$
$$3y + 4z = 2$$
$$5z = 3$$

We solve for z in the third equation:

$$5z = 3$$
$$z = \frac{3}{5}$$

Substitute into the second equation:

$$3y + 4z = 2$$
$$3y + (4)\frac{3}{5} = 2$$
$$3y + \frac{12}{5} = 2$$
$$3y = -\frac{2}{5}$$
$$y = -\frac{2}{15}$$

Substitute into the first equation:

$$8x + 5y + 3z = 1$$
$$8x + 5\left(-\frac{2}{15}\right) + (3)\frac{3}{5} = 1$$
$$8x - \frac{2}{3} + \frac{9}{5} = 1$$
$$8x - \frac{10}{15} + \frac{27}{15} = 1$$
$$8x = -\frac{2}{15}$$
$$x = -\frac{1}{60}$$

So the solution is (-1/60, -2/15, 3/5).

5.   Given:
$$-4x + 5y = 0$$
$$3y + 2z = 1$$
$$3z = -1$$

We solve for z in the third equation:
$$3z = -1$$
$$z = -\frac{1}{3}$$

Substitute into the second equation:
$$3y + 2z = 1$$
$$3y + 2\left(-\frac{1}{3}\right) = 1$$
$$3y - \frac{2}{3} = 1$$
$$3y = \frac{5}{3}$$
$$y = \frac{5}{9}$$

Substitute into the first equation:
$$-4x + 5y = 0$$
$$-4x + (5)\frac{5}{9} = 0$$
$$-4x + \frac{25}{9} = 0$$
$$-4x = -\frac{25}{9}$$
$$x = \frac{25}{36}$$

So the solution is $\left(\frac{25}{36}, \frac{5}{9}, -\frac{1}{3}\right)$.

7.   Given:
$$-x + 8y + 3z = 0$$
$$2z = 0$$

We solve for z in the second equation:
$$2z = 0$$
$$z = 0$$

Substitute into the first equation:
$$-x + 8y + 3z = 0$$
$$-x + 8y + 3(0) = 0$$
$$-x + 8y = 0$$
$$8y = x$$
$$y = \frac{x}{8}$$

So the solution is $(x, x/8, 0)$, where x is any real number.

9.   Given:
$$2x + 3y + z + w = -6$$
$$y + 3z - 4w = 23$$
$$6z - 5w = 31$$
$$-2w = 10$$
We solve for w in the fourth equation:
$$-2w = 10$$
$$w = -5$$
Substitute into the third equation:
$$6z - 5w = 31$$
$$6z - 5(-5) = 31$$
$$6z + 25 = 31$$
$$6z = 6$$
$$z = 1$$
Substitute into the second equation:
$$y + 3z - 4w = 23$$
$$y + 3(1) - 4(-5) = 23$$
$$y + 23 = 23$$
$$y = 0$$
Substitute into the first equation:
$$2x + 3y + z + w = -6$$
$$2x + 3(0) + 1 + (-5) = -6$$
$$2x - 4 = -6$$
$$2x = -2$$
$$x = -1$$
So the solution is (-1, 0, 1, -5).

11.   We must arrange this according to echelon form. First add negative two times the first equation to the second one, and -3 times it to the third:
$$x + y + z = 12$$
$$-3y - 3z = -25$$
$$-y - 2z = -14$$
We want to eliminate the y term from the third equation so let's interchange the 2nd and 3rd equations:
$$x + y + z = 12$$
$$-y - 2z = -14$$
$$-3y - 3z = -25$$
Add -3 times the 2nd to the third:
$$x + y + z = 12$$
$$-y - 2z = -14$$
$$3z = 17$$
Solve for z in the third equation:
$$3z = 17$$
$$z = \frac{17}{3}$$

Sustitute into the second equation:

$$-y - 2z = -14$$

$$-y - (2)\frac{17}{3} = -14$$

$$-y - \frac{34}{3} = -14$$

$$-y = -\frac{8}{3}$$

$$y = \frac{8}{3}$$

Substitute into the first equation:

$$x + y + z = 12$$

$$x + \frac{8}{3} + \frac{17}{3} = 12$$

$$x + \frac{25}{3} = 12$$

$$x = \frac{11}{3}$$

So the solution is $\left(\frac{11}{3}, \frac{8}{3}, \frac{17}{3}\right)$.

13. We must arrange the system in echelon form. Multiply the first equation by -2 and add it to the second equation:

$$-4x + 6y - 4z = -8$$
$$\underline{4x + 2y + 3z = 7}$$
$$8y - z = -1$$

Multiply the first equation by $-\frac{5}{2}$ and add it to the third equation:

$$-5x + \frac{15}{2}y - 5z = -10$$
$$\underline{5x + 4y + 2z = 7\quad}$$
$$\frac{23}{2}y - 3z = -3$$
$$23y - 6z = -6$$

So we have the system:

$$2x - 3y + 2z = 4$$
$$8y - z = -1$$
$$23y - 6z = -6$$

Multiply the second equation by $-\frac{23}{8}$ and add it to the third equation:

$$-23y + \frac{23}{8}z = \frac{23}{8}$$
$$\underline{23y - 6z = -6}$$
$$-\frac{25}{8}z = -\frac{25}{8}$$

So we have the system in echelon form:

$$2x - 3y + 2z = 4$$
$$8y - z = -1$$
$$-\frac{25}{8}z = -\frac{25}{8}$$

Solve for z in the third equation:

$$-\frac{25}{8}z = -\frac{25}{8}$$
$$z = 1$$

Substitute into the second equation:

$$8y - z = -1$$
$$8y - 1 = -1$$
$$8y = 0$$
$$y = 0$$

Substitute into the first equation:

$$2x - 3y + 2z = 4$$
$$2x - 3(0) + 2(1) = 4$$
$$2x + 2 = 4$$
$$2x = 2$$
$$x = 1$$

So the solution is $(1, 0, 1)$.

15. We must arrange the system in echelon form. Multiply the first equation by -2 and add it to the second equation:

$$-6x - 6y + 4z = -26$$
$$\underline{6x + 2y - 5z = 13}$$
$$-4y - z = -13$$

Multiply the first equation by $-\frac{7}{3}$ and add it to the third equation:

$$-7x - 7y + \frac{14}{3}z = -\frac{91}{3}$$
$$\underline{7x + 5y - 3z = 26}$$
$$-2y + \frac{5}{3}z = -\frac{13}{3}$$
$$-6y + 5z = -13$$

So we have the system:

$$3x + 3y - 2z = 13$$
$$-4y - z = -13$$
$$-6y + 5z = -13$$

Multiply the second equation by $-\frac{3}{2}$ and add it to the third equation:

$$6y + \frac{3}{2}z = \frac{39}{2}$$
$$\underline{-6y + 5z = -13}$$
$$\frac{13}{2}z = \frac{13}{2}$$

So we have the system in echelon form:

$$3x + 3y - 2z = 13$$
$$-4y - z = -13$$
$$\frac{13}{2}z = \frac{13}{2}$$

Solve for z in the third equation:

$$\frac{13}{2}z = \frac{13}{2}$$
$$z = 1$$

Substitute into the second equation:

$$-4y - z = -13$$
$$-4y - 1 = -13$$
$$-4y = -12$$
$$y = 3$$

Substitute into the first equation:

$$3x + 3y - 2z = 13$$
$$3x + 3(3) - 2(1) = 13$$
$$3x + 7 = 13$$
$$3x = 6$$
$$x = 2$$

So the solution is $(2, 3, 1)$.

17. We must arrange the system in echelon form. Multiply the first equation by 2 and add it to the second equation:

$$2x + 2y + 2z = 2$$
$$\underline{-2x + y + z = -2}$$
$$3y + 3z = 0$$
$$y + z = 0$$

Multiply the first equation by -3 and add it to the third equation:

$$-3x - 3y - 3z = -3$$
$$\underline{3x + 6y + 6z = 5}$$
$$3y + 3z = 2$$

So we have the system:

$$x + y + z = 1$$
$$y + z = 0$$
$$3y + 3z = 2$$

Multiply the second equation by -3 and add it to the third equation:

$$-3y - 3z = 0$$
$$\underline{3y + 3z = 2}$$
$$0 = 2$$

Since this equation is false, there is no solution. This system is inconsistent.

19. We first re-arrange the system as:

$$x + 3y - 2z = 2$$
$$2x - y + z = -1$$
$$-5x + 6y - 5z = 5$$

Multiply the first equation by -2 and add it to the second equation:

$$-2x - 6y + 4z = -4$$
$$\underline{2x - y + z = -1}$$
$$-7y + 5z = -5$$

Multiply the first equation by 5 and add it to the third equation:

$$5x + 15y - 10z = 10$$
$$\underline{-5x + 6y - 5z = 5}$$
$$21y - 15z = 15$$
$$7y - 5z = 5$$

So we have the system:

$$x + 3y - 2z = 2$$
$$-7y + 5z = -5$$
$$7y - 5z = 5$$

Adding the second and third equations yields $0 = 0$, so the system is dependent. Solving for x and y in terms of z yields the solution $\left(\dfrac{z + 1}{-7}, \dfrac{5(z + 1)}{7}, z\right)$, where z is any real number.

21. We first re-arrange the system as:

$$x + 3y + 2z = -1$$
$$2x - y + z = 4$$
$$7x + 5z = 11$$

Multiply the first equation by -2 and add it to the second equation:

$$-2x - 6y - 4z = 2$$
$$\underline{2x - y + z = 4}$$
$$-7y - 3z = 6$$

Multiply the first equation by -7 and add it to the third equation:

$$-7x - 21y - 14z = 7$$
$$\underline{7x + 5z = 11}$$
$$-21y - 9z = 18$$
$$-7y - 3z = 6$$

So we have the system:

$$x + 3y + 2z = -1$$
$$-7y - 3z = 6$$
$$-7y - 3z = 6$$

Multiply the second equation by -1 and add it to the third equation:

$$7y + 3z = -6$$
$$\underline{-7y - 3z = 6}$$
$$0 = 0$$

So we have the system:

$$x + 3y + 2z = -1$$
$$-7y - 3z = 6$$

We solve the second equation for y:

$$-7y - 3z = 6$$
$$-7y = 3z + 6$$
$$y = \frac{-3z - 6}{7}$$

Substitute into the first equation:

$$x + 3y + 2z = -1$$
$$x + 3\left(\frac{-3z - 6}{7}\right) + 2z = -1$$
$$x + \frac{-9z - 18 + 14z}{7} = -1$$
$$x + \frac{5z - 18}{7} = -1$$
$$x = \frac{-7 - 5z + 18}{7}$$
$$x = \frac{-5z + 11}{7}$$

So the solution is $\left(\frac{11 - 5z}{7}, \frac{-3z - 6}{7}, z\right)$ where z is any real number.

23. Multiply the first equation by -1 and add it to the second equation:

$$-x - y - z - w = -4$$
$$\underline{x - 2y - z - w = 3}$$
$$-3y - 2z - 2w = -1$$
$$3y + 2z + 2w = 1$$

Multiply the first equation by -2 and add it to the third equation:

$$-2x - 2y - 2z - 2w = -8$$
$$\underline{2x - y + z - w = 2}$$
$$-3y - z - 3w = -6$$
$$3y + z + 3w = 6$$

Multiply the first equation by -1 and add it to the fourth equation:

$$-x - y - z - w = -4$$
$$\underline{x - y + 2z - 2w = -7}$$
$$-2y + z - 3w = -11$$
$$2y - z + 3w = 11$$

So we have the system:

$$\begin{aligned} x + y + z + w &= 4 \\ 3y + 2z + 2w &= 1 \\ 3y + z + 3w &= 6 \\ 2y - z + 3w &= 11 \end{aligned}$$

Multiply the second equation by -1 and add it to the third equation:

$$\begin{aligned} -3y - 2z - 2w &= -1 \\ \underline{3y + z + 3w} &= \underline{6} \\ -z + w &= 5 \\ z - w &= -5 \end{aligned}$$

Multiply the second equation by $-\frac{2}{3}$ and add it to the fourth equation:

$$\begin{aligned} -2y - \frac{4}{3}z - \frac{4}{3}w &= -\frac{2}{3} \\ \underline{2y - z + 3w} &= \underline{11} \\ -\frac{7}{3}z + \frac{5}{3}w &= \frac{31}{3} \\ -7z + 5w &= 31 \end{aligned}$$

So we have the system:

$$\begin{aligned} x + y + z + w &= 4 \\ 3y + 2z + 2w &= 1 \\ z - w &= -5 \\ -7z + 5w &= 31 \end{aligned}$$

Multiply the third equation by 7 and add it to the fourth equation:

$$\begin{aligned} 7z - 7w &= -35 \\ \underline{-7z + 5w} &= \underline{31} \\ -2w &= -4 \end{aligned}$$

So we have the system:

$$\begin{aligned} x + y + z + w &= 4 \\ 3y + 2z + 2w &= 1 \\ z - w &= -5 \\ -2w &= -4 \end{aligned}$$

We solve the fourth equation for w:

$$\begin{aligned} -2w &= -4 \\ w &= 2 \end{aligned}$$

Substitute into the third equation:

$$\begin{aligned} z - w &= -5 \\ z - 2 &= -5 \\ z &= -3 \end{aligned}$$

Substitute into the second equation:

$$\begin{aligned} 3y + 2z + 2w &= 1 \\ 3y + 2(-3) + 2(2) &= 1 \\ 3y - 2 &= 1 \\ 3y &= 3 \\ y &= 1 \end{aligned}$$

Substitute into the first equation:
$$x + y + z + w = 4$$
$$x + 1 - 3 + 2 = 4$$
$$x = 4$$
So the solution is $(4, 1, -3, 2)$

25. We first re-arrange the system as:
$$x + 4y - 3z = 1$$
$$2x + 3y + 2z = 5$$
Multiply the first equation by -2 and add it to the second equation:
$$-2x - 8y + 6z = -2$$
$$\underline{2x + 3y + 2z = 5}$$
$$-5y + 8z = 3$$
So we have the system:
$$x + 4y - 3z = 1$$
$$-5y + 8z = 3$$
We solve the second equation for y:
$$-5y + 8z = 3$$
$$-5y = 3 - 8z$$
$$y = \frac{8z - 3}{5}$$
Substitute into the first equation:
$$x + 4y - 3z = 1$$
$$x + 4\left(\frac{8z - 3}{5}\right) - 3z = 1$$
$$x + \frac{17z - 12}{5} = 1$$
$$x = \frac{17 - 17z}{5}$$
So the solution is $\left(\dfrac{17 - 17z}{5}, \dfrac{8z - 3}{5}, z\right)$, where z is any real number.

27. Multiply the first equation by -3 and add it to the second equation:
$$-3x + 6y + 6z - 6w = 30$$
$$\underline{3x + 4y - z - 3w = 11}$$
$$10y + 5z - 9w = 41$$
Multiply the first equation by 4 and add it to the third equation:
$$4x - 8y - 8z + 8w = -40$$
$$\underline{-4x - 3y - 3z + 8w = -21}$$
$$-11y - 11z + 16w = -61$$
So we have the system:
$$x - 2y - 2z + 2w = -10$$
$$10y + 5z - 9w = 41$$
$$-11y - 11z + 16w = -61$$

We add the second and third equations:

$$10y + 5z - 9w = 41$$
$$\underline{-11y - 11z + 16w = -61}$$
$$-y - 6z + 7w = -20$$
$$y + 6z - 7w = 20$$

So we have the system:

$$x - 2y - 2z + 2w = -10$$
$$y + 6z - 7w = 20$$
$$-11y - 11z + 16w = -61$$

Multiply the second equation by 11 and add it to the third equation:

$$11y + 66z - 77w = 220$$
$$\underline{-11y - 11z + 16w = -61}$$
$$55z - 61w = 159$$

So we have the system:

$$x - 2y - 2z + 2w = -10$$
$$y + 6z - 7w = 20$$
$$55z - 61w = 159$$

We solve the third equation for z:

$$55z - 61w = 159$$
$$55z = 61w + 159$$
$$z = \frac{61w + 159}{55}$$

Substitute into the second equation:

$$y + 6z - 7w = 20$$
$$y + 6\left(\frac{61w + 159}{55}\right) - 7w = 20$$
$$y + \frac{954 - 19w}{55} = 20$$
$$y = \frac{146 + 19w}{55}$$

Substitute into the first equation:

$$x - 2y - 2z + 2w = -10$$
$$x - 2\left(\frac{146 + 19w}{55}\right) - 2\left(\frac{61w + 159}{55}\right) + 2w = -10$$
$$x + \frac{-122 - 10w}{11} = -10$$
$$x = \frac{12 + 10w}{11}$$

So the solution is $\left(\dfrac{12 + 10w}{11}, \dfrac{146 + 19w}{55}, \dfrac{61w + 159}{55}, w\right)$, where w is any real number.

29.   Solving the second equation for y yields $y = \dfrac{2z + 3}{3}$. We substitute this into

the first equation to get $x = -\dfrac{5z}{12}$. So the solution is $\left(-\dfrac{5z}{12}, \dfrac{2z + 3}{3}, z \right)$, where

z is any real number.

31.   (a)   Multiply by (x - 2)(x + 2), so:
$$1 = A(x + 2) + B(x - 2)$$
$$1 = Ax + 2A + Bx - 2B$$
$$1 = (A + B)x + (2A - 2B)$$
Since A and B are constants (cannot contain x), then we must have:
$$A + B = 0$$
$$2A - 2B = 1$$
Multiply the first equation by -2 and add it to the second equation:
$$-2A - 2B = 0$$
$$\underline{2A - 2B = 1}$$
$$-4B = 1$$
$$B = -\dfrac{1}{4}$$
Substituting into the first equation:
$$A + B = 0$$
$$A - \dfrac{1}{4} = 0$$
$$A = \dfrac{1}{4}$$
So $A = \dfrac{1}{4}$ and $B = -\dfrac{1}{4}$

(b)   Multiply by (x - 2)(x + 2), so:
$$x = A(x + 2) + B(x - 2)$$
$$x = Ax + 2A + Bx - 2B$$
$$x = (A + B)x + (2A - 2B)$$
Since A and B are constants then we have the system:
$$A + B = 1$$
$$2A - 2B = 0$$
Multiply the first equation by -2 and add it to the second equation:
$$-2A - 2B = -2$$
$$\underline{2A - 2B = 0}$$
$$-4B = -2$$
$$B = \dfrac{1}{2}$$

Substituting into the first equation:

$$A + B = 1$$

$$A + \frac{1}{2} = 1$$

$$A = \frac{1}{2}$$

So $A = \frac{1}{2}$ and $B = \frac{1}{2}$.

33.   Multiply by $(x + 4)(x - 5)$, so:

$$3x = A(x - 5) + B(x + 4)$$
$$3x = Ax - 5A + Bx + 4B$$
$$3x = (A + B)x + (-5A + 4B)$$

Since A and B are constants, then we have the system:

$$A + B = 3$$
$$-5A + 4B = 0$$

Multiply the first equation by 5 and add it to the second equation:

$$5A + 5B = 15$$
$$\underline{-5A + 4B = 0}$$
$$9B = 15$$
$$B = \frac{5}{3}$$

Substituting into the first equation:

$$A + B = 3$$

$$A + \frac{5}{3} = 3$$

$$A = \frac{4}{3}$$

So $A = \frac{4}{3}$ and $B = \frac{5}{3}$

35.   (a)   Multiply by $(x - 4)(x + 4)$, so:

$$3 = A(x + 4) + B(x - 4)$$
$$3 = Ax + 4A + Bx - 4B$$
$$3 = (A + B)x + (4A - 4B)$$

Since A and B are constants, we have:

$$A + B = 0$$
$$4A - 4B = 3$$

Multiply the first equation by -4 and add it to the second equation:

$$-4A - 4B = 0$$
$$\underline{4A - 4B = 3}$$
$$-8B = 3$$
$$B = -\frac{3}{8}$$

Substituting into the first equation:

$$A + B = 0$$

$$A - \frac{3}{8} = 0$$

$$A = \frac{3}{8}$$

So $A = \frac{3}{8}$ and $B = -\frac{3}{8}$

(b)   Multiply by $(x - 4)(x + 4)^2$, so:

$$3 = A(x + 4)^2 + B(x - 4)(x + 4) + C(x - 4)$$

$$3 = Ax^2 + 8Ax + 16A + Bx^2 - 16B + Cx - 4C$$

$$3 = (A + B)x^2 + (8A + C)x + (16A - 16B - 4C)$$

Since A, B, and C are constants, we have:

$$A + \quad B \qquad = 0$$

$$8A \qquad\quad + C = 0$$

$$16A - 16B - 4C = 3$$

Multiply the first equation by -8 and add it to the second equation:

$$-8A - 8B \qquad = 0$$

$$\underline{8A + \qquad C = 0}$$

$$-8B + C = 0$$

Multiply the first equation by -16 and add it to the third equation:

$$-16A - 16B \qquad = 0$$

$$\underline{16A - 16B - 4C = 3}$$

$$-32B - 4C = 3$$

So we have the system:

$$A + B \qquad = 0$$

$$-8B + \quad C = 0$$

$$-32B - 4C = 3$$

Multiply the second equation by -4 and add it to the third equation:

$$32B - 4C = 0$$

$$\underline{-32B - 4C = 3}$$

$$-8C = 3$$

$$C = -\frac{3}{8}$$

Substitute into the second equation:

$$-8B + C = 0$$

$$-8B - \frac{3}{8} = 0$$

$$-8B = \frac{3}{8}$$

$$B = -\frac{3}{64}$$

Substitute into the first equation:

$$A + B = 0$$

$$A - \frac{3}{64} = 0$$

$$A = \frac{3}{64}$$

So $A = \frac{3}{64}$, $B = -\frac{3}{64}$, and $C = -\frac{3}{8}$

37. Multiply by $(x + 1)(x^2 - x + 1)$, so:

$$1 = A(x^2 - x + 1) + (Bx + C)(x + 1)$$
$$1 = Ax^2 - Ax + A + Bx^2 + Cx + Bx + C$$
$$1 = (A + B)x^2 + (-A + B + C)x + (A + C)$$

Since A, B, and C are constants, we have:

$$A + B \quad = 0$$
$$-A + B + C = 0$$
$$A \quad + C = 1$$

Add the first two equations:

$$A + B \quad = 0$$
$$\underline{-A + B + C = 0}$$
$$2B + C = 0$$

Multiply the first equation by -1 and add it to the third equation:

$$-A - B \quad = 0$$
$$\underline{A \quad + C = 1}$$
$$-B + C = 1$$

So we have the system:

$$A + B \quad = 0$$
$$-B + C = 1$$
$$2B + C = 0$$

Multiply the second equation by 2 and add it to the third equation:

$$-2B + 2C = 2$$
$$\underline{2B + \quad C = 0}$$
$$3C = 2$$

$$C = \frac{2}{3}$$

Substitute into the second equation:

$$-B + C = 1$$

$$-B + \frac{2}{3} = 1$$

$$-B = \frac{1}{3}$$

$$B = -\frac{1}{3}$$

Substitute into the first equation:

$$A + B = 0$$

$$A - \frac{1}{3} = 0$$

$$A = \frac{1}{3}$$

So $A = \frac{1}{3}$, $B = -\frac{1}{3}$, and $C = \frac{2}{3}$.

39. Multiply by $x(1 - x)$, so:

$$4 = A(1 - x) + B(x)$$
$$4 = (-A + B)x + A$$

Since A and B are constants, wehave:

$$-A + B = 0$$
$$A = 4$$

Substituting yields $-4 + B = 0$, so $B = 4$. So $A = 4$ and $B = 4$.

41. Multiply by $(x^2 + x + 1)(x^2 - x + 1)$, so:

$$1 = (Ax + B)(x^2 - x + 1) + (Cx + D)(x^2 + x + 1)$$
$$1 = (A + C)x^3 + (-A + B + C + D)x^2 + (A - B + C + D)x + (B + D)$$

Since A, B, C, and D are constants, we have:

$$A \quad + C \quad = 0$$
$$-A + B + C + D = 0$$
$$A - B + C + D = 0$$
$$B \quad + D = 1$$

Add the first and second equations:

$$\begin{array}{r} A \quad + C \quad = 0 \\ \underline{-A + B + C + D = 0} \\ B + 2C + D = 0 \end{array}$$

Multiply the first equation by -1 and add it to the third equation:

$$\begin{array}{r} -A \quad - C \quad = 0 \\ \underline{A - B + C + D = 0} \\ -B \quad + D = 0 \end{array}$$

So we have the system:

$$A \quad + C \quad = 0$$
$$-B \quad + D = 0$$
$$B + 2C + D = 0$$
$$B \quad + D = 1$$

Add the second and third equations:

$$\begin{array}{r} -B \quad + D = 0 \\ \underline{B + 2C + D = 0} \\ 2C + 2D = 0 \\ C + D = 0 \end{array}$$

Add the second and the fourth equations:

$$-B + D = 0$$
$$B + D = 1$$
$$2D = 1$$
$$D = \frac{1}{2}$$

So we have the system:

$$A \quad + C \qquad = 0$$
$$-B \qquad + D = 0$$
$$C + D = 0$$
$$D = \frac{1}{2}$$

Substituting into the third equation yields $C = -\frac{1}{2}$. Substitution into the second equation yields $B = \frac{1}{2}$. Substituting into the first equation yields $A = \frac{1}{2}$.

So $A = \frac{1}{2}$, $B = \frac{1}{2}$, $C = -\frac{1}{2}$, and $D = \frac{1}{2}$.

43. We know its form is $(x - h)^2 + (y - k)^2 = r^2$, so:

$$(-1 - h)^2 + (-5 - k)^2 = r^2$$
$$(1 - h)^2 + (2 - k)^2 = r^2$$
$$(-2 - h)^2 + k^2 = r^2$$

Or:

$$1 + 2h + h^2 + 25 + 10k + k^2 = r^2$$
$$1 - 2h + h^2 + 4 - 4k + k^2 = r^2$$
$$4 + 4h + h^2 + k^2 = r^2$$

Setting the first two equations equal yields $4h + 14k = -21$ and setting the last two equations equal yields $6h + 4k = 1$. So we solve the system:

$$4h + 14k = -21$$
$$6h + 4k = 1$$

Multiplying the first equation by -3 and the second equation by 2, then adding, yields $k = -\frac{65}{34}$, and substituting into the second equation yields $h = \frac{49}{34}$.

We find r by the original third equation:

$$r^2 = 4 + 4h + h^2 + k^2$$
$$= 4 + \frac{98}{17} + \left(\frac{49}{34}\right)^2 + \left(-\frac{65}{34}\right)^2$$
$$= \frac{17914}{34^2}$$
$$= \frac{8957}{578}$$

So we have $\left(x - \dfrac{49}{34}\right)^2 + \left(y + \dfrac{65}{34}\right)^2 = \dfrac{8957}{578}$, which simplifies to:

$17x^2 + 17y^2 - 49x + 65y - 166 = 0$

45. Using the hint, we let $A = e^x$, $B = e^y$, and $C = e^z$. Then we have the system:

$$A +\ B - 2C\ =\ 2a$$
$$A + 2B - 4C\ =\ 3a$$
$$\frac{1}{2}A\ - 3B\ + C\ =\ -5a$$

Multiply the first equation by -1 and add it to the second equation:

$$-A\ -\ B + 2C\ =\ -2a$$
$$\underline{A + 2B\ - 4C\ =\ 3a}$$
$$B\ - 2C\ =\ a$$

Multiply the first equation by -1 and the third equation by 2, then add the resulting equations:

$$-A -\ B + 2C\ =\ -2a$$
$$\underline{A - 6B + 2C\ =\ -10a}$$
$$-7B + 4C\ =\ -12a$$

So we have the system:

$$A + B - 2C\ =\ 2a$$
$$B - 2C\ =\ \ a$$
$$-7B + 4C\ =\ -12a$$

Multiply the second equation by 7 and add it to the third equation:

$$7B - 14C\ =\ \ 7a$$
$$\underline{-7B + \ 4C\ =\ -12a}$$
$$-10C\ =\ -\ 5a$$
$$C\ =\ \frac{a}{2}$$

Substituting into the second equation:

$$B -\ 2C\ =\ a$$
$$B - 2\left(\frac{a}{2}\right)\ =\ a$$
$$B - a\ =\ a$$
$$B\ =\ 2a$$

Substituting into the first equation:

$$A + B - 2C\ =\ 2a$$
$$A + 2a - a\ =\ 2a$$
$$A + a\ =\ 2a$$
$$A\ =\ a$$

So $A = a$, $B = 2a$, $C = \dfrac{a}{2}$. Since $A = e^x$, $B = e^y$, $C = e^z$, then $x = \ln a$, $y = \ln 2a$,

and $z = \ln \dfrac{a}{2}$

47. From the figure in the text, we obtain the system of three equations:

$$r_1 + r_2 = a$$
$$r_2 + r_3 = b$$
$$r_1 + r_3 = c$$

This system can be solved by repeated substitution, or by using the following technique. Add the three equations and then divide by 2 to obtain $r_1 + r_2 + r_3 = \dfrac{a+b+c}{2}$. Now replace $r_2 + r_3$ in this last equation by b. The result is $r_1 = \dfrac{a+b+c}{2} - b$. Thus $r_1 = \dfrac{a-b+c}{2}$. Similarly, we find that $r_2 = \dfrac{a+b-c}{2}$, and $r_3 = \dfrac{b+c-a}{2}$.

49. (a) Multiply by $(x-a)(x-b)$, so:

$$1 = A(x-b) + B(x-a)$$
$$1 = (A+B)x + (-bA - aB)$$

Since A and B are constants, we have:

$$A + B = 0$$
$$-bA - aB = 1$$

Multiplying the first equation by b and adding it to the second equation, yields $B = \dfrac{1}{b-a}$. We re-solve for A. Multiplying the first equation by a and adding it to the second equation, yields $A = \dfrac{1}{a-b}$.

So $A = \dfrac{1}{a-b}$ and $B = \dfrac{1}{b-a}$.

(b) Multiply by $(x-a)(x-b)$, so:

$$px + q = A(x-b) + B(x-a)$$
$$px + q = (A+B)x + (-bA - aB)$$

Since A and B are constants, we have:

$$A + B = p$$
$$-bA - aB = q$$

Multiplying the first equation by b and adding it to the second equation yields $B = \dfrac{bp+q}{b-a}$. We re-solve for A. Multiplying the first equation by a and adding it to the second equation yields $A = \dfrac{ap+q}{a-b}$.

So $A = \dfrac{ap+q}{a-b}$ and $B = \dfrac{bp+q}{b-a}$.

51. We multiply by $(x - a)(x - b)(x - c)$ to get:

$$x^2 + px + q = A(x - b)(x - c) + B(x - a)(x - c) + C(x - a)(x - b)$$

For this problem, I'll show you a different method. Since this equation is an identity for all x, then it must be an identity for $x = a$, $x = b$, and $x = c$.

$x = a$: $a^2 + pa + q = A(a - b)(a - c) + 0 + 0$

$$A = \frac{a^2 + pa + q}{(a - b)(a - c)}$$

$x = b$: $b^2 + pb + q = 0 + B(b - a)(b - c) + 0$

$$B = \frac{b^2 + pb + q}{(b - a)(b - c)}$$

$x = c$: $c^2 + pc + q = 0 + 0 + C(c - a)(c - b)$

$$C = \frac{c^2 + pc + q}{(c - a)(c - b)}$$

So $A = \dfrac{a^2 + pa + q}{(a - b)(a - c)}$, $B = \dfrac{b^2 + pb + q}{(b - a)(b - c)}$, and $C = \dfrac{c^2 + pc + q}{(c - a)(c - b)}$

53. Let α, β, and γ be the distances opposite towns A, B, and C. The walking, riding, and driving rates are, respectively, $\frac{1}{a}$ mi/min, $\frac{1}{b}$ mi/min, and $\frac{1}{c}$ mi/min.

From the statement of the problem we can obtain the following system of three equations:

$$\alpha a + \beta b + \gamma c = 60(a + c - b)$$
$$\beta a + \gamma b + \alpha c = 60(b + a - c)$$
$$\gamma a + \alpha b + \beta c = 60(c + b - a)$$

By adding all three equations, we obtain:

$$\alpha(a + b + c) + \beta(a + b + c) + \gamma(a + b + c) = 60(a + b + c)$$

Now divide through by the quantity $a + b + c$. This yields $\alpha + \beta + \gamma = 60$ miles, as required.

7.3 Matrices

1. (a)   two by three (2 x 3)
   (b)   three by two (3 x 2)

3. five by four (5 x 4)

5. coefficient matrix: $\begin{pmatrix} 2 & 3 & 4 \\ 5 & 6 & 7 \\ 8 & 9 & 10 \end{pmatrix}$

   augmented matix: $\begin{pmatrix} 2 & 3 & 4 & 10 \\ 5 & 6 & 7 & 9 \\ 8 & 9 & 10 & 8 \end{pmatrix}$

7.   coefficient matix:
$$\begin{pmatrix} 1 & 0 & 1 & 1 \\ 1 & 1 & 0 & 2 \\ 0 & 1 & 1 & 1 \\ 2 & -1 & -1 & 0 \end{pmatrix}$$

augmented matix:
$$\begin{pmatrix} 1 & 0 & 1 & 1 & -1 \\ 1 & 1 & 0 & 2 & 0 \\ 0 & 1 & 1 & 1 & 1 \\ 2 & -1 & -1 & 0 & 2 \end{pmatrix}$$

9.   Form the augmented matrix:
$$\begin{pmatrix} 1 & -1 & 2 & 7 \\ 3 & 2 & -1 & -10 \\ -1 & 3 & 1 & -2 \end{pmatrix}$$

Adding -3 times row 1 to row 2 and adding row 1 to row 3 yields:
$$\begin{pmatrix} 1 & -1 & 2 & 7 \\ 0 & 5 & -7 & -31 \\ 0 & 2 & 3 & 5 \end{pmatrix}$$

Multiplying row 3 by -3 and adding to row 2 yields:
$$\begin{pmatrix} 1 & -1 & 2 & 7 \\ 0 & -1 & -16 & -46 \\ 0 & 2 & 3 & 5 \end{pmatrix}$$

Multiplying row 2 by 2 and adding to row 3 yields:
$$\begin{pmatrix} 1 & -1 & 2 & 7 \\ 0 & -1 & -16 & -46 \\ 0 & 0 & -29 & -87 \end{pmatrix}$$

So we have the system of equations:
$$x - y + 2z = 7$$
$$-y - 16z = -46$$
$$-29z = -87$$

Solve equation 3 for z:
$$-29z = -87$$
$$z = 3$$

Substitute into equation 2:
$$-y - 48 = -46$$
$$-y = 2$$
$$y = -2$$

Substitute into equation 1:
$$x + 2 + 6 = 7$$
$$x = -1$$

So the solution is $(-1, -2, 3)$

11. Form the augmented matrix:
$$\begin{pmatrix} 1 & 0 & 1 & -2 \\ -3 & 2 & 0 & 17 \\ 1 & -1 & -1 & -9 \end{pmatrix}$$

Adding 3 times row 1 to row 2, and -1 times row 1 to row 3 yields:
$$\begin{pmatrix} 1 & 0 & 1 & -2 \\ 0 & 2 & 3 & 11 \\ 0 & -1 & -2 & -7 \end{pmatrix}$$

Switching row 2 and row 3:
$$\begin{pmatrix} 1 & 0 & 1 & -2 \\ 0 & -1 & -2 & -7 \\ 0 & 2 & 3 & 11 \end{pmatrix}$$

Multiplying row 2 by 2 and adding it to row 3 yields:
$$\begin{pmatrix} 1 & 0 & 1 & -2 \\ 0 & -1 & -2 & -7 \\ 0 & 0 & -1 & -3 \end{pmatrix}$$

So we have the system:

$$x \quad + \quad z = -2$$
$$-y - 2z = -7$$
$$-z = -3$$

Solve equation 3 for z:
$$-z = -3$$
$$z = 3$$

Substitute into equation 2:
$$-y - 6 = -7$$
$$-y = -1$$
$$y = 1$$

Substitute into equation 1:
$$x + 3 = -2$$
$$x = -5$$

So the solution is (-5, 1, 3)

13. Form the augmented matrix:
$$\begin{pmatrix} 1 & 1 & 1 & -4 \\ 2 & -3 & 1 & -1 \\ 4 & 2 & -3 & 33 \end{pmatrix}$$

Adding -2 times row 1 to row 2, and -4 times row 1 to row 4 yields:
$$\begin{pmatrix} 1 & 1 & 1 & -4 \\ 0 & -5 & -1 & 7 \\ 0 & -2 & -7 & 49 \end{pmatrix}$$

Adding -3 times row 3 to row 2 (to get a 1 entry) yields:
$$\begin{pmatrix} 1 & 1 & 1 & -4 \\ 0 & 1 & 20 & -140 \\ 0 & -2 & -7 & 49 \end{pmatrix}$$

Adding 2 times row 2 to row 3 yields:

$$\begin{pmatrix} 1 & 1 & 1 & -4 \\ 0 & 1 & 20 & -140 \\ 0 & 0 & 33 & -231 \end{pmatrix}$$

So we have the system of equations:

$$\begin{aligned} x + y + z &= -4 \\ y + 20z &= -140 \\ 33z &= -231 \end{aligned}$$

Solving the last equation for z:

$$\begin{aligned} 33z &= -231 \\ z &= -7 \end{aligned}$$

Substituting into the second equation:

$$\begin{aligned} y + 20z &= -140 \\ y - 140 &= -140 \\ y &= 0 \end{aligned}$$

Substituting into the first equation:

$$\begin{aligned} x + y + z &= -4 \\ x + 0 - 7 &= -4 \\ x &= 3 \end{aligned}$$

So the solution is $(3, 0, -7)$

15.   Form the augmented matrix:

$$\begin{pmatrix} 3 & -2 & 6 & 0 \\ 1 & 3 & 20 & 15 \\ 10 & -11 & -10 & -9 \end{pmatrix}$$

Switching row 1 and row 2 yields:

$$\begin{pmatrix} 1 & 3 & 20 & 15 \\ 3 & -2 & 6 & 0 \\ 10 & -11 & -10 & -9 \end{pmatrix}$$

Adding -3 times row 1 to row 2, and -10 times row 1 to row 3 yields:

$$\begin{pmatrix} 1 & 3 & 20 & 15 \\ 0 & -11 & -54 & -45 \\ 0 & -41 & -210 & -159 \end{pmatrix}$$

Multiplying row 2 by -4 and adding it to row 3 yields:

$$\begin{pmatrix} 1 & 3 & 20 & 15 \\ 0 & -11 & -54 & -45 \\ 0 & 3 & 6 & 21 \end{pmatrix}$$

Dividing row 3 by 3 and then switching it with row 2 yields:

$$\begin{pmatrix} 1 & 3 & 20 & 15 \\ 0 & 1 & 2 & 7 \\ 0 & -11 & -54 & -45 \end{pmatrix}$$

Multiplying row 2 by 11 and adding it to row 3 yields:

$$\begin{pmatrix} 1 & 3 & 20 & 15 \\ 0 & 1 & 2 & 7 \\ 0 & 0 & -32 & 32 \end{pmatrix}$$

So we have the system of equations:

$$x + 3y + 20z = 15$$
$$y + 2z = 7$$
$$-32z = 32$$

Solve equation 3 for z:

$$-32z = 32$$
$$z = -1$$

Substitute into equation 2:

$$y - 2 = 7$$
$$y = 9$$

Substitute into equation 1:

$$x + 27 - 20 = 15$$
$$x + 7 = 15$$
$$x = 8$$

So the solution is (8, 9, -1)

17.   Form the augmented matrix: $\begin{pmatrix} 4 & -3 & 3 & 2 \\ 5 & 1 & -4 & 1 \\ 9 & -2 & -1 & 3 \end{pmatrix}$

Subtracting row 1 from row 2 yields:

$$\begin{pmatrix} 4 & -3 & 3 & 2 \\ 1 & 4 & -7 & -1 \\ 9 & -2 & -1 & 3 \end{pmatrix}$$

Switching row 1 and row 2 yields:

$$\begin{pmatrix} 1 & 4 & -7 & -1 \\ 4 & -3 & 3 & 2 \\ 9 & -2 & -1 & 3 \end{pmatrix}$$

Adding -4 times row 1 to row 2, and -9 times row 1 to row 3 yields:

$$\begin{pmatrix} 1 & 4 & -7 & -1 \\ 0 & -19 & 31 & 6 \\ 0 & -38 & 62 & 12 \end{pmatrix}$$

Multiplying row 2 by -2 and adding it to row 3 yields:

$$\begin{pmatrix} 1 & 4 & -7 & -1 \\ 0 & -19 & 31 & 6 \\ 0 & 0 & 0 & 0 \end{pmatrix}$$

So we have the system of equations:

$$x + 4y - 7z = -1$$
$$-19y + 31z = 6$$

We solve equation 2 for y:

$$-19y = 6 - 31z$$
$$y = \frac{31z - 6}{19}$$

Substitute into equation 1:

$$x + 4\left(\frac{31z - 6}{19}\right) - 7z = -1$$

$$x + \frac{-9z - 24}{19} = -1$$

$$x = \frac{9z + 5}{19}$$

So the solution is $\left(\dfrac{9z + 5}{19}, \dfrac{31z - 6}{19}, z\right)$ for any real number z.

19. Form the augmented matrix:

$$\begin{pmatrix} 1 & -1 & 1 & 1 & 6 \\ 1 & 1 & -1 & 1 & 4 \\ 1 & 1 & 1 & -1 & -2 \\ -1 & 1 & 1 & 1 & 0 \end{pmatrix}$$

Adding -1 times row 1 to both row 2 and row 3, and adding row 1 to row 4 yields:

$$\begin{pmatrix} 1 & -1 & 1 & 1 & 6 \\ 0 & 2 & -2 & 0 & -2 \\ 0 & 2 & 0 & -2 & -8 \\ 0 & 0 & 2 & 2 & 6 \end{pmatrix}$$

Dividing rows 2, 3, and 4 by 2 and subtracting row 2 from row 3 yields:

$$\begin{pmatrix} 1 & -1 & 1 & 1 & 6 \\ 0 & 1 & -1 & 0 & -1 \\ 0 & 0 & 1 & -1 & -3 \\ 0 & 0 & 1 & 1 & 3 \end{pmatrix}$$

Multiplying row 3 by -1 and adding it to row 4 yields:

$$\begin{pmatrix} 1 & -1 & 1 & 1 & 6 \\ 0 & 1 & -1 & 0 & -1 \\ 0 & 0 & 1 & -1 & -3 \\ 0 & 0 & 0 & 2 & 6 \end{pmatrix}$$

So we have the system of equations:

$$\begin{aligned} x - y + z + w &= 6 \\ y - z &= -1 \\ z - w &= -3 \\ 2w &= 6 \end{aligned}$$

Solve equation 4 for w:

$$2w = 6$$
$$w = 3$$

Substitute into equation 3:

$$z - 3 = -3$$
$$z = 0$$

Substitute into equation 2:

$$y - 0 = -1$$
$$y = -1$$

Substitute into equation 1:

$$x + 1 + 0 + 3 = 6$$
$$x + 4 = 6$$
$$x = 2$$

So the solution is $(2, -1, 0, 3)$.

21. Form the augmented matrix:
$$\begin{pmatrix} 15 & 14 & 26 & 1 \\ 18 & 17 & 32 & -1 \\ 21 & 20 & 38 & 0 \end{pmatrix}$$

We reduce coefficients by subtracting row 2 from row 3, and row 1 from row 2:
$$\begin{pmatrix} 15 & 15 & 26 & 1 \\ 3 & 3 & 6 & -2 \\ 3 & 3 & 6 & 1 \end{pmatrix}$$

Subtracting row 2 from row 3 yields:
$$\begin{pmatrix} 15 & 15 & 26 & 1 \\ 3 & 3 & 6 & -2 \\ 0 & 0 & 0 & 3 \end{pmatrix}$$

But this last row corresponds to the equation $0 = 3$, which is false. So the system has no solution.

23. $A + B$ will be:
$$\begin{pmatrix} 2 & 3 \\ -1 & 4 \end{pmatrix} + \begin{pmatrix} 1 & -1 \\ 3 & 0 \end{pmatrix} = \begin{pmatrix} 3 & 2 \\ 2 & 4 \end{pmatrix}$$

We simply add the corresponding terms.

25. We have:
$$2A = \begin{pmatrix} 4 & 6 \\ -2 & 8 \end{pmatrix} \text{ and } 2B = \begin{pmatrix} 2 & -2 \\ 6 & 0 \end{pmatrix}$$

So:
$$2A + 2B = \begin{pmatrix} 6 & 4 \\ 4 & 8 \end{pmatrix}$$

27. The multiplication is defined, since # col in A = # rows in B:

row 1, col 1: $2(1) + 3(3) = 2 + 9 = 11$
row 1, col 2: $2(-1) + 3(0) = -2 + 0 = -2$
row 2, col 1: $-1(1) + 4(3) = -1 + 12 = 11$
row 2, col 2: $-1(-1) + 4(0) = 1 + 0 = 1$

So $AB = \begin{pmatrix} 11 & -2 \\ 11 & 1 \end{pmatrix}$

29. The multiplication is defined, since # col in A = # rows in C:
     row 1, col 1: $2(1) + 3(0) = 2 + 0 = 2$
     row 1, col 2: $2(0) + 3(1) = 0 + 3 = 3$
     row 2, col 1: $-1(1) + 4(0) = -1 + 0 = -1$
     row 2, col 2: $-1(0) + 4(1) = 0 + 4 = 4$

So $AC = \begin{pmatrix} 2 & 3 \\ -1 & 4 \end{pmatrix}$

31. This operation is not defined, since D and E do not have the same size.

33. We have:

$$2F - 3G = \begin{pmatrix} 10 & -2 \\ -8 & 0 \\ 4 & 6 \end{pmatrix} - \begin{pmatrix} 0 & 0 \\ 0 & 0 \\ 0 & 0 \end{pmatrix} = \begin{pmatrix} 10 & -2 \\ -8 & 0 \\ 4 & 6 \end{pmatrix}$$

35. The multiplication is defined, since # col of E = # rows of D.
     row 1, col 1: $2(-1) + 1(4) = -2 + 4 = 2$
     row 1, col 2: $2(2) + 1(0) = 4 + 0 = 4$
     row 1, col 3: $2(3) + 1(5) = 6 + 5 = 11$
     row 2, col 1: $8(-1) - 1(4) = -8 - 4 = -12$
     row 2, col 2: $8(2) - 1(0) = 16 - 0 = 16$
     row 2, col 3: $8(3) - 1(5) = 24 - 5 = 19$
     row 3, col 1: $6(-1) + 5(4) = -6 + 20 = 14$
     row 3, col 2: $6(2) + 5(0) = 12 + 0 = 12$
     row 3, col 3: $6(3) + 5(5) = 18 + 25 = 43$

So $ED = \begin{pmatrix} 2 & 4 & 11 \\ -12 & 16 & 19 \\ 14 & 12 & 43 \end{pmatrix}$

37. The multiplication is defined, since # col of F = # rows of D.
     row 1, col 1: $5(-1) - 1(4) = -5 - 4 = -9$
     row 1, col 2: $5(2) - 1(0) = 10 - 0 = 10$
     row 1, col 3: $5(3) - 1(5) = 15 - 5 = 10$
     row 2, col 1: $-4(-1) + 0(4) = 4 + 0 = 4$
     row 2, col 2: $-4(2) + 0(0) = -8 + 0 = -8$
     row 2, col 3: $-4(3) + 0(5) = -12 + 0 = -12$
     row 3, col 1: $2(-1) + 3(4) = -2 + 12 = 10$
     row 3, col 2: $2(2) + 3(0) = 4 + 0 = 4$
     row 3, col 3: $2(3) + 3(5) = 6 + 15 = 21$

So $FD = \begin{pmatrix} -9 & 10 & 10 \\ 4 & -8 & -12 \\ 10 & 4 & 21 \end{pmatrix}$

39. The operation is not defined, since G and A are not the same size.

41. The multiplication is defined, since # col of G = # rows of D.

$$GD = \begin{pmatrix} 0 & 0 & 0 \\ 0 & 0 & 0 \\ 0 & 0 & 0 \end{pmatrix}$$

43. $A + (B + C) = \begin{pmatrix} 2 & 3 \\ -1 & 4 \end{pmatrix} + \begin{pmatrix} 2 & -1 \\ 3 & 1 \end{pmatrix} = \begin{pmatrix} 4 & 2 \\ 2 & 5 \end{pmatrix}$

45. The multiplication is not defined, since # col of D ≠ # rows of C.

47. The multiplication is defined, since # col of A = # rows of A.
     row 1, col 1: 2(2) + 3(-1) = 4 - 3 = 1
     row 1, col 2: 2(3) + 3(4) = 6 + 12 = 18
     row 2, col 1: -1(2) + 4(-1) = -2 - 4 = -6
     row 2, col 2: -1(3) + 4(4) = -3 + 16 = 13

$$\text{So } A^2 = \begin{pmatrix} 1 & 18 \\ -6 & 13 \end{pmatrix}$$

49. $AA^2 = \begin{pmatrix} 2 & 3 \\ -1 & 4 \end{pmatrix} \begin{pmatrix} 1 & 18 \\ -6 & 13 \end{pmatrix} = \begin{pmatrix} -16 & 75 \\ -25 & 34 \end{pmatrix}$

51. (a) $A(B + C) = \begin{pmatrix} -1 & 3 & 4 \\ 3 & 2 & -3 \\ 9 & 1 & 6 \end{pmatrix} \begin{pmatrix} 11 & 6 & 2 \\ 2 & 1 & 6 \\ -2 & 1 & 6 \end{pmatrix} = \begin{pmatrix} -13 & 1 & 40 \\ 43 & 17 & 0 \\ 89 & 61 & 60 \end{pmatrix}$

     (b) $AB + AC = \begin{pmatrix} -1 & 3 & 4 \\ 3 & 2 & -3 \\ 9 & 1 & 6 \end{pmatrix} \begin{pmatrix} 7 & 0 & 1 \\ 0 & 0 & 3 \\ -1 & 2 & 4 \end{pmatrix} + \begin{pmatrix} -1 & 3 & 4 \\ 3 & 2 & -3 \\ 9 & 1 & 6 \end{pmatrix} \begin{pmatrix} 4 & 6 & 1 \\ 2 & 1 & 3 \\ -1 & -1 & 2 \end{pmatrix}$

$$= \begin{pmatrix} -11 & 8 & 24 \\ 24 & -6 & -3 \\ 57 & 12 & 36 \end{pmatrix} + \begin{pmatrix} -2 & -7 & 16 \\ 19 & 23 & 3 \\ 32 & 49 & 24 \end{pmatrix}$$

$$= \begin{pmatrix} -13 & 1 & 40 \\ 43 & 17 & 0 \\ 89 & 61 & 60 \end{pmatrix}$$

(c) $(AB)C = \left[\begin{pmatrix} -1 & 3 & 4 \\ 3 & 2 & -3 \\ 9 & 1 & 6 \end{pmatrix}\begin{pmatrix} 7 & 0 & 1 \\ 0 & 0 & 3 \\ -1 & 2 & 4 \end{pmatrix}\right]\begin{pmatrix} 4 & 6 & 1 \\ 2 & 1 & 3 \\ -1 & -1 & 2 \end{pmatrix}$

$= \begin{pmatrix} -11 & 8 & 24 \\ 24 & -6 & -3 \\ 57 & 12 & 36 \end{pmatrix}\begin{pmatrix} 4 & 6 & 1 \\ 2 & 1 & 3 \\ -1 & -1 & 2 \end{pmatrix}$

$= \begin{pmatrix} -52 & -82 & 61 \\ 87 & 141 & 0 \\ 216 & 318 & 165 \end{pmatrix}$

(d) $A(BC) = \begin{pmatrix} -1 & 3 & 4 \\ 3 & 2 & -3 \\ 9 & 1 & 6 \end{pmatrix}\begin{pmatrix} 27 & 41 & 9 \\ -3 & -3 & 6 \\ -4 & -8 & 13 \end{pmatrix} = \begin{pmatrix} -52 & -82 & 61 \\ 87 & 141 & 0 \\ 216 & 318 & 165 \end{pmatrix}$

53. (a) $A^2 = \begin{pmatrix} 3 & 5 \\ 7 & 9 \end{pmatrix}\begin{pmatrix} 3 & 5 \\ 7 & 9 \end{pmatrix} = \begin{pmatrix} 44 & 60 \\ 84 & 116 \end{pmatrix}$

$B^2 = \begin{pmatrix} 2 & 4 \\ 6 & 8 \end{pmatrix}\begin{pmatrix} 2 & 4 \\ 6 & 8 \end{pmatrix} = \begin{pmatrix} 28 & 40 \\ 60 & 88 \end{pmatrix}$

So $A^2 - B^2 = \begin{pmatrix} 16 & 20 \\ 24 & 28 \end{pmatrix}$

(b) $A - B = \begin{pmatrix} 1 & 1 \\ 1 & 1 \end{pmatrix}$ and $A + B = \begin{pmatrix} 5 & 9 \\ 13 & 17 \end{pmatrix}$, so:

$(A - B)(A + B) = \begin{pmatrix} 1 & 1 \\ 1 & 1 \end{pmatrix}\begin{pmatrix} 5 & 9 \\ 13 & 17 \end{pmatrix} = \begin{pmatrix} 18 & 26 \\ 18 & 26 \end{pmatrix}$

(c) Here we want $(A + B)(A - B) = \begin{pmatrix} 5 & 9 \\ 13 & 17 \end{pmatrix}\begin{pmatrix} 1 & 1 \\ 1 & 1 \end{pmatrix} = \begin{pmatrix} 14 & 14 \\ 30 & 30 \end{pmatrix}$

(d) We compute $AB = \begin{pmatrix} 3 & 5 \\ 7 & 9 \end{pmatrix}\begin{pmatrix} 2 & 4 \\ 6 & 8 \end{pmatrix} = \begin{pmatrix} 36 & 52 \\ 68 & 100 \end{pmatrix}$

$BA = \begin{pmatrix} 2 & 4 \\ 6 & 8 \end{pmatrix}\begin{pmatrix} 3 & 5 \\ 7 & 9 \end{pmatrix} = \begin{pmatrix} 34 & 46 \\ 74 & 102 \end{pmatrix}$

So $A^2 + AB - BA - B^2 =$

$\begin{pmatrix} 44 & 60 \\ 84 & 116 \end{pmatrix} + \begin{pmatrix} 36 & 52 \\ 68 & 100 \end{pmatrix} - \begin{pmatrix} 34 & 46 \\ 74 & 102 \end{pmatrix} - \begin{pmatrix} 28 & 40 \\ 60 & 88 \end{pmatrix}$

which is equal to $\begin{pmatrix} 18 & 26 \\ 18 & 26 \end{pmatrix}$

55. (a) $AZ = \begin{pmatrix} 1 & 0 \\ 0 & -1 \end{pmatrix}\begin{pmatrix} x \\ y \end{pmatrix} = \begin{pmatrix} x \\ -y \end{pmatrix}$

(b) $BZ = \begin{pmatrix} -1 & 0 \\ 0 & 1 \end{pmatrix}\begin{pmatrix} x \\ y \end{pmatrix} = \begin{pmatrix} -x \\ y \end{pmatrix}$

(c) $AB = \begin{pmatrix} 1 & 0 \\ 0 & -1 \end{pmatrix}\begin{pmatrix} -1 & 0 \\ 0 & 1 \end{pmatrix} = \begin{pmatrix} -1 & 0 \\ 0 & -1 \end{pmatrix}$

So $(AB)Z = \begin{pmatrix} -1 & 0 \\ 0 & -1 \end{pmatrix}\begin{pmatrix} x \\ y \end{pmatrix} = \begin{pmatrix} -x \\ -y \end{pmatrix}$

This would represent a reflection about the origin. Or, if you prefer, a reflection about the x-axis followed by a reflection about the y-axis.

57. (a) $f(A) = 1(4) - 2(3) = 4 - 6 = -2$
$f(B) = 3(8) - (-1)5 = 24 + 5 = 29$
$AB = \begin{pmatrix} 1 & 2 \\ 3 & 4 \end{pmatrix}\begin{pmatrix} 3 & -1 \\ 5 & 8 \end{pmatrix} = \begin{pmatrix} 13 & 15 \\ 29 & 29 \end{pmatrix}$, so
$f(AB) = 13(29) - 15(29) = 377 - 435 = -58$
So $f(A) \bullet f(B) = -2(29) = -58 = f(AB)$

(b) $f(A) = ad - bc$ and $f(B) = eh - fg$, so
$f(A) \bullet f(B) = (ad - bc)(eh - fg) = adeh - bceh - adfg + bcfg$
Now $AB = \begin{pmatrix} a & b \\ c & d \end{pmatrix}\begin{pmatrix} e & f \\ g & h \end{pmatrix} = \begin{pmatrix} ae + bg & af + bh \\ ce + dg & cf + dh \end{pmatrix}$
Thus $f(AB) = (ae + bg)(cf + dh) - (af + bh)(ce + dg)$
$= (acef + bcfg + adeh + bdgh) - (acef + bceh + adfg + bdgh)$
$= bcfg + adeh - bceh - adfg$
$= f(A) \bullet f(B)$

59. (a) Let $A = \begin{pmatrix} a & b \\ c & d \end{pmatrix}$ and $B = \begin{pmatrix} e & f \\ g & h \end{pmatrix}$
Then $A + B = \begin{pmatrix} a + e & b + f \\ c + g & d + h \end{pmatrix}$, so $(A + B)^T = \begin{pmatrix} a + e & c + g \\ b + f & d + h \end{pmatrix}$
Now $A^T = \begin{pmatrix} a & c \\ b & d \end{pmatrix}$ and $B^T = \begin{pmatrix} e & g \\ f & h \end{pmatrix}$, so we have
$A^T + B^T = \begin{pmatrix} a + e & c + g \\ b + f & d + h \end{pmatrix}$ Thus $(A + B)^T = A^T + B^T$

(b) $A^T = \begin{pmatrix} a & c \\ b & d \end{pmatrix}$, so $(A^T)^T = \begin{pmatrix} a & b \\ c & d \end{pmatrix}$. Thus $(A^T)^T = A$.

(c) $AB = \begin{pmatrix} ae + bg & af + bh \\ ce + dg & cf + dh \end{pmatrix}$, so $(AB)^T = \begin{pmatrix} ae + bg & ce + dg \\ af + bh & cf + dh \end{pmatrix}$

$B^T A^T = \begin{pmatrix} e & g \\ f & h \end{pmatrix} \begin{pmatrix} a & c \\ b & d \end{pmatrix} = \begin{pmatrix} ae + bg & ce + dg \\ af + bh & cf + dh \end{pmatrix}$

So we see that $(AB)^T = B^T A^T$.

7.4 The Inverse of a Square Matrix

1. $AI_2 = \begin{pmatrix} 4 & -1 \\ -5 & 2 \end{pmatrix} \begin{pmatrix} 1 & 0 \\ 0 & 1 \end{pmatrix} = \begin{pmatrix} 4 & -1 \\ -5 & 2 \end{pmatrix} = A$

$I_2 A = \begin{pmatrix} 1 & 0 \\ 0 & 1 \end{pmatrix} \begin{pmatrix} 4 & -1 \\ -5 & 2 \end{pmatrix} = \begin{pmatrix} 4 & -1 \\ -5 & 2 \end{pmatrix} = A$

3. $CI_3 = \begin{pmatrix} 3 & 0 & -2 \\ 0 & 5 & 6 \\ 1 & 4 & -7 \end{pmatrix} \begin{pmatrix} 1 & 0 & 0 \\ 0 & 1 & 0 \\ 0 & 0 & 1 \end{pmatrix} = \begin{pmatrix} 3 & 0 & -2 \\ 0 & 5 & 6 \\ 1 & 4 & -7 \end{pmatrix} = C$

$I_3 C = \begin{pmatrix} 1 & 0 & 0 \\ 0 & 1 & 0 \\ 0 & 0 & 1 \end{pmatrix} \begin{pmatrix} 3 & 0 & -2 \\ 0 & 5 & 6 \\ 1 & 4 & -7 \end{pmatrix} = \begin{pmatrix} 3 & 0 & -2 \\ 0 & 5 & 6 \\ 1 & 4 & -7 \end{pmatrix} = C$

5.   We need to find numbers a, b, c, and d such that:

$\begin{pmatrix} 7 & 9 \\ 4 & 5 \end{pmatrix} \begin{pmatrix} a & b \\ c & d \end{pmatrix} = \begin{pmatrix} 1 & 0 \\ 0 & 1 \end{pmatrix}$ and $\begin{pmatrix} a & b \\ c & d \end{pmatrix} \begin{pmatrix} 7 & 9 \\ 4 & 5 \end{pmatrix} = \begin{pmatrix} 1 & 0 \\ 0 & 1 \end{pmatrix}$

We compute the left-hand product:

$\begin{pmatrix} 7 & 9 \\ 4 & 5 \end{pmatrix} \begin{pmatrix} a & b \\ c & d \end{pmatrix} = \begin{pmatrix} 7a + 9c & 7b + 9d \\ 4a + 5c & 4b + 5d \end{pmatrix} = \begin{pmatrix} 1 & 0 \\ 0 & 1 \end{pmatrix}$

So we have the following systems of equations:

$$7a + 9c = 1 \quad \text{and} \quad 7b + 9d = 0$$
$$4a + 5c = 0 \qquad\qquad 4b + 5d = 1$$

Multiplying the first equation by 5 and the second equation by -9, then adding the results, yields:

$$35a + 45c = 5 \quad \text{and} \quad 35b + 45d = 0$$
$$\underline{-36a - 45c = 0} \qquad\qquad \underline{-36b - 45d = -9}$$
$$-a = 5 \qquad\qquad\qquad -b = -9$$
$$a = -5 \qquad\qquad\qquad b = 9$$

Substituting for c and d, respectively:

$$4a + 5c = 0 \qquad 4b + 5d = 1$$
$$-20 + 5c = 0 \qquad 36 + 5d = 1$$
$$5c = 20 \qquad 5d = -35$$
$$c = 4 \qquad d = -7$$

So the inverse matrix is $A^{-1} = \begin{pmatrix} -5 & 9 \\ 4 & -7 \end{pmatrix}$.

7. We need to find numbers a, b, c, and d such that:

$$\begin{pmatrix} -3 & 1 \\ 5 & 6 \end{pmatrix}\begin{pmatrix} a & b \\ c & d \end{pmatrix} = \begin{pmatrix} 1 & 0 \\ 0 & 1 \end{pmatrix}$$

We compute the left-hand product:

$$\begin{pmatrix} -3a + c & -3b + d \\ 5a + 6c & 5b + 6d \end{pmatrix} = \begin{pmatrix} 1 & 0 \\ 0 & 1 \end{pmatrix}$$

So we have the following systems of equations:

$$-3a + c = 1 \quad \text{and} \quad -3b + d = 0$$
$$5a + 6c = 0 \qquad 5b + 6d = 1$$

Solving for c and d, respectively, then substituting:

$$-3a + c = 1 \qquad -3b + d = 0$$
$$c = 3a + 1 \qquad d = 3b$$

Substituting:

$$5a + 6(3a + 1) = 0 \qquad 5b + 6(3b) = 1$$
$$23a + 6 = 0 \qquad 23b = 1$$
$$23a = -6 \qquad b = \frac{1}{23}$$
$$a = \frac{-6}{23}$$

Now substituting to find c and d:

$$c = 3a + 1 \qquad d = 3b$$
$$c = \frac{-18}{23} + 1 \qquad d = \frac{3}{23}$$
$$c = \frac{5}{23}$$

So the inverse matrix is $A^{-1} = \begin{pmatrix} -6/23 & 1/23 \\ 5/23 & 3/23 \end{pmatrix}$

9. We need to find numbers a, b, c, and d such that:

$$\begin{pmatrix} -2 & 3 \\ -4 & 6 \end{pmatrix}\begin{pmatrix} a & b \\ c & d \end{pmatrix} = \begin{pmatrix} 1 & 0 \\ 0 & 1 \end{pmatrix}$$

We compute the left hand product:

$$\begin{pmatrix} -2a + 3c & -2b + 3d \\ -4a + 6c & -4b + 6d \end{pmatrix} = \begin{pmatrix} 1 & 0 \\ 0 & 1 \end{pmatrix}$$

So we have the following systems of equations:

$$-2a + 3c = 1 \qquad \text{and} \qquad -2b + 3d = 0$$
$$-4a + 6c = 0 \qquad\qquad\qquad -4b + 6d = 1$$

Multiplying the top equation by -2 and adding yields:

$$
\begin{array}{rcr}
4a - 6c &=& -2 \\
\underline{-4a + 6c} &=& \underline{0} \\
0 &=& -2
\end{array}
\qquad
\begin{array}{rcr}
4b - 6d &=& 0 \\
\underline{-4b + 6d} &=& \underline{1} \\
0 &=& 1
\end{array}
$$

Since both of these equations are false, no A^{-1} exists.

11. We need to find numbers a, b, c, and d such that:

$$\begin{pmatrix} 1/3 & 1/3 \\ -1/9 & 2/9 \end{pmatrix} \begin{pmatrix} a & b \\ c & d \end{pmatrix} = \begin{pmatrix} 1 & 0 \\ 0 & 1 \end{pmatrix}$$

We compute the left-hand product:

$$\begin{pmatrix} \frac{1}{3}a + \frac{1}{3}c & \frac{1}{3}b + \frac{1}{3}d \\ -\frac{1}{9}a + \frac{2}{9}c & -\frac{1}{9}b + \frac{2}{9}d \end{pmatrix} = \begin{pmatrix} 1 & 0 \\ 0 & 1 \end{pmatrix}$$

So we have the following systems of equations:

$$\frac{1}{3}a + \frac{1}{3}c = 1 \qquad \text{and} \qquad \frac{1}{3}b + \frac{1}{3}d = 0$$

$$-\frac{1}{9}a + \frac{2}{9}c = 0 \qquad\qquad -\frac{1}{9}b + \frac{2}{9}d = 1$$

Multiplying the first equation by 3 and the second by 9, then adding yields:

$$
\begin{array}{rcr}
a + c &=& 3 \\
\underline{-a + 2c} &=& \underline{0} \\
3c &=& 3 \\
c &=& 1
\end{array}
\qquad
\begin{array}{rcr}
b + d &=& 0 \\
\underline{-b + 2d} &=& \underline{9} \\
3d &=& 9 \\
d &=& 3
\end{array}
$$

Now substituting to find a and b:

$$
\begin{array}{rcr}
a + c &=& 3 \\
a + 1 &=& 3 \\
a &=& 2
\end{array}
\qquad
\begin{array}{rcr}
b + d &=& 0 \\
b + 3 &=& 0 \\
b &=& -3
\end{array}
$$

So the inverse is $A^{-1} = \begin{pmatrix} 2 & -3 \\ 1 & 3 \end{pmatrix}$

13. Form the augmented matrix: $\begin{pmatrix} 2 & 1 & 1 & 0 \\ 3 & 2 & 0 & 1 \end{pmatrix}$

Multiply row 1 by -1 and add to row 2:

$$\begin{pmatrix} 2 & 1 & 1 & 0 \\ 1 & 1 & -1 & 1 \end{pmatrix}$$

Switch rows 1 and 2:

$$\begin{pmatrix} 1 & 1 & -1 & 1 \\ 2 & 1 & 1 & 0 \end{pmatrix}$$

Multiply row 1 by -2 and add to row 2:

$$\begin{pmatrix} 1 & 1 & -1 & 1 \\ 0 & -1 & 3 & -2 \end{pmatrix}$$

Add row 2 to row 1:

$$\begin{pmatrix} 1 & 0 & 2 & -1 \\ 0 & -1 & 3 & -2 \end{pmatrix}$$

Multiply row 2 by -1:

$$\begin{pmatrix} 1 & 0 & 2 & -1 \\ 0 & 1 & -3 & 2 \end{pmatrix}$$

So the inverse is $\begin{pmatrix} 2 & -1 \\ -3 & 2 \end{pmatrix}$.

15. Form the augmented matrix: $\begin{pmatrix} 0 & -11 & 1 & 0 \\ 1 & 6 & 0 & 1 \end{pmatrix}$

Switch rows 1 and 2:

$$\begin{pmatrix} 1 & 6 & 0 & 1 \\ 0 & -11 & 1 & 0 \end{pmatrix}$$

Multiply row 2 by $-\frac{1}{11}$:

$$\begin{pmatrix} 1 & 6 & 0 & 1 \\ 0 & 1 & -1/11 & 0 \end{pmatrix}$$

Multiply row 2 by -6 and add to row 1:

$$\begin{pmatrix} 1 & 0 & 6/11 & 1 \\ 0 & 1 & -1/11 & 0 \end{pmatrix}$$

So the inverse is $\begin{pmatrix} 6/11 & 1 \\ -1/11 & 0 \end{pmatrix}$.

17. Form the augmented matrix: $\begin{pmatrix} 2/3 & -1/4 & 1 & 0 \\ -8 & 3 & 0 & 1 \end{pmatrix}$

Multiply row 1 by 12:

$$\begin{pmatrix} 8 & -3 & 12 & 0 \\ -8 & 3 & 0 & 1 \end{pmatrix}$$

Add row 1 to row 2:

$$\begin{pmatrix} 8 & -3 & 12 & 0 \\ 0 & 0 & 12 & 1 \end{pmatrix}$$

So the inverse does not exist.

19. Form the augmented matrix:
$$\begin{pmatrix} -5 & 4 & -3 & 1 & 0 & 0 \\ 10 & -7 & 6 & 0 & 1 & 0 \\ 8 & -6 & 5 & 0 & 0 & 1 \end{pmatrix}$$

Multiply row 1 by 2 and add to row 2:
$$\begin{pmatrix} -5 & 4 & -3 & 1 & 0 & 0 \\ 0 & 1 & 0 & 2 & 1 & 0 \\ 8 & -6 & 5 & 0 & 0 & 1 \end{pmatrix}$$

Add row 3 to row 1 (to reduce the numbers):
$$\begin{pmatrix} 3 & -2 & 2 & 1 & 0 & 1 \\ 0 & 1 & 0 & 2 & 1 & 0 \\ 8 & -6 & 5 & 0 & 0 & 1 \end{pmatrix}$$

Multiply row 2 by 2 and add to row 1, and also multiply row 2 by 6 and add to row 3:
$$\begin{pmatrix} 3 & 0 & 2 & 5 & 2 & 1 \\ 0 & 1 & 0 & 2 & 1 & 0 \\ 8 & 0 & 5 & 12 & 6 & 1 \end{pmatrix}$$

Multiply row 1 by $-\dfrac{8}{3}$ and add to row 3:
$$\begin{pmatrix} 3 & 0 & 2 & 5 & 2 & 1 \\ 0 & 1 & 0 & 2 & 1 & 0 \\ 0 & 0 & -1/3 & -4/3 & 2/3 & -5/3 \end{pmatrix}$$

Multiply row 3 by -3:
$$\begin{pmatrix} 3 & 0 & 2 & 5 & 2 & 1 \\ 0 & 1 & 0 & 2 & 1 & 0 \\ 0 & 0 & 1 & 4 & -2 & 5 \end{pmatrix}$$

Multiply row 3 by -2 and add to row 1:
$$\begin{pmatrix} 3 & 0 & 0 & -3 & 6 & -9 \\ 0 & 1 & 0 & 2 & 1 & 0 \\ 0 & 0 & 1 & 4 & -2 & 5 \end{pmatrix}$$

Multiply row 1 by $\dfrac{1}{3}$:
$$\begin{pmatrix} 1 & 0 & 0 & -1 & 2 & -3 \\ 0 & 1 & 0 & 2 & 1 & 0 \\ 0 & 0 & 1 & 4 & -2 & 5 \end{pmatrix}$$

So the inverse is $\begin{pmatrix} -1 & 2 & -3 \\ 2 & 1 & 0 \\ 4 & -2 & 5 \end{pmatrix}$.

21. Form the augmented matrix:

$$\begin{pmatrix} 1 & 2 & -1 & 1 & 0 & 0 \\ 0 & 3 & 0 & 0 & 1 & 0 \\ -4 & 0 & 5 & 0 & 0 & 1 \end{pmatrix}$$

Multiply row 1 by 4 and add to row 3:

$$\begin{pmatrix} 1 & 2 & -1 & 1 & 0 & 0 \\ 0 & 3 & 0 & 0 & 1 & 0 \\ 0 & 8 & 1 & 4 & 0 & 1 \end{pmatrix}$$

Multiply row 2 by $\frac{1}{3}$:

$$\begin{pmatrix} 1 & 2 & -1 & 1 & 0 & 0 \\ 0 & 1 & 0 & 0 & 1/3 & 0 \\ 0 & 8 & 1 & 4 & 0 & 1 \end{pmatrix}$$

Multiply row 2 by -2 and add to row 1, and multiply row 2 by -8 and add to row 3:

$$\begin{pmatrix} 1 & 0 & -1 & 1 & -2/3 & 0 \\ 0 & 1 & 0 & 0 & 1/3 & 0 \\ 0 & 0 & 1 & 4 & -8/3 & 1 \end{pmatrix}$$

Add row 3 to row 1:

$$\begin{pmatrix} 1 & 0 & 0 & 5 & -10/3 & 1 \\ 0 & 1 & 0 & 0 & 1/3 & 0 \\ 0 & 0 & 1 & 4 & -8/3 & 1 \end{pmatrix}$$

So the inverse is $\begin{pmatrix} 5 & -10/3 & 1 \\ 0 & 1/3 & 0 \\ 4 & -8/3 & 1 \end{pmatrix}$.

23. Form the augmented matrix:

$$\begin{pmatrix} -7 & 5 & 3 & 1 & 0 & 0 \\ 3 & -2 & -2 & 0 & 1 & 0 \\ 3 & -2 & -1 & 0 & 0 & 1 \end{pmatrix}$$

Multiply row 2 by -1 and add to row 3:

$$\begin{pmatrix} -7 & 5 & 3 & 1 & 0 & 0 \\ 3 & -2 & -2 & 0 & 1 & 0 \\ 0 & 0 & 1 & 0 & -1 & 1 \end{pmatrix}$$

Multiply row 2 by 2 and add to row 1:

$$\begin{pmatrix} -1 & 1 & -1 & 1 & 2 & 0 \\ 3 & -2 & -2 & 0 & 1 & 0 \\ 0 & 0 & 1 & 0 & -1 & 1 \end{pmatrix}$$

Multiply row 1 by 3 and add to row 2:

$$\begin{pmatrix} -1 & 1 & -1 & 1 & 2 & 0 \\ 0 & 1 & -5 & 3 & 7 & 0 \\ 0 & 0 & 1 & 0 & -1 & 1 \end{pmatrix}$$

Multiply row 3 by 5 and add to row 2, and add row 3 to row 1:

$$\begin{pmatrix} -1 & 1 & 0 & 1 & 1 & 1 \\ 0 & 1 & 0 & 3 & 2 & 5 \\ 0 & 0 & 1 & 0 & -1 & 1 \end{pmatrix}$$

Mutiply row 1 by -1:

$$\begin{pmatrix} 1 & -1 & 0 & -1 & -1 & -1 \\ 0 & 1 & 0 & 3 & 2 & 5 \\ 0 & 0 & 1 & 0 & -1 & 1 \end{pmatrix}$$

Add row 2 to row 1:

$$\begin{pmatrix} 1 & 0 & 0 & 2 & 1 & 4 \\ 0 & 1 & 0 & 3 & 2 & 5 \\ 0 & 0 & 1 & 0 & -1 & 1 \end{pmatrix}$$

So the inverse is $\begin{pmatrix} 2 & 1 & 4 \\ 3 & 2 & 5 \\ 0 & -1 & 1 \end{pmatrix}$.

25. Form the augmented matrix: $\begin{pmatrix} 1 & 2 & 3 & 1 & 0 & 0 \\ 4 & 5 & 6 & 0 & 1 & 0 \\ 7 & 8 & 9 & 0 & 0 & 1 \end{pmatrix}$

Multiply row 1 by -4 and add to row 2, and multiply row 1 by -7 and add to row 3:

$$\begin{pmatrix} 1 & 2 & 3 & 1 & 0 & 0 \\ 0 & -3 & -6 & -4 & 1 & 0 \\ 0 & -6 & -12 & -7 & 0 & 1 \end{pmatrix}$$

Multiply row 2 by -2 and add to row 3:

$$\begin{pmatrix} 1 & 2 & 3 & 1 & 0 & 0 \\ 0 & -3 & -6 & -4 & 1 & 0 \\ 0 & 0 & 0 & 1 & -2 & 1 \end{pmatrix}$$

So the inverse does not exist.

27. (a) Since the system can be written as $A \bullet X = B$, where

$X = \begin{pmatrix} x \\ y \end{pmatrix}$ and $B = \begin{pmatrix} 5 \\ 7 \end{pmatrix}$, then $X = A^{-1} \bullet B$.

So $X = \begin{pmatrix} 11 & -8 \\ -4 & 3 \end{pmatrix} \begin{pmatrix} 5 \\ 7 \end{pmatrix} = \begin{pmatrix} -1 \\ 1 \end{pmatrix}$, thus $x = -1$ and $y = 1$.

(b) Again this system can be written as $A \bullet X = B$, where

$X = \begin{pmatrix} x \\ y \end{pmatrix}$ and $B = \begin{pmatrix} -12 \\ 0 \end{pmatrix}$, so $X = A^{-1} \bullet B$.

So $X = \begin{pmatrix} 11 & -8 \\ -4 & 3 \end{pmatrix} \begin{pmatrix} -12 \\ 0 \end{pmatrix} = \begin{pmatrix} -132 \\ 48 \end{pmatrix}$, thus $x = -132$ and $y = 48$.

29. (a) Since the system can be written as $A \bullet X = B$, where

$$X = \begin{pmatrix} x \\ y \\ z \end{pmatrix} \text{ and } B = \begin{pmatrix} 28 \\ 9 \\ 22 \end{pmatrix}, \text{ then } X = A^{-1} \bullet B.$$

So $X = \begin{pmatrix} 1 & 2 & -2 \\ -1 & 3 & 0 \\ 0 & -2 & 1 \end{pmatrix} \begin{pmatrix} 28 \\ 9 \\ 22 \end{pmatrix} = \begin{pmatrix} 2 \\ -1 \\ 4 \end{pmatrix}$, thus $x = 2$, $y = -1$, $z = 4$.

(b) Again this system can be written as $A \bullet X = B$, where

$$X = \begin{pmatrix} x \\ y \\ z \end{pmatrix} \text{ and } B = \begin{pmatrix} -7 \\ -2 \\ -6 \end{pmatrix}, \text{ so } X = A^{-1} \bullet B.$$

So $X = \begin{pmatrix} 1 & 2 & -2 \\ -1 & 3 & 0 \\ 0 & -2 & 1 \end{pmatrix} \begin{pmatrix} -7 \\ -2 \\ -6 \end{pmatrix} = \begin{pmatrix} 1 \\ 1 \\ -2 \end{pmatrix}$, thus $x = 1$, $y = 1$, and $z = -2$.

31. (a) $AA = \begin{pmatrix} 1 & -6 & 3 \\ 2 & -7 & 3 \\ 4 & -12 & 5 \end{pmatrix} \begin{pmatrix} 1 & -6 & 3 \\ 2 & -7 & 3 \\ 4 & -12 & 5 \end{pmatrix} = \begin{pmatrix} 1 & 0 & 0 \\ 0 & 1 & 0 \\ 0 & 0 & 1 \end{pmatrix}$

The product is the identity matrix I_3, and thus $A^{-1} = A$.

(b) Since this can be written as $A \bullet X = B$, where $X = \begin{pmatrix} x \\ y \\ z \end{pmatrix}$ and $B = \begin{pmatrix} 19/2 \\ 11 \\ 19 \end{pmatrix}$

then $X = A^{-1} \bullet B$. Recall from part (a) that $A^{-1} = A$, so:

$$X = \begin{pmatrix} 1 & -6 & 3 \\ 2 & -7 & 3 \\ 4 & -12 & 5 \end{pmatrix} \begin{pmatrix} 19/2 \\ 11 \\ 19 \end{pmatrix} = \begin{pmatrix} 1/2 \\ -1 \\ 1 \end{pmatrix}, \text{ thus } x = \frac{1}{2}, y = -1, \text{ and } z = 1.$$

33. We find $\begin{pmatrix} a & b \\ c & d \end{pmatrix}$ where $\begin{pmatrix} 2 & 5 \\ 6 & 15 \end{pmatrix} \begin{pmatrix} a & b \\ c & d \end{pmatrix} = \begin{pmatrix} 1 & 0 \\ 0 & 1 \end{pmatrix}$. Carrying out the multiplication, we have:

$$\begin{pmatrix} 2a + 5c & 2b + 5d \\ 6a + 15c & 6b + 15d \end{pmatrix} = \begin{pmatrix} 1 & 0 \\ 0 & 1 \end{pmatrix}$$

So we have the following systems of equations:

$$\begin{array}{rcl} 2a + 5c &=& 1 \\ 6a + 15c &=& 0 \end{array} \quad \text{and} \quad \begin{array}{rcl} 2b + 5d &=& 0 \\ 6b + 15d &=& 1 \end{array}$$

Multiplying the first equation by -3 and adding to the second equation:

$$\begin{array}{rcl} -6a - 15c &=& -3 \\ \underline{6a + 15c} &=& \underline{0} \\ 0 &=& -3 \end{array} \qquad \begin{array}{rcl} -6b - 15d &=& 0 \\ \underline{6b + 15d} &=& \underline{1} \\ 0 &=& 1 \end{array}$$

Neither of these systems has a solution, thus the matrix has no inverse.

35. (a)   Form the augmented matrix: $\begin{pmatrix} 2 & 3 & 1 & 0 \\ 4 & 5 & 0 & 1 \end{pmatrix}$

Multiply row 1 by -2 and add to row 2:
$$\begin{pmatrix} 2 & 3 & 1 & 0 \\ 0 & -1 & -2 & 1 \end{pmatrix}$$

Multiply row 2 by 3 and add to row 1:
$$\begin{pmatrix} 2 & 0 & -5 & 3 \\ 0 & -1 & -2 & 1 \end{pmatrix}$$

Multiply row 1 by $\frac{1}{2}$ and row 2 by -1:
$$\begin{pmatrix} 1 & 0 & -5/2 & 3/2 \\ 0 & 1 & 2 & -1 \end{pmatrix}$$

So $A^{-1} = \begin{pmatrix} -5/2 & 3/2 \\ 2 & -1 \end{pmatrix}$

Now form the augmented matrix: $\begin{pmatrix} 7 & 8 & 1 & 0 \\ 6 & 7 & 0 & 1 \end{pmatrix}$

Subtract row 2 from row 1:
$$\begin{pmatrix} 1 & 1 & 1 & -1 \\ 6 & 7 & 0 & 1 \end{pmatrix}$$

Multiply row 1 by -6 and add to row 2:
$$\begin{pmatrix} 1 & 1 & 1 & -1 \\ 0 & 1 & -6 & 7 \end{pmatrix}$$

Subtract row 2 from row 1:
$$\begin{pmatrix} 1 & 0 & 7 & -8 \\ 0 & 1 & -6 & 7 \end{pmatrix}$$

So $B^{-1} = \begin{pmatrix} 7 & -8 \\ -6 & 7 \end{pmatrix}$.

Then $B^{-1} A^{-1} = \begin{pmatrix} 7 & -8 \\ -6 & 7 \end{pmatrix} \begin{pmatrix} -5/2 & 3/2 \\ 2 & -1 \end{pmatrix} = \begin{pmatrix} -67/2 & 37/2 \\ 29 & -16 \end{pmatrix}$.

(b)   We first find AB:
$$AB = \begin{pmatrix} 2 & 3 \\ 4 & 5 \end{pmatrix} \begin{pmatrix} 7 & 8 \\ 6 & 7 \end{pmatrix} = \begin{pmatrix} 32 & 37 \\ 58 & 67 \end{pmatrix}$$

Now form the augmented matrix: $\begin{pmatrix} 32 & 37 & 1 & 0 \\ 58 & 67 & 0 & 1 \end{pmatrix}$

Subtract row 1 from row 2 (to reduce numbers):
$$\begin{pmatrix} 32 & 37 & 1 & 0 \\ 26 & 30 & -1 & 1 \end{pmatrix}$$

Subtract row 2 from row 1 (to reduce numbers):
$$\begin{pmatrix} 6 & 7 & 2 & -1 \\ 26 & 30 & -1 & 1 \end{pmatrix}$$

Multiply row 1 by -4 and add to row 2:

$$\begin{pmatrix} 6 & 7 & 2 & -1 \\ 2 & 2 & -9 & 5 \end{pmatrix}$$

Multiply row 2 by -3 and add to row 1:

$$\begin{pmatrix} 0 & 1 & 29 & -16 \\ 2 & 2 & -9 & 5 \end{pmatrix}$$

Multiply row 1 by -2 and add to row 2:

$$\begin{pmatrix} 0 & 1 & 29 & -16 \\ 2 & 0 & -67 & 37 \end{pmatrix}$$

Multiply row 2 by $\frac{1}{2}$, then swith rows 1 and 2:

$$\begin{pmatrix} 1 & 0 & -67/2 & 37/2 \\ 0 & 1 & 29 & -16 \end{pmatrix}$$

So $(AB)^{-1} = \begin{pmatrix} -67/2 & 37/2 \\ 29 & -16 \end{pmatrix}$, which is the same as $B^{-1} A^{-1}$ from part (a).

7.5 Determinants and Cramer's Rule

1. (a) $\begin{vmatrix} 2 & -17 \\ 1 & 6 \end{vmatrix} = 2(6) - (-17)(1) = 12 + 17 = 29$

    (b) $\begin{vmatrix} 1 & 6 \\ 2 & -17 \end{vmatrix} = 1(-17) - 6(2) = -17 - 12 = -29$

3. (a) $\begin{vmatrix} 7 & 7 \\ 500 & 700 \end{vmatrix} = 100 \begin{vmatrix} 5 & 7 \\ 5 & 7 \end{vmatrix} = 100 [5(7) - 7(5)] = 100(35 - 35) = 0$

    (b) $\begin{vmatrix} 5 & 500 \\ 7 & 700 \end{vmatrix} = 100 \begin{vmatrix} 5 & 5 \\ 7 & 7 \end{vmatrix} = 100 [5(7) - 5(7)] = 100(35 - 35) = 0$

5. $\begin{vmatrix} \sqrt{2} - 1 & \sqrt{2} \\ \sqrt{2} & \sqrt{2} + 1 \end{vmatrix} = (\sqrt{2} - 1)(\sqrt{2} + 1) - \sqrt{2}(\sqrt{2}) = (2 - 1) - 2 = -1$

7. $\begin{vmatrix} 5 & 1 \\ 10 & -10 \end{vmatrix} = 10 \begin{vmatrix} 5 & 1 \\ 1 & -1 \end{vmatrix} = 10 [5(-1) - 1(1)] = 10(-6) = -60$

9. $\begin{vmatrix} -6 & 3 \\ 5 & -4 \end{vmatrix} = 3 \begin{vmatrix} -2 & 1 \\ 5 & -4 \end{vmatrix} = 3 [-2(-4) - 1(5)] = 3(3) = 9$

11. (a) $-6\begin{vmatrix} -4 & 1 \\ 9 & -10 \end{vmatrix} + 3\begin{vmatrix} 5 & 1 \\ 10 & -10 \end{vmatrix} + 8\begin{vmatrix} 5 & -4 \\ 10 & 9 \end{vmatrix}$ $= -6(31) + 3(-60) + 8(85) = 314$

  (b) $-6\begin{vmatrix} -4 & 1 \\ 9 & -10 \end{vmatrix} - 3\begin{vmatrix} 5 & 1 \\ 10 & -10 \end{vmatrix} + 8\begin{vmatrix} 5 & -4 \\ 10 & 9 \end{vmatrix}$ $= -6(31) - 3(-60) + 8(85) = 674$

  (c) The answer in part (b) would be the determinant.

13. (a) $-4\begin{vmatrix} 2 & 3 \\ 8 & 9 \end{vmatrix} + 5\begin{vmatrix} 1 & 3 \\ 7 & 9 \end{vmatrix} - 6\begin{vmatrix} 1 & 2 \\ 7 & 8 \end{vmatrix}$ $= -4(-6) + 5(-12) - 6(-6) = 0$

  (b) $7\begin{vmatrix} 2 & 3 \\ 5 & 6 \end{vmatrix} - 8\begin{vmatrix} 1 & 3 \\ 4 & 6 \end{vmatrix} + 9\begin{vmatrix} 1 & 2 \\ 4 & 5 \end{vmatrix}$ $= 7(-3) - 8(-6) + 9(-3) = 0$

  (c) $1\begin{vmatrix} 5 & 6 \\ 8 & 9 \end{vmatrix} - 4\begin{vmatrix} 2 & 3 \\ 8 & 9 \end{vmatrix} + 7\begin{vmatrix} 2 & 3 \\ 5 & 6 \end{vmatrix}$ $= 1(-3) - 4(-6) + 7(-3) = 0$

  (d) $3\begin{vmatrix} 4 & 5 \\ 7 & 8 \end{vmatrix} - 6\begin{vmatrix} 1 & 2 \\ 7 & 8 \end{vmatrix} + 9\begin{vmatrix} 1 & 2 \\ 4 & 5 \end{vmatrix}$ $= 3(-3) - 6(-6) + 9(-3) = 0$

15. $\begin{vmatrix} 5 & 10 & 15 \\ 1 & 2 & 3 \\ -9 & 11 & 7 \end{vmatrix} = 5\begin{vmatrix} 1 & 2 & 3 \\ 1 & 2 & 3 \\ -9 & 11 & 7 \end{vmatrix} = 5\begin{vmatrix} 0 & 0 & 0 \\ 1 & 2 & 3 \\ -9 & 11 & 7 \end{vmatrix} = 0$

17. $\begin{vmatrix} 1 & 2 & -3 \\ 4 & 5 & -9 \\ 0 & 0 & 1 \end{vmatrix} = 0\begin{vmatrix} 2 & -3 \\ 5 & -9 \end{vmatrix} - 0\begin{vmatrix} 1 & -3 \\ 4 & -9 \end{vmatrix} + 1\begin{vmatrix} 1 & 2 \\ 4 & 5 \end{vmatrix} = 1(-3) = -3$

19. $\begin{vmatrix} -6 & -8 & 18 \\ 25 & 12 & 15 \\ -9 & 4 & 13 \end{vmatrix} = 2\begin{vmatrix} -3 & -4 & 9 \\ 25 & 12 & 15 \\ -9 & 4 & 13 \end{vmatrix} = 8\begin{vmatrix} -3 & -1 & 9 \\ 25 & 3 & 15 \\ -9 & 1 & 13 \end{vmatrix}$

  Now $\begin{vmatrix} -3 & -1 & 9 \\ 25 & 3 & 15 \\ -9 & 1 & 13 \end{vmatrix} = -3\begin{vmatrix} 3 & 15 \\ 1 & 13 \end{vmatrix} + 1\begin{vmatrix} 25 & 15 \\ -9 & 13 \end{vmatrix} + 9\begin{vmatrix} 25 & 3 \\ -9 & 1 \end{vmatrix}$

  $= -3(24) + 1(460) + 9(52)$

  $= 856$

  So $8\begin{vmatrix} -3 & -1 & 9 \\ 25 & 3 & 15 \\ -9 & 1 & 13 \end{vmatrix} = 8(856) = 6848$

21. $\begin{vmatrix} 16 & 0 & -64 \\ -8 & 15 & -12 \\ 30 & -20 & 10 \end{vmatrix} = 16 \begin{vmatrix} 1 & 0 & -4 \\ -8 & 15 & -12 \\ 30 & -20 & 10 \end{vmatrix} = 160 \begin{vmatrix} 1 & 0 & -4 \\ -8 & 15 & -12 \\ 3 & -2 & 1 \end{vmatrix}$

Now $\begin{vmatrix} 1 & 0 & -4 \\ -8 & 15 & -12 \\ 3 & -2 & 1 \end{vmatrix} = 1 \begin{vmatrix} 15 & -12 \\ -2 & 1 \end{vmatrix} - 0 \begin{vmatrix} -8 & -12 \\ 3 & 1 \end{vmatrix} - 4 \begin{vmatrix} -8 & 15 \\ 3 & 2 \end{vmatrix}$

$= 1(-9) - 4(-29)$
$= 107$

So $160 \begin{vmatrix} 1 & 0 & -4 \\ -8 & 15 & -12 \\ 3 & -2 & 1 \end{vmatrix} = 160(107) = 17120$

23. $\begin{vmatrix} 1 & x & x^2 \\ 1 & y & y^2 \\ 1 & z & z^2 \end{vmatrix} = \begin{vmatrix} 1 & x & x^2 \\ 0 & y-x & y^2-x^2 \\ 0 & z-x & z^2-x^2 \end{vmatrix}$

$= \begin{vmatrix} y-x & y^2-x^2 \\ z-x & z^2-x^2 \end{vmatrix}$

$= \begin{vmatrix} y-x & (y+x)(y-x) \\ z-x & (z+x)(z-x) \end{vmatrix}$

$= (y-x)(z-x) \begin{vmatrix} 1 & y+x \\ 1 & z+x \end{vmatrix}$

$= (y-x)(z-x)[z+x-y-x]$
$= (y-x)(z-x)(z-y)$

25. $\begin{vmatrix} 1 & 1 & 1 \\ 1 & 1+x & 1 \\ 1 & 1 & 1+y \end{vmatrix}$

Subtract row 1 from row 2 and row 1 from row 3:

$= \begin{vmatrix} 1 & 1 & 1 \\ 0 & x & 0 \\ 0 & 0 & y \end{vmatrix} = 1 \begin{vmatrix} x & 0 \\ 0 & y \end{vmatrix} = xy$

27. $\begin{vmatrix} 1 & -1 & 0 & 2 \\ 0 & 1 & -1 & 0 \\ 2 & 1 & 0 & -1 \\ -2 & 2 & 1 & 1 \end{vmatrix}$

Add column 2 to column 3:

$$= \begin{vmatrix} 1 & -1 & -1 & 2 \\ 0 & 1 & 0 & 0 \\ 2 & 1 & 1 & -1 \\ -2 & 2 & 3 & 1 \end{vmatrix}$$

$$= 1 \begin{vmatrix} 1 & -1 & 2 \\ 2 & 1 & -1 \\ -2 & 3 & 1 \end{vmatrix}$$

Add twice column 3 to column 1:

$$= \begin{vmatrix} 5 & -1 & 2 \\ 0 & 1 & -1 \\ 0 & 3 & 1 \end{vmatrix} = 5 \begin{vmatrix} 1 & -1 \\ 3 & 1 \end{vmatrix} = 5(4) = 20$$

29. $\begin{vmatrix} 2 & 0 & 0 & 0 \\ 0 & 3 & 0 & 0 \\ 0 & 0 & 4 & 0 \\ 0 & 0 & 0 & 5 \end{vmatrix} = 2 \begin{vmatrix} 3 & 0 & 0 \\ 0 & 4 & 0 \\ 0 & 0 & 5 \end{vmatrix} = 2(3) \begin{vmatrix} 4 & 0 \\ 0 & 5 \end{vmatrix} = 6(20) = 120$

31. (a) Subtract the first column from the second; add twice the first column to the third. The result is:

$$\begin{vmatrix} -20 & 22 & -43 \\ 6 & -10 & 13 \\ -1 & 0 & 0 \end{vmatrix} = -1[22(13) - (-43)(-10)] = 144$$

(b) Multiply the second row by 2 and subtract it from the first row; multiply the second row by 4 and subtract it from the third row. This yields:

$$\begin{vmatrix} 0 & -32 & -5 \\ 1 & 6 & 1 \\ 0 & -25 & -2 \end{vmatrix} = -1[(-32)(-2) - (-5)(-25)] = 61$$

(c) Subtract the first column from the second; add 10 times the first column to the third. This yields:

$$\begin{vmatrix} 2 & 0 & 0 \\ 1 & -5 & 16 \\ 4 & -5 & 39 \end{vmatrix} = 2[(-5)(39) - 16(-5)] = -230$$

33. Compute $D = \begin{vmatrix} 3 & 4 & -1 \\ 1 & -3 & 2 \\ 5 & 0 & -6 \end{vmatrix} = 5 \begin{vmatrix} 4 & -1 \\ -3 & 2 \end{vmatrix} - 6 \begin{vmatrix} 3 & 4 \\ 1 & -3 \end{vmatrix} = 5(5) - 6(-13) = 103$

$D_x = \begin{vmatrix} 5 & 4 & -1 \\ 2 & -3 & 2 \\ -7 & 0 & -6 \end{vmatrix} = -7 \begin{vmatrix} 4 & -1 \\ -3 & 2 \end{vmatrix} - 6 \begin{vmatrix} 5 & 4 \\ 2 & -3 \end{vmatrix} = -7(5) - 6(-23) = 103$

$D_y = \begin{vmatrix} 3 & 5 & -1 \\ 1 & 2 & 2 \\ 5 & -7 & -6 \end{vmatrix}$

Adding -2 times column 1 to both column 2 and column 3 yields:

$= \begin{vmatrix} 3 & -1 & -7 \\ 1 & 0 & 0 \\ 5 & -17 & -16 \end{vmatrix} = -1 \begin{vmatrix} -1 & -7 \\ -17 & -16 \end{vmatrix} = -(-103) = 103$

$D_z = \begin{vmatrix} 3 & 4 & 5 \\ 1 & -3 & 2 \\ 5 & 0 & -7 \end{vmatrix}$

Adding 3 times column 1 to column 2, and -2 times column 1 to column 3 yields:

$= \begin{vmatrix} 3 & 13 & -1 \\ 1 & 0 & 0 \\ 5 & 15 & -17 \end{vmatrix} = -1 \begin{vmatrix} 13 & 1 \\ 15 & -17 \end{vmatrix} = -(-206) = 206$

So $x = \dfrac{D_x}{D} = 1$, $y = \dfrac{D_y}{D} = 1$, and $z = \dfrac{D_z}{D} = 2$.

So the solution is $(1, 1, 2)$.

35. $D = \begin{vmatrix} 3 & 2 & -1 \\ 2 & -3 & -4 \\ 1 & 1 & 1 \end{vmatrix}$

Subtracting column 1 from both column 2 and column 3 yields:

$= \begin{vmatrix} 3 & -1 & -4 \\ 2 & -5 & -6 \\ 1 & 0 & 0 \end{vmatrix} = 1 \begin{vmatrix} -1 & -4 \\ -5 & -6 \end{vmatrix} = -14$

$D_x = \begin{vmatrix} -6 & 2 & -1 \\ -11 & -3 & -4 \\ 5 & 1 & 1 \end{vmatrix}$

Adding -5 times column 3 to column 1, and subtracting column 3 from column 2 yields:

$= \begin{vmatrix} -1 & 3 & -1 \\ 9 & 1 & -4 \\ 0 & 0 & 1 \end{vmatrix} = 1 \begin{vmatrix} -1 & 3 \\ 9 & 1 \end{vmatrix} = -28$

$$D_y = \begin{vmatrix} 3 & -6 & -1 \\ 2 & -11 & -4 \\ 1 & 5 & 1 \end{vmatrix}$$

Adding row 3 to row 1, and 4 times row 3 to row 2 yields:

$$= \begin{vmatrix} 4 & -1 & 0 \\ 6 & 9 & 0 \\ 1 & 5 & 1 \end{vmatrix} = 1 \begin{vmatrix} 4 & -1 \\ 6 & 9 \end{vmatrix} = 42$$

$$D_z = \begin{vmatrix} 3 & 2 & -6 \\ 2 & -3 & -11 \\ 1 & 1 & 5 \end{vmatrix}$$

Adding -2 times row 3 to row 1, and 3 times row 3 to row 2 yields:

$$= \begin{vmatrix} 1 & 0 & -16 \\ 5 & 0 & 4 \\ 1 & 1 & 5 \end{vmatrix} = -1 \begin{vmatrix} 1 & -16 \\ 5 & 4 \end{vmatrix} = -(84) = -84$$

So $x = \dfrac{D_x}{D} = 2$, $y = \dfrac{D_y}{D} = -3$, and $z = \dfrac{D_z}{D} = 6$

So the solution is (2, -3, 6).

37. $D = \begin{vmatrix} 2 & 5 & 2 \\ 3 & -1 & -4 \\ 1 & 2 & -3 \end{vmatrix}$

Adding -2 times row 3 to row 1, and -3 times row 3 to row 2 yields:

$$= \begin{vmatrix} 0 & 1 & 8 \\ 0 & -7 & 5 \\ 1 & 2 & -3 \end{vmatrix} = 1 \begin{vmatrix} 1 & 8 \\ -7 & 5 \end{vmatrix} = 61$$

$$D_x = \begin{vmatrix} 0 & 5 & 2 \\ 0 & -1 & -4 \\ 0 & 2 & 3 \end{vmatrix} = 0$$

$$D_y = \begin{vmatrix} 2 & 0 & 2 \\ 3 & 0 & -4 \\ 1 & 0 & -3 \end{vmatrix} = 0$$

$$D_z = \begin{vmatrix} 2 & 5 & 0 \\ 3 & -1 & 0 \\ 1 & 2 & 0 \end{vmatrix} = 0$$

So $x = \dfrac{D_x}{D} = 0$, $y = \dfrac{D_y}{D} = 0$, and $z = \dfrac{D_z}{D} = 0$

So the solution is (0, 0, 0).

39. $D = \begin{vmatrix} 12 & 0 & -11 \\ 6 & 6 & -4 \\ 6 & 2 & -5 \end{vmatrix} = 6 \begin{vmatrix} 2 & 0 & -11 \\ 1 & 6 & -4 \\ 1 & 2 & -5 \end{vmatrix} = 12 \begin{vmatrix} 2 & 0 & -11 \\ 1 & 3 & -4 \\ 1 & 1 & -5 \end{vmatrix}$

Adding -3 times row 3 to row 2 yields:

$= 12 \begin{vmatrix} 2 & 0 & -11 \\ -2 & 0 & 11 \\ 1 & 1 & -5 \end{vmatrix} = 12(-1) \begin{vmatrix} 2 & -11 \\ -2 & 11 \end{vmatrix} = -12(0) = 0$

So Cramer's Rule will not work. We form the augmented matrix (using equation 2 as row 1):

$$\begin{pmatrix} 6 & 6 & -4 & 26 \\ 12 & 0 & -11 & 13 \\ 6 & 2 & -5 & 13 \end{pmatrix}$$

Adding -2 times row 1 to row 2 and -1 times row 1 to row 3 yields:

$$\begin{pmatrix} 6 & 6 & -4 & 26 \\ 0 & -12 & -3 & -39 \\ 0 & -4 & -1 & -13 \end{pmatrix}$$

Multiply row 1 by $\frac{1}{2}$ and row 2 by $\frac{1}{3}$:

$$\begin{pmatrix} 3 & 3 & -2 & 13 \\ 0 & 4 & 1 & 13 \\ 0 & -4 & -1 & -13 \end{pmatrix}$$

Adding row 2 to row 3 yields:

$$\begin{pmatrix} 3 & 3 & -2 & 13 \\ 0 & 4 & 1 & 13 \\ 0 & 0 & 0 & 0 \end{pmatrix}$$

So:

$$3x + 3y - 2z = 13$$
$$4y + z = 13$$

Solve equation 2 for z:

$$4y + z = 13$$
$$z = 13 - 4y$$

Substitute into equation 1:

$$3x + 3y - 26 + 8y = 13$$
$$3x = 39 - 11y$$
$$x = 13 - \frac{11}{3}y$$

So the solution is $\left(13 - \frac{11}{3}y, y, 13 - 4y\right)$, for any real number y.

41. $D = \begin{vmatrix} 1 & 1 & 1 & 1 \\ 1 & -1 & 1 & -1 \\ 2 & -2 & -3 & -3 \\ 3 & 2 & 1 & -1 \end{vmatrix}$

Adding row 1 to row 2, 3 times row 1 to row 3, and row 1 to row 4 yields:

$= \begin{vmatrix} 1 & 1 & 1 & 1 \\ 2 & 0 & 2 & 0 \\ 5 & 1 & 0 & 0 \\ 4 & 3 & 2 & 0 \end{vmatrix} = -1 \begin{vmatrix} 2 & 0 & 2 \\ 5 & 1 & 0 \\ 4 & 3 & 2 \end{vmatrix}$

Subtracting column 3 from col 1 yields:

$= -1 \begin{vmatrix} 0 & 0 & 2 \\ 5 & 1 & 0 \\ 2 & 3 & 2 \end{vmatrix} = -2 \begin{vmatrix} 5 & 1 \\ 2 & 3 \end{vmatrix} = -2(13) = -26$

$D_x = \begin{vmatrix} -7 & 1 & 1 & 1 \\ -11 & -1 & 1 & -1 \\ 26 & -2 & -3 & -3 \\ -9 & 2 & 1 & -1 \end{vmatrix}$

Adding row 1 ro row 2, 3 times row 1 to row 3, and row 1 to row 4 yields:

$= \begin{vmatrix} -7 & 1 & 1 & 1 \\ -18 & 0 & 2 & 0 \\ 5 & 1 & 0 & 0 \\ -16 & 3 & 2 & 0 \end{vmatrix} = -1 \begin{vmatrix} -18 & 0 & 2 \\ 5 & 1 & 0 \\ -16 & 3 & 2 \end{vmatrix}$

Subtracting row 3 from row 1 yields:

$= -1 \begin{vmatrix} -2 & -3 & 0 \\ 5 & 1 & 0 \\ -16 & 3 & 2 \end{vmatrix} = -2 \begin{vmatrix} -2 & -3 \\ 5 & 1 \end{vmatrix} = -2 (13) = -26$

$D_y = \begin{vmatrix} 1 & -7 & 1 & 1 \\ 1 & -11 & 1 & -1 \\ 2 & 26 & -3 & -3 \\ 3 & -9 & 1 & -1 \end{vmatrix}$

Adding row 1 to row 2, 3 times row 1 to row 3, and row 1 to row 4 yields:

$= \begin{vmatrix} 1 & -7 & 1 & 1 \\ 2 & -18 & 2 & 0 \\ 5 & 5 & 0 & 0 \\ 4 & -16 & 2 & 0 \end{vmatrix} = -1 \begin{vmatrix} 2 & -18 & 2 \\ 5 & 5 & 0 \\ 4 & -16 & 2 \end{vmatrix}$

Subtracting row 3 from row 1 yields:

$= -1 \begin{vmatrix} -2 & -2 & 0 \\ 5 & 5 & 0 \\ 4 & -16 & 2 \end{vmatrix} = -2 \begin{vmatrix} -2 & -2 \\ 5 & 5 \end{vmatrix} = -2(0) = 0$

$$D_z = \begin{vmatrix} 1 & 1 & -7 & 1 \\ 1 & -1 & -11 & -1 \\ 2 & -2 & 26 & -3 \\ 3 & 2 & -9 & -1 \end{vmatrix}$$

Adding row 1 to row 2, 3 times row 1 to row 3, and row 1 to row 4 yields:

$$= \begin{vmatrix} 1 & 1 & -7 & 1 \\ 2 & 0 & -18 & 0 \\ 5 & 1 & 5 & 0 \\ 4 & 3 & -16 & 0 \end{vmatrix} = -1\begin{vmatrix} 2 & 0 & -18 \\ 5 & 1 & 5 \\ 4 & 3 & -16 \end{vmatrix}$$

Adding -3 times row 2 to row 3 yields:

$$= -1\begin{vmatrix} 2 & 0 & -18 \\ 5 & 1 & 5 \\ 11 & 0 & -31 \end{vmatrix} = -1\begin{vmatrix} 2 & -18 \\ -11 & -31 \end{vmatrix} = -1(-260) = 260$$

$$D_w = \begin{vmatrix} 1 & 1 & 1 & -7 \\ 1 & -1 & 1 & -11 \\ 2 & -2 & -3 & 26 \\ 3 & 2 & 1 & -9 \end{vmatrix}$$

Adding row 1 to row 2, 2 times row 1 to row 3, and -2 times row 1 to row 4 yields:

$$= \begin{vmatrix} 1 & 1 & 1 & -7 \\ 2 & 0 & 2 & -18 \\ 4 & 0 & -1 & 12 \\ 1 & 0 & -1 & 5 \end{vmatrix} = -1\begin{vmatrix} 2 & 2 & -18 \\ 4 & -1 & 12 \\ 1 & -1 & 5 \end{vmatrix} = -2\begin{vmatrix} 1 & 1 & -9 \\ 4 & -1 & 12 \\ 1 & -1 & 5 \end{vmatrix}$$

Adding row 1 to both row 2 and row 3 yields:

$$= -2\begin{vmatrix} 1 & 1 & -9 \\ 5 & 0 & 3 \\ 2 & 0 & -4 \end{vmatrix} = 2\begin{vmatrix} 5 & 3 \\ 2 & -4 \end{vmatrix} = 2(-26) = -52$$

So $x = \dfrac{D_x}{D} = 1$, $y = \dfrac{D_y}{D} = 0$, $z = \dfrac{D_z}{D} = -10$, and $w = \dfrac{D_w}{D} = 2$.

So the solution is $(1, 0, -10, 2)$

43. $\begin{vmatrix} x-4 & 0 & 0 \\ 0 & x+4 & 0 \\ 0 & 0 & x+1 \end{vmatrix} = (x-4)\begin{vmatrix} x+4 & 0 \\ 0 & x+1 \end{vmatrix} = (x-4)(x+4)(x+1)$

This will equal 0 when $x = 4$, $x = -4$, or $x = -1$.

45. $\begin{vmatrix} a & b & c \\ a & b & c \\ d & e & f \end{vmatrix} = a\begin{vmatrix} b & c \\ e & f \end{vmatrix} - a\begin{vmatrix} b & c \\ e & f \end{vmatrix} + d\begin{vmatrix} b & c \\ b & c \end{vmatrix}$

$= a(bf - ec) - a(bf - ec) + d(bc - bc)$
$= abf - aec - abf + aec + 0$
$= 0$

47.
$$\begin{vmatrix} a_1 + A_1 & b_1 & c_1 \\ a_2 + A_2 & b_2 & c_2 \\ a_3 + A_3 & b_3 & c_3 \end{vmatrix}$$

$$= (a_1 + A_1)\begin{vmatrix} b_2 & c_2 \\ b_3 & c_3 \end{vmatrix} - (a_2 + A_2)\begin{vmatrix} b_1 & c_1 \\ b_3 & c_3 \end{vmatrix} + (a_3 + A_3)\begin{vmatrix} b_1 & c_1 \\ b_2 & c_2 \end{vmatrix}$$

$$= \left\{ a_1 \begin{vmatrix} b_2 & c_2 \\ b_3 & c_3 \end{vmatrix} - a_2 \begin{vmatrix} b_1 & c_1 \\ b_3 & c_3 \end{vmatrix} + a_3 \begin{vmatrix} b_1 & c_1 \\ b_2 & c_2 \end{vmatrix} \right\}$$

$$+ \left\{ A_1 \begin{vmatrix} b_2 & c_2 \\ b_3 & c_3 \end{vmatrix} - A_2 \begin{vmatrix} b_1 & c_1 \\ b_3 & c_3 \end{vmatrix} + A_3 \begin{vmatrix} b_1 & c_1 \\ b_2 & c_2 \end{vmatrix} \right\}$$

Now observe that the expression in the first set of braces is

$$\begin{vmatrix} a_1 & b_1 & c_1 \\ a_2 & b_2 & c_2 \\ a_3 & b_3 & c_3 \end{vmatrix}$$

the expression in the second set of braces is

$$\begin{vmatrix} A_1 & b_1 & c_1 \\ A_2 & b_2 & c_2 \\ A_3 & b_3 & c_3 \end{vmatrix}$$

49. Expanding the determinant on the left-hand side of the given equation along its first row, we obtain:

$$\begin{vmatrix} a_1 & b_1 & c_1 \\ a_2 & b_2 & c_2 \\ a_3 & b_3 & c_3 \end{vmatrix} = a_1 \begin{vmatrix} b_2 & c_2 \\ b_3 & c_3 \end{vmatrix} - b_1 \begin{vmatrix} a_2 & c_2 \\ a_3 & c_3 \end{vmatrix} + c_1 \begin{vmatrix} a_2 & b_2 \\ a_3 & b_3 \end{vmatrix}$$

Next, expanding the determinant on the right-hand side of the given equation along its second row, we obtain:

$$\begin{vmatrix} a_2 & b_2 & c_2 \\ a_1 & b_1 & c_1 \\ a_3 & b_3 & c_3 \end{vmatrix} = -a_1 \begin{vmatrix} b_2 & c_2 \\ b_3 & c_3 \end{vmatrix} + b_1 \begin{vmatrix} a_2 & c_2 \\ a_3 & c_3 \end{vmatrix} - c_1 \begin{vmatrix} a_2 & b_2 \\ a_3 & b_3 \end{vmatrix}$$

By inspection now, we observe that the two expressions for the determinants are negatives of one another.

51. Subtract the fourth row from each of the other three rows. After that, we have:

$$\begin{vmatrix} a & 0 & 0 & -d \\ 0 & b & 0 & -d \\ 0 & 0 & c & -d \\ 1 & 1 & 1 & 1+d \end{vmatrix} = abcd \begin{vmatrix} 1 & 0 & 0 & -1 \\ 0 & 1 & 0 & -1 \\ 0 & 0 & 1 & -1 \\ 1/a & 1/b & 1/c & 1+1/d \end{vmatrix}$$

$$= abcd \begin{vmatrix} 1 & 0 & 0 & 0 \\ 0 & 1 & 0 & -1 \\ 0 & 0 & 1 & -1 \\ 1/a & 1/b & 1/c & 1+1/a+1/d \end{vmatrix}$$

$$= abcd \begin{vmatrix} 1 & 0 & -1 \\ 0 & 1 & -1 \\ 1/b & 1/c & 1+1/a+1/d \end{vmatrix}$$

$$= abcd \begin{vmatrix} 1 & 0 & 0 \\ 0 & 1 & -1 \\ 1/b & 1/c & 1+1/a+1/b+1/d \end{vmatrix}$$

$$= abcd \begin{vmatrix} 1 & -1 \\ 1/c & 1+1/a+1/b+1/d \end{vmatrix}$$

$$= abcd \left(1 + \frac{1}{a} + \frac{1}{b} + \frac{1}{c} + \frac{1}{d} \right)$$

53. By expanding D along its first column, we obtain the equation:

$$a_1 D = a_1 [\, a_1(b_2 c_3 - b_3 c_2) - a_2(b_1 c_3 - b_3 c_1) + a_3(b_1 c_2 - b_2 c_1) \,] \quad **$$

On the other hand $\begin{vmatrix} B_2 & C_2 \\ B_3 & C_3 \end{vmatrix}$ is equal to:

$$\begin{aligned} B_2 C_3 - B_3 C_2 &= (a_1 c_3 - a_3 c_1)(a_1 b_2 - a_2 b_1) - (a_1 c_2 - a_2 c_1)(a_1 b_3 - a_3 b_1) \\ &= a_1^2 b_2 c_3 - a_1 a_3 b_2 c_1 - a_1 a_2 b_1 c_3 + a_2 a_3 b_1 c_1 \\ &\quad - a_1^2 b_3 c_2 + a_1 a_3 b_1 c_2 + a_1 a_2 b_3 c_1 - a_2 a_3 b_1 c_1 \\ &= a_1 [\, a_1 b_2 c_3 - a_3 b_2 c_1 - a_2 b_1 c_3 - a_1 b_3 c_2 + a_3 b_1 c_2 + a_2 b_3 c_1 \,] \\ &= a_1 [\, a_1(b_2 c_3 - b_3 c_2) - a_2(b_1 c_3 - b_3 c_1) + a_3(b_1 c_2 - b_2 c_1) \,] \end{aligned}$$

By inspection now, we see that this last expression agrees with the right-hand side of equation ** . This proves that:

$$\begin{vmatrix} B_2 & C_2 \\ B_3 & C_3 \end{vmatrix} = a_1 D, \text{ as required.}$$

55. (a) $\begin{vmatrix} 1 & 0 & 0 \\ x & 1 & 0 \\ x & y & 1 \end{vmatrix} = 1 \begin{vmatrix} 1 & 0 \\ y & 1 \end{vmatrix} = 1(1) = 1$

(b) $\begin{vmatrix} 1 & 0 & 0 & 0 \\ x & 1 & 0 & 0 \\ x & y & 1 & 0 \\ x & y & z & 1 \end{vmatrix} = 1 \begin{vmatrix} 1 & 0 & 0 \\ y & 1 & 0 \\ y & z & 1 \end{vmatrix} = 1 \begin{vmatrix} 1 & 0 \\ z & 1 \end{vmatrix} = 1(1) = 1$

57.
$$\begin{vmatrix} 1 & a & a & a \\ 1 & b & a & a \\ 1 & a & b & a \\ 1 & a & a & b \end{vmatrix}$$

Subtracting row 1 from each of row 2, row 3, and row 4 yields:

$$= \begin{vmatrix} 1 & a & a & a \\ 0 & b-a & 0 & 0 \\ 0 & 0 & b-a & 0 \\ 0 & 0 & 0 & b-a \end{vmatrix}$$

$$= 1 \begin{vmatrix} b-a & 0 & 0 \\ 0 & b-a & 0 \\ 0 & 0 & b-a \end{vmatrix}$$

$$= (b-a) \begin{vmatrix} b-a & 0 \\ 0 & b-a \end{vmatrix}$$

$$= (b-a)(b-a)^2$$

$$= (b-a)^3$$

59. Just for some variety, let's use augmented matrices.

Form the augmented matrix:
$$\begin{pmatrix} a & b & c & k \\ a^2 & b^2 & c^2 & k^2 \\ a^3 & b^3 & c^3 & k^3 \end{pmatrix}$$

Adding $-a$ times row 1 to row 2 and $-a^2$ times row 1 to row 3:
$$\begin{pmatrix} a & b & c & k \\ 0 & b^2-ab & c^2-ac & k^2-ak \\ 0 & b^3-a^2b & c^3-a^2c & k^3-a^2k \end{pmatrix}$$

Factoring:
$$\begin{pmatrix} a & b & c & k \\ 0 & b(b-a) & c(c-a) & k(k-a) \\ 0 & b(b+a)(b-a) & c(c+a)(c-a) & k(k+a)(k-a) \end{pmatrix}$$

Adding $-(b+a)$ times row 2 to row 3:
$$\begin{pmatrix} a & b & c & k \\ 0 & b(b-a) & c(c-a) & k(k-a) \\ 0 & 0 & c(c-a)(c-b) & k(k-a)(k-b) \end{pmatrix}$$

So:
$$\begin{aligned} ax + by + cz &= k \\ b(b-a)y + c(c-a)z &= k(k-a) \\ c(c-a)(c-b)z &= k(k-a)(k-b) \end{aligned}$$

Solving the third equation for z:
$$c(c-a)(c-b)z = k(k-a)(k-b)$$
$$z = \frac{k(k-a)(k-b)}{c(c-a)(c-b)}$$

Substitute into the second equation:

$$b(b-a)y + \frac{k(k-a)(k-b)}{c-b} = k(k-a)$$

$$b(b-a)(c-b)y = k(k-a)(c-b-k+b)$$

$$y = \frac{k(k-a)(k-c)}{b(b-a)(b-c)}$$

Substitute into the first equation:

$$ax + \frac{k(k-a)(k-c)}{(b-a)(b-c)} + \frac{k(k-a)(k-b)}{(c-a)(c-b)} = k$$

$$ax = \frac{k(k-b)(k-c)}{(b-a)(c-a)}$$

$$x = \frac{k(k-b)(k-c)}{a(a-b)(a-c)}$$

So the solution is $\left(\dfrac{k(k-b)(k-c)}{a(a-b)(a-c)}, \dfrac{k(k-a)(k-c)}{b(b-a)(b-c)}, \dfrac{k(k-a)(k-b)}{c(c-a)(c-b)} \right)$.

61.   We re-draw the figure:

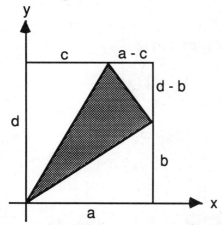

The area of the rectangle is ad, and the three triangles have areas of $\frac{1}{2}(ab)$,

$\frac{1}{2}(a-c)(d-b)$, and $\frac{1}{2}(cd)$, so the area of the shaded triangle is:

$$ad - [\tfrac{1}{2}ab + \tfrac{1}{2}ad - \tfrac{1}{2}cd - \tfrac{1}{2}ab + \tfrac{1}{2}bc + \tfrac{1}{2}cd] = \tfrac{1}{2}ad - \tfrac{1}{2}bc$$

$$= \tfrac{1}{2}(ad - bc)$$

$$= \frac{1}{2} \begin{vmatrix} a & b \\ c & d \end{vmatrix}$$

63. (a) From exercise #36 of the previous section, we found $A^{-1} = \begin{pmatrix} \dfrac{d}{ad-bc} & \dfrac{-b}{ad-bc} \\ \dfrac{-c}{ad-bc} & \dfrac{a}{ad-bc} \end{pmatrix}$

   Since $D = ad - bc$, then $A^{-1} = \dfrac{1}{D}\begin{pmatrix} d & -b \\ -c & a \end{pmatrix}$

   (b) $D = -6(9) - 7(1) = -54 - 7 = -61$, so the inverse is:

   $-\dfrac{1}{61}\begin{pmatrix} 9 & -7 \\ -1 & -6 \end{pmatrix}$ or $\begin{pmatrix} -9/61 & 7/61 \\ 1/61 & 6/61 \end{pmatrix}$

65. The parabola has a form of $y = ax^2 + bx$, since it passes through the origin. Now (x_1, y_1) and (x_2, y_2) will set up a system of equations:

   $$y_1 = ax_1^2 + bx_1$$
   $$y_2 = ax_2^2 + bx_2$$

   Thus:

   $$x_1^2 a + x_1 b = y_1$$
   $$x_2^2 a + x_2 b = y_2$$

   Using Cramer's Rule, this will have a solution of:

   $$a = \frac{\begin{vmatrix} y_1 & x_1 \\ y_2 & x_2 \end{vmatrix}}{\begin{vmatrix} x_1^2 & x_1 \\ x_2^2 & x_2 \end{vmatrix}} \quad \text{and} \quad b = \frac{\begin{vmatrix} x_1^2 & y_1 \\ x_2^2 & y_2 \end{vmatrix}}{\begin{vmatrix} x_1^2 & x_1 \\ x_2^2 & x_2 \end{vmatrix}}$$

   By the vertex formula, $x = -\dfrac{b}{2a}$, so:

   $$x = \frac{-\begin{vmatrix} x_1^2 & y_1 \\ x_2^2 & y_2 \end{vmatrix}}{2\begin{vmatrix} y_1 & x_1 \\ y_2 & x_2 \end{vmatrix}} = \frac{\begin{vmatrix} x_1^2 & y_1 \\ x_2^2 & y_2 \end{vmatrix}}{2\begin{vmatrix} x_1 & y_1 \\ x_2 & y_2 \end{vmatrix}}$$

7.6 Nonlinear Systems of Equations

1. $y = 3x$
    $y = x^2$
    Substituting, we get:
    $$x^2 = 3x$$
    $$x^2 - 3x = 0$$
    $$x(x - 3) = 0$$
    From which we get $x = 0$ or $x = 3$. If $x = 0$, $y = 3 \cdot 0 = 0$ and if $x = 3$, $y = 9$. Our solutions are $(0, 0)$ and $(3, 9)$. Note that we have found the points of intersection of a line and a parabola.

3. Since $x^2 = 24y$, $x^2 + y^2 = 25$ becomes:
    $$24y + y^2 = 25$$
    $$y^2 + 24y - 25 = 0$$
    $$(y + 25)(y - 1) = 0$$
    $$y = -25 \text{ and } y = 1$$
    When $y = 1$ we get $x^2 = 24$ or $x = \pm 2\sqrt{6}$ but $y = -25$ means $x^2 = -600$ which is impossible. Our two solutions are $(2\sqrt{6}, 1)$ and $(-2\sqrt{6}, 1)$.

5. Substitute into the first equation:
    $$x(-x^2) = 1$$
    $$-x^3 = 1$$
    $$x = -1$$
    Since $y = \dfrac{1}{x}$, then $y = -1$.
    So the only solution is $(-1, -1)$.

7. Multiply the first equation by -2:
    $$-4x^2 - 2y^2 = -34$$
    $$x^2 + 2y^2 = 22$$
    Adding, we get:
    $$-3x^2 = -12$$
    $$x^2 = 4$$
    $$x = \pm 2$$
    When $x = 2$, we have:
    $$2(4) + y^2 = 17$$
    $$y^2 = 9$$
    $$y = \pm 3$$

When x = -2, we have:

$$2(4) + y^2 = 17$$
$$y^2 = 9$$
$$y = \pm 3$$

So the solutions are (2, 3), (2, -3), (-2, 3), and (-2, -3).

9. Substitute into the first equation:

$$x^2 - 1 = 1 - x^2$$
$$2x^2 = 2$$
$$x^2 = 1$$
$$x = \pm 1$$

So y = 1 - 1 = 0 for each value of x.
So the solutions are (1, 0) and (-1, 0).

11. Substitute into the first equation:

$$x(4x + 1) = 4$$
$$4x^2 + x - 4 = 0$$

$$x = \frac{-1 \pm \sqrt{1 + 64}}{8} = \frac{-1 \pm \sqrt{65}}{8}$$

When $x = \dfrac{-1 + \sqrt{65}}{8}$, we have $y = \dfrac{-1 + \sqrt{65}}{2} + 1 = \dfrac{1 + \sqrt{65}}{2}$

When $x = \dfrac{-1 - \sqrt{65}}{8}$, we have $y = \dfrac{-1 - \sqrt{65}}{2} + 1 = \dfrac{1 - \sqrt{65}}{2}$

So the solutions are $\left(\dfrac{-1 + \sqrt{65}}{8}, \dfrac{1 + \sqrt{65}}{2} \right)$ and $\left(\dfrac{-1 - \sqrt{65}}{8}, \dfrac{1 - \sqrt{65}}{2} \right)$.

13. Let $a = \dfrac{1}{x^2}$ and $b = \dfrac{1}{y^2}$, so

$$a - 3b = 14$$
$$2a + b = 35$$

Multiply the first equation by -2:

$$-2a + 6b = -28$$
$$2a + b = 35$$

Adding, we get:

$$7b = 7$$
$$b = 1$$

So a - 3 = 14, and a = 17.

Since $a = \dfrac{1}{x^2}$ and $b = \dfrac{1}{y^2}$, we have $x^2 = \dfrac{1}{17}$ and $y^2 = 1$

So $x = \dfrac{\pm\sqrt{17}}{17}$ and $y = \pm 1$

So the solutions are $\left(\dfrac{\sqrt{17}}{17}, 1 \right)$, $\left(\dfrac{\sqrt{17}}{17}, -1 \right)$, $\left(\dfrac{-\sqrt{17}}{17}, 1 \right)$, and $\left(\dfrac{-\sqrt{17}}{17}, -1 \right)$.

15. Substitute into the second equation:
$$(x - 3)^2 + (-\sqrt{x - 1})^2 = 4$$
$$x^2 - 6x + 9 + x - 1 = 4$$
$$x^2 - 5x + 4 = 0$$
$$(x - 1)(x - 4) = 0$$
$$x = 1 \text{ or } x = 4$$

When $x = 1$, $y = -\sqrt{1 - 1} = 0$ and when $x = 4$, $y = -\sqrt{4 - 1} = -\sqrt{3}$.

So the solutions are $(1, 0)$ and $(4, -\sqrt{3})$.

17. Since $y = 2^{2x} - 12 = (2^x)^2 - 12$, we substitute into the second equation:
$$y = y^2 - 12$$
$$0 = y^2 - y - 12$$
$$0 = (y - 4)(y + 3)$$
$$y = 4 \text{ or } y = -3$$

When $y = 4$, we have $2^x = 4$, so $x = 2$. $y = -3$ will not have a solution.

So the only solution is $(2, 4)$.

19. Let $u = \log_{10} x$ and $v = \log_{10} y$, so:
$$2u^2 - v^2 = -1$$
$$4u^2 - 3v^2 = -11$$

Multiply the first equation by -2:
$$-4u^2 + 2v^2 = 2$$
$$4u^2 - 3v^2 = -11$$

Adding, we get:
$$-v^2 = -9$$
$$v^2 = 9$$
$$v = \pm 3$$

Substitute into the first equation:
$$2u^2 - 9 = -1$$
$$2u^2 = 8$$
$$u^2 = 4$$
$$u^2 = \pm 2$$

Since $u = \log_{10} x$, then $x = 10^{\pm 2}$. Similarly, $y = 10^{\pm 3}$

So the solutions are $(100, 1000)$, $\left(100, \dfrac{1}{1000}\right)$, $\left(\dfrac{1}{100}, 1000\right)$,

and $\left(\dfrac{1}{100}, \dfrac{1}{1000}\right)$.

21. First take the logarithm (ln) of each side of the first equation:

$$\ln (2^x 3^y) = \ln 4$$
$$\ln (2^x) + \ln (3^y) = \ln 2^2$$
$$(\ln 2)x + (\ln 3)y = 2 \ln 2$$

Multiply the second equation by $-\ln 2$

$$(\ln 2)x + (\ln 3)y = 2 \ln 2$$
$$(-\ln 2)x - (\ln 2)y = -5 \ln 2$$

Adding, we get:

$$(\ln 3 - \ln 2)y = -3 \ln 2$$
$$y = \frac{3 \ln 2}{\ln 2 - \ln 3}$$

Substitute into the second equation:

$$x = 5 - \frac{3 \ln 2}{\ln 2 - \ln 3} = \frac{2 \ln 2 - 5 \ln 3}{\ln 2 - \ln 3}$$

So the solution is $\left(\dfrac{2 \ln 2 - 5 \ln 3}{\ln 2 - \ln 3} , \dfrac{3 \ln 2}{\ln 2 - \ln 3} \right)$.

23. $y = 3x + 1 = \dfrac{-3 + 3\sqrt{13}}{6} + 1 = \dfrac{3 + 3\sqrt{13}}{6} = \dfrac{1 + \sqrt{13}}{2}$

$y = \dfrac{1}{x} = \dfrac{6}{-1 + \sqrt{13}} \cdot \dfrac{-1 - \sqrt{13}}{-1 - \sqrt{13}} = \dfrac{-6(1 + \sqrt{13})}{1 - 13} = \dfrac{-6(1 + \sqrt{13})}{-12} = \dfrac{1 + \sqrt{13}}{2}$

So they both yield the same y-value.

25. Since $ax + by = 2$, then $by = 2 - ax$. Substitute into the second equation:

$$ax(by) = 1$$
$$ax(2 - ax) = 1$$
$$2ax - a^2 x^2 = 1$$
$$a^2 x^2 - 2ax + 1 = 0$$
$$(ax - 1)^2 = 0$$
$$ax = 1$$
$$x = \frac{1}{a}$$

When $ax = 1$, $by = 2 - 1 = 1$, so $y = \dfrac{1}{b}$.

So the solution is $\left(\dfrac{1}{a} , \dfrac{1}{b} \right)$.

27. Solve the second equation for y to get $y = 23 - x$. Substitute into the first equation:

$$x^3 + (23 - x)^3 = 3473$$
$$x^3 + 12167 - 1587x + 69x^2 - x^3 = 3473$$
$$69x^2 - 1587x + 8694 = 0$$
$$x^2 - 23x + 126 = 0$$
$$(x - 9)(x - 14) = 0$$
$$x = 9 \text{ or } x = 14$$

When $x = 9$, $y = 14$ and when $x = 14$, $y = 9$.
So the solutions are $(9, 14)$ and $(14, 9)$.

29. First draw the rectangle:

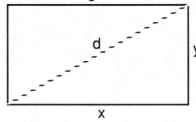

Now $x^2 + y^2 = d^2$ and $2x + 2y = 2p$. Solve the second equation for y:

$$2x + 2y = 2p$$
$$2y = 2p - 2x$$
$$y = p - x$$

Substitute into the first equation:

$$x^2 + (p - x)^2 = d^2$$
$$x^2 + p^2 - 2px + x^2 = d^2$$
$$2x^2 - 2px + p^2 - d^2 = 0$$
$$x = \frac{2p \pm \sqrt{4p^2 - 8(p^2 - d^2)}}{4}$$
$$= \frac{2p \pm 2\sqrt{2d^2 - p^2}}{4}$$
$$= \frac{p \pm \sqrt{2d^2 - p^2}}{2}$$

When $x = \dfrac{p + \sqrt{2d^2 - p^2}}{2}$, $y = p - \dfrac{p + \sqrt{2d^2 - p^2}}{2} = \dfrac{p - \sqrt{2d^2 - p^2}}{2}$

When $x = \dfrac{p - \sqrt{2d^2 - p^2}}{2}$, $y = p - \dfrac{p - \sqrt{2d^2 - p^2}}{2} = \dfrac{p + \sqrt{2d^2 - p^2}}{2}$

So the rectangle has dimensions $\dfrac{p - \sqrt{2d^2 - p^2}}{2}$ by $\dfrac{p + \sqrt{2d^2 - p^2}}{2}$.

31.   If we follow the lead offered we have:

$$(\sqrt{u+v} + \sqrt{u-v})^2 = 4^2$$

$$u + v + 2\sqrt{u^2 - v^2} + u - v = 16$$

But since $u^2 - v^2 = 9$ from the first equation:

$$2u + 2\sqrt{9} = 16$$
$$2u + 6 = 16$$
$$2u = 10, \text{ so } u = 5$$

When $u = 5$, we have:

$$5^2 - v^2 = 9$$
$$v^2 = 16$$
$$v = \pm 4$$

So the solutions are $(5, 4)$ and $(5, -4)$.

33.   Let $w = x + y + z$, so:

$$xw = p^2$$
$$yw = q^2$$
$$zw = r^2$$

Adding the three equations, we get:

$$(x + y + z)w = p^2 + q^2 + r^2$$
$$w^2 = p^2 + q^2 + r^2$$
$$w = \pm\sqrt{p^2 + q^2 + r^2}$$

Substitute into the first equation:

$$x = \frac{p^2}{\pm\sqrt{p^2 + q^2 + r^2}}$$

Similarly $y = \frac{q^2}{\pm A}$ and $z = \frac{r^2}{\pm A}$ where $A = \sqrt{p^2 + q^2 + r^2}$.

So the solutions are $\left(\frac{p^2}{A}, \frac{q^2}{A}, \frac{r^2}{A}\right)$ and $\left(\frac{-p^2}{A}, \frac{-q^2}{A}, \frac{-r^2}{A}\right)$

where $A = \sqrt{p^2 + q^2 + r^2}$.

35. $A = \frac{1}{2}bh$, where b and h are the missing legs. We have:

$180 = \frac{1}{2}bh$, so bh = 360, so $b = \frac{360}{h}$

Also from the Pythagorean Theorem $b^2 + h^2 = 41^2$. so:

$$\left(\frac{360}{h}\right)^2 + h^2 = 41^2$$

$$\frac{129600}{h^2} + h^2 = 1681$$

$$129600 + h^4 = 1681h^2$$

$$h^4 - 1681h^2 + 129600 = 0$$

$$(h^2 - 1600)(h^2 - 81) = 0$$

$$h^2 = 1600 \quad \text{or} \quad h^2 = 81$$

$$h = \pm 40 \quad \text{or} \quad h = \pm 9$$

Since these must be the length of sides, we can neglect the negative values.
So the legs are 9 cm and 40 cm.

37. We have LW = 60 and 2L + 2W = 46, so L + W = 23 and L = 23 - W. We
substitute this into the first equation:

$$(23 - W)(W) = 60$$

$$23W - W^2 = 60$$

$$W^2 - 23w + 60 = 0$$

$$(W - 20)(W - 3) = 0$$

$$W = 20 \text{ or } W = 3$$

When W = 20 we have L = 3, and when W = 3 we have L = 20. So the
rectangle must be 3 cm by 20 cm.

39. Solve xy = 2 to get $y = \frac{2}{x}$. Now substitute into the first equation:

$$x^2 + \frac{4}{x^2} = 5$$

$$x^4 + 4 = 5x^2$$

$$x^4 - 5x^2 + 4 = 0$$

$$(x^2 - 1)(x^2 - 4) = 0$$

$$x^2 = 1 \quad \text{or} \quad x^2 = 4$$

$$x = \pm 1 \qquad x = \pm 2$$

When x = 1, y = 2; when x = -1, y = -2; when x = 2, y = 1; when x = -2, y = -1.
So the solutions are (1, 2), (-1, -2), (2, 1) and (-2, -1).

41. Multiply the second equation by 2:

$$2xy = 6$$

Adding to the first we get:

$$x^2 + 2xy + y^2 = 13$$
$$(x + y)^2 = 13$$
$$x + y = \pm\sqrt{13}$$

Subtracting from the first equation, we get:

$$x^2 - 2xy + y^2 = 1$$
$$(x - y)^2 = 1$$
$$x - y = \pm 1$$

We solve the four systems of equations:

$x + y = \sqrt{13}$	$x + y = \sqrt{13}$	$x + y = -\sqrt{13}$	$x + y = -\sqrt{13}$
$\underline{x - y = 1}$	$\underline{x - y = -1}$	$\underline{x - y = 1}$	$\underline{x - y = -1}$
$2x = 1 + \sqrt{13}$	$2x = -1 + \sqrt{13}$	$2x = 1 - \sqrt{13}$	$2x = -1 - \sqrt{13}$
$x = \dfrac{1 + \sqrt{13}}{2}$	$x = \dfrac{-1 + \sqrt{13}}{2}$	$x = \dfrac{1 - \sqrt{13}}{2}$	$x = \dfrac{-1 - \sqrt{13}}{2}$
$y = \dfrac{-1 + \sqrt{13}}{2}$	$y = \dfrac{1 + \sqrt{13}}{2}$	$y = \dfrac{-1 - \sqrt{13}}{2}$	$y = \dfrac{1 - \sqrt{13}}{2}$

So the solutions are $\left(\dfrac{1 + \sqrt{13}}{2}, \dfrac{-1 + \sqrt{13}}{2}\right)$, $\left(\dfrac{-1 + \sqrt{13}}{2}, \dfrac{1 + \sqrt{13}}{2}\right)$,

$\left(\dfrac{1 - \sqrt{13}}{2}, \dfrac{-1 - \sqrt{13}}{2}\right)$, and $\left(\dfrac{-1 - \sqrt{13}}{2}, \dfrac{1 - \sqrt{13}}{2}\right)$.

43. $2m^2 - 7m + 6 = 0$
$(2m - 3)(m - 2) = 0$

$$m = \frac{3}{2} \quad \text{or} \quad m = 2$$

So $x^2(\frac{9}{2} - 4) = 2$ or $x^2(6 - 4) = 2$

$x^2 = 4$	$x^2 = 1$
$x = \pm 2$	$x = \pm 1$
$y = \pm 3$	$y = \pm 2$

So the solutions are $(2, 3)$, $(-2, -3)$, $(1, 2)$, and $(-1, -2)$.

45. Using the hint, we square the first equation:

$$x^2y^2 + 2pqxy + p^2q^2 = 4p^2x^2$$
$$x^2y^2 \qquad\quad + p^2q^2 = 2q^2y^2$$

Subtracting the second equation from the first:

$$2pqxy = 4p^2x^2 - 2q^2y^2$$
$$pqxy = 2p^2x^2 - q^2y^2$$
$$0 = 2p^2x^2 - pqxy - q^2y^2$$
$$0 = (2px + qy)(px - qy)$$

So, we have:

$$2px + qy = 0, \text{ so } y = -\frac{2p}{q}x$$

$$px - qy = 0, \text{ so } y = \frac{p}{q}x$$

Substituting into the first equation:

$$x\left(-\frac{2p}{q}x\right) + pq = 2px$$

$$x\left(\frac{p}{q}x\right) + pq = 2px$$

Multiplying each side by $\frac{q}{p}$:

$$-2x^2 - 2qx + q^2 = 0$$
$$x^2 - 2qx + q^2 = 0$$

The second equation factors to $(x - q)^2 = 0$, so $x = q$ and thus $y = \frac{p}{q} \cdot q = p$.

Thus one solution is (q,p). This solution checks in the original (non-squared) first equation. For the second equation, we use the quadratic formula:

$$x = \frac{2q \pm \sqrt{4q^2 + 8q^2}}{-4} = \frac{2q \pm 2q\sqrt{3}}{-4} = \frac{-1 \pm \sqrt{3}}{2}q$$

$$y = -\frac{2p}{q}\left(\frac{-1 \pm \sqrt{3}}{2}\right)q = (1 \pm \sqrt{3})p$$

This results in two other solutions, $\left(\frac{-1 + \sqrt{3}}{2}q, (1 - \sqrt{3})p\right)$ and

$\left(\frac{-1 - \sqrt{3}}{2}q, (1 + \sqrt{3})p\right)$. Both of these solutions check in the original

(non-squared) first equation.

47. Taking logs in the first equation:

$$\ln(x^4) = \ln(y^6)$$
$$4\ln x = 6\ln y$$
$$2\ln x = 3\ln y$$

The second equation is: $\ln x - \ln y = \frac{\ln x}{\ln y}$

$$\ln x \ln y - (\ln y)^2 = \ln x$$

Let $u = \ln x$ and $v = \ln y$, so we have the equations $2u = 3v$ and $uv - v^2 = u$.

Solving the first equation for u yields $u = \frac{3v}{2}$, and substituting into the second equation yields:

$$\left(\frac{3v}{2}\right) v - v^2 = \frac{3v}{2}$$
$$3v^2 - 2v^2 = 3v$$
$$v^2 - 3v = 0$$
$$v(v - 3) = 0$$
$$v = 0 \quad \text{or} \quad v = 3$$

When $v = 0$, $u = 0$ and when $v = 3$, $u = \frac{9}{2}$. Since $v = \ln y$, $v = 0$ cannot be a solution to the original second equation ($\ln y$ is in the denominator). Thus $u = \ln x$ and $v = \ln y$ yields:

$$\ln x = \frac{9}{2} \quad \text{so} \quad x = e^{9/2}$$
$$\ln y = 3, \quad \text{so} \quad y = e^3$$

So the only solution is $(e^{9/2}, e^3)$.

7.7 Systems of Inequalities

1. (a) Since substituting the pair (1,2) into $4x - 6y + 3 \geq 0$ gives $4(1) - 6(2) + 3 \geq 0$, which says $-5 \geq 0$, our answer is no.

   (b) Substitute $\left(0, \frac{1}{2}\right)$: $4(0) - 6\left(\frac{1}{2}\right) + 3 \geq 0$
   $$0 \geq 0$$
   Our answer is yes.

3. $2x - 3y > 6$

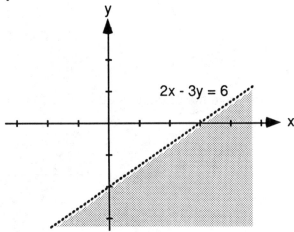

5. $2x - 3y \geq 6$

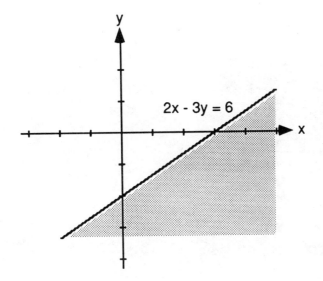

2x - 3y = 6

7. $x - y < 0$

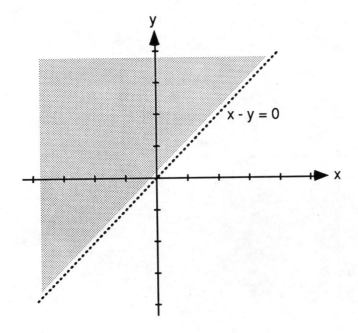

x - y = 0

9.   x ≥ 1

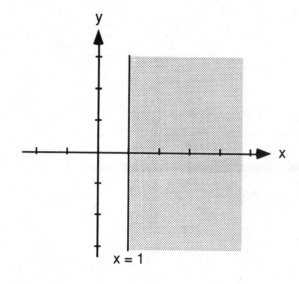

11.   x > 0

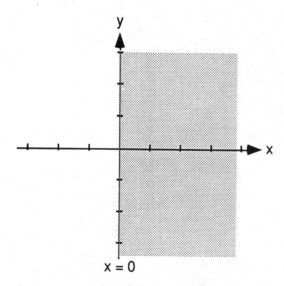

13. $y > x^3 + 1$

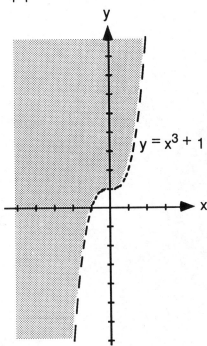

$y = x^3 + 1$

15. $x^2 + y^2 \geq 25$
We know $x^2 + y^2 = 25$ is a circle, so we must shade the area outside the circle:

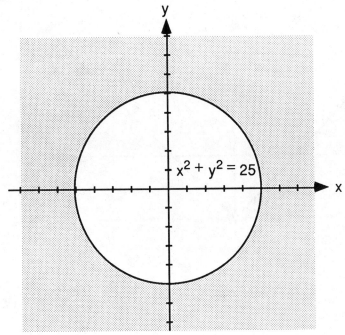

$x^2 + y^2 = 25$

17. $y \le x^2$
     $x^2 + y^2 \le 1$

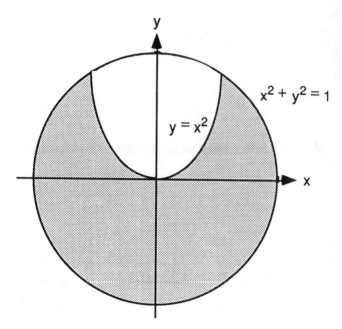

19. $y \ge 1$
     $y \le |x|$

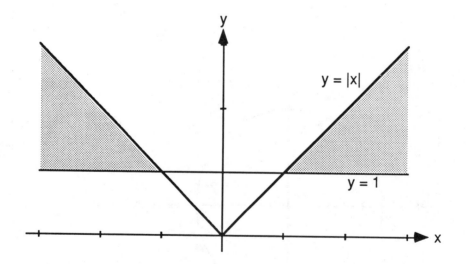

21. $x \geq 0$
     $y \geq 0$
     $y \leq 1 - x^2$

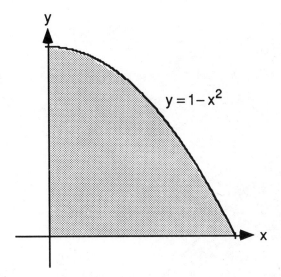

23. convex: yes; bounded: yes
     vertices: $(0, 0)$, $(7, 0)$, $(3, 8)$, $(0, 5)$

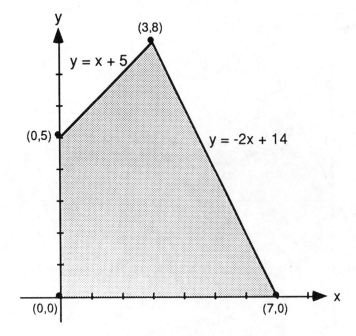

25. We simply graph each inequality, and where necessary solve to find vertices.
     In this case:
$$-x + 3y = 12$$
$$x + y = 8$$
So $4y = 20$, thus $y = 5$ and $x = 3$
convex: yes; bounded: yes
vertices: $(0, 0)$, $(0, 4)$, $(3, 5)$, $(8, 0)$

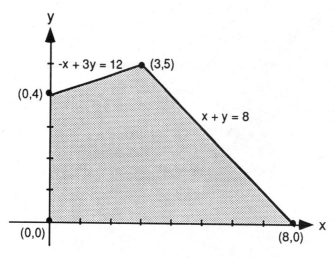

27. convex: yes; bounded: no
     vertices: $(2, 7)$, $(8, 5)$

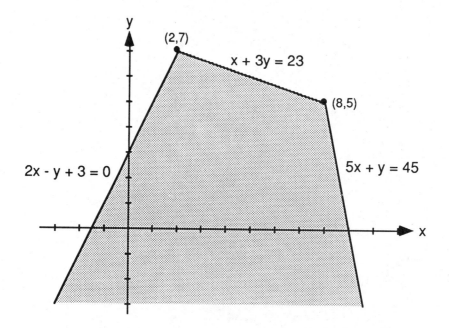

29. convex: yes; bounded: no
     vertex: (6, 0)

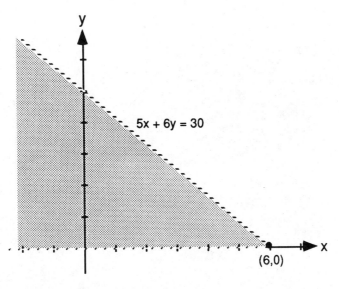

31. convex: yes; bounded: yes
     vertices: (0, 0), (0, 5), (6, 0)

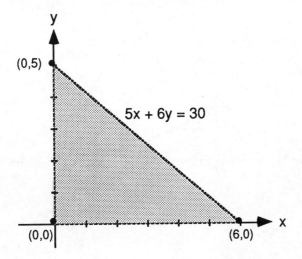

33. convex: yes; bounded: yes
     vertices: (5, 30), (10, 30), (20, 15), (20, 20)

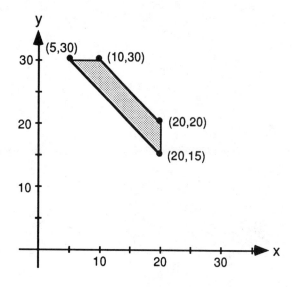

35. vertices: $(-e, 0)$, $(-e, e^{-e})$, $(0, 1)$, (e, e^{-e}), $(e, 0)$

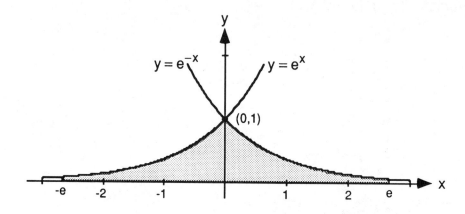

37. The domain results from the inequality $x + y + 2 \geq 0$, or $x + y \geq -2$. We sketch the graph:

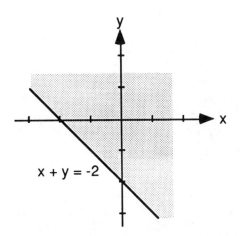

39. The domain results from the inequality $25 - x^2 - y^2 \geq 0$, or $x^2 + y^2 \leq 25$. We sketch the graph:

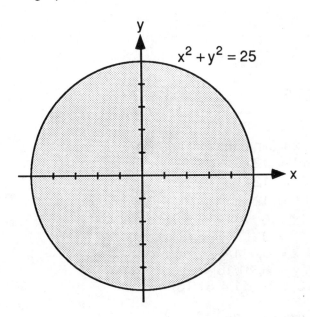

41.   The domain results from the inequality $xy > 0$. This consists of two planes:
  $x > 0$ and $y > 0$ (first quadrant)   or $x < 0$ and $y < 0$ (third quadrant)
We sketch the graph:

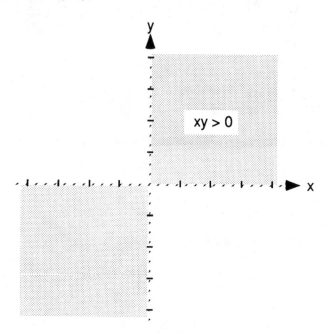

Chapter 7 Review Exercises

1.   We substitute $y = x^2 + 2x + 3$ into the first equation:
$$3x + 4y = 12$$
$$3x + 4(x^2 + 2x + 3) = 12$$
$$3x + 4x^2 + 8x + 12 = 12$$
$$4x^2 + 11x = 0$$
$$x(4x + 11) = 0$$
$$x = 0, -11/4$$
$$y = 3, 81/16$$
So the solutions are $(0, 3)$ and $(-11/4, 81/16)$.

2.   We multiply the first equation by -3:
$$-3x + 6y = -39$$
$$3x + 5y = -16$$
Adding, we have:
$$11y = -55$$
$$y = -5$$

Substitute into the first equation:
$$x - 2y = 13$$
$$x - 2(-5) = 13$$
$$x + 10 = 13$$
$$x = 3$$
So the solution is $(3, -5)$.

3.   (a)   Adding -3 times the first equation to the second equation, and also adding -4 times the first equation to the third equation results in the system:
$$x + 4y - z = 0$$
$$-11y + 4z = -1$$
$$-20y + 9z = -7$$
To reduce coefficients, multiply the second equation by -2 and add it to the third equation:
$$x + 4y - z = 0$$
$$2y + z = -5$$
$$-20y + 9z = -7$$
Multiply the second equation by 10 and add it to the third equation:
$$x + 4y - z = 0$$
$$2y + z = -5$$
$$19z = -57$$
Solving the third equation for z yields $z = -3$. Substitute into the second equation:
$$2y - 3 = -5$$
$$2y = -2$$
$$y = -1$$
Substitute into the first equation:
$$x + 4(-1) - (-3) = 0$$
$$x - 4 + 3 = 0$$
$$x = 1$$
So the solution is $(1, -1, -3)$.

(b) $D = \begin{vmatrix} 1 & 4 & -1 \\ 3 & 1 & 1 \\ 4 & -4 & 5 \end{vmatrix}$

Adding row 1 to row 2, and 5 times row 1 to row 3:
$$= \begin{vmatrix} 1 & 4 & -1 \\ 4 & 5 & 0 \\ 9 & 16 & 0 \end{vmatrix}$$
Now expand along column 3:
$$= -1 \begin{vmatrix} 4 & 5 \\ 9 & 16 \end{vmatrix} = -(64 - 45) = -19$$

$$D_x = \begin{vmatrix} 0 & 4 & -1 \\ -1 & 1 & 1 \\ -7 & -4 & 5 \end{vmatrix}$$

Adding column 1 to columns 2 and 3:

$$= \begin{vmatrix} 0 & 4 & -1 \\ -1 & 0 & 0 \\ -7 & -11 & -2 \end{vmatrix}$$

Now expand along row 2:

$$= -(-1) \begin{vmatrix} 4 & -1 \\ -11 & -2 \end{vmatrix} = 1(-8 - 11) = -19$$

$$D_y = \begin{vmatrix} 1 & 0 & -1 \\ 3 & -1 & 1 \\ 4 & -7 & 5 \end{vmatrix}$$

Adding column 1 to column 3:

$$= \begin{vmatrix} 1 & 0 & 0 \\ 3 & -1 & 4 \\ 4 & -7 & 9 \end{vmatrix}$$

Now expand along row 1:

$$= 1 \begin{vmatrix} -1 & 4 \\ -7 & 9 \end{vmatrix} = -9 + 28 = 19$$

$$D_z = \begin{vmatrix} 1 & 4 & 0 \\ 3 & 1 & -1 \\ 4 & -4 & -7 \end{vmatrix}$$

Adding -4 times column 1 to column 2:

$$= \begin{vmatrix} 1 & 0 & 0 \\ 3 & -11 & -1 \\ 4 & -20 & -7 \end{vmatrix}$$

Now expand along row 1:

$$= 1 \begin{vmatrix} -11 & -1 \\ -20 & -7 \end{vmatrix} = 77 - 20 = 57$$

So $x = \dfrac{D_x}{D} = \dfrac{-19}{-19} = 1$, $y = \dfrac{D_y}{D} = \dfrac{19}{-19} = -1$, $z = \dfrac{D_z}{D} = \dfrac{57}{-19} = -3$.

So the solution is (1, -1, -3), which verifies our answer from (a).

4. (a) $2A - B = \begin{pmatrix} 2 & -6 \\ 4 & -2 \end{pmatrix} - \begin{pmatrix} 0 & 4 \\ 1 & 3 \end{pmatrix} = \begin{pmatrix} 2 & -10 \\ 3 & -5 \end{pmatrix}$

(b) $BA = \begin{pmatrix} 0 & 4 \\ 1 & 3 \end{pmatrix}\begin{pmatrix} 1 & -3 \\ 2 & -1 \end{pmatrix} = \begin{pmatrix} 8 & -4 \\ 7 & -6 \end{pmatrix}$

5.   We first graph the region:

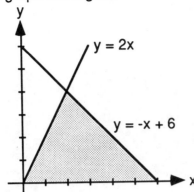

The base of the triangle is the x-intercept of $y = -x + 6$, which is 6. To find the height, we find the intersection points of the lines $y = 2x$ and $y = -x + 6$:

$$2x = -x + 6$$
$$3x = 6$$
$$x = 2$$
$$y = 4$$

So the height is 4. We find the area:

$$\text{Area} = \frac{1}{2}(\text{base})(\text{height}) = \frac{1}{2}(6)(4) = 12 \text{ sq. units}$$

6.   Let $u = \frac{1}{x}$ and $v = \frac{1}{y}$, so we have the system:

$$\frac{1}{2}u + \frac{1}{3}v = 10$$
$$-5u - 4v = -4$$

Multiply the first equation by 10:

$$5u + \frac{10}{3}v = 100$$
$$-5u - 4v = -4$$

Adding, we have:

$$-\frac{2}{3}v = 96$$
$$v = -144$$

Substitute into the first equation to find u:

$$\frac{1}{2}u + \frac{1}{3}(-144) = 10$$
$$\frac{1}{2}u - 48 = 10$$
$$\frac{1}{2}u = 58$$
$$u = 116$$

So $\dfrac{1}{x} = 116$, thus $x = \dfrac{1}{116}$, and $\dfrac{1}{y} = -144$, thus $y = -\dfrac{1}{144}$.

So the solution is $\left(\dfrac{1}{116}, -\dfrac{1}{144}\right)$.

7.   coefficient matrix: $\begin{pmatrix} 1 & 1 & -1 \\ 2 & -1 & 2 \\ 1 & -2 & 1 \end{pmatrix}$

augmented matrix: $\begin{pmatrix} 1 & 1 & -1 & -1 \\ 2 & -1 & 2 & 11 \\ 1 & -2 & 1 & 10 \end{pmatrix}$

8.   Using the augmented matrix formed in the preceeding exercise, add -2 times row 1 to row 2 and -1 times row 1 to row 3:

$$\begin{pmatrix} 1 & 1 & -1 & -1 \\ 0 & -3 & 4 & 13 \\ 0 & -3 & 2 & 11 \end{pmatrix}$$

Multiply row 2 by -1 and add to row 3:

$$\begin{pmatrix} 1 & 1 & -1 & -1 \\ 0 & -3 & 4 & 13 \\ 0 & 0 & -2 & -2 \end{pmatrix}$$

So we have the system of equations:

$$\begin{aligned} x + y - z &= -1 \\ -3y + 4z &= 13 \\ -2z &= -2 \end{aligned}$$

Solving the third equation for z yields z = 1. Substitute into the second equation:

$$\begin{aligned} -3y + 4(1) &= 13 \\ -3y &= 9 \\ y &= -3 \end{aligned}$$

Substitute into the first equation:

$$\begin{aligned} x - 3 - 1 &= -1 \\ x - 4 &= -1 \\ x &= 3 \end{aligned}$$

So the solution is (3, -3, 1).

9.   We first find the point of intersection:

$$\begin{aligned} x + y &= 11 \\ 3x + 2y &= 7 \end{aligned}$$

Multiply the first equation by -2:

$$\begin{aligned} -2x - 2y &= -22 \\ 3x + 2y &= 7 \end{aligned}$$

Adding, we get:

$$x = -15$$

Substitute into the first equation:
$$-15 + y = 11$$
$$y = 26$$
So the point of intersection is (-15, 26). We now find the slope of the line
$2x - 4y = 7$:
$$-4y = -2x + 7$$
$$y = \frac{1}{2}x - \frac{7}{4}$$

Since this slope is $\frac{1}{2}$, the perpendicular slope must be -2. We use this slope
and the point (-15, 26) in the point-slope formula:
$$y - 26 = -2(x + 15)$$
$$y - 26 = -2x - 30$$
$$y = -2x - 4$$

10. Multiply by $(x + 1)(x - 1)^2$:
$$x - 2 = A(x - 1)^2 + B(x + 1)(x - 1) + C(x + 1)$$
$$x - 2 = A(x^2 - 2x + 1) + B(x^2 - 1) + C(x + 1)$$
$$x - 2 = (A + B)x^2 + (-2A + C)x + (A - B + C)$$
Equating coefficients, we have the system:
$$A + B \qquad = 0$$
$$-2A \qquad + C = 1$$
$$A - B + C = -2$$
Adding 2 times the first equation to the second equation, and -1 times the first
equation to the third equation:
$$A + B \qquad = 0$$
$$2B + C = 1$$
$$-2B + C = -2$$
Adding the second equation to the third equation:
$$A + B \qquad = 0$$
$$2B + C = 1$$
$$2C = -1$$
Solving the third equation for C yields C = -1/2. Substitute into the second
equation:
$$2B - 1/2 = 1$$
$$B = 3/4$$
Substitute into the first equation:
$$A + 3/4 = 0$$
$$A = -3/4$$
So A = -3/4, B = 3/4, C = -1/2.

11. (a) The minor is $\begin{vmatrix} 2 & -1 \\ 0 & 4 \end{vmatrix} = 8$.

(b) The cofactor is $-1 \begin{vmatrix} 2 & -1 \\ 0 & 4 \end{vmatrix} = -1(8) = -8$.

12.   Adding 2 times row 1 to row 2, and -4 times row 1 to row 3:

$$\begin{vmatrix} 4 & -5 & 0 \\ 0 & 0 & 7 \\ 0 & 40 & 14 \end{vmatrix}$$

Expanding along column 1, we have:

$$= 4 \begin{vmatrix} 0 & 7 \\ 40 & 14 \end{vmatrix} = 4(0 - 280) = -1120$$

13.   If we multiply the first equation by 2 we have $2xy = 10$. Adding the two equations, we get:

$$x^2 + 2xy + y^2 = 25$$
$$(x + y)^2 = 25$$
$$x + y = \pm 5$$

Subtracting the two equations, we get:

$$x^2 - 2xy + y^2 = 5$$
$$(x - y)^2 = 5$$
$$x - y = \pm\sqrt{5}$$

So we have the following four systems of equations:

$$\begin{array}{llll} x + y = 5 & x + y = 5 & x + y = -5 & x + y = -5 \\ x - y = \sqrt{5} & x - y = -\sqrt{5} & x - y = \sqrt{5} & x - y = -\sqrt{5} \end{array}$$

Adding, we have:

$$\begin{array}{llll} 2x = 5 + \sqrt{5} & 2x = 5 - \sqrt{5} & 2x = -5 + \sqrt{5} & 2x = -5 - \sqrt{5} \\[2mm] x = \dfrac{5 + \sqrt{5}}{2} & x = \dfrac{5 - \sqrt{5}}{2} & x = \dfrac{-5 + \sqrt{5}}{2} & x = \dfrac{-5 - \sqrt{5}}{2} \\[4mm] y = \dfrac{5 - \sqrt{5}}{2} & y = \dfrac{5 + \sqrt{5}}{2} & y = \dfrac{-5 - \sqrt{5}}{2} & y = \dfrac{-5 + \sqrt{5}}{2} \end{array}$$

So the solutions are $\left(\dfrac{5 + \sqrt{5}}{2}, \dfrac{5 - \sqrt{5}}{2} \right)$, $\left(\dfrac{5 - \sqrt{5}}{2}, \dfrac{5 + \sqrt{5}}{2} \right)$,

$\left(\dfrac{-5 + \sqrt{5}}{2}, \dfrac{-5 - \sqrt{5}}{2} \right)$ and $\left(\dfrac{-5 - \sqrt{5}}{2}, \dfrac{-5 + \sqrt{5}}{2} \right)$.

14.   Multiply the first equation by -2:

$$-2A - 4B - 6C = -2$$
$$2A - B - C = 2$$

Adding, we have:

$$-5B - 7C = 0$$
$$-5B = 7C$$
$$B = -\frac{7}{5} C$$

Substitute into the (original) first equation:

$$A + 2B + 3C = 1$$

$$A - \frac{14}{5}C + 3C = 1$$

$$A + \frac{1}{5}C = 1$$

$$A = 1 - \frac{1}{5}C$$

So the solution is $\left(1 - \frac{1}{5}C, -\frac{7}{5}C, C\right)$, where C = any real number.

15. (a)   We form the augmented matrix:

$$\begin{pmatrix} 10 & -2 & 5 & 1 & 0 & 0 \\ 6 & -1 & 4 & 0 & 1 & 0 \\ 1 & 0 & 1 & 0 & 0 & 1 \end{pmatrix}$$

Switching rows, we have:

$$\begin{pmatrix} 1 & 0 & 1 & 0 & 0 & 1 \\ 6 & -1 & 4 & 0 & 1 & 0 \\ 10 & -2 & 5 & 1 & 0 & 0 \end{pmatrix}$$

Adding -6 times row 1 to row 2, and -10 times row 1 to row 3, we have:

$$\begin{pmatrix} 1 & 0 & 1 & 0 & 0 & 1 \\ 0 & -1 & -2 & 0 & 1 & -6 \\ 0 & -2 & -5 & 1 & 0 & -10 \end{pmatrix}$$

Multiply row 2 by -1, and adding 2 times this new row 2 to row 3, we have:

$$\begin{pmatrix} 1 & 0 & 1 & 0 & 0 & 1 \\ 0 & 1 & 2 & 0 & -1 & 6 \\ 0 & 0 & -1 & 1 & -2 & 2 \end{pmatrix}$$

Adding 2 times row 3 to row 2, row 3 to row 1, then multiplying row 3 by -1, we have:

$$\begin{pmatrix} 1 & 0 & 0 & 1 & -2 & 3 \\ 0 & 1 & 0 & 2 & -5 & 10 \\ 0 & 0 & 1 & -1 & 2 & -2 \end{pmatrix}$$

So the inverse is $\begin{pmatrix} 1 & -2 & 3 \\ 2 & -5 & 10 \\ -1 & 2 & -2 \end{pmatrix}$.

(b)   Calling A the coefficient matrix, we know the solution will be given by $A^{-1}b$:

$$\begin{pmatrix} u \\ v \\ w \end{pmatrix} = \begin{pmatrix} 1 & -2 & 3 \\ 2 & -5 & 10 \\ -1 & 2 & -2 \end{pmatrix}\begin{pmatrix} -1 \\ -2 \\ 3 \end{pmatrix} = \begin{pmatrix} 12 \\ 38 \\ -9 \end{pmatrix}$$

So the solution is $(12, 38, -9)$.

16.   We graph $5x - 6y \geq 30$:

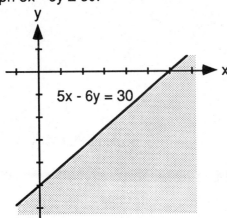

17.   Substituting the two points into $y = Px^2 + Qx - 5$, we have:
$$-1 = 4P - 2Q - 5$$
$$-2 = P - Q - 5$$
So we have the system:
$$4P - 2Q = 4$$
$$P - Q = 3$$
Divide the first equation by 2, and multiply the second equation by -1:
$$2P - Q = 2$$
$$-P + Q = -3$$
Adding, we have $P = -1$. Substitute into the second equation:
$$-1 - Q = 3$$
$$-Q = 4$$
$$Q = -4$$
So $P = -1$ and $Q = -4$.

18.   We complete the square on x:
$$x^2 - 4x + y^2 > -3$$
$$(x^2 - 4x + 4) + y^2 > -3 + 4$$
$$(x - 2)^2 + y^2 > 1$$

We now graph the inequality:

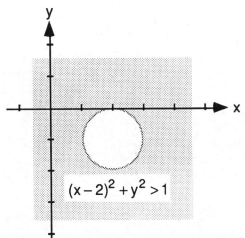

$$(x-2)^2 + y^2 > 1$$

The solution set is neither bounded nor convex.

19.   vertices: $(0,0), (0,7), (6,10), (261/26, 225/26), (11,0)$

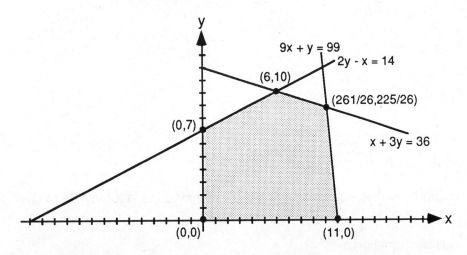

20.   Since $y = x$ is one of the lines, we substitute for y in the second equation:

$$x - 2x = -3$$
$$-x = -3$$
$$x = 3$$

Let $x = 3, y = 3$ in the first equation:

$$3k + 3(3) = -4$$
$$3k + 9 = -4$$
$$3k = -13$$
$$k = -13/3$$

21. Adding the two equations yields:
$$2x = 6$$
$$x = 3$$
Substitute into equation 1:
$$3xy = -2$$
$$y = -5$$
So the solution is (3, -5).

23. Multiply the first equation by -2:
$$-4x - 2y = -4$$
$$x + 2y = 7$$
Adding , we get:
$$-3x = 3$$
$$x = -1$$
Substitute into equation 1:
$$-2 + y = 2$$
$$y = 4$$
So the solution is (-1, 4).

25. Multiply equation 1 by -5 and equation 2 by 2:
$$-35x - 10y = -45$$
$$8x + 10y = 126$$
Adding, we get:
$$-27x = 81$$
$$x = -3$$
Substitute into equation 1:
$$-21 + 2y = 9$$
$$2y = 30$$
$$y = 15$$
So the solution is (-3, 15).

27. Multiply the first equation by 2 and the second equation by 24 to clear fractions:
$$4x - y = -16$$
$$8x + 3y = -24$$
Multiply equation 1 by -2:
$$-8x + 2y = 32$$
$$8x + 3y = -24$$
Adding, we get:
$$5y = 8$$
$$y = \frac{8}{5}$$

Substitute into equation 1:

$$4x - \frac{8}{5} = -16$$

$$4x = -\frac{72}{5}$$

$$x = -\frac{18}{5}$$

So the solution is (-18/5, 8/5).

29. Multiply the first equation by 2:
$$6x + 10y = 2$$
$$9x - 10y = 8$$
Adding, we get:
$$15x = 10$$
$$x = \frac{2}{3}$$
Substitute into equation 1:
$$2 + 5y = 1$$
$$5y = -1$$
$$y = -\frac{1}{5}$$
So the solution is (2/3, -1/5).

31. Multiply the first equation by 6 and the second equation by 2 to clear fractions:
$$4x + 3y = -72$$
$$x - 2y = 4$$
Multiply the second by -4:
$$4x + 3y = -72$$
$$-4x + 8y = -16$$
Adding, we get:
$$11y = -88$$
$$y = -8$$
Substitute into equation 2:
$$x + 16 = 4$$
$$x = -12$$
So the solution is (-12, -8).

33. Let $a = \frac{1}{x}$ and $b = \frac{1}{y}$. So we have:
$$a + b = -1$$
$$2a + 5b = -14$$
Multiply the first equation by -2:
$$-2a - 2b = 2$$
$$2a + 5b = -14$$

Adding, we get:
$$3b = -12$$
$$b = -4$$
Substitute into equation 1:
$$a - 4 = -1$$
$$a = 3$$
Since $x = \dfrac{1}{a}$ and $y = \dfrac{1}{b}$, then $x = \dfrac{1}{3}$ and $y = -\dfrac{1}{4}$.
So the solution is (1/3, -1/4).

35. Multiply the second equation by $a - 1$:
$$ax + (1 - a)y = 1$$
$$(-a^2 + 2a - 1)x + (a - 1)y = 0$$
Adding, we get:
$$(-a^2 + 3a - 1)x = 1$$
$$x = \dfrac{-1}{a^2 - 3a + 1}$$
Substitute into equation 2:
$$\dfrac{a - 1}{a^2 - 3a + 1} + y = 0$$
$$y = \dfrac{1 - a}{a^2 - 3a + 1}$$
So the solution is $\left(\dfrac{-1}{a^2 - 3a + 1}, \dfrac{1 - a}{a^2 - 3a + 1} \right)$. We must assume that

$a^2 - 3a + 1 \neq 0$, or $a \neq \dfrac{3 \pm \sqrt{5}}{2}$.

37. Multiply the first equation by 2:
$$4x - 2y = 6a^2 - 2$$
$$x + 2y = -a^2 + 2$$
Adding, we get:
$$5x = 5a^2$$
$$x = a^2$$
Substitute into equation 2:
$$2y + a^2 = 2 - a^2$$
$$2y = 2 - 2a^2$$
$$y = 1 - a^2$$
So the solution is $(a^2, 1 - a^2)$.

39.   Multiply the first equation by 3:

$$15x - 3y = 12a^2 - 18b^2$$
$$2x + 3y = 5a^2 + b^2$$

Adding, we get:

$$17x = 17a^2 - 17b^2$$
$$x = a^2 - b^2$$

Substitute into equation 1:

$$5a^2 - 5b^2 - y = 4a^2 - 6b^2$$
$$-y = -a^2 - b^2$$
$$y = a^2 + b^2$$

So the solution is $(a^2 - b^2, a^2 + b^2)$.

41.   Multiply the first equation by p and the second equation by q:

$$p^2x - pqy = pq^2$$
$$q^2x + pqy = p^2q$$

Adding, we get:

$$(p^2 + q^2)x = pq(p + q)$$
$$x = \frac{pq(p + q)}{p^2 + q^2}$$

We re-solve the system to find y. Multiply the first equation by -q and the second equation by p:

$$-pqx + q^2y = -q^3$$
$$pqx + p^2y = p^3$$

Adding, we get:

$$(p^2 + q^2)y = p^3 - q^3$$
$$y = \frac{p^3 - q^3}{p^2 + q^2}$$

So the solution is $\left(\dfrac{pq(p + q)}{p^2 + q^2}, \dfrac{p^3 - q^3}{p^2 + q^2} \right)$. We must assume that $(p, q) \neq (0, 0)$.

43.   Let $u = \dfrac{1}{x}$ and $v = \dfrac{1}{y}$, so we have:

$$4au - 3bv = a - 7b$$
$$2a^2u - 2b^2v = 3a^2 - 5ab - 2b^2$$

Multiply the first equation by -2b and the second equation by 3:

$$-8abu + 6b^2v = 14b^2 - 2ab$$
$$9a^2u - 6b^2v = 9a^2 - 15ab - 6b^2$$

Adding, we get:

$$(9a^2 - 8ab)u = 9a^2 - 17ab + 8b^2$$

$$u = \frac{9a^2 - 17ab + 8b^2}{9a^2 - 8ab}$$

$$= \frac{(9a - 8b)(a - b)}{a(9a - 8b)}$$

$$= \frac{a - b}{a}$$

Substitute into equation 1:

$$4a\left(\frac{a - b}{a}\right) - 3bv = a - 7b$$

$$4a - 4b - 3bv = a - 7b$$

$$-3bv = -3a - 3b$$

$$v = \frac{a + b}{b}$$

Since $x = \frac{1}{u}$ and $y = \frac{1}{v}$, then $x = \frac{a}{a - b}$ and $y = \frac{b}{a + b}$.

So the solution is $\left(\frac{a}{a - b}, \frac{b}{a + b}\right)$. We must assume that $ab \neq 0$, $9a - 8b \neq 0$, $a \neq \pm b$.

45.   Form the augmented matrix:

$$\begin{pmatrix} 1 & 1 & 1 & 9 \\ 1 & -1 & -1 & -5 \\ 2 & 1 & -2 & -1 \end{pmatrix}$$

Add -1 times row 1 to row 2 and -2 times row 1 to row 3:

$$\begin{pmatrix} 1 & 1 & 1 & 9 \\ 0 & -2 & -2 & -14 \\ 0 & -1 & -4 & -19 \end{pmatrix}$$

Switch row 2 and row 3, multiply each by -1:

$$\begin{pmatrix} 1 & 1 & 1 & 9 \\ 0 & 1 & 4 & 19 \\ 0 & 2 & 2 & 14 \end{pmatrix}$$

Add -2 times row 2 to row 3:

$$\begin{pmatrix} 1 & 1 & 1 & 9 \\ 0 & 1 & 4 & 19 \\ 0 & 0 & -6 & -24 \end{pmatrix}$$

So:
$$x + y + z = 9$$
$$y + 4z = 19$$
$$-6z = -24$$

Solve equation 3 for z:
$$-6z = -24$$
$$z = 4$$

Substitute into equation 2:
$$y + 16 = 19$$
$$y = 3$$
Substitute into equation 1:
$$x + 3 + 4 = 9$$
$$x = 2$$
So the solution is $(2, 3, 4)$.

47.   Switching equations 1 and 3, form the augmented matrix:

$$\begin{pmatrix} 1 & 1 & 1 & -3 \\ 2 & 3 & 3 & -8 \\ 4 & -4 & 1 & 4 \end{pmatrix}$$

Add -2 times row 1 to row 2 and -4 times row 1 to row 3:

$$\begin{pmatrix} 1 & 1 & 1 & -3 \\ 0 & 1 & 1 & -2 \\ 0 & -8 & -3 & 16 \end{pmatrix}$$

Add 8 times row 2 to row 3:

$$\begin{pmatrix} 1 & 1 & 1 & -3 \\ 0 & 1 & 1 & -2 \\ 0 & 0 & 5 & 0 \end{pmatrix}$$

So: $x + y + z = -3$
$$y + z = -2$$
$$5z = 0$$
Solve equation 3 for z:
$$5z = 0$$
$$z = 0$$
Substitute into equation 2:
$$y + 0 = -2$$
$$y = -2$$
Substitute into equation 1:
$$x - 2 + 0 = -3$$
$$x = -1$$
So the solution is $(-1, -2, 0)$.

49.   Using equation 3 as row 1, form the augmented matrix:

$$\begin{pmatrix} 1 & 1 & -2 & 4 \\ 1 & -2 & 1 & -2 \\ -2 & 1 & 1 & 1 \end{pmatrix}$$

Add -1 times row 1 to row 2 and 2 times row 1 to row 3:

$$\begin{pmatrix} 1 & 1 & -2 & 4 \\ 0 & -3 & 3 & -6 \\ 0 & 3 & -3 & 9 \end{pmatrix}$$

Multiply row 2 by $\frac{1}{3}$ and row 3 by $\frac{1}{3}$:

$$\begin{pmatrix} 1 & 1 & -2 & 4 \\ 0 & -1 & 1 & -2 \\ 0 & 1 & -1 & 3 \end{pmatrix}$$

Add row 2 to row 3:

$$\begin{pmatrix} 1 & 1 & -2 & 4 \\ 0 & -1 & 1 & -2 \\ 0 & 0 & 0 & 1 \end{pmatrix}$$

Since $0 = 1$ is false, there is no solution to the system.

51. Multiply the second equation by -2:
$$4x + 2y - 3z = 15$$
$$-4x - 2y - 6z = -6$$
Adding, we get:
$$-9z = 9$$
$$z = -1$$
Substitute into the original equation:
$$2x + y - 3 = 3$$
$$2x + y = 6$$
$$y = 6 - 2x$$
So the solution is $(x, 6 - 2x, -1)$, for any real number x.

53. Form the augmented matrix:

$$\begin{pmatrix} 1 & 2 & -3 & -2 \\ 2 & -1 & 1 & 1 \\ 3 & -4 & 5 & 1 \end{pmatrix}$$

Add -2 times row 1 to row 2 and -3 times row 1 to row 3:

$$\begin{pmatrix} 1 & 2 & -3 & -2 \\ 0 & -5 & 7 & 5 \\ 0 & -10 & 14 & 7 \end{pmatrix}$$

Add -2 times row 2 to row 3:

$$\begin{pmatrix} 1 & 2 & -3 & -2 \\ 0 & -5 & 7 & 5 \\ 0 & 0 & 0 & -3 \end{pmatrix}$$

Since $0 = -3$ is false, there is no solution to the system.

55. Form the augmented matrix:
$$\begin{pmatrix} 1 & 1 & 1 & a+b \\ 2 & -1 & 2 & -a+5b \\ 1 & -2 & 1 & -2a+4b \end{pmatrix}$$
Add -2 times row 1 to row 2 and -1 times row 1 to row 3:
$$\begin{pmatrix} 1 & 1 & 1 & a+b \\ 0 & -3 & 0 & -3a+3b \\ 0 & -3 & 0 & -3a+3b \end{pmatrix}$$
Add -1 times row 2 to row 3:
$$\begin{pmatrix} 1 & 1 & 1 & a+b \\ 0 & -3 & 0 & -3a+3b \\ 0 & 0 & 0 & 0 \end{pmatrix}$$
So: $x+y+z = a+b$
$-3y = -3a+3b$
Solve equation 2 for y:
$-3y = -3a+3b$
$y = a-b$
Substitute into equation 1:
$x+a-b+z = a+b$
$x = 2b-z$
So the solution is $(2b-z, a-b, z)$, for any real number z.

57. Form the augmented matrix:
$$\begin{pmatrix} 1 & 1 & 1 & 1 & 8 \\ 3 & 3 & -1 & -1 & 20 \\ 4 & -1 & -1 & 2 & 18 \\ 2 & 5 & 5 & -5 & 8 \end{pmatrix}$$
Add -3 times row 1 to row 2, -4 times row 1 ro row 3, and -2 times row 1 to row 4:
$$\begin{pmatrix} 1 & 1 & 1 & 1 & 8 \\ 0 & 0 & -4 & -4 & -4 \\ 0 & -5 & -5 & -2 & -14 \\ 0 & 3 & 3 & -7 & -8 \end{pmatrix}$$
Switch row 2 and row 3, and multiply row 3 by $-\frac{1}{4}$:
$$\begin{pmatrix} 1 & 1 & 1 & 1 & 8 \\ 0 & -5 & -5 & -2 & -14 \\ 0 & 0 & 1 & 1 & 1 \\ 0 & 3 & 3 & -7 & -8 \end{pmatrix}$$
Add 2 times row 4 to row 2:
$$\begin{pmatrix} 1 & 1 & 1 & 1 & 8 \\ 0 & 1 & 1 & -16 & -30 \\ 0 & 0 & 1 & 1 & 1 \\ 0 & 3 & 3 & -7 & -8 \end{pmatrix}$$

Add -3 times row 2 to row 4:

$$\begin{pmatrix} 1 & 1 & 1 & 1 & 8 \\ 0 & 1 & 1 & -16 & -30 \\ 0 & 0 & 1 & 1 & 1 \\ 0 & 0 & 0 & 41 & 82 \end{pmatrix}$$

So:

$$x + y + z + w = 8$$
$$y + z - 16w = -30$$
$$z + w = 1$$
$$41w = 82$$

Solve equation 4 for w:

$$41w = 82$$
$$w = 2$$

Substitute into equation 3:

$$z + 2 = 1$$
$$z = -1$$

Substitute into equation 2:

$$y - 1 - 32 = -30$$
$$y = 3$$

Substitute into equation 1:

$$x + 3 - 1 + 2 = 8$$
$$x = 4$$

So the solution is $(4, 3, -1, 2)$.

59. Multiply by $(x - 10)(x + 10)$, so:

$$1 = A(x + 10) + B(x - 10)$$
$$1 = (A + B)x + (10A - 10B)$$

Since A and B are constants:

$$A + B = 0$$
$$10A - 10B = 1$$

Multiply equation 1 by 10:

$$10A + 10B = 0$$
$$10A - 10B = 1$$

Adding, we get:

$$20A = 1$$
$$A = \frac{1}{20}$$

Substitute into equation 1:

$$\frac{1}{20} + B = 0$$
$$B = -\frac{1}{20}$$

So $A = \frac{1}{20}$ and $B = -\frac{1}{20}$.

61.   Multiply by $(x + 1)^2$, so:

$$2x = A(x + 1) + B$$
$$2x = Ax + (A + B)$$

Since A and B are constants:

$$A = 2$$
$$A + B = 0$$

Substitute into equation 2:

$$2 + B = 0$$
$$B = -2$$

So A = 2 and B = -2.

63.   Multiply by $x(x - 4)$, so:

$$5 = A(x - 4) + Bx$$
$$5 = (A + B)x - 4A$$

Since A and B are constants:

$$A + B = 0$$
$$-4A = 5$$

Solve equation 2 for A:

$$-4A = 5$$
$$A = -\frac{5}{4}$$

Substitute into equation 1:

$$-\frac{5}{4} + B = 0$$
$$B = \frac{5}{4}$$

So $A = -\frac{5}{4}$ and $B = \frac{5}{4}$.

65.   Multiply by $(x - 1)(x + 3)^2$, so:

$$1 = A(x + 3)^2 + B(x - 1)(x + 3) + C(x - 1)$$
$$1 = A(x^2 + 6x + 9) + B(x^2 + 2x - 3) + C(x - 1)$$
$$1 = (A + B)x^2 + (6A + 2B + C)x + (9A - 3B - C)$$

Since A, B, and C are constants:

$$A + B = 0$$
$$6A + 2B + C = 0$$
$$9A - 3B - C = 1$$

Add -6 times equation 1 to equation 2 and -9 times equation 1 to equation 3:

$$A + B = 0$$
$$-4B + C = 0$$
$$-12B - C = 1$$

Add equation 2 and 3:

$$-16B = 1$$
$$B = -\frac{1}{16}$$

Substitute into equation 2:
$$\frac{1}{4} + C = 0$$
$$C = -\frac{1}{4}$$
Substitute into equation 1:
$$A - \frac{1}{16} = 0$$
$$A = \frac{1}{16}$$
So $A = \frac{1}{16}$, $B = -\frac{1}{16}$, $C = -\frac{1}{4}$.

67. Multiply by $(x - 1)(x^2 + x + 5)$, so:
$$4x^2 + 2x + 15 = A(x^2 + x + 5) + (Bx + C)(x - 1)$$
$$4x^2 + 2x + 15 = (A + B)x^2 + (A - B + C)x + (5A - C)$$
Since A, B, and C are constants:
$$A + B = 4$$
$$A - B + C = 2$$
$$5A - C = 15$$
Add -1 times equation 1 to equation 2 and -5 times equation 1 to equation 3:
$$A + B = 4$$
$$-2B + C = -2$$
$$-5B - C = -5$$
Add equation 2 and equation 3:
$$-7B = -7$$
$$B = 1$$
Substitute into equation 2:
$$-2 + C = -2$$
$$C = 0$$
Substitute into equation 1:
$$A + 1 = 4$$
$$A = 3$$
So $A = 3$, $B = 1$, and $C = 0$.

69. Multiply by $(x + 4)(x^2 - 4x + 16)$, so:
$$1 = A(x^2 - 4x + 16) + (Bx + C)(x + 4)$$
$$1 = (A + B)x^2 + (-4A + 4B + C)x + (16A + 4C)$$
Since A, B, and C are constants:
$$A + B = 0$$
$$-4A + 4B + C = 0$$
$$16A + 4C = 1$$

Add 4 times equation 1 to equation 2, and -16 times equation 1 to equation 3:

$$A + B \quad\quad = 0$$
$$8B + \ C = 0$$
$$-16B + 4C = 1$$

Add 2 times equation 2 to equation 3:

$$A + B \quad\quad = 0$$
$$8B + C = 0$$
$$6C = 1$$

Solve equation 3 for C:

$$6C = 1$$
$$C = \frac{1}{6}$$

Substitute into equation 2:

$$8B + \frac{1}{6} = 0$$
$$8B = -\frac{1}{6}$$
$$B = -\frac{1}{48}$$

Substitute into equation 1:

$$A - \frac{1}{48} = 0$$
$$A = \frac{1}{48}$$

So $A = \frac{1}{48}$, $B = -\frac{1}{48}$, and $C = \frac{1}{6}$.

71. Multiply by $(x - a)^3$, so:

$$x = A(x - a)^2 + B(x - a) + C$$
$$x = Ax^2 + (-2aA + B)x + (a^2A - aB + C)$$

Since A, B, and C are constants:

$$A = 0$$
$$-2aA + B = 1$$
$$a^2A - aB + C = 0$$

Substitute into equation 2:

$$0 + B = 1$$
$$B = 1$$

Substitute into equation 3:

$$0 - a + C = 0$$
$$C = a$$

So $A = 0$, $B = 1$ and $C = a$.

73.   Multiply by (x - a)(x - b), so:
$$(a - b)(a + b - x) = A(x - b) + B(x - a)$$
$$(a - b)(a + b) - (a - b)x = (A + B)x + (-bA - aB)$$
Since A and B are constants:
$$A + B = b - a$$
$$-bA - aB = a^2 - b^2$$
Multiply equation 1 by b:
$$bA + bB = b^2 - ab$$
$$-bA - aB = a^2 - b^2$$
Adding, we get:
$$(b - a)B = a^2 - ab$$
$$B = \frac{a(a - b)}{b - a}$$
$$B = -a$$
Substitute into equation 1:
$$A - a = b - a$$
$$A = b$$
So A = b and B = -a.

75. $\begin{vmatrix} 1 & 5 \\ -6 & 4 \end{vmatrix} = 1(4) - 5(-6) = 4 + 30 = 34$

77. $\begin{vmatrix} 4 & 0 & 3 \\ -2 & 1 & 5 \\ 0 & 2 & -1 \end{vmatrix}$
Adding -2 times row 2 to row 3 yields:
$$= \begin{vmatrix} 4 & 0 & 3 \\ -2 & 1 & 5 \\ 4 & 0 & -11 \end{vmatrix} = 1 \bullet \begin{vmatrix} 4 & 3 \\ 4 & -11 \end{vmatrix} = -56$$

79. $\begin{vmatrix} 1 & 5 & 7 \\ 1 & 5 & 7 \\ 17 & 19 & 21 \end{vmatrix}$
Subtracting row 2 from row 1 yields:
$$= \begin{vmatrix} 0 & 0 & 0 \\ 1 & 5 & 7 \\ 17 & 19 & 21 \end{vmatrix} = 0$$

81. $\begin{vmatrix} 1 & 0 & 0 & 0 \\ 0 & 2 & 0 & 0 \\ 0 & 0 & 3 & 0 \\ 0 & 0 & 0 & 4 \end{vmatrix} = 1 \begin{vmatrix} 2 & 0 & 0 \\ 0 & 3 & 0 \\ 0 & 0 & 4 \end{vmatrix} = 2 \begin{vmatrix} 3 & 0 \\ 0 & 4 \end{vmatrix} = 2(12) = 24$

83. By expanding along column 1:

$$\begin{vmatrix} a & b & c \\ b & c & a \\ c & a & b \end{vmatrix} = a\begin{vmatrix} c & a \\ a & b \end{vmatrix} - b\begin{vmatrix} b & c \\ a & b \end{vmatrix} + c\begin{vmatrix} b & c \\ c & a \end{vmatrix}$$

$$= a(bc - a^2) - b(b^2 - ac) + c(ab - c^2)$$
$$= abc - a^3 - b^3 + abc + abc - c^3$$
$$= 3abc - a^3 - b^3 - c^3$$

85.
$$\begin{vmatrix} a^2 + x & b & c & d \\ -b & 1 & 0 & 0 \\ -c & 0 & 1 & 0 \\ -d & 0 & 0 & 1 \end{vmatrix}$$

Adding b times column 2 to column 1 yields:

$$= \begin{vmatrix} a^2 + b^2 + x & b & c & d \\ 0 & 1 & 0 & 0 \\ -c & 0 & 1 & 0 \\ -d & 0 & 0 & 1 \end{vmatrix} = 1\begin{vmatrix} a^2 + b^2 + x & c & d \\ -c & 1 & 0 \\ -d & 0 & 1 \end{vmatrix}$$

Adding c times column 2 to column 1 yields:

$$= \begin{vmatrix} a^2 + b^2 + c^2 + x & c & d \\ 0 & 1 & 0 \\ -d & 0 & 1 \end{vmatrix}$$

$$= 1\begin{vmatrix} a^2 + b^2 + c^2 + x & d \\ -d & 1 \end{vmatrix}$$
$$= a^2 + b^2 + c^2 + x - (-d^2)$$
$$= a^2 + b^2 + c^2 + d^2 + x$$

87. Substituting $(x, y) = (-2, 5)$ and $(x, y) = (2, 9)$, we get:

$$5 = 4a - 2b - 1$$
$$9 = 4a + 2b - 1$$

Adding, we get:

$$14 = 8a - 2$$
$$16 = 8a$$
$$2 = a$$

Substitute into the first equation:

$$5 = 8 - 2b - 1$$
$$-2 = -2b$$
$$1 = b$$

So $a = 2$ and $b = 1$.

89.   (a)   Let's first graph the triangle:

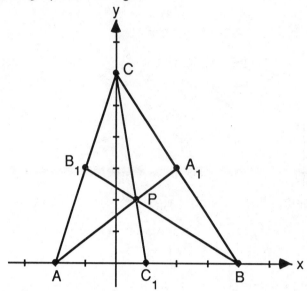

By the midpoint formula:

$$A_1 = \left(\frac{4+0}{2}, \frac{0+6}{2}\right) = (2,3)$$

$$B_1 = \left(\frac{-2+0}{2}, \frac{0+6}{2}\right) = (-1,3)$$

$$C_1 = \left(\frac{-2+4}{2}, \frac{0+0}{2}\right) = (1,0)$$

AA_1:

$$\text{slope} = \frac{3-0}{2-(-2)} = \frac{3}{4}$$

$$\text{point} = (-2,0)$$

$$y - 0 = \frac{3}{4}(x+2)$$

$$y = \frac{3}{4}x + \frac{3}{2}$$

BB_1:

$$\text{slope} = \frac{3-0}{-1-4} = -\frac{3}{5}$$

$$\text{point} = (4,0)$$

$$y - 0 = -\frac{3}{5}(x-4)$$

$$y = -\frac{3}{5}x + \frac{12}{5}$$

We solve $\frac{3}{4}x + \frac{3}{2} = -\frac{3}{5}x + \frac{12}{5}$:

Multiply by 20 to clear fractions:
$$15x + 30 = -12x + 48$$
$$27x = 18$$
$$x = \frac{2}{3}$$

So $y = \frac{3}{4} \cdot \frac{2}{3} + \frac{3}{2} = 2$. Thus the point of intersection is $(2/3, 2)$.

(b) CC_1:
$$\text{slope} = \frac{6 - 0}{0 - 1} = -6$$
$$y = -6x + 6$$

We solve $-6x + 6 = -\frac{3}{5}x + \frac{12}{5}$

Multiply by 5 to clear fractions:
$$-30x + 30 = -3x + 12$$
$$18 = 27x$$
$$\frac{2}{3} = x$$

So $y = -6\left(\frac{2}{3}\right) + 6 = 2$. Thus the point of intersection is $(2/3, 2)$.

(c)   We solve $-6x + 6 = \frac{3}{4}x + \frac{3}{2}$

Multiply by 4 to clear fractions:
$$-24x + 24 = 3x + 6$$
$$18 = 27x$$
$$\frac{2}{3} = x$$

So $y = -6\left(\frac{2}{3}\right) + 6 = 2$. Thus the point of intersection is $(2/3, 2)$.

(d)   We use the distance formula:
$$AP = \sqrt{\left(-2 - \frac{2}{3}\right)^2 + (0 - 2)^2} = \sqrt{\frac{64}{9} + \frac{36}{9}} = \frac{10}{3}$$
$$PA_1 = \sqrt{\left(\frac{2}{3} - 2\right)^2 + (2 - 3)^2} = \sqrt{\frac{16}{9} + \frac{9}{9}} = \frac{5}{3}$$

So $\dfrac{AP}{PA_1} = \dfrac{\frac{10}{3}}{\frac{5}{3}} = 2$

$$BP = \sqrt{\left(4 - \frac{2}{3}\right)^2 + (0 - 2)^2} = \sqrt{\frac{100}{9} + \frac{36}{9}} = \frac{2\sqrt{34}}{3}$$

$$PB_1 = \sqrt{\left(\frac{2}{3} + 1\right)^2 + (2 - 3)^2} = \sqrt{\frac{25}{9} + \frac{9}{9}} = \frac{\sqrt{34}}{3}$$

So $\dfrac{BP}{PB_1} = \dfrac{\frac{2\sqrt{34}}{3}}{\frac{\sqrt{34}}{3}} = 2$

$$CP = \sqrt{\left(0 - \frac{2}{3}\right)^2 + (6 - 2)^2} = \sqrt{\frac{4}{9} + \frac{144}{9}} = \frac{2\sqrt{37}}{3}$$

$$PC_1 = \sqrt{\left(\frac{2}{3} - 1\right)^2 + (2 - 0)^2} = \sqrt{\frac{1}{9} + \frac{36}{9}} = \frac{\sqrt{37}}{3}$$

So $\dfrac{CP}{PC_1} = \dfrac{\frac{2\sqrt{37}}{3}}{\frac{\sqrt{37}}{3}} = 2$

These ratios are all equal.

91. See the figure:

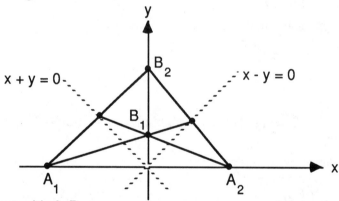

We start with A_2B_2:

$$m = -\frac{b_2}{a_2}$$

point: (a, a)

By the point slope formula:

$$a_2y + b_2x = aa_2 + ab_2$$

Since $(a_2, 0)$ lies on this curve, we have $a_2b_2 = aa_2 + ab_2$ (*)

Now for A_1B_1:

$$m = -\frac{b_1}{a_1}$$

point: (a, a)

By the point-slope formula:

$$a_1 y + b_1 x = a a_1 + a b_1$$

Since $(a_1, 0)$ lies on this curve, we have $a_1 b_1 = a a_1 + a b_1$ (*)

Now we look at A_1B_2:

$$m = -\frac{b_2}{a_1}$$

$$b_2 x + a_1 y = a_1 b_2$$

Also look at A_2B_1:

$$m = -\frac{b_1}{a_2}, \text{ so:}$$

$$b_1 x + a_2 y = a_2 b_1$$

We solve the system:

$$b_2 x + a_1 y = a_1 b_2$$
$$b_1 x + a_2 y = a_2 b_1$$

Multiply equation 1 by $-b_1$ and equation 2 by b_2:

$$-b_1 b_2 x - a_1 b_1 y = -a_1 b_1 b_2$$
$$b_1 b_2 x + a_2 b_2 y = a_2 b_1 b_2$$

Adding:

$$(a_2 b_2 - a_1 b_1)y = a_2 b_1 b_2 - a_1 b_1 b_2 ,$$

So: $$y = \frac{b_1 b_2 (a_2 - a_1)}{a_2 b_2 - a_1 b_1}$$

Substituting into equation 1, we have:

$$b_2 x + \frac{a_1 b_1 b_2 (a_2 - a_1)}{a_2 b_2 - a_1 b_1} = a_1 b_2$$

So: $$x = \frac{a_1 a_2 (b_2 - b_1)}{a_2 b_2 - a_1 b_1}$$

Now, we are asked to show that $x + y = 0$, so:

$$x + y = \frac{a_1 a_2 (b_2 - b_1) + b_1 b_2 (a_2 - a_1)}{a_2 b_2 - a_1 b_1}$$

$$= \frac{a_1 a_2 b_2 - a_1 a_2 b_1 + a_2 b_1 b_2 - a_1 b_1 b_2}{a_2 b_2 - a_1 b_1}$$

Replacing a_1b_1 and a_2b_2 by equations (*):

$$= \frac{a_1(aa_2+ab_2) - a_2(aa_1+ab_1) + b_1(aa_2+ab_2) - b_2(aa_1+ab_1)}{a_2b_2 - a_1b_1}$$

$$= \frac{a(a_1a_2 + a_1b_2 - a_1a_2 - a_2b_1 + a_2b_1 + b_1b_2 - a_1b_2 - b_1b_2)}{a_2b_2 - a_1b_1}$$

$$= 0 \; ! \text{ All terms cancel.}$$

If you followed this one through, then perhaps you should take a break. . .

93.   We find each intersection point:

$$
\begin{array}{lll}
y = x - 1 & y = x - 1 & y = -x - 2 \\
\underline{y = -x - 2} & \underline{y = 2x + 3} & \underline{y = 2x + 3} \\
2y = -3 & x - 1 = 2x + 3 & -x - 2 = 2x + 3 \\
y = -\dfrac{3}{2} & -4 = x & -5 = 3x \\
 & & x = -\dfrac{5}{3} \\
x = -\dfrac{1}{2} & y = -5 & y = -\dfrac{1}{3} \\
\left(-\dfrac{1}{2}, -\dfrac{3}{2}\right) & (-4, -5) & \left(-\dfrac{5}{3}, -\dfrac{1}{3}\right)
\end{array}
$$

We now substitute into the equation $(x - h)^2 + (y - k)^2 = r^2$:

$$\left(-\frac{1}{2} - h\right)^2 + \left(-\frac{3}{2} - k\right)^2 = r^2$$

$$(-4 - h)^2 + (-5 - k)^2 = r^2$$

$$\left(-\frac{5}{3} - h\right)^2 + \left(-\frac{1}{3} - k\right)^2 = r^2$$

These equations, when multiplied out, become:

$$\frac{5}{2} + h + h^2 + 3k + k^2 = r^2$$

$$41 + 8h + h^2 + 10k + k^2 = r^2$$

$$\frac{26}{9} + \frac{10}{3}h + h^2 + \frac{2}{3}k + k^2 = r^2$$

Subtracting the first equation from the other two yields:

$$\frac{77}{2} + 7h + 7k = 0$$

$$\frac{7}{18} + \frac{7}{3}h - \frac{7}{3}k = 0$$

Which simplify to:

$$6h + 6k = -33$$
$$6h - 6k = -1$$

Adding, we get:
$$12h = -34$$
$$h = -\frac{17}{6}$$

To find k, we subtract the two equations:
$$12k = -32$$
$$k = -\frac{8}{3}$$

Finally, we find r:
$$r^2 = (-4 - h)^2 + (-5 - k)^2 = \left(-\frac{7}{6}\right)^2 + \left(-\frac{7}{3}\right)^2 = \frac{245}{36}$$

The equation of the circle is:
$$\left(x + \frac{17}{6}\right)^2 + \left(y + \frac{8}{3}\right)^2 = \frac{245}{36}$$

95. $2A + 2B = \begin{pmatrix} 6 & -4 \\ 2 & 10 \end{pmatrix} + \begin{pmatrix} 4 & 2 \\ 2 & 16 \end{pmatrix} = \begin{pmatrix} 10 & -2 \\ 4 & 26 \end{pmatrix}$

97. $4B = \begin{pmatrix} 8 & 4 \\ 4 & 32 \end{pmatrix}$

99. $AB = \begin{pmatrix} 4 & -13 \\ 7 & 41 \end{pmatrix}$

101. $AB - BA = \begin{pmatrix} 7 & -13 \\ 7 & 41 \end{pmatrix} - \begin{pmatrix} 7 & 1 \\ 11 & 38 \end{pmatrix} = \begin{pmatrix} -3 & -14 \\ -4 & 3 \end{pmatrix}$

103. $B + C = \begin{pmatrix} 1 & 1 \\ 1 & 7 \end{pmatrix}$

105. $AB + AC = \begin{pmatrix} 4 & -13 \\ 7 & 41 \end{pmatrix} + \begin{pmatrix} -3 & 2 \\ -1 & -5 \end{pmatrix} = \begin{pmatrix} 1 & -11 \\ 6 & 36 \end{pmatrix}$

107. $BA + CA = \begin{pmatrix} 7 & 1 \\ 11 & 38 \end{pmatrix} + \begin{pmatrix} -3 & 2 \\ -1 & -5 \end{pmatrix} = \begin{pmatrix} 4 & 3 \\ 10 & 33 \end{pmatrix}$

109. $DE = \begin{pmatrix} -42 & 58 \\ 5 & 20 \end{pmatrix}$

111. undefined

113. undefined

115. $(A + B) + C = \begin{pmatrix} 5 & -1 \\ 2 & 13 \end{pmatrix} + \begin{pmatrix} -1 & 0 \\ 0 & -1 \end{pmatrix} = \begin{pmatrix} 4 & -1 \\ 2 & 12 \end{pmatrix}$

117. $(AB)C = \begin{pmatrix} 4 & -13 \\ 7 & 41 \end{pmatrix} \begin{pmatrix} -1 & 0 \\ 0 & -1 \end{pmatrix} = \begin{pmatrix} -4 & 13 \\ -7 & -41 \end{pmatrix}$

119. $A^2 = \begin{pmatrix} 1 & 1 \\ 0 & 1 \end{pmatrix} \begin{pmatrix} 1 & 1 \\ 0 & 1 \end{pmatrix} = \begin{pmatrix} 1 & 2 \\ 0 & 1 \end{pmatrix}$

   $A^3 = A \bullet A^2 = \begin{pmatrix} 1 & 1 \\ 0 & 1 \end{pmatrix} \begin{pmatrix} 1 & 2 \\ 0 & 1 \end{pmatrix} = \begin{pmatrix} 1 & 3 \\ 0 & 1 \end{pmatrix}$

121.   (a)   Form the augmented matrix: $\begin{pmatrix} 1 & 5 & 1 & 0 \\ 2 & 9 & 0 & 1 \end{pmatrix}$

   Multiply row 1 by -2 and add to row 2:
   $\begin{pmatrix} 1 & 5 & 1 & 0 \\ 0 & -1 & -2 & 1 \end{pmatrix}$
   Multiply row 2 by 5 and add to row 1:
   $\begin{pmatrix} 1 & 0 & -9 & 5 \\ 0 & -1 & -2 & 1 \end{pmatrix}$
   Multiply row 2 by -1:
   $\begin{pmatrix} 1 & 0 & -9 & 5 \\ 0 & 1 & 2 & -1 \end{pmatrix}$
   So the inverse is $\begin{pmatrix} -9 & 5 \\ 2 & -1 \end{pmatrix}$.

   (b)   Since the system is equivalent to $A \bullet X = B$, where $A = \begin{pmatrix} 1 & 5 \\ 2 & 9 \end{pmatrix}$,

   $X = \begin{pmatrix} x \\ y \end{pmatrix}$, and $B = \begin{pmatrix} 3 \\ -4 \end{pmatrix}$ then $X = A^{-1} \bullet B$

   $= \begin{pmatrix} -9 & 5 \\ 2 & -1 \end{pmatrix} \begin{pmatrix} 3 \\ -4 \end{pmatrix}$

   $= \begin{pmatrix} -47 \\ 10 \end{pmatrix}$

   So x = -47, y = 10.

123. (a) Form the augmented matrix:
$$\begin{pmatrix} 1 & -2 & 3 & 1 & 0 & 0 \\ 2 & -5 & 10 & 0 & 1 & 0 \\ -1 & 2 & -2 & 0 & 0 & 1 \end{pmatrix}$$

Multiply row 1 by -2 and add to row 2, then add row 1 to row 3:
$$\begin{pmatrix} 1 & -2 & 3 & 1 & 0 & 0 \\ 0 & -1 & 4 & -2 & 1 & 0 \\ 0 & 0 & 1 & 1 & 0 & 1 \end{pmatrix}$$

Multiply row 2 by -1:
$$\begin{pmatrix} 1 & -2 & 3 & 1 & 0 & 0 \\ 0 & 1 & -4 & 2 & -1 & 0 \\ 0 & 0 & 1 & 1 & 0 & 1 \end{pmatrix}$$

Multiply row 2 by 2 and add to row 1:
$$\begin{pmatrix} 1 & 0 & -5 & 5 & -2 & 0 \\ 0 & 1 & -4 & 2 & -1 & 0 \\ 0 & 0 & 1 & 1 & 0 & 1 \end{pmatrix}$$

Multiply row 3 by 4 and add to row 2, then multiply row 3 by 5 and add to row 1:
$$\begin{pmatrix} 1 & 0 & 0 & 10 & -2 & 5 \\ 0 & 1 & 0 & 6 & -1 & 4 \\ 0 & 0 & 1 & 1 & 0 & 1 \end{pmatrix}$$

So the inverse is $\begin{pmatrix} 10 & -2 & 5 \\ 6 & -1 & 4 \\ 1 & 0 & 1 \end{pmatrix}$.

(b) Since the system is equivalent to $A \bullet X = B$, where $A = \begin{pmatrix} 1 & -2 & 3 \\ 2 & -5 & 10 \\ -1 & 2 & -2 \end{pmatrix}$,

$X = \begin{pmatrix} x \\ y \\ z \end{pmatrix}$, and $B = \begin{pmatrix} -2 \\ -3 \\ 6 \end{pmatrix}$, then $X = A^{-1} \bullet B$

$$= \begin{pmatrix} 10 & -2 & 5 \\ 6 & -1 & 4 \\ 1 & 0 & 1 \end{pmatrix} \begin{pmatrix} -2 \\ -3 \\ 6 \end{pmatrix}$$

$$= \begin{pmatrix} 16 \\ 15 \\ 4 \end{pmatrix}$$

So $x = 16$, $y = 15$ and $z = 4$.

125.   Form the augmented matrix:

$$\begin{pmatrix} 5 & 3 & 6 & -7 & 1 & 0 & 0 & 0 \\ 3 & -4 & 0 & -9 & 0 & 1 & 0 & 0 \\ 0 & 1 & -1 & -1 & 0 & 0 & 1 & 0 \\ 2 & 2 & 3 & -2 & 0 & 0 & 0 & 1 \end{pmatrix}$$

Multiply row 4 by -2 and add to row 1 (to get a 1 value):

$$\begin{pmatrix} 1 & -1 & 0 & -3 & 1 & 0 & 0 & -2 \\ 3 & -4 & 0 & -9 & 0 & 1 & 0 & 0 \\ 0 & 1 & -1 & -1 & 0 & 0 & 1 & 0 \\ 2 & 2 & 3 & -2 & 0 & 0 & 0 & 1 \end{pmatrix}$$

Multiply row 1 by -3 and add to row 2, and multiply row 1 by -2 and add to row 4:

$$\begin{pmatrix} 1 & -1 & 0 & -3 & 1 & 0 & 0 & -2 \\ 0 & -1 & 0 & 0 & -3 & 1 & 0 & 6 \\ 0 & 1 & -1 & -1 & 0 & 0 & 1 & 0 \\ 0 & 4 & 3 & 4 & -2 & 0 & 0 & 5 \end{pmatrix}$$

Add row 2 to row 3, then multiply row 2 by 4 and add to row 4:

$$\begin{pmatrix} 1 & -1 & 0 & -3 & 1 & 0 & 0 & -2 \\ 0 & -1 & 0 & 0 & -3 & 1 & 0 & 6 \\ 0 & 0 & -1 & -1 & -3 & 1 & 1 & 6 \\ 0 & 0 & 3 & 4 & -14 & 4 & 0 & 29 \end{pmatrix}$$

Multiply row 3 by 3 and add to row 4:

$$\begin{pmatrix} 1 & -1 & 0 & -3 & 1 & 0 & 0 & -2 \\ 0 & -1 & 0 & 0 & -3 & 1 & 0 & 6 \\ 0 & 0 & -1 & -1 & -3 & 1 & 1 & 6 \\ 0 & 0 & 0 & 1 & -23 & 7 & 3 & 47 \end{pmatrix}$$

Add row 4 to row 3, then multiply row 4 by 3 and add to row 1:

$$\begin{pmatrix} 1 & -1 & 0 & 0 & -68 & 21 & 9 & 139 \\ 0 & -1 & 0 & 0 & -3 & 1 & 0 & 6 \\ 0 & 0 & -1 & 0 & -26 & 8 & 4 & 53 \\ 0 & 0 & 0 & 1 & -23 & 7 & 3 & 47 \end{pmatrix}$$

Multiply row 2 by -1 and row 3 by -1:

$$\begin{pmatrix} 1 & -1 & 0 & 0 & -68 & 21 & 9 & 139 \\ 0 & 1 & 0 & 0 & 3 & -1 & 0 & -6 \\ 0 & 0 & 1 & 0 & 26 & -8 & -4 & -53 \\ 0 & 0 & 0 & 1 & -23 & 7 & 3 & 47 \end{pmatrix}$$

Add row 2 to row 1:

$$\begin{pmatrix} 1 & 0 & 0 & 0 & -65 & 20 & 9 & 133 \\ 0 & 1 & 0 & 0 & 3 & -1 & 0 & -6 \\ 0 & 0 & 1 & 0 & 26 & -8 & -4 & -53 \\ 0 & 0 & 0 & 1 & -23 & 7 & 3 & 47 \end{pmatrix}$$

So the inverse is:

$$\begin{pmatrix} -65 & 20 & 9 & 133 \\ 3 & -1 & 0 & -6 \\ 26 & -8 & -4 & -53 \\ -23 & 7 & 3 & 47 \end{pmatrix}$$

127. $D = \begin{vmatrix} 2 & -1 & 1 \\ 3 & 2 & 2 \\ 1 & -5 & -3 \end{vmatrix}$

Adding 2 times column 2 to column 1 and column 2 to column 3 yields:

$= \begin{vmatrix} 0 & -1 & 0 \\ 7 & 2 & 4 \\ -9 & -5 & -8 \end{vmatrix} = -(-1)\begin{vmatrix} 7 & 4 \\ -9 & -8 \end{vmatrix} = 1(-20) = -20$

$D_x = \begin{vmatrix} 1 & -1 & 1 \\ 0 & 2 & 2 \\ -2 & -5 & -3 \end{vmatrix}$

Adding 2 times row 1 to row 3 yields:

$= \begin{vmatrix} 1 & -1 & 1 \\ 0 & 2 & 2 \\ 0 & -7 & -1 \end{vmatrix} = 1\begin{vmatrix} 2 & 2 \\ -7 & -1 \end{vmatrix} = 12$

$D_y = \begin{vmatrix} 2 & 1 & 1 \\ 3 & 0 & 2 \\ 1 & -2 & -3 \end{vmatrix}$

Adding 2 times row 1 to row 3 yields:

$= \begin{vmatrix} 2 & 1 & 1 \\ 3 & 0 & 2 \\ 5 & 0 & -1 \end{vmatrix} = -1\begin{vmatrix} 3 & 2 \\ 5 & -1 \end{vmatrix} = -(-13) = 13$

$D_z = \begin{vmatrix} 2 & -1 & 1 \\ 3 & 2 & 0 \\ 1 & -5 & -2 \end{vmatrix}$

Adding 2 times row 1 to row 3 yields:

$= \begin{vmatrix} 2 & -1 & 1 \\ 3 & 2 & 0 \\ 5 & -7 & 0 \end{vmatrix} = 1\begin{vmatrix} 3 & 2 \\ 5 & -7 \end{vmatrix} = -31$

So $x = \dfrac{D_x}{D} = -\dfrac{12}{20} = -\dfrac{3}{5}$, $y = \dfrac{D_y}{D} = -\dfrac{13}{20}$, and $z = \dfrac{D_z}{D} = \dfrac{31}{20}$.

So the solution is $\left(-\dfrac{3}{5}, -\dfrac{13}{20}, \dfrac{31}{20}\right)$.

129. $D = \begin{vmatrix} 1 & 2 & 3 \\ 4 & 5 & 6 \\ 7 & 8 & 9 \end{vmatrix}$

Subtracting column 2 from column 3 and column 1 from column 2 yields:

$= \begin{vmatrix} 1 & 1 & 1 \\ 4 & 1 & 1 \\ 7 & 1 & 1 \end{vmatrix}$

Subtracting column 3 from column 2 yields:

$= \begin{vmatrix} 1 & 0 & 1 \\ 4 & 0 & 1 \\ 7 & 0 & 1 \end{vmatrix} = 0$

So Cramer's Rule will not work. Form the augmented matrix:

$\begin{pmatrix} 1 & 2 & 3 & -1 \\ 4 & 5 & 6 & 2 \\ 7 & 8 & 9 & -3 \end{pmatrix}$

Add -4 times row 1 to row 2 and -7 times row 1 to row 3:

$\begin{pmatrix} 1 & 2 & 3 & -1 \\ 0 & -3 & -6 & 6 \\ 0 & -6 & -12 & 4 \end{pmatrix}$

Add -2 times row 2 to row 3:

$\begin{pmatrix} 1 & 2 & 3 & -1 \\ 0 & -3 & -6 & 6 \\ 0 & 0 & 0 & -8 \end{pmatrix}$

So $0 = -8$, which is false. The system has no solution.

131. $D = 0$ (See problem 110), so form the augmented matrix:

$\begin{pmatrix} 3 & 2 & -2 & 1 \\ 2 & 3 & -1 & -2 \\ 8 & 7 & -5 & 0 \end{pmatrix}$

Subtract row 2 from row 1:

$\begin{pmatrix} 1 & -1 & -1 & 3 \\ 2 & 3 & -1 & -2 \\ 8 & 7 & -5 & 0 \end{pmatrix}$

Add -2 times row 1 to row 2 and -8 times row 1 to row 3:

$\begin{pmatrix} 1 & -1 & -1 & 3 \\ 0 & 5 & 1 & -8 \\ 0 & 15 & 3 & -24 \end{pmatrix}$

Add -3 times row 2 to row 3:

$\begin{pmatrix} 1 & -1 & -1 & 3 \\ 0 & 5 & 1 & -8 \\ 0 & 0 & 0 & 0 \end{pmatrix}$

So: $x - y - z = 3$
        $5y + z = -8$

Solve equation 2 for z:
$$z = -8 - 5y$$
Substitute into equation 1:
$$x - y + 8 + 5y = 3$$
$$x = -5 - 4y$$
So the solution is $(-5 - 4y, y, -8 - 5y)$, for any real number y.

133. $D = \begin{vmatrix} 2 & -1 & 1 & 3 \\ 1 & 2 & 0 & 2 \\ 0 & 3 & 3 & 4 \\ -4 & 1 & -4 & 0 \end{vmatrix}$

Adding 4 times column 2 to both column 1 and column 3 yields:

$$= \begin{vmatrix} -2 & -1 & -3 & 3 \\ 9 & 2 & 8 & 2 \\ 12 & 3 & 15 & 4 \\ 0 & 1 & 0 & 0 \end{vmatrix}$$

$$= 1 \begin{vmatrix} -2 & -3 & 3 \\ 9 & 8 & 2 \\ 12 & 15 & 4 \end{vmatrix}$$

Subtracting row 2 from row 3 yields:

$$= \begin{vmatrix} -2 & -3 & 3 \\ 9 & 8 & 2 \\ 3 & 7 & 2 \end{vmatrix}$$

Adding $\frac{2}{3}$ times column 3 to column 1, and column 3 to column 2 yields:

$$= \begin{vmatrix} 0 & 0 & 3 \\ 31/3 & 10 & 2 \\ 13/3 & 9 & 2 \end{vmatrix} = 3 \begin{vmatrix} 31/3 & 10 \\ 13/3 & 9 \end{vmatrix} = \begin{vmatrix} 31 & 10 \\ 13 & 9 \end{vmatrix} = 149$$

$$D_x = \begin{vmatrix} 15 & -1 & 1 & 3 \\ 12 & 2 & 0 & 2 \\ 12 & 3 & 3 & 4 \\ -11 & 1 & -4 & 0 \end{vmatrix}$$

Adding 11 times column 2 to column 1 and 4 times column 2 to column 3 yields:

$$= \begin{vmatrix} 4 & -1 & -3 & 3 \\ 34 & 2 & 8 & 2 \\ 45 & 3 & 15 & 4 \\ 0 & 1 & 0 & 0 \end{vmatrix}$$

$$= 1 \begin{vmatrix} 4 & -3 & 3 \\ 34 & 8 & 2 \\ 45 & 15 & 4 \end{vmatrix}$$

Subtracting row 2 from row 3 yields:

$$= \begin{vmatrix} 4 & -3 & 3 \\ 34 & 8 & 2 \\ 11 & 7 & 2 \end{vmatrix}$$

Subtracting row 3 from row 2 yields:

$$= \begin{vmatrix} 4 & -3 & 3 \\ 23 & 1 & 0 \\ 11 & 7 & 2 \end{vmatrix}$$

Adding -23 times column 2 to column 1:

$$= \begin{vmatrix} 73 & -3 & 3 \\ 0 & 1 & 0 \\ -150 & 7 & 2 \end{vmatrix} = \begin{vmatrix} 73 & 3 \\ -150 & 2 \end{vmatrix} = 596$$

$$D_y = \begin{vmatrix} 2 & 15 & 1 & 3 \\ 1 & 12 & 0 & 2 \\ 0 & 12 & 3 & 4 \\ -4 & -11 & -4 & 0 \end{vmatrix}$$

Adding -2 times row 2 to row 1 and 4 times row 2 to row 4 yields:

$$= \begin{vmatrix} 0 & -9 & 1 & -1 \\ 1 & 12 & 0 & 2 \\ 0 & 12 & 3 & 4 \\ 0 & 37 & -4 & 8 \end{vmatrix}$$

$$= -1 \begin{vmatrix} -9 & 1 & -1 \\ 12 & 3 & 4 \\ 37 & -4 & 8 \end{vmatrix}$$

Adding 9 times column 2 to column 1 and column 2 to column 3 yields:

$$= -1 \begin{vmatrix} 0 & 1 & 0 \\ 39 & 3 & 7 \\ 1 & -4 & 4 \end{vmatrix} = 1 \begin{vmatrix} 39 & 7 \\ 1 & 4 \end{vmatrix} = 149$$

$$D_z = \begin{vmatrix} 2 & -1 & 15 & 3 \\ 1 & 2 & 12 & 2 \\ 0 & 3 & 12 & 4 \\ -4 & 1 & -11 & 0 \end{vmatrix}$$

Adding -2 times row 2 to row 1 and 4 times row 2 to row 4 yields:

$$= \begin{vmatrix} 0 & -5 & -9 & -1 \\ 1 & 2 & 12 & 2 \\ 0 & 3 & 12 & 4 \\ 0 & 9 & 37 & 8 \end{vmatrix}$$

$$= -1 \begin{vmatrix} -5 & -9 & -1 \\ 3 & 12 & 4 \\ 9 & 37 & 8 \end{vmatrix}$$

Adding 4 times row 1 to row 2 and 8 times row 1 to row 3:

$$= -1 \begin{vmatrix} -5 & -9 & -1 \\ -17 & -24 & 0 \\ -31 & -25 & 0 \end{vmatrix} = 1 \begin{vmatrix} -17 & -24 \\ -31 & -35 \end{vmatrix} = -149$$

$$D_w = \begin{vmatrix} 2 & -1 & 1 & 15 \\ 1 & 2 & 0 & 12 \\ 0 & 3 & 3 & 12 \\ -4 & 1 & -4 & -11 \end{vmatrix}$$

Adding -2 times row 2 to row 1 and 4 times row 2 to row 4:

$$= \begin{vmatrix} 0 & -5 & 1 & -9 \\ 1 & 2 & 0 & 12 \\ 0 & 3 & 3 & 12 \\ 0 & 9 & -4 & 37 \end{vmatrix}$$

$$= -1 \begin{vmatrix} -5 & 1 & -9 \\ 3 & 3 & 12 \\ 9 & -4 & 37 \end{vmatrix}$$

Factoring 3 out of row 2 yields:

$$= -3 \begin{vmatrix} -5 & 1 & -9 \\ 1 & 1 & 4 \\ 9 & -4 & 37 \end{vmatrix}$$

Adding -1 times row 2 to row 1 and 4 times row 2 to row 3:

$$= -3 \begin{vmatrix} -6 & 0 & -13 \\ 1 & 1 & 4 \\ 13 & 0 & 53 \end{vmatrix} = -3 \begin{vmatrix} -6 & -13 \\ 13 & 53 \end{vmatrix} = -3(-149) = 447$$

So $x = \dfrac{D_x}{D} = \dfrac{596}{149} = 4$, $y = \dfrac{D_y}{D} = \dfrac{149}{149} = 1$, $z = \dfrac{D_z}{D} = -\dfrac{149}{149} = -1$,

and $w = \dfrac{D_w}{D} = \dfrac{447}{149} = 3$.

So the solution is $(4, 1, -1, 3)$.

135.   Substitute to get

$$x^2 = 6x$$
$$x^2 - 6x = 0$$
$$x(x - 6) = 0$$
$$x = 0 \quad \text{or} \quad x = 6$$

When $x = 0$, $y = 0$ and when $x = 6$, $y = 36$.
So the solutions are $(0, 0)$ and $(6, 36)$.

137.   Substitute to get

$$x^2 - 9 = 9 - x^2$$
$$2x^2 = 18$$
$$x^2 = 9$$
$$x = \pm 3$$

When $x = \pm 3$, $y = 0$.
So the solutions are $(3, 0)$ and $(-3, 0)$

139.   Adding the two equations yields $2x^2 = 25$

$$x^2 = \frac{25}{2}$$

$$x = \frac{\pm 5\sqrt{2}}{2}$$

So: $\frac{25}{2} + y^2 = 16$

$$y^2 = \frac{7}{2}$$

$$y = \frac{\pm\sqrt{14}}{2}$$

So the solutions are $\left(\frac{5\sqrt{2}}{2}, \frac{\sqrt{14}}{2}\right)$, $\left(-\frac{5\sqrt{2}}{2}, \frac{\sqrt{14}}{2}\right)$, $\left(\frac{5\sqrt{2}}{2}, -\frac{\sqrt{14}}{2}\right)$,

and $\left(-\frac{5\sqrt{2}}{2}, -\frac{\sqrt{14}}{2}\right)$.

141.   Substitute to get: $x^2 + x = 1$

$$x^2 + x - 1 = 0$$

$$x = \frac{-1 \pm \sqrt{1+4}}{2} = \frac{-1 \pm \sqrt{5}}{2}$$

Now $x = \frac{-1 - \sqrt{5}}{2}$ doesn't make sense ($y = \sqrt{x}$).

So the only solution is $\left(\frac{-1 + \sqrt{5}}{2}, \sqrt{\frac{-1 + \sqrt{5}}{2}}\right)$ or $\left(\frac{-1 + \sqrt{5}}{2}, \frac{\sqrt{-2 + 2\sqrt{5}}}{2}\right)$.

143.   Substitute to get $x^2 + (2x^2)^2 = 1$

$$x^2 + 4x^4 = 1$$

$$4x^4 + x^2 - 1 = 0$$

$$x^2 = \frac{-1 \pm \sqrt{1+16}}{8} = \frac{-1 \pm \sqrt{17}}{8}$$

Since $x^2 \neq \frac{-1 - \sqrt{17}}{8}$, we have $x^2 = \frac{-1 + \sqrt{17}}{8}$, so $x = \frac{\pm\sqrt{-2 + 2\sqrt{17}}}{4}$

Since $y = 2x^2$, we have $y = \frac{-1 + \sqrt{17}}{4}$

So the solutions are:

$$\left(\frac{\sqrt{-2 + 2\sqrt{17}}}{4}, \frac{-1 + \sqrt{17}}{4}\right) \text{ and } \left(\frac{-\sqrt{-2 + 2\sqrt{17}}}{4}, \frac{-1 + \sqrt{17}}{4}\right)$$

145.   Multiply the second equation by -3:
$$-9x^2 + 3xy - 3y^2 = -54$$
$$x^2 + 2xy + 3y^2 = 68$$
Adding, we get:
$$-8x^2 + 5xy = 14$$
$$-5xy = 8x^2 + 14$$
$$y = \frac{8x^2 + 14}{5x}$$
Now substitute into the second equation:
$$3x^2 - \frac{8x^2 + 14}{5} + \frac{(8x^2 + 14)^2}{25x^2} = 18$$
Multiply by $25x^2$:
$$75x^4 - 5x^2(8x^2 + 14) + (8x^2 + 14)^2 = 450x^2$$
$$75x^4 - 40x^4 - 70x^2 + 64x^4 + 224x^2 + 196 = 450x^2$$
$$99x^4 - 296x^2 + 196 = 0$$
$$(99x^2 - 98)(x^2 - 2) = 0$$
So: $x^2 = \dfrac{98}{99}$ or $x^2 = 2$

$x = \dfrac{\pm 7\sqrt{22}}{33}$ or $x = \pm\sqrt{2}$

Now $y = \dfrac{8x^2 + 14}{5x}$, so:

When $x = \sqrt{2}$, $y = \dfrac{16 + 14}{5\sqrt{2}} = 3\sqrt{2}$

When $x = -\sqrt{2}$, $y = \dfrac{16 + 14}{-5\sqrt{2}} = -3\sqrt{2}$

When $x = \dfrac{7\sqrt{22}}{33}$, $y = \dfrac{31\sqrt{22}}{33}$

When $x = \dfrac{-7\sqrt{22}}{33}$, $y = \dfrac{-31\sqrt{22}}{33}$

So the solutions are $(\sqrt{2}, 3\sqrt{2})$, $(-\sqrt{2}, -3\sqrt{2})$, $\left(\dfrac{7\sqrt{22}}{33}, \dfrac{31\sqrt{22}}{33}\right)$, and $\left(\dfrac{-7\sqrt{22}}{33}, \dfrac{-31\sqrt{22}}{33}\right)$.

147.   Let $u = x - 3$ and $v = y + 1$, so:
$$2u^2 - v^2 = -1$$
$$-3u^2 + 2v^2 = 6$$
Multiply the first equation by 2 and add:
$$u^2 = 4$$
$$u = \pm 2$$

Substituting, we get:

$$8 - v^2 = -1$$
$$-v^2 = -9$$
$$v = \pm 3$$

So the solutions (u, v) are $(2, 3)$, $(2, -3)$, $(-2, 3)$, and $(-2, -3)$.
Since $u = x - 3$ and $v = y + 1$, then $x = u + 3$ and $y = v - 1$.
So the solutions are $(5, 2)$, $(5, -4)$, $(1, 2)$, $(1, -4)$.

149.   Call the numbers x and y. So $x + y = s$ and $\dfrac{x}{y} = \dfrac{a}{b}$.

So $y = s - x$, and substituting:

$$\frac{x}{s - x} = \frac{a}{b}$$
$$bx = as - ax$$
$$(a + b)x = as$$
$$x = \frac{as}{a + b}$$

So $y = s - \dfrac{as}{a + b} = \dfrac{bs}{a + b}$

So the two numbers are $\dfrac{as}{a + b}$ and $\dfrac{bs}{a + b}$.

151.   We have:

$$\frac{1}{2}x + \frac{1}{3}y + \frac{1}{4}z = 62$$
$$\frac{1}{3}x + \frac{1}{4}y + \frac{1}{5}z = 47$$
$$\frac{1}{4}x + \frac{1}{5}y + \frac{1}{6}z = 38$$

Multiply the first equation by 12, the second equation by 60, and the third by 60 to clear the fractions:

$$6x + 4y + 3z = 744$$
$$20x + 15y + 12z = 2820$$
$$15x + 12y + 10z = 2280$$

We use Cramer's Rule:

$$D = \begin{vmatrix} 6 & 4 & 3 \\ 20 & 15 & 12 \\ 15 & 12 & 10 \end{vmatrix}$$

Subtracting row 3 from row 2 yields:

$$= \begin{vmatrix} 6 & 4 & 3 \\ 5 & 3 & 2 \\ 15 & 12 & 10 \end{vmatrix}$$

Subtracting row 2 from row 1 and adding -3 times row 2 to row 3 yields:

$$= \begin{vmatrix} 1 & 1 & 1 \\ 5 & 3 & 2 \\ 0 & 3 & 4 \end{vmatrix}$$

Subtracting column 1 from column 2 and column 3 yields:

$$= \begin{vmatrix} 1 & 0 & 0 \\ 5 & -2 & -3 \\ 0 & 3 & 4 \end{vmatrix} = 1 \begin{vmatrix} -2 & -3 \\ 3 & 4 \end{vmatrix} = 1(1) = 1$$

$$D_x = \begin{vmatrix} 744 & 4 & 3 \\ 2820 & 15 & 12 \\ 2280 & 12 & 10 \end{vmatrix}$$

Subtracting row 3 from row 2 yields:

$$= \begin{vmatrix} 744 & 4 & 3 \\ 540 & 3 & 2 \\ 2280 & 12 & 10 \end{vmatrix}$$

Subtracting row 2 from row 1, and adding -4 times row 2 to row 3 yields:

$$= \begin{vmatrix} 204 & 1 & 1 \\ 540 & 3 & 2 \\ 120 & 0 & 2 \end{vmatrix}$$

Adding -3 times row 1 to row 2 yields:

$$= \begin{vmatrix} 204 & 1 & 1 \\ -72 & 0 & -1 \\ 120 & 0 & 2 \end{vmatrix} = -1 \begin{vmatrix} -72 & -1 \\ 120 & 2 \end{vmatrix} = -(-24) = 24$$

$$D_y = \begin{vmatrix} 6 & 744 & 3 \\ 20 & 2820 & 12 \\ 15 & 2280 & 10 \end{vmatrix}$$

Subtracting row 3 from row 2 yields:

$$= \begin{vmatrix} 6 & 744 & 3 \\ 5 & 540 & 2 \\ 15 & 2280 & 10 \end{vmatrix}$$

Subtracting row 2 from row 1 and adding -3 times row 2 to row 3 yields:

$$= \begin{vmatrix} 1 & 204 & 1 \\ 5 & 540 & 2 \\ 0 & 660 & 4 \end{vmatrix}$$

Adding -5 times row 1 to row 2 yields:

$$= \begin{vmatrix} 1 & 204 & 1 \\ 0 & -480 & -3 \\ 0 & 660 & 4 \end{vmatrix} = 1 \begin{vmatrix} -480 & -3 \\ 660 & 4 \end{vmatrix} = 1(60) = 60$$

$$D_z = \begin{vmatrix} 6 & 4 & 744 \\ 20 & 15 & 2820 \\ 15 & 12 & 2280 \end{vmatrix}$$

Subtracting row 3 from row 2 yields:

$$= \begin{vmatrix} 6 & 4 & 744 \\ 5 & 3 & 540 \\ 15 & 12 & 2280 \end{vmatrix}$$

Subtracting row 2 from row 1 and adding -3 times row 2 to row 3 yields:

$$= \begin{vmatrix} 1 & 1 & 204 \\ 5 & 3 & 540 \\ 0 & 3 & 660 \end{vmatrix}$$

Adding -5 times row 1 to row 2 yields:

$$= \begin{vmatrix} 1 & 1 & 204 \\ 0 & -2 & -480 \\ 0 & 3 & 660 \end{vmatrix} = 1 \begin{vmatrix} -2 & -480 \\ 3 & 660 \end{vmatrix} = 1(120) = 120$$

So $x = \dfrac{D_x}{D} = 24$, $y = \dfrac{D_y}{D} = 60$, and $z = \dfrac{D_z}{D} = 120$

So the numbers are 24, 60, 120.

153.   We have:

$$xy = m$$
$$x^2 + y^2 = n$$

Add twice the first equation to the second and get:

$$x^2 + 2xy + y^2 = n + 2m$$
$$(x + y)^2 = n + 2m$$
$$x + y = \pm\sqrt{n + 2m}$$

Subtract twice the first equation from the second to get:

$$x^2 - 2xy + y^2 = n - 2m$$
$$(x - y)^2 = n - 2m$$
$$x - y = \pm\sqrt{n - 2m}$$

We solve the systems:

$$
\begin{aligned}
x + y &= \sqrt{n + 2m} \\
\underline{x - y} &= \underline{\sqrt{n - 2m}} \\
2x &= \sqrt{n + 2m} + \sqrt{n - 2m} \\
x &= \frac{\sqrt{n + 2m} + \sqrt{n - 2m}}{2} \\
y &= \frac{\sqrt{n + 2m} - \sqrt{n - 2m}}{2}
\end{aligned}
\qquad
\begin{aligned}
x + y &= \sqrt{n + 2m} \\
\underline{x - y} &= \underline{-\sqrt{n - 2m}} \\
2x &= \sqrt{n + 2m} - \sqrt{n - 2m} \\
x &= \frac{\sqrt{n + 2m} - \sqrt{n - 2m}}{2} \\
y &= \frac{\sqrt{n + 2m} + \sqrt{n - 2m}}{2}
\end{aligned}
$$

$$x + y = -\sqrt{n + 2m}$$
$$\underline{x - y = \sqrt{n - 2m}}$$
$$2x = \sqrt{n - 2m} - \sqrt{n + 2m}$$
$$x = \frac{\sqrt{n - 2m} - \sqrt{n + 2m}}{2}$$
$$y = \frac{-\sqrt{n - 2m} - \sqrt{n + 2m}}{2}$$

$$x + y = -\sqrt{n + 2m}$$
$$\underline{x - y = -\sqrt{n - 2m}}$$
$$2x = -\sqrt{n + 2m} - \sqrt{n - 2m}$$
$$x = \frac{-\sqrt{n + 2m} - \sqrt{n - 2m}}{2}$$
$$y = \frac{\sqrt{n - 2m} - \sqrt{n + 2m}}{2}$$

So the possible pairs of numbers are:

$$\frac{\sqrt{n + 2m} + \sqrt{n - 2m}}{2} \quad \text{and} \quad \frac{\sqrt{n + 2m} - \sqrt{n - 2m}}{2},$$

$$\frac{\sqrt{n - 2m} - \sqrt{n + 2m}}{2} \quad \text{and} \quad \frac{-\sqrt{n - 2m} - \sqrt{n + 2m}}{2}$$

155.   convex: no; bounded: no

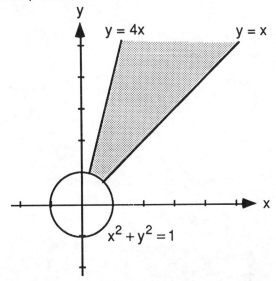

157.   convex: yes; bounded: yes

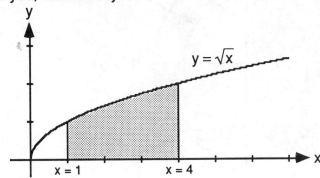

159.   convex: no; bounded: no

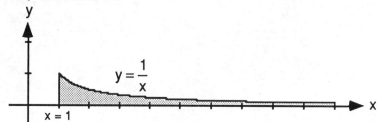

161.   We must solve the inequality $2x + y \geq 0$, so $y \geq -2x$:

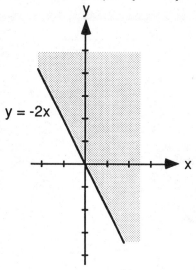

163.   We must have both of the following inequalities satisfied:

$9 - x^2 - y^2 \geq 0$, so $x^2 + y^2 \leq 9$

$x^2 + y^2 - 4 \geq 0$, so $x^2 + y^2 \geq 4$

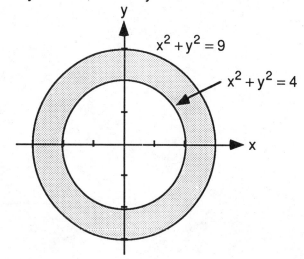

165.   We first square each equation:
$$y^2\cos^2 x = a^2$$
$$y^2\sin^2 x = b^2$$
Adding these two equations yields:
$$y^2(\cos^2 x + \sin^2 x) = a^2 + b^2$$
$$y^2 = a^2 + b^2$$
$$y = \sqrt{a^2 + b^2}$$
To find x, we can divide the second equation by the first to get:
$$\tan x = \frac{b}{a}, \text{ so } x = \tan^{-1}\frac{b}{a}$$

So a solution is $\left(\tan^{-1}\frac{b}{a}, \sqrt{a^2 + b^2}\right)$.

CHAPTER EIGHT
ANALYTIC GEOMETRY

8.1 The Basic Equations

1. $d = \sqrt{(-5 - 3)^2 + (-6 + 1)^2} = \sqrt{64 + 25} = \sqrt{89}$

3. We find the perpendicular slope :

$$4x - 5y - 20 = 0$$
$$-5y = -4x + 20$$
$$y = \frac{4}{5}x - 4$$

So the perpendicular slope is $m = -\frac{5}{4}$. We now find the y-intercept:

$$x - y + 1 = 0$$
$$-y = -x - 1$$
$$y = x + 1$$

So b = 1, and the equation is $y = -\frac{5}{4}x + 1$. Multiplying by 4, we have
4y = -5x + 4, or 5x + 4y - 4 = 0.

5.   We find the slope of the line segment:
$$m = \frac{7-1}{6-2} = \frac{6}{4} = \frac{3}{2}$$

So the perpendicular slope is $m = -\frac{2}{3}$. We find the midpoint:
$$M = \left(\frac{2+6}{2}, \frac{1+7}{2}\right) = \left(\frac{8}{2}, \frac{8}{2}\right) = (4, 4)$$
Now use the point-slope formula:
$$y - 4 = -\frac{2}{3}(x - 4)$$
$$y - 4 = -\frac{2}{3}x + \frac{8}{3}$$
$$y = -\frac{2}{3}x + \frac{20}{3}$$
Multiplying by 3, we have $3y = -2x + 20$, or $2x + 3y - 20 = 0$.

7.   Since the center is $(1, 0)$ and the radius is 5, the equation must be
$(x - 1)^2 + y^2 = 25$.

x-intercepts :
$$y = 0$$
$$(x - 1)^2 = 25$$
$$x - 1 = \pm 5$$
$$x = 6, -4$$

y-intercepts:
$$x = 0$$
$$(-1)^2 + y^2 = 25$$
$$y^2 = 24$$
$$y = \pm\sqrt{24} = \pm 2\sqrt{6}$$

x-intercepts: 6, -4; y-intercepts: $\pm 2\sqrt{6}$

9.   We first find the midpoint of AB:
$$M = \left(\frac{1+6}{2}, \frac{2+1}{2}\right) = \left(\frac{7}{2}, \frac{3}{2}\right)$$
Now find the slope of the line:
$$m = \frac{8 - \frac{3}{2}}{7 - \frac{7}{2}} = \frac{\frac{13}{2}}{\frac{7}{2}} = \frac{13}{7}$$
Using the point $(7, 8)$ in the point-slope formula:
$$y - 8 = \frac{13}{7}(x - 7)$$
$$y - 8 = \frac{13}{7}x - 13$$
$$y = \frac{13}{7}x - 5$$
Multiply by 7 to get $7y = 13x - 35$, or $13x - 7y - 35 = 0$.

11. Since $\frac{x}{7} + \frac{y}{5} = 1$ is in two-intercept form, the coordinates of B and C must be B(0, 5) and C(7, 0). We find BC by the distance formula:

$$BC = \sqrt{(7-0)^2 + (0-5)^2} = \sqrt{49 + 25} = \sqrt{74}$$

So, the perimeter is given by:

$$P = AB + BC + AC = 5 + \sqrt{74} + 7 = 12 + \sqrt{74}$$

13. $\tan\theta = \sqrt{3}$, so $\theta = \frac{\pi}{3}$ or $60°$

15. (a) $\tan\theta = 5$, so $\theta = 1.37$ or $78.69°$
     (b) $\tan\theta = -5$, so $\theta = 1.77$ or $101.31°$

17. (a) Here $(x_0, y_0) = (1, 4)$, $m = 1$, $b = -2$, so:

$$d = \frac{|1 - 2 - 4|}{\sqrt{1 + 1}} = \frac{5}{\sqrt{2}} = \frac{5\sqrt{2}}{2}$$

     (b) Using $x - y - 2 = 0$, we have $A = 1$, $B = -1$, $C = -2$:

$$d = \frac{|1 - 4 - 2|}{\sqrt{1 + 1}} = \frac{5}{\sqrt{2}} = \frac{5\sqrt{2}}{2}$$

19. (a) Here $(x_0, y_0) = (-3, 5)$. We convert to slope-intercept form:

$$4x + 5y + 6 = 0$$
$$5y = -4x - 6$$
$$y = -\frac{4}{5}x - \frac{6}{5}$$

So $m = -\frac{4}{5}$ and $b = -\frac{6}{5}$:

$$d = \frac{\left|\frac{12}{5} - \frac{6}{5} - 5\right|}{\sqrt{1 + \frac{16}{25}}} = \frac{\frac{19}{5}}{\frac{\sqrt{41}}{5}} = \frac{19}{\sqrt{41}} = \frac{19\sqrt{41}}{41}$$

     (b) We have $A = 4$, $B = 5$, $C = 6$:

$$d = \frac{|-12 + 25 + 6|}{\sqrt{16 + 25}} = \frac{19}{\sqrt{41}} = \frac{19\sqrt{41}}{41}$$

21. (a) The radius of the circle is the distance from the point $(-2, -3)$ to the line $2x + 3y - 6 = 0$. Using $(x_0, y_0) = (-2, -3)$, $A = 2$, $B = 3$, $C = -6$:

$$r = \frac{|-4 - 9 - 6|}{\sqrt{4 + 9}} = \frac{19}{\sqrt{13}}$$

So the equation of the circle is $(x + 2)^2 + (y + 3)^2 = \frac{361}{13}$.

(b)   Since the radius is the distance from the point $(1, 3)$ to the line $y = \frac{1}{2}x + 5$,

we have $(x_0, y_0) = (1, 3)$, $m = \frac{1}{2}$, $b = 5$:

$$r = \frac{\left|\frac{1}{2} + 5 - 3\right|}{\sqrt{1 + \frac{1}{4}}} = \frac{\frac{5}{2}}{\frac{\sqrt{5}}{2}} = \sqrt{5}$$

23.   Using the suggestion, we work with $\triangle ABC$ and $\triangle CDA$.
For $\triangle ABC$, we find the base using the distance formula:
$$AB = \sqrt{(8 - 0)^2 + (2 - 0)^2} = \sqrt{64 + 4} = \sqrt{68} = 2\sqrt{17}$$
Now we find the equation of the line through A and B. We find the slope:
$$m = \frac{2 - 0}{8 - 0} = \frac{1}{4}$$
So the equation is $y = \frac{1}{4}x$. We find the distance from $C(4, 7)$ to this line:
$$h = \frac{|1 + 0 - 7|}{\sqrt{1 + \frac{1}{16}}} = \frac{6}{\frac{\sqrt{17}}{4}} = \frac{24}{\sqrt{17}}$$
So $\triangle ABC$ will have an area of:
$$A(\triangle ABC) = \frac{1}{2}(\text{base})(\text{height}) = \frac{1}{2}(2\sqrt{17})\left(\frac{24}{\sqrt{17}}\right) = 24$$
For $\triangle CDA$, we find the base using the distance formula:
$$CD = \sqrt{(1 - 4)^2 + (6 - 7)^2} = \sqrt{9 + 1} = \sqrt{10}$$
Now we find the equation of the line through C and D. We find the slope:
$$m = \frac{6 - 7}{1 - 4} = \frac{-1}{-3} = \frac{1}{3}$$
Using $C(4, 7)$ in the point-slope formula:
$$y - 7 = \frac{1}{3}(x - 4)$$
$$y - 7 = \frac{1}{3}x - \frac{4}{3}$$
$$y = \frac{1}{3}x + \frac{17}{3}$$
$$3y = x + 17 \text{ or } x - 3y + 17 = 0$$
We find the distance from $A(0, 0)$ to this line:
$$h = \frac{|0 + 0 + 17|}{\sqrt{1 + 9}} = \frac{17}{\sqrt{10}}$$
So $\triangle CDA$ will have an area of:
$$A(\triangle CDA) = \frac{1}{2}(\text{base})(\text{height}) = \frac{1}{2}(\sqrt{10})\left(\frac{17}{\sqrt{10}}\right) = \frac{17}{2}$$

Thus, the total combined area of quadrilateral ABCD is:
$$24 + \frac{17}{2} = \frac{65}{2}$$

25. Using the point $(0, -5)$ in the point-slope formula:
$$y + 5 = m(x - 0)$$
$$y = mx - 5$$
Now, since the distance from the center $(3, 0)$ to this line is 2, we have:
$$2 = \frac{|3m - 5 - 0|}{\sqrt{1 + m^2}} = \frac{|3m - 5|}{\sqrt{1 + m^2}}$$
Squaring each side, we have:
$$4 = \frac{9m^2 - 30m + 25}{1 + m^2}$$
$$4 + 4m^2 = 9m^2 - 30m + 25$$
$$0 = 5m^2 - 30m + 21$$
$$m = \frac{30 \pm \sqrt{900 - 420}}{10}$$
$$= \frac{30 \pm \sqrt{480}}{10}$$
$$= \frac{30 \pm 4\sqrt{30}}{10}$$
$$= \frac{15 \pm 2\sqrt{30}}{5}$$

27. We use the same approach as in the preceeding exercise. Let d_1 and d_2 represent the distances from $(0, 0)$ to the lines $3x + 4y - 12 = 0$ and $3x + 4y - 24 = 0$, respectively.
For d_1, we have $(x_0, y_0) = (0, 0)$, $A = 3$, $B = 4$, $C = -12$:
$$d_1 = \frac{|0 + 0 - 12|}{\sqrt{9 + 16}} = \frac{12}{\sqrt{25}} = \frac{12}{5}$$
For d_2, we have $(x_0, y_0) = (0, 0)$, $A = 3$, $B = 4$, $C = -24$:
$$d_2 = \frac{|0 + 0 - 24|}{\sqrt{9 + 16}} = \frac{24}{\sqrt{25}} = \frac{24}{5}$$
So the distance between the lines is:
$$d_2 - d_1 = \frac{24}{5} - \frac{12}{5} = \frac{12}{5}$$

29. For the described line segment to be bisected by the point $(2, 6)$, then $(2, 6)$ must be the midpoint of the x- and y-intercepts (as points) of the line.
Using the point-slope formula:
$$y - 6 = m(x - 2)$$
$$y - 6 = mx - 2m$$
$$y = mx - 2m + 6$$

We find the x- and y- intercepts:

x-intercept:
$$y = 0$$
$$mx - 2m + 6 = 0$$
$$mx = 2m - 6$$
$$x = \frac{2m - 6}{m}$$

y-intercepts:
$$x = 0$$
$$y = -2m + 6$$

Since $(2, 6)$ must be the midpoint of $\left(\frac{2m - 6}{m}, 0\right)$ and $(0, -2m + 6)$, we have:

$$\frac{2m - 6}{2m} = 2 \qquad \text{and} \qquad \frac{-2m + 6}{2} = 6$$
$$2m - 6 = 4m \qquad\qquad -2m + 6 = 12$$
$$-6 = 2m \qquad\qquad -2m = 6$$
$$-3 = m \qquad\qquad m = -3$$

Now use the point-slope formula with the point $(2, 6)$:
$$y - 6 = -3(x - 2)$$
$$y - 6 = -3x + 6$$
$$y = -3x + 12$$

31. Using the hint, we let d_1 and d_2 represent the distances from (x, y) to $x - y + 1 = 0$ and $x + 7y - 49 = 0$, respextively. Then:

$$d_1 = \frac{|x - y + 1|}{\sqrt{1 + 1}} = \frac{|x - y + 1|}{\sqrt{2}}$$

$$d_2 = \frac{|x + 7y - 49|}{\sqrt{1 + 49}} = \frac{|x + 7y - 49|}{\sqrt{50}}$$

Since $d_1 = d_2$, we have:

$$\frac{|x - y + 1|}{\sqrt{2}} = \frac{|x + 7y - 49|}{\sqrt{50}}$$

Multiplying each side by $\sqrt{2}$, we have:

$$|x - y + 1| = \frac{|x + 7y - 49|}{5}$$

$$5|x - y + 1| = |x + 7y - 49|$$

Rather than squaring each side, we will note that:

$$5(x - y + 1) = x + 7y - 49 \qquad \text{or} \qquad 5(x - y + 1) = -x - 7y + 49$$
$$5x - 5y + 5 = x + 7y - 49 \qquad\qquad 5x - 5y + 5 = -x - 7y + 49$$
$$4x - 12y + 54 = 0 \qquad\qquad 6x + 2y - 44 = 0$$
$$2x - 6y + 27 = 0 \qquad\qquad 3x + y - 22 = 0$$
$$y = \frac{1}{3}x + \frac{9}{2} \qquad\qquad y = -3x + 22$$

Note that the first of these lines, $y = \frac{1}{3}x + \frac{9}{2}$, is the solution as indicated in the figure. The second line we found is the second angle bisector passing through the same intersection point but bisecting the larger vertical angles

33. (a) We solve for y:

$$A(x + x_0) + B(y + y_0) + C = 0$$
$$By + By_0 = -Ax - Ax_0 - C$$
$$By = -Ax \cdot Ax_0 - By_0 - C$$
$$y = -\frac{A}{B}x - \frac{Ax_0 + By_0 + C}{B}$$

So $m = -\dfrac{A}{B}$ and $b = -\dfrac{Ax_0 + By_0 + C}{B}$

(b) Applying our formula from the preceeding exercise, we have:

$$d = \frac{\left| -\dfrac{Ax_0 + By_0 + C}{B} \right|}{\sqrt{1 + \dfrac{A^2}{B^2}}}$$

$$= \frac{\dfrac{|Ax_0 + By_0 + C|}{|B|}}{\dfrac{\sqrt{A^2 + B^2}}{|B|}}$$

$$= \frac{|Ax_0 + By_0 + C|}{\sqrt{A^2 + B^2}}$$

35. (a) The standard form for a circle is $(x - h)^2 + (y - k)^2 = r^2$. We substitute each point for (x, y):

$$(-12 - h)^2 + (1 - k)^2 = r^2$$
$$(2 - h)^2 + (1 - k)^2 = r^2$$
$$(0 - h)^2 + (7 - k)^2 = r^2$$

Setting the first two equations equal, we have:

$$(-12 - h)^2 + (1 - k)^2 = (2 - h)^2 + (1 - k)^2$$
$$144 + 24h + h^2 + 1 - 2k + k^2 = 4 - 4h + h^2 + 1 - 2k + k^2$$
$$28h = -140$$
$$h = -5$$

Setting the second two equations equal, we have:

$$(2 - h)^2 + (1 - k)^2 = (0 - h)^2 + (7 - k)^2$$
$$4 - 4h + h^2 + 1 - 2k + k^2 = h^2 + 49 - 14k + k^2$$
$$-4h + 12k = 44$$
$$h - 3k = -11$$

Substituting $h = -5$, we have:

$$-5 - 3k = -11$$
$$-3k = -6$$
$$k = 2$$

Now substitute into the second equation to find r:
$$(7)^2 + (-1)^2 = r^2$$
$$50 = r^2$$
$$5\sqrt{2} = r$$

So the center is (-5, 2) and the radius is $5\sqrt{2}$.

(b)   We first draw the sketch:

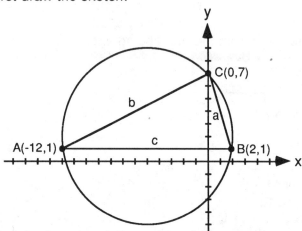

We find the lengths of three sides (using the distance formula):
$$a = \sqrt{(2-0)^2 + (1-7)^2} = \sqrt{4+36} = \sqrt{40} = 2\sqrt{10}$$
$$b = \sqrt{(-12-0)^2 + (1-7)^2} = \sqrt{144+36} = \sqrt{180} = 6\sqrt{5}$$
$$c = \sqrt{(-12-2)^2 + (1-1)^2} = \sqrt{196+0} = \sqrt{196} = 14$$

Using $R = 5\sqrt{2}$ from part (a), we have:
$$\frac{abc}{4R} = \frac{(2\sqrt{10})(6\sqrt{5})(14)}{4(5\sqrt{2})} = \frac{42\sqrt{50}}{5\sqrt{2}} = 42$$

For the area of the triangle, we have base = 14 and height = 6, so:
$$\text{area} = \frac{1}{2}\text{(base)(height)} = \frac{1}{2}(14)(6) = 42$$

This verifies the result.

37.   We will first find points P and Q. Solving for x, we have x = 7y - 44.
Now substitute:
$$(7y-44)^2 - 4(7y-44) + y^2 - 6y = 12$$
$$49y^2 - 616y + 1936 - 28y + 176 + y^2 - 6y = 12$$
$$50y^2 - 650y + 2100 = 0$$
$$50(y^2 - 13y + 42) = 0$$
$$50(y-7)(y-6) = 0$$
$$y = 7, 6$$

When y = 7, x = 49 - 44 = 5. When y = 6, x = 42 - 44 = -2. So the two points are P(5, 7) and Q(-2, 6). We now use the distance formula:

$$PQ = \sqrt{(-2 - 5)^2 + (6 - 7)^2} = \sqrt{49 + 1} = \sqrt{50} = 5\sqrt{2}$$

39. Let d_1 be the distance from (0, c) to ax + y = 0:

$$d_1 = \frac{|0 + c + 0|}{\sqrt{a^2 + 1}} = \frac{|c|}{\sqrt{a^2 + 1}}$$

Let d_2 be the distance from (0, c) to x + by = 0:

$$d_2 = \frac{|0 + bc + 0|}{\sqrt{1 + b^2}} = \frac{|bc|}{\sqrt{1 + b^2}}$$

So the product of these distances is given by:

$$d_1 d_2 = \frac{|c|}{\sqrt{a^2 + 1}} \bullet \frac{|bc|}{\sqrt{1 + b^2}} = \frac{|bc^2|}{\sqrt{a^2 + a^2 b^2 + b^2 + 1}}$$

41. (a)   We draw the triangle:

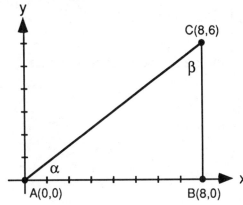

Since the triangle is a right triangle, note that $\sin \alpha = \frac{6}{10} = \frac{3}{5}$,

$\cos \alpha = \frac{8}{10} = \frac{4}{5}$, $\sin \beta = \frac{8}{10} = \frac{4}{5}$ and $\cos \beta = \frac{6}{10} = \frac{3}{5}$.

To find the bisector for A, note that:

$$m = \tan \frac{\alpha}{2} = \frac{\sin \alpha}{1 + \cos \alpha} = \frac{\frac{3}{5}}{1 + \frac{4}{5}} = \frac{3}{9} = \frac{1}{3}$$

Since this line passes through the point (0, 0), its equation is $y = \frac{1}{3}x$.

To find the bisector for B, note that its slope is -1 and that it passes through (8, 0), so:

$$y - 0 = -1(x - 8)$$
$$y = -x + 8$$

To find the bisector for C, first draw the figure:

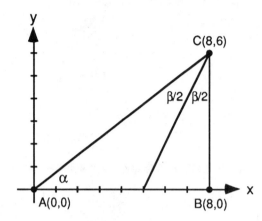

Now note that:

$$m = \tan\left(90° - \frac{\beta}{2}\right) = \cot\frac{\beta}{2} = \frac{1 + \cos\beta}{\sin\beta} = \frac{1 + \frac{3}{5}}{\frac{4}{5}} = 2$$

Using the point $(8, 6)$, we use the point-slope formula:

$$y - 6 = 2(x - 8)$$
$$y - 6 = 2x - 16$$
$$y = 2x - 10$$

So the bisectors at each vertex are:

A: $y = \frac{1}{3}x$

B: $y = -x + 8$

C: $y = 2x - 10$

(b)   Setting A and B equal:

$$\frac{1}{3}x = -x + 8$$
$$\frac{4}{3}x = 8$$
$$x = 6$$
$$y = 2$$

Setting B and C equal:

$$-x + 8 = 2x - 10$$
$$18 = 3x$$
$$6 = x$$
$$2 = y$$

Setting A and C equal:

$$\frac{1}{3}x = 2x - 10$$

$$-\frac{5}{3}x = -10$$

$$x = 6$$
$$y = 2$$

So the intersection point is $(6, 2)$ for all three bisectors.

43. Call $P(x_1, y_1)$ and $Q(x_2, y_2)$. Then the tangent line through P has equation $x_1 x + y_1 y = a^2$ and the tangent line through Q has equation $x_2 x + y_2 y = a^2$. We find the distance from $P(x_1, y_1)$ to $x_2 x + y_2 y - a^2 = 0$:

$$d_1 = \frac{|x_1 x_2 + y_1 y_2 - a^2|}{\sqrt{x_2^2 + y_2^2}} = \frac{|x_1 x_2 + y_1 y_2 - a^2|}{a}$$

We find the distance from $Q(x_2, y_2)$ to $x_1 x + y_1 y - a^2 = 0$:

$$d_2 = \frac{|x_1 x_2 + y_1 y_2 - a^2|}{\sqrt{x_1^2 + y_1^2}} = \frac{|x_1 x_2 + y_1 y_2 - a^2|}{a}$$

Note that these two distances are equal.

45. The distance from the point (x, y) to $\left(0, \frac{1}{4}\right)$ is:

$$d = \sqrt{(x - 0)^2 + \left(y - \frac{1}{4}\right)^2} = \sqrt{x^2 + y^2 - \frac{1}{2}y + \frac{1}{16}}$$

The distance from the point (x, y) to $y = -\frac{1}{4}$ is:

$$d = \frac{|0 - \frac{1}{4} - y|}{\sqrt{1 + 0}} = |y + \frac{1}{4}|$$

Setting these distances equal:

$$|y + \frac{1}{4}| = \sqrt{x^2 + y^2 - \frac{1}{2}y + \frac{1}{16}}$$

Squaring, we have:

$$y^2 + \frac{1}{2}y + \frac{1}{16} = x^2 + y^2 - \frac{1}{2}y + \frac{1}{16}$$

$$y = x^2$$

Thus, the points satisfy the equation $y = x^2$.

47. (a) We write the line in slope-intercept form:

$$Ax + By + C = 0$$
$$By = -Ax - C$$
$$y = -\frac{A}{B}x - \frac{C}{B}$$

slope: $-\frac{A}{B}$; y-intercept: $-\frac{C}{B}$

(b) $d = \dfrac{|mx_0 + b - y_0|}{\sqrt{1 + m^2}}$

$$= \dfrac{\left| -\dfrac{Ax_0 + By_0 + C}{B} \right|}{\sqrt{1 + \dfrac{A^2}{B^2}}}$$

$$= \dfrac{\dfrac{|Ax_0 + By_0 + C|}{|B|}}{\dfrac{\sqrt{A^2 + B^2}}{|B|}}$$

$$= \dfrac{|Ax_0 + By_0 + C|}{\sqrt{A^2 + B^2}}$$

49. We first find the slope of the line passing through (x_2, y_2) and (x_3, y_3):

$$m = \frac{y_2 - y_3}{x_2 - x_3}$$

Using the point-slope formula:

$$y - y_2 = \frac{y_2 - y_3}{x_2 - x_3}(x - x_2)$$
$$(x_2 - x_3)y - x_2 y_2 + x_3 y_2 = (y_2 - y_3)x - x_2 y_2 + x_2 y_3$$
$$(y_3 - y_2)x + (x_2 - x_3)y + (x_3 y_2 - x_2 y_3) = 0$$

We now find the distance from (x_1, y_1) to the line:

$$d = \frac{|x_1(y_3 - y_2) + y_1(x_2 - x_3) + x_3 y_2 - x_2 y_3|}{\sqrt{(y_3 - y_2)^2 + (x_2 - x_3)^2}}$$

$$= \frac{|x_1 y_3 - x_1 y_2 + x_2 y_1 - x_3 y_1 + x_3 y_2 - x_2 y_3|}{\sqrt{(x_2 - x_3)^2 + (y_2 - y_3)^2}}$$

Expanding D along the third column, we find that its terms exactly match the numerator of d.

51. Since the center can be written as $(x, 2x - 7)$, we find the distance to each point. Let d_1 represent the distance to $(6, 3)$ and d_2 represent the distance to $(-4, -3)$, then:

$$\begin{aligned}
d_1 &= \sqrt{(x - 6)^2 + (2x - 7 - 3)^2} \\
&= \sqrt{x^2 - 12x + 36 + 4x^2 - 40x + 100} \\
&= \sqrt{5x^2 - 52x + 136} \\
d_2 &= \sqrt{(x + 4)^2 + (2x - 7 + 3)^2} \\
&= \sqrt{x^2 + 8x + 16 + 4x^2 - 16x + 16} \\
&= \sqrt{5x^2 - 8x + 32}
\end{aligned}$$

Since $d_1 = d_2$ (they both represent the radius of the circle), we have:

$$\sqrt{5x^2 - 52x + 136} = \sqrt{5x^2 - 8x + 32}$$

Squaring each side:

$$\begin{aligned}
5x^2 - 52x + 136 &= 5x^2 - 8x + 32 \\
-44x &= -104 \\
x &= \frac{26}{11}
\end{aligned}$$

$$y = 2\left(\frac{26}{11}\right) - 7 = \frac{52}{11} - \frac{77}{11} = -\frac{25}{11}$$

So the center is $\left(\frac{26}{11}, -\frac{25}{11}\right)$. We find the radius using the point $(6, 3)$ in the distance formula:

$$r = \sqrt{\left(6 - \frac{26}{11}\right)^2 + \left(3 + \frac{25}{11}\right)^2} = \sqrt{\frac{1600}{121} + \frac{3364}{121}} = \frac{\sqrt{4964}}{11}$$

So the equation of the circle is:

$$\left(x - \frac{26}{11}\right)^2 + \left(y + \frac{25}{11}\right)^2 = \frac{4964}{121}$$

53. Since the line $2x + 3y = 26$ has a slope of $-\frac{2}{3}$, then the radial line will have a slope of $\frac{3}{2}$. Call (h, k) the center of the circle, so:

$$\begin{aligned}
\frac{k - 6}{h - 4} &= \frac{3}{2} \\
2k - 12 &= 3h - 12 \\
2k &= 3h \\
k &= \frac{3}{2}h
\end{aligned}$$

The circle has an equation of $(x - h)^2 + (y - k)^2 = 25$, so using the point $(4, 6)$ we have:

$$(4 - h)^2 + (6 - k)^2 = 25$$
$$16 - 8h + h^2 + 36 - 12k + k^2 = 25$$
$$h^2 - 8h + k^2 - 12k = -27$$

Substituting $k = \frac{3}{2}h$:

$$h^2 - 8h + \frac{9}{4}h^2 - 18h = -27$$
$$4h^2 - 32h + 9h^2 - 72h = -108$$
$$13h^2 - 104h + 108 = 0$$

$$h = \frac{104 \pm \sqrt{5200}}{26} = 4 \pm \frac{10\sqrt{13}}{13}$$

$$k = 6 \pm \frac{15\sqrt{13}}{13}$$

So the two circles are:

$$\left(x - 4 - \frac{10\sqrt{13}}{13}\right)^2 + \left(y - 6 - \frac{15\sqrt{13}}{13}\right)^2 = 25$$

$$\left(x - 4 + \frac{10\sqrt{13}}{13}\right)^2 + \left(y - 6 + \frac{15\sqrt{13}}{13}\right)^2 = 25$$

8.2 The Parabola

1. $x^2 = 4y$
    $4p = 4$, so $p = 1$
    focus: $(0, 1)$; directrix: $y = -1$; focal width: 4

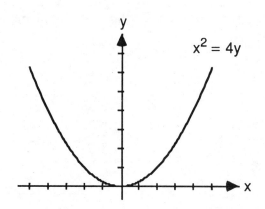

3. $y^2 = -8x$
    $4p = -8$, so $p = -2$
    focus: $(-2, 0)$
    directrix: $x = 2$
    focal width: 8

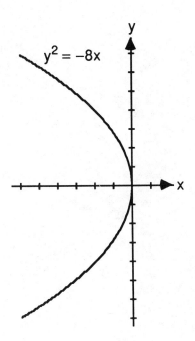

5. $x^2 = -20y$
    $4p = -20$, so $p = -5$
    focus: $(0, -5)$
    directrix: $y = 5$
    focal width: 20

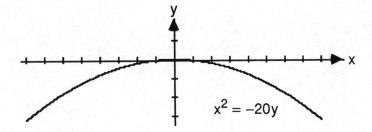

7. $y^2 + 28x = 0$
$$y^2 = -28x$$
$4p = -28$, so $p = -7$
focus: $(-7, 0)$; directrix: $x = 7$; focal width: 28

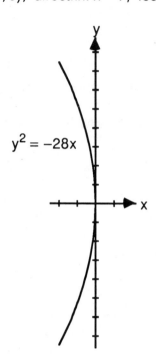

$y^2 = -28x$

9. $x^2 = 6y$
$4p = 4$, so $p = \dfrac{3}{2}$

focus: $(0, 3/2)$; directrix: $y = -\dfrac{3}{2}$; focal width: 6

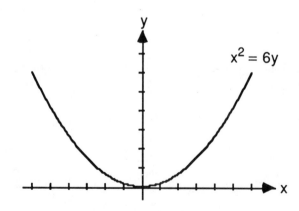

$x^2 = 6y$

11. $4x^2 = 7y$

   $x^2 = \dfrac{7}{4}y$

   $4p = \dfrac{7}{4}$, so $p = \dfrac{7}{16}$

   focus: $(0, 7/16)$; directrix: $y = -\dfrac{7}{16}$; focal width: $\dfrac{7}{4}$

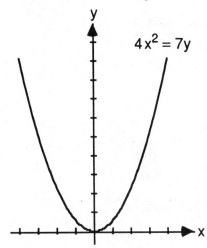

$4x^2 = 7y$

13. $y^2 - 6y - 4x + 17 = 0$

   $y^2 - 6y = 4x - 17$

   $y^2 - 6y + 9 = 4x - 17 + 9$

   $(y - 3)^2 = 4x - 8$

   $(y - 3)^2 = 4(x - 2)$

   vertex: $(2, 3)$

   $4p = 4$, so $p = 1$

   focus: $(3, 3)$; directrix: $x = 1$; focal width: 4

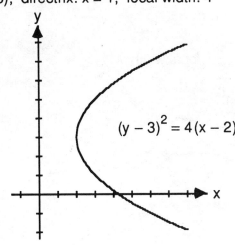

$(y - 3)^2 = 4(x - 2)$

15. $x^2 - 8x - y + 18 = 0$
$$x^2 - 8x = y - 18$$
$$x^2 - 8x + 16 = y - 18 + 16$$
$$(x - 4)^2 = y - 2$$
vertex: $(4, 2)$

$4p = 1$, so $p = \dfrac{1}{4}$

focus: $(4, 9/4)$; directrix: $y = \dfrac{7}{4}$; focal width: 1

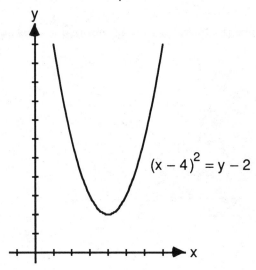

$(x - 4)^2 = y - 2$

17. $y^2 + 2y - x + 1 = 0$
$$y^2 + 2y = x - 1$$
$$y^2 + 2y + 1 = x - 1 + 1$$
$$(y + 1)^2 = x$$
vertex: $(0, -1)$

$4p = 1$, so $p = \dfrac{1}{4}$

focus: $(1/4, -1)$; directrix: $x = -\dfrac{1}{4}$; focal width: 1

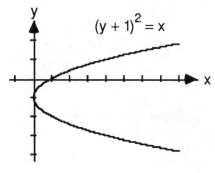

$(y + 1)^2 = x$

19. $2x^2 - 12x - y + 18 = 0$

$$2x^2 - 12x = y - 18$$

$$x^2 - 6x = \frac{1}{2}y - 9$$

$$x^2 - 6x + 9 = \frac{1}{2}y - 9 + 9$$

$$(x - 3)^2 = \frac{1}{2}y$$

vertex: (3, 0)

$4p = \dfrac{1}{2}$, so $p = \dfrac{1}{8}$

focus: (3, 1/8)

directrix: $y = -\dfrac{1}{8}$

focal width: $\dfrac{1}{2}$

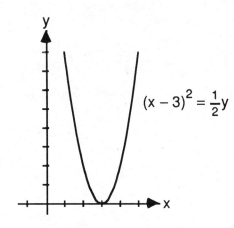

$(x - 3)^2 = \frac{1}{2}y$

21. $2x^2 - 16x - y + 33 = 0$

$$2x^2 - 16x = y - 33$$

$$2(x - 4)^2 = y - 1$$

$$(x - 4)^2 = \frac{1}{2}(y - 1)$$

vertex: $(4, 1)$

$4p = \frac{1}{2}$, so $p = \frac{1}{8}$

focus: $(4, 9/8)$

directrix: $y = \frac{7}{8}$

focal width: $\frac{1}{2}$

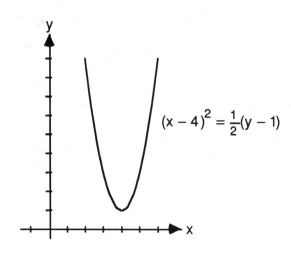

$$(x - 4)^2 = \frac{1}{2}(y - 1)$$

23. We re-draw the figure:

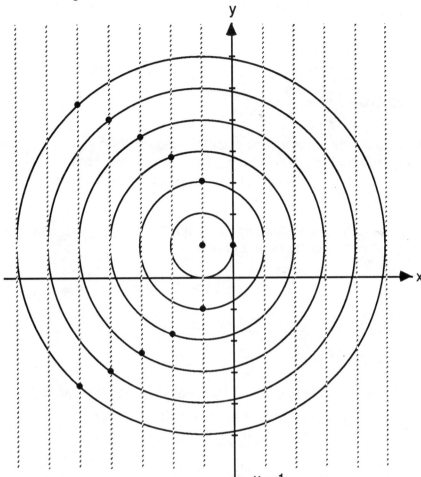

line of symmetry: y = 1

25. Given that the focus is at (0, 3), we see that p = 3 and 4p = 12. Since the parabola opens up, it has the $x^2 = 4py$ form, and its equation must be $x^2 = 12y$

27. The directrix is x = -32, so (32, 0) is the focus and the parabola opens to the right. So the parabola is of the form $y^2 = 4px$, where p = 32. Thus the equation is $y^2 = 128x$.

29. Since the parabola passes through the points $(5, 6)$ and $(5, -6)$, we know its basic equation is $y^2 = 4px$. Using the points $(5, 6)$ and $(5, -6)$, we have:

$$36 = 4p(5)$$
$$36 = 20p$$
$$\frac{9}{5} = p$$

So the equation is $y^2 = \frac{36}{5} x$.

31. Since the parabola is symmetric about the x-axis, then $y^2 = 4px$ is the form (here p can be positive or negative). Since the x-coordinate of the focus is negative, then $y^2 = -4px$ where $p > 0$. Finally we are given $4p = 9$, so the equation is $y^2 = -9x$.

33. Since $4p = 4$, then $p = 1$. By symmetry, if $P(2, 1)$ is one endpoint of focal chord, then $Q(-2, 1)$ is the other endpoint.

35. We have $4p = 1$, so $p = \frac{1}{4}$. Thus the focus is at $(0, 1/4)$. We find the equation of the focal chord PQ:

$$m = \frac{9 - \frac{1}{4}}{-3 - 0} = \frac{\frac{35}{4}}{-3} = -\frac{35}{12}$$

So $y = -\frac{35}{12} x + \frac{1}{4}$. We find where this line intersects the parabola (we already know P is one intersection point, but Q will be the other):

$$x^2 = -\frac{35}{12} x + \frac{1}{4}$$
$$12x^2 = -35x + 3$$
$$12x^2 + 35x - 3 = 0$$
$$(12x - 1)(x + 3) = 0$$
$$x = -3, \frac{1}{12}$$
$$y = 9, \frac{1}{144}$$

So $Q\left(\frac{1}{12}, \frac{1}{144}\right)$. Since $P(-3, 9)$, we can use the distance formula:

$$PQ = \sqrt{\left(-3 - \frac{1}{12}\right)^2 + \left(9 - \frac{1}{144}\right)^2} = \frac{1369}{144}$$

37. We draw the sketch:

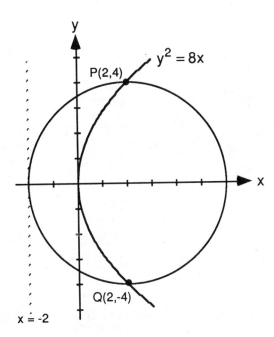

We have 4p = 8, so p = 2, and thus the coordinates of Q are (2, -4). Thus the diameter of the circle is 8, its radius is thus 4, and its equation is $(x - 2)^2 + y^2 = 16$. Since the directrix is x = -2, we can see that the circle is tangent to the directrix.

39. Call (0, 0) the vertex, thus the ends of the arch are at (20, -15) and (-20, -15). The parabola is of the form $x^2 = -4py$, so we substitute:

$$400 = -4p(-15)$$

$$-\frac{80}{3} = -4p$$

So the equation is $x^2 = -\frac{80}{3} y$. We wish to find the y-coordinate when the base is 20 ft, so we substitute x = ±10 into the equation:

$$100 = -\frac{80}{3} y$$

$$-\frac{15}{4} = y$$

So the height above the base is $15 - \frac{15}{4} = \frac{45}{4} = 11.25$ ft.

41. (a) We have $4p = 2$, so $p = \dfrac{1}{2}$, and thus the focus is $(0, 1/2)$. To find A', we find the equation of the line containing A and the focus:

$$m = \frac{8 - \dfrac{1}{2}}{4 - 0} = \frac{\dfrac{15}{2}}{4} = \frac{15}{8}$$

So $y = \dfrac{15}{8}x + \dfrac{1}{2}$. Now substitute into the parabola:

$$x^2 = 2\left(\frac{15}{8}x + \frac{1}{2}\right)$$

$$x^2 = \frac{15}{4}x + 1$$

$$4x^2 = 15x + 4$$

$$4x^2 - 15x - 4 = 0$$

$$x = -\frac{1}{4}, 4$$

$$y = \frac{1}{32}, 8$$

So $A' = \left(-\dfrac{1}{4}, \dfrac{1}{32}\right)$. To find B', we find the equation of the line containing B and the focus:

$$m = \frac{2 - \dfrac{1}{2}}{-2 - 0} = \frac{\dfrac{3}{2}}{-2} = -\frac{3}{4}$$

So $y = -\dfrac{3}{4}x + \dfrac{1}{2}$. Now substitute into the parabola:

$$x^2 = 2\left(-\frac{3}{4}x + \frac{1}{2}\right)$$

$$x^2 = -\frac{3}{2}x + 1$$

$$2x^2 + 3x - 2 = 0$$

$$x = \frac{1}{2}, -2$$

$$y = \frac{1}{8}, 2$$

So $B' = \left(\dfrac{1}{2}, \dfrac{1}{8}\right)$. We now find the equation through A and B':

$$m = \frac{8 - \dfrac{1}{8}}{4 - \dfrac{1}{2}} = \frac{\dfrac{63}{8}}{\dfrac{7}{2}} = \frac{9}{4}$$

Using $(4, 8)$ in the point-slope formula:

$$y - 8 = \frac{9}{4}(x - 4)$$

$$y - 8 = \frac{9}{4}x - 9$$

$$y = \frac{9}{4}x - 1$$

(b) We find the slope:

$$m = \frac{2 - \frac{1}{32}}{-2 + \frac{1}{4}} = \frac{\frac{63}{32}}{-\frac{7}{4}} = -\frac{9}{8}$$

Using $(-2, 2)$ in the point-slope formula:

$$y - 2 = -\frac{9}{8}(x + 2)$$

$$y - 2 = -\frac{9}{8}x - \frac{9}{4}$$

$$y = -\frac{9}{8}x - \frac{1}{4}$$

(c) Setting the y-coordinates equal:

$$\frac{9}{4}x - 1 = -\frac{9}{8}x - \frac{1}{4}$$

$$18x - 8 = -9x - 2$$

$$27x = 6$$

$$x = \frac{2}{9}$$

$$y = \frac{1}{2} - 1 = -\frac{1}{2}$$

So the lines intersect at the point $\left(\frac{2}{9}, -\frac{1}{2}\right)$. Since the directrix is $y = -\frac{1}{2}$, then this point lies on the directrix.

43. (a) Since $4p = 1$, $p = \frac{1}{4}$, thus the focus is $(0, 1/4)$. We find the equation of the focal chord from P:

$$m = \frac{4 - \frac{1}{4}}{2 - 0} = \frac{\frac{15}{4}}{2} = \frac{15}{8}$$

So the equation is $y = \frac{15}{8}x + \frac{1}{4}$. We now find the intersection of this line with the parabola $y = x^2$:

$$x^2 = \frac{15}{8}x + \frac{1}{4}$$
$$8x^2 = 15x + 2$$
$$8x^2 - 15x - 2 = 0$$
$$(8x + 1)(x - 2) = 0$$
$$x = -\frac{1}{8}, 2$$
$$y = \frac{1}{64}, 4$$

So the coordinates of Q are $Q\left(-\frac{1}{8}, \frac{1}{64}\right)$.

(b)   We find the midpoint of PQ:

$$M = \left(\frac{2 - \frac{1}{8}}{2}, \frac{4 + \frac{1}{64}}{2}\right) = \left(\frac{15}{16}, \frac{257}{128}\right)$$

(c)   The coordinates of S are $\left(0, \frac{17}{8}\right)$. We can find T, since the slope of this line (which is perpendicular to PQ) is $-\frac{8}{15}$, and thus by the point-slope formula:

$$y - \frac{17}{8} = -\frac{8}{15}\left(x - \frac{15}{16}\right)$$
$$y - \frac{17}{8} = -\frac{8}{15}x + \frac{1}{2}$$
$$y = -\frac{8}{15}x + \frac{21}{8}$$

Now let $x = 0$:

$$y = \frac{21}{8}$$

So the coordinates of T are $\left(0, \frac{21}{8}\right)$.

Thus the length of ST is $\frac{21}{8} - \frac{17}{8} = \frac{4}{8} = \frac{1}{2}$. Since the focal width is $4p = 1$, this verifies that ST is one-half the focal width.

45. Call m the slope of the tangent line, so:
$$y - 2 = m(x - 4)$$

Solving $x^2 = 8y$ for y yields $y = \dfrac{x^2}{8}$, now substitute:

$$\frac{x^2}{8} - 2 = m(x - 4)$$
$$x^2 - 16 = 8m(x - 4)$$
$$(x + 4)(x - 4) = 8m(x - 4)$$
$$x + 4 = 8m$$
$$x = -4 + 8m$$

Since this x-coordinate must also equal 4, we have:

$$4 = -4 + 8m$$
$$8 = 8m$$
$$1 = m$$

Thus the tangent line is given by:

$$y - 2 = 1(x - 4)$$
$$y - 2 = x - 4$$
$$y = x - 2$$

We sketch the parabola and tangent line:

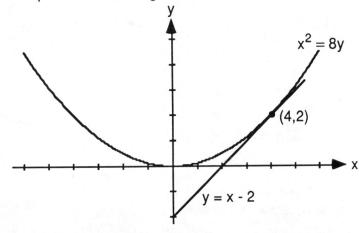

47. Call m the slope of the tangent line, so:
$$y + 9 = m(x + 3)$$

Solving $x^2 = -y$ for y yields $y = -x^2$, now substitute:

$$-x^2 + 9 = m(x + 3)$$
$$x^2 - 9 = -m(x + 3)$$
$$(x + 3)(x - 3) = -m(x + 3)$$
$$x - 3 = -m$$
$$x = 3 - m$$

Since this x-coordinate must also equal -3, we have:
$$-3 = 3 - m$$
$$-6 = -m$$
$$6 = m$$
Thus the tangent line is given by:
$$y + 9 = 6(x + 3)$$
$$y + 9 = 6x + 18$$
$$y = 6x + 9$$
We sketch the parabola and tangent line:

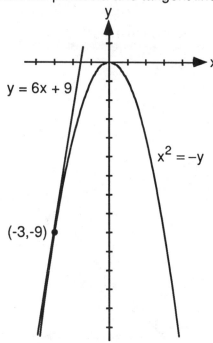

49.   Call m the slope of the tangent line, so:
$$y - 4 = m(x + 2)$$

Solving $y^2 = -8x$ for x yields $x = -\frac{y^2}{8}$, now substitute:

$$y - 4 = m\left(-\frac{y^2}{8} + 2\right)$$
$$8(y - 4) = m(-y^2 + 16)$$
$$8(y - 4) = -m(y + 4)(y - 4)$$
$$8 = -m(y + 4)$$
$$-\frac{8}{m} - 4 = y$$

Since this y-coordinate must also equal 4, we have:

$$-\frac{8}{m} - 4 = 4$$

$$-\frac{8}{m} = 8$$

$$-8 = 8m$$

$$-1 = m$$

Thus the tangent line is given by:

$$y - 4 = -(x + 2)$$

$$y - 4 = -x - 2$$

$$y = -x + 2$$

We sketch the parabola and tangent line:

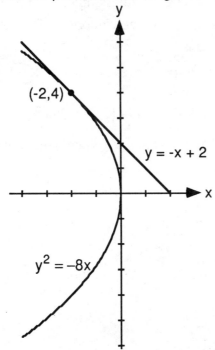

51.   The sketch in the book will have the following coordinates:

$$O(0,0), \; B\left(x, \frac{x^2}{4p}\right), \; A\left(-x, \frac{x^2}{4p}\right)$$

We require that AB = OB. So:

$$2x = \sqrt{(x-0)^2 + \left(\frac{x^2}{4p} - 0\right)^2}$$

$$2x = \sqrt{x^2 + \frac{x^4}{16p^2}}$$

Squaring, we have:

$$4x^2 = x^2 + \frac{x^4}{16p^2}$$

$$0 = -3x^2 + \frac{x^4}{16p^2}$$

$$0 = -48x^2p^2 + x^4$$

$$0 = x^2(-48p^2 + x^2)$$

So $x^2 = 0$ or $x = 0$ is one root and $x^2 = 48p^2$ or $x = \pm 4\sqrt{3}\,p$ is the other. The distance from A to B is therefore:

$$2(4\sqrt{3}\,p) = 8\sqrt{3}\,p \text{ units}$$

To find the area we note that this is an equilateral triangle. Half of it is a 30°-60°-90° triangle whose height will be $\sqrt{3}$ times its base. The height is therefore $\sqrt{3} \bullet 4\sqrt{3}\,p = 12p$. The area is:

$$\frac{1}{2}(8\sqrt{3}\,p)(12p) = 48\sqrt{3}\,p^2 \text{ sq. units}$$

53. (a) Let $y_0 = 1$, so $x_0 = 2$. We find the tangent at $(2, 1)$. Call m the slope, so $y - 1 = m(x - 2)$. Since $x^2 = 4y$ implies $y = \frac{x^2}{4}$, we substitute:

$$\frac{x^2}{4} - 1 = m(x - 2)$$

$$x^2 - 4 = 4m(x - 2)$$

$$(x + 2)(x - 2) = 4m(x - 2)$$

$$x + 2 = 4m$$

$$x = 4m - 2$$

Since $x = 2$, then $2 = 4m - 2$, thus $m = 1$. So the tangent line is:

$$y - 1 = x - 2$$

$$y = x - 1$$

So the y-intercept is -1.

(b) Let $y_0 = 2$, so $x_0 = 2\sqrt{2}$. We find the tangent at $(2\sqrt{2}, 2)$. Call m the slope, so $y - 2 = m(x - 2\sqrt{2})$. Substitute:

$$\frac{x^2}{4} - 2 = m(x - 2\sqrt{2})$$

$$x^2 - 8 = 4m(x - 2\sqrt{2})$$

$$(x + 2\sqrt{2})(x - 2\sqrt{2}) = 4m(x - 2\sqrt{2})$$

$$x + 2\sqrt{2} = 4m$$

$$x = 4m - 2\sqrt{2}$$

Since $x = 2\sqrt{2}$, then $2\sqrt{2} = 4m - 2\sqrt{2}$, thus $m = \sqrt{2}$. So the tangent line is:

$$y - 2 = \sqrt{2}\,(x - 2\sqrt{2})$$
$$y - 2 = \sqrt{2}\,x - 4$$
$$y = \sqrt{2}\,x - 2$$

So the y-intercept is -2.

(c)   Repeating the steps outlined in (a) and (b), we find the y-intercept is -3.

(d)   Conjecture: the y-intercept of the tangent line at (x_0, y_0) is $-y_0$. Call m the slope, so $y - y_0 = m(x - x_0)$. Substituting $y = \dfrac{x^2}{4}$ and $y_0 = \dfrac{x_0^2}{4}$, we have:

$$\frac{x^2}{4} - \frac{x_0^2}{4} = m(x - x_0)$$
$$x^2 - x_0^2 = 4m(x - x_0)$$
$$(x + x_0)(x - x_0) = 4m(x - x_0)$$
$$x + x_0 = 4m$$
$$x = 4m - x_0$$

Since this value of x must be x_0, then $x_0 = 4m - x_0$, and thus $m = \dfrac{1}{2}x_0$. So the tangent line is:

$$y - y_0 = \frac{1}{2}x_0(x - x_0)$$
$$y - y_0 = \frac{1}{2}x_0 x - \frac{1}{2}x_0^2$$

But $x_0^2 = 4y_0$, so:

$$y - y_0 = \frac{1}{2}x_0 x - 2y_0$$
$$y = \frac{1}{2}x_0 y - y_0$$

Thus the y-intercept is $-y_0$.

55.   Let m be the slope, so $y - 2 = m(x - 4)$. Since $y = \sqrt{x}$, then $x = y^2$:

$$y - 2 = m(y^2 - 4)$$
$$y - 2 = m(y + 2)(y - 2)$$
$$1 = m(y + 2)$$
$$\frac{1}{m} - 2 = y$$

Since this y-coordinate must also equal 2, we have:

$$\frac{1}{m} \cdot 2 = 2$$

$$\frac{1}{m} = 4$$

$$m = \frac{1}{4}$$

57. Let m be the slope, so $y - 8 = m(x - 2)$. Substitute $y = x^3$:

$$x^3 - 8 = m(x - 2)$$
$$(x - 2)(x^2 + 2x + 4) = m(x - 2)$$
$$x^2 + 2x + 4 = m$$

Since $x = 2$, we have:

$$m = 2^2 + 4 + 4 = 12$$

59. Since the focus is $(p, 0)$, then the slope of the focal chord is:

$$m = \frac{y_0 - 0}{\dfrac{y_0^2}{4p} - p} = \frac{4py_0}{y_0^2 - 4p^2}$$

Using the point-slope formula, the equation of this focal chord is:

$$y - y_0 = m\left(x - \frac{y_0^2}{4p}\right)$$

This line intersects the parabola when $x = \dfrac{y^2}{4p}$, so:

$$y - y_0 = m\left(\frac{y^2}{4p} - \frac{y_0^2}{4p}\right)$$
$$4p(y - y_0) = m(y + y_0)(y - y_0)$$
$$4p = m(y + y_0)$$

Substitute $m = \dfrac{4py_0}{y_0^2 - 4p^2}$:

$$4p = \frac{4py_0}{y_0^2 - yp^2}(y + y_0)$$

$$\frac{y_0^2 - 4p^2}{y_0} = y + y_0$$

$$-\frac{4p^2}{y_0} = y$$

So $x = \dfrac{1}{4p}\left(-\dfrac{4p^2}{y_0}\right)^2 = \dfrac{1}{4p}\left(\dfrac{16p^4}{y_0^2}\right) = \dfrac{4p^3}{y_0^2}$

But $y_0{}^2 = 4px_0$, so $x = \dfrac{4p^3}{4px_0} = \dfrac{p^2}{x_0}$

Thus the coordinates of Q are $\left(\dfrac{p^2}{x_0} , \dfrac{-4p^2}{y_0} \right)$.

61. The following results summarize the calculations required for this problem. Note: At each step we have replaced the quantity $y_0{}^2$ by $4px_0$. This simplifies matters a great deal.

Coordinates of M: $\left(\dfrac{x_0{}^2 + p}{2x_0} , \dfrac{2p(x_0 - p)}{y_0} \right)$

Coordinates of S: $\left(\dfrac{p^2 + x_0{}^2}{2x_0} , 0 \right)$

Slope of PQ: $\dfrac{4px_0}{y_0(x_0 - p)}$

Slope of perpendicular: $\dfrac{y_0(p - x_0)}{4px_0}$

Equation for line through M and T (using point-slope):

$$y - \dfrac{2p(x_0 - p)}{y_0} = \dfrac{p - x_0}{4px_0} \; x - \dfrac{x_0{}^2 + p_0{}^2}{2x_0}$$

To determine the x-intercept of this line, set $y = 0$ and then divide out the factor $x_0 - p$ from both sides of the equation. After doing this, we find that the coordinates of T are:

$$\left(\dfrac{4px_0 + x_0{}^2 + p^2}{2x_0} , 0 \right)$$

Thus $ST = \dfrac{4px_0 + x_0{}^2 + p^2}{2x_0} - \dfrac{p^2 + x_0{}^2}{2x_0} = \dfrac{4px_0}{2x_0} = 2p$, which is one-half of the focal width.

63. Denote the coordinates of A and B by $\left(a, \dfrac{a^2}{4p} \right)$ and $\left(b, \dfrac{b^2}{4p} \right)$, respectively. Then by using the result in exercise #58, we find that the coordinates of A' and B' are $\left(-\dfrac{4p^2}{a} , \dfrac{4p^3}{a^2} \right)$ and $\left(-\dfrac{4p^2}{b} , \dfrac{4p^3}{b} \right)$, respectively. Using these coordinates, the equations of the lines AB and A'B' can be determined. The results are as follows:

Line AB: $y = \dfrac{a + b}{4p} x - \dfrac{ab}{4p}$

Line A'B': $y = \dfrac{-p(a + b)}{ab} x - \dfrac{4p^3}{ab}$

By solving the first of these two equations for x, and then using that result to substitute for y in the second equation, we obtain y = -p. That implies that the two lines intersect on the directrix, as required.

65.   (a)   Since the focus is $(0, p)$, then the slope of the focal chord is:

$$m = \frac{\dfrac{x_0^2}{4p} - p}{x_0 - 0} = \frac{x_0^2 - 4p^2}{4px_0}$$

Using the point-slope formula, the equation of this focal chord is:

$$y - \frac{x_0^2}{4p} = m(x - x_0)$$

This line intersects the parabola when $y = \dfrac{x^2}{4p}$, so:

$$\frac{x^2}{4p} - \frac{x_0^2}{4p} = m(x - x_0)$$
$$x^2 - x_0^2 = 4pm(x - x_0)$$
$$(x + x_0)(x - x_0) = 4pm(x - x_0)$$
$$x + x_0 = 4pm$$

Now substitute $m = \dfrac{x_0^2 - 4p^2}{4px_0}$:

$$x + x_0 = 4p\left(\frac{x_0^2 - 4p^2}{4px_0}\right)$$

$$x + x_0 = \frac{x_0^2 - 4p^2}{x_0}$$

$$x = \frac{x_0^2 - 4p^2 - x_0^2}{x_0} = -\frac{4p^2}{x_0}$$

So $y = \dfrac{1}{4p}\left(\dfrac{-4p^2}{x_0}\right)^2 = \dfrac{1}{4p}\left(\dfrac{16p^4}{x_0^2}\right) = \dfrac{4p^3}{x_0^2}$

But $x_0^2 = 4py_0$, so $y = \dfrac{4p^3}{4py_0} = \dfrac{p^2}{y_0}$.

Thus the coordinates of Q are $\left(-\dfrac{4p^2}{x_0}, \dfrac{p^2}{y_0}\right)$.

(b)   By the midpoint formula:

$$PQ = \left(\frac{x_0 - \dfrac{4p^2}{x_0}}{2}, \frac{y_0 + \dfrac{p^2}{y_0}}{2}\right) = \left(\frac{x_0^2 - 4p^2}{2x_0}, \frac{y_0^2 + p^2}{2y_0}\right)$$

(c)   The distance from P to the directrix is $y_0 + p$. Therefore $PF = y_0 + p$. The distance from Q to the directrix is $\dfrac{p^2}{y_0} + p$. So we have $QF = \dfrac{p^2}{y_0} + p$ and consequently:

$$
\begin{aligned}
PQ &= QF + PF \\
&= \frac{p^2}{y_0} + p + y_0 + p \\
&= \frac{p^2 + 2p + y_0{}^2}{y_0} \\
&= \frac{(p + y_0)^2}{y_0}
\end{aligned}
$$

(d)   The distance from the center of the circle to the directrix is found by adding p to the y coordinate of the midpoint of PQ. This yields:

$$
\frac{y_0{}^2 + p^2}{2y_0} + p = \frac{y_0{}^2 + p^2 + 2py_0}{2y_0} = \frac{(y_0 + p)^2}{2y_0}
$$

Comparing this result with the expression for PQ determined in part (c), we conclude that the distance from the center of the circle to the directrix equals the radius of the circle. This implies that the circle is tangent to the directrix, as we wished to show.

67.   Let the equation of the tangent line be $y - y_0 = m(x - x_0)$. Replacing x by $\dfrac{y^2}{4p}$ and x_0 by $\dfrac{y_0{}^2}{4p}$ we obtain:

$$
\begin{aligned}
y - y_0 &= m\left(\frac{y^2}{4p} - \frac{y_0{}^2}{4p}\right) \\
4p(y - y_0) &= m(y + y_0)(y - y_0) \\
4p &= m(y + y_0) \\
y &= \frac{4p}{m} - y_0
\end{aligned}
$$

But since $y = y_0$, we have:

$$
\begin{aligned}
y_0 &= \frac{4p}{m} - y_0 \\
2y_0 &= \frac{4p}{m} \\
m &= \frac{2p}{y_0}
\end{aligned}
$$

So the equation of the tangent line is:

$$y - y_0 = \frac{2p}{y_0}(x - x_0)$$

$$y - y_0 = \frac{2p}{y_0}x - \frac{2px_0}{y_0}$$

$$y = \frac{2p}{y_0}x + \frac{y_0^2 - 2px_0}{y_0}$$

Replacing $x_0 = \frac{y_0^2}{4p}$, we have:

$$y = \frac{2p}{y_0}x + \frac{y_0^2 - 2p \cdot \frac{y_0}{4p}}{y_0} = \frac{2p}{y_0}x + \frac{y_0}{2}$$

To find the x-intercept, we set $y = 0$:

$$\frac{2p}{y_0}x + \frac{y_0}{2} = 0$$

$$4px + y_0^2 = 0$$

$$x = -\frac{y_0^2}{4p} = -x_0$$

69. The slope of the normal is $-\frac{1}{2p/y_0} = -\frac{y_0}{2p}$. The axis is the line $y = 0$, so A is the x-intercept of the normal line, which has equation:

$$y - y_0 = -\frac{y_0}{2p}(x - x_0)$$

Setting $y = 0$ we get:

$$-y_0 = \frac{-y_0}{2p}(x - x_0)$$

$$2py_0 = y_0(x - x_0)$$

$$2p = x - x_0$$

$$x = x_0 + 2p$$

So A is $(x_0 + 2p, 0)$. Since B is $(x_0, 0)$, AB = 2p as required.

71. (a)   Let A and B have coordinates (x_1, y_1) and (x_2, y_2) respectively.

Then M has coordinates $\left(\frac{x_1 + y_1}{2}, \frac{y_1 + y_2}{2} \right)$.

The tangent line at A is:

$$y = \frac{x_1}{2p}x - y_1 = \frac{x_1}{2p}x - \frac{x_1^2}{4p}$$

The tangent line at B is:

$$y = \frac{x_2}{2p}x - y_2 = \frac{x_2}{2p}x - \frac{x_2^2}{4p}$$

The x-coordinate of C, then, is the solution of:

$$\frac{x_1}{2p}x - \frac{x_1^2}{4p} = \frac{x_2}{2p}x - \frac{x_2^2}{4p}$$

$$2x_1 x - x_1^2 = 2x_2 x - x_2^2$$

$$x = \frac{x_1^2 - x_2^2}{2(x_1 - x_2)}$$

$$x = \frac{x_1 + x_2}{2}$$

So C and M have same x-coordinate, thus MC is parallel to the axis x = 0.

(b)   The coordinates of D are $\left(\dfrac{x_1 + x_2}{2}, \dfrac{x_1^2 + 2x_1 x_2 + x_2^2}{16p} \right)$.

The y-coordinate of C is:

$$\frac{x_1}{2p}\left(\frac{x_1 + x_2}{2}\right) - \frac{x_1^2}{4p} = \frac{x_1 x_2}{4p}$$

The y-coordinate of M is:

$$\frac{y_1 + y_2}{2} = \frac{\dfrac{x_1^2}{4p} + \dfrac{x_2^2}{4p}}{2} = \frac{x_1^2 + x_2^2}{8p}$$

Thus we have:

$$CD = \frac{x_1^2 + 2x_1 x_2 + x_2^2}{16p} - \frac{4x_1 x_2}{16p} = \frac{x_1^2 - 2x_1 x_2 + x_2^2}{16p}$$

$$DM = \frac{2x_1^2 + 2x_2^2}{16p} - \frac{x_1^2 + 2x_1 x_2 + x_2^2}{16p} = \frac{x_1^2 - 2x_1 x_2 + x_2^2}{16p}$$

Thus CD = DM as required.

73.   (a)   We must show the y-coordinate of B is 0. The tangent line through P has equation:

$$y = \frac{x_0}{2p}x - y_0 = \frac{x_0}{2p}x - \frac{x_0^2}{4p}$$

So the normal through F, which contains B, has slope $-\dfrac{2p}{x_0}$. The equation of this normal is:

$$y - p = -\frac{2p}{x_0}(x - 0)$$

$$y = -\frac{2p}{x_0}x + p$$

Since F has coordinates $(0, p)$, the x-intercept of this line is $\frac{x_0}{2}$, and this is also the x-intercept of the tangent through P, so these two lines intersect at B in the x-axis, as required.

(b)   B has coordinates $\left(\frac{x_0}{2}, 0\right)$, C has coordinates $(x_0, -p)$ (since the directrix is $y = -p$), and F has coordinates $(0, p)$. Thus the midpoint of FC is $\left(\frac{x_0 + 0}{2}, \frac{-p + p}{2}\right) = \left(\frac{x_0}{2}, 0\right)$ which is B, as required.

75.   Since $p = 1$, the coordinates of B are $\left(\frac{1}{4}, -\frac{4}{4}\right) = \left(\frac{1}{4}, -1\right)$ using exercise #59.

The tangent through A has slope $\frac{2}{4} = \frac{1}{2}$, so the normal has slope -2 and equation:
$$y - 4 = -2(x - 4)$$
$$y = -2x + 12$$
The points of intersection of this line with the parabola can now be found:
$$y = -2x + 12$$
$$-2x = y - 12$$
$$x = \frac{-y + 12}{2}$$
Thus $y^2 = 4x$ becomes:
$$y^2 = 4\left(\frac{-y + 12}{2}\right)$$
$$y^2 = -2y + 24$$
$$y^2 + 2y - 24 = 0$$
$$(y - 4)(y + 6) = 0$$
$$y = 4, -6$$
Thus the y-coordinate of A' is -6, so A' is $(9, -6)$. By a similar procedure we obtain the coordinates of B' to be $\left(\frac{81}{4}, 9\right)$. Now we compute the distances:

$$\begin{aligned}
AB &= \sqrt{\left(4 - \frac{1}{4}\right)^2 + (4 + 1)^2} \\
&= \sqrt{\frac{225}{16} + \frac{400}{16}} \\
&= \sqrt{\frac{625}{16}} \\
&= \frac{25}{4}
\end{aligned}$$

$$A'B' = \sqrt{\left(\frac{36-81}{4}\right)^2 + (-6-9)^2}$$

$$= \sqrt{\frac{2025}{16} + \frac{3600}{16}}$$

$$= \sqrt{\frac{5625}{16}}$$

$$= \frac{75}{4}$$

Thus A'B' = 3AB as required.

8.3 The Ellipse

1. $4x^2 + 9y^2 = 36$

$\frac{x^2}{9} + \frac{y^2}{4} = 1$

major axis: 6
minor axis: 4

$c^2 = 9 - 4 = 5$, so $c = \sqrt{5}$

foci: $(\pm\sqrt{5}, 0)$

eccentricity: $\frac{\sqrt{5}}{3}$

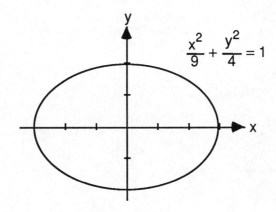

$\frac{x^2}{9} + \frac{y^2}{4} = 1$

3. $x^2 + 16y^2 = 16$

$\dfrac{x^2}{16} + \dfrac{y^2}{1} = 1$

major axis: 8
minor axis: 2

$c^2 = 16 - 1 = 15$, so $c = \sqrt{15}$

foci: $(\pm\sqrt{15}, 0)$

eccentricity: $\dfrac{\sqrt{15}}{4}$

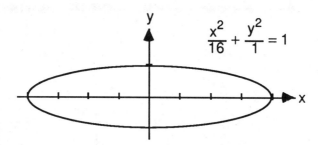

$\dfrac{x^2}{16} + \dfrac{y^2}{1} = 1$

5. $x^2 + 2y^2 = 2$

$\dfrac{x^2}{2} + \dfrac{y^2}{1} = 1$

major axis: $2\sqrt{2}$
minor axis: 2

$c^2 = 2 - 1 = 1$, so $c = 1$

foci: $(\pm 1, 0)$

eccentricity: $\dfrac{\sqrt{2}}{2}$

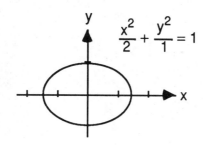

$\dfrac{x^2}{2} + \dfrac{y^2}{1} = 1$

7. $16x^2 + 9y^2 = 144$

$\dfrac{x^2}{9} + \dfrac{y^2}{16} = 1$

major axis: 8
minor axis: 6

$c^2 = 16 - 9 = 7$, so $c = \sqrt{7}$

foci: $(0, \pm\sqrt{7})$

eccentricity: $\dfrac{\sqrt{7}}{4}$

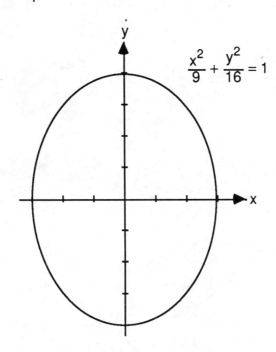

$\dfrac{x^2}{9} + \dfrac{y^2}{16} = 1$

9. $15x^2 + 3y^2 = 5$

$\dfrac{x^2}{1/3} + \dfrac{y^2}{5/3} = 1$

major axis: $2\sqrt{\dfrac{5}{3}} = \dfrac{2\sqrt{15}}{3}$

minor axis: $2\sqrt{\dfrac{1}{3}} = \dfrac{2\sqrt{3}}{3}$

$c^2 = \dfrac{5}{3} - \dfrac{1}{3} = \dfrac{4}{3}$, so $c = \dfrac{2}{\sqrt{3}} = \dfrac{2\sqrt{3}}{3}$

foci: $\left(0, \pm\dfrac{2\sqrt{3}}{3}\right)$

eccentricity: $\dfrac{2\sqrt{3}/3}{\sqrt{15}/3} = \dfrac{2\sqrt{3}}{\sqrt{15}} = \dfrac{2}{\sqrt{5}} = \dfrac{2\sqrt{5}}{5}$

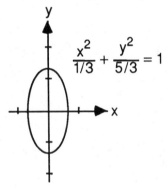

$\dfrac{x^2}{1/3} + \dfrac{y^2}{5/3} = 1$

11. $2x^2 + y^2 = 4$

$\dfrac{x^2}{2} + \dfrac{y^2}{4} = 1$

major axis: 4; minor axis: $2\sqrt{2}$

$c^2 = 4 - 2 = 2$, so $c = \sqrt{2}$

foci: $(0, \pm\sqrt{2})$; eccentricity: $\dfrac{\sqrt{2}}{2}$

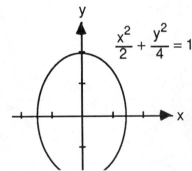

$\dfrac{x^2}{2} + \dfrac{y^2}{4} = 1$

13. $\dfrac{(x-5)^2}{5^2} + \dfrac{(y+1)^2}{3^2} = 1$

center: $(5,-1)$; major axis: 10; minor axis: 6

$c^2 = 25 - 9 = 16$, so $c = 4$

foci: $(5+4,-1)$ and $(5-4,-1)$, or $(9,-1)$ and $(1,-1)$

eccentricity: $\dfrac{4}{5}$

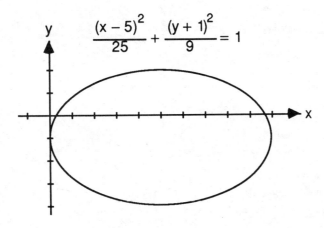

15. $\dfrac{(x-1)^2}{1^2} + \dfrac{(y-2)^2}{2^2} = 1$

center: $(1,2)$; major axis: 4; minor axis: 2

$c^2 = 4 - 1 = 3$, so $c = \sqrt{3}$

foci: $(1, 2 \pm \sqrt{3})$; eccentricity: $\dfrac{\sqrt{3}}{2}$

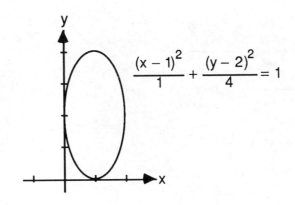

17. $\dfrac{(x + 3)^2}{3^2} + \dfrac{y^2}{1^2} = 1$

center: (-3, 0); major axis: 6; minor axis: 2

$c^2 = 9 - 1 = 8$, so $c = \sqrt{8} = 2\sqrt{2}$

foci: $(-3 \pm 2\sqrt{2}, 0)$; eccentricity: $\dfrac{2\sqrt{2}}{3}$

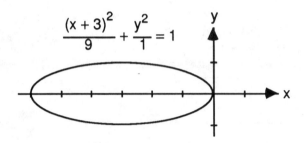

19. $3x^2 + 4y^2 - 6x + 16y + 7 = 0$

$3(x^2 - 2x) + 4(y^2 + 4y) = -7$

$3(x^2 - 2x + 1) + 4(y^2 + 4y + 4) = -7 + 3 + 16$

$3(x - 1)^2 + 4(y + 2)^2 = 12$

$\dfrac{(x - 1)^2}{4} + \dfrac{(y + 2)^2}{3} = 1$

center: (1, -2); major axis: 4; minor axis: $2\sqrt{3}$

$c^2 = 4 - 3 = 1$, so $c = 1$

foci: (1 + 1, -2) and (1 - 1, -2), or (2, -2) and (0, -2)

eccentricity: $\dfrac{1}{2}$

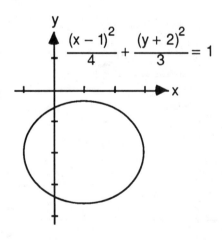

21. $$5x^2 + 3y^2 - 40x - 36y + 188 = 0$$
$$5(x^2 - 8x) + 3(y^2 - 12y) = -188$$
$$5(x^2 - 8x + 16) + 3(y^2 - 12y + 36) = -188 + 80 + 108$$
$$5(x - 4)^2 + 3(y - 6)^2 = 0$$

Notice that the only solution to this is the center $(4, 6)$. This is called a degenerate ellipse.

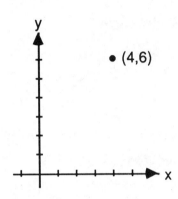

23. $$16x^2 + 25y^2 - 64x - 100y + 564 = 0$$
$$16(x^2 - 4x) + 25(y^2 - 4y) = -564$$
$$16(x^2 - 4x + 4) + 25(y^2 - 4y + 4) = -564 + 64 + 100$$
$$16(x - 2)^2 + 25(y - 2)^2 = -400$$

Notice that there is no solution to this equation, since the left-hand side is non-negative. So there is no graph.

25. We are given $c = 3$ and $a = 5$, so we have the equation in the form:
$$\frac{x^2}{5^2} + \frac{y^2}{b^2} = 1$$
Since $c^2 = a^2 - b^2$, we find b:
$$9 = 25 - b^2$$
$$16 = b^2$$
$$4 = b$$
So the equation is $\frac{x^2}{5^2} + \frac{y^2}{4^2} = 1$, or $16x^2 + 25y^2 = 400$.

27. We are given $a = 4$, so the equation has a form of:
$$\frac{x^2}{16} + \frac{y^2}{b^2} = 1$$
Now $\frac{c}{a} = \frac{1}{4}$, so: $\frac{c}{4} = \frac{1}{4}$, thus $c = 1$

We find b:

$$c^2 = a^2 - b^2$$
$$1 = 16 - b^2$$
$$b^2 = 15$$

So the equation is $\dfrac{x^2}{16} + \dfrac{y^2}{15} = 1$, or $15x^2 + 16y^2 = 240$.

29.   We have $c = 2$ and $a = 5$, so the equation has a form of:

$$\dfrac{x^2}{b^2} + \dfrac{y^2}{25} = 1$$

We find b:

$$c^2 = a^2 - b^2$$
$$4 = 25 - b^2$$
$$21 = b^2$$

So the equation is $\dfrac{x^2}{21} + \dfrac{y^2}{25} = 1$, or $25x^2 + 21y^2 = 525$.

31.   We know $a = 2b$ and that the equation has a form of:

$$\dfrac{x^2}{a^2} + \dfrac{y^2}{b^2} = 1$$

Using the point $(1, \sqrt{2})$ and $a = 2b$, we have:

$$\dfrac{1}{(2b)^2} + \dfrac{2}{b^2} = 1$$

$$\dfrac{1}{4b^2} + \dfrac{2}{b^2} = 1$$

Multiply by $4b^2$:

$$1 + 8 = 4b^2$$
$$\dfrac{9}{4} = b^2$$
$$\dfrac{3}{2} = b$$

Since $a = 2b$, then $a = 3$.

So the equation is $\dfrac{x^2}{3^2} + \dfrac{y^2}{(3/2)^2} = 1$, or $x^2 + 4y^2 = 9$.

33. (a) Using the equation $\dfrac{x_1 x}{a^2} + \dfrac{y_1 y}{b^2} = 1$, where $(x_1, y_1) = (8, 2)$, $a^2 = 76$,

$b^2 = \dfrac{76}{3}$, we have:

$$\dfrac{8x}{76} + \dfrac{2y}{76/3} = 1$$
$$8x + 6y = 76$$
$$6y = -8x + 76$$
$$y = -\dfrac{4}{3}x + \dfrac{38}{3}$$

(b) Here $(x_1, y_1) = (-7, 3)$, $a^2 = 76$, $b^2 = \dfrac{76}{3}$:

$$-\dfrac{7x}{76} + \dfrac{3y}{76/3} = 1$$
$$-7x + 9y = 76$$
$$9y = 7x + 76$$
$$y = \dfrac{7}{9}x + \dfrac{76}{9}$$

(c) Here $(x_1, y_1) = (1, -5)$, $a^2 = 76$, $b^2 = \dfrac{76}{3}$:

$$\dfrac{x}{76} - \dfrac{5y}{76/3} = 1$$
$$x - 15y = 76$$
$$-15y = -x + 76$$
$$y = \dfrac{1}{15}x - \dfrac{76}{15}$$

35. (a) Using the tangent formula where $(x_1, y_1) = (4, 2)$, $a^2 = \dfrac{52}{3}$, $b^2 = 52$:

$$\dfrac{4x}{52/3} + \dfrac{2y}{52} = 1$$
$$12x + 2y = 52$$
$$2y = -12x + 52$$
$$y = -6x + 26$$

(b) The y-intercept is 26 and the x-intercept is $\dfrac{13}{3}$, so the area is:

$$\dfrac{1}{2}\,(\text{base})(\text{height}) = \dfrac{1}{2}\left(\dfrac{13}{3}\right)(26) = \dfrac{169}{3}$$

37. (a)   Substituting the point, we have:

$$9x^2 + 25y^2 = 9(1)^2 + 25\left(\frac{6\sqrt{6}}{5}\right)^2 = 9 + 216 = 225$$

(b)   Here $(x_1, y_1) = \left(1, \frac{6\sqrt{6}}{5}\right)$, $a^2 = 25$, $b^2 = 9$:

$$\frac{x}{25} + \frac{\frac{6\sqrt{6}}{5}y}{9} = 1$$
$$9x + 30\sqrt{6}\,y = 225$$
$$3x + 10\sqrt{6}\,y - 75 = 0$$

(c) $c^2 = a^2 - b^2 = 25 - 9 = 16$, so $c = 4$. Thus the coordinates of F_1 and F_2 are $F_1\,(-4, 0)$ and $F_2\,(4, 0)$. We now find each distance:

$$d_1 = \frac{|-12 + 0 - 75|}{\sqrt{9 + 600}} = \frac{87}{\sqrt{609}}$$
$$d_2 = \frac{|12 + 0 - 75|}{\sqrt{9 + 600}} = \frac{63}{\sqrt{609}}$$

(d) $d_1 d_2 = \frac{87}{\sqrt{609}} \bullet \frac{63}{\sqrt{609}} = \frac{5481}{609} = 9$, which is b^2.

39. $\dfrac{x^2}{1} + \dfrac{y^2}{16} = 1$

$$\frac{y^2}{16} = 1 - x^2$$
$$y^2 = 16(1 - x^2)$$
$$y = \pm\sqrt{16(1 - x^2)}$$
$$y = \pm 4\sqrt{1 - x^2}$$

We use a calculator to fill in the table:

x	0	0.1	0.2	0.3	0.4	0.5	0.6	0.7	0.8	0.9	1.0
y	±4	±3.98	±3.92	±3.82	±3.67	±3.46	±3.2	±2.86	±2.4	±1.74	0

Now draw the graph:

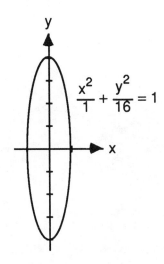

$$\frac{x^2}{1} + \frac{y^2}{16} = 1$$

41. From Figure 4, we have $F_1P + F_2P > F_1F_2$. But by definition, $F_1P + F_2P = 2a$, while $F_1F_2 = 2c$. Thus $2a > 2c$, or $a > c$, so $a^2 > c^2$ (since a, c positive), and consequently $a^2 - c^2 > 0$.

43. The tangent at (x_1, y_1) has equation:
$$\frac{x_1x}{a^2} + \frac{y_1y}{b^2} = 1$$
which has slope $\frac{-x_1b^2}{y_1a^2}$. Thus the normal has slope $\frac{y_1a^2}{x_1b^2}$ and equation:
$$y - y_1 = \frac{y_1a^2}{x_1b^2}(x - x_1)$$
$$b^2x_1y - b^2x_1y_1 = y_1a^2x - a^2x_1y_1$$
$$a^2y_1x - b^2x_1y = (a^2 - b^2)x_1y_1$$

45. If we first multiply each equation by a^2b^2, we have:
$$b^2x^2 + a^2y^2 = a^2b^2$$
$$a^2x^2 + b^2y^2 = a^2b^2$$
Multiply the first equation by $-a^2$ and the second equation by b^2:
$$-a^2b^2x^2 - a^4y^2 = -a^4b^2$$
$$a^2b^2x^2 + b^4y^2 = a^2b^4$$

Adding, we have:

$$(b^4 - a^4)y^2 = a^2b^2(b^2 - a^2)$$

$$y^2 = \frac{a^2b^2}{b^2 + a^2}$$

$$y = \pm\frac{ab}{\sqrt{a^2 + b^2}}$$

Substituting into the first equation:

$$b^2x^2 + \frac{a^4b^2}{a^2 + b^2} = a^2b^2$$

$$b^2x^2 = \frac{a^2b^4}{a^2 + b^2}$$

$$x^2 = \frac{a^2b^2}{a^2 + b^2}$$

$$x = \pm\frac{ab}{\sqrt{a^2 + b^2}}$$

So there are four intersection points:

$$\left(\frac{ab}{A}, \frac{ab}{A}\right), \left(\frac{ab}{A}, -\frac{ab}{A}\right), \left(-\frac{ab}{A}, \frac{ab}{A}\right), \left(-\frac{ab}{A}, -\frac{ab}{A}\right), \text{ where } A = \sqrt{a^2 + b^2}$$

We sketch the intersection:

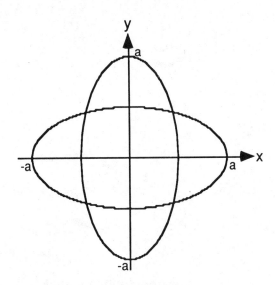

47. Using exercise #43, we find that N is the point $\left(\frac{(a^2 - b^2)x_1}{a^2}, 0\right)$. Thus:

$$FN = \frac{(a^2 - b^2)x_1}{a^2} + c = \frac{c^2}{a^2}x_1 + c = e^2x_1 + c$$

It can be shown using $\dfrac{x_1^2}{a^2} + \dfrac{y_1^2}{b^2} = 1$ that $y_1 = a^2 - c^2 - x_1^2 + e^2 x_1^2$. Now:

$$
\begin{aligned}
FP &= \sqrt{(x_1 + c)^2 + y_1^2} \\
&= \sqrt{x_1^2 + 2x_1 c + c^2 + a^2 - c^2 - x_1^2 + e^2 x_1^2} \\
&= \sqrt{e^2 x_1^2 + 2aex_1 + a^2} \\
&= ex_1 + a
\end{aligned}
$$

Thus:

$$
\frac{FN}{FP} = \frac{e^2 x_1 + c}{ex_1 + a} = \frac{e(ex_1 + a)}{ex_1 + a} = e
$$

49. (a) $5^2 + 3(1)^2 = 25 + 3 = 28$
    $4^2 + 3(-2)^2 = 16 + 12 = 28$
    $(-1)^2 + 3(3)^2 = 1 + 27 = 28$

(b) AB has slope $\dfrac{-2 - 1}{4 - 5} = 3$. The line containing C parallel to AB has equation:

$$
\begin{aligned}
y - 3 &= 3(x + 1) \\
y &= 3x + 6
\end{aligned}
$$

The intersections of this line with the ellipse have x-coordinates such that:

$$
\begin{aligned}
x^2 + 3(3x + 6)^2 &= 28 \\
x^2 + 27x^2 + 108x + 108 &= 28 \\
7x^2 + 27x + 20 &= 0 \\
(7x + 20)(x + 1) &= 0 \\
x &= -\frac{20}{7}, -1
\end{aligned}
$$

Thus the point D we want is $\left(-\dfrac{20}{7}, -\dfrac{18}{7}\right)$.

(c) O is $(0, 0)$. We use the suggested formula:

$$
\text{Area of } \triangle OAC = \frac{1}{2}\left| 0 - 0 + 5 \bullet 3 - (-1)(1) + 0 - 0 \right| = 8
$$

$$
\text{Area of } \triangle OBD = \frac{1}{2}\left| 0 - 0 + 4\left(-\frac{18}{7}\right) - (-2)\left(-\frac{20}{7}\right) + 0 - 0 \right| = 8
$$

Thus the areas are equal.

51. (a) $a\sqrt{(x + c)^2 + y^2} = a^2 + xc$

Dividing by a and noting that $e = \dfrac{c}{a}$:

$\sqrt{(x + c)^2 + y^2} = a + xe$
But the radical is F_1P by the distance formula, so:
$F_1P = a + xe$

(b) We have:
$$F_1P + F_2P = 2a$$
$$(a + xe) + F_2P = 2a$$
$$F_2P = a - xe$$

53. (a) We know from the formula:
$$\frac{x_1x}{a^2} + \frac{y_1y}{b^2} = 1$$
Multiply by a^2b^2:
$$b^2x_1x + a^2y_1y = a^2b^2$$

(b) Since (h, k) lies on this line, replacing (x, y) with (h, k) results in:
$$b^2x_1h + a^2y_1k = a^2b^2$$

(c) Repeating part (a), we have $b^2x_2x + a^2y_2y = a^2b^2$. Now substitute (h, k) to get $b^2x_2h + a^2y_2k = a^2b^2$

(d) Replacing (x, y) with (x_1, y_1) and (x_2, y_2), respectively, results in the equations we have proved in (b) and (c). Thus thus line must pass through the points (x_1, y_1) and (x_2, y_2).

55. By exercise #51(b), $F_2P = a - ex$, and $PR = \dfrac{a}{e} - x$. Thus:

$$\frac{F_2P}{PR} = \frac{a - ex}{\dfrac{a}{e} - x} \bullet \frac{e}{e} = \frac{e(a - ex)}{a - ex} = e$$

57. Since (0, 0) is the center, then $D = \dfrac{a}{e}$ and $d = \dfrac{a}{e} - c$, thus:

$$\frac{D}{d} = \frac{\dfrac{a}{e}}{\dfrac{a}{e} - c} = \frac{a}{a - ce} = \frac{a}{a - c \bullet (c/a)} = \frac{a^2}{a^2 - c^2} = \frac{a^2}{b^2}$$

59. (a) Substituting in, we see that:

$$\frac{c^2}{a^2} + \frac{(b^2/a)^2}{b^2} = \frac{a^2 - b^2}{a^2} + \frac{b^2}{a^2} = 1$$

So $\left(c, \dfrac{b^2}{2a}\right)$ lies on the ellipse.

(b) The equation of the tangent is:

$$\frac{cx}{a^2} + \frac{\dfrac{b^2}{a}y}{b^2} = 1$$

$$\frac{cx}{a^2} + \frac{y}{a} = 1$$

The x-coordinate of the point of intersection is $\dfrac{a}{e}$, and the y-coordinate is the solution of:

$$\frac{c(a/e)}{a^2} + \frac{y}{a} = 1$$

$$\frac{a^2}{a^2} + \frac{y}{a} = 1$$

$$y = 0$$

Thus, the required point is $\left(\dfrac{a}{e}, 0\right)$.

61. Let P have coordinates (x_1, y_1) and Q have coordinates (x_1, y_2). The center of the circle is $(0, 0)$, and the slope of the normal through P is thus $\dfrac{y_1 - 0}{x_1 - 0} = \dfrac{y_1}{x_1}$. Thus the slope of the tangent through P is $-\dfrac{x_1}{y_1}$, and its equation is:

$$y - y_1 = -\frac{x_1}{y_1}(x - x_1)$$

$$yy_1 - y_1^2 = -x_1 x + x_1^2$$

$$x_1 x = -y_1 y + x_1^2 + y_1^2$$

$$x_1 x = -y_1 y + a^2$$

The tangent of the ellipse through Q has equation $\dfrac{x_1 x}{a^2} + \dfrac{y_2 y}{b^2} = 1$. Thus the y-coordinate of the point of intersection is the solution of:

$$\frac{-y_1 y + a^2}{a^2} + \frac{y_2 y}{b^2} = 1$$

$$\left(\frac{y_2}{b^2} - \frac{y_1}{a^2}\right)y = 0$$

If $\dfrac{y_2}{b^2} - \dfrac{y_1}{a^2} = 0$ then any y-value corresponds to a point of intersection, so the lines are the same. So the points are the same, contradicting our hypothesis that the points are distinct. Otherwise, $y = 0$, as required.
Note: We implicitly assumed $x_1 \neq 0$ earlier, when assuming $x_1 x \neq 0$. Note that the lines do not intersect if $x_1 = 0$.

63. Let P have coordinates (x_1, y_1). Then by exercise #62(a), Q has coordinates $(-x_1, -y_1)$. The tangent through P has equation:

$$\frac{x_1 x}{a^2} + \frac{y_1 y}{b^2} = 1$$

$$y = \frac{b^2}{y_1}\left(\frac{-x_1 x}{a^2} + 1\right)$$

So its slope is $-\dfrac{b^2 x_1}{y_1 a^2}$. The tangent through Q has equation:

$$-\frac{x_1 x}{a^2} + \frac{-y_1 y}{b^2} = 1$$

$$y = \frac{b^2}{y_1}\left(\frac{x_1 x}{a^2} + 1\right)$$

So its slope is $\dfrac{b^2 x_1}{y_1 a^2}$, the same as that of the other tangent. Thus the two tangents are parallel, as required.

65. (a)   Using the formula $d = \dfrac{\left|Ax_0 + By_0 + c\right|}{\sqrt{A^2 + B^2}}$, we have:

$$F_1 A = \frac{\left|-c\left(\dfrac{x_1}{a^2}\right) + 0 - 1\right|}{\sqrt{A^2 + B^2}} = \frac{\left|\dfrac{x_1 c}{a^2} + 1\right|}{\sqrt{A^2 + B^2}},$$

where $A = \dfrac{x_1}{a^2}$ and $B = \dfrac{y_1}{b^2}$.

(b)   Making the substitution $c = ae$ and $a + ex_1 = F_1 P$, we have:

$$F_1 A = \frac{\left|\dfrac{x_1 e}{a} + 1\right|}{\sqrt{A^2 + B^2}} = \frac{\left|x_1 e + a\right|}{a\sqrt{A^2 + B^2}} = \frac{F_1 P}{a\sqrt{A^2 + B^2}}$$

(c) F_2B is the distance from the point $(c, 0)$ to $\dfrac{x_1 x}{a^2} + \dfrac{y_1 y}{b^2} = 1$, so:

$$F_2B = \frac{\left| c\left(\dfrac{x_1}{a^2}\right) + 0 - 1 \right|}{\sqrt{A^2 + B^2}} = \frac{\left| \dfrac{x_1 c}{a^2} - 1 \right|}{\sqrt{A^2 + B^2}}$$

Now making the substitution $c = ae$ and $a - ex_1 = F_2P$, we have:

$$F_2B = \frac{\left| \dfrac{x_1 e}{a} - 1 \right|}{\sqrt{A^2 + B^2}} = \frac{|x_1 e - a|}{a\sqrt{A^2 + B^2}} = \frac{|a - x_1 e|}{a\sqrt{A^2 + B^2}} = \frac{F_2P}{a\sqrt{A^2 + B^2}}$$

(d)   We evaluate each quotient:

$$\frac{F_1A}{F_1P} = \frac{1}{a\sqrt{A^2 + B^2}} \quad \text{and} \quad \frac{F_2B}{F_2P} = \frac{1}{a\sqrt{A^2 + B^2}}$$

Thus they are equal.

8.4 The Hyperbola

1. $x^2 - 4y^2 = 4$

$\dfrac{x^2}{4} - \dfrac{y^2}{1} = 1$

vertices: $(\pm 2, 0)$; transverse axis: 4; conjugate axis: 2

asymptotes: $y = \pm \dfrac{1}{2} x$; foci: $(\pm\sqrt{5}, 0)$; eccentricity: $\dfrac{\sqrt{5}}{2}$

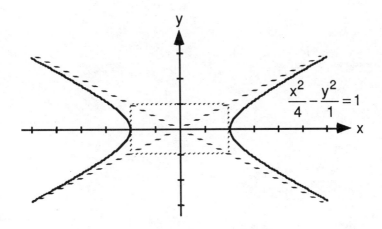

3. $y^2 - 4x^2 = 4$

$\dfrac{y^2}{4} - \dfrac{x^2}{1} = 1$

vertices: $(0, \pm 2)$
transverse axis: 4
conjugate axis: 2
asymptotes: $y = \pm 2x$
foci: $(0, \pm\sqrt{5})$

eccentricity: $\dfrac{\sqrt{5}}{2}$

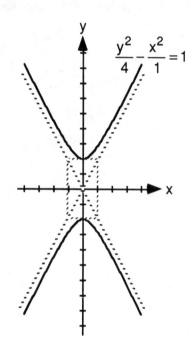

$\dfrac{y^2}{4} - \dfrac{x^2}{1} = 1$

5. $16x^2 - 25y^2 = 400$

$$\frac{x^2}{25} - \frac{y^2}{16} = 1$$

vertices: $(\pm 5, 0)$

transverse axis: 10

conjugate axis: 8

asymptotes: $y = \pm \frac{4}{5} x$

foci: $(\pm \sqrt{41}, 0)$

eccentricity: $\frac{\sqrt{41}}{5}$

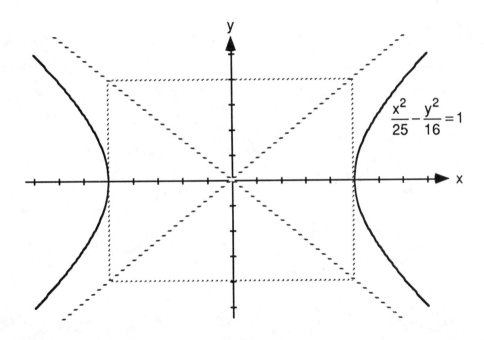

$$\frac{x^2}{25} - \frac{y^2}{16} = 1$$

7. $2y^2 - 3x^2 = 4$

$\dfrac{y^2}{1/2} - \dfrac{x^2}{1/3} = 1$

vertices: $\left(0, \pm\sqrt{\dfrac{1}{2}}\right)$

transverse axis: $\sqrt{2}$

conjugate axis: $\dfrac{2\sqrt{3}}{3}$

asymptotes: $y = \pm\sqrt{\dfrac{3}{2}}\,x$

foci: $\left(0, \pm\sqrt{\dfrac{5}{6}}\right)$

eccentricity: $\sqrt{\dfrac{5}{3}} = \dfrac{\sqrt{15}}{3}$

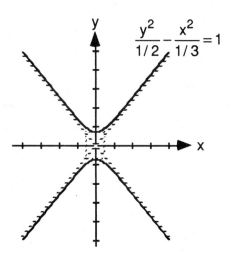

$$\dfrac{y^2}{1/2} - \dfrac{x^2}{1/3} = 1$$

9. $4y^2 - 25x^2 = 100$

$$\frac{y^2}{25} - \frac{x^2}{4} = 1$$

vertices: $(0, \pm 5)$

transverse axis: 10

conjugate axis: 4

asymptotes: $y = \pm \frac{5}{2} x$

foci: $(0, \pm \sqrt{29})$

eccentricity: $\frac{\sqrt{29}}{5}$

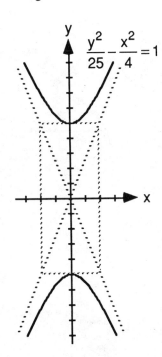

11. $\dfrac{(x-5)^2}{25} - \dfrac{(y+1)^2}{9} = 1$

center: (5, -1)
vertices: (10, -1), (0, -1)
transverse axis: 10
conjugate axis: 6

asymptotes: $y = \dfrac{3}{5}x - 4$, $y = -\dfrac{3}{5}x + 2$

foci: $(5 \pm \sqrt{34}, -1)$

eccentricity: $\dfrac{\sqrt{34}}{5}$

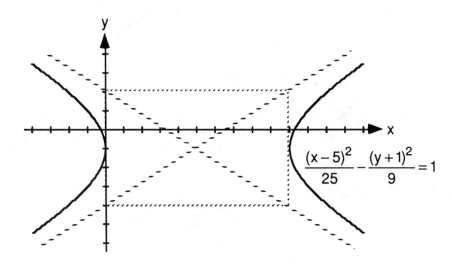

13. $\dfrac{(y-2)^2}{4} - \dfrac{(x-1)^2}{1} = 1$

center: $(1, 2)$
vertices: $(1, 4)$, $(1, 0)$
transverse axis: 4
conjugate axis: 2
asymptotes: $y = 2x$, $y = -2x + 4$
foci: $(1, 2 \pm \sqrt{5})$
eccentricity: $\dfrac{\sqrt{5}}{2}$

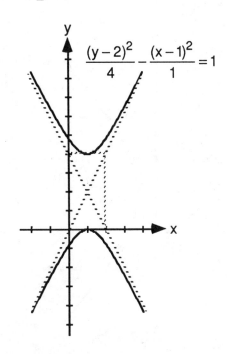

$$\dfrac{(y-2)^2}{4} - \dfrac{(x-1)^2}{1} = 1$$

15. $\dfrac{(x+3)^2}{16} - \dfrac{(y-4)^2}{16} = 1$

center: (-3, 4)
vertices: (1, 4), (-7, 4)
transverse axis: 8
conjugate axis: 8
asymptotes: $y = x + 7$, $y = -x + 1$

foci: $(-3 \pm 4\sqrt{2}, 4)$

eccentricity: $\dfrac{4\sqrt{2}}{4} = \sqrt{2}$

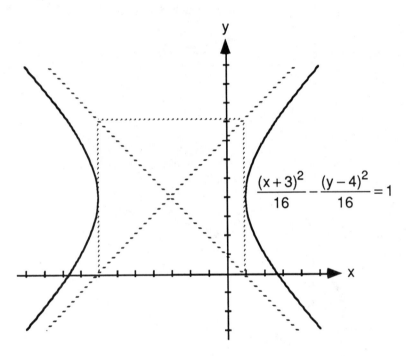

$\dfrac{(x+3)^2}{16} - \dfrac{(y-4)^2}{16} = 1$

17. $x^2 - y^2 + 2y - 5 = 0$

$x^2 - (y^2 - 2y) = 5$

$x^2 - (y^2 - 2y + 1) = 5 - 1$

$x^2 - (y - 1)^2 = 4$

$\dfrac{x^2}{4} - \dfrac{(y - 1)^2}{4} = 1$

center: $(0, 1)$

vertices: $(\pm 2, 1)$

transverse axis: 4

conjugate axis: 4

asymptotes: $y = x + 1,\ y = -x + 1$

foci: $(\pm 2\sqrt{2}, 1)$

eccentricity: $\dfrac{2\sqrt{2}}{2} = \sqrt{2}$

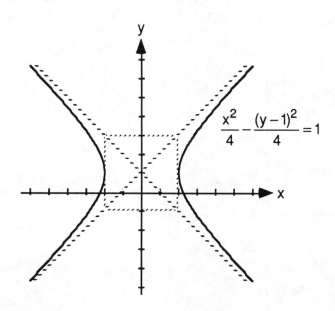

$$\dfrac{x^2}{4} - \dfrac{(y - 1)^2}{4} = 1$$

19.
$$x^2 - y^2 - 4x + 2y - 6 = 0$$
$$(x^2 - 4x) - (y^2 - 2y) = 6$$
$$(x^2 - 4x + 4) - (y^2 - 2y + 1) = 6 + 4 - 1$$
$$(x - 2)^2 - (y - 1)^2 = 9$$
$$\frac{(x - 2)^2}{9} - \frac{(y - 1)^2}{9} = 1$$

center: (2, 1)
vertices: (-1, 1), (5, 1)
transverse axis: 6
conjugate axis: 6
asymptotes: $y = x - 1$, $y = -x + 3$
foci: $(2 \pm 3\sqrt{2}, 1)$
eccentricity: $\dfrac{3\sqrt{2}}{3} = \sqrt{2}$

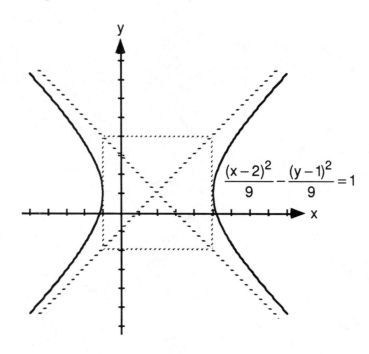

$$\frac{(x-2)^2}{9} - \frac{(y-1)^2}{9} = 1$$

21.　　　$y^2 - 25x^2 + 8y - 9 = 0$

$(y^2 + 8y) - 25x^2 = 9$

$(y^2 + 8y + 16) - 25x^2 = 9 + 16$

$(y + 4)^2 - 25x^2 = 25$

$$\frac{(y + 4)^2}{25} - \frac{x^2}{1} = 1$$

center: (0, -4)

vertices: (0, -9), (0, 1)

transverse axis: 10

conjugate axis: 2

asymptotes: $y = 5x - 4$, $y = -5x - 4$

foci: $(0, -4 \pm \sqrt{26})$

eccentricity: $\dfrac{\sqrt{26}}{5}$

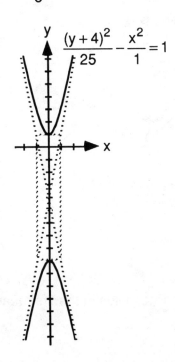

23.
$$x^2 + 7x - y^2 - y + 12 = 0$$
$$(x^2 + 7x) - (y^2 + y) = -12$$
$$\left(x^2 + 7x + \frac{49}{4}\right) - \left(y^2 + y + \frac{1}{4}\right) = -12 + \frac{49}{4} - \frac{1}{4}$$
$$\left(x + \frac{7}{2}\right)^2 - \left(y + \frac{1}{2}\right)^2 = 0$$

Notice that this is a degenerate hyperbola, and the graph consists of the two lines: $y = x + 3$ and $y = -x - 4$

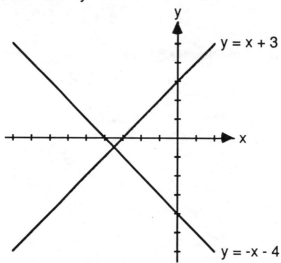

25. Since $P(x, y)$ lies on $\frac{x^2}{4} - \frac{y^2}{1} = 1$, we can find y in terms of x:

$$y^2 = \frac{x^2}{4} - 1$$
$$y^2 = \frac{x^2 - 4}{4}$$

Taking roots, we have $y = \frac{\sqrt{x^2 - 4}}{2}$, since $P(x, y)$ lies in the first quadrant.

So the coordinates of P are $\left(x, \frac{\sqrt{x^2 - 4}}{2}\right)$.

Since $Q(x, y)$ lies in the first quadrant on the asymptote, we find the equation of the asymptote:

$$y - 0 = \frac{1}{2}(x - 0)$$
$$y = \frac{1}{2}x$$

So the coordinates of Q are $\left(x, \frac{1}{2}x\right)$.

We find PQ by using the distance formula:

$$PQ = \sqrt{(x - x)^2 + \left(\frac{\sqrt{x^2 - 4}}{2} - \frac{x}{2}\right)^2}$$

$$= \sqrt{\left(\frac{\sqrt{x^2 - 4} - x}{2}\right)^2}$$

$$= \frac{x - \sqrt{x^2 - 4}}{2}$$

The choice of signs is because the asymptote lies above the hyperbola in the first quadrant, and thus $\frac{x}{2}$ is larger than $\frac{\sqrt{x^2 - 4}}{2}$. This proves the desired result.

27. Since the foci are $(\pm 4, 0)$ and the vertices are $(\pm 1, 0)$, then $c = 4$, $a = 1$, and the hyperbola has the form:

$$\frac{x^2}{1} - \frac{y^2}{b^2} = 1$$

We find b:

$$c^2 = a^2 + b^2$$
$$16 = 1 + b^2$$
$$15 = b^2$$

So the equation is $\frac{x^2}{1} - \frac{y^2}{15} = 1$, or $15x^2 - y^2 = 15$.

29. The slope of the asymptotes, $\pm\frac{1}{2}$, tells us that the ratio $\frac{b}{a} = \frac{1}{2}$ in this hyperbola. Also, since the vertices are $(\pm 2, 0)$, $a = 2$. The required ratio is therefore:

$$\frac{b}{2} = \frac{1}{2} \text{ and } b = 1$$

The equation is:

$$\frac{x^2}{4} - \frac{y^2}{1} = 1, \text{ or } x^2 - 4y^2 = 4$$

31. Since the asymptotes are $y = \pm\frac{\sqrt{10}}{5}x$, then $\frac{b}{a} = \frac{\sqrt{10}}{5}$, so $b = \frac{\sqrt{10}}{5}a$.

Now, since the foci are $(\pm\sqrt{7}, 0)$, then $c = \sqrt{7}$ and the hyperbola has the form:

$$\frac{x^2}{a^2} - \frac{y^2}{b^2} = 1$$

Since $b = \dfrac{\sqrt{10}}{5}\, a$ and $c = \sqrt{7}$, we have:

$$c^2 = a^2 + b^2$$
$$7 = a^2 + \left(\dfrac{\sqrt{10}}{5}\, a\right)^2$$
$$7 = a^2 + \dfrac{2}{5}\, a^2$$
$$35 = 7a^2$$
$$5 = a^2$$
$$b^2 = \dfrac{2}{5}\, a^2 = \dfrac{2}{5}\, (5) = 2$$

So the equation is $\dfrac{x^2}{5} - \dfrac{y^2}{2} = 1$, or $2x^2 - 5y^2 = 10$.

33. The vertices are at $(0, \pm 7)$ so we know it is a "vertical" hyperbola. Its equation will be $\dfrac{y^2}{49} - \dfrac{x^2}{b^2} = 1$, but we also know that $(1, 9)$ is a point satisfying the equation. We use it to find b:

$$\dfrac{81}{49} - \dfrac{1}{b^2} = 1$$
$$81b^2 - 49 = 49b^2$$
$$-49 = -32b^2$$
$$b^2 = \dfrac{49}{32}$$
$$\dfrac{y^2}{49} - \dfrac{32x^2}{49} = 1, \text{ or } y^2 - 32x^2 = 49$$

35. We have $2a = 6$, so $a = 3$. Also $2b = 2$, so $b = 1$. Since the foci are on the y-axis, the hyperbola will have the form:

$$\dfrac{y^2}{a^2} - \dfrac{x^2}{b^2} = 1$$

So the equation is $\dfrac{y^2}{9} - \dfrac{x^2}{1} = 1$, or $y^2 - 9x^2 = 9$.

37. Writing the equation as $\dfrac{x^2}{16} - \dfrac{y^2}{16} = 1$, we have $a = b = 4$. So the slopes of the asymptotes are $\pm \dfrac{b}{a} = \pm \dfrac{4}{4} = \pm 1$. But these are negative reciprocals of each other, so the asymptotes are perpendicular to each other.

39. (a) Let's substitute:
$$5(6)^2 - 4(5)^2 = 5(36) - 4(25) = 180 - 100 = 80 \text{ yes!}$$

(b) $$\frac{5y^2}{80} - \frac{4x^2}{80} = \frac{80}{90}$$

$$\frac{y^2}{16} - \frac{x^2}{20} = 1$$

So $a = 4$ and $b = 2\sqrt{5}$
$$c^2 = a^2 + b^2 = 16 + 20 = 36$$
So $c = 6$ and the foci will be at $(0, \pm 6)$.

(c) $$F_1P = \sqrt{(5-0)^2 + (6-6)^2} = 5$$
$$F_2P = \sqrt{(5-0)^2 + (6-(-6))^2} = \sqrt{25 + 144} = 13$$

(d) $$\left| F_1P - F_2P \right| = \left| 5 - 13 \right| = \left| -8 \right| = 8 = 2a$$

41. (a) Since the asymptotes must have slopes of $\pm \dfrac{b}{a}$, then:

$$-\frac{b}{a} = \frac{-1}{b/a}$$

$$\frac{b^2}{a^2} = 1$$

$$b^2 = a^2$$

$$b = a$$

Now, since $c^2 = a^2 + b^2 = 2a^2$, then the eccentricity is:

$$\frac{c}{a} = \frac{\sqrt{2a^2}}{a} = \frac{\sqrt{2}\,a}{a} = \sqrt{2}$$

(b) The slopes of the asymptotes are $\dfrac{\pm a}{a} = \pm 1$, so the hyperbola will have perpendicular asymptotes.

The eccentricity is: $\dfrac{\sqrt{2}\,a}{a} = \sqrt{2}$

43. (a) This equation is just $F_1P - F_2P = 2a$, the defining relation of a hyperbola. (Since P is on the right-hand branch, $F_1P > F_2P$)

(b)
$$\sqrt{(x + c)^2 + y^2} = 2a + \sqrt{(x - c)^2 + y^2}$$
$$(x + c)^2 + y^2 = 4a^2 + 4a\sqrt{(x - c)^2 + y^2} + (x - c)^2 + y^2$$
$$4xc = 4a^2 + 4a\sqrt{(x - c)^2 + y^2}$$
$$xc - a^2 = a\sqrt{(x - c)^2 + y^2}$$
$$xc - a^2 = a(F_2P)$$

(c)
$$\frac{xc}{a} - a = F_2P$$
$$xe - a = F_2P$$

45. For this hyperbola we find $a^2 = b^2 = k^2$, and $e = \sqrt{2}$. Also $d^2 = x^2 + y^2 = x^2 + (x^2 - k^2) = 2x^2 - k^2$. Thus we want to show that $F_1P \cdot F_2P = 2x^2 - k^2$. Using the formulas for F_1P and F_2P developed in exercises #43-44, we have:
$$F_1P \cdot F_2P = (xe + a)(xe - a)$$
$$= x^2e^2 - a^2$$
$$= x^2(2) - k^2$$
$$= 2x^2 - k^2$$
$$= d^2$$

47. The coordinates of D are $\left(\frac{a}{e}, \frac{b}{e}\right)$ and those of F are $(c, 0)$. Let O denote the center $(0, 0)$. We show that $\angle ODF$ is a right angle by showing $OD^2 + DF^2 = OF^2$:
$$OF^2 = c^2$$
$$OD^2 = \left(\frac{a}{e}\right)^2 + \left(\frac{b}{e}\right)^2 = \frac{a^2 + b^2}{e^2} = \frac{c^2}{e^2} = a^2$$
$$DF^2 = \left(\frac{a}{e} - c\right)^2 + \left(\frac{b}{e}\right)^2$$
$$= \frac{(a - ec)^2 + b^2}{e^2}$$
$$= \frac{a^2 + b^2 - 2aec + e^2c^2}{e^2}$$
$$= \frac{c^2 - 2c^2}{e^2} + c^2$$
$$= -\frac{c^2}{e^2} + c^2$$
$$= -a^2 + c^2$$

Thus $OD^2 + DF^2 = OF^2$ as required.

49. We draw the sketch:

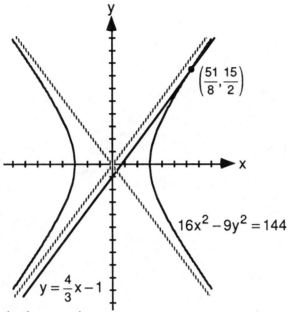

By substitution, we have:

$$16x^2 - 9\left(\frac{4}{3}x - 1\right)^2 = 144$$

$$16x^2 - 9\left(\frac{16}{9}x^2 - \frac{8}{3}x + 1\right) = 144$$

$$16x^2 - 16x^2 + 24x - 9 = 144$$

$$24x = 153$$

$$x = \frac{51}{8}$$

$$y = \frac{4}{3} \bullet \frac{51}{8} - 1 = \frac{17}{2} - 1 = \frac{15}{2}$$

Therefore $\left(\frac{51}{8}, \frac{15}{2}\right)$ is the intersection point.

51. (a) $e = \dfrac{c}{a} = \dfrac{\sqrt{a^2 + b^2}}{a} = \sqrt{\dfrac{a^2 + b^2}{a^2}} = \sqrt{1 + \dfrac{b^2}{a^2}}$

   (b) (i) Converting to standard form, we have: $\dfrac{x^2}{1} - \dfrac{y^2}{.0201} = 1$

   So $c^2 = 1 + .0201 = 1.0201$, thus $c = 1.01$.

   Then $e = \dfrac{c}{a} = 1.01$.

(ii)   Converting to standard form, we have: $\dfrac{x^2}{1} - \dfrac{y^2}{3} = 1$

So $c^2 = 1 + 3 = 4$, thus $c = 2$.

Then $e = \dfrac{c}{a} = 2$.

(iii)   Converting to standard form, we have: $\dfrac{x^2}{1} - \dfrac{y^2}{8} = 1$

So $c^2 = 1 + 8 = 9$, thus $c = 3$.

Then $e = \dfrac{c}{a} = 3$.

(iv)   Converting to standard form, we have: $\dfrac{x^2}{1} - \dfrac{y^2}{15} = 1$

So $c^2 = 1 + 15 = 16$, thus $c = 4$.

Then $e = \dfrac{c}{a} = 4$.

(v)   Converting to standard form, we have: $\dfrac{x^2}{1} - \dfrac{y^2}{99} = 1$

So $c^2 = 1 + 99 = 100$, thus $c = 10$.

Then $e = \dfrac{c}{a} = 10$.

(c)   We draw the graphs:

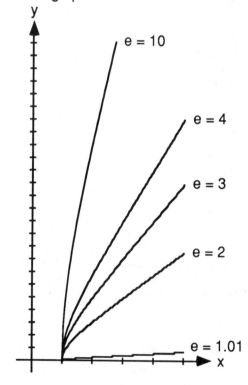

(d) It appears the eccentricity affects the width of the hyperbola. That is, larger eccentricities result in a much wider curve than eccentricities closer to 1.

53. We have $(x_1, y_1) = (4, 6)$, $a^2 = 4$, $b^2 = 12$:

$$\frac{4x}{4} - \frac{6y}{12} = 1$$

$$x - \frac{y}{2} = 1$$

$$2x - y = 2$$

$$-y = -2x + 2$$

$$y = 2x - 2$$

55. The equation $\dfrac{x^2}{a^2} - \dfrac{y^2}{b^2} = 1$ is equivalent to $b^2x^2 - a^2y^2 = a^2b^2$ (1)

So (x_1, y_1) is on the hyperbola if and only if:

$$b^2x_1{}^2 - a^2y_1{}^2 = a^2b^2$$

Thus if (x_1, y_1) is on the hyperbola then the equation of the hyperbola can be written as:

$$b^2(x^2 - x_1{}^2) - a^2(y^2 - y_1{}^2) = 0$$

Let $y - y_1 = m(x - x_1)$ be the equation of the tangent to the hyperbola through (x_1, y_1). Then as in the referenced exercise from the preceeding section, the system:

$$b^2(x^2 - x_1{}^2) - a^2(y^2 - y_1{}^2) = 0 \qquad (2)$$
$$y - y_1 = m(x - x_1)$$

has exactly one solution, (x_1, y_1). Substutituting $y = m(x - x_1) + y_1$ into (2), we get:

$$b^2(x^2 - x_1{}^2) - a^2[(m(x - x_1) + y_1)^2 - y_1{}^2] = 0$$
$$b^2(x^2 - x_1{}^2) - a^2m^2(x - x_1)^2 - 2a^2my_1(x - x_1) = 0$$
$$(x - x_1)\,[b^2(x + x_1) - a^2m^2(x - x_1) - 2a^2my_1] = 0$$

Since x_1 is the only solution, it is a double root, so:

$$b^2(x_1 + x_1) - a^2m^2(x_1 - x_1) - 2a^2my_1 = 0$$
$$2a^2my_1 = 2b^2x_1$$
$$m = \frac{b^2x_1}{a^2y_1}$$

Thus the tangent line has equation:

$$y - y_1 = \frac{b^2 x_1}{a^2 y_1}(x - x_1)$$

$$a^2 y_1 y - a^2 y_1^2 = b^2 x_1 x - b^2 x_1^2$$

$$b^2 x_1 x - a^2 y_1 y = b^2 x_1 - a^2 y_1^2$$

$$b^2 x_1 x - a^2 y_1 y = a^2 b^2$$

$$\frac{x_1 x}{a^2} - \frac{y_1 y}{b^2} = 1$$

Note that $m = \dfrac{b^2 x_1}{a^2 y_1}$ cannot be the slope $\pm\dfrac{b}{a}$ of as asymtote if (x_1, y_1) lies on the hyperbola, since if so then:

$$\pm\frac{b}{a} = \frac{b^2 x_1}{a^2 y_1}$$

$$\pm\frac{a}{b} y_1 = x_1$$

So:

$$\frac{\dfrac{a^2}{b^2} y_1^2}{a^2} - \frac{y_1^2}{b^2} = 0 \neq 1$$

57. By the Law of Sines:

$$\frac{F_2 P}{\sin\theta} = \frac{F_2 A}{\sin\alpha}$$

$$\frac{F_2 P}{F_2 A} = \frac{\sin\theta}{\sin\alpha}$$

Also by the Law of Sines:

$$\frac{F_1 P}{\sin(180° - \theta)} = \frac{F_1 A}{\sin\beta}$$

$$\frac{F_1 P}{F_1 A} = \frac{\sin\theta}{\sin\beta}$$

Thus if $\dfrac{F_2 P}{F_2 A} = \dfrac{F_1 P}{F_1 A}$, then $\dfrac{\sin\theta}{\sin\alpha} = \dfrac{\sin\theta}{\sin\beta}$ so $\sin\alpha = \sin\beta$. By construction α and β are acute, so $\alpha = \beta$ as required.

59. We know the slope of the tangent line at P is $\dfrac{b^2 x_1}{a^2 y_1}$, so the slope of the normal

is $\dfrac{-a^2 y_1}{b^2 x_1}$ and its equation is:

$$y - y_1 = \frac{-a^2 y_1}{b^2 x_1}(x - x_1)$$
$$b^2 x_1 y - b^2 x_1 y_1 = -a^2 y_1 x + a^2 y_1 x_1$$
$$a^2 y_1 x + b^2 x_1 y = x_1 y_1 (a^2 + b^2)$$

61. The equation of the normal line is $a^2 y_1 x + b^2 x_1 y = x_1 y_1 (a^2 + b^2)$.

Letting $y = 0$ we see that the x-intercept of the line is $x = \dfrac{x_1(a^2 + b^2)}{a^2}$.

Similarily, the y-intercept is found to be $y = \dfrac{y_1(a^2 + b^2)}{b^2}$. Thus the

coordinates of Q and R are $\left(\dfrac{x_1(a^2 + b^2)}{a^2}, 0 \right)$ and $\left(0, \dfrac{y_1(a^2 + b^2)}{b^2} \right)$.
The area of $\triangle OQR$ is :

$$\frac{1}{2} OQ \bullet OR = \frac{x_1 y_1 (a^2 + b^2)^2}{2 a^2 b^2}$$

63. The equation of the tangent line at the point P with coordinates (x_1, y_1) is

$\dfrac{x_1 x}{a^2} - \dfrac{y_1 y}{b^2} = 1$. The asymtotes are $y = \pm \dfrac{b}{a} x$. Suppose the tangent

intersects $y = \dfrac{b}{a} x$ at A and $y = -\dfrac{b}{a} x$ at B. The x-coordinate of A is found by
solving:

$$\frac{x_1 x}{a^2} - \frac{y_1 \frac{b}{a} x}{b^2} = 1$$
$$b x_1 x - a y_1 x = ba^2$$
$$x = \frac{ba^2}{bx_1 - ay_1}$$

So $y = \dfrac{b}{a} x = \dfrac{b^2 a}{bx_1 - ay_1}$. So A is the point $\left(\dfrac{ba^2}{bx_1 - ay_1}, \dfrac{b^2 a}{bx_1 - ay_1} \right)$.

The point B is similarly found to be $\left(\dfrac{ba^2}{bx_1 + ay_1}, \dfrac{b^2 a}{bx_1 + ay_1} \right)$.

The midpoint of AB has x-coordinate:

$$\frac{1}{2}\left(\frac{ba^2}{bx_1 - ay_1} + \frac{ba^2}{bx_1 - ay_1}\right) = \frac{1}{2}\left(\frac{ba^2(2bx_1)}{b^2x_1^2 - a^2y_1^2}\right)$$

$$= \frac{b^2a^2x_1}{b^2x_1^2 - a^2y_1^2}$$

Since $b^2x_1^2 - a^2y_1^2 = a^2b^2$, then:

$$= \frac{b^2a^2x_1}{a^2b^2}$$

$$= x_1$$

Similarly the y-coordinate of the midpoint is found to be y_1, so P is the midpoint of AB as required.

65. (a) The foci of the ellipse are given by $(\pm c, 0)$, where $c = \sqrt{a^2 - b^2}$.
The foci of the hyperbola are given by $(\pm d, 0)$ where

$d = \sqrt{a^2 - 2b^2 + b^2} = \sqrt{a^2 - b^2} = c$. Thus the two curves are confocal.

(b) Four. This can be shown algebraically, but it is easier to note that

$0 < \sqrt{a^2 - 2b^2} < a$ and look at the following sketch:

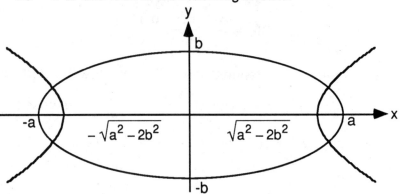

Note there is exactly one point of intersection in each quadrant.

(c) $e = \dfrac{c}{a} = \dfrac{C}{a}$

$E = \dfrac{C}{\sqrt{a^2 - 2b^2}}$

We will show that $\left(\dfrac{C}{eE}, \dfrac{b^2}{C}\right)$ lies on both curves. Note that:

$$\frac{C}{eE} = \frac{C}{\dfrac{C}{a} \bullet \dfrac{C}{\sqrt{a^2 + 2b^2}}} = \frac{a\sqrt{a^2 - 2b^2}}{C}$$

Thus:

$$\frac{(C/eE)^2}{a^2} + \frac{(b^2/C)^2}{b^2} = \frac{a^2(a^2 - 2b^2)}{a^2C^2} + \frac{b^4}{C^2b^2}$$

$$= \frac{a^2 - 2b^2 + b^2}{C^2}$$

$$= \frac{a^2 - b^2}{C^2}$$

$$= 1$$

So the point lies on the ellipse. Now checking the hyperbola:

$$\frac{(C/eE)^2}{a^2 - 2b^2} - \frac{(b^2/C)^2}{b^2} = \frac{a^2(a^2 - 2b^2)}{C^2(a^2 - 2b^2)} - \frac{b^4}{C^2b^2}$$

$$= \frac{a^2 - b^2}{C^2}$$

$$= 1$$

Thus the point lies on both the hyperbola and the ellipse. Since by part (b) only one point in the first quadrant lies on both curves, this is the one.

(d) Using exercise #64(f) from the preceeding section, we see that the slope of the tangent to the ellipse at P is:

$$-\frac{b^2(C/eE)}{a^2(b^2/C)} = -\frac{C^2}{a^2eE}$$

$$= \frac{-e^2}{eE} \quad (\text{since } e = \frac{C}{a})$$

$$= -\frac{e}{E}$$

Using exercise #55 we see that the slope of the tangent of the hyperbola at P is:

$$\frac{b^2(C/eE)}{(a^2 - 2b^2)(b^2/C)} = \frac{C^2}{a^2 - 2b^2} \cdot \frac{1}{eE}$$

$$= \frac{E^2}{eE} \quad \left(\text{since } E^2 = \frac{C^2}{a^2 - 2b^2}\right)$$

$$= \frac{E}{e}$$

Since the slopes of these two tangent lines at P are negative reciprocals of one another, the tangents are perpendicular.

8.5 Rotation of Axes

1.   For x, we have:

$$x = x' \cos \theta - y' \sin \theta$$
$$= \sqrt{3} \cos 30° - 2 \sin 30°$$
$$= \sqrt{3} \cdot \frac{\sqrt{3}}{2} - 2 \cdot \frac{1}{2}$$
$$= \frac{3}{2} - 1$$
$$= \frac{1}{2}$$

For y, we have:

$$y = x' \sin \theta + y' \cos \theta$$
$$= \sqrt{3} \sin 30° + 2 \cos 30°$$
$$= \sqrt{3} \cdot \frac{1}{2} + 2 \cdot \frac{\sqrt{3}}{2}$$
$$= \frac{\sqrt{3}}{2} + \sqrt{3}$$
$$= \frac{3\sqrt{3}}{2}$$

So the coordinates in the x-y system are $\left(\frac{1}{2}, \frac{3\sqrt{3}}{2} \right)$.

3.   For x, we have:

$$x = x' \cos \theta - y' \sin \theta$$
$$= \sqrt{2} \cos 45° + \sqrt{2} \sin 45°$$
$$= \sqrt{2} \cdot \frac{1}{\sqrt{2}} + \sqrt{2} \cdot \frac{1}{\sqrt{2}}$$
$$= 1 + 1$$
$$= 2$$

For y, we have:

$$y = x' \sin \theta + y' \cos \theta$$
$$= \sqrt{2} \sin 45° - \sqrt{2} \cos 45°$$
$$= \sqrt{2} \cdot \frac{1}{\sqrt{2}} - \sqrt{2} \cdot \frac{1}{\sqrt{2}}$$
$$= 1 - 1$$
$$= 0$$

So the coordinates in the x-y system are (2, 0).

5.   For x', we have:

$$x' = x \cos \theta + y \sin \theta$$

$$= -3 \cos \left(\sin^{-1} \frac{5}{13} \right) + 1 \sin \left(\sin^{-1} \frac{5}{13} \right)$$

$$= -3 \cdot \frac{12}{13} + 1 \cdot \frac{5}{13}$$

$$= -\frac{31}{13}$$

For y', we have:

$$y' = -x \sin \theta + y \cos \theta$$

$$= 3 \sin \left(\sin^{-1} \frac{5}{13} \right) + 1 \cos \left(\sin^{-1} \frac{5}{13} \right)$$

$$= 3 \cdot \frac{5}{13} + 1 \cdot \frac{12}{13}$$

$$= \frac{27}{13}$$

So the coordinates in the x'-y' system are $\left(-\frac{31}{13}, \frac{27}{13} \right)$.

7.   We have:

$$\cot 2\theta = \frac{A - C}{B} = \frac{25 - 18}{-24} = -\frac{7}{24}, \text{ so } \tan 2\theta = -\frac{24}{7}$$

$$\sec^2 2\theta = 1 + \tan^2 2\theta$$

$$= 1 + \left(-\frac{24}{7} \right)^2$$

$$= \frac{625}{49}$$

So $\sec 2\theta = -\frac{25}{7}$ (2nd quadrant, since $\cot 2\theta < 0$), and thus $\cos 2\theta = -\frac{7}{25}$.

Since θ is in the first quadrant, we have:

$$\sin \theta = \sqrt{\frac{1 - \cos 2\theta}{2}} = \sqrt{\frac{1 + \frac{7}{25}}{2}} = \sqrt{\frac{16}{25}} = \frac{4}{5}$$

$$\cos \theta = \sqrt{\frac{1 + \cos 2\theta}{2}} = \sqrt{\frac{1 - \frac{7}{25}}{2}} = \sqrt{\frac{9}{25}} = \frac{3}{5}$$

9.   We have:

$$\cot 2\theta = \frac{1-8}{-24} = \frac{-7}{-24} = \frac{7}{24}, \text{ so } \tan 2\theta = \frac{24}{7}$$

$$\sec^2 2\theta = 1 + \tan^2 2\theta = 1 + \left(\frac{24}{7}\right)^2 = \frac{625}{49}$$

So $\sec 2\theta = \frac{25}{7}$ (1st quadrant, since $\cot 2\theta > 0$), and thus $\cos 2\theta = \frac{7}{25}$.
Since θ is in the first quadrant, we have:

$$\sin\theta = \sqrt{\frac{1-\cos 2\theta}{2}} = \sqrt{\frac{1-\frac{7}{25}}{2}} = \sqrt{\frac{9}{25}} = \frac{3}{5}$$

$$\cos\theta = \sqrt{\frac{1+\cos 2\theta}{2}} = \sqrt{\frac{1+\frac{7}{25}}{2}} = \sqrt{\frac{16}{25}} = \frac{4}{5}$$

11.   We have:

$$\cot 2\theta = \frac{A-C}{B} = \frac{1-(-1)}{-2\sqrt{3}} = -\frac{1}{\sqrt{3}}, \text{ so } \tan 2\theta = -\sqrt{3}$$

Therefore $2\theta = 120°$, and thus $\theta = 60°$. So:

$$\sin\theta = \sin 60° = \frac{\sqrt{3}}{2}$$

$$\cos\theta = \cos 60° = \frac{1}{2}$$

13.   We have:

$$\cot 2\theta = \frac{A-C}{B} = \frac{0-(-240)}{161} = \frac{240}{161}, \text{ so } \tan 2\theta = \frac{161}{240}$$

$$\sec^2 2\theta = 1 + \tan^2 2\theta = 1 + \left(\frac{161}{240}\right)^2 = \frac{83521}{57600}$$

So $\sec 2\theta = \frac{289}{240}$ (1st quadrant, since $\cot 2\theta > 0$), and thus $\cos 2\theta = \frac{240}{289}$.
Since θ is in the first quadrant, we have:

$$\sin\theta = \sqrt{\frac{1-\cos 2\theta}{2}} = \sqrt{\frac{1-\frac{240}{289}}{2}} = \sqrt{\frac{49}{578}} = \frac{7\sqrt{2}}{34}$$

$$\cos\theta = \sqrt{\frac{1+\cos 2\theta}{2}} = \sqrt{\frac{1+\frac{240}{289}}{2}} = \sqrt{\frac{529}{578}} = \frac{23\sqrt{2}}{34}$$

15. Using the rotation equations:

$$x = x' \cos \theta - y' \sin \theta = x' \cos 45° - y' \sin 45° = \frac{\sqrt{2}}{2} x' - \frac{\sqrt{2}}{2} y'$$

$$y = x' \sin \theta + y' \cos \theta = x' \sin 45° + y' \cos 45° = \frac{\sqrt{2}}{2} x' + \frac{\sqrt{2}}{2} y'$$

So the equation $2xy = 9$ becomes:

$$2\left(\frac{\sqrt{2}}{2} x' - \frac{\sqrt{2}}{2} y'\right)\left(\frac{\sqrt{2}}{2} x' + \frac{\sqrt{2}}{2} y'\right) = 9$$

$$2\left(\frac{1}{2} x'^2 - \frac{1}{2} y'^2\right) = 9$$

$$x'^2 - y'^2 = 9$$

We graph the equation:

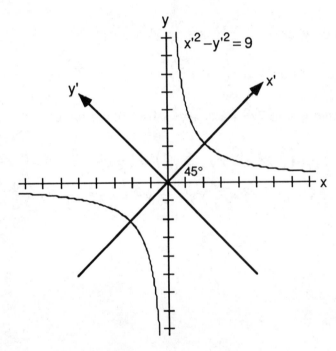

17. We find:

$$\cot 2\theta = \frac{7 - 1}{8} = \frac{3}{4}, \text{ so } \tan 2\theta = \frac{4}{3}$$

$$\sec^2 2\theta = 1 + \tan^2 2\theta = 1 + \left(\frac{4}{3}\right)^2 = \frac{25}{9}, \text{ so } \sec 2\theta = \frac{5}{3} \text{ (since } 2\theta < 90°\text{)}.$$

Thus $\cos 2\theta = \dfrac{3}{5}$, and thus:

$$\sin \theta = \sqrt{\dfrac{1 - \cos 2\theta}{2}} = \sqrt{\dfrac{1 - \dfrac{3}{5}}{2}} = \sqrt{\dfrac{1}{5}} = \dfrac{\sqrt{5}}{5}$$

$$\cos \theta = \sqrt{\dfrac{1 + \cos 2\theta}{2}} = \sqrt{\dfrac{1 + \dfrac{3}{5}}{2}} = \sqrt{\dfrac{4}{5}} = \dfrac{2\sqrt{5}}{5}$$

Thus $\theta = \sin^{-1} \dfrac{\sqrt{5}}{5} \approx 26.6°$. Now:

$$x = x' \cos \theta - y' \sin \theta = \dfrac{2\sqrt{5}}{5} x' - \dfrac{\sqrt{5}}{5} y'$$

$$y = x' \sin \theta + y' \cos \theta = \dfrac{\sqrt{5}}{5} x' + \dfrac{2\sqrt{5}}{5} y'$$

Making the substitutions into $7x^2 + 8xy + y^2 - 1 = 0$, we have:

$$7\left(\dfrac{4}{5} x'^2 - \dfrac{4}{5} x'y' + \dfrac{1}{5} y'^2\right) + 8\left(\dfrac{2}{5} x'^2 + \dfrac{3}{5} x'y' - \dfrac{2}{5} y'^2\right) + \left(\dfrac{1}{5} x'^2 + \dfrac{4}{5} x'y' + \dfrac{4}{5} y'^2\right) - 1 = 0$$

$$\dfrac{28}{5} x'^2 - \dfrac{28}{5} x'y' + \dfrac{7}{5} y'^2 + \dfrac{16}{5} x'^2 + \dfrac{24}{5} x'y' - \dfrac{16}{5} y'^2 + \dfrac{1}{5} x'^2 + \dfrac{4}{5} x'y' + \dfrac{4}{5} y'^2 - 1 = 0$$

$$9x'^2 - y'^2 = 1$$

$$\dfrac{x'^2}{\dfrac{1}{9}} - \dfrac{y'^2}{1} = 1$$

So, rotating $\theta = 26.6°$, we sketch the hyperbola:

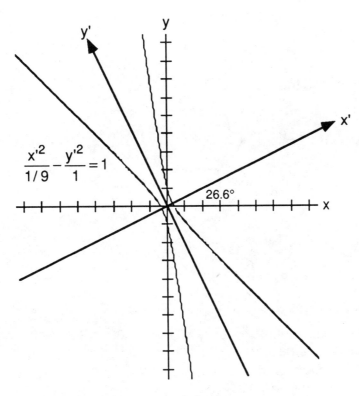

$$\frac{x'^2}{1/9} - \frac{y'^2}{1} = 1$$

19. We can use an alternate approach here:

$$x^2 + 4xy + 4y^2 = 1$$
$$(x + 2y)^2 = 1$$
$$x + 2y = 1 \qquad \text{or} \qquad x + 2y = -1$$
$$y = -\frac{1}{2}x + \frac{1}{2} \qquad\qquad\qquad y = -\frac{1}{2}x - \frac{1}{2}$$

So the graph consists of two lines:

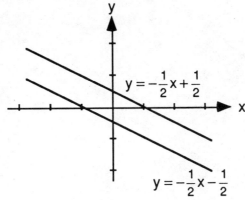

$$y = -\frac{1}{2}x + \frac{1}{2}$$

$$y = -\frac{1}{2}x - \frac{1}{2}$$

21. We find:

$$\cot 2\theta = \frac{9-16}{-24} = \frac{7}{24}, \text{ so } \tan 2\theta = \frac{24}{7}$$

$$\sec^2 2\theta = 1 + \tan^2 2\theta = 1 + \left(\frac{24}{7}\right)^2 = \frac{625}{49}, \text{ so } \sec 2\theta = \frac{25}{7} \text{ (since } 2\theta < 90°).$$

Thus $\cos 2\theta = \frac{7}{25}$, and thus:

$$\sin \theta = \sqrt{\frac{1 - \cos 2\theta}{2}} = \sqrt{\frac{1 - \frac{7}{25}}{2}} = \sqrt{\frac{9}{25}} = \frac{3}{5}$$

$$\cos \theta = \sqrt{\frac{1 + \cos 2\theta}{2}} = \sqrt{\frac{1 + \frac{7}{25}}{2}} = \sqrt{\frac{16}{25}} = \frac{4}{5}$$

Thus $\theta = \sin^{-1}\frac{3}{5} \approx 36.9°$. Now:

$$x = x' \cos \theta - y' \sin \theta = \frac{4}{5}x' - \frac{3}{5}y'$$

$$y = x' \sin \theta + y' \cos \theta = \frac{3}{5}x' + \frac{4}{5}y'$$

Making the substitutions into $9x^2 - 24xy + 16y^2 - 400x - 300y = 0$ and collecting like terms, we have:

$$25y'^2 - 500x' = 0$$
$$y'^2 = 20x'$$

So, rotating 36.9°, we sketch the parabola:

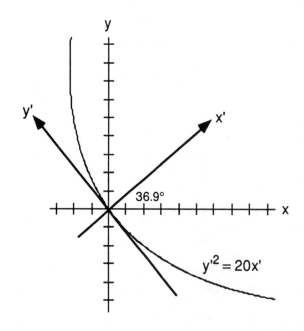

23. We find:

$$\cot 2\theta = \frac{0-3}{4} = -\frac{3}{4}, \text{ so } \tan 2\theta = -\frac{4}{3}$$

$$\sec^2 2\theta = 1 + \tan^2 2\theta = 1 + \left(-\frac{4}{3}\right)^2 = \frac{25}{9},$$

$$\text{so } \sec 2\theta = -\frac{5}{3} \text{ (since } 2\theta > 90°)$$

Thus $\cos 2\theta = -\frac{3}{5}$, and thus:

$$\sin\theta = \sqrt{\frac{1-\cos 2\theta}{2}} = \sqrt{\frac{1+\frac{3}{5}}{2}} = \sqrt{\frac{4}{5}} = \frac{2\sqrt{5}}{5}$$

$$\cos\theta = \sqrt{\frac{1+\cos 2\theta}{2}} = \sqrt{\frac{1-\frac{3}{5}}{2}} = \sqrt{\frac{1}{5}} = \frac{\sqrt{5}}{5}$$

Thus $\theta = \cos^{-1}\frac{\sqrt{5}}{5} \approx 63.4°$. Now:

$$x = x'\cos\theta - y'\sin\theta = \frac{\sqrt{5}}{5}x' - \frac{2\sqrt{5}}{5}y'$$

$$y = x'\sin\theta + y'\cos\theta = \frac{2\sqrt{5}}{5}x' + \frac{\sqrt{5}}{5}y'$$

Making the substitutions into $4xy + 3y^2 + 4x + 6y = 1$ and completing the square on x' and y' terms, we have:

$$\frac{\left(x'+\frac{2\sqrt{5}}{5}\right)^2}{1} - \frac{\left(y'+\frac{\sqrt{5}}{5}\right)^2}{4} = 1$$

So, rotating 63.4°, we sketch the hyperbola:

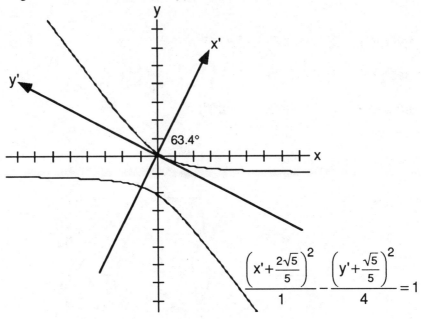

$$\frac{\left(x'+\frac{2\sqrt{5}}{5}\right)^2}{1} - \frac{\left(y'+\frac{\sqrt{5}}{5}\right)^2}{4} = 1$$

25.   We find:

$$\cot 2\theta = \frac{3-3}{-2} = 0, \text{ so } 2\theta = 90° \text{ and thus } \theta = 45°$$

Thus:

$$x = x' \cos\theta - y' \sin\theta = x' \cos 45° - y' \sin 45° = \frac{\sqrt{2}}{2} x' - \frac{\sqrt{2}}{2} y'$$

$$y = x' \sin\theta + y' \cos\theta = x' \sin 45° + y' \cos 45° = \frac{\sqrt{2}}{2} x' + \frac{\sqrt{2}}{2} y'$$

Making the substitutions into $3x^2 - 2xy + 3y^2 - 6\sqrt{2}\, x + 2\sqrt{2}\, y + 4 = 0$ and completing the sguare on x' and y' terms, we have:

$$\frac{(x'-1)^2}{1} + \frac{(y'+1)^2}{1/2} = 1$$

So, rotating 45°, we sketch the ellipse:

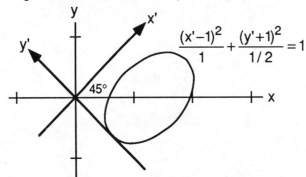

$$\frac{(x'-1)^2}{1} + \frac{(y'+1)^2}{1/2} = 1$$

27. We first multiply out, to get:
$$x^2 - 2xy + y^2 = 8y - 48$$
$$x^2 - 2xy + y^2 - 8y + 48 = 0$$

Now:
$$\cot 2\theta = \frac{1-1}{-2} = 0, \text{ so } 2\theta = 90° \text{ and thus } \theta = 45°$$

Thus:
$$x = x' \cos\theta - y' \sin\theta = \frac{\sqrt{2}}{2}x' - \frac{\sqrt{2}}{2}y'$$
$$y = x' \sin\theta + y' \cos\theta = \frac{\sqrt{2}}{2}x' + \frac{\sqrt{2}}{2}y'$$

Making the substitutions and completing the square on x' and y' terms yields:
$$(y' - \sqrt{2})^2 = 2\sqrt{2}\left(x' - \frac{11\sqrt{2}}{2}\right)$$

So, rotating 45°, we sketch the parabola:

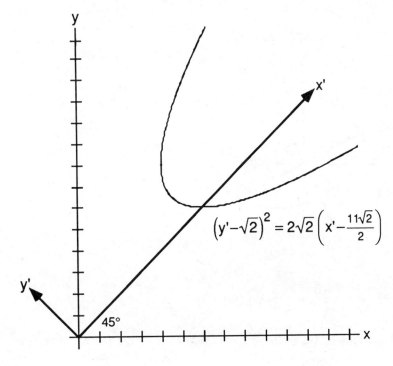

$$\left(y'-\sqrt{2}\right)^2 = 2\sqrt{2}\left(x'-\frac{11\sqrt{2}}{2}\right)$$

29. We find:
$$\cot 2\theta = \frac{3-6}{4} = -\frac{3}{4}, \text{ so } \tan 2\theta = -\frac{4}{3}$$
$$\sec^2 2\theta = 1 + \tan^2 2\theta = 1 + \left(-\frac{4}{3}\right)^2 = \frac{25}{9}$$

So $\sec 2\theta = -\frac{5}{3}$ (since $2\theta > 90°$) , and thus $\cos 2\theta = -\frac{3}{5}$

Then:

$$\sin \theta = \sqrt{\frac{1 - \cos 2\theta}{2}} = \sqrt{\frac{1 + \frac{3}{5}}{2}} = \frac{2\sqrt{5}}{5}$$

$$\cos \theta = \sqrt{\frac{1 + \cos 2\theta}{2}} = \sqrt{\frac{1 - \frac{3}{5}}{2}} = \frac{\sqrt{5}}{5}$$

Thus $\theta = \cos^{-1} \frac{\sqrt{5}}{5} \approx 63.4°$. Now:

$$x = x' \cos \theta - y' \sin \theta = \frac{\sqrt{5}}{5} x' - \frac{2\sqrt{5}}{5} y'$$

$$y = x' \sin \theta + y' \cos \theta = \frac{2\sqrt{5}}{5} x' + \frac{\sqrt{5}}{5} y'$$

Making the substitutions into $3x^2 + 4xy + 6y^2 = 7$, we have:

$$\frac{x'^2}{1} + \frac{y'^2}{7/2} = 1$$

So, rotating 63.4°, sketch the ellipse:

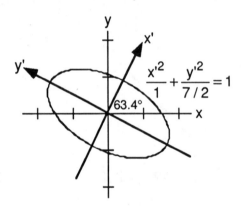

31. We find:

$$\cot 2\theta = \frac{17 - 8}{-12} = -\frac{3}{4}, \text{ so } \tan 2\theta = -\frac{4}{3}$$

As with the preceeding exercise we find $\sin \theta = \frac{2\sqrt{5}}{5}$ and $\cos \theta = \frac{\sqrt{5}}{5}$, so:

$$x = \frac{\sqrt{5}}{5} x' - \frac{2\sqrt{5}}{5} y'$$

$$y = \frac{2\sqrt{5}}{5} x' + \frac{\sqrt{5}}{5} y'$$

Substituting into $17x^2 - 12xy + 8y^2 - 80 = 0$ yields:

$$\frac{x'^2}{16} + \frac{y'^2}{4} = 1$$

So, rotating 63.4°, we sketch the ellipse:

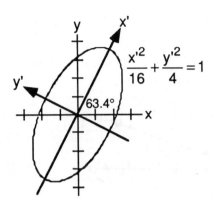

$$\frac{x'^2}{16} + \frac{y'^2}{4} = 1$$

33. We find:

$$\cot 2\theta = \frac{0+4}{3} = \frac{4}{3}, \text{ so } \tan 2\theta = \frac{3}{4}$$

$$\sec^2 2\theta = 1 + \tan^2 2\theta = 1 + \frac{9}{16} = \frac{25}{16}, \text{ so } \sec 2\theta = \frac{5}{4}$$

Then $\cos 2\theta = \frac{4}{5}$, and thus:

$$\sin \theta = \sqrt{\frac{1 - \cos 2\theta}{2}} = \sqrt{\frac{1 - \frac{4}{5}}{2}} = \frac{\sqrt{10}}{10}$$

$$\cos \theta = \sqrt{\frac{1 + \cos 2\theta}{2}} = \sqrt{\frac{1 + \frac{4}{5}}{2}} = \frac{3\sqrt{10}}{10}$$

Then $\theta = \sin^{-1} \frac{\sqrt{10}}{10} \approx 18.4°$, and:

$$x = \frac{3\sqrt{10}}{10} x' - \frac{\sqrt{10}}{10} y'$$

$$y = \frac{\sqrt{10}}{10} x' + \frac{3\sqrt{10}}{10} y'$$

Substituting into $3xy - 4y^2 + 18 = 0$ results in:

$$\frac{y'^2}{4} - \frac{x'^2}{36} = 1$$

So, rotating 18.4°, we sketch the hyperbola:

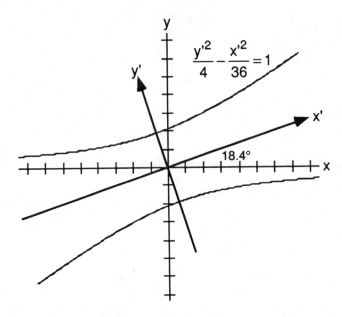

35. We first multiply out terms to obtain:

$$x^2 + 2xy + y^2 + 4\sqrt{2}\,x - 4\sqrt{2}\,y = 0$$

We find:

$$\cot 2\theta = \frac{1-1}{2} = 0, \text{ so } 2\theta = 90° \text{ and thus } \theta = 45°$$

Now:

$$x = \frac{\sqrt{2}}{2}x' - \frac{\sqrt{2}}{2}y'$$

$$y = \frac{\sqrt{2}}{2}x' + \frac{\sqrt{2}}{2}y'$$

Substituting into $x^2 + 2xy + y^2 + 4\sqrt{2}\,x - 4\sqrt{2}\,y = 0$ results in:

$$x'^2 = 4y'$$

So, rotating 45°, we sketch the parabola:

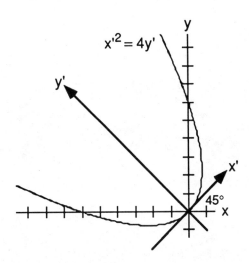

37. We find:

$$\cot 2\theta = \frac{3 - 2}{-\sqrt{15}} = -\frac{1}{\sqrt{15}}, \text{ so } \tan 2\theta = -\sqrt{15}$$

$$\sec^2 2\theta = 1 + \tan^2 2\theta = 1 + 15 = 16, \text{ so } \sec 2\theta = -4 \ \ (\text{since } 2\theta > 90°)$$

Thus $\cos 2\theta = -\frac{1}{4}$ and we find:

$$\sin \theta = \sqrt{\frac{1 - \cos 2\theta}{2}} = \sqrt{\frac{1 + \frac{1}{4}}{2}} = \sqrt{\frac{5}{8}} = \frac{\sqrt{10}}{4}$$

$$\cos \theta = \sqrt{\frac{1 + \cos 2\theta}{2}} = \sqrt{\frac{1 - \frac{1}{4}}{2}} = \sqrt{\frac{3}{8}} = \frac{\sqrt{6}}{4}$$

Then $\theta = \cos^{-1} \frac{\sqrt{6}}{4} \approx 52.2°$, and:

$$x = \frac{\sqrt{6}}{4} x' - \frac{\sqrt{10}}{4} y'$$

$$y = \frac{\sqrt{10}}{4} x' + \frac{\sqrt{6}}{4} y'$$

Substituting into $3x^2 - \sqrt{15} xy + 2y^2 = 3$ results in:

$$\frac{x'^2}{6} + \frac{y'^2}{2/3} = 1$$

So, rotating 52.2°, we sketch the ellipse:

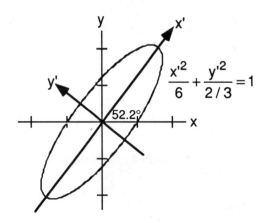

$$\frac{x'^2}{6} + \frac{y'^2}{2/3} = 1$$

39. We find:

$$\cot 2\theta = \frac{3 - 3}{-2} = 0, \text{ so } 2\theta = 90° \text{ and thus } \theta = 45°$$

Now:

$$x = \frac{\sqrt{2}}{2}x' - \frac{\sqrt{2}}{2}y'$$

$$y = \frac{\sqrt{2}}{2}x' + \frac{\sqrt{2}}{2}y'$$

Substituting into $3x^2 - 2xy + 3y^2 + 2 = 0$ results in:

$$x'^2 + 2y'^2 = -1$$

But clearly this is impossible, so there is no graph.

41. Multiplying the first equation by $\sin \theta$ and the second equation by $\cos \theta$ yields:

$$\sin \theta \cos \theta \, x + \sin^2\theta \, y = x' \sin \theta$$
$$-\sin \theta \cos \theta \, x + \cos^2\theta \, y = y' \cos \theta$$

Adding, we get:

$$(\sin^2\theta + \cos^2\theta)y = x' \sin \theta + y' \cos \theta$$
$$y = x' \sin \theta + y' \cos \theta$$

Multiplying the first equation by $\cos \theta$ and the second equation by $-\sin \theta$ yields:

$$\cos^2\theta \, x + \sin \theta \cos \theta \, y = x' \cos \theta$$
$$\sin^2\theta \, x - \sin \theta \cos \theta \, y = -y' \sin \theta$$

Adding, we get:

$$(\sin^2\theta + \cos^2\theta)x = x' \cos \theta - y' \sin \theta$$
$$x = x' \cos \theta - y' \sin \theta$$

43. (a) Since $\cot 2\theta = -\frac{7}{24}$, $\tan 2\theta = -\frac{24}{7}$ so:

$$\sec^2 2\theta = 1 + \left(\frac{24}{7}\right)^2$$

$$= \frac{49}{49} + \frac{576}{49}$$

$$= \frac{625}{49}$$

Thus $\sec 2\theta = \pm\frac{25}{7}$. Since 2θ is in either the 1st or 2nd quadrant, and

$\cot 2\theta < 0$, 2θ is in the 2nd quadrant, so $\sec 2\theta = -\frac{25}{7}$, so $\cos 2\theta = -\frac{7}{25}$.

(b) $\sin\theta = \sqrt{\dfrac{1 - \cos 2\theta}{2}} = \sqrt{\dfrac{1 + \frac{7}{25}}{2}} = \sqrt{\dfrac{32}{50}} = \sqrt{\dfrac{16}{25}} = \dfrac{4}{5}$

$\cos\theta = \sqrt{\dfrac{1 + \cos 2\theta}{2}} = \sqrt{\dfrac{1 - \frac{7}{25}}{2}} = \sqrt{\dfrac{18}{50}} = \sqrt{\dfrac{9}{25}} = \dfrac{3}{5}$

(c) $16\left(\frac{1}{5}(3x' - 4y')\right)^2 - 24\left(\frac{1}{5}(3x' - 4y')\right)\left(\frac{1}{5}(4x' + 3y')\right) + 9\left(\frac{1}{5}(4x' + 3y')\right)^2$

$$+ 110\left(\frac{1}{5}(3x' - 4y')\right) - 20 \bullet \frac{1}{5}(4x' + 3y') + 100 = 0$$

$\dfrac{16}{25}(9x'^2 - 24x'y' + 16y'^2) - \dfrac{24}{25}(12x'^2 - 7x'y' - 12y'^2)$

$$+ \frac{9}{25}(16x'^2 + 24x'y' + 9y'^2) + 22(3x' - 4y') - 4(4x' + 3y') + 100 = 0$$

$$\frac{144 - 288 + 144}{25}x'^2 + \frac{-384 + 168 + 216}{25}x'y' + \frac{256 + 288 + 81}{25}y'^2$$

$$+ (66 - 16)x' + (-88 - 12)y' + 110 = 0$$

$$25y'^2 + 50x' - 100y' + 100 = 0$$

$$y'^2 + 2x' - 4y' + 4 = 0$$

45. $A' + C' = A\cos^2\theta + B\sin\theta\cos\theta + C\sin^2\theta + A\sin^2\theta - B\sin\theta\cos\theta + C\cos^2\theta$
$= (A + C)(\cos^2\theta + \sin^2\theta)$
$= A + C$

8.6 Introduction to Polar Coordinates

1.   (a) $x = 3 \cos \frac{2\pi}{3} = 3\left(-\frac{1}{2}\right) = -\frac{3}{2}$

   $y = 3 \sin \frac{2\pi}{3} = 3\left(\frac{\sqrt{3}}{2}\right) = \frac{3\sqrt{3}}{2}$

   So the rectangular coordinates are $\left(-\frac{3}{2}, \frac{3\sqrt{3}}{2}\right)$

   (b) $x = 4 \cos \frac{11\pi}{6} = 4\left(\frac{\sqrt{3}}{2}\right) = 2\sqrt{3}$

   $y = 4 \sin \frac{11\pi}{6} = 4\left(-\frac{1}{2}\right) = -2$

   So the rectangular coordinates are $(2\sqrt{3}, -2)$

   (c) $x = 4 \cos \left(-\frac{\pi}{6}\right) = 4\left(\frac{\sqrt{3}}{2}\right) = 2\sqrt{3}$

   $y = 4 \sin \left(-\frac{\pi}{6}\right) = 4\left(-\frac{1}{2}\right) = -2$

   So the rectangular coordinates are $(2\sqrt{3}, -2)$

3.   (a) $x = 1 \cos \frac{\pi}{2} = 1(0) = 0$

   $y = 1 \sin \frac{\pi}{2} = 1(1) = 1$

   So the rectangular coordinates are $(0, 1)$

   (b) $x = 1 \cos \frac{5\pi}{2} = 1(0) = 0$

   $y = 1 \sin \frac{5\pi}{2} = 1(1) = 1$

   So the rectangular coordinates are $(0, 1)$

   (c) $x = 1 \cos \frac{\pi}{8} = 1\left(\sqrt{\frac{1 + \frac{\sqrt{2}}{2}}{2}}\right) = \sqrt{\frac{2 + \sqrt{2}}{4}} = \frac{\sqrt{2 + \sqrt{2}}}{2}$

   $y = 1 \sin \frac{\pi}{8} = 1\left(\sqrt{\frac{1 - \frac{\sqrt{2}}{2}}{2}}\right) = \sqrt{\frac{2 - \sqrt{2}}{4}} = \frac{\sqrt{2 - \sqrt{2}}}{2}$

   So the rectangular coordinates are $\left(\frac{\sqrt{2 + \sqrt{2}}}{2}, \frac{\sqrt{2 - \sqrt{2}}}{2}\right)$

5.   We have:
$$r^2 = 1 + 1 = 2, \text{ so } r = \sqrt{2}$$
$$\theta = \tan^{-1}\left(\frac{-1}{-1}\right) + \pi = \frac{\pi}{4} + \pi = \frac{5\pi}{4}$$
So the polar form is $\left(\sqrt{2}, \frac{5\pi}{4}\right)$

7.   If we first multiply by r, we have:
$$r^2 = 2r\cos\theta$$
$$x^2 + y^2 = 2x$$
$$x^2 - 2x + y^2 = 0$$
$$x^2 - 2x + 1 + y^2 = 1$$
$$(x - 1)^2 + y^2 = 1$$

9.
$$\sqrt{x^2 + y^2} = \frac{y}{x}$$
$$x^2 + y^2 = \frac{y^2}{x^2}$$
$$x^4 + x^2y^2 = y^2$$
$$x^4 + x^2y^2 - y^2 = 0$$

11. Using the double-angle identity, we have:
$$r = 3(\cos^2\theta - \sin^2\theta)$$
Multplying by r^2:
$$r^3 = 3\,(r^2\cos^2\theta - r^2\sin^2\theta)$$
$$(x^2 + y^2)^{3/2} = 3\,(x^2 - y^2)$$
$$(x^2 + y^2)^3 = 9\,(x^2 - y^2)^2$$
Multiplying out parentheses yields:
$$x^6 + 3x^4y^2 + 3x^2y^4 + y^6 = 9x^4 - 18x^2y^2 + 9y^4$$
$$x^6 - 9x^4 + 3x^4y^2 + 18x^2y^2 + 3x^2y^4 - 9y^4 + y^6 = 0$$

13. Multiplying each side by $2 - \sin^2\theta$ yields:
$$2r^2 - r^2\sin^2\theta = 8$$
$$2(x^2 + y^2) - y^2 = 8$$
$$2x^2 + 2y^2 - y^2 = 8$$
$$2x^2 + y^2 = 8$$
$$\frac{x^2}{4} + \frac{y^2}{8} = 1$$

15.
$$r \cos \left(\theta - \frac{\pi}{6}\right) = 2$$
$$r \left(\cos \theta \cos \frac{\pi}{6} + \sin \theta \sin \frac{\pi}{6}\right) = 2$$
$$\frac{\sqrt{3}}{2} r \cos \theta + \frac{1}{2} r \sin \theta = 2$$
$$\frac{\sqrt{3}}{2} x + \frac{1}{2} y = 2$$
$$\sqrt{3} x + y = 4$$
$$y = -\sqrt{3} x + 4$$

17.
$$3r \cos \theta - 4r \sin \theta = 2$$
$$r (3 \cos \theta - 4 \sin \theta) = 2$$
$$r = \frac{2}{3 \cos \theta - 4 \sin \theta}$$

19.
$$r^2 \sin^2 \theta = r^3 \cos^3 \theta$$
$$\sin^2 \theta = r \cos^3 \theta$$
$$r = \frac{\sin^2 \theta}{\cos^3 \theta}$$
$$r = \tan^2 \theta \sec \theta$$

21.
$$2(r \cos \theta)(r \sin \theta) = 1$$
$$r^2(2 \sin \theta \cos \theta) = 1$$
$$r^2 \sin 2\theta = 1$$
$$r^2 = \frac{1}{\sin 2\theta}$$
$$r^2 = \csc 2\theta$$

23.
$$9r^2 \cos^2 \theta + r^2 \sin^2 \theta = 9$$
$$r^2 (9 \cos^2 \theta + \sin^2 \theta) = 9$$
$$r^2 = \frac{9}{9 \cos^2 \theta + \sin^2 \theta}$$

25. (a)   r cos θ = 3
                 x = 3

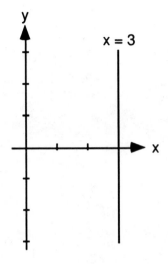

     (b)   r cos θ = -2
                 x = -2

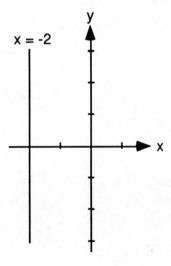

27. $r \cos \theta = 5$
     $x = 5$

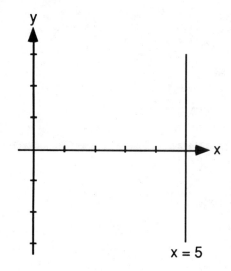

29.   To help gain familiarity with polar equations, it may help to convert to rectangular form. Multiplying by r, we have:

$$r^2 = 3r \cos \theta$$
$$x^2 + y^2 = 3x$$
$$x^2 - 3x + y^2 = 0$$
$$\left(x - \frac{3}{2}\right)^2 + y^2 = \frac{9}{4}$$

This is a circle of radius $\frac{3}{2}$ centered at $\left(\frac{3}{2}, 0\right)$:

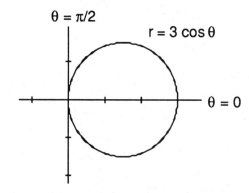

31.   Converting to rectangular form does not help here, so we plot points directly:

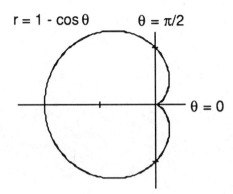

33.   Again we plot points in polar form, noting that ±r values are the same and that
$0 \leq \theta \leq \dfrac{\pi}{2}$ or $\pi \leq \theta \leq \dfrac{3\pi}{2}$:

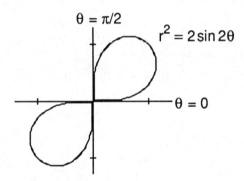

35.   Converting to rectangular coordinates:
$$r^2 = 1$$
$$x^2 + y^2 = 1$$
This is a circle of radius 1 centered at the origin:

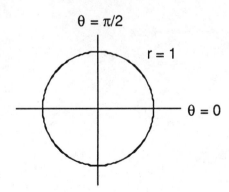

37.   We graph in polar coordinates, noting ±r values:

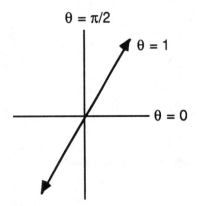

39.   We first multiply by r:

$$r^2 = 4r \sin \theta + 2r \cos \theta$$
$$x^2 + y^2 = 4y + 2x$$
$$x^2 - 2x + y^2 - 4y = 0$$
$$x^2 - 2x + 1 + y^2 - 4y + 4 = 1 + 4$$
$$(x - 1)^2 + (y - 2)^2 = 5$$

The graph is a circle with center $(1, 2)$ and radius $= \sqrt{5}$:

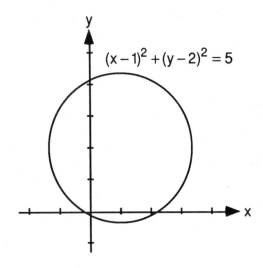

41. We graph in polar coordinates:

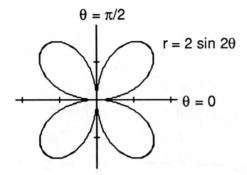

43. We graph in polar coordinates:

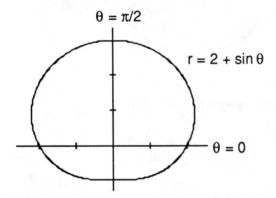

45. We graph in polar coordinates:

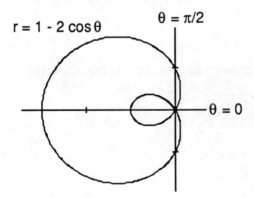

47.   We graph in polar coordinates, noting symmetry of ±r values:

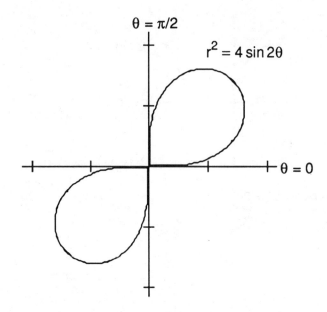

49.   We graph in polar coordinates:

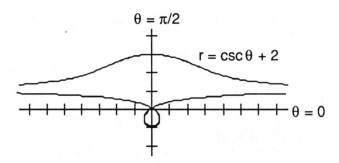

51.   To aid in graphing, we convert to rectangular coordinates:

$$r = \frac{1}{\cos^2 \frac{\theta}{2}}$$

$$r = \frac{2}{1 + \cos \theta}$$

$$r + r \cos \theta = 2$$

$$\sqrt{x^2 + y^2} + x = 2$$

$$\sqrt{x^2 + y^2} = 2 - x$$

$$x^2 + y^2 = 4 - 4x + x^2$$

$$y^2 = -4(x - 1)$$

This is a parabola, opening to the left, with vertex $(1, 0)$:

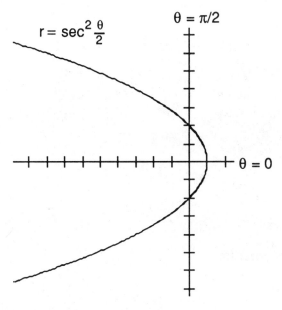

53. We first multiply by r:

$$r^2 = ar \cos \theta + br \sin \theta$$
$$x^2 + y^2 = ax + by$$
$$x^2 - ax + y^2 - by = 0$$
$$\left(x - \frac{a}{2}\right)^2 + \left(y - \frac{b}{2}\right)^2 = \frac{a^2 + b^2}{4}$$

This is the equation of a circle with center $\left(\frac{a}{2}, \frac{b}{2}\right)$ and radius $\frac{\sqrt{a^2 + b^2}}{2}$.

55. We multiply by $1 - a \cos \theta$ to get:

$$r - ar \cos \theta = ab$$
$$\sqrt{x^2 + y^2} - ax = ab$$
$$\sqrt{x^2 + y^2} = a(x + b)$$
$$x^2 + y^2 = a^2(x + b)^2$$
$$x^2 + y^2 = a^2 x^2 + 2a^2 bx + a^2 b^2$$
$$x^2 - a^2 x^2 + y^2 - 2a^2 bx - a^2 b^2 = 0$$
$$(1 - a^2)x^2 + y^2 - 2a^2 bx - a^2 b^2 = 0$$

57. (a) $F_1P = \sqrt{(x+k)^2 + y^2}$ and $F_2P = \sqrt{(x-k)^2 + y^2}$, so the equation becomes:

$$\sqrt{(x+k)^2 + y^2} \; \sqrt{(x-k)^2 + y^2} = k^2$$
$$\sqrt{(x^2 + k^2 + y^2)^2 - (2kx)^2} = k^2$$
$$(x^2 + y^2)^2 + 2k^2(x^2 + y^2) + k^4 - 4k^2x^2 = k^4$$
$$(x^2 + y^2)^2 = 2k^2(x^2 - y^2)$$

(b)   Substituting, we have:

$$r^4 = 2k^2\,(r^2\cos^2\theta - r^2\sin^2\theta)$$
$$r^2 = 2k^2\,(\cos^2\theta - \sin^2\theta)$$
$$r^2 = 2k^2\cos 2\theta$$

(c)   We graph in polar form:

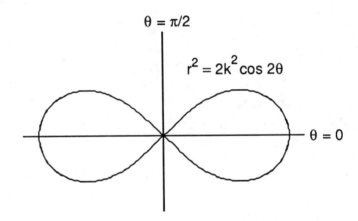

Chapter 8 Review Exercises

1. $4p = -12$, so $p = -3$
    focus: $(-3, 0)$; directrix: $x = 3$

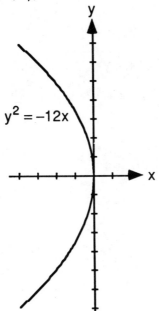

$$y^2 = -12x$$

2. Dividing by 4, we have:

    $$\frac{x^2}{4} - \frac{y^2}{1} = 1$$

    $c^2 = 4 + 1 = 5$, so $c = \sqrt{5}$

    foci: $(\pm\sqrt{5}, 0)$; asymptotes: $y = \pm\frac{1}{2}x$

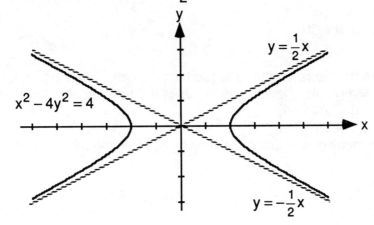

$$x^2 - 4y^2 = 4$$

$$y = \frac{1}{2}x$$

$$y = -\frac{1}{2}x$$

3.   (a) $\cot 2\theta = \dfrac{A - C}{B} = \dfrac{1 - 3}{2\sqrt{3}} = -\dfrac{1}{\sqrt{3}}$, so $\tan 2\theta = -\sqrt{3}$.

Thus $2\theta = 120°$, or $\theta = 60°$.

(b)   Applying the rotation formulas, we have:

$$x = x' \cos 60° - y' \sin 60° = \frac{1}{2}x' - \frac{\sqrt{3}}{2}y'$$

$$y = x' \sin 60° + y' \cos 60° = \frac{\sqrt{3}}{2}x' + \frac{1}{2}y'$$

Substituting into $x^2 + 2\sqrt{3}\, xy + 3y^2 - 12\sqrt{3}\, x + 12y = 0$ yields:

$$x'^2 = -6y'$$

Rotating 60°, we graph the parabola:

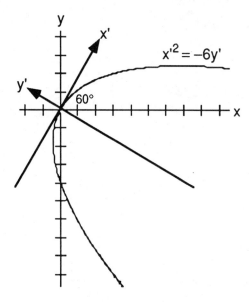

4. $\tan \theta = \dfrac{1}{\sqrt{3}}$, so $\theta = 30°$

5.   Let m denote the slope for the required tangent line. Then the equation of the
line is $y - 8 = m(x - 4)$. Now because this is the tangent line, the system:

$$y - 8 = m(x - 4)$$
$$x^2 = 2y$$

must have exactly one solution, namely $(4, 8)$. Solving the second equation

yields $y = \dfrac{x^2}{2}$.

Now substitute into the first equation:

$$\frac{x^2}{2} - 8 = m(x - 4)$$

$$x^2 - 16 = 2m(x - 4)$$

$$(x - 4)(x + 4) - 2m(x - 4) = 0$$

$$(x - 4)(x + 4 - 2m) = 0$$

From this last equation we obtain $x = 4$ or $x = 2m - 4$. Now we equate these two x-values because the system is known to have only one solution. This yields $2m - 4 = 4$, so $2m = 8$ and thus $m = 4$. With this value for m, the equation $y - 8 = m(x - 4)$ becomes $y - 8 = 4(x - 4)$, or $y = 4x - 8$. This is the required tangent line.

6.   We first draw the sketch:

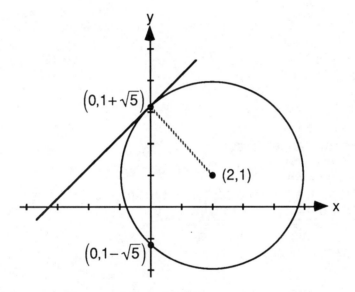

To determine the y-intercepts, we set $x = 0$:

$$(0 - 2)^2 + (y - 1)^2 = 9$$

$$(y - 1)^2 = 5$$

$$y - 1 = \pm\sqrt{5}$$

$$y = 1 \pm \sqrt{5}$$

From the sketch we see that $(0, 1 + \sqrt{5})$ has a positive tangent slope. The slope of the radius line (drawn from the center of the circle) is:

$$\frac{1 + \sqrt{5} - 1}{0 - 2} = -\frac{\sqrt{5}}{2}$$

So the slope of the tangent line is $\dfrac{2}{\sqrt{5}}$. Now use the point-slope formula:

$$y - (1 + \sqrt{5}) = \frac{2}{\sqrt{5}} (x - 0)$$

$$y - 1 - \sqrt{5} = \frac{2}{\sqrt{5}} x$$

$$\sqrt{5}\,y - \sqrt{5} - 5 = 2x$$

$$2x - \sqrt{5}\,y + (5 + \sqrt{5}) = 0$$

7.   Since $e = \dfrac{c}{a}$, then $\dfrac{c}{a} = \dfrac{1}{2}$, so $a = 2c$. Since the foci are $(0, \pm 2)$, then $c = 2$ and thus $a = 4$. Now we find b^2:

$$c^2 = a^2 - b^2$$

$$4 = 16 - b^2$$

$$b^2 = 12$$

Thus the equation of the ellipse is:

$$\frac{x^2}{12} + \frac{y^2}{16} = 1$$

8.   Call m the slope of the tangents, so:

$$y - 0 = m(x + 4)$$

$$y = mx + 4m$$

We now find the distance from the center of the circle $(0, 0)$ to this line:

$$r = \frac{|0 + 0 - 4m|}{\sqrt{1 + m^2}} = \frac{|4m|}{\sqrt{1 + m^2}}$$

Since this radius is 1, we have:

$$1 = \frac{|4m|}{\sqrt{1 + m^2}}$$

Squaring, we have:

$$1 = \frac{16m^2}{1 + m^2}$$

$$1 + m^2 = 16m^2$$

$$1 = 15m^2$$

$$m^2 = \frac{1}{15}$$

$$m = \pm \frac{\sqrt{15}}{15}$$

9. $m = \tan 60° = \sqrt{3}$. Using the point $(2, 0)$ in the point-slope formula:

$$y - 0 = \sqrt{3}\,(x - 2)$$
$$y = \sqrt{3}\,x - 2\sqrt{3}$$
$$\sqrt{3}\,x - y - 2\sqrt{3} = 0$$

10. Since the foci are $(\pm 2, 0)$, then $c = 2$. Also $\dfrac{b}{a} = \dfrac{1}{\sqrt{3}}$, so $a = b\sqrt{3}$. So:

$$c^2 = a^2 + b^2$$
$$4 = (b\sqrt{3})^2 + b^2$$
$$4 = 4b^2$$
$$1 = b^2$$
$$1 = b$$

So $a = 1\sqrt{3} = \sqrt{3}$, thus the equation is:

$$\frac{x^2}{3} - \frac{y^2}{1} = 1$$

11. We draw the graph:

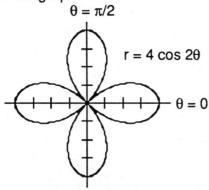

12. (a)   Replace x by 6 and y by 5:

$$5(6)^2 - 4(5)^2 = 80$$
$$180 - 100 = 80$$
$$80 = 80 \;\text{ True}$$

This shows that $P(6, 5)$ lies on the hyperbola $5x^2 - 4y^2 = 80$.

(b)   The quantity $(F_1P - F_2P)^2$ can be computed without determining the coordinates of F_1 and F_2. By definition we have $|F_1P - F_2P| = 2a$, for any point P on the hyperbola. Squaring both sides here yields $(F_1P - F_2P)^2 = 4a^2$. Now to compute a, we convert the equation $5x^2 - 4y^2 = 80$ to standard form. The result is $\dfrac{x^2}{4^2} - \dfrac{y^2}{(2\sqrt{5})^2} = 1$.

Therefore $a = 4$ and we obtain $(F_1P - F_2P)^2 = 4a^2 = 4(16) = 64$.

13. $\dfrac{x^2}{25} + \dfrac{y^2}{4} = 1$

length of major axis: 10; length of minor axis: 4

$c = \sqrt{25 - 4} = \sqrt{21}$

foci: $(\pm\sqrt{21}, 0)$

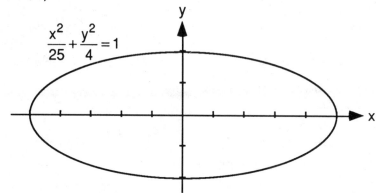

14. $r^2 = \cos 2\theta$

$r^2 = \cos^2\theta - \sin^2\theta$

$x^2 + y^2 = \left(\dfrac{x}{\sqrt{x^2 + y^2}}\right)^2 - \left(\dfrac{y}{\sqrt{x^2 + y^2}}\right)^2$

$x^2 + y^2 = \dfrac{x^2}{x^2 + y^2} - \dfrac{y^2}{x^2 + y^2}$

$(x^2 + y^2)^2 = x^2 - y^2$

15. Here $(x_0, y_0) = (-1, 0)$, $A = 2$, $B = -1$, $C = -1$:

$$d = \dfrac{|Ax_0 + By_0 + C|}{\sqrt{A^2 + B^2}} = \dfrac{|-2 + 0 - 1|}{\sqrt{4 + 1}} = \dfrac{3}{\sqrt{5}} = \dfrac{3\sqrt{5}}{5}$$

16. $16x^2 + y^2 - 64x + 2y + 65 = 0$

$16(x^2 - 4x) + (y^2 + 2y) = -65$

$16(x^2 - 4x + 4) + (y^2 + 2y + 1) = -65 + 64 + 1$

$16(x - 2)^2 + (y + 1)^2 = 0$

Thus the graph of the equation consists of the point $(2, -1)$:

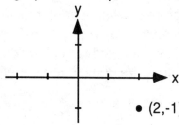

17. We draw the graph:

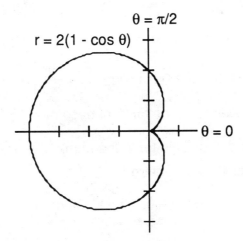

18. We draw the graph:

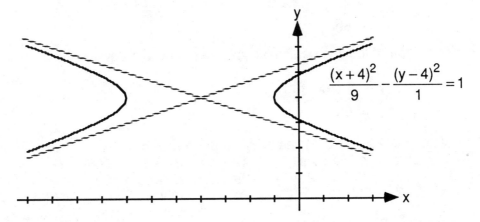

$$\frac{(x+4)^2}{9} - \frac{(y-4)^2}{1} = 1$$

19. focal width: 8; vertex: (1, 2)

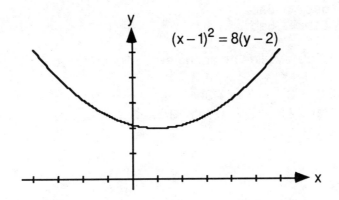

$$(x-1)^2 = 8(y-2)$$

20. The equation of the tangent line is $\dfrac{x_1 x}{a^2} + \dfrac{y_1 y}{b^2} = 1$. With $x_1 = -2$ and $y_1 = 4$, this becomes $\dfrac{-2x}{a^2} + \dfrac{4y}{b^2} = 1$. Now to determine a^2 and b^2, we divide both sides of the equation $x^2 + 3y^2 = 52$ by 52. This yields $\dfrac{x^2}{52} + \dfrac{y^2}{52/3} = 1$. Thus $a^2 = 52$ and $b^2 = \dfrac{52}{3}$, and the equation of the tangent becomes $\dfrac{-2x}{52} + \dfrac{4y}{52/3} = 1$. When we simplify and solve for y, the result is $y = \dfrac{1}{6}x + \dfrac{13}{3}$. This is the equation of the tangent line, as required.

21. The x-axis contains AB and has equation $y = 0$. The slope of the line containing BC is $-\dfrac{1}{b}$ and the equation is:

$$y = -\dfrac{1}{b}(x - 6b)$$
$$by = 6b - x$$
$$x + by = 6b$$

The slope of the line containing AC is $-\dfrac{1}{a}$ and the equation is:

$$y = -\dfrac{1}{a}(x - 6a)$$
$$x + ay = 6a$$

23. We show $G(2a + 2b, 2)$ lies on all three medians:
$$2(2a + 2b) + (a + b)(2) = 4a + 4b + 2a + 2b = 6(a + b)$$
$$2a + 2b - (b - 2a)(2) = 2a + 2b - 2b + 4a = 6a$$
$$2a + 2b - (a - 2b)(2) = 2a + 2b - 2a + 4b = 6b$$

25. We show $H(0, -6ab)$ lies on each altitude:
$$x = 0$$
$$-6ab = b \bullet 0 - 6ab = -6ab$$
$$-6ab = a \bullet 0 - 6ab = -6ab$$

27. We show $O(3a + 3b, 3ab + 3)$ lies on each perpendicular bisector:
$$x = 3a + 3b$$
$$b(3a + 3b) - (3ab + 3) = 3ab + 3b^2 - 3ab - 3 = 3b^2 - 3$$
$$a(3a + 3b) - (3ab + 3) = 3a^2 + 3ab - 3ab - 3 = 3a^2 - 3$$

29. We find each distance:

$$p = \sqrt{(6b)^2 + 6^2} = 6\sqrt{b^2 + 1}$$
$$q = \sqrt{(6a)^2 + 6^2} = 6\sqrt{a^2 + 1}$$
$$r = 6(a - b)$$
$$R = 3\sqrt{(a^2 + 1)(b^2 + 1)}$$

Thus:

$$\frac{pqr}{4R} = \frac{\left(6\sqrt{b^2 + 1}\right)\left(6\sqrt{a^2 + 1}\right)(6(a - b))}{4 \cdot 3 \sqrt{(a^2 + 1)(b^2 + 1)}} = 18(a - b)$$

area of $\triangle ABC = \frac{1}{2}\left(6(a - b)\right)(6) = 18(a - b)$

So the area is $\frac{pqr}{4R}$ as required.

31. $OH^2 = (3a + 3b - 0)^2 + (3ab + 3 + 6ab)^2$
$\qquad = 9(a^2 + 2ab + b^2) + 9(3ab + 1)^2$
$\qquad = 9(a^2 + 2ab + b^2 + 9a^2b^2 + 6ab + 1)$
$\qquad = 81a^2b^2 + 9a^2 + 9b^2 + 72ab + 9$

$9R^2 - (p^2 + q^2 + r^2)$
$\qquad = 9\left(9(a^2 + 1)(b^2 + 1)\right) - 36(b^2 + 1) - 36(a^2 + 1) - 36(a^2 - 2ab + b^2)$
$\qquad = 81a^2b^2 + 81a^2 + 81b^2 + 81 - 36b^2 - 36a^2 - 36 - 36a^2 + 72ab - 36b^2$
$\qquad = 81a^2b^2 + 9a^2 + 9b^2 + 72ab + 9$

Thus $OH^2 = 9R^2 - (p^2 + q^2 + r^2)$.

33. $HA^2 = (6a)^2 + (-6ab)^2 = 36a^2 + 36a^2b^2$
$HB^2 = (6b)^2 + (-6ab)^2 = 36b^2 + 36a^2b^2$
$HC^2 = 0^2 + (6 + 6ab)^2 = 36 + 72ab + 36a^2b^2$

So $HA^2 + HB^2 + HC^2 = 108a^2b^2 + 36a^2 + 36b^2 + 72ab + 36$

$12R^2 - (p^2 + q^2 + r^2)$
$\qquad = 12\left(9(a^2 + 1)(b^2 + 1)\right) - \left(36(b^2 + 1) + 36(a^2 + 1) + 36(a^2 - 2ab + b^2)\right)$
$\qquad = 108a^2b^2 + 108a^2 + 108b^2 + 108 - 36b^2 - 36 - 36a^2 - 36 - 36a^2 + 72ab - 36b^2$
$\qquad = 108a^2b^2 + 36a^2 + 36b^2 + 72ab + 36$

Thus $HA^2 + HB^2 + HC^2 = 12R^2 - (p^2 + q^2 + r^2)$.

35. In exercise #32 we saw that:

$GH = 4(9a^2b^2 + a^2 + b^2 + 8ab + 1)$

So:

$$GH^2 = 2\sqrt{9a^2b^2 + a^2 + b^2 + 8ab + 1}$$

Now:

$$2GO = 2\sqrt{(2a + 2b - 3a - 3b)^2 + (2 - 3ab - 3)^2}$$
$$= 2\sqrt{a^2 + 2ab + b^2 + 1 + 6ab + 9a^2b^2}$$
$$= 2\sqrt{9a^2b^2 + a^2 + b^2 + 8ab + 1}$$

Thus GH = 2GO.

37. $\tan \theta = -\dfrac{2}{3}$, so $\theta \approx 146.3°$

39. We have $(x_0, y_0) = (-1, -3)$, A = 5, B = 6, C = -30:

$$d = \frac{|5(-1) + 6(-3) - 30|}{\sqrt{5^2 + 6^2}} = \frac{53}{\sqrt{61}} = \frac{53\sqrt{61}}{61}$$

41. Label A(-6, 0), B(6, 0) and C(0, $6\sqrt{3}$). The height of the triangle is $6\sqrt{3}$. The slope of the line containing AB is 0, and its equation is y = 0, so the distance from (1, 2) to AB is $\dfrac{|0 + 0 - 2|}{\sqrt{1 + 0^2}} = 2$. The line containing AC has slope $\sqrt{3}$ and equation:

$$y - 0 = \sqrt{3}(x + 6)$$
$$y = \sqrt{3}x + 6\sqrt{3}$$

The distance from (1, 2) to AC is thus:

$$\frac{|\sqrt{3}(1) + 6\sqrt{3} - 2|}{\sqrt{1^2 + (-\sqrt{3})^2}} = \frac{7\sqrt{3} - 2}{2}$$

The line containing BC has slope $-\sqrt{3}$ and equation:

$$y - 0 = -\sqrt{3}(x - 6)$$
$$y = -\sqrt{3}x + 6\sqrt{3}$$

The distance from (1, 2) to BC is thus:

$$\frac{|-\sqrt{3}(1) + 6\sqrt{3} - 2|}{\sqrt{1^2 + (\sqrt{3^2})}} = \frac{5\sqrt{3} - 2}{2}$$

The sum of these distances is $6\sqrt{3}$, which is also the height.

43. (a)   We have the form $y^2 = 4px$, where p = 4. Thus the equation is $y^2 = 16x$.

     (b)   We have the form $x^2 = 4py$, where p = 4. Thus the equation is $x^2 = 16y$.

45. Since the parabola is symmetric about the positive y-axis, its equation must be of the form $x^2 = 4py$, where p > 0. Now the focal width is 12, so 4p = 12. Thus the equation is $x^2 = 12y$.

47.   We have c = 2 and a = 8, and the ellipse must have the form:

$$\frac{x^2}{8^2} + \frac{y^2}{b^2} = 1$$

Since $c^2 = a^2 - b^2$, we can find b:

$$4 = 64 - b^2$$
$$b^2 = 60$$

So the equation is $\frac{x^2}{64} + \frac{y^2}{60} = 1$, or $15x^2 + 16y^2 = 960$.

49.   Since one end of the minor axis is (-6, 0), then b = 6 and the ellipse has a form of:

$$\frac{x^2}{36} + \frac{y^2}{a^2} = 1$$

Now $\frac{c}{a} = \frac{4}{5}$, so $c = \frac{4}{5}a$. We find a:

$$c^2 = a^2 - b^2$$
$$\left(\frac{4}{5}a\right)^2 = a^2 - 36$$
$$\frac{16}{25}a^2 = a^2 - 36$$
$$36 = \frac{9}{25}a^2$$
$$100 = a^2$$

So the equation is $\frac{x^2}{36} + \frac{y^2}{100} = 1$, or $25x^2 + 9y^2 = 900$.

51.   Since the foci are (±6, 0) and the vertices are (±2, 0), then c = 6, a = 2, and the equation has the form:

$$\frac{x^2}{4} - \frac{y^2}{b^2} = 1$$

We find b:

$$c^2 = a^2 + b^2$$
$$36 = 4 + b^2$$
$$32 = b^2$$

So the equation is $\frac{x^2}{4} - \frac{y^2}{36} = 1$, or $8x^2 - y^2 = 32$.

53. Since the foci are $(\pm 3, 0)$, then $c = 3$ and the equation has the form:

$$\frac{x^2}{a^2} - \frac{y^2}{b^2} = 1$$

Now $\frac{c}{a} = 4$, so $\frac{3}{a} = 4$, thus $a = \frac{3}{4}$. We substitute to find b:

$$c^2 = a^2 + b^2$$
$$9 = \frac{9}{16} + b^2$$
$$144 = 9 + 16b^2$$
$$135 = 16b^2$$
$$\frac{135}{16} = b^2$$

So the equation is $\dfrac{x^2}{9/16} - \dfrac{y^2}{135/16} = 1$, or $240x^2 - 16y^2 = 135$

55. $x^2 = 10y$

$4p = 10$, so $p = \frac{5}{2}$

vertex: $(0, 0)$; focus: $(0, 5/2)$

directrix: $y = -\frac{5}{2}$; focal width: 10

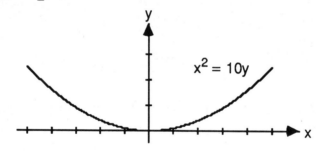

57. $x^2 = -12(y - 3)$
$4p = -12$, so $p = -3$
vertex: $(0, 3)$; focus: $(0, 0)$
directrix: $y = 6$; focal width: 12

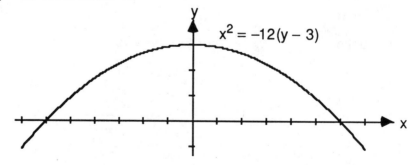

59. $(y - 1)^2 = -4(x - 1)$
$4p = -4$, so $p = -1$
vertex: $(1, 1)$; focus: $(0, 1)$
directrix: $x = 2$; focal width: 4

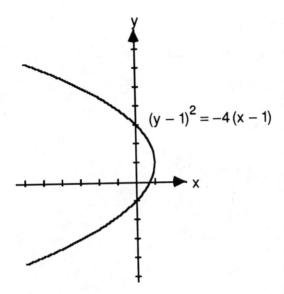

61. $x^2 + 2y^2 = 4$
$\dfrac{x^2}{4} + \dfrac{y^2}{2} = 1$
$a = 2, b = \sqrt{2}, c = \sqrt{2}$
center: $(0, 0)$; foci: $(\pm\sqrt{2}, 0)$

major axis: 4; minor axis: $2\sqrt{2}$; eccentricity: $\dfrac{\sqrt{2}}{2}$

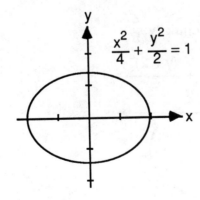

63. $49x^2 + 9y^2 = 441$

$$\frac{x^2}{9} + \frac{y^2}{49} = 1$$

$a = 7, b = 3, c = \sqrt{40} = 2\sqrt{10}$

center: $(0, 0)$; foci: $(0, \pm 2\sqrt{10})$

major axis: 14; minor axis: 6; eccentricity: $\dfrac{2\sqrt{10}}{7}$

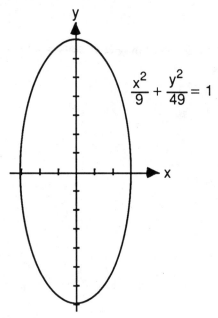

65. $\dfrac{(x - 1)^2}{25} + \dfrac{(y + 2)^2}{9} = 1$

$a = 5, b = 3, c = 4$

center: $(1, -2)$; foci: $(5, -2), (-3, -2)$

major axis: 10; minor axis: 6; eccentricity: $\dfrac{4}{5}$

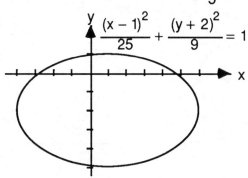

67. $x^2 - 2y^2 = 4$

$\dfrac{x^2}{4} - \dfrac{y^2}{2} = 1$

$a = 2$, $b = \sqrt{2}$, $c = \sqrt{6}$

center: $(0, 0)$

vertices: $(\pm 2, 0)$

foci: $(\pm\sqrt{6}, 0)$

asymptotes: $y = \pm\dfrac{\sqrt{2}}{2}x$

eccentricity: $\dfrac{\sqrt{6}}{2}$

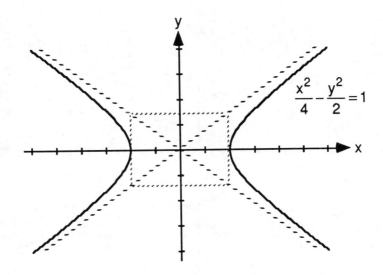

$\dfrac{x^2}{4} - \dfrac{y^2}{2} = 1$

69. $49y^2 - 9x^2 = 441$

$$\frac{y^2}{9} - \frac{x^2}{49} = 1$$

$a = 3, b = 7, c = \sqrt{58}$
center: $(0, 0)$
vertices: $(0, \pm 3)$
foci: $(0, \pm\sqrt{58})$

asymptotes: $y = \pm\frac{3}{7}x$

eccentricity: $\dfrac{\sqrt{58}}{3}$

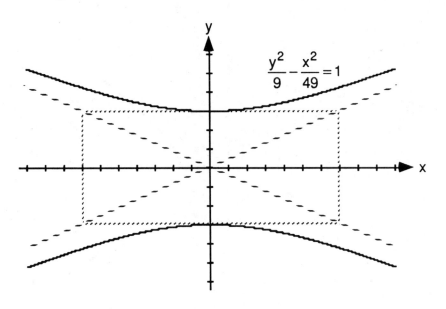

71. $\dfrac{(x - 1)^2}{25} - \dfrac{(y + 2)^2}{9} = 1$

a = 5, b = 3, c = $\sqrt{34}$

center: (1, -2); vertices: (6, -2), (-4, -2); foci: (1 $\pm \sqrt{34}$, -2)

asymptotes: $y + 2 = \pm\dfrac{3}{5}(x - 1)$; eccentricity: $\dfrac{\sqrt{34}}{5}$

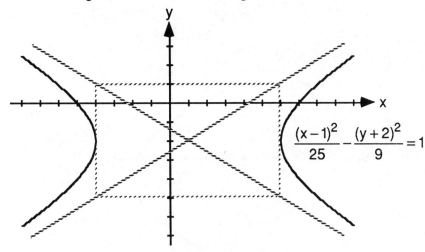

73. $3x^2 - 6x + 4y^2 + 16 = -7$

$3(x^2 - 2x + 1) + 4(y^2 + 4y + 4) = -7 + 3 + 16$

$3(x - 1)^2 + 4(y + 2)^2 = 12$

$\dfrac{(x - 1)^2}{4} + \dfrac{(y + 2)^2}{3} = 1$

Ellipse
center: (1, -2); foci: (0, -2), (2, -2)

major axis: 4; minor axis: $2\sqrt{3}$

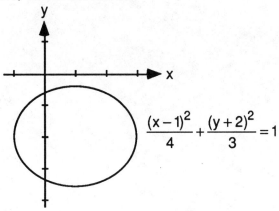

75. $y^2 + 2y = -4x + 15$

$y^2 + 2y + 1 = -4x + 15 + 1$

$(y + 1)^2 = -4(x - 4)$

Parabola: vertex: $(4, -1)$

axis: $y = -1$

focus: $(3, -1)$

directrix: $x = 5$

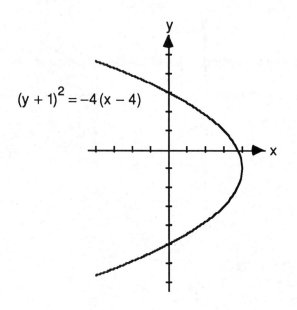

$(y + 1)^2 = -4(x - 4)$

77. $16(x^2 - 2x) - 9(y^2 - 10y) = 353$

$16(x^2 - 2x + 1) - 9(y^2 - 10y + 25) = 353 + 16 - 225$

$16(x - 1)^2 - 9(y - 5)^2 = 144$

$$\frac{(x - 1)^2}{9} - \frac{(y - 5)^2}{16} = 1$$

Hyperbola: center: $(1, 5)$;   vertices: $(-2, 5)$, $(4, 5)$

foci: $(-4, 5)$, $(6, 5)$;   asymptotes: $y = \frac{4}{3}x + \frac{11}{3}$; $y = -\frac{4}{3}x + \frac{19}{3}$

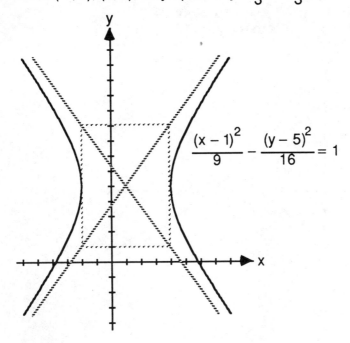

$$\frac{(x - 1)^2}{9} - \frac{(y - 5)^2}{16} = 1$$

79. $5x^2 + 3y^2 - 40x - 36y + 188 = 0$

$5(x^2 - 8x) + 3(y^2 - 12y) = -188$

$5(x - 4)^2 + 3(y - 6)^2 = -188 + 80 + 108$

$5(x - 4)^2 + 3(y - 6)^2 = 0$

one point: $(4, 6)$

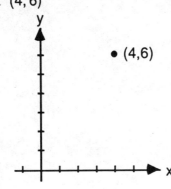

81. $9x^2 - 90x - 16y^2 + 32y = -209$
        $9(x^2 - 10x) - 16(y^2 - 2y) = -209$
        $9(x - 5)^2 - 16(y - 1)^2 = -209 + 225 - 16$
        $9(x - 5)^2 - 16(y - 1)^2 = 0$
        $9(x - 5)^2 = 16(y - 1)^2$
        $\pm 3(x - 5) = 4(y - 1)$

Two lines:
$3x - 15 = 4y - 4$ or $-3x + 15 = 4y - 4$
$3x - 4y = 11$ $3x + 4y = 19$

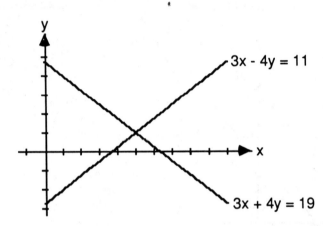

83. $y^2 + 8y - 25x^2 = 9$

$(y + 4)^2 - 25x^2 = 25$

$\dfrac{(y + 4)^2}{25} - \dfrac{x^2}{1} = 1$

Hyperbola: center: $(0, -4)$; vertices: $(0, 1)$, $(0, -9)$; foci: $(0, -4 \pm \sqrt{26})$

asymptotes: $y = 5x - 4$; $y = -5x - 4$

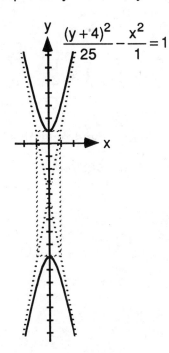

85. $16x^2 - 64x + 25y^2 - 100y = -564$

$16(x^2 - 4x) + 25(y^2 - 4y) = -564$

$16(x - 2)^2 + 25(y - 2)^2 = -564 + 64 + 100$

$16(x - 2)^2 + 25(y - 2)^2 = -400$

No graph (right side is negative).

87. (a)   Using the point $(6, 5)$:

$5(36) - 4(25) = 80$

$180 - 100 = 80$ $\checkmark$

(b)   Since P lies on the hyperbola with foci F_1, F_2, then the quantity
$F_1P - F_2P = \pm 2a$ (by the definition of the hyperbola). Thus
$(F_1P - F_2P)^2 = 4a^2$. It remains to find a:

$$5x^2 - 4y^2 = 80$$

$$\frac{x^2}{16} - \frac{y^2}{20} = 1$$

So $a^2 = 16$, thus the quantity is $4(16) = 64$.

89.   Completing the square, we obtain:

$$A\left(x^2 + \frac{D}{A}x + \frac{D^2}{4A^2}\right) + C\left(y^2 + \frac{E}{C}y + \frac{E^2}{4C^2}\right) = \frac{D^2}{4A} + \frac{E^2}{4C} - F$$

$$A\left(x + \frac{D}{2A}\right)^2 + C\left(y + \frac{E}{2C}\right)^2 = \frac{CD^2 + AE^2 - 4ACF}{4AC}$$

Now if the curve represents an ellipse or a hyperbola, this last equation

shows that the center is $\left(-\frac{D}{2A}, -\frac{E}{2C}\right)$, as required.

91.   Call the slope of the tangent line m, so:

$$y - 16 = m(x + 8)$$

Solving $x^2 = 4y$ for y yields $y = \frac{x^2}{4}$, so:

$$\frac{x^2}{4} - 16 = m(x + 8)$$

$$x^2 - 64 = 4m(x + 8)$$

$$(x + 8)(x - 8) = 4m(x + 8)$$

$$x - 8 = 4m$$

$$x = 4m + 8$$

Since $x = -8$, we have:

$$-8 = 4m + 8$$

$$-16 = 4m$$

$$-4 = m$$

Using the point-slope formula, we have:

$$y - 16 = -4(x + 8)$$

$$y - 16 = -4x - 32$$

$$y = -4x - 16$$

93. Writing the ellipse in the form $\dfrac{x^2}{52} + \dfrac{y^2}{52/3} = 1$, we have:

$$\frac{2x}{52} + \frac{4y}{52/3} = 1$$
$$2x + 12y = 52$$
$$x + 6y = 26$$
$$6y = -x + 26$$
$$y = -\frac{1}{6}x + \frac{13}{3}$$

95. Writing the hyperbola in the form $\dfrac{x^2}{9} - \dfrac{y^2}{12} = 1$, we have:

$$\frac{6x}{9} - \frac{6y}{12} = 1$$
$$\frac{2x}{3} - \frac{y}{2} = 1$$
$$4x - 3y = 6$$
$$-3y = -4x + 6$$
$$y = \frac{4}{3}x - 2$$

97. For the parabola, the vertex is $(5, 0)$, so we know $y^2 = -4p\,(x - 5)$. Since the focus is $(3, 0)$, then $p = 2$, so the equation is $y^2 = -8(x - 5)$. For the ellipse, $a = 5$ and $c = 3$, so $b^2 = a^2 - c^2 = 25 - 9 = 16$, so $b = 4$. Thus the equation of the ellipse is $\dfrac{x^2}{25} + \dfrac{y^2}{16} = 1$.

99. We use $a = 5$ and $b = 3$ in each formula:

	Approximation Obtained	Percentage Error
C_1	25.531776	0.019
C_2	25.526986	0.000049
C_3	25.519489	0.029

Since C_2 has the smallest percentage error, it would be the best approximation of the circumference of the three.

101.   We have:

$$\cot 2\theta = \frac{4-1}{4} = \frac{3}{4}, \text{ so } \tan 2\theta = \frac{4}{3}$$

$$\sec^2 2\theta = 1 + \tan^2 2\theta = 1 + \frac{16}{9} = \frac{25}{9}$$

So $\sec 2\theta = \frac{5}{3}$ and $\cos 2\theta = \frac{3}{5}$. Thus:

$$\sin\theta = \sqrt{\frac{1 - \cos 2\theta}{2}} = \sqrt{\frac{1 - \frac{3}{5}}{2}} = \sqrt{\frac{1}{5}} = \frac{\sqrt{5}}{5}$$

$$\cos\theta = \sqrt{\frac{1 + \cos 2\theta}{2}} = \sqrt{\frac{1 + \frac{3}{5}}{2}} = \sqrt{\frac{4}{5}} = \frac{2\sqrt{5}}{5}$$

So $\theta = \sin^{-1}\frac{\sqrt{5}}{5} \approx 26.6°$, and:

$$x = \frac{2\sqrt{5}}{5}x' - \frac{\sqrt{5}}{5}y'$$

$$y = \frac{\sqrt{5}}{5}x' + \frac{2\sqrt{5}}{5}y'$$

Substituting, we obtain:

$$\left(x' + \frac{3\sqrt{5}}{5}\right)^2 = \frac{8\sqrt{5}}{5}\left(y' + \frac{9\sqrt{5}}{40}\right)$$

So, rotating 26.6°, we graph the parabola:

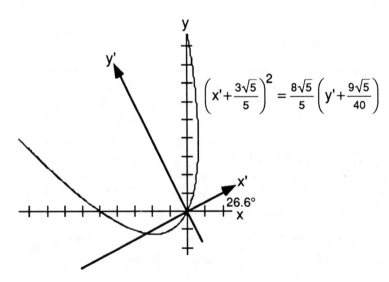

103.   We have:

$$\cot 2\theta = \frac{13 - 13}{10} = 0, \text{ so } 2\theta = 90° \text{ and } \theta = 45°$$

Thus:

$$\sin \theta = \frac{\sqrt{2}}{2} \text{ and } \cos \theta = \frac{\sqrt{2}}{2}$$

$$x = \frac{\sqrt{2}}{2} x' - \frac{\sqrt{2}}{2} y'$$

$$y = \frac{\sqrt{2}}{2} x' + \frac{\sqrt{2}}{2} y'$$

Substituting, we obtain:

$$\frac{x'^2}{16} + \frac{(y' - \sqrt{2})^2}{36} = 1$$

So, rotating 45°, we graph the ellipse:

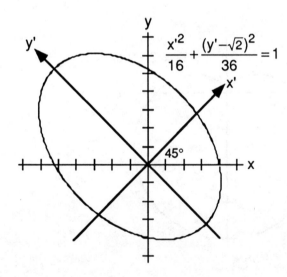

105. (a) We graph in polar coordinates:

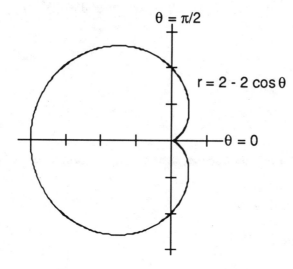

$r = 2 - 2\cos\theta$

(b) We graph in polar coordinates:

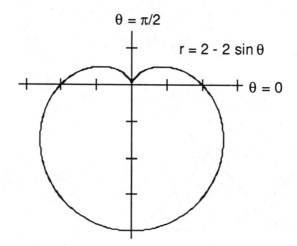

$r = 2 - 2\sin\theta$

107.   (a)   We graph in polar coordinates:

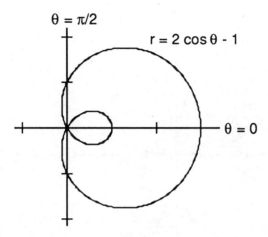

$\theta = \pi/2$

$r = 2 \cos \theta - 1$

$\theta = 0$

(b)   We graph in polar coordinates:

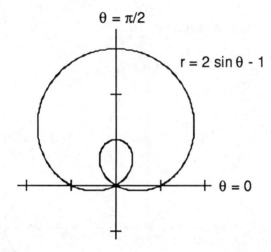

$\theta = \pi/2$

$r = 2 \sin \theta - 1$

$\theta = 0$

109.   (a)   We graph in polar coordinates:

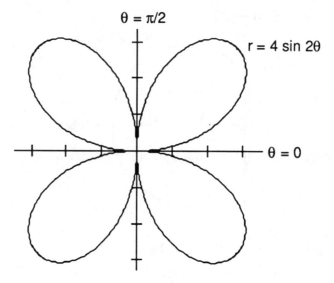

(b)   We graph in polar coordinates:

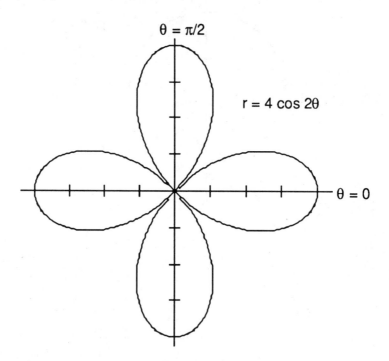

111.   (a)   We graph in polar coordinates:

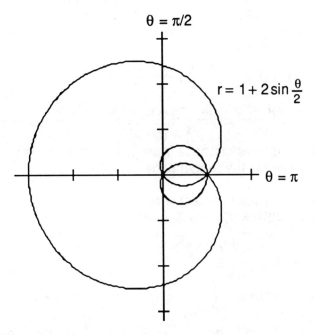

$$r = 1 + 2\sin\frac{\theta}{2}$$

(b)   We graph in polar coordinates:

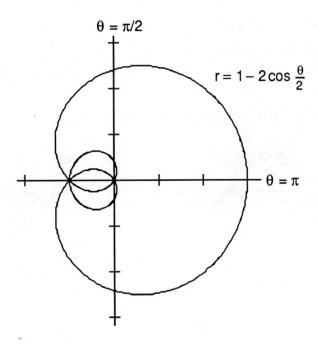

$$r = 1 - 2\cos\frac{\theta}{2}$$

113.   The given line will be tangent to the circle at (a, b) if and only if (a, b) lies on the line and the perpendicular distance from the center of the circle (h, k) to the line is the radius r. Since (a, b) is on the given circle:

$$(a - h)(a - h) + (b - k)(b - k) = (a - h)^2 + (b - k)^2 = r^2$$

So (a, b) lies on the line.

Using the formula $d = \dfrac{|Ax_0 + By_0 + C|}{\sqrt{A^2 + B^2}}$ we get:

$$d = \frac{|(a - h)h + (b - k)k - ah + h^2 - bk + k^2 - r^2|}{\sqrt{(a - h)^2 + (b - k)^2}} = \frac{|-r^2|}{\sqrt{r^2}} = r$$

Thus the perpendicular distance from (h, k) to the line is r.
Thus the given line is the tangent line at (a, b).

115.   (a)   The first two lines intersect where:

$$(2p - 2q)x = r(q - p)$$
$$2x = -r$$
$$x = -\frac{r}{2}$$

Thus one vertex is $A\left(-\dfrac{r}{2}, -\dfrac{r}{2}(p + q)\right)$. Similarly, we find that

$B\left(-\dfrac{q}{2}, -\dfrac{q}{2}(p + r)\right)$ and $C\left(-\dfrac{p}{2}, -\dfrac{p}{2}(q + r)\right)$ are the other vertices.

(b)   We use the formula $A = \dfrac{1}{2}|x_1y_2 - x_2y_1 + x_2y_3 - x_3y_2 + x_3y_1 - x_1y_3|$

for the area of a triangle with vertices (x_1, y_1), (x_2, y_2), and (x_3, y_3):

$$A = \frac{1}{2}\left|\frac{rq(p+r)}{4} - \frac{rq(p+q)}{4} + \frac{pq(q+r)}{4} - \frac{pq(p+r)}{4} + \frac{pr(p+q)}{4} - \frac{pr(q+r)}{4}\right|$$

$$= \frac{1}{8}|r^2q - rq^2 + pq^2 - p^2q + p^2r - pr^2|$$

Thus

$$\frac{|(p - q)(q - r)(r - p)|}{8}$$

$$= \frac{|pqr - p^2q - pr^2 + p^2r - q^2r + q^2p + qr^2 - prq|}{8}$$

$$= A$$

117.   We have $\tan \theta = \dfrac{y}{a + x}$ and $\tan \beta = \dfrac{y}{a - x}$, thus:

$$\tan \theta \ \tan \beta = 2$$

$$\frac{y}{a + x} \cdot \frac{y}{a - x} = 2$$

$$\frac{y^2}{a^2 - x^2} = 2$$

$$y^2 = 2a^2 - 2x^2$$

$$2x^2 + y^2 = 2a^2$$

CHAPTER NINE
ROOTS OF POLYNOMIAL EQUATIONS

9.1 Division of Polynomials

1. We use long division:

$$
\begin{array}{r}
x - 5 \\
x - 3 \enclose{longdiv}{x^2 - 8x + 4} \\
\underline{x^2 - 3x} \\
-5x + 4 \\
\underline{-5x + 15} \\
-11
\end{array}
$$

quotient: x - 5; remainder: -11

$x^2 - 8x + 4 = (x - 3)(x - 5) - 11$

3. We use long division:

$$
\begin{array}{r}
x - 11 \\
x + 5 \enclose{longdiv}{x^2 - 6x - 2} \\
\underline{x^2 + 5x} \\
-11x - 2 \\
\underline{-11x - 55} \\
53
\end{array}
$$

quotient: x - 11; remainder: 53

$x^2 - 6x - 2 = (x + 5)(x - 11) + 53$

5.   We use long division:

$$3x^2 - \tfrac{3}{2}x \;-\; \tfrac{1}{4}$$

$$2x + 1 \;\big)\; 6x^3 + 0x^2 - 2x + 3$$

$$\underline{6x^3 + 3x^2}$$

$$-3x^2 - 2x$$

$$\underline{-3x^2 - \tfrac{3}{2}x}$$

$$-\tfrac{1}{2}x + 3$$

$$\underline{-\tfrac{1}{2}x - \tfrac{1}{4}}$$

$$\tfrac{13}{4}$$

quotient: $3x^2 - \tfrac{3}{2}x - \tfrac{1}{4}$; remainder: $\tfrac{13}{4}$

$$6x^3 - 2x + 3 = (2x + 1)\left(3x^2 - \tfrac{3}{2}x - \tfrac{1}{4}\right) + \tfrac{13}{4}$$

7.   We use long division:

$$x^4 - 3x^3 + 9x^2 - 27x + 81$$

$$x + 3 \;\big)\; x^5 + 0x^4 + 0x^3 + 0x^2 + 0x + 2$$

$$\underline{x^5 + 3x^4}$$

$$-3x^4 + 0x^3$$

$$\underline{-3x^4 - 9x^3}$$

$$9x^3 + 0x^2$$

$$\underline{9x^3 + 27x^2}$$

$$-27x^2 + 0x$$

$$\underline{-27x^2 - 81x}$$

$$81x + 2$$

$$\underline{81x + 243}$$

$$-241$$

quotient: $x^4 - 3x^3 + 9x^2 - 27x + 81$; remainder: -241

$x^5 + 2 = (x + 3)(x^4 - 3x^3 + 9x^2 - 27x + 81) - 241$

9. We use long division:

$$x - 2 \enclose{longdiv}{\begin{array}{l} x^5 + 2x^4 + 4x^3 + 8x^2 + 16x + 32 \\ \hline x^6 + 0x^5 + 0x^4 + 0x^3 + 0x^2 + 0x - 64 \end{array}}$$

$$\begin{array}{l}
\underline{x^6 - 2x^5} \\
2x^5 + 0x^4 \\
\underline{2x^5 - 4x^4} \\
4x^4 + 0x^3 \\
\underline{4x^4 - 8x^3} \\
8x^3 + 0x^2 \\
\underline{8x^3 - 16x^2} \\
16x^2 + 0x \\
\underline{16x^2 - 32x} \\
32x - 64 \\
\underline{32x - 64} \\
0
\end{array}$$

quotient: $x^5 + 2x^4 + 4x^3 + 8x^2 + 16x + 32$; remainder: 0

$x^6 - 64 = (x - 2)(x^5 + 2x^4 + 4x^3 + 8x^2 + 16x + 32) + 0$

11. We use long division:

$$x^2 - 3x + 5 \enclose{longdiv}{\begin{array}{l} 5x^2 + 15x + 17 \\ \hline 5x^4 + 0x^3 - 3x^2 + 0x + 2 \end{array}}$$

$$\begin{array}{l}
\underline{5x^4 - 15x^3 + 25x^2} \\
15x^3 - 28x^2 + 0x \\
\underline{15x^3 - 45x^2 + 75x} \\
17x^2 - 75x + 2 \\
\underline{17x^2 - 51x + 85} \\
-24x - 83
\end{array}$$

quotient: $5x^2 + 15x + 17$; remainder: $-24x - 83$

$5x^4 - 3x^2 + 2 = (x^2 - 3x + 5)(5x^2 + 15x + 17) + (-24x - 83)$

13. We use long division:

$$
\begin{array}{r}
3y \quad - \quad 19 \\
y^2 + 5y + 2 \overline{\big)\, 3y^3 - 4y^2 + 0y - 3} \\
3y^3 + 15y^2 + 6y \\
\hline
-19y^2 - 6y - 3 \\
-19y^2 - 95y - 38 \\
\hline
89y + 35
\end{array}
$$

quotient: $3y - 19$; remainder: $89y + 35$

$3y^3 - 4y^2 - 3 = (y^2 + 5y + 2)(3y - 19) + (89y + 35)$

15. We use long division:

$$
\begin{array}{r}
t^2 - 2t \quad - 4 \\
t^2 - 2t - 4 \overline{\big)\, t^4 - 4t^3 + 4t^2 + 0t - 16} \\
t^4 - 2t^3 + 4t^2 \\
\hline
-2t^3 + 0t^2 + 0t \\
-2t^3 + 4t^2 - 8t \\
\hline
-4t^2 + 8t - 16 \\
-4t^2 + 8t - 16 \\
\hline
0
\end{array}
$$

quotient: $t^2 - 2t - 4$; remainder: 0

$t^4 - 4t^3 + 4t^2 - 16 = (t^2 - 2t + 4)(t^2 - 2t - 4) + 0$

17. We use long division:

$$
\begin{array}{r}
z^4 + z^3 + z^2 + z + 1 \\
z - 1 \overline{\smash{)}\ z^5 + 0z^4 + 0z^3 + 0z^2 + 0z - 1} \\
\underline{z^5 - z^4} \\
z^4 + 0z^3 \\
\underline{z^4 - z^3} \\
z^3 + 0z^2 \\
\underline{z^3 - z^2} \\
z^2 + 0z \\
\underline{z^2 - z} \\
z - 1 \\
\underline{z - 1} \\
0
\end{array}
$$

quotient: $z^4 + z^3 + z^2 + z + 1$; remainder: 0

$z^5 - 1 = (z - 1)(z^4 + z^3 + z^2 + z + 1) + 0$

19. We use long division:

$$
\begin{array}{r}
ax + (b + ar) \\
x - r \overline{\smash{)}\ ax^2 + bx + c} \\
\underline{ax^2 - arx} \\
(b + ar)x + c \\
\underline{(b + ar)x + (-ar^2 - br)} \\
ar^2 + br + c
\end{array}
$$

quotient: $ax + (ar + b)$; remainder: $ar^2 + br + c$

$ax^2 + bx + c = (x - r)\big(ax + (ar + b)\big) + (ar^2 + br + c)$

21. We use synthetic division:

$$
\begin{array}{r|rrr}
5 & 1 & -6 & -2 \\
  &   & 5 & -5 \\
\hline
  & 1 & -1 & -7
\end{array}
$$

The quotient is $x - 1$ and the remainder is -7.

So $x^2 - 6x - 2 = (x - 5)(x - 1) - 7$

23. We use synthetic division:

$$-1 \, \big|\, \begin{array}{rrr} 4 & -1 & -5 \\ & -4 & 5 \\ \hline 4 & -5 & 0 \end{array}$$

The quotient is $4x - 5$ and the remainder is 0.
So $4x^2 - x - 5 = (x + 1)(4x - 5) + 0$

25. We use synthetic division:

$$4 \, \big|\, \begin{array}{rrrr} 6 & -5 & 2 & 1 \\ & 24 & 76 & 312 \\ \hline 6 & 19 & 78 & 313 \end{array}$$

The quotient is $6x^2 + 19x + 78$ and the remainder is 313.
So $6x^3 - 5x^2 + 2x + 1 = (x - 4)(6x^2 + 19x + 78) + 313$

27. We use synthetic division:

$$2 \, \big|\, \begin{array}{rrrr} 1 & 0 & 0 & -1 \\ & 2 & 4 & 8 \\ \hline 1 & 2 & 4 & 7 \end{array}$$

The quotient is $x^2 + 2x + 4$ and the remainder is 7.
So $x^3 - 1 = (x - 2)(x^2 + 2x + 4) + 7$

29. We use synthetic division:

$$-2 \, \big|\, \begin{array}{rrrrrr} 1 & 0 & 0 & 0 & 0 & -1 \\ & -2 & 4 & -8 & 16 & -32 \\ \hline 1 & -2 & 4 & -8 & 16 & -33 \end{array}$$

The quotient is $x^4 - 2x^3 + 4x^2 - 8x + 16$ and the remainder is -33.
So $x^5 - 1 = (x + 2)(x^4 - 2x^3 + 4x^2 - 8x + 16) - 33$

31. We use synthetic division:

$$-4 \, \big|\, \begin{array}{rrrrr} 1 & -6 & 0 & 0 & 2 \\ & -4 & 40 & -160 & 640 \\ \hline 1 & -10 & 40 & -160 & 642 \end{array}$$

The quotient is $x^3 - 10x^2 + 40x - 160$ and the remainder is 642.
So $x^4 - 6x^3 + 2 = (x + 4)(x^3 - 10x^2 + 40x - 160) + 642$

33. We use synthetic division:

$$
\begin{array}{r|rrrr}
10 & 1 & -4 & -3 & 6 \\
   &   & 10 & 60 & 570 \\
\hline
   & 1 & 6 & 57 & 576 \\
\end{array}
$$

The quotient is $x^2 + 6x + 57$ and the remainder is 576.
So $x^3 - 4x^2 - 3x + 6 = (x - 10)(x^2 + 6x + 57) + 576$

35. We use synthetic division:

$$
\begin{array}{r|rrrr}
-5 & 1 & -1 & 0 & 0 \\
   &   & -5 & 30 & -150 \\
\hline
   & 1 & -6 & 30 & -150 \\
\end{array}
$$

The quotient is $x^2 - 6x + 30$ and the remainder is -150.
So $x^3 - x^2 = (x + 5)(x^2 - 6x + 30) - 150$

37. We use synthetic division:

$$
\begin{array}{r|rrrr}
2/3 & 54 & -27 & -27 & 14 \\
   &   & 36 & 6 & -14 \\
\hline
   & 54 & 9 & -21 & 0 \\
\end{array}
$$

The quotient is $54x^2 + 9x - 21$ and the remainder is 0.

So $54x^3 - 27x^2 - 27x + 14 = \left(x - \dfrac{2}{3}\right)(54x^2 + 9x - 21) + 0$

39. We use synthetic division:

$$
\begin{array}{r|rrrrr}
-1/2 & 5 & -4 & 3 & -2 & 1 \\
   &   & -5/2 & 13/4 & -25/8 & 41/16 \\
\hline
   & 5 & -13/2 & 25/4 & -41/8 & 57/16 \\
\end{array}
$$

The quotient is $5x^3 - \dfrac{13}{2}x^2 + \dfrac{25}{4}x - \dfrac{41}{8}$ and the remainder is $\dfrac{57}{16}$.

So $5x^4 - 4x^3 + 3x^2 - 2x + 1 = \left(x + \dfrac{1}{2}\right)\left(5x^3 - \dfrac{13}{2}x^2 + \dfrac{25}{4}x - \dfrac{41}{8}\right) + \dfrac{57}{16}$.

41. Since the two quotients are the same, we can now perform synthetic division:

$$
\begin{array}{r|rrr}
4/3 & 2 & -8/3 & 1/3 \\
   &   & 8/3 & 0 \\
\hline
   & 2 & 0 & 1/3 \\
\end{array}
$$

The quotient is $2x$ and the remainder is $\dfrac{1}{3}$.

43.   Using the hint from the previous exercise, we first divide the numerator and

denominator by 2 to form the quotient: $\dfrac{3x^3 + \frac{1}{2}}{x + \frac{1}{2}}$

We use synthetic division:

$$
\begin{array}{r|rrrr}
-1/2 & 3 & 0 & 0 & 1/2 \\
     &   & -3/2 & 3/4 & -3/8 \\
\hline
     & 3 & -3/2 & 3/4 & 1/8
\end{array}
$$

The quotient is $3x^2 - \dfrac{3}{2}x + \dfrac{3}{4}$ and the remainder is $\dfrac{1}{8}$.

45.   We use synthetic division:

$$
\begin{array}{r|rrrr}
-1 & 1 & 0 & k & 1 \\
   &   & -1 & 1 & -k-1 \\
\hline
   & 1 & -1 & k+1 & -k
\end{array}
$$

So $-k = -4$, and thus $k = 4$.

47.   We use synthetic division:

$$
\begin{array}{r|rrr}
p & 1 & 2p & -3q^2 \\
  &   & p & 3p^2 \\
\hline
  & 1 & 3p & 3p^2 - 3q^2
\end{array}
$$

Since the remainder is 0, we have:

$$
\begin{aligned}
3p^2 - 3q^2 &= 0 \\
3p^2 &= 3q^2 \\
p^2 &= q^2
\end{aligned}
$$

49.   We use synthetic division:

$$
\begin{array}{r|rrr}
i & 1 & -4 & 1 \\
  &   & i & -1-4i \\
\hline
  & 1 & -4+i & -4i
\end{array}
$$

The quotient is $x + (-4 + i)$ and the remainder is $-4i$.

51.   We use synthetic division:

$$
\begin{array}{r|rrr}
1+i & 1 & -2 & 2 \\
    &   & 1+i & -2 \\
\hline
    & 1 & -1+i & 0
\end{array}
$$

The quotient is $x + (-1 + i)$ and the remainder is 0.

53. We use long division:

$$
\begin{array}{r}
x^2 - 5x\ -\ 8 \\
2x+1\ \overline{\big)\ 2x^3 - 9x^2 - 21x + k} \\
\underline{2x^3 +\ x^2} \\
-10x^2 - 21x \\
\underline{-10x^2 -\ 5x} \\
-16x + k \\
\underline{-16x - 8} \\
k + 8
\end{array}
$$

Since this remainder must be 0, we have $k + 8 = 0$, so $k = -8$.

55. We use long division:

$$
\begin{array}{r}
x\ +1 \\
x^2 + x + 3\ \overline{\big)\ x^3 + 2x^2 +\ \ \ \ \ kx + 3} \\
\underline{x^3 +\ x^2 +\ \ \ \ \ 3x} \\
x^2 + (k-3)x + 3 \\
\underline{x^2 +\ \ \ \ \ \ \ x + 3} \\
(k-4)x
\end{array}
$$

Since this remainder must be 0, we have $k - 4 = 0$, so $k = 4$.

57. Since $d(\sqrt{3}) = 3 - 3 = 0$, then $f(\sqrt{3}) = R(\sqrt{3}) = -6\sqrt{3} + 57$.

59. We use synthetic division:

$$
\begin{array}{c|cccccc}
\underline{a} & 1 & 0 & 0 & 0 & -5a^4 & 4a^5 \\
& & a & a^2 & a^3 & a^4 & -4a^5 \\
\hline
& 1 & a & a^2 & a^3 & -4a^4 & 0
\end{array}
$$

The remainder is 0.

9.2 The Remainder Theorem and the Factor Theorem

1. $\quad 12(10) - 8 = 112$
    $\quad\ \ \ 120 - 8 = 112\ \ \sqrt{}$
    Yes, it is a root.

3. $(1 - \sqrt{5})^2 - 2(1 - \sqrt{5}) - 4 = 0$

$1 - 2\sqrt{5} + 5 - 2 + 2\sqrt{5} - 4 = 0$

$4 - 4 = 0 \quad \sqrt{}$

Yes, it is a root.

5. $2\left(\dfrac{1}{2}\right)^2 - 3\left(\dfrac{1}{2}\right) + 1 = 0$

$\dfrac{1}{2} - \dfrac{3}{2} + 1 = 0$

$-1 + 1 = 0 \quad \sqrt{}$

Yes, it is a root.

7. $f\left(\dfrac{2}{3}\right) = 3\left(\dfrac{2}{3}\right) - 2 = 2 - 2 = 0$

$x = \dfrac{2}{3}$ is a zero of f(x).

9. $h(-1) = 5(-1)^3 - (-1)^2 + 2(-1) + 8 = -5 - 1 - 2 + 8 = 0$

$x = -1$ is a zero of h(x).

11. $f(2) = 1 + 2(2) + (2)^3 - (2)^5 = 1 + 4 + 8 - 32 = -19$

$t = 2$ is not a zero of f(t).

13. (a) $f\left(\dfrac{\sqrt{3} - 1}{2}\right) = 2\left(\dfrac{\sqrt{3} - 1}{2}\right)^3 - 3\left(\dfrac{\sqrt{3} - 1}{2}\right) + 1$

$= \dfrac{3\sqrt{3} - 5}{2} - \dfrac{3\sqrt{3} - 3}{2} + 1$

$= -1 + 1$

$= 0$

$x = \dfrac{\sqrt{3} - 1}{2}$ is a zero of f(x).

(b) $f\left(\dfrac{\sqrt{3} + 1}{2}\right) = 2\left(\dfrac{\sqrt{3} + 1}{2}\right)^3 - 3\left(\dfrac{\sqrt{3} + 1}{2}\right) + 1$

$= \dfrac{5 + 3\sqrt{3}}{2} - \dfrac{3\sqrt{3} - 3}{2} + 1$

$= 4 + 1$

$= 5$

$x = \dfrac{\sqrt{3} + 1}{2}$ is not a zero of f(x).

15. (a)   1, 2 (multiplicity 3), 3
    (b)   1 (multiplicity 3)
    (c)   5 (multiplicity 6), -1 (multiplicity 4)
    (d)   0 (multiplicity 5), 1

17. We use synthetic division:

$$\begin{array}{r|rrrr} -3 & 4 & -6 & 1 & -5 \\ & & -12 & 54 & -165 \\ \hline & 4 & -18 & 55 & -170 \end{array}$$

So $f(-3) = -170$.

19. We use synthetic division:

$$\begin{array}{r|rrrrr} 1/2 & 6 & 5 & -8 & -10 & -3 \\ & & 3 & 4 & -2 & -6 \\ \hline & 6 & 8 & -4 & -12 & -9 \end{array}$$

So $f\left(\dfrac{1}{2}\right) = -9$.

21. We use synthetic division:

$$\begin{array}{r|rrr} -\sqrt{2} & 1 & 3 & -4 \\ & & -\sqrt{2} & -3\sqrt{2}+2 \\ \hline & 1 & 3-\sqrt{2} & -3\sqrt{2}-2 \end{array}$$

So $f(-\sqrt{2}) = -3\sqrt{2} - 2$.

23. We use synthetic division:

$$\begin{array}{r|rrrr} 12 & 1/2 & -5 & -13 & -10 \\ & & 6 & 12 & -12 \\ \hline & 1/2 & 1 & -1 & -22 \end{array}$$

So $f(12) = -22$.

25. We use synthetic division:

$$\begin{array}{r|rrrr} -3 & 1 & -4 & -9 & 36 \\ & & -3 & 21 & -36 \\ \hline & 1 & -7 & 12 & 0 \end{array}$$

So $x^3 - 4x^2 - 9x + 36 = (x + 3)(x^2 - 7x + 12) = (x + 3)(x - 4)(x - 3)$.
So the roots are $\pm 3, 4$.

27.   We use synthetic division:

$$\begin{array}{r|rrrr} 1 & 1 & 1 & -7 & 5 \\ & & 1 & 2 & -5 \\ \hline & 1 & 2 & -5 & 0 \end{array}$$

So $x^3 + x^2 - 7x + 5 = (x - 1)(x^2 + 2x - 5)$.
$x = 1$ is a root. We use the quadratic formula:

$$x = \frac{-2 \pm \sqrt{4 + 20}}{2} = \frac{-2 \pm 2\sqrt{6}}{2} = -1 \pm \sqrt{6}$$

So the roots are $1, -1 \pm \sqrt{6}$

29.   We use synthetic division:

$$\begin{array}{r|rrrr} -2 & 3 & -5 & -16 & 12 \\ & & -6 & 22 & -12 \\ \hline & 3 & -11 & 6 & 0 \end{array}$$

So $3x^3 - 5x^2 - 16x + 12 = (x + 2)(3x^2 - 11x + 6) = (x + 2)(3x - 2)(x - 3)$.
So the roots are $-2, \frac{2}{3}, 3$.

31.   We use synthetic division:

$$\begin{array}{r|rrrr} -3/2 & 2 & 1 & -5 & -3 \\ & & -3 & 3 & 3 \\ \hline & 2 & -2 & -2 & 0 \end{array}$$

So $2x^3 + x^2 - 5x - 3 = \left(x + \frac{3}{2}\right)(2x^2 - 2x - 2) = 2\left(x + \frac{3}{2}\right)(x^2 - x - 1)$.

$x = -\frac{3}{2}$ is a root. We use the quadratic formula:

$$x = \frac{1 \pm \sqrt{1 + 4}}{2} = \frac{1 \pm \sqrt{5}}{2}$$

So the roots are $-\frac{3}{2}, \frac{1 \pm \sqrt{5}}{2}$.

33.   We use synthetic division:

$$\begin{array}{r|rrrrr} 5 & 1 & -15 & 75 & -125 & 0 \\ & & 5 & -50 & 125 & 0 \\ \hline & 1 & -10 & 25 & 0 & 0 \end{array}$$

So $x^4 - 15x^3 + 75x^2 - 125x = (x - 5)(x^3 - 10x^2 + 25x)$
$= x(x - 5)(x^2 - 10x + 25)$
$= x(x - 5)^3$

So the roots are 0 and 5.

35. We use synthetic division:

$$
\begin{array}{r|rrrrr}
-4 & 1 & 2 & -23 & -24 & 144 \\
   &   & -4 & 8 & 60 & -144 \\
\hline
   & 1 & -2 & -15 & 36 & 0
\end{array}
$$

Use synthetic division again:

$$
\begin{array}{r|rrrr}
3 & 1 & -2 & -15 & 36 \\
  &   & 3 & 3 & -36 \\
\hline
  & 1 & 1 & -12 & 0
\end{array}
$$

So $x^4 + 2x^3 - 23x^2 - 24x + 144 = (x + 4)(x - 3)(x^2 + x - 12) = (x + 4)^2(x - 3)^2$.
So the roots are -4 and 3.

37. We use synthetic division:

$$
\begin{array}{r|rrrr}
-9 & 1 & 7 & -19 & -9 \\
   &   & -9 & 18 & 9 \\
\hline
   & 1 & -2 & -1 & 0
\end{array}
$$

So $x^3 + 7x^2 - 19x - 9 = (x + 9)(x^2 - 2x - 1)$.
So $x = -9$ is a root. Use the quadratic formula:

$$x = \frac{2 \pm \sqrt{4 + 4}}{2} = \frac{2 \pm 2\sqrt{2}}{2} = 1 \pm \sqrt{2}$$

So the roots are -9, $1 \pm \sqrt{2}$.

39. We use long division:

$$
\begin{array}{r}
2x^2 - 3x - 1 \\
2x^2 - 3x - 1 \overline{\smash{\big)}\ 4x^4 - 12x^3 + 5x^2 + 6x + 1} \\
\underline{4x^4 - 6x^3 - 2x^2} \\
-6x^3 + 7x^2 + 6x \\
\underline{-6x^3 + 9x^2 + 3x} \\
-2x^2 + 3x + 1 \\
\underline{-2x^2 + 3x + 1} \\
0
\end{array}
$$

We use the quadratic formula to solve $2x^2 - 3x - 1 = 0$:

$$x = \frac{3 \pm \sqrt{9 + 8}}{4} = \frac{3 \pm \sqrt{17}}{4}$$

So the solutions are $\dfrac{3 \pm \sqrt{17}}{4}$ (multiplicity 2).

41. (a) $R(1/2) = f(1/2) = 1.125$

    (b) $R(1.25) = f(1.25) = -0.046875$

    (c)   Since $f(1) = 0$, then $t - 1$ is a linear factor of $f(t)$.

    (d)   Since 1 is a solution, we use synthetic division:

$$\begin{array}{r|rrrr}
1 & 1 & 0 & -4 & 3 \\
  &   & 1 & 1 & -3 \\
\hline
  & 1 & 1 & -3 & 0
\end{array}$$

Using the quadratic formula to solve $t^2 + t - 3 = 0$:

$$t = \frac{-1 \pm \sqrt{1 + 12}}{2} = \frac{-1 \pm \sqrt{13}}{2}$$

So the solutions are $1, \dfrac{-1 \pm \sqrt{13}}{2}$.

43. $f(x) = (x - 3)(x - 5)(x + 4) = 0$. Multiplying out, we have $x^3 - 4x^2 - 17x + 60 = 0$.

45. $f(x) = (x + 1)^2(x + 6) = 0$. Multiplying out, we have $x^3 + 8x^2 + 13x + 6 = 0$.

47.   We know that such an equation must have $f(x) = (x^2 - 3x - 4)(x - 1/2)^3$, which has degree 5. Thus no such polynomial equation of degree 4 exists.

49.   We must have $x^2 - 3x + 1$ and $x + 6$ as factors, and thus we can write $f(x) = (x^2 - 3x + 1)(x + 6)(ax + b) = 0$, for any real numbers a and b. Multiplying out, we have $ax^4 + (3a + b)x^3 + (-17a + 3b)x^2 + (6a - 17b)x + 6b = 0$.

51.   We use synthetic division:

$$\begin{array}{r|rrrr}
1.16 & 1 & -3 & 12 & 9 \\
     &   & 1.16 & -2.1344 & 11.44 \\
\hline
     & 1 & -1.84 & 9.8656 & 20.44
\end{array}$$

So $f(1.16)$ is approximately equal to 20.44.

53. (a)   We use synthetic division:

$$\begin{array}{r|rrrr}
2.41 & 1 & 0 & -5 & -2 \\
     &   & 2.41 & 5.8081 & 1.9475 \\
\hline
     & 1 & 2.41 & 0.8081 & -0.05
\end{array}$$

So $f(2.41)$ is approximately equal to -0.05.

(b)   We use synthetic division:

$$2.42 \,\big|\; \begin{array}{cccc} 1 & 0 & -5 & -2 \\ & 2.42 & 5.8564 & 2.0725 \\ \hline 1 & 2.42 & 0.8564 & 0.07 \end{array}$$

So $f(2.42)$ is approximately equal to 0.07.

55. $f(-b - \sqrt{b^2 - 2c}) = \dfrac{1}{2}(-b - \sqrt{b^2 - 2c})^2 + b(-b - \sqrt{b^2 - 2c}) + c$

$\qquad\qquad\qquad\quad = \dfrac{1}{2}(b^2 + 2b\sqrt{b^2 - 2c} + b^2 - 2c) - b^2 - b\sqrt{b^2 - 2c} + c$

$\qquad\qquad\qquad\quad = b^2 + b\sqrt{b^2 - 2c} - c - b^2 - b\sqrt{b^2 - 2c} + c$

$\qquad\qquad\qquad\quad = 0$

$x = -b - \sqrt{b^2 - 2c}$ is a zero of $f(x)$.

57. $F\left(\dfrac{-\sqrt{2} + \sqrt{2\sqrt{2} - 2}}{2}\right) = 2\left(\dfrac{-\sqrt{2} + \sqrt{2\sqrt{2} - 2}}{2}\right)^4 + 4\left(\dfrac{-\sqrt{2} + \sqrt{2\sqrt{2} - 2}}{2}\right) + 1$

$\qquad\qquad\qquad\qquad = -1 + 2\sqrt{2} - 2\sqrt{2\sqrt{2} - 2} - 2\sqrt{2} + 2\sqrt{2\sqrt{2} - 2} + 1$

$\qquad\qquad\qquad\qquad = 0$

Yes, it is a zero.

59.   We use synthetic division:

$$1 \,\big|\; \begin{array}{cccc} 1 & 1 & a & b \\ & 1 & 2 & a+2 \\ \hline 1 & 2 & a+2 & a+b+2 \end{array}$$

Using synthetic division again:

$$1 \,\big|\; \begin{array}{cccc} 1 & -1 & -a & b \\ & 1 & 0 & -a \\ \hline 1 & 0 & -a & -a+b \end{array}$$

If 1 is a root, then:

$$a + b + 2 = 0$$
$$-a + b = 0$$

Adding these, we get $2b + 2 = 0$, so $b = -1$. Substituting we get $a = -1$.
So $a = -1$ and $b = -1$.

61.   Let r_1 and r_2 be the roots, so $r_2 = 2r_1$.
Then $x^2 + bx + 1 = (x - r_1)(x - 2r_1) = x^2 - 3r_1 x + 2r_1^2$.

Since r_1 is a constant, then $-3r_1 = b$ and $2r_1^2 = 1$, so $r_1^2 = \dfrac{1}{2}$ and thus

$r_1 = \dfrac{\pm\sqrt{2}}{2}$. So $b = \dfrac{\pm 3\sqrt{2}}{2}$.

63. Let r denote the root with multiplicity 2. We use synthetic division:

$$\begin{array}{r|cccc}
r & 1 & 0 & -12 & 16 \\
& & r & r^2 & r^3 - 12r \\
\hline
& 1 & r & r^2 - 12 & r^3 - 12r + 16
\end{array}$$

Since r is a double root, then the equation $x^2 + rx + (r^2 - 12) = 0$ must also have r as a root. Substituting $x = r$, we have:

$$r^2 + r^2 + r^2 - 12 = 0$$
$$3r^2 = 12$$
$$r^2 = 4$$
$$r = \pm 2$$

But $r = -2$ does not check in the original equation, thus $r = 2$. Thus the quadratic equation becomes $x^2 + 2x - 8 = 0$, which factors to $(x + 4)(x - 2) = 0$, and thus $x = -4$ is also a solution. So the solutions are 2 (multiplicity 2) and -4.

9.3 The Fundamental Theorem of Algebra

1. (a) yes
    (b) yes
    (c) yes
    (d) no -- not a polynomial equation

3. $x^2 - 2x - 3 = (x + 1)(x - 3) = \left(x - (-1)\right)(x - 3)$

5. $4x^2 + 23x - 6 = (4x - 1)(x + 6) = 4\left(x - \frac{1}{4}\right)\left(x - (-6)\right)$

7. $x^2 - 5 = (x + \sqrt{5})(x - \sqrt{5}) = \left(x - (-\sqrt{5})\right)(x - \sqrt{5})$

9. $x^2 - 10x + 26 = 0$

$$x = \frac{10 \pm \sqrt{100 - 104}}{2} = \frac{10 \pm 2i}{2} = 5 \pm i$$

So $x^2 - 10x + 26 = \left(x - (5 + i)\right)\left(x - (5 - i)\right)$

11. $f(x) = (x - 1)^2(x + 3) = x^3 + x^2 - 5x + 3$

13. $f(x) = (x - 2)(x + 2)(x - 2i)(x + 2i) = x^4 - 16$

15. $f(x) = \left(x - \sqrt{3}\right)^2\left(x - (-\sqrt{3})\right)^2\left(x - 4i\right)\left(x - (-4i)\right) = x^6 + 10x^4 - 87x^2 + 144$

17. $f(x) = a(x + 4)(x - 9)$
Since $f(3) = 5$, then:
$$5 = a(7)(-6)$$
$$a = -\frac{5}{42}$$
So $f(x) = -\frac{5}{42}(x^2 - 5x - 36) = -\frac{5}{42}x^2 + \frac{25}{42}x + \frac{30}{7}$.

19. $f(x) = a(x + 5)(x - 2)(x - 3)$
Since $f(0) = 1$, then:
$$1 = a(5)(-2)(-3)$$
$$a = \frac{1}{30}$$
So $f(x) = \frac{1}{30}(x^3 - 19x + 30) = \frac{1}{30}x^3 - \frac{19}{30}x + 1$.

21. $-b = -i - \sqrt{3}$, so $b = i + \sqrt{3}$
$c = -i(-\sqrt{3}) = i\sqrt{3}$
So $x^2 + (i + \sqrt{3})x + i\sqrt{3} = 0$.

23. $-b = 3$, so $b = -3$
$c = (9)(-6) = -54$
So $x^2 - 3x - 54 = 0$.

25. $-b = 2$, so $b = -2$
$c = (1 + \sqrt{5})(1 - \sqrt{5}) = -4$
So $x^2 - 2x - 4 = 0$.

27. $-B = 2a$, so $B = -2a$
$C = (a + \sqrt{b})(a - \sqrt{b}) = a^2 - b$
So $x^2 - 2ax + a^2 - b = 0$.

29. $x^4 + 64 = x^4 + 16x^2 + 64 - 16x^2$
$$= (x^2 + 8)^2 - (4x)^2$$
$$= (x^2 + 8 + 4x)(x^2 + 8 - 4x)$$
$$= (x^2 + 4x + 8)(x^2 - 4x + 8)$$

Now $x^2 + 4x + 8 = 0$ when $x = \dfrac{-4 \pm \sqrt{16 - 32}}{2} = \dfrac{-4 \pm 4i}{2} = -2 \pm 2i$

and $x^2 - 4x + 8 = 0$ when $x = \dfrac{4 \pm \sqrt{16 - 32}}{2} = \dfrac{4 \pm 4i}{2} = 2 \pm 2i$

So $x^4 + 64 = (x^2 + 4x + 8)(x^2 - 4x + 8)$
$$= \left(x - (-2 + 2i)\right)\left(x - (-2 - 2i)\right)\left(x - (2 + 2i)\right)\left(x - (2 - 2i)\right)$$
$$= (x + 2 - 2i)(x + 2 + 2i)(x - 2 - 2i)(x - 2 + 2i)$$

31.   We know $x^3 + bx^2 + cx + d = (x - r_1)(x - r_2)(x - r_3)$
$$= x^3 - (r_1 + r_2 + r_3)x^2 + (r_1 r_2 + r_1 r_3 + r_2 r_3)x - r_1 r_2 r_3$$

So: $r_1 + r_2 + r_3 = -b$
$$r_1 r_2 + r_1 r_3 + r_2 r_3 = c$$
$$r_1 r_2 r_3 = -d$$

33.   Let r_1, r_2, and r_3 be the roots and assume $r_2 = -r_1$ (their sum is therefore, 0).
The identities from exercise #31 give us:

$r_1 + r_2 + r_3 = 4$ $r_1 r_2 r_3 = -36$

$r_1 - r_1 + r_3 = 4$ $-r_1^2(4) = -36$

$r_3 = 4$ $r_1^2 = 9$

$r_1 = \pm 3$

So $r_1 = 3$ and $r_2 = -3$ (or switch them, it doesn't matter).
So the roots are 4, 3, and -3.

35.   (a) $\alpha^2 + \beta^2 = (\alpha + \beta)^2 - 2\alpha\beta$
$$= (-b)^2 - 2c$$
$$= b^2 - 2c$$

(b) $\left(\dfrac{1}{\alpha}\right)^2 + \left(\dfrac{1}{\beta}\right)^2 = \dfrac{\alpha^2 + \beta^2}{(\alpha\beta)^2} = \dfrac{b^2 - 2c}{c^2}$

(c) $\alpha^3 + \beta^3 = (\alpha + \beta)(\alpha^2 - \alpha\beta + \beta^2)$
$$= (-b)(\alpha^2 + \beta^2 - \alpha\beta)$$
$$= (-b)(b^2 - 2c - c)$$
$$= -b(b^2 - 3c)$$

37.   (a)   Suppose $A \neq 0$ or $B \neq 0$. Then $f(x) = Ax^2 + Bx + C = 0$ can have at
most two distinct roots by the Linear Factor Theorem (re-read it!).
So $A = B = 0$. But this implies $C = 0$, and thus $f(x) = 0$ for all values of x.

(b)   Using the hint, let:

$$f(x) = \frac{a^2 - x^2}{(a - b)(a - c)} + \frac{b^2 - x^2}{(b - c)(b - a)} + \frac{c^2 - x^2}{(c - a)(c - b)} - 1$$

$$f(a) = 0 + \frac{b^2 - a^2}{(b - c)(b - a)} + \frac{c^2 - a^2}{(c - a)(c - b)} - 1$$

$$= \frac{b + a}{b - c} + \frac{c + a}{c - b} - 1$$

$$= \frac{-b - a + c + a}{c - b} - 1$$

$$= \frac{c - b}{c - b} - 1$$

$$= 0$$

$$f(b) = \frac{a^2 - b^2}{(a - b)(a - c)} + 0 + \frac{c^2 - b^2}{(c - a)(c - b)} - 1$$

$$= \frac{a + b}{a - c} + \frac{c + b}{c - a} - 1$$

$$= \frac{-a - b + c + b}{c - a} - 1$$

$$= \frac{c - a}{c - a} - 1$$

$$= 0$$

$$f(c) = \frac{a^2 - c^2}{(a - b)(a - c)} + \frac{b^2 - c^2}{(b - c)(b - a)} + 0 - 1$$

$$= \frac{a + c}{a - b} + \frac{b + c}{b - a} - 1$$

$$= \frac{-a - c + b + c}{b - a} - 1$$

$$= \frac{b - a}{b - a} - 1$$

$$= 0$$

Since a, b, and c are distinct (for denominators to be nonzero), and all three are roots, then by part (a) $f(x) = 0$ for all values of x. Thus the equation is an identity.

9.4 Rational and Irrational Roots

1.   p-factors: $\pm 1, \pm 3$
     q-factors: $\pm 1, \pm 2, \pm 4$

possible rational roots $\frac{p}{q}$: $\pm 1, \pm \frac{1}{2}, \pm \frac{1}{4}, \pm 3, \pm \frac{3}{2}, \pm \frac{3}{4}$

3.   p-factors: ±1, ±3, ±9
      q-factors: ±1, ±2, ±4, ±8
      possible rational roots $\frac{p}{q}$: ±1, $\pm\frac{1}{2}$, $\pm\frac{1}{4}$, $\pm\frac{1}{8}$, ±3, $\pm\frac{3}{2}$, $\pm\frac{3}{4}$, $\pm\frac{3}{8}$,

      ±9, $\pm\frac{9}{2}$, $\pm\frac{9}{4}$, $\pm\frac{9}{8}$

5.   First multiply by 3 (we need integer coefficients) to get:
      $$2x^3 - 3x^2 - 15x + 6 = 0$$
      p-factors: ±1, ±2, ±3, ±6
      q-factors: ±1, ±2
      possible rational roots $\frac{p}{q}$: ±1, $\pm\frac{1}{2}$, ±2, ±3, $\pm\frac{3}{2}$, ±6

7.   The possible rational roots are ±1.
      We use synthetic division:

```
  1 | 1    0   -3    1
    |      1    1   -2
    ───────────────────
      1    1   -2   -1
```

      So x = 1 is not a root.

```
 -1 | 1    0   -3    1
    |     -1    1    2
    ───────────────────
      1   -1   -2    3
```

      So x = -1 is not a root. There are no rational roots.

9.   The possible rational roots are ±1.
      We use synthetic division:

```
  1 | 1    1   -1    1
    |      1    2    1
    ───────────────────
      1    2    1    2
```

      So x = 1 is not a root.

```
 -1 | 1    1   -1    1
    |     -1    0    1
    ───────────────────
      1    0   -1    2
```

      So x = -1 is not a root. There are no rational roots.

11. possible rational roots: $\pm 1, \pm\frac{1}{2}, \pm\frac{1}{3}, \pm\frac{1}{4}, \pm\frac{1}{6}, \pm\frac{1}{12}, \pm 2, \pm\frac{2}{3}, \pm 3, \pm\frac{3}{2}, \pm\frac{3}{4}, \pm 6$

We use synthetic division:

```
1 |  12    0    -1    0    -6
   |        12   12   11    11
   ------------------------------
      12    12   11   11    5
```

So $x = 1$ is not a root. Since this row is all positive, we can exclude $x = 2$, $x = 3$, $x = \frac{3}{2}$ and $x = 6$.

```
-1 |  12    0    -1    0    -6
   |       -12   12  -11    11
   ------------------------------
      12   -12   11  -11    5
```

So $x = -1$ is not a root. Since this row alternates signs, we can exclude $x = -2$, $x = -3$, $x = -\frac{3}{2}$, and $x = -6$.

```
1/4 |  12    0     -1      0      -6
    |        3    3/4    -1/16    -1/64
    ------------------------------------
       12    3    -1/4   -1/16   -6 1/64
```

So $x = \frac{1}{4}$ is not a root.

```
1/3 |  12    0    -1     0       -6
    |        4    4/3   1/9      1/27
    -----------------------------------
       12    4    1/3   1/9    -5 26/27
```

Proceeding in a similar fashion, we find that none of the candidates are rational roots.

13. possible rational roots: $\pm 1, \pm 3$
We use synthetic division:

```
1 |  1    3    -1    -3
  |       1     4     3
  ----------------------
     1    4     3     0
```

So $x^3 + 3x^2 - x - 3 = (x - 1)(x^2 + 4x + 3) = (x - 1)(x + 1)(x + 3)$
So the roots are 1, -1, and -3.

15. possible rational roots: $\pm 1, \pm\frac{1}{2}, \pm\frac{1}{4}, \pm 5, \pm\frac{5}{2}, \pm\frac{5}{4}$

We use synthetic division:

$$\begin{array}{r|rrrr} -1/4 & 4 & 1 & -20 & -5 \\ & & -1 & 0 & 5 \\ \hline & 4 & 0 & -20 & 0 \end{array}$$

So $4x^3 + x^2 - 20x - 5 = \left(x + \frac{1}{4}\right)(4x^2 - 20)$

$$= 4\left(x + \frac{1}{4}\right)(x^2 - 5)$$

$$= 4\left(x + \frac{1}{4}\right)(x + \sqrt{5})(x - \sqrt{5})$$

So the roots are $-\frac{1}{4}, -\sqrt{5}$, and $\sqrt{5}$.

17. possible rational roots: $\pm 1, \pm\frac{1}{3}, \pm\frac{1}{9}, \pm 2, \pm\frac{2}{3}, \pm\frac{2}{9}$

We use synthetic division:

$$\begin{array}{r|rrrr} 1 & 9 & 18 & 11 & 2 \\ & & 9 & 27 & 38 \\ \hline & 9 & 27 & 38 & 40 \end{array}$$

So $x = 2$ is excluded also (the row is positive).

$$\begin{array}{r|rrrr} -1 & 9 & 18 & 11 & 2 \\ & & -9 & -9 & -2 \\ \hline & 9 & 9 & 2 & 0 \end{array}$$

So $9x^3 + 18x^2 + 11x + 2 = (x + 1)(9x^2 + 9x + 2) = (x + 1)(3x + 2)(3x + 1)$

So the roots are $-1, -\frac{2}{3}$, and $-\frac{1}{3}$.

19. possible rational roots: $\pm 1, \pm 2, \pm 3, \pm 4, \pm 6, \pm 8, \pm 12, \pm 24$

We use synthetic division:

$$\begin{array}{r|rrrrr} 1 & 1 & 1 & -25 & -1 & 24 \\ & & 1 & 2 & -23 & -24 \\ \hline & 1 & 2 & -23 & -24 & 0 \end{array}$$

Using synthetic division again:

$$\begin{array}{r|rrrr} -1 & 1 & 2 & -23 & -24 \\ & & -1 & -1 & 24 \\ \hline & 1 & 1 & -24 & 0 \end{array}$$

So $x^4 + x^3 - 25x^2 - x + 24 = (x - 1)(x + 1)(x^2 + x - 24)$

Use the quadratic formula: $x = \dfrac{-1 \pm \sqrt{1+96}}{2} = \dfrac{-1 \pm \sqrt{97}}{2}$

So the roots are 1, -1, $\dfrac{-1 + \sqrt{97}}{2}$, and $\dfrac{-1 - \sqrt{97}}{2}$.

21. possible rational roots: ± 1
We use synthetic division:

$$
\begin{array}{r|rrrrr}
1 & 1 & -4 & 6 & -4 & 1 \\
  &   & 1 & -3 & 3 & -1 \\
\hline
  & 1 & -3 & 3 & -1 & 0
\end{array}
$$

Using synthetic division again:

$$
\begin{array}{r|rrrr}
1 & 1 & -3 & 3 & -1 \\
  &   & 1 & -2 & 1 \\
\hline
  & 1 & -2 & 1 & 0
\end{array}
$$

So $x^4 - 4x^3 + 6x^2 - 4x + 1 = (x-1)^2(x^2 - 2x + 1) = (x-1)^4$
So the only root is 1 (with multiplicity 4).

23. First multiply by 2 to get integer coefficients:
$2x^3 - 5x^2 - 46x + 24 = 0$

possible rational roots: $\pm 1, \pm \dfrac{1}{2}, \pm 2, \pm 3, \pm \dfrac{3}{2}, \pm 4, \pm 6, \pm 8, \pm 12, \pm 24$

We use synthetic division:

$$
\begin{array}{r|rrrr}
1/2 & 2 & -5 & -46 & 24 \\
    &   & 1 & -2 & -24 \\
\hline
    & 2 & -4 & -48 & 0
\end{array}
$$

So $2x^3 - 5x^2 - 46x + 24 = \left(x - \dfrac{1}{2}\right)(2x^2 - 4x - 48)$

$$= 2\left(x - \dfrac{1}{2}\right)(x^2 - 2x - 24)$$

$$= 2\left(x - \dfrac{1}{2}\right)(x - 6)(x + 4)$$

So the roots are $\dfrac{1}{2}$, 6, and -4.

25. First multiply by 20 to get integer coefficients:
$40x^4 - 18x^3 - 58x^2 + 27x - 3 = 0$

possible rational roots: $\pm 1, \pm \dfrac{1}{2}, \pm \dfrac{1}{4}, \pm \dfrac{1}{5}, \pm \dfrac{1}{8}, \pm \dfrac{1}{10}, \pm \dfrac{1}{20}, \pm \dfrac{1}{40}, \pm 3,$

$\pm \dfrac{3}{2}, \pm \dfrac{3}{4}, \pm \dfrac{3}{5}, \pm \dfrac{3}{8}, \pm \dfrac{3}{10}, \pm \dfrac{3}{20}, \pm \dfrac{3}{40}$

We use synthetic division:

$$
\begin{array}{r|rrrrr}
1/4 & 40 & -18 & -58 & 27 & -3 \\
    &   & 10 & -2 & -15 & 3 \\
\hline
    & 40 & -8 & -60 & 12 & 0
\end{array}
$$

Using synthetic division again:

$$
\begin{array}{r|rrrr}
1/5 & 40 & -8 & -60 & 12 \\
    &   & 8 & 0   & -12 \\
\hline
    & 40 & 0 & -60 & 0
\end{array}
$$

So

$$
\begin{aligned}
40x^4 - 18x^3 - 58x^2 + 27x - 3 &= \left(x - \tfrac{1}{4}\right)\left(x - \tfrac{1}{5}\right)(40x^2 - 60) \\
&= 10\left(x - \tfrac{1}{4}\right)\left(x - \tfrac{1}{5}\right)(4x^2 - 6) \\
&= 10\left(x - \tfrac{1}{4}\right)\left(x - \tfrac{1}{5}\right)(2x + \sqrt{6})(2x - \sqrt{6})
\end{aligned}
$$

So the roots are $\dfrac{1}{4}$, $\dfrac{1}{5}$, $-\dfrac{\sqrt{6}}{2}$, and $\dfrac{\sqrt{6}}{2}$.

27. (a)   possible rational roots: ± 1, $\pm\dfrac{1}{5}$, ± 2, $\pm\dfrac{2}{5}$, ± 3, $\pm\dfrac{3}{5}$, ± 4, $\pm\dfrac{4}{5}$, ± 6,

$$\pm\dfrac{6}{5},\ \pm 12,\ \pm\dfrac{12}{5}$$

We use synthetic division:

$$
\begin{array}{r|rrrrr}
2 & 5 & 0 & 0 & -10 & -12 \\
  &   & 10 & 20 & 40 & 60 \\
\hline
  & 5 & 10 & 20 & 30 & 48
\end{array}
$$

Since this row is all positive, $x = 2$ is the upper bound.

$$
\begin{array}{r|rrrrr}
-1 & 5 & 0 & 0 & -10 & -12 \\
   &   & -5 & 5 & -5 & 15 \\
\hline
   & 5 & -5 & 5 & -15 & 3
\end{array}
$$

Since this row alternates signs, $x = -1$ is the lower bound.
Final results: 2 upper, -1 lower

(b)   possible rational roots: ± 1, $\pm\dfrac{1}{3}$, ± 2, $\pm\dfrac{2}{3}$, ± 4, $\pm\dfrac{4}{3}$

We use synthetic division:

$$
\begin{array}{r|rrrrr}
4/3 & 3 & -4 & 5 & -2 & -4 \\
    &   & 4 & 0 & 20/3 & 56/9 \\
\hline
    & 3 & 0 & 5 & 14/3 & 20/9
\end{array}
$$

So $x = \dfrac{4}{3}$ is the upper bound.

-2 / 3	3	-4	5	-2	-4
		-2	4	-6	16 / 3
	3	-6	9	-8	4 / 3

So $x = -\frac{2}{3}$ is the lower bound.

Final results: $\frac{4}{3}$ upper, $-\frac{2}{3}$ lower

To have integral bounds, we have: 2 upper, -1 lower

(c)   possible rational roots: $\pm 1, \pm \frac{1}{2}, \pm 2, \pm 3, \pm \frac{3}{2}, \pm 4, \pm 6, \pm 12$

We use synthetic division:

6	2	-7	-5	28	-12
		12	30	150	1068
	2	5	25	178	1056

So $x = 6$ is the upper bound

-2	2	-7	-5	28	-12
		-4	22	-34	12
	2	-11	17	-6	0

Actually, -2 is a root, but also a lower bound.
Final results: 6 upper, -2 lower

29. Let $f(x) = x^3 + x - 1$
$f(0) = -1$
$f(1) = 1$
So the root lies between 0 and 1.
$f(0.5) = -0.375$
$f(0.7) = 0.043$
$f(0.6) = -0.373$
So the root lies between 0.6 and 0.7.
$f(0.65) = -0.075$
$f(0.66) = -0.052$
$f(0.67) = -0.029$
$f(0.68) = -0.005$
$f(0.69) = 0.018$
So the root lies between 0.68 and 0.69.

31. Let $f(x) = x^5 - 200$
$f(2) = -168$
$f(3) = 43$
So the root lies between 2 and 3.
$f(2.5) = -102$
$f(2.8) = -27.9$
$f(2.9) = 5.11$
So the root lies between 2.8 and 2.9.
$f(2.87) = -5.28$
$f(2.88) = -1.86$
$f(2.89) = 1.60$
So the root lies between 2.88 and 2.89.

33. Let $f(x) = x^3 - 8x^2 + 21x - 22$
$f(4) = -2$
$f(8) = 8$
So the root lies between 4 and 5.
$f(4.5) = 1.63$
$f(4.4) = 0.704$
$f(4.3) = -0.113$
So the root lies between 4.3 and 4.4.
$f(4.33) = 0.12$
$f(4.32) = 0.04$
$f(4.31) = -0.03$
So the root lies between 4.31 and 4.32.

35. Let $f(x) = x^3 + x^2 - 2x + 1$
$f(-2) = 1$
$f(-3) = -11$
So the root lies between -3 and -2.
$f(-2.1) = 0.35$
$f(-2.2) = -0.41$
So the root lies between -2.2 and -2.1.
$f(-2.15) = -0.02$
$f(-2.14) = 0.05$
So the root lies between -2.15 and -2.14.

37. Let $f(x) = x^3 + 2x^2 + 2x + 101$
$f(-5) = 16$
$f(-6) = -55$
So the root lies between -6 and -5.
$f(-5.4) = -8.94$
$f(-5.3) = -2.30$
$f(-5.2) = 4.07$
So the root lies between -5.3 and -5.2.

f(-5.26) = 0.28
f(-5.27) = -0.36
So the root lies between -5.27 and -5.26.

39. (a) Since 2 is a factor of $8 \cdot 5 = 40$, and 2 is not a factor of 5, then 2 must be a factor of 8, which is true.

(b) The result guarantees only that A is a factor of B in the case where A and C have no factor in common. Here A and C have a common factor of 5, so the result does not apply.

(c) Since $x = \dfrac{p}{q}$ is a root of the equation, this statement must be true.

(d) Subtract a_0 and multiply by q^n to get:
$$a_n p^n + a_{n-1} q p^{n-1} + a_{n-2} q^2 p^{n-2} + \ldots + a_1 q^{n-1} p = -a_0 q^n$$
So:
$$p(a_n p^{n-1} + a_{n-1} q p^{n-2} + a_{n-2} q^2 p^{n-3} + \ldots + a_1 q^{n-1}) = -a_0 q^n$$

41. We sketch the graph:

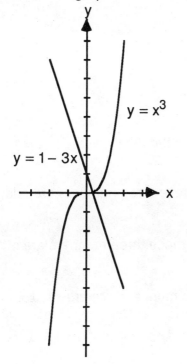

We find where $x^3 = 1 - 3x$, so $x^3 + 3x - 1 = 0$

Let $f(x) = x^3 + 3x - 1$

$f(0) = -1$

$f(1) = 3$

So the root lies between 0 and 1.

$f(0.3) = -0.07$

$f(0.4) = 0.264$

So the root lies between 0.3 and 0.4.

$f(0.32) = -0.007$

$f(0.33) = 0.02$

So the root lies between 0.32 and 0.33.

$f(0.325) = 0.009$

So the root lies between 0.32 and 0.325, thus the x-coordinate is x = 0.32, accurate to two decimal places.

43.   We find where $\sqrt{x} = x^2 - 1$

$x = x^4 - 2x^2 + 1$

$x^4 - 2x^2 - x + 1 = 0$

Let $f(x) = x^4 - 2x^2 - x + 1$

$f(1) = -1$

$f(2) = 7$

So the root lies between 1 and 2.

$f(1.4) = -0.48$

$f(1.5) = 0.06$

So the root lies between 1.4 and 1.5.

$f(1.48) = -0.06$

$f(1.49) = -0.001$

So the root lies between 1.49 and 1.50.

$f(1.495) = 0.03$

So the root lies between 1.49 and 1.495, thus the x-coordinate is x = 1.49, accurate to two decimal places.

45.   (a) $a_n = 9$, $a_0 = 27$, and $f(1) = 29$. Since these three numbers are odd, then the equation has no rational roots.

(b) $a_n = 5$, $a_0 = -25$, and $f(1) = -29$. Since these three numbers are odd, then the equation has no rational roots.

47.   Since p is a prime number, the only possible rational roots are ±1, $\pm p$.

Let $f(x) = x^3 + x^2 + x - p$

$f(1) = 1 + 1 + 1 - p = 3 - p$

p = 3 is a root to this.

$f(-1) = -1 + 1 - 1 - p = -1 - p$

p = -1 is the only root to this, and it is not prime.

$f(p) = p^3 + p^2 + p - p = p^3 + p^2 = p^2(p + 1)$

So p = 0 or p = -1, neither of which is prime.

$$f(-p) = -p^3 + p^2 - p - p = -p^3 + p^2 - 2p = -p(p^2 - p + 2)$$

So $p = 0$ or $p = \dfrac{1 \pm \sqrt{1 - 8}}{2}$, neither of which is prime.

So $p = 3$ is the only prime number such that $f(x) = 0$ will have rational roots.

When $p = 3$, we have $x^3 + x^2 + x - 3 = 0$

We use synthetic division:

```
        1   1   1  -3
   1│        1   2   3
        1   2   3   0
```

So $x = 1$ is a root.

Now $x^2 + 2x + 3 = 0$ has no real roots, so $x = 1$ is the only root.

49. Following the suggestion, we substitute:

  $x = 1$: $1 + 1 - pq = 0$, so $pq = 2$, which is impossible for prime numbers p and q.

  $x = -1$: $1 - 1 - pq = 0$, so $pq = 0$, which is impossible.

  $x = p$: $p^2 + p - pq = 0$
         $p(p + 1 - q) = 0$
         Clearly $p \neq 0$, so $p = q - 1$, which occurs when $p = 2$ and $q = 3$.
         Thus the equation is $x^2 + x - 6 = 0$, which factors to
         $(x + 3)(x - 2) = 0$, thus the solutions are -3 and 2.

  $x = -p$: $p^2 - p - pq = 0$
         $p(p - 1 - q) = 0$
         Clearly $p \neq 0$, so $p = q + 1$, which occurs when $p = 3$ and $q = 2$.
         This results in identical solutions as when $x = p$.

  $x = q$: $q^2 + q - pq = 0$
         $q(q + 1 - p) = 0$
         Clearly $q \neq 0$, so $p = q + 1$, as above.

  $x = -q$: $q^2 - q - pq = 0$
         $q(q - 1 - p) = 0$
         Clearly $q \neq 0$, so $q = p + 1$, again as above.

  $x = pq$: $p^2q^2 + pq - pq = 0$
              $p^2q^2 = 0$
         Clearly this is impossible.

  $x = -pq$: $p^2q^2 - pq - pq = 0$
            $pq(pq - 2) = 0$
         Since $pq \neq 0$, then $pq = 2$. But this is impossible for prime numbers p and q.

Thus if the equation has rational roots they must be -3 and 2.

51.   The possible rational roots are ±1, ±2, ±4.
      We use synthetic division:

$$\underline{1|} \quad 1 \qquad -b^2 \qquad\qquad 3b \qquad\qquad -4$$

$$\qquad\quad 1 \qquad\quad -b^2+1 \qquad -b^2+3b+1$$

$$\overline{\quad 1 \quad -b^2+1 \quad -b^2+3b+1 \quad -b^2+3b-3}$$

Solve:

$$-3 + 3b - b^2 = 0$$
$$b^2 - 3b + 3 = 0$$

$$b = \frac{3 \pm \sqrt{9 - 12}}{2}, \text{ which is not an integer.}$$

Use synthetic division again:

$$\underline{-1|} \quad 1 \qquad -b^2 \qquad\qquad 3b \qquad\qquad -4$$

$$\qquad\quad -1 \qquad\quad b^2+1 \qquad -b^2-3b-1$$

$$\overline{\quad 1 \quad -b^2-1 \quad b^2+3b+1 \quad -b^2-3b-5}$$

Solve:

$$-b^2 - 3b - 5 = 0$$
$$b^2 + 3b + 5 = 0$$

$$b = \frac{-3 \pm \sqrt{9 - 20}}{2}, \text{ which is not an integer.}$$

Use synthetic division again:

$$\underline{2|} \quad 1 \qquad -b^2 \qquad\qquad 3b \qquad\qquad -4$$

$$\qquad\quad 2 \qquad\quad -2b^2+4 \qquad -4b^2+6b+8$$

$$\overline{\quad 1 \quad -b^2+2 \quad -2b^2+3b+4 \quad -4b^2+6b+4}$$

Solve:

$$4 + 6b - 4b^2 = 0$$
$$2b^2 - 3b - 2 = 0$$
$$(2b + 1)(b - 2) = 0$$

$$b = -\frac{1}{2} \quad \text{or} \quad b = 2$$

So b = 2 is a possible value.
Use synthetic division again:

$$\underline{-2|} \quad 1 \qquad -b^2 \qquad\qquad 3b \qquad\qquad -4$$

$$\qquad\quad -2 \qquad\quad 2b^2+4 \qquad -4b^2-6b-8$$

$$\overline{\quad 1 \quad -b^2-2 \quad 2b^2+3b+4 \quad -4b^2-6b-12}$$

Solve:

$$-4b^2 - 6b - 12 = 0$$
$$2b^2 + 3b + 6 = 0$$

$$b = \frac{-3 \pm \sqrt{9 - 48}}{4}, \text{ which is not an integer.}$$

Use synthetic division again:

$$\begin{array}{r|rrrr} 4 & 1 & -b^2 & 3b & -4 \\ & & 4 & -4b^2+16 & -16b^2+12b+64 \\ \hline & 1 & -b^2+4 & -4b^2+3b+16 & -16b^2+12b+60 \end{array}$$

Solve:

$$60 + 12b - 16b^2 = 0$$
$$4b^2 - 3b - 15 = 0$$
$$b = \frac{3 \pm \sqrt{9 + 240}}{8}, \text{ which is not an integer.}$$

Use synthetic division again:

$$\begin{array}{r|rrrr} -4 & 1 & -b^2 & 3b & -4 \\ & & -4 & 4b^2+16 & -16b^2-12b-64 \\ \hline & 1 & -b^2-4 & 4b^2+3b+16 & -16b^2-12b-68 \end{array}$$

Solve:

$$-16b^2 - 12b - 68 = 0$$
$$4b^2 + 3b + 17 = 0$$
$$b = \frac{-3 \pm \sqrt{9 - 272}}{8}, \text{ which is not an integer.}$$

So $b = 2$ is the only integer value of b.

9.5 Conjugate Roots and Descartes's Rule of Signs

1.   The other root must be $7 + 2i$.

3.   One other root must be $5 - 2i$. So $\big(x - (5 - 2i)\big)\big(x - (5 + 2i)\big)$ are factors, or $x^2 - 10x + 29$. We divide:

$$\require{enclose}\begin{array}{r} x \phantom{{}^3} - 3 \phantom{{}x} \\ x^2 - 10x + 29 \enclose{longdiv}{x^3 - 13x^2 + 59x - 87} \\ \underline{x^3 - 10x^2 + 29x} \phantom{{}- 87} \\ -3x^2 + 30x - 87 \\ \underline{-3x^2 + 30x - 87} \\ 0 \end{array}$$

Since $x - 3$ is the other factor, then 3 is the other root. So the other two roots are $5 - 2i$ and 3.

5.   One other root must be -2 - i, so $\left(x - (-2 + i)\right)\left(x - (-2 - i)\right)$ are factors, or $x^2 + 4x + 5$. We divide:

$$
\begin{array}{r}
x^2 + 6x + 9 \\
x^2 + 4x + 5 \overline{\smash{\big)}\ x^4 + 10x^3 + 38x^2 + 66x + 45} \\
\underline{x^4 + 4x^3 + 5x^2} \\
6x^3 + 33x^2 + 66x \\
\underline{6x^3 + 24x^2 + 30x} \\
9x^2 + 36x + 45 \\
\underline{9x^2 + 36x + 45} \\
0
\end{array}
$$

Since $x^2 + 6x + 9 = (x + 3)^2$, the other root is -3. So the remaining roots are -2 - i and -3 (multiplicity 2).

7.   One other root must be 6 + 5i, so $\left(x - (6 - 5i)\right)\left(x - (6 + 5i)\right)$ are factors, or $x^2 - 12x + 61$. We divide:

$$
\begin{array}{r}
4x + 1 \\
x^2 - 12x + 61 \overline{\smash{\big)}\ 4x^3 - 47x^2 + 232x + 61} \\
\underline{4x^3 - 48x^2 + 244x} \\
x^2 - 12x + 61 \\
\underline{x^2 - 12x + 61} \\
0
\end{array}
$$

Since 4x + 1 is the other factor, then $-\dfrac{1}{4}$ is the other root. So the remaining roots are 6 + 5i and $-\dfrac{1}{4}$.

9. One other root must be $4 - \sqrt{2}\,i$, so $\left(x - (4 + \sqrt{2}i)\right)\left(x - (4 - \sqrt{2}i)\right)$ are factors, or $x^2 - 8x + 18$. We divide:

$$
\begin{array}{r}
4x^2 + 9 \\
x^2 - 8x + 18 \enclose{longdiv}{4x^4 - 32x^3 + 81x^2 - 72x + 162} \\
\underline{4x^4 - 32x^3 + 72x^2} \\
9x^2 - 72x + 162 \\
\underline{9x^2 - 72x + 162} \\
0
\end{array}
$$

Since $4x^2 + 9 = (2x + 3i)(2x - 3i)$, the other roots are $-\dfrac{3i}{2}$ and $\dfrac{3i}{2}$. So the remaining roots are $4 - \sqrt{2}\,i$, $-\dfrac{3i}{2}$, and $\dfrac{3i}{2}$.

11. One other root must be $10 - 2i$, so $\left(x - (10 + 2i)\right)\left(x - (10 - 2i)\right)$ are factors, or $x^2 - 20x + 104$. We divide:

$$
\begin{array}{r}
x^2 - 2x - 4 \\
x^2 - 20x + 104 \enclose{longdiv}{x^4 - 22x^3 + 140x^2 - 128x - 416} \\
\underline{x^4 - 20x^3 + 104x^2} \\
-2x^3 + 36x^2 - 128x \\
\underline{-2x^3 + 40x^2 - 208x} \\
-4x^2 + 80x - 416 \\
\underline{-4x^2 + 80x - 416} \\
0
\end{array}
$$

So the other factor is $x^2 - 2x - 4$. We use the quadratic formula:

$$
x = \frac{2 \pm \sqrt{4 + 16}}{2} = \frac{2 \pm 2\sqrt{5}}{2} = 1 \pm \sqrt{5}
$$

So the remaining roots are $10 - 2i$, $1 + \sqrt{5}$, and $1 - \sqrt{5}$.

13.   One other root must be $\dfrac{1 - \sqrt{2}i}{3}$, so $\left(x - \dfrac{1 + \sqrt{2}i}{2}\right)\left(x - \dfrac{1 - \sqrt{2}i}{2}\right)$ are factors, or $x^2 - \dfrac{2}{3}x + \dfrac{1}{3}$. We divide:

$$
\begin{array}{r}
15x - 6 \\
x^2 - 2/3x + 1/3 \overline{\smash{\big)}\, 15x^3 - 16x^2 + 9x - 2} \\
\underline{15x^3 - 10x^2 + 5x} \\
-6x^2 + 4x - 2 \\
\underline{-6x^2 + 4x - 2} \\
0
\end{array}
$$

So the other factor is $15x - 6$, so $x = \dfrac{2}{5}$ is a root. The remaining roots are $\dfrac{1 - i\sqrt{2}}{3}$ and $\dfrac{2}{5}$.

15.   We know $3 + 2i$ is a root, so $\big(x - (3 - 2i)\big)\big(x - (3 + 2i)\big)$ are factors, which is $x^2 - 6x + 13$. We divide:

$$
\begin{array}{r}
x^5 + 3x^4 + x^3 - 3x^2 - 4x + 2 \\
x^2 - 6x + 13 \overline{\smash{\big)}\, x^7 - 3x^6 - 4x^5 + 30x^4 + 27x^3 - 13x^2 - 64x + 26} \\
\underline{x^7 - 6x^6 + 13x^5} \\
3x^6 - 17x^5 + 30x^4 \\
\underline{3x^6 - 18x^5 + 39x^4} \\
x^5 - 9x^4 + 27x^3 \\
\underline{x^5 - 6x^4 + 13x^3} \\
-3x^4 + 14x^3 - 13x^2 \\
\underline{-3x^4 + 18x^3 - 39x^2} \\
-4x^3 + 26x^2 - 64x \\
\underline{-4x^3 + 24x^2 - 52x} \\
2x^2 - 12x + 26 \\
\underline{2x^2 - 12x + 26} \\
0
\end{array}
$$

We know x = -1 - i will be a root, so $\left(x - (-1 + i)\right)\left(x - (-1 - i)\right)$ are factors, which is $x^2 + 2x + 2$. We divide:

$$
\require{enclose}
\begin{array}{r}
x^3 + x^2 - 3x + 1 \\[2pt]
x^2 + 2x + 2 \enclose{longdiv}{x^5 + 3x^4 + x^3 - 3x^2 - 4x + 2} \\
\end{array}
$$

$$
\begin{aligned}
&x^5 + 2x^4 + 2x^3 \\
&\quad\; x^4 - x^3 - 3x^2 \\
&\quad\; x^4 + 2x^3 + 2x^2 \\
&\qquad\quad -3x^3 - 5x^2 - 4x \\
&\qquad\quad -3x^3 - 6x^2 - 6x \\
&\qquad\qquad\qquad x^2 + 2x + 2 \\
&\qquad\qquad\qquad x^2 + 2x + 2 \\
&\qquad\qquad\qquad\qquad\qquad 0
\end{aligned}
$$

Finally, we know x = 1 is a root, so we synthetically divide:

$$
\begin{array}{r|rrrr}
1 & 1 & 1 & -3 & 1 \\
  &   & 1 & 2 & -1 \\
\hline
  & 1 & 2 & -1 & 0
\end{array}
$$

So we are left with $x^2 + 2x - 1 = 0$. Using the quadratic formula:

$$
x = \frac{-2 \pm \sqrt{4 + 4}}{2} = \frac{-2 \pm 2\sqrt{2}}{2} = -1 \pm \sqrt{2}
$$

So the remaining roots are 3 + 2i, -1 - i, $-1 + \sqrt{2}$, and $-1 - \sqrt{2}$.

17. $r_1 = 1 + \sqrt{6}$ and $r_2 = 1 - \sqrt{6}$, so $\left(x - (1 + \sqrt{6})\right)\left(x - (1 - \sqrt{6})\right) = 0$.
Multiplied out, we get $x^2 - 2x - 5 = 0$.

19. $r_1 = \dfrac{2 + \sqrt{10}}{3}$ and $r_2 = \dfrac{2 - \sqrt{10}}{3}$, so $\left(x - \dfrac{2 + \sqrt{10}}{3}\right)\left(x - \dfrac{2 - \sqrt{10}}{3}\right) = 0$.

Multiplied out, we get $x^2 - \dfrac{4}{3}x - \dfrac{2}{3} = 0$.

21. Let $f(x) = x^3 + 5$. Since there are no sign changes, there will be no positive roots. Now $f(-x) = -x^3 + 5$. Since there is one sign change, there is one negative root. So the equation has two complex roots and one negative real root.

23. Let $f(x) = 2x^5 + 3x + 4$. Since there are no sign changes, there will be no positive roots. Now $f(-x) = -2x^5 - 3x + 4$. Since there is one sign change, there is 1 negative root. So the equation has 4 complex roots and 1 negative real root.

25. Let $f(x) = 5x^4 + 2x - 7$. Since there is one sign change, there will be 1 positive root. Now $f(-x) = 5x^4 - 2x - 7$. Since there is one sign change, there will be 1 negative root. So the equation has 2 complex roots, 1 positive real root, and 1 negative real root.

27. Let $f(x) = x^3 - 4x^2 - x - 1$. Since there is one sign change, there will be 1 positive root. Now $f(-x) = -x^3 - 4x^2 + x - 1$. Since there are two sign changes, there will be 0 or 2 negative roots. So the equation has either 1 positive real root and 2 negative real roots, or 1 positive real root and 2 complex roots.

29. Let $f(x) = 3x^8 + x^6 - 2x^2 - 4$. Since there is one sign change, there is 1 positive root. Now $f(-x) = 3x^8 + x^6 - 2x^2 - 4$. Since there is one sign change, there is one negative root. So the equation has 1 positive real root, 1 negative real root, and 6 complex roots.

31. Let $f(x) = x^9 - 2$. Since there is one sign change, there is 1 positive root. Now $f(-x) = -x^9 - 2$. Since there are no sign changes, there are no negative roots. So the equation has 1 positive real root and 8 complex roots.

33. Let $f(x) = x^8 - 2$. Since there is one sign change, there is one positive root. Now $f(-x) = x^8 - 2$. Since there is one sign change, there is one negative root. So the equation has 1 positive real root, 1 negative real root, and 6 complex roots.

35. Let $f(x) = x^6 + x^2 - x - 1$. Since there is one sign change, there is one positive root. Now $f(-x) = x^6 + x^2 + x - 1$. Since there is one sign change, there is one negative root. So the equation has 1 positive real root, 1 negative real root and 4 complex roots.

37. Let $f(x) = x^4 + cx^2 + dx - e$. Since there is one sign change, there is one positive root. Now $f(-x) = x^4 + cx^2 - dx - e$. Since there is one sign change, there is one negative root. So the equation has 1 positive real root, 1 negative real root, and 2 complex roots.

39. The two roots $\sqrt{3} + 2i$ and $\sqrt{3} - 2i$ must be included, so:

$$f(x) = \left(x - (\sqrt{3} + 2i)\right)\left(x - (\sqrt{3} - 2i)\right) = x^2 - 2\sqrt{3}\,x + 7 = 0$$

Unfortunately, not all coefficients are rational:

$$x^2 + 7 = 2\sqrt{3}\,x$$

Squaring, we get:

$$x^4 + 14x^2 + 49 = 12x^2$$
$$x^4 + 2x^2 + 29 = 0$$

So $f(x) = x^4 + 2x^2 + 49$ is the desired polynomial.

41. (a) If $b = 0$, then $a + b\sqrt{c} = a = a - b\sqrt{c}$, so $a - b\sqrt{c}$ is also a root.

(b) $\begin{aligned} d(a + b\sqrt{c}) &= \left(a + b\sqrt{c} - (a + b\sqrt{c})\right)\left(a + b\sqrt{c} - (a - b\sqrt{c})\right) \\ &= 0\left(2b\sqrt{c}\right) \\ &= 0 \end{aligned}$

(c) $d(x) = x^2 - 2ax + a^2 - b^2c = (x - a)^2 - b^2c$

(d) If $x = a + b\sqrt{c}$, we have:

$$\begin{aligned} f(a + b\sqrt{c}) &= d(a + b\sqrt{c})\,Q(a + b\sqrt{c}) + C(a + b\sqrt{c}) + D \\ 0 &= 0 \bullet Q(a + b\sqrt{c}) + Ca + D + bC\sqrt{c} \\ 0 &= Ca + D + bC\sqrt{c} \end{aligned}$$

But if C and D are rational, then $C = 0$ (otherwise $\sqrt{c}$ will not be "cancelled" out). If $C = D$, then $D = 0$. So $C = D = 0$.

(e) $\begin{aligned} f(a - b\sqrt{c}) &= \left(a - b\sqrt{c} - (a + b\sqrt{c})\right)\left(a - b\sqrt{c} - (a - b\sqrt{c})\right) Q(x) \\ &= \left(-2b\sqrt{c}\right)\left(0\right) Q(x) \\ &= 0 \end{aligned}$

So $x = a - b\sqrt{c}$ is also a root of $f(x) = 0$.

Chapter 9 Review Exercises

1. Since $f(1/2)$ will be the remainder after synthetic division, we synthetically divide by $1/2$:

$$
\begin{array}{r|rrrrr}
1/2 & 6 & -5 & 7 & -2 & -2 \\
    &   & 3 & -1 & 3 & 1/2 \\
\hline
    & 6 & -2 & 6 & 1 & -3/2
\end{array}
$$

So $f(1/2) = -3/2$.

2.   Use synthetic division:

$$
\begin{array}{r|rrrr}
-3 & 1 & 1 & -11 & -15 \\
   &   & -3 & 6 & 15 \\
\hline
   & 1 & -2 & -5 & 0
\end{array}
$$

So $x^3 + x^2 - 11x - 15 = (x + 3)(x^2 - 2x - 5)$
Using the quadratic equation, we get:

$$x = \frac{2 \pm \sqrt{4 + 20}}{2} = \frac{2 \pm 2\sqrt{6}}{2} = 1 \pm \sqrt{6}$$

So the roots of the equation are -3, $1 + \sqrt{6}$, and $1 - \sqrt{6}$.

3. $\pm 1, \pm 1/2, \pm 2, \pm 3, \pm 3/2, \pm 6$

4.   Such a function would be $y = a(x - 1)(x + 8)$. Now $y = -24$ when $x = 0$, so $-24 = a(-1)(8)$, so $a = 3$. So the function is $y = 3(x - 1)(x + 8)$, or $f(x) = 3x^2 + 21x - 24$.

5.   We use synthetic division:

$$
\begin{array}{r|rrrr}
-1 & 4 & 1 & -8 & 3 \\
   &   & -4 & 3 & 5 \\
\hline
   & 4 & -3 & -5 & 8
\end{array}
$$

quotient: $4x^2 - 3x - 5$; remainder: 8

6.   (a)   Let $f(x)$ be a polynomial. If $f(r) = 0$, then $x - r$ is a factor of $f(x)$.
        Conversely, if $x - r$ is a factor of $f(x)$, then $f(r) = 0$.

    (b)   Every polynomial equation of the form
            $a_n x^n + a_{n-1} x^{n-1} + \ldots + a_1 x + a_0 = 0$ $(n \geq 1, a_n \neq 0)$
        has at least one root among the complex numbers. (This root may be a real number.)

7.   (a)   We use synthetic division with 1:

$$
\begin{array}{r|rrrr}
1 & 1 & -2 & 0 & -1 \\
  &   & 1 & -1 & -1 \\
\hline
  & 1 & -1 & -1 & -2
\end{array}
$$

Now we use 2:

$$
\begin{array}{r|rrrr}
2 & 1 & -2 & 0 & -1 \\
  &   & 2 & 0 & 0 \\
\hline
  & 1 & 0 & 0 & -1
\end{array}
$$

Now use 3:

$$3 \underline{|} \quad 1 \quad -2 \quad 0 \quad -1$$

$$ 3 \quad 3 \quad 9$$

$$\underline{} $$

$$ \quad 1 \quad 1 \quad 3 \quad 8$$

So 3 is an upper bound for the roots.

(b) $f(2.2) = -0.032$ and $f(2.3) = 0.587$, so the root lies between 2.2 and 2.3.

8.   Two other roots are 1 - i and 3 + 2i, so $x^2 - 2x + 2$ and $x^2 - 6x + 13$ are factors. We use long division:

$$
\begin{array}{r}
x^3 - 4x^2 + x + 26 \\
x^2 - 2x + 2 \enclose{longdiv}{x^5 - 6x^4 + 11x^3 + 16x^2 - 50x + 52} \\
\underline{x^5 - 2x^4 + 2x^3} \\
-4x^4 + 9x^3 + 16x^2 \\
\underline{-4x^4 + 8x^3 - 8x^2} \\
x^3 + 24x^2 - 50x \\
\underline{x^3 - 2x^2 + 2x} \\
26x^2 - 52x + 52 \\
\underline{26x^2 - 52x + 52} \\
0
\end{array}
$$

We use long division again:

$$
\begin{array}{r}
x + 2 \\
x^2 - 6x + 13 \enclose{longdiv}{x^3 - 4x^2 + x + 26} \\
\underline{x^3 - 6x^2 + 13x} \\
2x^2 - 12x + 26 \\
\underline{2x^2 - 12x + 26} \\
0
\end{array}
$$

So the roots are $1 \pm i$, $3 \pm 2i$ and -2.

9.   We use long division:

$$\begin{array}{r}
x^2 + 2x - 1 \\
x^2 + 1 \overline{\smash{\big)}\ x^4 + 2x^3 + 0x^2 - x + 6} \\
\underline{x^4 \qquad\quad + x^2} \\
2x^3 - x^2 - x \\
\underline{2x^3 \qquad\quad + 2x} \\
-x^2 - 3x + 6 \\
\underline{-x^2 \qquad\quad - 1} \\
-3x + 7
\end{array}$$

So $q(x) = x^2 + 2x - 1$ and $R(x) = -3x + 7$.

10.   We first find the roots by the quadratic formula:

$$x = \frac{6 \pm \sqrt{36 - 40}}{4} = \frac{6 \pm 2i}{4} = \frac{3}{2} \pm \frac{1}{2}i$$

So $2x^2 - 6x + 5 = 2(x^2 - 3x + 5/2) = 2\big(x - (3/2 + 1/2\ i)\big)\big(x - (3/2 - 1/2\ i)\big)$.

11.   (a) $\pm 1, \pm 2, \pm 3, \pm 4, \pm 6, \pm 8, \pm 12, \pm 24$

(b)   We use synthetic division:

$$\begin{array}{r|rrrrr}
2 & 1 & -1 & 0 & 0 & 24 \\
  &   & 2 & 2 & 4 & 8 \\
\hline
  & 1 & 1 & 2 & 4 & 32
\end{array}$$

Since this last row consists of all positive numbers, we know that 2 is an upper bound for the roots of this equation.

(c)   Only $x = 1$, since $x = 2$ is an upper bound and not a root.

(d)   We use synthetic division:

$$\begin{array}{r|rrrrr}
1 & 1 & -1 & 0 & 0 & 24 \\
  &   & 1 & 0 & 0 & 1 \\
\hline
  & 1 & 0 & 0 & 0 & 25
\end{array}$$

Since $x = 1$ was the only possibility, there are no positive rational roots.

12. (a) The possible rational roots are $\pm 1, \pm\frac{1}{2}, \pm 3, \pm\frac{3}{2}$

We use synthetic division:

```
3/2 │  2   −1   −1   −3
    │       3    3    3
    └──────────────────
       2    2    2    0
```

So $2x^3 - x^2 - x - 3 = \left(x - \frac{3}{2}\right)(2x^2 + 2x + 2) = 2\left(x - \frac{3}{2}\right)(x^2 + x + 1)$

Using the quadratic equation, we have:

$$x = \frac{-1 \pm \sqrt{1-4}}{2} = \frac{-1 \pm i\sqrt{3}}{2}$$

So the only rational root is $\frac{3}{2}$.

(b) All solutions are $\frac{3}{2}, \frac{-1 + i\sqrt{3}}{2}$, and $\frac{-1 - i\sqrt{3}}{2}$.

13. Let $f(x) = 3x^4 + x^2 - 5x - 1$. Since there is one sign change, there is one positive root. $f(-x) = 3x^4 + x^2 + 5x - 1$. Since there is one sign change, there is 1 negative root. So the equation has 1 positive real root, 1 negative real root, and 2 complex roots.

14. The factors are $x + 2$, $x - (1 - 3i)$ and $x - (1 + 3i)$, so:

$$\left(x + 2\right)\left(x - (1 - 3i)\right)\left(x - (1 + 3i)\right) = 0$$
$$(x + 2)(x^2 - 2x + 10) = 0$$
$$x^3 + 6x + 20 = 0$$

15. $f(x) = (x - 2)(x - 3i)^3\left(x - (1 + \sqrt{2})\right)^2$
Note that had a restriction of rational coefficients been added, we would also have $-3i$ (multiplicity 3) and $1 - \sqrt{2}$ (muliplicity 2) as roots.

17. (a) We use synthetic division:

```
2 │  1    2   −1    4   12
  │       2    8   14   36
  └────────────────────────
     1    4    7   18   48
```

Since the remainder is non-zero, $x - 2$ is not a factor of $f(x)$.

(b)   We use synthetic division:

$$-2 \, \rfloor \quad \begin{array}{ccccc} 1 & 2 & -1 & 4 & 12 \\ & -2 & 0 & 2 & -12 \\ \hline 1 & 0 & -1 & 6 & 0 \end{array}$$

Since the remainder is zero, x + 2 is a factor of f(x).

19. (a)   We use synthetic division:

$$1 \, \rfloor \quad \begin{array}{ccccc} 1 & 3 & -1 & 3 & -18 \\ & 1 & 4 & 3 & 6 \\ \hline 1 & 4 & 3 & 6 & -12 \end{array}$$

Since the remainder is non-zero, x - 1 is not a factor of f(x).

(b)   We use synthetic division:

$$-3 \, \rfloor \quad \begin{array}{ccccc} 1 & 3 & -1 & 3 & -18 \\ & -3 & 0 & 3 & -18 \\ \hline 1 & 0 & -1 & 6 & -36 \end{array}$$

Since the remainder is non-zero, x + 3 is not a factor of f(x).

21. We use long division:

$$
\begin{array}{r}
x^3 + x^2 - 3x + 1 \\
x + 2 \overline{\smash{\big)}\, x^4 + 3x^3 - x^2 - 5x + 1} \\
\underline{x^4 + 2x^3} \\
x^3 - x^2 \\
\underline{x^3 + 2x^2} \\
-3x^2 - 5x \\
\underline{-3x^2 - 6x} \\
x + 1 \\
\underline{x + 2} \\
-1
\end{array}
$$

So q(x) = $x^3 + x^2 - 3x + 1$ and R(x) = -1.

23. We use synthetic division:

$$3 \, \rfloor \quad \begin{array}{ccccc} 1 & 0 & -2 & 0 & 8 \\ & 3 & 9 & 21 & 63 \\ \hline 1 & 3 & 7 & 21 & 71 \end{array}$$

So the quotient is $x^3 + 3x^2 + 7x + 21$ and the remainder is 71.

25. We use synthetic division:

$$\begin{array}{r|rrrr} -4 & 2 & -5 & -6 & -3 \\ & & -8 & 52 & -184 \\ \hline & 2 & -13 & 46 & -187 \end{array}$$

So the quotient is $2x^2$ - 13x + 46 and the remainder is -187.

27. We use synthetic division:

$$\begin{array}{r|rrr} -0.2 & 5 & -19 & -4 \\ & & -1 & 4 \\ \hline & 5 & -20 & 0 \end{array}$$

So the quotient is 5x - 20 and the remainder is zero.

29. We use synthetic division:

$$\begin{array}{r|rrrrrr} 10 & 1 & 0 & 0 & 0 & -10 & 4 \\ & & 10 & 100 & 1000 & 10000 & 99900 \\ \hline & 1 & 10 & 100 & 1000 & 9990 & 99904 \end{array}$$

So f(10) = 99,904.

31. We use synthetic division:

$$\begin{array}{r|rrrr} 1/10 & 1 & -10 & 1 & -1 \\ & & 1/10 & -99/100 & 1/1000 \\ \hline & 1 & -99/10 & 1/100 & -999/1000 \end{array}$$

So $f\left(\dfrac{1}{10}\right) = -\dfrac{999}{1000}$.

33. We use synthetic division:

$$\begin{array}{r|rrrr} a-1 & 1 & 3 & 3 & 1 \\ & & a-1 & a^2+a-2 & a^3-1 \\ \hline & 1 & a+2 & a^2+a+1 & a^3 \end{array}$$

So f(a - 1) = a^3.

35. (a) We use synthetic division:

$$\begin{array}{r|rrrrr} -0.3 & 1 & 4 & -6 & -8 & -2 \\ & & -0.3 & -1.11 & 2.133 & 1.7601 \\ \hline & 1 & 3.7 & -7.11 & -5.867 & -0.24 \end{array}$$

So f(-0.3) ≈ -0.24.

(b)   We use synthetic division:

-0.39	1	4	-6	-8	-2
		-0.39	-1.4079	2.8891	1.9933
	1	3.61	-7.4079	-5.1109	-0.007

So $f(-0.39) \approx -0.007$.

(c)   We use synthetic division:

-0.394	1	4	-6	-8	-2
		-0.394	-1.420764	2.92378	2.00003
	1	3.606	-7.420764	-5.07622	0.00003

So $f(-0.394) \approx 0.00003$.

37.   We use synthetic division:

3	1	-4	$-a$	-6
		3	-3	$-3a-9$
	1	-1	$-a-3$	$-3a-15$

So if 3 is a root, then:
$$-3a - 15 = 0$$
$$-3a = 15$$
$$a = -5$$

39.   We use synthetic division:

1	a^2	$3a$	0	2
		a^2	a^2+3a	a^2+3a
	a^2	a^2+3a	a^2+3a	a^2+3a+2

So, if $x - 1$ is a factor, then:
$$a^2 + 3a + 2 = 0$$
$$(a + 1)(a + 2) = 0$$
$$a = -1, -2$$
So $a = -1$ or $a = -2$.

41.   (a)   Let $f(x + h) = 0$, and let $x = r - h$. Then $f(r - h + h) = f(r) = 0$, since r is a root of $f(x) = 0$.

(b)   Let $f(-x) = 0$, and let $x = -r$. Then $f\left(-(-r)\right) = f(r) = 0$, since r is a root of $f(x) = 0$.

(c)   Let $f\left(\dfrac{x}{k}\right) = 0$, and let $x = kr$. Then $f\left(\dfrac{kr}{k}\right) = f(r) = 0$, since r is a root of $f(x) = 0$.

43. p-factors: ±1, ±2, ±3, ±6, ±9, ±18
     q-factors: ±1
     possible rational roots: ±1, ±2, ±3, ±6, ±9, ±18

45. p-factors: ±1, ±2, ±4, ±8
     q-factors: ±1, ±2
     possible rational roots: ±1, ±1/2, ±2, ±4, ±8

47. p-factors: ±p, ±1
     q-factors: ±1
     possible rational roots: ±p, ±1

49. possible rational roots: $\pm 1, \pm \frac{1}{2}, \pm 2, \pm 3, \pm \frac{3}{2}, \pm 6$

     We use synthetic division:

     $$\begin{array}{r|rrrr} 2 & 2 & 1 & -7 & -6 \\ & & 4 & 10 & 6 \\ \hline & 2 & 5 & 3 & 0 \end{array}$$

     So $2x^3 + x^2 - 7x - 6 = (x - 2)(2x^2 + 5x + 3) = (x - 2)(2x + 3)(x + 1)$

     So the roots are 2, $-\frac{3}{2}$, and -1.

51. possible rational roots: $\pm 1, \pm \frac{1}{2}, \pm 2, \pm 5, \pm \frac{5}{2}, \pm 10$

     We use synthetic division:

     $$\begin{array}{r|rrrr} 5/2 & 2 & -1 & -14 & 10 \\ & & 5 & 10 & -10 \\ \hline & 2 & 4 & -4 & 0 \end{array}$$

     So $2x^3 - x^2 - 14x + 10 = \left(x - \frac{5}{2}\right)(2x^2 + 4x - 4) = 2\left(x - \frac{5}{2}\right)(x^2 + 2x - 2)$

     We use the quadratic formula: $x = \dfrac{-2 \pm \sqrt{4 + 8}}{2} = \dfrac{-2 \pm 2\sqrt{3}}{2} = -1 \pm \sqrt{3}$

     So the roots are $\frac{5}{2}$, $-1 + \sqrt{3}$, and $-1 - \sqrt{3}$.

53. First multiply by 2: $3x^3 + x^2 + x - 2 = 0$
     possible rational roots: $\pm 1, \pm \frac{1}{3}, \pm 2, \pm \frac{2}{3}$
     We use synthetic division:

     $$\begin{array}{r|rrrr} 2/3 & 3 & 1 & 1 & -2 \\ & & 2 & 2 & 2 \\ \hline & 3 & 3 & 3 & 0 \end{array}$$

So $3x^3 + x^2 + x - 2 = \left(x - \dfrac{2}{3}\right)(3x^2 + 3x + 3) = 3\left(x - \dfrac{2}{3}\right)(x^2 + x + 1)$

Using the quadratic formula: $x = \dfrac{-1 \pm \sqrt{1-4}}{2} = \dfrac{-1 \pm i\sqrt{3}}{2}$

So the roots are $\dfrac{2}{3}$, $\dfrac{-1 + i\sqrt{3}}{2}$, and $\dfrac{-1 - i\sqrt{3}}{2}$.

55. possible rational roots: $\pm 1, \pm 7, \pm 49$
We use synthetic division:

$$
\begin{array}{r|rrrrrr}
-1 & 1 & 1 & -14 & -14 & 49 & 49 \\
   &   & -1 & 0 & 14 & 0 & -49 \\
\hline
   & 1 & 0 & -14 & 0 & 49 & 0
\end{array}
$$

So $x^5 + x^4 - 14x^3 - 14x^2 + 49x + 49 = (x + 1)(x^4 - 14x^2 + 49)$
$$= (x + 1)(x^2 - 7)^2$$
$$= (x + 1)(x + \sqrt{7})^2(x - \sqrt{7})^2$$

So the roots are -1, $-\sqrt{7}$ (multiplicity 2), and $\sqrt{7}$ (multiplicity 2).

57. Since $x^3 - 9x^2 + 24x - 20 = 0$ has a root r with multiplicity 2, we can use synthetic division by r twice, each time the remainder must be 0:

$$
\begin{array}{r|rrrr}
r & 1 & -9 & 24 & -20 \\
  &   & r & r^2 - 9r & r^3 - 9r^2 + 24r \\
\hline
  & 1 & r-9 & r^2 - 9r + 24 & r^3 - 9r^2 + 24r - 20
\end{array}
$$

We continue the division:

$$
\begin{array}{r|rrr}
r & 1 & r-9 & r^2 - 9r + 24 \\
  &   & r & 2r^2 - 9r \\
\hline
  & 1 & 2r-9 & 3r^2 - 18r + 24
\end{array}
$$

So $3r^2 - 18r + 24 = 3(r^2 - 6r + 8) = 3(r - 4)(r - 2) = 0$, thus $r = 4$ or
$r = 2$. We check these in $r^3 - 9r^2 + 24r - 20 = 0$:
$r = 4$: $(4)^3 - 9(4)^2 + 24(4) - 20 = 64 - 144 + 96 - 20 = -4 \neq 0$
        So $r = 4$ cannot be a root.
$r = 2$: $(2)^3 - 9(2)^2 + 24(2) - 20 = 8 - 36 + 48 - 20 = 0$
So $r = 2$ is the root with multiplicity two. SInce the synthetic division resulted
in $x + (2r - 9) = 0$, then $x + (-5) = 0$, thus $x = 5$.
So the roots are 2 (multiplicity 2) and 5.

Note: Actually, an easier (and more direct) approach is to find the roots directly:

possible rational roots: $\pm 1, \pm 2, \pm 4, \pm 5, \pm 10, \pm 20$

Note that there are 3 sign changes, so there can be 1 or 3 positive real roots. Since $f(-x)$ has no sign changes, all 3 roots must be positive real numbers for one of them to have multiplicity of 2 (note that it cannot have a radical or be complex - why?). We use synthetic division:

$$\begin{array}{r|rrrr} 2 & 1 & -9 & 24 & -20 \\ & & 2 & -14 & 20 \\ \hline & 1 & -7 & 10 & 0 \end{array}$$

So $x^3 - 9x^2 + 24x - 20 = (x - 2)(x^2 - 7x + 10) = (x - 2)^2(x - 5)$

So the roots are 2 (with multiplicity 2) and 5.

59. (a)   Let $p(x)$ and $d(x)$ be polynomials where $d(x) \neq 0$. Then there are unique polynomials $q(x)$ and $R(x)$ such that
$$p(x) = d(x) \bullet q(x) + R(x)$$
where either $R(x) = 0$ or the degree of $R(x)$ is less than the degree of $d(x)$.

(b)   When a polynomial $f(x)$ is divided by $x - r$, the remainder is $f(r)$.

(c)   Let $f(x)$ be a polynomial. If $f(r) = 0$, then $x - r$ is a factor of $f(x)$. Conversely, if $x - r$ is a factor of $f(x)$, then $f(r) = 0$.

(d)   Every polynomial equation of the form
$$a_n x^n + a_{n-1} x^{n-1} + \ldots + a_1 x + a_0 = 0 \ (n \geq 1, a_n \neq 0)$$
has at least one root among the complex numbers. (This root may be a real number.)

61. $6x^2 + 7x - 20 = (3x - 4)(2x + 5) = 6\left(x - \frac{4}{3}\right)\left(x - \left(-\frac{5}{2}\right)\right)$

63. $x^4 - 4x^3 + 5x - 20 = x^3(x - 4) + 5(x - 4)$
$$= (x - 4)(x^3 + 5)$$
$$= (x - 4)(x + \sqrt[3]{5})(x^2 - \sqrt[3]{5}\,x + \sqrt[3]{25})$$

We solve $x^2 - \sqrt[3]{5}\,x + \sqrt[3]{25} = 0$ in the quadratic formula, which yields:

$$x = \frac{\sqrt[3]{5} \pm i\sqrt{3\sqrt[3]{25}}}{2}$$

So $x^4 - 4x^3 + 3x - 20 = (x - 4)\left(x - (-\sqrt[3]{5})\right)\left(x - \frac{\sqrt[3]{5} + i\sqrt{3\sqrt[3]{25}}}{2}\right)\left(x - \frac{\sqrt[3]{5} - i\sqrt{3\sqrt[3]{25}}}{2}\right)$

65. One other root is $2 + 3i$, so $\left(x - (2 - 3i)\right)\left(x - (2 + 3i)\right)$ are factors, which is $x^2 - 4x + 13$. We divide:

$$
\begin{array}{r}
x - 3 \\
x^2 - 4x + 13 \;\big|\; \overline{x^3 - 7x^2 + 25x - 39} \\
\underline{x^3 - 4x^2 + 13x} \\
-3x^2 + 12x - 39 \\
\underline{-3x^2 + 12x - 39} \\
0
\end{array}
$$

So $x - 3$ is the other factor. So the roots are $2 - 3i$, $2 + 3i$, and 3.

67. One other root is $1 - i\sqrt{2}$, so $\left(x - (1 + i\sqrt{2})\right)\left(x - (1 - i\sqrt{2})\right)$ are factors, which is $x^2 - 2x + 3$. We divide:

$$
\begin{array}{r}
x^2 - 4 \\
x^2 - 2x + 3 \;\big|\; \overline{x^4 - 2x^3 - 4x^2 + 14x - 21} \\
\underline{x^4 - 2x^3 + 3x^2} \\
-7x^2 + 14x - 21 \\
\underline{-7x^2 + 14x - 21} \\
0
\end{array}
$$

So $x^2 - 7 = (x + \sqrt{7})(x - \sqrt{7})$ is the other factor. So the roots are $1 + i\sqrt{2}$, $1 - i\sqrt{2}$, $\sqrt{7}$, and $-\sqrt{7}$.

69. Let $f(x) = x^3 + 8x - 7$. There is one sign change, so there is one positive root. Now $f(-x) = -x^3 - 8x - 7$. Since there are no sign changes, there are no negative roots. So the equation has 1 positive real root and 2 complex roots.

71. Let $f(x) = x^3 + 3x + 1$. There are no sign changes, so there are no positive roots. Now $f(-x) = -x^3 - 3x + 1$. Since there is one sign change, there is one negative root. So the equation has 1 negative real root and 2 complex roots.

73. Let $f(x) = x^4 - 10$. There is one sign change, so there is 1 positive root. Since $f(-x) = f(x)$, there is also 1 negative root. So the equation has 1 positive real root, 1 negative real root, and 2 complex roots.

75. (a) Let $f(x) = x^3 + x^2 + x + 1$, so $f(-x) = -x^3 + x^2 - x + 1$. There are three sign changes, so there are either 1 or 3 negative roots.

(b) $(x - 1)(x^3 + x^2 + x + 1) = x^4 - 1$. Let $g(x) = x^4 - 1$. Then $g(-x) = x^4 - 1$, so this can only have 1 negative root. Since $x = 1$ is a positive root, then $x^3 + x^2 + x + 1 = 0$ can only have 1 negative root also.

(c) $x^3 + x^2 + x + 1 = x^2(x + 1) + (x + 1) = (x + 1)(x^2 + 1)$
So $x = -1$ is a root. Also:
$$x^2 + 1 = 0$$
$$x^2 = -1$$
$$x = \pm i$$
So the roots are -1, i, and -i.

77. $x^2 + (x^3)^2 = 1$, so $x^6 + x^2 - 1 = 0$
Let $f(x) = x^6 + x^2 - 1$
  $f(0) = -1$
  $f(1) = 1$
So there is a root between 0 and 1.
  $f(0.8) = -0.09$
  $f(0.9) = 0.34$
So there is a root between 0.8 and 0.9.
  $f(0.82) = -0.02$
  $f(0.83) = 0.01$
So there is a root between 0.82 and 0.83.
So the x-coordinate lies between 0.82 and 0.83.

79. (a) Let $f(x) = x^3 - 36x - 84$. Since there is only one sign change, there is 1 positive real root.

(b) Use synthetic division:

$$\begin{array}{r|rrrr} 7 & 1 & 0 & -36 & -84 \\ & & 7 & 49 & 91 \\ \hline & 1 & 7 & 13 & 7 \end{array}$$

Since the row is all positive, there are no roots to the equation greater than 7.

(c) $f(6) = -84$ and $f(7) = 7$, so there is a root between 6 and 7.
$f(6.8) = -14.3$ and $f(6.9) = -3.89$, so there is a root between 6.9 and 7.0.
$f(6.93) = -0.66$ and $f(6.94) = 0.42$, so there is a root between 6.93 and 6.94.

81.   Another root will be $4 + \sqrt{5}$, so:
$$\left(x - (4 - \sqrt{5})\right)\left(x - (4 + \sqrt{5})\right) = 0$$
$$x^2 - 8x + 11 = 0$$

83.   Other roots will be $6 + 2i$ and $-\sqrt{5}$:
$$\left(x - \sqrt{5}\right)\left(x - (-\sqrt{5})\right)\left(x - (6 - 2i)\right)\left(x - (6 + 2i)\right) = 0$$
$$(x^2 - 5)(x^2 - 12x + 40) = 0$$
$$x^4 - 12x^3 + 35x^2 + 60x - 200 = 0$$

85. $x - 1 = \sqrt{2} + \sqrt{3}$
Squaring both sides, we get:
$$x^2 - 2x + 1 = 5 + 2\sqrt{6}$$
$$x^2 - 2x - 4 = 2\sqrt{6}$$
Squaring both sides again, we get:
$$x^4 - 4x^3 - 4x^2 + 16x + 16 = 24$$
$$x^4 - 4x^3 - 4x^2 + 16x - 8 = 0$$

87. $y = x^3 - 2x^2 - 3x = x(x^2 - 2x - 3) = x(x - 3)(x + 1)$
zeros: 0, 3, -1

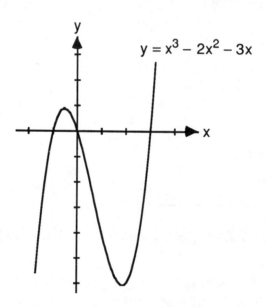

$$y = x^3 - 2x^2 - 3x$$

89. $y = x^4 - 4x^2 = x^2(x^2 - 4) = x^2(x + 2)(x - 2)$
     zeros: 0, -2, 2

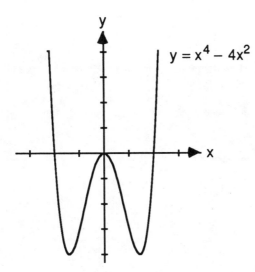

$y = x^4 - 4x^2$

91. $y = x^5 - 8x^4 + 25x^3 - 38x^2 + 28x - 8$

Using synthetic division to find rational roots:

```
1 |  1   -8    25   -38    28   -8
   |      1    -7    18   -20    8
   ------------------------------------
      1   -7    18   --20    8    0
```

Use synthetic division again:

```
1 |  1   -7    18   -20    8
   |      1    -6    12   -8
   ----------------------------
      1   -6    12    -8    0
```

Use synthetic division again:

```
2 |  1   -6    12   -8
   |      2    -8    8
   ----------------------
      1   -4    4    0
```

$$y = (x - 1)^2(x - 2)(x^2 - 4x + 4) = (x - 1)^2(x - 2)^3$$
zeros: 1, 2

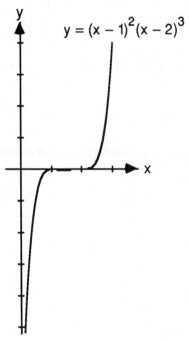

$$y = (x - 1)^2(x - 2)^3$$

93. T

95. F (±1, ±3 are the possiblities)

97. F (f(a) and f(b) must have different signs)

99. T

CHAPTER TEN
ADDITIONAL TOPICS IN ALGEBRA
AND TRIGONOMETRY

10.1   Mathematical Induction

1.   Here P_n denotes the statement:

$$1 + 2 + 3 + \ldots + n = \frac{n(n+1)}{2}$$

Since $1 = \frac{1(1+1)}{2} = 1$, then P_1 is true. It remains to show that P_k implies P_{k+1}. Form P_k:

$$1 + 2 + \ldots + k = \frac{k(k+1)}{2}$$

Hence:

$$1 + 2 + \ldots + k + k + 1 = \frac{k(k+1)}{2} + k + 1$$

$$= (k+1)\left(\frac{k}{2} + 1\right)$$

$$= \frac{(k+1)(k+2)}{2}$$

$$= \frac{(k+1)\big((k+1)+1\big)}{2}$$

which is P_{k+1} and the induction is complete.

3.   Here P_n denotes the statement:

$$1 + 4 + 7 + \ldots + (3n - 2) = \frac{n(3n - 1)}{2}$$

Since $1 = \dfrac{1\big(3(1) - 1\big)}{2} = 1$, then P_1 is true.

Form P_k:

$$1 + 4 + \ldots + (3k - 2) = \frac{k(3k - 1)}{2}$$

Therefore:

$$1 + 4 + \ldots + (3k - 2) + \big(3(k + 1) - 2\big)$$

$$= \frac{k(3k - 1)}{2} + 3(k + 1) - 2$$

$$= \frac{1}{2}\big(k(3k - 1) + 6(k + 1) - 4\big)$$

$$= \frac{1}{2}(3k^2 - k + 6k + 2)$$

$$= \frac{1}{2}(3k^2 + 5k + 2)$$

$$= \frac{(k + 1)(3k + 2)}{2}$$

$$= \frac{(k + 1)\big(3(k + 1) - 1\big)}{2}$$

which is P_{k+1} and the induction is complete.

5.   Here P_n denotes:

$$1^2 + 2^2 + 3^2 + \ldots + n^2 = \frac{n(n + 1)(2n + 1)}{6}$$

Since $1^2 = 1 = \dfrac{1(1 + 1)\big(2(1) + 1\big)}{6} = \dfrac{1(2)(3)}{6} = 1$ then P_1 is true.

Form P_k:

$$1^2 + 2^2 + \ldots + k^2 = \frac{k(k + 1)(2k + 1)}{6}$$

Thus:

$$1^2 + 2^2 + \ldots + k^2 + (k + 1)^2$$

$$= \frac{k(k + 1)(2k + 1)}{6} + (k + 1)^2$$

$$= \frac{(k + 1)\big(k(2k + 1)\big) + 6(k + 1)^2}{6}$$

$$= \frac{(k + 1)(2k^2 + k + 6k + 6)}{6}$$

$$= \frac{(k + 1)(2k^2 + 7k + 6)}{6}$$

$$= \frac{(k + 1)(k + 2)(2k + 3)}{6}$$

$$= \frac{(k + 1)\big((k + 1) + 1\big)\big(2(k + 1) + 1\big)}{6}$$

which is P_{k+1} and the induction is complete.

7.   Here P_n denotes:

$$1^2 + 3^2 + 5^2 + \ldots + (2n - 1)^2 = \frac{n(2n - 1)(2n + 1)}{3}$$

Since $1^2 = 1 = \dfrac{1\big(2(1) - 1\big)\big(2(1) + 1\big)}{3} = 1$, then P_1 is true.

Form P_k:

$$1^2 + 3^2 + \ldots + (2k - 1)^2 = \frac{k(2k - 1)(2k + 1)}{3}$$

Thus:

$$1^2 + 3^2 + \ldots + (2k - 1)^2 + \big(2(k + 1) - 1\big)^2$$

$$= \frac{k(2k - 1)(2k + 1)}{3} + \big(2(k + 1) - 1\big)^2$$

$$= \frac{k(2k - 1)(2k + 1)}{3} + \frac{3(2k + 1)^2}{3}$$

$$= \frac{2k + 1}{3}\big(k(2k - 1) + 3(2k + 1)\big)$$

$$= \frac{\big(2(k + 1) - 1\big)}{3}(2k^2 + 5k + 3)$$

$$= \frac{(k + 1)\big(2(k + 1) - 1\big)(2k + 3)}{3}$$

$$= \frac{(k + 1)\big(2(k + 1) - 1\big)\big(2(k + 1) + 1\big)}{3}$$

which is P_{k+1} and the induction is complete.

9.   Here P_n denotes:

$$3 + 3^2 + 3^3 + \ldots + 3^n = \frac{1}{2}(3^{n+1} - 3)$$

Since $3 = \frac{1}{2}(3^2 - 3) = \frac{1}{2}(6) = 3$ then P_1 is true.

Form P_k:

$$3 + 3^2 + \ldots + 3^k = \frac{1}{2}(3^{k+1} - 3)$$

Thus:

$$
\begin{aligned}
3 + 3^2 + \ldots + 3^k + 3^{k+1} &= \frac{1}{2}(3^{k+1} - 3) + 3^{k+1} \\
&= \frac{3}{2}(3^{k+1}) - \frac{3}{2} \\
&= \frac{1}{2}\left(3(3^{k+1}) - 3\right) \\
&= \frac{1}{2}(3^{k+2} - 3) \\
&= \frac{1}{2}\left(3^{(k+1)+1} - 3\right)
\end{aligned}
$$

which is P_{k+1} and the induction is complete.

11.   Here P_n denotes:

$$1^3 + 2^3 + 3^3 + \ldots + n^3 = \left(\frac{n(n+1)}{2}\right)^2$$

Since $1^3 = 1 = \left(\frac{1(2)}{2}\right)^2 = 1$, then P_1 is true.

Form P_k:

$$1^3 + 2^3 + \ldots + k^3 = \left(\frac{k(k+1)}{2}\right)^2$$

Thus:

$$1^3 + 2^3 + \ldots + k^3 + (k + 1)^3 = \left(\frac{k(k + 1)}{2}\right)^2 + (k + 1)^3$$

$$= (k +1)^2\left[\frac{k^2}{4} + (k + 1)\right]$$

$$= \frac{(k + 1)^2}{4}\left[k^2 + 4k + 4\right]$$

$$= \frac{(k + 1)^2(k + 2)^2}{4}$$

$$= \frac{(k + 1)^2\left((k + 1) + 1\right)^2}{2^2}$$

$$= \left(\frac{(k + 1)\left((k + 1) + 1\right)}{2}\right)^2$$

which is P_{k+1} and the induction is complete.

13. Here P_n denotes:

$$1^3 + 3^3 + 5^3 + \ldots + (2n - 1)^3 = n^2(2n^2 - 1)$$

Since $1^3 = 1(1)^2\left(2(1)^2 - 1\right) = (1)(1) = 1$, then P_1 is true.

Form P_K:

$$1^3 + 3^3 + \ldots + (2k - 1)^3 = k^2(2k^2 - 1)$$

Thus:

$$1^3 + 3^3 + \ldots + (2k - 1)^3 + \left(2(k + 1) - 1\right)^3$$

$$= k^2(2k^2 - 1) + (2k + 1)^3$$

$$= 2k^4 - k^2 + 8k^3 + 12k^2 + 6k + 1$$

$$= 2k^4 + 8k^3 + 11k^2 + 6k + 1$$

$$= (k + 1)^2(2k^2 + 4k + 1)$$

$$= (k + 1)^2\left(2(k^2 + 2k + 1) - 1\right)$$

$$= (k + 1)^2\left(2(k + 1)^2 - 1\right)$$

which is P_{k+1} and the induction is complete.

15. Here P_n denotes:

$$1 \times 3 + 3 \times 5 + 5 \times 7 + \ldots + (2n -1)(2n +1) = \frac{n(4n^2 + 6n - 1)}{3}$$

Since $1 \times 3 = 3 = \dfrac{(1)\left(4(1)^2 + 6(1) - 1\right)}{3} = \dfrac{9}{3} = 3 = 1 \times 3$, then P_1 is true.

Form P_k:

$$1 \times 3 + 3 \times 5 + \ldots + (2k - 1)(2k + 1) = \frac{k(4k^2 + 6k - 1)}{3}$$

Thus:

$$1 \times 3 + 3 \times 5 + \ldots + (2k - 1)(2k + 1) + \big(2(k + 1) - 1\big)\big(2(k + 1) + 1\big)$$

$$= \frac{k(4k^2 + 6k - 1)}{3} + (2k + 1)(2k + 3)$$

$$= \frac{4k^3 + 6k^2 - k + 12k^2 + 24k + 9}{3}$$

$$= \frac{4k^3 + 18k^2 + 23k + 9}{3}$$

Noting that -1 is a root:

$$= \frac{(k + 1)(4k^2 + 14k + 9)}{3}$$

$$= \frac{(k + 1)\big(4(k + 1)^2 + 6(k + 1) - 1\big)}{3}$$

which is P_{k+1} and the induction is complete.

17. Here P_n denotes:

$$1 + \frac{3}{2} + \frac{5}{2^2} + \ldots + \frac{2n - 1}{2^{n-1}} = 6 - \frac{2n + 3}{2^{n-1}}$$

Since $1 = 6 - \dfrac{\big(2(1) + 3\big)}{2^0} = 6 - 5 = 1$, then P_1 is true.

Form P_k:

$$1 + \frac{3}{2} + \ldots + \frac{2k - 1}{2^{k-1}} = 6 - \frac{2k + 3}{2^{k-1}}$$

Thus:

$$1 + \frac{3}{2} + \ldots + \frac{2k - 1}{2^{k-1}} + \frac{2(k + 1) - 1}{2^k}$$

$$= 6 - \frac{2k + 3}{2^{k-1}} + \frac{2k + 1}{2^k}$$

$$= 6 - \frac{4k + 6 - 2k - 1}{2^k}$$

$$= 6 - \frac{2k + 5}{2^k}$$

$$= 6 - \frac{2(k + 1) + 3}{2^{(k+1)-1}}$$

which is P_{k+1} and the induction is complete.

19. Let P_n denote the statement:

$$n \leq 2^{n-1}$$

Since $2^{1-1} = 2^0 = 1 \geq 1$, then P_1 is true.

Form P_k:

$$k \leq 2^{k-1}$$

Hence:

$$k + 1 \leq 2^{k-1} + 1$$

Since $1 \leq 2^{k-1}$ (use induction to prove this), then:

$$
\begin{aligned}
k + 1 &\leq 2^{k-1} + 1 \\
&\leq 2^{k-1} + 2^{k-1} \\
&= 2(2^{k-1}) \\
&= 2^k \\
&= 2^{(k+1)-1}
\end{aligned}
$$

which is P_{k+1} and the induction is complete.

21. For $n = 2$:

$$2^2 + 4 = 8 < (2 + 1)^2$$

Assuming:

$$k^2 + 4 < (k + 1)^2$$

Then:

$$
\begin{aligned}
k^2 + 2k + 4 &< (k + 1)^2 + 2k \\
(k + 1)^2 + 3 &< k^2 + 4k + 1 \\
(k + 1)^2 + 4 &< k^2 + 4k + 2 \\
(k + 1)^2 + 4 &< k^2 + 4k + 4 \\
(k + 1)^2 + 4 &< (k + 2)^2
\end{aligned}
$$

completing the induction for $n \geq 2$.

23. For $n = 7$, we have:

$$(1.5)^7 \approx 17.09 > 2(7)$$

Assume P_k is true, so:

$$(1.5)^k > 2k$$

Form P_{k+1}:

$$
\begin{aligned}
(1.5)^{k+1} &= 1.5(1.5)^k \\
&> 1.5(2k) \\
&= 3k \\
&= 2k + k \\
&> 2k + 2 \qquad \text{since } k > 2 \\
&= 2(k + 1)
\end{aligned}
$$

This completes the induction.

25. For n = 39, we have:
$$(1.1)^{39} \approx 41.1 > 39$$
Assume P_k is true, so:
$$(1.1)^k > k$$
Form P_{k+1}:
$$
\begin{aligned}
(1.1)^{k+1} &= 1.1(1.1)^k \\
&> 1.1k \\
&= k + 0.1k \\
&> k + 1 \qquad \text{since } k > 10
\end{aligned}
$$
This completes the induction.

27. (a) We complete the table:

n	1	2	3	4	5
f(n)	1/2	2/3	3/4	4/5	5/6

(b) $\frac{6}{7}$, $f(6) = f(5) + \frac{1}{42} = \frac{5}{6} + \frac{1}{42} = \frac{36}{42} = \frac{6}{7}$

(c) $f(n) = \frac{1}{1 \times 2} + \frac{1}{2 \times 3} + \cdots + \frac{1}{n(n+1)} = \frac{n}{n+1}$

$f(1) = \frac{1}{2} = \frac{1}{1+1} = \frac{1}{2}$

Assuming $f(k) = \frac{k}{k+1}$ then:

$$
\begin{aligned}
f(k+1) &= f(k) + \frac{1}{(k+1)(k+2)} \\
&= \frac{k}{k+1} + \frac{1}{(k+1)(k+2)} \\
&= \frac{k(k+2) + 1}{(k+1)(k+2)} \\
&= \frac{k^2 + 2k + 1}{(k+1)(k+2)} \\
&= \frac{(k+1)^2}{(k+1)(k+2)} \\
&= \frac{k+1}{k+2}
\end{aligned}
$$
completing the induction.

29. (a) We complete the table:

n	1	2	3	4	5
f(n)	1	4	9	16	25

(b) 36, $f(6) = f(5) + 2\sqrt{f(5)} + 1 = 25 + 2\sqrt{25} + 1 = 36$

(c) $f(n) = n^2$
     $f(1) = 1 = 1^2$
     Assume that for some $k \geq 1$ that $f(k) = k^2$. Then since $k + 1 \geq 2$, we have:

$$\begin{aligned} f(k + 1) &= f(k) + 2\sqrt{f(k)} + 1 \\ &= k^2 + 2\sqrt{k^2} + 1 \\ &= k^2 + 2k + 1 \\ &= (k + 1)^2 \end{aligned}$$

and the induction is complete.

31. For n = 1:   13 is prime and P_1 is true
     For n = 2:   17 is prime and P_2 is true
     For n = 3:   23 is prime and P_3 is true
     For n = 4:   31 is prime and P_4 is true
     For n = 5:   41 is prime and P_5 is true
     For n = 6:   53 is prime and P_6 is true
     For n = 7:   67 is prime and P_7 is true
     For n = 8:   83 is prime and P_8 is true
     For n = 9:   101 is prime and P_9 is true
     However, for n = 10, we have $(10)^2 + 10 + 11 = 121 = (11)(11)$ and so P_{10} is false.

33. Let P_n denote:

$$1 + r + r^2 + \ldots + r^{n-1} = \frac{r^n - 1}{r - 1} \text{ when } r \neq 1$$

Then since $1 = \frac{r - 1}{r - 1} = 1$, then P_1 is true.

Assuming P_k is true, then:

$$1 + r + \ldots + r^{k-1} = \frac{r^k - 1}{r - 1}$$

Thus:

$$1 + r + \ldots + r^{k-1} + r^k = \frac{r^k - 1}{r - 1} + r^k$$

$$= \frac{r^k - 1 + r^k(r - 1)}{r - 1}$$

$$= \frac{r^{k+1} - 1}{r - 1}$$

which is P_{k+1} and the induction is complete.

35. Let P_n denote:

$n^5 - n = 5R$ for some natural number R.

Since $2^5 - 2 = 32 - 2 = 30 = 5(6)$, then P_2 is true.

Since:

$$(k + 1)^5 - (k + 1) = k^5 + 5k^4 + 10k^3 + 10k^2 + 4k$$

$$= k^5 - k + 5(k^4 + 2k^3 + 2k^2 + k)$$

then assuming P_k is true results in:

$$(k + 1)^5 - (k + 1) = 5(R + k^4 + 2k^3 + 2k^2 + k)$$

which is P_{k+1} and the induction is complete.

37. For $n = 0$, we have:

$$2^1 + 3^1 = 5 = 5(1)$$

Assume P_k is true, so:

$$2^{2k+1} + 3^{2k+1} = 5A, \text{ for some natural number A}$$

Form P_{k+1}:

$$2^{2k+3} + 3^{2k+3} = 4 \bullet 2^{2k+1} + 9 \bullet 3^{2k+1}$$

$$= 4 \bullet 2^{2k+1} + 9(5A - 2^{2k+1})$$

$$= 4 \bullet 2^{2k+1} + 45A - 9 \bullet 2^{2k+1}$$

$$= 45A - 5 \bullet 2^{2k+1}$$

$$= 5(9A - 2^{2k+1})$$

Since 5 is a factor of this expression, this completes the induction.

39. For n = 0, we have:
$$2^1 + (-1)^0 = 2 + 1 = 3 = 3(1)$$
Assume P_k is true, so:
$$2^{k+1} + (-1)^k = 3A, \text{ for some natural number A}$$
Form P_{k+1}:
$$\begin{aligned}2^{k+2} + (-1)^{k+1} &= 2 \cdot 2^{k+1} - (-1)^k \\ &= 2\left(3A - (-1)^k\right) - (-1)^k \\ &= 6A - 2(-1)^k - (-1)^k \\ &= 6A - 3(-1)^k \\ &= 3\left(2A - (-1)^k\right)\end{aligned}$$
Since 3 is a factor of this expression, this completes the induction.

41. Let P_n denote:
$$x^n - y^n = (x - y)\left(Q(x,y)\right) \text{ where } Q(x,y) \text{ is a polynomial in x and y.}$$
Then:
$$x - y = (x - y)(1) \text{ and } P_1 \text{ is true.}$$
While using the suggested identity:
$$x^{k+1} - y^{k+1} = x^k(x - y) + (x^k - y^k)y$$
So assuming P_k:
$$x^{k+1} - y^{k+1} = \left(x^k + yQ(x,y)\right)(x - y)$$
which is P_{k+1} and the induction is complete.

43. For n = 1:
$$(1 + p) \geq (1 + p)$$
When $p > -1$ then $p + 1 > 0$
Assuming $(1 + p)^k \geq 1 + kp$ then:
$$\begin{aligned}(1 + p)^{k+1} &\geq (1 + kp)(1 + p) \\ &\geq 1 + p + kp + kp^2 \\ &\geq 1 + (k + 1)p\end{aligned}$$
and the induction is complete.

45. For n = 1, we have:
$$1^5 = \frac{1(2)^2(3)}{12} = \frac{12}{12} = 1$$
Let P_k denote:
$$1^5 + 2^5 + \ldots + k^5 = \frac{k^2(k + 1)^2(2k^2 + 2k - 1)}{12}$$

Form P_{k+1}:

$$1^5 + 2^5 + \ldots + k^5 + (k+1)^5 = \frac{k^2(k+1)^2(2k^2 + 2k - 1)}{12} + (k+1)^5$$

$$= \frac{(k+1)^2}{12}(2k^4 + 14k^3 + 35k^2 + 36k + 12)$$

$$= \frac{(k+1)^2}{12}(k+2)^2(2k^2 + 6k + 3)$$

$$= \frac{(k+1)^2(k+2)^2\big(2(k+1)^2 + 2(k+1) - 1\big)}{12}$$

This completes the induction.

47. For $n = 1$, we have:

$$\frac{0+1}{1+1} = \frac{1}{4} + \frac{1}{4} \text{, so } \frac{1}{2} = \frac{1}{2}$$

Let P_k denote:

$$\frac{0^3 + 1^3 + \ldots + k^3}{(k+1)k^3} = \frac{1}{4} + \frac{1}{4k}$$

Form P_{k+1}:

$$\frac{0^3 + 1^3 + \ldots + k^3 + (k+1)^3}{(k+2)(k+1)^3} = \frac{(k+1)k^3\left(\frac{1}{4} + \frac{1}{4k}\right) + (k+1)^3}{(k+2)(k+1)^3}$$

$$= \frac{\frac{k^3}{4}\left(1 + \frac{1}{k}\right) + (k+1)^2}{(k+2)(k+1)^2}$$

$$= \frac{\frac{k^2}{4}(k+1) + (k+1)^2}{(k+2)(k+1)^2}$$

$$= \frac{\frac{k^2}{4} + (k+1)}{(k+2)(k+1)}$$

$$= \frac{k^2 + 4k + 4}{4(k+2)(k+1)}$$

$$= \frac{(k+2)^2}{4(k+2)(k+1)}$$

$$= \frac{k+2}{4(k+1)}$$

$$= \frac{k+1}{4(k+1)} + \frac{1}{4(k+1)}$$

$$= \frac{1}{4} + \frac{1}{4(k+1)}$$

This completes the induction.

10.2 The Binomial Theorem

1. (a) $(a + b)^2 = (a + b)(a + b)$
$$= a^2 + ab + ba + b^2$$
$$= a^2 + 2ab + b^2$$

   (b) $(a + b)^3 = (a + b)(a + b)^2$
$$= (a + b)(a^2 + 2ab + b^2)$$
$$= a^3 + 2a^2b + ab^2 + ba^2 + 2ab^2 + b^3$$
$$= a^3 + 3a^2b + 3ab^2 + b^3$$

3. $(a + b)^9 = \binom{9}{0}a^9 + \binom{9}{1}a^8b + \binom{9}{2}a^7b^2 + \binom{9}{3}a^6b^3 + \binom{9}{4}a^5b^4$
$$+ \binom{9}{5}a^4b^5 + \binom{9}{6}a^3b^6 + \binom{9}{7}a^2b^7 + \binom{9}{8}ab^8 + \binom{9}{9}b^9$$
$$= a^9 + 9a^8b + 36a^7b^2 + 84a^6b^3 + 126a^5b^4 + 126a^4b^5 + 84a^3b^6$$
$$+ 36a^2b^7 + 9ab^8 + b^9$$

5. $(2A + B)^3 = \binom{3}{0}(2A)^3 + \binom{3}{1}(2A)^2B + \binom{3}{2}(2A)B^2 + \binom{3}{3}B^3$
$$= 8A^3 + 12A^2B + 6AB^2 + B^3$$

7. $(1 - 2x)^6 = \binom{6}{0}1^6 - \binom{6}{1}1^5(2x) + \binom{6}{2}1^4(2x)^2 - \binom{6}{3}1^3(2x)^3 + \binom{6}{4}1^2(2x)^4$
$$- \binom{6}{5}1(2x)^5 + \binom{6}{6}(2x)^6$$
$$= 1 - 12x + 60x^2 - 160x^3 + 240x^4 - 192x^5 + 64x^6$$

9. $(\sqrt{x} + \sqrt{y})^4$
$$= \binom{4}{0}(\sqrt{x})^4 + \binom{4}{1}(\sqrt{x})^3(\sqrt{y}) + \binom{4}{2}(\sqrt{x})^2(\sqrt{y})^2 + \binom{4}{3}(\sqrt{x})(\sqrt{y})^3 + \binom{4}{4}(\sqrt{y})^4$$
$$= x^2 + 4x\sqrt{xy} + 6xy + 4y\sqrt{xy} + y^2$$

11. $(x^2 + y^2)^5 = \binom{5}{0}(x^2)^5 + \binom{5}{1}(x^2)^4y^2 + \binom{5}{2}(x^2)^3(y^2)^2 + \binom{5}{3}(x^2)^2(y^2)^3$
$$+ \binom{5}{4}(x^2)(y^2)^4 + \binom{5}{5}(y^2)^5$$
$$= x^{10} + 5x^8y^2 + 10x^6y^4 + 10x^4y^6 + 5x^2y^8 + y^{10}$$

13. $\left(1 - \dfrac{1}{x}\right)^6$

$= \dbinom{6}{0} - \dbinom{6}{1}\dfrac{1}{x} + \dbinom{6}{2}\left(\dfrac{1}{x}\right)^2 - \dbinom{6}{3}\left(\dfrac{1}{x}\right)^3 + \dbinom{6}{4}\left(\dfrac{1}{x}\right)^4 - \dbinom{6}{5}\left(\dfrac{1}{x}\right)^5 + \dbinom{6}{6}\left(\dfrac{1}{x}\right)^6$

$= 1 - \dfrac{6}{x} + \dfrac{15}{x^2} - \dfrac{20}{x^3} + \dfrac{15}{x^4} - \dfrac{6}{x^5} + \dfrac{1}{x^6}$

15. $\left(\dfrac{x}{2} - \dfrac{y}{3}\right)^3 = \dbinom{3}{0}\left(\dfrac{x}{2}\right)^3 - \dbinom{3}{1}\left(\dfrac{x}{2}\right)^2\left(\dfrac{y}{3}\right) + \dbinom{3}{2}\left(\dfrac{x}{2}\right)\left(\dfrac{y}{3}\right)^2 - \dbinom{3}{3}\left(\dfrac{y}{3}\right)^3$

$= \dfrac{x^3}{8} - \dfrac{x^2 y}{4} + \dfrac{xy^2}{6} - \dfrac{y^3}{27}$

17. $(ab^2 + c)^7 = \dbinom{7}{0}(ab^2)^7 + \dbinom{7}{1}(ab^2)^6 c + \dbinom{7}{2}(ab^2)^5 c^2 + \dbinom{7}{3}(ab^2)^4 c^3$

$\qquad + \dbinom{7}{4}(ab^2)^3 c^4 + \dbinom{7}{5}(ab^2)^2 c^5 + \dbinom{7}{6}(ab^2)c^6 + \dbinom{7}{7}c^7$

$= a^7 b^{14} + 7a^6 b^{12} c + 21a^5 b^{10} c^2 + 35a^4 b^8 c^3 + 35a^3 b^6 c^4$
$\quad + 21a^2 b^4 c^5 + 7ab^2 c^6 + c^7$

19. $(x + \sqrt{2})^8$

$= \dbinom{8}{0}x^8 + \dbinom{8}{1}x^7\sqrt{2} + \dbinom{8}{2}x^6(\sqrt{2})^2 + \dbinom{8}{3}x^5(\sqrt{2})^3 + \dbinom{8}{4}x^4(\sqrt{2})^4$

$\qquad + \dbinom{8}{5}x^3(\sqrt{2})^5 + \dbinom{8}{6}x^2(\sqrt{2})^6 + \dbinom{8}{7}x(\sqrt{2})^7 + \dbinom{8}{8}(\sqrt{2})^8$

$= x^8 + 8\sqrt{2}\,x^7 + 56x^6 + 112\sqrt{2}\,x^5 + 280x^4 + 224\sqrt{2}\,x^3 + 224x^2 + 64\sqrt{2}\,x +$

16

21. $(\sqrt{2} - 1)^3 = \dbinom{3}{0}(\sqrt{2})^3 - \dbinom{3}{1}(\sqrt{2})^2 + \dbinom{3}{2}(\sqrt{2}) - \dbinom{3}{3}$

$= 2\sqrt{2} - 6 + 3\sqrt{2} - 1$
$= 5\sqrt{2} - 7$

23. $(\sqrt{2} + \sqrt{3})^5$

$= \dbinom{5}{0}(\sqrt{2})^5 + \dbinom{5}{1}(\sqrt{2})^4\sqrt{3} + \dbinom{5}{2}(\sqrt{2})^3(\sqrt{3})^2 + \dbinom{5}{3}(\sqrt{2})^2(\sqrt{3})^3$

$\qquad + \dbinom{5}{4}(\sqrt{2})(\sqrt{3})^4 + \dbinom{5}{5}(\sqrt{3})^5$

$= 4\sqrt{2} + 20\sqrt{3} + 60\sqrt{2} + 60\sqrt{3} + 45\sqrt{2} + 9\sqrt{3}$
$= 89\sqrt{3} + 109\sqrt{2}$

25. $\left(2\sqrt[3]{2} - \sqrt[3]{4}\right)^3$

$$= \binom{3}{0}(2\sqrt[3]{2})^3 - \binom{3}{1}(2\sqrt[3]{2})^2\,(\sqrt[3]{4}) + \binom{3}{2}(2\sqrt[3]{2})\,(\sqrt[3]{4})^2 - \binom{3}{3}(\sqrt[3]{4})^3$$

$$= 16 - 12\sqrt[3]{16} + 6\sqrt[3]{32} - 4$$

$$= 12 - 24\sqrt[3]{2} + 12\sqrt[3]{4}$$

27. $\left(x^2 - (2x + 1)\right)^5$

$$= \binom{5}{0}(x^2)^5 - \binom{5}{1}(x^2)^4\,(2x + 1) + \binom{5}{2}(x^2)^3(2x + 1)^2 - \binom{5}{3}(x^2)^2(2x + 1)^3$$

$$+ \binom{5}{4}(x^2)(2x + 1)^4 - \binom{5}{5}(2x + 1)^5$$

$$= x^{10} - \left(5x^8(2x + 1)\right) + \left(10x^6(4x^2 + 4x + 1)\right)$$

$$- \left(10x^4(8x^3 + 12x^2 + 6x + 1)\right)$$

$$+ \left(5x^2(16x^4 + 32x^3 + 24x^2 + 8x + 1)\right)$$

$$- \left(32x^5 + 80x^4 + 80x^3 + 40x^2 + 10x + 1\right)$$

$$= x^{10} - (10x^9 + 5x^8) + (40x^8 + 40x^7 + 10x^6) - (80x^7 + 120x^6 + 60x^5 + 10x^4)$$

$$+ (80x^6 + 160x^5 + 120x^4 + 40x^3 + 5x^2)$$

$$- (32x^5 + 80x^4 + 80x^3 + 40x^2 + 10x + 1)$$

$$= x^{10} - 10x^9 + 35x^8 - 40x^7 - 30x^6 + 68x^5 + 30x^4 - 40x^3 - 35x^2 - 10x - 1$$

29. $5! = (5)(4)(3)(2)(1) = 120$

31. $\binom{7}{3}\binom{3}{2} = \dfrac{7!}{3!(4!)} \bullet \dfrac{3!}{2!(1!)} = \dfrac{7 \bullet 6 \bullet 5}{3 \bullet 2} \bullet 3 = 105$

33. (a) $\binom{5}{3} = \dfrac{5!}{3!(5 - 3)!} = \dfrac{5(4)}{2} = 10$

    (b) $\binom{5}{4} = \dfrac{5!}{4!(5 - 4)!} = 5$

35. $\dfrac{(n + 2)!}{n!} = \dfrac{(n + 2)(n + 1)n!}{n!} = n^2 + 3n + 2$

37. $\binom{6}{4} + \binom{6}{3} - \binom{7}{4}$ $= \dfrac{6!}{4!2!} + \dfrac{6!}{3!3!} - \dfrac{7!}{4!3!}$

$= \dfrac{6(5)}{2} + \dfrac{6(5)(4)}{6} - \dfrac{7(6)(5)}{6}$

$= 15 + 20 - 35$

$= 0$

39. $\binom{16}{14} a^2 b^{14} = 120 a^2 b^{14}$

41. $\binom{100}{99} x^{99} = 100 x^{99}$

43. Here $n - r + 1 = 8$, so $10 - r + 1 = 8$, so $r = 3$. Hence, the coefficient is:

$\binom{10}{2} = 45$

45. Here $r - 1 = 8$, thus $r = 9$. Hence, the coefficient is:

$\dfrac{1}{2}(-4)^8 \binom{9}{8} = 9 \cdot \dfrac{1}{2}(65536) = 294{,}912$

47. Here $r - 1 = 6$. Hence, $r = 7$, and the coefficient is:

$\binom{8}{6} = \dfrac{8(7)}{2} = 28$

49. Here $(12 - r + 1)(-1) + 2(r - 1) = 0$, so $-12 + r - 1 + 2r - 2 = 0$, then $3r = 15$, so $r = 5$ and the coefficient is:

$(3)^4 \binom{12}{4} = \dfrac{(12)(11)(10)(9)}{(4)(3)(2)} (3)^4 = 495(81) = 40095$

51. Here $r - 1 = n$; so $r = n + 1$, so the coefficient is:

$\binom{2n}{n} = \dfrac{(2n)!}{n!n!} = \dfrac{(2n)!}{(n!)^2}$

53. (a) We fill in the table:

k	0	1	2	3	4	5	6	7	8
$\binom{8}{k}$	1	8	28	56	70	56	28	8	1

(b) $1 + 8 + 28 + 56 + 70 + 56 + 28 + 8 + 1 = 256$
While $2^8 = 256$

(c) Since a^L and b^L equal 1 for any L since $a = b = 1$, then from the binomial theorem:

$$2^n = (1 + 1)^n = \binom{n}{0} + \binom{n}{1} + \ldots + \binom{n}{n}$$

55. (a) $(1 + x)^n \left(1 + \dfrac{1}{x}\right)^n = (1 + x)^n \left(\dfrac{x + 1}{x}\right)^n$

$$= (1 + x)^n \bullet \dfrac{(1 + x)^n}{x^n}$$

$$= \dfrac{(1 + x)^{2n}}{x^n}$$

(b) The nth term of expansion on the right is $\dfrac{\binom{2n}{n}(1)^n(x)^n}{x^n} = \binom{2n}{n}$, which verifies the result.

(c) $(1 + x)^n = \binom{n}{0} + \binom{n}{1}x + \binom{n}{2}x^2 + \binom{n}{3}x^3 + \ldots + \binom{n}{n}x^n$, and

$\left(1 + \dfrac{1}{x}\right)^n = \binom{n}{0} + \binom{n}{1}x^{-1} + \binom{n}{2}x^{-2} + \binom{n}{3}x^{-3} + \ldots + \binom{n}{n}x^{-n}$.

When multiplied, the terms do not contain x come from terms with corresponding positive and negative exponents:

$$\binom{n}{1}x \bullet \binom{n}{1}x^{-1} + \binom{n}{2}x^2 \bullet \binom{n}{2}x^{-2} + \ldots + \binom{n}{n}x^n \bullet \binom{n}{n}x^{-n}$$

$$= \binom{n}{1}^2 + \binom{n}{2}^2 + \ldots + \binom{n}{n}^2$$

This verifies the identity.

10.3   Introduction to Sequences and Series

1.   Since $a_n = \dfrac{n}{n+1}$, we can write out the first five terms by setting n equal to the natural numbers 1 through 5:

$$a_1 = \frac{1}{1+1} = \frac{1}{2}$$

$$a_2 = \frac{2}{2+1} = \frac{2}{3}$$

$$a_3 = \frac{3}{3+1} = \frac{3}{4}$$

$$a_4 = \frac{4}{4+1} = \frac{4}{5}$$

$$a_5 = \frac{5}{5+1} = \frac{5}{6}$$

So the first five terms are $\dfrac{1}{2}, \dfrac{2}{3}, \dfrac{3}{4}, \dfrac{4}{5}, \dfrac{5}{6}$

3.   Again, letting n be successively 1 through 5, we get:

$$a_1 = (1-1)^2$$
$$a_2 = (2-1)^2$$
$$a_3 = (3-1)^2$$
$$a_4 = (4-1)^2$$
$$a_5 = (5-1)^2$$

So the first five terms are 0, 1, 4, 9, 16

5. $b_n = \left(1 + \dfrac{1}{n}\right)^n$

So, $b_1 = 2$, $b_2 = \dfrac{9}{4}$, $b_3 = \dfrac{64}{27}$, $b_4 = \dfrac{625}{256}$, $b_5 = \dfrac{7776}{3125}$

7. $u_n = (-1)^n$

So, $u_1 = -1$, $u_2 = 1$, $u_3 = -1$, $u_4 = 1$, $u_5 = -1$

9. $a_n = \dfrac{(-1)^{n+1}}{n!}$

So, $a_1 = 1$, $a_2 = -\dfrac{1}{2}$, $a_3 = \dfrac{1}{6}$, $a_4 = -\dfrac{1}{24}$, $a_5 = \dfrac{1}{120}$

11. $a_n = 3n$

So, $a_1 = 3$, $a_2 = 6$, $a_3 = 9$, $a_4 = 12$, $a_5 = 15$

13. $a_1 = 1$
$a_n = (1 + a_{n-1})^2$ for $n \geq 2$
So:

$a_1 = 1$
$a_2 = (1 + a_1)^2 = 2^2 = 4$
$a_3 = (1 + a_2)^2 = 5^2 = 25$
$a_4 = (1 + a_3)^2 = 26^2 = 676$
$a_5 = (1 + a_4)^2 = 677^2 = 458,329$

and the first five terms are 1, 4, 25, 676, 458329.

15. $a_1 = 2$
$a_2 = 2$
$a_n = a_{n-1}a_{n-2}$, for $n \geq 3$
So, $a_1 = 2$, $a_2 = 2$, $a_3 = 4$, $a_4 = 8$, $a_5 = 32$.

17. $a_1 = 1$
$a_{n+1} = na_n$ for $n \geq 1$
So, $a_1 = 1$, $a_2 = 1$, $a_3 = 2$, $a_4 = 6$, $a_5 = 24$

19. $a_1 = 0$
$a_n = 2^{a_{n-1}}$ for $n \geq 2$
So, $a_1 = 0$, $a_2 = 1$, $a_3 = 2$, $a_4 = 4$, $a_5 = 16$

21. First, we compute the required values of a_n as shown in the table:

n	1	2	3	4
a_n	−1	1	−1	1

Now graph these values:

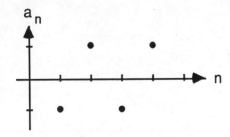

23.   First, we compute the required values of a_n as shown in the table:

n	1	2	3	4
a_n	1	$\frac{1}{2}$	$\frac{1}{3}$	$\frac{1}{4}$

Now graph these values:

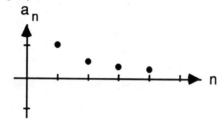

25.   First, we compute the required values of a_n as shown in the table:

n	1	2	3
a_n	0	$\frac{1}{3}$	$\frac{1}{2}$

Now graph these values:

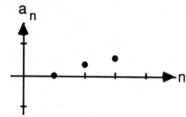

27. $a_n = 2^n$
So the sum is $2 + 4 + 8 + 16 + 32 = 62$

29. $a_n = n^2 - n$
So the sum is $0 + 2 + 6 + 12 + 20 = 40$

31. $a_n = \dfrac{(-1)^n}{n!}$

So the sum is $-1 + \dfrac{1}{2} - \dfrac{1}{6} + \dfrac{1}{24} - \dfrac{1}{120} = -\dfrac{19}{30}$

33. $a_1 = 1$
$a_2 = 2$
$a_n = a^2_{n-1} + a^2_{n-2}$ $n \geq 3$
So the sum is $1 + 2 + 5 + 29 + 866 = 903$

35. $a_1 = 2$
     $a_n = (a_{n-1})^2 \quad n \geq 2$
     So the sum is $2 + 4 + 16 + 256 = 278$

37. $\displaystyle\sum_{k=1}^{3} (k - 1) = 0 + 1 + 2 = 3$

39. $\displaystyle\sum_{k=4}^{5} k^2 = 16 + 25 = 41$

41. $\displaystyle\sum_{n=1}^{3} x^n = x + x^2 + x^3$

43. $\displaystyle\sum_{n=1}^{4} \frac{1}{n} = 1 + \frac{1}{2} + \frac{1}{3} + \frac{1}{4} = \frac{25}{12}$

45. $\displaystyle\sum_{j=1}^{9} \log_{10} \frac{j}{j+1} = \log_{10} \frac{1}{2} + \log_{10} \frac{2}{3} + \log_{10} \frac{3}{4} + \log_{10} \frac{4}{5} + \log_{10} \frac{5}{6}$

$$+ \log_{10} \frac{6}{7} + \log_{10} \frac{7}{8} + \log_{10} \frac{8}{9} + \log_{10} \frac{9}{10}$$

$$= \log_{10} \left(\frac{1}{2} \cdot \frac{2}{3} \cdot \frac{3}{4} \cdot \frac{4}{5} \cdot \frac{5}{6} \cdot \frac{6}{7} \cdot \frac{7}{8} \cdot \frac{8}{9} \cdot \frac{9}{10} \right)$$

$$= \log_{10} \frac{1}{10}$$

$$= -1$$

47. $\displaystyle\sum_{j=1}^{6} \left(\frac{1}{j} - \frac{1}{j+1} \right)$

$$= \left(1 - \frac{1}{2} \right) + \left(\frac{1}{2} - \frac{1}{3} \right) + \left(\frac{1}{3} - \frac{1}{4} \right) + \left(\frac{1}{4} - \frac{1}{5} \right) + \left(\frac{1}{5} - \frac{1}{6} \right) + \left(\frac{1}{6} - \frac{1}{7} \right)$$

$$= 1 - \frac{1}{7}$$

$$= \frac{6}{7}$$

49. $5 + 5^2 + 5^3 + 5^4 = \sum_{j=1}^{4} 5^j$

51. $x + x^2 + x^3 + x^4 + x^5 + x^6 = \sum_{j=1}^{6} x^j$

53. $1 + \dfrac{1}{2} + \dfrac{1}{3} + \ldots + \dfrac{1}{12} = \sum_{k=1}^{12} \dfrac{1}{k}$

55. $2 - 2^2 + 2^3 - 2^4 + 2^5 = \sum_{j=1}^{5} (-1)^{j+1} 2^j$

57. $1 - 2 + 3 - 4 + 5 = \sum_{j=1}^{5} (-1)^{j+1} j$

59. (a) $F_1 = 1$
          $F_2 = 1$
          $F_{n+2} = F_n + F_{n+1} \quad n \geq 1$
          Evaluating the first 10 terms, we obtain the table:

F_1	F_2	F_3	F_4	F_5	F_6	F_7	F_8	F_9	F_{10}
1	1	2	3	5	8	13	21	34	55

(b)   We complete the chart:

n	$F_1 + F_2 + \ldots + F_n$	$F_{n+2} - 1$
1	1	1
2	2	2
3	4	4
4	7	7
5	12	12

(c)   The chart completed in (b) shows the hypothesis to be true for n = 1.
Assuming:
$$F_1 + F_2 + \ldots + F_k = F_{k+2} - 1$$
Therefore:
$$\begin{aligned} F_1 + F_2 + \ldots + F_k + F_{k+1} &= F_{k+2} - 1 + F_{k+1} \\ &= F_{k+3} - 1 \\ &= F_{(k+1)+2} - 1 \end{aligned}$$
which completes the induction.

(d)   From (a), $F_5 = 5 \geq 5$, so the hypothesis is true for n = 5. For some
$k \geq 5$, assume:
$$F_k \geq k$$
Then:
$$F_{k+1} = F_k + F_{k-1} \geq F_k + 1 \geq k + 1$$
and the induction is complete.

(e)   Since $F_1^2 = 1^2 = 1 = F_1 F_2 = 1(1) = 1$, then the hypothesis is true
for n = 1. Assuming:
$$F_1^2 + F_2^2 + \ldots + F_k^2 = F_k F_{k+1}$$
Then:
$$\begin{aligned} F_1^2 + F_2^2 + \ldots + F_k^2 + F_{k+1}^2 &= F_k F_{k+1} + F_{k+1}^2 \\ &= F_{k+1}(F_k + F_{k+1}) \\ &= F_{k+1}(F_{k+2}) \end{aligned}$$
and the induction is complete.

(f)   Since $F_2^2 = 1^2 = 1 = F_1 F_3 + (-1)^1 = 2 - 1 = 1$, the hypothesis is
true for n = 1. Assume:
$$F_{k+1}^2 = F_k F_{k+2} + (-1)^k$$
Then:
$$\begin{aligned} F_{k+1} F_{k+2} + F_{k+1}^2 &= F_k F_{k+2} + F_{k+1} F_{k+2} + (-1)^k \\ F_{k+1}(F_{k+2} + F_{k+1}) &= F_{k+2}(F_k + F_{k+1}) + (-1)^k \\ F_{k+1} F_{k+3} &= F_{k+2}^2 + (-1)^k \\ F_{k+2}^2 &= F_{k+1} F_{k+3} + (-1)^{k+1} \end{aligned}$$
and the induction is complete.

(g)   Since $\begin{pmatrix} 1 & 1 \\ 1 & 0 \end{pmatrix}^2 = \begin{pmatrix} 2 & 1 \\ 1 & 1 \end{pmatrix} = \begin{pmatrix} F_3 & F_2 \\ F_2 & F_1 \end{pmatrix}$ then the hypothesis is true for
n = 2. Assuming:
$$\begin{pmatrix} 1 & 1 \\ 1 & 0 \end{pmatrix}^k = \begin{pmatrix} F_{k+1} & F_k \\ F_k & F_{k-1} \end{pmatrix}$$

Then:

$$\begin{pmatrix} 1 & 1 \\ 1 & 0 \end{pmatrix}^{k+1} = \begin{pmatrix} 1 & 1 \\ 1 & 0 \end{pmatrix} \begin{pmatrix} F_{k+1} & F_k \\ F_k & F_{k-1} \end{pmatrix}$$

$$= \begin{pmatrix} F_k + F_{k+1} & F_k + F_{k-1} \\ F_{k+1} & F_k \end{pmatrix}$$

$$= \begin{pmatrix} F_{k+2} & F_{k+1} \\ F_{k+1} & F_k \end{pmatrix}$$

and the induction is complete.

10.4   Arithmetic Sequences and Series

1. (a) To find the common difference, d, we simply subtract any term from the succeeding term. Here, that can be:

$$3 - 1 = 2$$
$$5 - 3 = 2$$
$$7 - 5 = 2$$

So 2 is the required common difference.

(b) Again we subtract terms:

$$6 - 10 = -4$$
$$2 - 6 = -4$$
$$-2 - 2 = -4$$

The common difference is -4. It is not necessary to try all three pairs, but this helps to verify that we have an arithmetic sequence.

(c) $1 - \dfrac{2}{3} = \dfrac{4}{3} - 1 = \dfrac{5}{3} - \dfrac{4}{3} = \dfrac{1}{3}$

So $\dfrac{1}{3}$ is the common difference.

(d) $1 + \sqrt{2} - 1 = \sqrt{2}$ or $(1 + 2\sqrt{2}) - (1 + \sqrt{2}) = \sqrt{2}$

Here, $\sqrt{2}$ is the common difference.

3. Since $a = 10$ and $d = 11$, then using $a_n = a + (n - 1)d$ we find:

$$a_{12} = 10 + (12 - 1)11 = 131$$

5. $a_{100} = 6 + (100 - 1)(5) = 6 + 495 = 501$

7. $a_{1000} = -1 + (1000 - 1)(1) = 998$

9. $a_4 = -6$, $a_{10} = 5$, thus:

$$-6 = a + 3d$$
$$5 = a + 9d$$

Subtracting the second equation from the first yields:

$$-6d = -11$$
$$d = \frac{11}{6}$$

So:

$$a = 5 - 9\left(\frac{11}{6}\right)$$
$$a = 5 - \frac{33}{2}$$
$$a = \frac{-23}{2}$$

11. $a_{60} = 105$, $d = 5$, so:

$$105 = a + 59(5)$$
$$105 = a + 295$$
$$a = -190$$

13. Since $a_{15} = a + 14d$ and $a_7 = a + 6d$, then:

$$a_{15} - a_7 = 8d$$
$$-1 = 8d$$
$$d = -\frac{1}{8}$$

15. Since $a = 1$ and $d = 1$, then:

$$S_{1000} = \frac{1000}{2}(2 + 999) = 500{,}500$$

17. For $\frac{\pi}{3} + \frac{2\pi}{3} + \pi + \frac{4\pi}{3} + \ldots + \frac{13\pi}{3}$, $a = \frac{\pi}{3}$, $d = \frac{\pi}{3}$, so the sum is:

$$S_{13} = \frac{13}{2}\left(\frac{2\pi}{3} + \frac{12\pi}{3}\right) = \frac{14(13)(\pi)}{6} = \frac{91\pi}{3}$$

19. Since $d = 5$ and $S_{38} = 3534$, then:

$$3534 = \frac{38}{2}\left(2a + 37(5)\right)$$
$$3534 = 38a + 3515$$
$$19 = 38a$$
$$a = \frac{1}{2}$$

21. Here $a = 4$, $a_{16} = -100$, therefore:

$$S_{16} = 16 \left(\frac{4 - 100}{2} \right)$$
$$S_{16} = -768$$

So we have:

$$-768 = \frac{16}{2} \left(2(4) + 15d \right)$$
$$-768 = 64 + 120d$$
$$-832 = 120d$$
$$d = \frac{-104}{15}$$

23. Since $a_8 = 5$ and $S_{10} = 20$, then:

$$5 = a + 7d$$
$$20 = 5(2a + 9d)$$
$$4 = 2a + 9d$$

We solve the system:

$$a + 7d = 5$$
$$2a + 9d = 4$$

Multiplying the first equation by -2 and adding to the second equation:

$$-2a - 14d = -10$$
$$\underline{2a + 9d = 4}$$
$$-5d = -6$$
$$d = \frac{6}{5}$$

So:

$$a = 5 - 7 \left(\frac{6}{5} \right) = -\frac{17}{5}$$

25. $S = S_{20} = \displaystyle\sum_{k=1}^{20} (4k + 3)$ so $a = 7$ and $a_{20} = 83$, thus:

$$S = 20 \left(\frac{7 + 83}{2} \right) = 900$$

27. Let x denote the middle term, so the three terms are $x - d$, x, $x + d$, and:
$(x - d) + x + (x + d) = 30$ while $x(x - d)(x + d) = 360$
equivalently:

$$3x = 30, \text{ so } x = 10$$
$$x(x^2 - d^2) = 360$$

and:

$$100 - d^2 = 36$$
$$d = \pm 8$$

So the terms are 2, 10, 18 or 18, 10, 2.

29. Using equations as in exercise #27:

$$3x = 6, \text{ so } x = 2$$

$$(x - d)^3 + x^3 + (x + d)^3 = 132$$

$$(2 - d)^3 + 8 + (2 + d)^3 = 132$$

$$(2 - d)^3 + (2 + d)^3 = 124$$

$$16 + 12d^2 = 124$$

$$d^2 = 9$$

$$d = \pm 3$$

So the terms are -1, 2, 5 or 5, 2, -1.

31. (a)

$$a_2 - a_1 = -1 - \frac{1}{1 + \sqrt{2}}$$

$$= \frac{-2 - \sqrt{2}}{1 + \sqrt{2}}$$

$$= \frac{(1 - \sqrt{2})(-2 - \sqrt{2})}{-1}$$

$$= -\sqrt{2}$$

$$a_3 - a_2 = \frac{1}{1 - \sqrt{2}} + 1$$

$$= \frac{2 - \sqrt{2}}{1 - \sqrt{2}}$$

$$= \frac{(2 - \sqrt{2})(1 + \sqrt{2})}{-1}$$

$$= -\sqrt{2}$$

So $a_2 - a_1 = a_3 - a_2$

(b) $a = \dfrac{1}{1 + \sqrt{2}}$, from (a) $d = -\dfrac{2 + \sqrt{2}}{1 + \sqrt{2}}$

$$\text{So } S_6 = 3\left(\frac{2}{1 + \sqrt{2}} - \frac{10 + 5\sqrt{2}}{1 + \sqrt{2}}\right)$$

$$= 3\left(\frac{-8 - 5\sqrt{2}}{1 + \sqrt{2}}\right)$$

$$= -\frac{24 + 15\sqrt{2}}{1 + \sqrt{2}}$$

$$= (24 + 15\sqrt{2})(1 - \sqrt{2})$$

$$= 24 - 30 - 9\sqrt{2}$$

$$= -6 - 9\sqrt{2}$$

33. $a = \dfrac{1}{1 + \sqrt{b}}$ while $d = \dfrac{1}{2}\left(\dfrac{1}{1 - \sqrt{b}} - \dfrac{1}{1 + \sqrt{b}}\right)$

$$= \dfrac{1}{2}\left(\dfrac{2\sqrt{b}}{1 - b}\right)$$

$$= \dfrac{\sqrt{b}}{1 - b}$$

Therefore:

$$S_n = \dfrac{n}{2}\left(\dfrac{2}{1 + \sqrt{b}} + (n - 1)\dfrac{\sqrt{b}}{1 - b}\right)$$

$$= \dfrac{n}{2}\left(\dfrac{(2 - 2\sqrt{b}) + (n - 1)\sqrt{b}}{1 - b}\right)$$

$$= \dfrac{n}{2(1 - b)}\left(2 + (n - 3)\sqrt{b}\right)$$

35.
$$\dfrac{n^2}{m^2} = \dfrac{S_n}{S_m} = \dfrac{\dfrac{n}{2}\left(2a + (n - 1)d\right)}{\dfrac{m}{2}\left(2a + (m - 1)d\right)}$$

$$\dfrac{2a + (n - 1)d}{2a + (m - 1)d} = \dfrac{n}{m}$$

$$m\left(2a + (n - 1)d\right) = n\left(2a + (m - 1)d\right)$$

$$2am + m(n - 1)d = 2an + n(m - 1)d$$

$$2a(m - n) = \left(n(m - 1) - m(n - 1)\right)d$$

$$d = \dfrac{2a(m - n)}{m - n}$$

$$d = 2a \quad (\text{assuming } m \neq n)$$

Consequently:

$$\dfrac{a_n}{a_m} = \dfrac{a + (n - 1)(2a)}{a + (m - 1)(2a)} = \dfrac{1 + 2n - 2}{1 + 2m - 2} = \dfrac{2n - 1}{2m - 1}$$

37. Let the three consecutive terms be: $x - d, x, x + d$, then because of the Pythagorean Theorem:

$$(x - d)^2 + x^2 = (x + d)^2$$

$$x^2 - 2xd + d^2 + x^2 = x^2 + 2xd + d^2$$

$$x^2 - 4xd = 0$$

$$x = 0 \text{ or } x = 4d$$

Since the side of a triangle cannot have zero length, then $x = 4d$ and the three terms are: $3d, 4d, 5d$, which is clearly similar to a 3 - 4 - 5 right triangle.

39. We have $\dfrac{1}{b} - \dfrac{1}{a} = \dfrac{1}{c} - \dfrac{1}{b}$, from which it follows that $b = \dfrac{2ac}{a+c}$. Therefore:

$$
\begin{aligned}
\ln(a+c) + \ln(a - 2b + c) &= \ln(a+c) + \ln\left(a - \frac{4ac}{a+c} + c\right) \\
&= \ln(a+c) + \ln\left(\frac{a^2 + ac - 4ac + ac + c^2}{a+c}\right) \\
&= \ln(a+c) + \ln\frac{(a-c)^2}{a+c} \\
&= \ln(a-c)^2 \\
&= 2\ln(a-c)
\end{aligned}
$$

10.5   Geometric Sequences and Series

1. The first three terms have a common ratio, hence:
$$\frac{x}{9} = \frac{4}{x}, \text{ therefore } x^2 = 36 \text{ and } x = \pm 6$$
Since the ratio is positive, then the second term is 6.

3. Letting the common ration be r, we have:
$$4, 4r, \text{ and } 4r^2 \text{ so } 64r^3 = 8000$$
Therefore, $r^3 = 125$, so $r = 5$, and the second and third terms are 20 and 100, respectively.

5. $a_1 = -1$, $r = -1$, so $a_{100} = -1(-1)^{99} = 1$

7. $a_1 = \dfrac{2}{3}$, $r = \dfrac{2}{3}$, so $a_8 = \dfrac{2}{3}\left(\dfrac{2}{3}\right)^7 = \dfrac{256}{6561}$

9. $4096 = a_7 = r^6$, so $r = \pm\sqrt[6]{4096} = \pm 4$

11. $S_{10} = \dfrac{7(1 - 2^{10})}{1 - 2} = -7(1 - 1024) = 7161$

13. $1 + \sqrt{2} + 2 + \ldots + 32 = S_{11}$
$$
\begin{aligned}
&= \frac{1(1 - (\sqrt{2})^{11})}{1 - \sqrt{2}} \\
&= \frac{1 - 32\sqrt{2}}{1 - \sqrt{2}} \\
&= 63 + 31\sqrt{2}
\end{aligned}
$$

15. $\displaystyle\sum_{k=1}^{6}\left(\frac{3}{2}\right)^k = S_6$

$$= \frac{\frac{3}{2}\left(1-\left(\frac{3}{2}\right)^6\right)}{1-\frac{3}{2}}$$

$$= -3\left(1-\frac{729}{64}\right)$$

$$= \frac{1995}{64}$$

17. $\displaystyle\sum_{k=2}^{6}\left(\frac{1}{10}\right)^k = S_6 - a_1$

$$= \frac{\frac{1}{10}\left(1-\left(\frac{1}{10}\right)^6\right)}{1-\frac{1}{10}} - \frac{1}{10}$$

$$= \frac{1}{9}\left(1-\frac{1}{1000000}\right) - \frac{1}{10}$$

$$= \frac{1}{9}\left(\frac{999999}{1000000}\right) - \frac{1}{10}$$

$$= \frac{111111}{1000000} - \frac{1}{10}$$

$$= \frac{11111}{1000000}$$

which is equivalent to 0.011111

19. $\dfrac{2}{3} - \dfrac{4}{9} + \dfrac{8}{27} - \ldots = \dfrac{\frac{2}{3}}{1+\frac{2}{3}} = \dfrac{2}{5}$

21. $1 + \dfrac{1}{1.01} + \dfrac{1}{(1.01)^2} + \ldots = \dfrac{1}{1-\frac{1}{1.01}} = 101$

23. $.555\ldots = \dfrac{5}{10} + \dfrac{5}{100} + \ldots = \dfrac{\frac{5}{10}}{1-\frac{1}{10}} = \dfrac{5}{9}$

25. $.12323\ldots = \dfrac{1}{10} + \dfrac{23}{1000} + \dfrac{23}{100000} + \cdots$

$= \dfrac{1}{10} + \dfrac{\dfrac{23}{1000}}{1 - \dfrac{1}{100}}$

$= \dfrac{1}{10} + \dfrac{23}{990}$

$= \dfrac{122}{990}$

$= \dfrac{61}{495}$

27. $.432\ldots = \dfrac{432}{1000} + \dfrac{432}{1000000} + \cdots$

$= \dfrac{\dfrac{432}{1000}}{1 - \dfrac{1}{1000}}$

$= \dfrac{432}{999}$

$= \dfrac{16}{37}$

29.   For $\dfrac{a}{r}$, a, ar we have:

$\dfrac{a}{r}(a)(ar) = -1000$

$a^3 = -1000$

$a = -10$

So we have:

$\dfrac{a}{r} + a + ar = 15$

$\dfrac{-10}{r} - 10 - 10r = 15$

$2r^2 + 5r + 2 = 0$

$(2r + 1)(r + 2) = 0$

$r = -\dfrac{1}{2}, -2$

31. $\dfrac{\sqrt{3}}{\sqrt{3}+1} + \dfrac{\sqrt{3}}{\sqrt{3}+3} + \ldots = \dfrac{\dfrac{\sqrt{3}}{\sqrt{3}+1}}{1 - \dfrac{\sqrt{3}+1}{\sqrt{3}+3}}$

$= \dfrac{\dfrac{\sqrt{3}}{\sqrt{3}+1}}{\dfrac{2}{\sqrt{3}+3}}$

$= \dfrac{\sqrt{3}(\sqrt{3}+3)}{(\sqrt{3}+1)2}$

$= \dfrac{3+3\sqrt{3}}{2(1+\sqrt{3})}$

$= \dfrac{3}{2}$

33. For $a_1, a_2, \ldots$ a geometric sequence,

$S = a_1 + a_2 + \ldots + a_n = \dfrac{a_1(1-r^n)}{1-r}$ where r is the common ratio.

Also, $T = \dfrac{1}{a_1} + \dfrac{1}{a_2} + \ldots + \dfrac{1}{a_n} = \dfrac{\dfrac{1}{a_1}\left(1 - \dfrac{1}{r^n}\right)}{1 - \dfrac{1}{r}}$

Therefore:

$\dfrac{S}{T} = \dfrac{\dfrac{a_1(1-r^n)}{1-r}}{\dfrac{\dfrac{1}{a_1}\left(1 - \dfrac{1}{r^n}\right)}{\dfrac{r-1}{r}}}$

$= \dfrac{a_1(1-r^n)a_1(r-1)r^n}{(1-r)r(r^n-1)}$

$= a_1{}^2r^{n-1}$

$= a_1(a_1r^{n-1})$

$= a_1a_n$

35. The total distance traveled by the ball consists of two infinite geometric series:

down: $6 + \frac{1}{3}(6) + \frac{1}{9}(6) + \ldots$

up: $2 + \frac{1}{3}(2) + \frac{1}{9}(2) + \ldots$

We now use the formula $S = \frac{a}{1 - r}$ to find each sum:

down: $a = 6, r = \frac{1}{3}$

$$S = \frac{6}{1 - 1/3} = \frac{6}{2/3} = 9 \text{ ft.}$$

up: $a = 2, r = \frac{1}{3}$

$$S = \frac{2}{1 - 1/3} = \frac{2}{2/3} = 3 \text{ ft.}$$

So the total distance traveled is 12 ft.

10.6   Vectors in the Plane, a Geometric Approach

1.   We graph the vector:

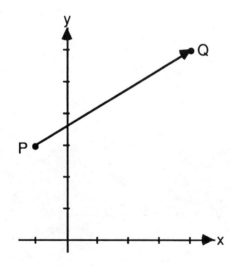

The magnitude is given by:

$$|\vec{PQ}| = \sqrt{(4 - (-1))^2 + (6 - 3)^2} = \sqrt{25 + 9} = \sqrt{34}$$

3.   We graph the vector:

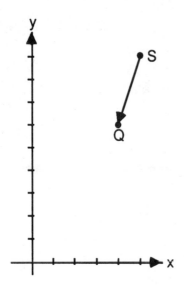

The magnitude is given by:

$$|\overrightarrow{SQ}| = \sqrt{(4-5)^2 + (6-9)^2} = \sqrt{1+9} = \sqrt{10}$$

5.   We graph the vector:

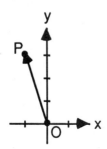

The magnitude is given by:

$$|\overrightarrow{OP}| = \sqrt{(-1-0)^2 + (3-0)^2} = \sqrt{1+9} = \sqrt{10}$$

7.   We graph the vector sum:

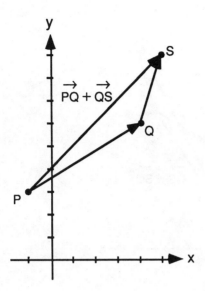

The magnitude is given by:

$$|\vec{PQ} + \vec{QS}| = |\vec{PS}| = \sqrt{(5 - (-1))^2 + (9 - 3)^2} = \sqrt{36 + 36} = 6\sqrt{2}$$

9.   We graph the vector sum:

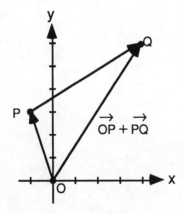

The magnitude is given by:

$$|\vec{OP} + \vec{PQ}| = |\vec{OQ}| = \sqrt{(4 - 0)^2 + (6 - 0)^2} = \sqrt{16 + 36} = 2\sqrt{13}$$

11. We graph the vector sum:

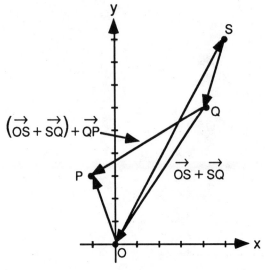

$(\overrightarrow{OS} + \overrightarrow{SQ}) + \overrightarrow{QP}$

$\overrightarrow{OS} + \overrightarrow{SQ}$

The magnitude is given by:

$$\left| (\overrightarrow{OS} + \overrightarrow{SQ}) + \overrightarrow{QP} \right| = \left| \overrightarrow{OQ} + \overrightarrow{QP} \right|$$

$$= \left| \overrightarrow{OP} \right|$$

$$= \sqrt{(-1 - 0)^2 + (3 - 0)^2}$$

$$= \sqrt{1 + 9}$$

$$= \sqrt{10}$$

13. We graph the vector sum:

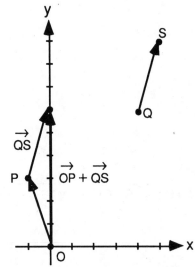

$\overrightarrow{QS}$

$\overrightarrow{OP} + \overrightarrow{QS}$

The magnitude is given by:

$$|\overrightarrow{OP} + \overrightarrow{QS}| = \sqrt{(0 - 0)^2 + (6 - 0)^2} = \sqrt{0 + 36} = 6$$

15. We graph the vector sum:

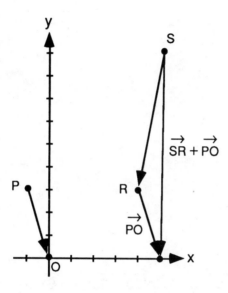

The magnitude is given by:

$$|\overrightarrow{SR} + \overrightarrow{PO}| = \sqrt{(5 - 5)^2 + (9 - 0)^2} = \sqrt{0 + 81} = 9$$

17. We graph the vector sum:

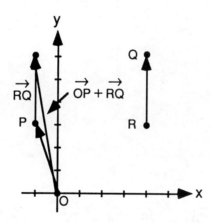

The magnitude is given by:

$$|\overrightarrow{OP} + \overrightarrow{RQ}| = \sqrt{(-1 - 0)^2 + (6 - 0)^2} = \sqrt{1 + 36} = \sqrt{37}$$

19. We graph the vector sum:

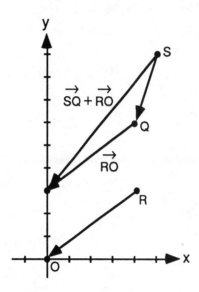

The magnitude is given by:

$$|\overrightarrow{SQ} + \overrightarrow{RO}| = \sqrt{(5-0)^2 + (9-3)^2} = \sqrt{25 + 36} = \sqrt{61}$$

21. We graph the vector sum:

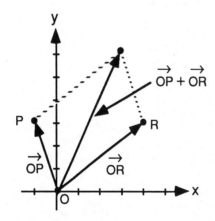

The magnitude is given by:

$$|\overrightarrow{OP} + \overrightarrow{OR}| = \sqrt{(3-0)^2 + (6-0)^2} = \sqrt{9 + 36} = 3\sqrt{5}$$

23. We graph the vector sum:

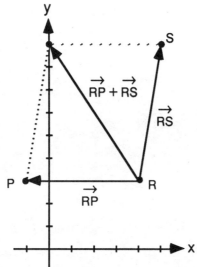

The magnitude is given by:

$$\left| \overrightarrow{RP} + \overrightarrow{RS} \right| = \sqrt{(0-4)^2 + (9-3)^2} = \sqrt{16+36} = 2\sqrt{13}$$

25. We graph the vector sum:

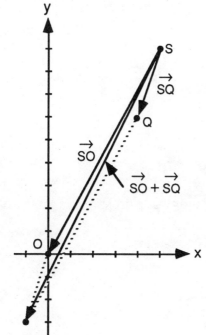

The magnitude is given by:

$$\left| \overrightarrow{SO} + \overrightarrow{SQ} \right| = \sqrt{(-1-5)^2 + (-3-9)^2} = \sqrt{36+144} = 6\sqrt{5}$$

27. We draw the figure:

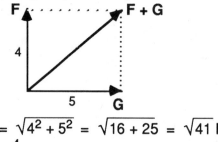

$|\mathbf{F} + \mathbf{G}| = \sqrt{4^2 + 5^2} = \sqrt{16 + 25} = \sqrt{41}$ N

$\theta = \tan^{-1} \dfrac{4}{5} \approx 38.7°$

29. We draw the figure:

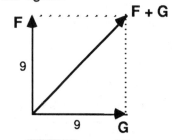

$|\mathbf{F} + \mathbf{G}| = \sqrt{9^2 + 9^2} = 9\sqrt{2}$ N

$\theta = \tan^{-1} \dfrac{9}{9} = \tan^{-1} 1 = 45°$

31. We draw the figure:

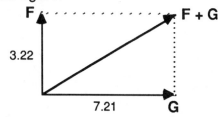

$|\mathbf{F} + \mathbf{G}| = \sqrt{3.22^2 + 7.21^2} = \sqrt{62.3525} \approx 7.90$ N

$\theta = \tan^{-1} \dfrac{3.22}{7.21} \approx 24.1°$

33. We draw the parallelogram:

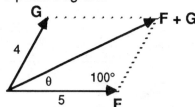

Let d = $|F + G|$. Then using the law of cosines:

$$d^2 = 5^2 + 4^2 - 2(5)(4) \cos 100°$$

$$d^2 = 41 - 40 \cos 100°$$

$$d = \sqrt{41 - 40 \cos 100°} \approx 6.92 \text{ N}$$

We find θ by the law of sines:

$$\frac{\sin \theta}{4} = \frac{\sin 100°}{d}$$

$$\sin \theta = \frac{4 \sin 100°}{\sqrt{41 - 40 \cos 100°}} \approx 0.5689$$

$$\theta \approx 34.67°$$

35. We draw the parallelogram:

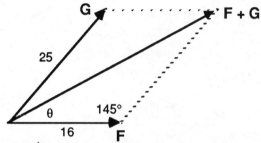

Let d = $|F + G|$. Then using the law of cosines:

$$d^2 = 16^2 + 25^2 - 2(16)(25) \cos 145°$$

$$d^2 = 881 - 800 \cos 145°$$

$$d = \sqrt{881 - 800 \cos 145°} \approx 39.20 \text{ N}$$

We find θ by the law of sines:

$$\frac{\sin \theta}{25} = \frac{\sin 145°}{d}$$

$$\sin \theta = \frac{25 \sin 145°}{\sqrt{881 - 800 \cos 145°}} \approx 0.3658$$

$$\theta \approx 21.46°$$

37. We draw the parallelogram:

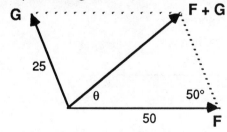

Let d = $|\mathbf{F} + \mathbf{G}|$. Then using the law of cosines:

$$d^2 = 50^2 + 25^2 - 2(50)(25) \cos 50°$$

$$d^2 = 3125 - 2500 \cos 50°$$

$$d = \sqrt{3125 - 2500 \cos 50°} \approx 38.96 \text{ N}$$

We find θ by the law of sines:

$$\frac{\sin θ}{25} = \frac{\sin 50°}{d}$$

$$\sin θ = \frac{25 \sin 50°}{\sqrt{3125 - 2500 \cos 50°}} \approx 0.4915$$

$$θ \approx 29.44°$$

39. $V_x = 16 \cos 30° \approx 13.86 \text{ cm/sec}$
     $V_y = 16 \sin 30° = 8 \text{ cm/sec}$

41. $F_x = 14 \cos 75° \approx 3.62 \text{ N}$
     $F_y = 14 \sin 75° \approx 13.52 \text{ N}$

43. $V_x = 1 \cos 135° \approx -0.71 \text{ cm/sec}$
     $V_y = 1 \sin 135° \approx 0.71 \text{ cm/sec}$

45. $F_x = 1.25 \cos 145° \approx -1.02 \text{ N}$
     $F_y = 1.25 \sin 145° \approx 0.72 \text{ N}$

47. We draw the vectors:

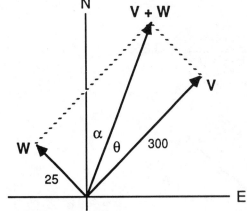

Let θ be the drift angle. Then:

$$\tan θ = \frac{25}{300} = \frac{1}{12}$$

$$θ = \tan^{-1} \frac{1}{12} \approx 4.76°$$

The ground speed is given by:
$$|\mathbf{V} + \mathbf{W}| = \sqrt{25^2 + 300^2} = \sqrt{90625} \approx 301.04 \text{ mph}$$
Let α be the bearing. Then:
$$\alpha = 30° - \theta \approx 30° - 4.76° \approx 25.24°$$

49. We draw the vectors:

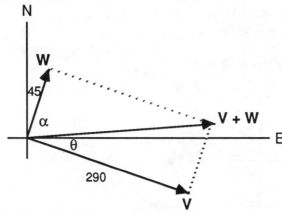

Let θ be the drift angle. Then:
$$\tan \theta = \frac{45}{290} = \frac{9}{58}$$
$$\theta = \tan^{-1} \frac{9}{58} \approx 8.82°$$
The ground speed is given by:
$$|\mathbf{V} + \mathbf{W}| = \sqrt{290^2 + 45^2} = \sqrt{86125} \approx 293.47 \text{ mph}$$
Let α be the bearing. Then:
$$\alpha = 100° - \theta \approx 100° - 8.82° \approx 91.18°$$

51. We draw a figure:

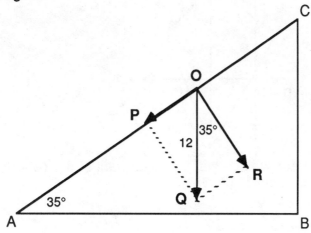

∠QOR = 35° since it is complementary to ∠POQ, but ∠POQ ≈ ∠ACB.

So: $|\overrightarrow{OR}|$ = 12 cos 35° ≈ 9.83 lb

       $|\overrightarrow{OP}|$ = 12 sin 35° ≈ 6.88 lb

53. Using the same approach as in #51, we have:
       perpendicular: 12 cos 10° ≈ 11.82 lb
       parallel: 12 sin 10° ≈ 2.08 lb

55. (a) We draw the vector sum **(A + B) + C**:

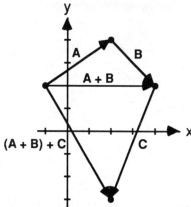

From the diagram, we see that the initial point of **(A + B) + C** is (-1, 2) and the terminal point is (2, -3).

     (b) We draw the vector sum **A + (B + C)**:

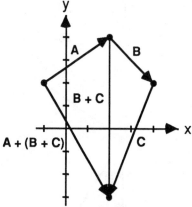

From the diagram, we see that the initial point of **A + (B + C)** is (-1, 2) and the terminal point is (2, -3).

10.7   Vectors in the Plane, an Algebraic Approach

1. $|\langle 4,3 \rangle| = \sqrt{4^2 + 3^2} = \sqrt{25} = 5$

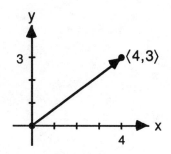

3. $|\langle -4,2 \rangle| = \sqrt{(-4)^2 + 2^2} = \sqrt{20} = 2\sqrt{5}$

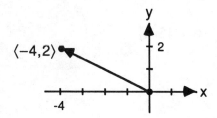

5. $\left|\left\langle \dfrac{3}{4}, -\dfrac{1}{2} \right\rangle\right| = \sqrt{\left(\dfrac{3}{4}\right)^2 + \left(-\dfrac{1}{2}\right)^2} = \sqrt{\dfrac{9}{16} + \dfrac{1}{4}} = \dfrac{\sqrt{13}}{4}$

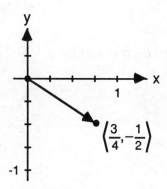

7. $\overrightarrow{PQ} = \langle 3 - 2, 7 - 3 \rangle = \langle 1, 4 \rangle$

9. $\overrightarrow{PQ} = \langle -3 - (-2), -2 - (-3) \rangle = \langle -3 + 2, -2 + 3 \rangle = \langle -1, 1 \rangle$

11. $\vec{PQ} = \langle 3 - (-5), -4 - 1 \rangle = \langle 3 + 5, -5 \rangle = \langle 8, -5 \rangle$

13. $\mathbf{a} + \mathbf{b} = \langle 2 + 5, 3 + 4 \rangle = \langle 7, 7 \rangle$

15. $\mathbf{2a} + \mathbf{4b} = \langle 4, 6 \rangle + \langle 20, 16 \rangle = \langle 24, 22 \rangle$

17. $\mathbf{b} + \mathbf{c} = \langle 5 + 6, 4 - 1 \rangle = \langle 11, 3 \rangle$, so:
$$|\mathbf{b} + \mathbf{c}| = \sqrt{11^2 + 3^2} = \sqrt{130}$$

19. $\mathbf{a} + \mathbf{c} = \langle 2 + 6, 3 - 1 \rangle = \langle 8, 2 \rangle$, so:
$$|\mathbf{a} + \mathbf{c}| = \sqrt{8^2 + 2^2} = \sqrt{68} = 2\sqrt{17}$$
$$|\mathbf{a}| = \sqrt{2^2 + 3^2} = \sqrt{13}$$
$$|\mathbf{c}| = \sqrt{6^2 + (-1)^2} = \sqrt{37}$$
So $|\mathbf{a} + \mathbf{c}| - |\mathbf{a}| - |\mathbf{c}| = 2\sqrt{17} - \sqrt{13} - \sqrt{37}$

21. $\mathbf{b} + \mathbf{c} = \langle 5 + 6, 4 - 1 \rangle = \langle 11, 3 \rangle$, so:
$$\mathbf{a} + (\mathbf{b} + \mathbf{c}) = \langle 2, 3 \rangle + \langle 11, 3 \rangle = \langle 13, 6 \rangle$$

23. $\mathbf{3a} + \mathbf{4a} = \langle 6, 9 \rangle + \langle 8, 12 \rangle = \langle 14, 21 \rangle$

25. $\mathbf{a} - \mathbf{b} = \langle 2, 3 \rangle - \langle 5, 4 \rangle = \langle -3, -1 \rangle$

27. $\mathbf{3b} - \mathbf{4d} = \langle 15, 12 \rangle - \langle -8, 0 \rangle = \langle 15 + 8, 12 - 0 \rangle = \langle 23, 12 \rangle$

29. $\mathbf{b} + \mathbf{c} = \langle 11, 3 \rangle$, so:
$$\mathbf{a} - (\mathbf{b} + \mathbf{c}) = \langle 2, 3 \rangle - \langle 11, 3 \rangle = \langle -9, 0 \rangle$$

31. $\mathbf{c} + \mathbf{d} = \langle 4, -1 \rangle$ and $\mathbf{c} - \mathbf{d} = \langle 8, -1 \rangle$, while:
$$|\mathbf{c} + \mathbf{d}| = \sqrt{16 + 1} = \sqrt{17} \text{ and } |\mathbf{c} - \mathbf{d}| = \sqrt{64 + 1} = \sqrt{65}$$
So:
$$|\mathbf{c} + \mathbf{d}|^2 - |\mathbf{c} - \mathbf{d}|^2 = 17 - 65 = -48$$

33. $\langle 3, 8 \rangle = \langle 3, 0 \rangle + \langle 0, 8 \rangle = 3\mathbf{i} + 8\mathbf{j}$

35. $\langle -8, -6 \rangle = \langle -8, 0 \rangle + \langle 0, -6 \rangle = -8\mathbf{i} - 6\mathbf{j}$

37. $3 \langle 5, 3 \rangle + 2 \langle 2, 7 \rangle = 3(5\mathbf{i} + 3\mathbf{j}) + 2(2\mathbf{i} + 7\mathbf{j})$
$$= 15\mathbf{i} + 9\mathbf{j} + 4\mathbf{i} + 14\mathbf{j}$$
$$= 19\mathbf{i} + 23\mathbf{j}$$

39. $\mathbf{i} + \mathbf{j} = \langle 1, 1 \rangle$

41. $5\mathbf{i} - 4\mathbf{j} = \langle 5, -4 \rangle$

43. $\left| \langle 4, 8 \rangle \right| = \sqrt{4^2 + 8^2} = \sqrt{80} = 4\sqrt{5}$, so a unit vector would be given by:

$$\frac{1}{4\sqrt{5}} \langle 4, 8 \rangle = \left\langle \frac{1}{\sqrt{5}}, \frac{2}{\sqrt{5}} \right\rangle = \left\langle \frac{\sqrt{5}}{5}, \frac{2\sqrt{5}}{5} \right\rangle$$

45. $\left| \langle 6, -3 \rangle \right| = \sqrt{6^2 + (-3)^2} = \sqrt{45} = 3\sqrt{5}$, so a unit vector would be given by:

$$\frac{1}{3\sqrt{5}} \langle 6, -3 \rangle = \left\langle \frac{2}{\sqrt{5}}, \frac{-1}{\sqrt{5}} \right\rangle = \left\langle \frac{2\sqrt{5}}{5}, \frac{-\sqrt{5}}{5} \right\rangle$$

47. $\left| 8\mathbf{i} - 9\mathbf{j} \right| = \sqrt{8^2 + (-9)^2} = \sqrt{145}$, so a unit vector would be given by:

$$\frac{1}{\sqrt{145}} (8\mathbf{i} - 9\mathbf{j}) = \frac{8}{\sqrt{145}}\mathbf{i} - \frac{9}{\sqrt{145}}\mathbf{j} = \frac{8\sqrt{145}}{145}\mathbf{i} - \frac{9\sqrt{145}}{145}\mathbf{j}$$

49. $u_1 = \cos\frac{\pi}{6} = \frac{\sqrt{3}}{2}$, $u_2 = \sin\frac{\pi}{6} = \frac{1}{2}$

51. $u_1 = \cos\frac{2\pi}{3} = -\frac{1}{2}$, $u_2 = \sin\frac{2\pi}{3} = \frac{\sqrt{3}}{2}$

53. $u_1 = \cos\frac{5\pi}{6} = -\frac{\sqrt{3}}{2}$, $u_2 = \sin\frac{5\pi}{6} = \frac{1}{2}$

55. property 1

$$
\begin{aligned}
\mathbf{u} + (\mathbf{v} + \mathbf{w}) &= \langle u_1, u_2 \rangle + \left(\langle v_1, v_2 \rangle + \langle w_1, w_2 \rangle \right) \\
&= \langle u_1, u_2 \rangle + \langle v_1 + w_1, v_2 + w_2 \rangle \\
&= \langle u_1 + v_1 + w_1, u_2 + v_2 + w_2 \rangle \\
&= \langle u_1 + v_1, u_2 + v_2 \rangle + \langle w_1, w_2 \rangle \\
&= \left(\langle u_1, u_2 \rangle + \langle v_1, v_2 \rangle \right) + \langle w_1, w_2 \rangle \\
&= (\mathbf{u} + \mathbf{v}) + \mathbf{w}
\end{aligned}
$$

property 2

$$
\begin{aligned}
\mathbf{0} + \mathbf{v} &= \langle 0, 0 \rangle + \langle v_1, v_2 \rangle \\
&= \langle 0 + v_1, 0 + v_2 \rangle \\
&= \langle v_1 + 0, v_2 + 0 \rangle \\
&= \langle v_1, v_2 \rangle + \langle 0, 0 \rangle \\
&= \mathbf{v} + \mathbf{0}
\end{aligned}
$$

$$
\begin{aligned}
\mathbf{v} + \mathbf{0} &= \langle v_1, v_2 \rangle + \langle 0, 0 \rangle \\
&= \langle v_1 + 0, v_2 + 0 \rangle \\
&= \langle v_1, v_2 \rangle \\
&= \mathbf{v}
\end{aligned}
$$

57.   property 5
$$\begin{aligned} a\,(\mathbf{u} + \mathbf{v}) &= a\,(\,\langle u_1, u_2 \rangle + \langle v_1, v_2 \rangle\,) \\ &= a\,\langle u_1 + v_1, u_2 + v_2 \rangle \\ &= \langle a(u_1 + v_1), a(u_2 + v_2) \rangle \\ &= \langle au_1 + av_1, au_2 + av_2 \rangle \\ &= \langle au_1, au_2 \rangle + \langle av_1, av_2 \rangle \\ &= a\,\langle u_1, u_2 \rangle + a\,\langle v_1, v_2 \rangle \\ &= a\mathbf{u} + a\mathbf{v} \end{aligned}$$

property 6
$$\begin{aligned} (a + b)\,\mathbf{v} &= (a + b)\,\langle v_1, v_2 \rangle \\ &= \langle (a + b)v_1, (a + b)v_2 \rangle \\ &= \langle av_1 + bv_1, av_2 + bv_2 \rangle \\ &= \langle av_1, av_2 \rangle + \langle bv_1, bv_2 \rangle \\ &= a\,\langle v_1, v_2 \rangle + b\,\langle v_1, v_2 \rangle \\ &= a\mathbf{v} + b\mathbf{v} \end{aligned}$$

59.   (a) $\mathbf{u} \cdot \mathbf{v} = \langle -4, 5 \rangle \cdot \langle 3, 4 \rangle = (-4)(3) + (5)(4) = -12 + 20 = 8$
        $\mathbf{v} \cdot \mathbf{u} = \langle 3, 4 \rangle \cdot \langle -4, 5 \rangle = (3)(-4) + (4)(5) = -12 + 20 = 8$

      (b) $\mathbf{v} \cdot \mathbf{w} = \langle 3, 4 \rangle \cdot \langle 2, -5 \rangle = (3)(2) + (4)(-5) = 6 - 20 = -14$
        $\mathbf{w} \cdot \mathbf{v} = \langle 2, -5 \rangle \cdot \langle 3, 4 \rangle = (2)(3) + (-5)(4) = 6 - 20 = -14$

      (c)   Let $\mathbf{A} = \langle x_1, y_1 \rangle$ and $\mathbf{B} = \langle x_2, y_2 \rangle$. We compute each dot product:
        $$\mathbf{A} \cdot \mathbf{B} = \langle x_1, y_1 \rangle \cdot \langle x_2, y_2 \rangle = x_1 x_2 + y_1 y_2$$
        $$\mathbf{B} \cdot \mathbf{A} = \langle x_2, y_2 \rangle \cdot \langle x_1, y_1 \rangle = x_2 x_1 + y_2 y_1$$
        Thus $\mathbf{A} \cdot \mathbf{B} = \mathbf{B} \cdot \mathbf{A}$.

61.   (a) $\mathbf{v} \cdot \mathbf{v} = \langle 3, 4 \rangle \cdot \langle 3, 4 \rangle = (3)(3) + (4)(4) = 9 + 16 = 25$
        $|\mathbf{v}| = \sqrt{3^2 + 4^2} = \sqrt{9 + 16} = \sqrt{25} = 5$, so $|\mathbf{v}|^2 = 25$

      (b) $\mathbf{w} \cdot \mathbf{w} = \langle 2, -5 \rangle \cdot \langle 2, -5 \rangle = (2)(2) + (-5)(-5) = 4 + 25 = 29$
        $|\mathbf{w}| = \sqrt{2^2 + (-5)^2} = \sqrt{4 + 25} = \sqrt{29}$, so $|\mathbf{u}|^2 = 29$

63.   We first do the computations:
        $$|\mathbf{A}| = \sqrt{16 + 1} = \sqrt{17}$$
        $$|\mathbf{B}| = \sqrt{4 + 36} = \sqrt{40} = 2\sqrt{10}$$
        $$\mathbf{A} \cdot \mathbf{B} = 8 + 6 = 14$$
      Thus:
        $$\cos\theta = \frac{14}{\sqrt{17} \cdot 2\sqrt{10}} = \frac{7}{\sqrt{170}}$$
      So $\theta \approx 57.53°$ or $\theta \approx 1.00$.

65. We first do the computations:
$$|\mathbf{A}| = \sqrt{25 + 36} = \sqrt{61}$$
$$|\mathbf{B}| = \sqrt{9 + 49} = \sqrt{58}$$
$$\mathbf{A} \cdot \mathbf{B} = -15 - 42 = -57$$
Thus:
$$\cos \theta = \frac{-57}{\sqrt{61} \cdot \sqrt{58}} = \frac{-57}{\sqrt{3538}}$$
So $\theta \approx 163.39°$ or $\theta \approx 2.85$.

67. (a) We first do the computations:
$$|\mathbf{A}| = \sqrt{64 + 4} = \sqrt{68} = 2\sqrt{17}$$
$$|\mathbf{B}| = \sqrt{1 + 9} = \sqrt{10}$$
$$\mathbf{A} \cdot \mathbf{B} = -8 - 6 = -14$$
Thus:
$$\cos \theta = \frac{-14}{2\sqrt{17} \cdot \sqrt{10}} = \frac{-7}{\sqrt{170}}$$
So $\theta \approx 122.47°$ or $\theta \approx 2.14$.

   (b) Again, we do the computations:
$$|\mathbf{A}| = \sqrt{64 + 4} = \sqrt{68} = 2\sqrt{17}$$
$$|\mathbf{B}| = \sqrt{1 + 9} = \sqrt{10}$$
$$\mathbf{A} \cdot \mathbf{B} = 8 + 6 = 14$$
Thus:
$$\cos \theta = \frac{14}{2\sqrt{17} \cdot \sqrt{10}} = \frac{7}{\sqrt{170}}$$
So $\theta \approx 57.53°$ or $\theta \approx 1.00$.

69. (a) We first compute:
$$|\langle 2, 5 \rangle| = \sqrt{4 + 25} = \sqrt{29}$$
$$|\langle -5, 2 \rangle| = \sqrt{25 + 4} = \sqrt{29}$$
$$\langle 2, 5 \rangle \cdot \langle -5, 2 \rangle = -10 + 10 = 0$$
So $\cos \theta = \frac{0}{29} = 0$

   (b) Since the angle between the vectors is 90°, the vectors must be perpendicular.

(c)   We draw the sketch:

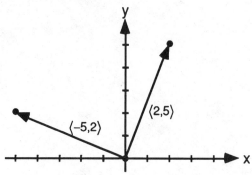

71.   Since $\cos \theta = \dfrac{\mathbf{A} \cdot \mathbf{B}}{|\mathbf{A}|\,|\mathbf{B}|}$, then $\mathbf{A} \cdot \mathbf{B} = 0$ implies $\cos \theta = 0$, and thus $\theta = 90°$. So the vectors are perpendicular.

73.   Call such a vector $\langle x, y \rangle$, so $x^2 + y^2 = 1$. Now we know $\langle x, y \rangle \cdot \langle -12, 5 \rangle = 0$, so:

$$-12x + 5y = 0$$
$$5y = 12x$$
$$y = \frac{12}{5}x$$

Substituting into $x^2 + y^2 = 1$, we have:

$$x^2 + \frac{144}{25}x^2 = 1$$
$$\frac{169}{25}x^2 = 1$$
$$x^2 = \frac{25}{169}$$
$$x = \pm\frac{5}{13}$$
$$y = \pm\frac{12}{13}$$

So the two unit vectors are $\langle 5/13, 12/13 \rangle$ and $\langle -5/13, -12/13 \rangle$.

75.   (a) $\mathbf{C} = \mathbf{B} - \mathbf{A} = \langle x_2, y_2 \rangle - \langle x_1, y_1 \rangle = \langle x_2 - x_1, y_2 - y_1 \rangle$

So $|\mathbf{C}| = \sqrt{(x_2 - x_1)^2 + (y_2 - y_1)^2}$

$\qquad\quad = \sqrt{x_1{}^2 + y_1{}^2 + x_2{}^2 + y_2{}^2 - 2x_1x_2 - 2y_1y_2}$

(b) $|\mathbf{C}|^2 = x_1{}^2 + y_1{}^2 + x_2{}^2 + y_2{}^2 - 2x_1x_2 - 2y_1y_2$

$\qquad\quad = |\mathbf{A}|^2 + |\mathbf{B}|^2 - 2(\mathbf{A} \cdot \mathbf{B})$

(c)   Using the suggestion given, we have:

$$|A|^2 + |B|^2 - 2|A||B|\cos\theta = |A|^2 + |B|^2 - 2(A \cdot B)$$
$$-2|A||B|\cos\theta = -2(A \cdot B)$$
$$|A||B|\cos\theta = A \cdot B$$
$$\cos\theta = \frac{A \cdot B}{|A||B|}$$

10.8   Trigonometric Form for Complex Numbers

1.   The complex number 4 + 2i is identified with the point (4, 2):

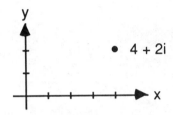

3.   The complex number -5 + i is identified with the point (-5, 1):

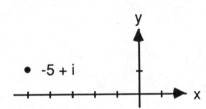

5.   The complex number 1 - 4i is identified with the point (1, -4):

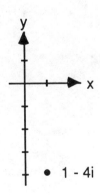

7.   The complex number -i, or 0 - 1i, is identified with the point (0, -1):

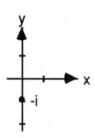

9. $2\left[\cos\dfrac{\pi}{4} + i\sin\dfrac{\pi}{4}\right] = 2\left[\dfrac{\sqrt{2}}{2} + \dfrac{\sqrt{2}}{2}i\right] = \sqrt{2} + \sqrt{2}\,i$

11. $4\left[\cos\dfrac{5\pi}{6} + i\sin\dfrac{5\pi}{6}\right] = 4\left[-\dfrac{\sqrt{3}}{2} + \dfrac{1}{2}i\right] = -2\sqrt{3} + 2i$

13. $\sqrt{2}\,[\cos 225° + i\sin 225°] = \sqrt{2}\left[-\dfrac{\sqrt{2}}{2} - \dfrac{\sqrt{2}}{2}i\right] = -1 - i$

15. $\sqrt{3}\left[\cos\dfrac{\pi}{2} + i\sin\dfrac{\pi}{2}\right] = \sqrt{3}\,(0 + 1i) = \sqrt{3}\,i$

17.   We use the hint to find cos 75° and sin 75°:

$$\begin{aligned}
\cos 75° &= \cos (30° + 45°)\\
&= \cos 30° \cos 45° - \sin 30° \sin 45°\\
&= \frac{\sqrt{3}}{2} \cdot \frac{\sqrt{2}}{2} - \frac{1}{2} \cdot \frac{\sqrt{2}}{2}\\
&= \frac{\sqrt{6} - \sqrt{2}}{4}
\end{aligned}$$

$$\begin{aligned}
\sin 75° &= \sin (30° + 45°)\\
&= \sin 30° \cos 45° + \cos 30° \sin 45°\\
&= \frac{1}{2} \cdot \frac{\sqrt{2}}{2} + \frac{\sqrt{3}}{2} \cdot \frac{\sqrt{2}}{2}\\
&= \frac{\sqrt{6} + \sqrt{2}}{4}
\end{aligned}$$

So $4\,[\cos 75° + i\sin 75°] = 4\left[\dfrac{\sqrt{6} - \sqrt{2}}{4} + \dfrac{\sqrt{6} + \sqrt{2}}{4}i\right]$

$$= (\sqrt{6} - \sqrt{2}) + (\sqrt{6} + \sqrt{2})i$$

19.   Here $a = \dfrac{\sqrt{3}}{2}$ and $b = \dfrac{1}{2}$, so $r = \sqrt{a^2 + b^2} = \sqrt{\dfrac{3}{4} + \dfrac{1}{4}} = 1$.

We now find θ such that $\cos \theta = \dfrac{a}{r} = \dfrac{\sqrt{3}}{2}$ and $\sin \theta = \dfrac{b}{r} = \dfrac{1}{2}$.

Such a θ is $\theta = \dfrac{\pi}{6}$. Thus $\dfrac{\sqrt{3}}{2} + \dfrac{1}{2}i = \cos \dfrac{\pi}{6} + i \sin \dfrac{\pi}{6}$.

21.   Here $a = -1$ and $b = \sqrt{3}$, so $r = \sqrt{a^2 + b^2} = \sqrt{1 + 3} = \sqrt{4} = 2$.

We now find θ such that $\cos \theta = \dfrac{a}{r} = -\dfrac{1}{2}$ and $\sin \theta = \dfrac{b}{r} = \dfrac{\sqrt{3}}{2}$.

Such a θ is $\theta = \dfrac{2\pi}{3}$. Thus $-1 + \sqrt{3} i = 2\left[\cos \dfrac{2\pi}{3} + i \sin \dfrac{2\pi}{3}\right]$.

23.   Here $a = -2\sqrt{3}$ and $b = -2$, so $r = \sqrt{a^2 + b^2} = \sqrt{12 + 4} = \sqrt{16} = 4$.

We now find θ such that $\cos \theta = \dfrac{a}{r} = -\dfrac{2\sqrt{3}}{4} = -\dfrac{\sqrt{3}}{2}$ and

$\sin \theta = \dfrac{b}{r} = -\dfrac{2}{4} = -\dfrac{1}{2}$. Such a θ is $\theta = \dfrac{7\pi}{6}$.

Thus $-2\sqrt{3} - 2i = 4\left[\cos \dfrac{7\pi}{6} + i \sin \dfrac{7\pi}{6}\right]$.

25.   Here $a = 0$ and $b = -6$, so $r = \sqrt{a^2 + b^2} = \sqrt{0 + 36} = 6$. We now find θ

such that $\cos \theta = \dfrac{a}{r} = \dfrac{0}{6} = 0$ and $\sin \theta = \dfrac{b}{r} = -\dfrac{6}{6} = -1$. Such a θ is

$\theta = \dfrac{3\pi}{2}$. Thus $-6i = 6\left[\cos \dfrac{3\pi}{2} + i \sin \dfrac{3\pi}{2}\right]$.

27.   Here $a = \dfrac{\sqrt{3}}{4}$ and $b = -\dfrac{1}{4}$, so $r = \sqrt{a^2 + b^2} = \sqrt{\dfrac{3}{16} + \dfrac{1}{16}} = \sqrt{\dfrac{1}{4}} = \dfrac{1}{2}$.

We now find θ such that $\cos \theta = \dfrac{a}{r} = \dfrac{\frac{\sqrt{3}}{4}}{\frac{1}{2}} = \dfrac{\sqrt{3}}{2}$ and $\sin \theta = \dfrac{b}{r} = \dfrac{-\frac{1}{4}}{\frac{1}{2}} = -\dfrac{1}{2}$.

Such a θ is $\theta = \dfrac{11\pi}{6}$. Thus $\dfrac{\sqrt{3}}{4} - \dfrac{1}{4}i = \dfrac{1}{2}\left[\cos \dfrac{11\pi}{6} + i \sin \dfrac{11\pi}{6}\right]$.

29. $2\left[\cos 22° + i \sin 22°\right] \bullet 3\left[\cos 38° + i \sin 38°\right] = 6\left[\cos 60° + i \sin 60°\right]$

$$= 6\left(\dfrac{1}{2} + \dfrac{\sqrt{3}}{2}i\right)$$

$$= 3 + 3\sqrt{3} i$$

31. $\sqrt{2}\left[\cos\dfrac{\pi}{3} + i\sin\dfrac{\pi}{3}\right] \bullet \sqrt{2}\left[\cos\dfrac{4\pi}{3} + i\sin\dfrac{4\pi}{3}\right] = 2\left[\cos\dfrac{5\pi}{3} + i\sin\dfrac{5\pi}{3}\right]$

$$= 2\left(\dfrac{1}{2} - \dfrac{\sqrt{3}}{2}i\right)$$

$$= 1 - \sqrt{3}\,i$$

33. $3\left[\cos\dfrac{\pi}{7} + i\sin\dfrac{\pi}{7}\right] \bullet \sqrt{2}\left[\cos\dfrac{\pi}{7} + i\sin\dfrac{\pi}{7}\right] = 3\sqrt{2}\left[\cos\dfrac{2\pi}{7} + i\sin\dfrac{2\pi}{7}\right]$

35. $6\,[\cos 50° + i\sin 50°] \div 2\,[\cos 5° + i\sin 5°] = 3\,[\cos 45° + i\sin 45°]$

$$= 3\left(\dfrac{\sqrt{2}}{2} + \dfrac{\sqrt{2}}{2}i\right)$$

$$= \dfrac{3\sqrt{2}}{2} + \dfrac{3\sqrt{2}}{2}i$$

37. $2^{4/3}\left[\cos\dfrac{5\pi}{12} + i\sin\dfrac{5\pi}{12}\right] \div 2^{1/3}\left[\cos\dfrac{\pi}{4} + i\sin\dfrac{\pi}{4}\right] = 2\left[\cos\dfrac{\pi}{6} + i\sin\dfrac{\pi}{6}\right]$

$$= 2\left(\dfrac{\sqrt{3}}{2} + \dfrac{1}{2}i\right)$$

$$= \sqrt{3} + i$$

39. $\left[\cos\dfrac{2\pi}{5} + i\sin\dfrac{2\pi}{5}\right] \div \left[\cos\dfrac{2\pi}{5} + i\sin\dfrac{2\pi}{5}\right] = \cos 0 + i\sin 0$

$$= 1 + 0i$$

$$= 1$$

41. $\left[3\left(\cos\dfrac{\pi}{3} + i\sin\dfrac{\pi}{3}\right)\right]^5 = 3^5\left[\cos\dfrac{5\pi}{3} + i\sin\dfrac{5\pi}{3}\right]$

$$= 243\left(\dfrac{1}{2} - \dfrac{\sqrt{3}}{2}i\right)$$

$$= \dfrac{243}{2} - \dfrac{243\sqrt{3}}{2}i$$

43. $\left[\dfrac{1}{2}\left(\cos\dfrac{\pi}{24} + i\sin\dfrac{\pi}{24}\right)\right]^6 = \left(\dfrac{1}{2}\right)^6\left[\cos\dfrac{\pi}{4} + i\sin\dfrac{\pi}{4}\right]$

$$= \dfrac{1}{64}\left(\dfrac{\sqrt{2}}{2} + \dfrac{\sqrt{2}}{2}i\right)$$

$$= \dfrac{\sqrt{2}}{128} + \dfrac{\sqrt{2}}{128}i$$

45. $\left[2^{1/5}(\cos 63° + i \sin 63°)\right]^{10} = (2^{1/5})^{10}[\cos 630° + i \sin 630°]$
$$= 4(0 - 1i)$$
$$= -4i$$

47. $2[\cos 200° + i \sin 200°] \bullet \sqrt{2}[\cos 20° + i \sin 20°] \bullet \dfrac{1}{2}[\cos 5° + i \sin 5°]$

$$= \dfrac{2\sqrt{2}}{2}[\cos 225° + i \sin 225°]$$

$$= \sqrt{2}\left(-\dfrac{\sqrt{2}}{2} - \dfrac{\sqrt{2}}{2}i\right)$$

$$= -1 - i$$

49. Since $\dfrac{1}{2} - \dfrac{\sqrt{3}}{2}i = \cos\dfrac{5\pi}{3} + i \sin\dfrac{5\pi}{3}$, then:

$$\left(\dfrac{1}{2} - \dfrac{\sqrt{3}}{2}i\right)^5 = \cos\dfrac{25\pi}{3} + i \sin\dfrac{25\pi}{3} = \dfrac{1}{2} + \dfrac{\sqrt{3}}{2}i$$

51. Since $-2 - 2i = 2\sqrt{2}\left(-\dfrac{\sqrt{2}}{2} - \dfrac{\sqrt{2}}{2}i\right) = 2\sqrt{2}\left[\cos\dfrac{5\pi}{4} + i \sin\dfrac{5\pi}{4}\right]$, then:

$$(-2 - 2i)^5 = (2\sqrt{2})^5\left[\cos\dfrac{25\pi}{4} + i \sin\dfrac{25\pi}{4}\right]$$

$$= 128\sqrt{2}\left(\dfrac{\sqrt{2}}{2} + \dfrac{\sqrt{2}}{2}i\right)$$

$$= 128 + 128i$$

53. Since $-2\sqrt{3} - 2i = 4\left(-\dfrac{\sqrt{3}}{2} - \dfrac{1}{2}i\right) = 4\left[\cos\dfrac{7\pi}{6} + i \sin\dfrac{7\pi}{6}\right]$, then:

$$(-2\sqrt{3} - 2i)^4 = 4^4\left[\cos\dfrac{14\pi}{3} + i \sin\dfrac{14\pi}{3}\right]$$

$$= 256\left(-\dfrac{1}{2} + \dfrac{\sqrt{3}}{2}i\right)$$

$$= -128 + 128\sqrt{3}i$$

55. We write $-27i = 27(0 - 1i) = 27\left[\cos\frac{3\pi}{2} + i\sin\frac{3\pi}{2}\right]$.

Now let $z = r(\cos\theta + i\sin\theta)$ denote a cube root of $-27i$. Then:

$$z^3 = r^3(\cos 3\theta + i\sin 3\theta) = 27\left[\cos\frac{3\pi}{2} + i\sin\frac{3\pi}{2}\right]$$

Then $r^3 = 27$ so $r = 3$, and $3\theta = \frac{3\pi}{2} + 2\pi k$, so $\theta = \frac{\pi}{2} + \frac{2\pi}{3}k$

When $k = 0$, we have: $z_1 = 3\left[\cos\frac{\pi}{2} + i\sin\frac{\pi}{2}\right] = 3(0 + i) = 3i$

When $k = 1$, we have: $z_2 = 3\left[\cos\frac{7\pi}{6} + i\sin\frac{7\pi}{6}\right]$

$$= 3\left(-\frac{\sqrt{3}}{2} - \frac{1}{2}i\right)$$

$$= -\frac{3\sqrt{3}}{2} - \frac{3}{2}i$$

When $k = 2$, we have: $z_3 = 3\left[\cos\frac{11\pi}{6} + i\sin\frac{11\pi}{6}\right]$

$$= 3\left(\frac{\sqrt{3}}{2} - \frac{1}{2}i\right)$$

$$= \frac{3\sqrt{3}}{2} - \frac{3}{2}i$$

So the cube roots are $3i$, $-\frac{3\sqrt{3}}{2} - \frac{3}{2}i$, and $\frac{3\sqrt{3}}{2} - \frac{3}{2}i$

57. We write $1 = 1(1 + 0i) = 1[\cos 0 + i\sin 0]$. Now let $z = r(\cos\theta + i\sin\theta)$ denote an eighth root of 1. Then:

$$z^8 = r^8(\cos 8\theta + i\sin 8\theta) = 1[\cos 0 + i\sin 0]$$

Then $r^8 = 1$ so $r = 1$, and $8\theta = 0 + 2\pi k$, so $\theta = 0 + \frac{\pi}{4}k$.

When $k = 0$, we have: $z_1 = 1[\cos 0 + i\sin 0] = 1(1 + 0i) = 1$

When $k = 1$, we have: $z_2 = 1\left[\cos\frac{\pi}{4} + i\sin\frac{\pi}{4}\right]$

$$= 1\left(\frac{\sqrt{2}}{2} + \frac{\sqrt{2}}{2}i\right)$$

$$= \frac{\sqrt{2}}{2} + \frac{\sqrt{2}}{2}i$$

When $k = 2$, we have: $z_3 = 1\left[\cos\frac{\pi}{2} + i\sin\frac{\pi}{2}\right] = 1(0 + i) = i$

When $k = 3$, we have: $z_4 = 1\left[\cos\frac{3\pi}{4} + i\sin\frac{3\pi}{4}\right] = -\frac{\sqrt{2}}{2} + \frac{\sqrt{2}}{2}i$

When $k = 4$, we have: $z_5 = 1[\cos\pi + i\sin\pi] = -1 + 0i = -1$

When k = 5, we have: $z_6 = 1\left[\cos \dfrac{5\pi}{4} + i \sin \dfrac{5\pi}{4}\right] = -\dfrac{\sqrt{2}}{2} - \dfrac{\sqrt{2}}{2} i$

When k = 6, we have: $z_7 = 1\left[\cos \dfrac{3\pi}{2} + i \sin \dfrac{3\pi}{2}\right] = 0 - i = -i$

When k = 7, we have: $z_8 = 1\left[\cos \dfrac{7\pi}{4} + i \sin \dfrac{7\pi}{4}\right] = \dfrac{\sqrt{2}}{2} - \dfrac{\sqrt{2}}{2} i$

So the eighth roots of 1 are 1, $\dfrac{\sqrt{2}}{2} + \dfrac{\sqrt{2}}{2} i$, i, $-\dfrac{\sqrt{2}}{2} + \dfrac{\sqrt{2}}{2} i$, -1, $-\dfrac{\sqrt{2}}{2} - \dfrac{\sqrt{2}}{2} i$, -i,

and $\dfrac{\sqrt{2}}{2} - \dfrac{\sqrt{2}}{2} i$.

59. We write 64 = 64 (1 + 0i) = 64 [cos 0 + i sin 0].
Now let z = r (cos θ + i sin θ) denote a cube root of 64. Then:
$$z^3 = r^3[\cos 3\theta + i \sin 3\theta] = 64 [\cos 0 + i \sin 0]$$
Then $r^3 = 64$ so r = 4, and 3θ = 0 + 2πk, so θ = $0 + \dfrac{2\pi}{3} k$.

When k = 0, we have: $z_1 = 4 [\cos 0 + i \sin 0] = 4(1 + 0i) = 4$

When k = 1, we have: $z_2 = 4\left[\cos \dfrac{2\pi}{3} + i \sin \dfrac{2\pi}{3}\right]$

$$= 4 \left(-\dfrac{1}{2} + \dfrac{\sqrt{3}}{2} i\right)$$

$$= -2 + 2\sqrt{3}\, i$$

When k = 2, we have: $z_3 = 4\left[\cos \dfrac{4\pi}{3} + i \sin \dfrac{4\pi}{3}\right]$

$$= 4 \left(-\dfrac{1}{2} - \dfrac{\sqrt{3}}{2} i\right)$$

$$= -2 - 2\sqrt{3}\, i$$

So the cube roots of 64 are 4, $-2 + 2\sqrt{3}\, i$, and $-2 - 2\sqrt{3}\, i$.

61. We write 729 = 729 (1 + 0i) = 729 [cos 0 + i sin 0] . Now let
z = r (cos θ + i sin θ) denote a sixth root of 729. Then:
$$z^6 = r^6 [\cos 6\theta + i \sin 6\theta] = 729 [\cos 0 + i \sin 0]$$
Then $r^6 = 729$ so r = 3, and 6θ = 0 + 2πk, so θ = $0 + \dfrac{\pi}{3} k$.

When k = 0, we have: $z_1 = 3 [\cos 0 + i \sin 0] = 3(1 + 0i) = 3$

When k = 1, we have: $z_2 = 3\left[\cos \dfrac{\pi}{3} + i \sin \dfrac{\pi}{3}\right]$

$$= 3 \left(\dfrac{1}{2} + \dfrac{\sqrt{3}}{2} i\right)$$

$$= \dfrac{3}{2} + \dfrac{3\sqrt{3}}{2} i$$

When $k = 2$, we have: $\quad z_3 = 3\left[\cos\dfrac{2\pi}{3} + i\sin\dfrac{2\pi}{3}\right]$

$$= 3\left(-\dfrac{1}{2} + \dfrac{\sqrt{3}}{2}\,i\right)$$

$$= -\dfrac{3}{2} + \dfrac{3\sqrt{3}}{2}\,i$$

When $k = 3$, we have: $\quad z_4 = 3\left[\cos\pi + i\sin\pi\right] = 3(-1 + 0i) = -3$

When $k = 4$, we have: $\quad z_5 = 3\left[\cos\dfrac{4\pi}{3} + i\sin\dfrac{4\pi}{3}\right]$

$$= 3\left(-\dfrac{1}{2} - \dfrac{\sqrt{3}}{2}\,i\right)$$

$$= -\dfrac{3}{2} - \dfrac{3\sqrt{2}}{2}\,i$$

When $k = 5$, we have: $\quad z_6 = 3\left[\cos\dfrac{5\pi}{3} + i\sin\dfrac{5\pi}{3}\right]$

$$= 3\left(\dfrac{1}{2} - \dfrac{\sqrt{3}}{2}\,i\right)$$

$$= \dfrac{3}{2} - \dfrac{3\sqrt{3}}{2}\,i$$

So the sixth roots of 729 are 3, $\dfrac{3}{2} + \dfrac{3\sqrt{3}}{2}\,i$, $-\dfrac{3}{2} + \dfrac{3\sqrt{3}}{2}\,i$, -3, $-\dfrac{3}{2} - \dfrac{3\sqrt{3}}{2}\,i$,

and $\dfrac{3}{2} - \dfrac{3\sqrt{3}}{2}\,i$.

63. $7 - 7i = 7\sqrt{2}\left(\dfrac{1}{\sqrt{2}} - \dfrac{1}{\sqrt{2}}\,i\right) = 7\sqrt{2}\left[\cos\dfrac{7\pi}{4} + i\sin\dfrac{7\pi}{4}\right]$. So:

$$(7 - 7i)^8 = (7\sqrt{2})^8[\cos 14\pi + i\sin 14\pi]$$
$$= (7^8)(2^4)(1 + 0i)$$
$$= 92{,}236{,}816$$

65. We have $i = 1\left[\cos\dfrac{\pi}{2} + i\sin\dfrac{\pi}{2}\right]$. Now let z be a fifth root of i, where

$z = r(\cos\theta + i\sin\theta)$. Then:

$$z^5 = r^5[\cos 5\theta + i\sin 5\theta] = 1\left[\cos\dfrac{\pi}{2} + i\sin\dfrac{\pi}{2}\right]$$

So $r^5 = 1$, thus $r = 1$, and $5\theta = \dfrac{\pi}{2} + 2\pi k = 90° + 360°k$, so $\theta = 18° + 72°k$

When $k = 0$: $\quad z_1 = 1\left[\cos 18° + i\sin 18°\right] = 0.95 + 0.31i$

When $k = 1$: $\quad z_2 = 1\left[\cos 90° + i\sin 90°\right] = i$

When $k = 2$: $\quad z_3 = 1\left[\cos 162° + i\sin 162°\right] = -0.95 + 0.31i$

When $k = 3$: $\quad z_4 = 1\left[\cos 234° + i\sin 234°\right] = -0.59 - 0.81i$

When $k = 4$: $z_5 = 1 [\cos 306° + i \sin 306°] = 0.59 - 0.81i$

So the fifth roots of i are $0.95 + 0.31i$, i, $-0.95 + 0.31i$, $-0.59 - 0.81i$, and $0.59 - 0.81i$. Each of the real and imaginary parts here has been rounded off to two decimal places.

67. We write $8 - 8\sqrt{3}\, i = 16 \left(\dfrac{1}{2} - \dfrac{\sqrt{3}}{2} i \right) = 16 \left[\cos \dfrac{5\pi}{3} + i \sin \dfrac{5\pi}{3} \right]$. Now let

$z = r(\cos \theta + i \sin \theta)$ denote a fourth root of $8 - 8\sqrt{3}\, i$. Then:

$$z^4 = r^4 [\cos 4\theta + i \sin 4\theta] = 16 \left[\cos \dfrac{5\pi}{3} + i \sin \dfrac{5\pi}{3} \right]$$

Then $r^4 = 16$ so $r = 2$, and $4\theta = \dfrac{5\pi}{3} + 2\pi k$, so $\theta = \dfrac{5\pi}{12} + \dfrac{\pi}{2} k$.

When $k = 0$, we have: $z_1 = 2 \left[\cos \dfrac{5\pi}{12} + i \sin \dfrac{5\pi}{12} \right]$

$$= 2 \left[\dfrac{\sqrt{6} - \sqrt{2}}{4} + \dfrac{\sqrt{6} + \sqrt{2}}{4} i \right]$$

(using the addition formulas)

$$= \dfrac{\sqrt{6} - \sqrt{2}}{2} + \dfrac{\sqrt{6} + \sqrt{2}}{2} i$$

When $k = 1$, we have: $z_2 = 2 \left[\cos \dfrac{11\pi}{12} + i \sin \dfrac{11\pi}{12} \right]$

$$= 2 \left[\dfrac{-\sqrt{2} - \sqrt{6}}{4} + \dfrac{\sqrt{6} - \sqrt{2}}{4} i \right]$$

$$= \dfrac{-\sqrt{2} - \sqrt{6}}{2} + \dfrac{\sqrt{6} - \sqrt{2}}{2} i$$

When $k = 2$, we have: $z_3 = 2 \left[\cos \dfrac{17\pi}{12} + i \sin \dfrac{17\pi}{12} \right]$

$$= 2 \left[\dfrac{\sqrt{2} - \sqrt{6}}{4} + \dfrac{-\sqrt{2} - \sqrt{6}}{4} i \right]$$

$$= \dfrac{\sqrt{2} - \sqrt{6}}{2} - \dfrac{\sqrt{2} + \sqrt{6}}{2} i$$

When $k = 3$, we have: $z_4 = 2 \left[\cos \dfrac{23\pi}{12} + i \sin \dfrac{23\pi}{12} \right]$

$$= 2 \left[\dfrac{\sqrt{2} + \sqrt{6}}{4} + \dfrac{\sqrt{2} - \sqrt{6}}{4} i \right]$$

$$= \dfrac{\sqrt{2} + \sqrt{6}}{2} + \dfrac{\sqrt{2} - \sqrt{6}}{2} i$$

So the fourth roots of $8 - 8\sqrt{3}$ are $\dfrac{\sqrt{6} - \sqrt{2}}{2} + \dfrac{\sqrt{6} + \sqrt{2}}{2}i,$

$\dfrac{-\sqrt{2} - \sqrt{6}}{2} + \dfrac{\sqrt{6} - \sqrt{2}}{2}i, \dfrac{\sqrt{2} - \sqrt{6}}{2} + \dfrac{-\sqrt{2} - \sqrt{6}}{2}i,$ and $\dfrac{\sqrt{2} + \sqrt{6}}{2} + \dfrac{\sqrt{2} - \sqrt{6}}{2}i.$

Note: If you used half-angle formulas, your answers, though identical in value, may "look" vastly different. Those answers (which are correct) are

$\sqrt{2 - \sqrt{3}} + i\sqrt{2 + \sqrt{3}}, -\sqrt{2 + \sqrt{3}} + i\sqrt{2 - \sqrt{3}}, -\sqrt{2 - \sqrt{3}} - i\sqrt{2 + \sqrt{3}},$

and $\sqrt{2 + \sqrt{3}} - i\sqrt{2 - \sqrt{3}}$

69. (a)   Let $z = r(\cos\theta + i\sin\theta)$, so $z^3 = r^3(\cos 3\theta + i\sin 3\theta)$.
Since $1 = 1(\cos 0 + i\sin 0)$, we have $r^3 = 1$ so $r = 1$, and
$3\theta = 0 + 2\pi k$, so $\theta = 0 + \dfrac{2\pi}{3}k$.

When $k = 0$: $z_1 = 1[\cos 0 + i\sin 0] = 1(1 + 0i) = 1$

When $k = 1$: $z_2 = 1\left[\cos\dfrac{2\pi}{3} + i\sin\dfrac{2\pi}{3}\right]$

$$= 1\left(-\dfrac{1}{2} + \dfrac{\sqrt{3}}{2}i\right)$$

$$= -\dfrac{1}{2} + \dfrac{\sqrt{3}}{2}i$$

When $k = 2$: $z_3 = 1\left[\cos\dfrac{4\pi}{3} + i\sin\dfrac{4\pi}{3}\right]$

$$= 1\left(-\dfrac{1}{2} - \dfrac{\sqrt{3}}{2}i\right)$$

$$= -\dfrac{1}{2} - \dfrac{\sqrt{3}}{2}i$$

So the cube roots of 1 are $1, -\dfrac{1}{2} + \dfrac{\sqrt{3}}{2}i$, and $-\dfrac{1}{2} - \dfrac{\sqrt{3}}{2}i$.

(b) $z_1 + z_2 + z_3 = 1 + \left(-\dfrac{1}{2} + \dfrac{\sqrt{3}}{2}i\right) + \left(-\dfrac{1}{2} - \dfrac{\sqrt{3}}{2}i\right) = 0 + 0i = 0$

$z_1 z_2 = 1\left[\cos\dfrac{2\pi}{3} + i\sin\dfrac{2\pi}{3}\right] = -\dfrac{1}{2} + \dfrac{\sqrt{3}}{2}i$ (Note this is z_3)

$z_2 z_3 = 1[\cos 2\pi + i\sin 2\pi] = 1$ (Note this is z_1)

$z_3 z_1 = 1\left[\cos\dfrac{4\pi}{3} + i\sin\dfrac{4\pi}{3}\right] = -\dfrac{1}{2} - \dfrac{\sqrt{3}}{2}i$ (Note this is z_2)

So $z_1 z_2 + z_2 z_3 + z_3 z_1 = z_1 + z_2 + z_3 = 0$

71. $\left[\dfrac{-1 + i\sqrt{3}}{2}\right]^5 = \left[-\dfrac{1}{2} + \dfrac{\sqrt{3}}{2}i\right]^5$

$\qquad\qquad = \left[\cos\dfrac{2\pi}{3} + i\sin\dfrac{2\pi}{3}\right]^5$

$\qquad\qquad = \cos\dfrac{10\pi}{3} + i\sin\dfrac{10\pi}{3}$

$\qquad\qquad = -\dfrac{1}{2} - \dfrac{\sqrt{3}}{2}i$

$\left[\dfrac{-1 - i\sqrt{3}}{2}\right]^5 = \left[-\dfrac{1}{2} - \dfrac{\sqrt{3}}{2}i\right]^5$

$\qquad\qquad = \left[\cos\dfrac{4\pi}{3} + i\sin\dfrac{4\pi}{3}\right]^5$

$\qquad\qquad = \cos\dfrac{20\pi}{3} + i\sin\dfrac{20\pi}{3}$

$\qquad\qquad = -\dfrac{1}{2} + \dfrac{\sqrt{3}}{2}i$

So $\left[\dfrac{-1 + i\sqrt{3}}{2}\right]^5 + \left[\dfrac{-1 - i\sqrt{3}}{2}\right]^5 = \left(-\dfrac{1}{2} - \dfrac{\sqrt{3}}{2}i\right) + \left(-\dfrac{1}{2} + \dfrac{\sqrt{3}}{2}i\right) = -1$

73. $(\cos\theta + i\sin\theta)(\cos\theta - i\sin\theta) = \cos^2\theta - i^2\sin^2\theta$

$\qquad\qquad\qquad\qquad\qquad\qquad = \cos^2\theta + \sin^2\theta,\ \text{since } i^2 = -1$

$\qquad\qquad\qquad\qquad\qquad\qquad = 1$

75. Using the hint, we have:

$\dfrac{r(\cos\alpha + i\sin\alpha)}{R(\cos\beta + i\sin\beta)} \bullet \dfrac{(\cos\beta - i\sin\beta)}{(\cos\beta - i\sin\beta)}$

$= \dfrac{r(\cos\alpha\cos\beta + i\sin\alpha\cos\beta - i\cos\alpha\sin\beta - i^2\sin\alpha\sin\beta)}{R(\cos^2\beta - i^2\sin^2\beta)}$

$= \dfrac{r[(\cos\alpha\cos\beta + \sin\alpha\sin\beta) + i(\sin\alpha\cos\beta - \cos\alpha\sin\beta)]}{R(\cos^2\beta + \sin^2\beta)}$

Using the difference identities for sine and cosine:

$= \dfrac{r[\cos(\alpha - \beta) + i\sin(\alpha - \beta)]}{R}$

$= \dfrac{r}{R}[\cos(\alpha - \beta) + i\sin(\alpha - \beta)]$

77.   Using the hint, $\dfrac{1}{z} = \dfrac{1\,(\cos 0 + i \sin 0)}{r\,(\cos \theta + i \sin \theta)}$

$\qquad\qquad\qquad = \dfrac{1}{r}\,[\cos (0 - \theta) + i \sin (0 - \theta)]$ by exercise #75

$\qquad\qquad\qquad = \dfrac{1}{r}\,[\cos (-\theta) + i \sin (-\theta)]$

$\qquad\qquad\qquad = \dfrac{1}{r}\,(\cos \theta - i \sin \theta)$

$\qquad\qquad$ since $\cos (-\theta) = \cos \theta$ and $\sin (-\theta) = -\sin \theta$

This proves the desired result.

79.   Let P_n denote the statement:

$\qquad [r(\cos \theta + i \sin \theta)]^n = r^n(\cos n\theta + i \sin n\theta)$

For n = 1, we have:

$\qquad r(\cos \theta + i \sin \theta) = r(\cos \theta + i \sin \theta)$

Assume P_k is true:

$\qquad [r(\cos \theta + i \sin \theta)]^k = r^k(\cos k\theta + i \sin k\theta)$

Form P_{k+1}:

$\qquad [r(\cos \theta + i \sin \theta)]^{k+1}$

$\qquad\qquad = r(\cos \theta + i \sin \theta) \bullet [r(\cos \theta + i \sin \theta)]^k$

$\qquad\qquad = r(\cos \theta + i \sin \theta) \bullet r^k(\cos k\theta + i \sin k\theta)$

$\qquad\qquad = r^{k+1}[(\cos \theta \cos k\theta - \sin \theta \sin k\theta) + i\,(\sin \theta \cos k\theta + \cos \theta \sin k\theta)]$

$\qquad\qquad = r^{k+1}(\cos (k+1)\theta + i \sin (k+1)\theta)$

This completes the induction.

Chapter 10 Review Exercises

1.   For n = 1, we have:

$\qquad 1^2 = \dfrac{1(1 + 1)(2 + 1)}{6} = \dfrac{6}{6} = 1$

Assume P_k is true, so:

$\qquad 1^2 + 2^2 + 3^2 + \ldots + k^2 = \dfrac{k(k + 1)(2k + 1)}{6}$

Let P_{k+1} denote:

$$1^2 + 2^2 + \ldots + k^2 + (k+1)^2 = \frac{k(k+1)(2k+1)}{6} + (k+1)^2$$

$$= (k+1)\left(\frac{k(2k+1)}{6} + k + 1\right)$$

$$= (k+1)\left(\frac{2k^2 + k + 6k + 6}{6}\right)$$

$$= \frac{(k+1)(2k^2 + 7k + 6)}{6}$$

$$= \frac{(k+1)(k+2)(2k+3)}{6}$$

$$= \frac{(k+1)(k+2)\big(2(k+1)+1\big)}{6}$$

This completes the induction.

2. (a) $\displaystyle\sum_{k=0}^{2}(10k-1) = -1 + 9 + 19 = 27$

    (b) $\displaystyle\sum_{k=1}^{3}(-1)^k k^2 = -1 + 4 - 9 = -6$

3. (a) $S_n = \dfrac{a(1-r^n)}{1-r}$

    (b) Here $a = \dfrac{3}{2}$, $r = \dfrac{3}{2}$, and $n = 10$, so:

    $$S_{10} = \frac{\frac{3}{2}\left(1 - (3/2)^{10}\right)}{1 - 3/2}$$

    $$= \frac{\frac{3}{2}\left(1 - \frac{59049}{1024}\right)}{-1/2}$$

    $$= -3\left(\frac{-58025}{1024}\right)$$

    $$= \frac{174075}{1024}$$

4.   (a)   Here $11 - r + 1 = 3$, so $r = 9$, and the coefficient is:

$$\binom{11}{8}(-2)^8 = \frac{11(10)(9)}{3(2)}(256) = 42240$$

(b)   The fifth term is:

$$\binom{11}{4}(a)^7(-2b^3)^4 = \frac{11(10)(9)(8)}{4(3)(2)}a^7(16b^{12}) = 5280a^7b^{12}$$

5. $(3x^2 + y^3)^5 = \binom{5}{0}(3x^2)^5 + \binom{5}{1}(3x^2)^4(y^3) + \binom{5}{2}(3x^2)^3(y^3)^2$

$$+ \binom{5}{3}(3x^2)^2(y^3)^3 + \binom{5}{4}(3x^2)(y^3)^4 + \binom{5}{5}(y^3)^5$$

$$= 243x^{10} + 405x^8y^3 + 270x^6y^6 + 90x^4y^9 + 15x^2y^{12} + y^{15}$$

6. $S_{12} = (12)\left(\dfrac{8 + \frac{43}{2}}{2}\right) = (6)\dfrac{59}{2} = 177$

7. $S = \dfrac{a}{1 - r} = \dfrac{7/10}{1 - 1/10} = \dfrac{7}{9}$

8. $a_1 = 1$ and $a_2 = 1$, so:

$$a_3 = a_2{}^2 + a_1 = 1 + 1 = 2$$
$$a_4 = a_3{}^2 + a_2 = 2^2 + 1 = 5$$
$$a_5 = a_4{}^2 + a_3 = 5^2 + 2 = 27$$

9.   Since $a_3 = 4$ and $a_5 = 10$, then $a_5 = a_3r^2$, so:

$$10 = 4r^2$$
$$\frac{5}{2} = r^2$$
$$r = -\sqrt{5/2} = -\frac{\sqrt{10}}{2}$$

Then $a_6 = ra_5 = -\dfrac{\sqrt{10}}{2}(10) = -5\sqrt{10}$.

10.   Here $a_n = -61 + 15(n - 1)$, so:

$$a_{20} = -61 + 15(19) = 224$$

11. We draw the figure:

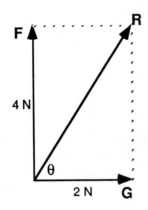

(a) $|\mathbf{R}| = \sqrt{2^2 + 4^2} = \sqrt{20} = 2\sqrt{5}$ N

(b) $\tan \theta = \dfrac{4}{2} = 2$

12. We draw the figure:

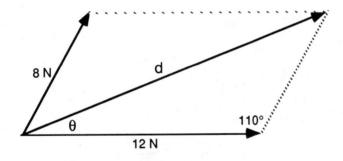

(a) $d = \sqrt{12^2 + 8^2 - 2(8)(12) \cos 110°}$

     $= \sqrt{208 - 192 \cos 110°}$

     $= 4\sqrt{13 - 12 \cos 110°}$ N

(b) Using the law of sines:

$$\frac{\sin \theta}{8} = \frac{\sin 110°}{4\sqrt{13 - 12 \cos 110°}}$$

$$\sin \theta = \frac{2 \sin 110°}{\sqrt{13 - 12 \cos 110°}}$$

13. We draw the figure:

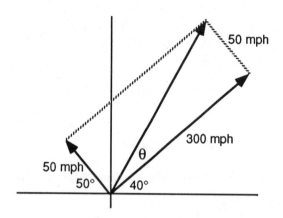

The heading vector and the wind vector are perpendicular to each other.

ground speed $= \sqrt{300^2 + 50^2} = 50\sqrt{37}$ mph

$\tan \theta = \dfrac{50}{300} = \dfrac{1}{6}$

14. (a) $2\mathbf{A} + 3\mathbf{B} = 2\langle 2, 4 \rangle + 3\langle 3, -1 \rangle = \langle 13, 5 \rangle$

(b) $\left| 2\mathbf{A} + 3\mathbf{B} \right| = \left| \langle 13, 5 \rangle \right| = \sqrt{194}$

(c) $\mathbf{C} - \mathbf{B} = \langle 4, -4 \rangle - \langle 3, -1 \rangle = \langle 1, -3 \rangle = \mathbf{i} - 3\mathbf{j}$

15. $\overrightarrow{PQ} = \langle -7, 2 \rangle - \langle 4, 5 \rangle = \langle -11, -3 \rangle$
The required unit vector is:

$$\frac{\overrightarrow{PQ}}{\left| \overrightarrow{PQ} \right|} = \frac{1}{\sqrt{130}}\langle -11, -3 \rangle = \left\langle \frac{-11\sqrt{130}}{130}, \frac{-3\sqrt{130}}{130} \right\rangle$$

16. $z = 2\left(\cos \dfrac{2\pi}{3} + i \sin \dfrac{2\pi}{3} \right)$

$= 2(-1/2 + \sqrt{3}/2\, i)$

$= -1 + \sqrt{3}\, i$

17. $\sqrt{2} - \sqrt{2}\, i = 2(\sqrt{2}/2 - \sqrt{2}/2\, i) = 2\left(\cos \dfrac{7\pi}{4} + i \sin \dfrac{7\pi}{4} \right)$

18. $r^n(\cos n\theta + i \sin n\theta)$

19. $zw = 3\left(\cos\frac{2\pi}{9} + i\sin\frac{2\pi}{9}\right) \bullet 5\left(\cos\frac{\pi}{9} + i\sin\frac{\pi}{9}\right)$

$= 15\left(\cos\frac{\pi}{3} + i\sin\frac{\pi}{3}\right)$

$= 15(1/2 + \sqrt{3}/2\ i)$

$= 15/2 + 15\sqrt{3}/2\ i$

20. Let $z = r(\cos\theta + i\sin\theta)$ be a cube root of 64i. We have:

$64i = 64(0 + 1i) = 64\left(\cos\frac{\pi}{2} + i\sin\frac{\pi}{2}\right)$

Thus:

$z^3 = r^3(\cos 3\theta + i\sin 3\theta) = 64\left(\cos\frac{\pi}{2} + i\sin\frac{\pi}{2}\right)$

So $r^3 = 64$ and thus $r = 4$, and $3\theta = \pi/2 + 2\pi k$ thus $\theta = \pi/6 + 2\pi/3\ k$.

When $k = 0$: $z_1 = 4\left(\cos\frac{\pi}{6} + i\sin\frac{\pi}{6}\right)$

$= 4(\sqrt{3}/2 + 1/2\ i)$

$= 2\sqrt{3} + 2i$

When $k = 1$: $z_2 = 4\left(\cos\frac{5\pi}{6} + i\sin\frac{5\pi}{6}\right)$

$= 4(-\sqrt{3}/2 + 1/2\ i)$

$= -2\sqrt{3} + 2i$

When $k = 2$: $z_3 = 4\left(\cos\frac{3\pi}{2} + i\sin\frac{3\pi}{2}\right)$

$= 4(0 - i)$

$= -4i$

So the cube roots of 64i are $2\sqrt{3} + 2i$, $-2\sqrt{3} + 2i$, and $-4i$.

21. When $n = 1$: $5 = \frac{5}{2}(1)(1 + 1) = 5$

Assuming: $5 + 10 + \ldots + 5k = \frac{5}{2}\ k(k + 1)$

Then: $5 + 10 + \ldots + 5k + 5(k + 1) = \frac{5}{2}k(k + 1) + 5(k + 1)$

$= (k + 1)\left(\frac{5}{2}k + 5\right)$

$= \frac{5}{2}(k + 1)(k + 2)$

which completes the induction.

23. When $n = 1$: $1 \cdot 2 = 2 = \frac{1}{3}(1)(1 + 1)(1 + 2) = 2$

Assuming: $1 \cdot 2 + 2 \cdot 3 + \ldots + k(k + 1) = \frac{1}{3}k(k + 1)(k + 2)$

Then: $1 \cdot 2 + 2 \cdot 3 + \ldots + k(k + 1) + (k + 1)(k + 2)$

$$= \frac{1}{3}k(k + 1)(k + 2) + (k + 1)(k + 2)$$

$$= \left(\frac{1}{3}k + 1\right)(k + 1)(k + 2)$$

$$= \frac{1}{3}(k + 1)(k + 2)(k + 3)$$

which completes the induction.

25. When $n = 1$: $1 = 3 + (2 - 3)2 = 3 - 2 = 1$

Assuming: $1 + 3 \cdot 2 + 5 \cdot 2^2 + \ldots + (2k - 1) \cdot 2^{k-1} = 3 + (2k - 3) \cdot 2^k$

Then: $1 + 3 \cdot 2 + \ldots + (2k - 1)2^{k-1} + (2k + 1)2^k$

$$= 3 + (2k - 3)2^k + (2k + 1)2^k$$

$$= 3 + (4k - 2)2^k$$

$$= 3 + (2k - 1)2^{k+1}$$

$$= 3 + (2(k + 1) - 3) \cdot 2^{k+1}$$

and the induction is complete.

27. When $n = 1$: $1 = (1^2 - 2 + 3)2 - 3 = 1$

Assuming:

$1 + 2^2 \cdot 2 + 3^2 \cdot 2^2 + 4^2 \cdot 2^3 + \ldots + k^2 \cdot 2^{k-1} = (k^2 - 2k + 3)2^k - 3$

Then:

$1 + 2^2 \cdot 2 + \ldots + (k + 1)^2 2^k = (k^2 - 2k + 3)2^k - 3 + (k + 1)^2 2^k$

$$= 2^k\left(k^2 - 2k + 3 + (k + 1)^2\right) - 3$$

$$= 2^k(2k^2 + 4) - 3$$

$$= 2^{k+1}(k^2 + 2) - 3$$

$$= 2^{k+1}\left((k + 1)^2 - 2k + 1\right) - 3$$

$$= 2^{k+1}\left((k + 1)^2 - 2(k + 1) + 3\right) - 3$$

and the induction is complete.

29. When $n = 1$: $7^1 - 1 = 6 = 3(2)$

Assuming: $7^k - 1 = 3L$

Then: $7^{k+1} - 1 = 3L + 7^{k+1} - 7^k$

$$= 3L + 7^k(7 - 1)$$

$$= 3L + 6(7^k)$$

$$= 3(L + 2 \cdot 7^k)$$

and the induction is complete.

31. $(3a + b^2)^4$

$$= \binom{4}{0}(3a)^4 + \binom{4}{1}(3a)^3(b^2) + \binom{4}{2}(3a)^2(b^2)^2 + \binom{4}{3}(3a)(b^2)^3 + \binom{4}{4}(b^2)^4$$

$$= 81a^4 + 108a^3b^2 + 54a^2b^4 + 12ab^6 + b^8$$

33. $(x + \sqrt{x})^4 = \binom{4}{0}x^4 + \binom{4}{1}x^3(\sqrt{x}) + \binom{4}{2}x^2(\sqrt{x})^2 + \binom{4}{3}x(\sqrt{x})^3 + \binom{4}{4}(\sqrt{x})^4$

$$= x^4 + 4x^3\sqrt{x} + 6x^3 + 4x^2\sqrt{x} + x^2$$

35. $(x^2 - 2y^2)^5 = \binom{5}{0}(x^2)^5 - \binom{5}{1}(x^2)^4(2y^2) + \binom{5}{2}(x^2)^3(2y^2)^2 - \binom{5}{3}(x^2)^2(2y^2)^3$

$$+ \binom{5}{4}(x^2)(2y^2)^4 - \binom{5}{5}(2y^2)^5$$

$$= x^{10} - 10x^8y^2 + 40x^6y^4 - 80x^4y^6 + 80x^2y^8 - 32y^{10}$$

37. $\left(1 + \dfrac{1}{x}\right)^5 = \binom{5}{0} + \binom{5}{1}\dfrac{1}{x} + \binom{5}{2}\left(\dfrac{1}{x}\right)^2 + \binom{5}{3}\left(\dfrac{1}{x}\right)^3 + \binom{5}{4}\left(\dfrac{1}{x}\right)^4 + \binom{5}{5}\left(\dfrac{1}{x}\right)^5$

$$= 1 + \dfrac{5}{x} + \dfrac{10}{x^2} + \dfrac{10}{x^3} + \dfrac{5}{x^4} + \dfrac{1}{x^5}$$

39. $(a\sqrt{b} - b\sqrt{a})^4 = a^2b^2(\sqrt{a} - \sqrt{b})^4$

$$= a^2b^2\left((\sqrt{a})^4 - 4(\sqrt{a})^3\sqrt{b} + 6(\sqrt{a})^2(\sqrt{b})^2 - 4(\sqrt{a})(\sqrt{b})^3 + (\sqrt{b})^4\right)$$

$$= a^2b^2(a^2 - 4a\sqrt{ab} + 6ab - 4b\sqrt{ab} + b^2)$$

$$= a^4b^2 - 4a^3b^2\sqrt{ab} + 6a^3b^3 - 4a^2b^3\sqrt{ab} + a^2b^4$$

41. $\binom{5}{5-1}(3x)(y^2)^4 = 5(3x)y^8 = 15xy^8$

43. Here $7 - r + 1 = 5$, so $r = 3$, and the coefficient of the third term is:

$$\binom{7}{2}(2)^2 = (4)\dfrac{7!}{5!2!} = 84$$

45. $r - 1 = 6$, so $r = 7$, and the coefficient of the seventh term is:

$$\binom{8}{6} = \dfrac{8(7)}{2} = 28$$

47. $\binom{2}{0}^2 + \binom{2}{1}^2 + \binom{2}{2}^2 = (1)^2 + (2)^2 + (1)^2 = 6$

$$\binom{4}{2} = \dfrac{4(3)}{2} = 6$$

49. $\binom{4}{0}^2 + \binom{4}{1}^2 + \binom{4}{2}^2 + \binom{4}{3}^2 + \binom{4}{4}^2 = 1^2 + 4^2 + 6^2 + 4^2 + 1^2 = 70$

$\binom{8}{4} = \frac{8(7)(6)(5)}{4(3)(2)} = 70$

51. $\binom{3}{0} + \binom{3}{1} + \binom{3}{2} + \binom{3}{3} = 1 + 3 + 3 + 1 = 8 = 2^3$

53. $a_1 = \frac{2}{1+1} = 1$

$a_2 = \frac{4}{2+1} = \frac{4}{3}$

$a_3 = \frac{6}{3+1} = \frac{3}{2}$

$a_4 = \frac{8}{4+1} = \frac{8}{5}$

$a_5 = \frac{10}{5+1} = \frac{5}{3}$

55. $a_1 = (-1)\left(1 - \frac{1}{2}\right) = -\frac{1}{2}$

$a_2 = (1)\left(1 - \frac{1}{3}\right) = \frac{2}{3}$

$a_3 = (-1)\left(1 - \frac{1}{4}\right) = -\frac{3}{4}$

$a_4 = (1)\left(1 - \frac{1}{5}\right) = \frac{4}{5}$

$a_5 = (-1)\left(1 - \frac{1}{6}\right) = -\frac{5}{6}$

57. $a_0 = -3$
$a_1 = 4(-3) = -12$
$a_2 = 4(-12) = -48$
$a_3 = 4(-48) = -192$
$a_4 = 4(-192) = -768$
The first five terms are -3, -12, -48, -192, -768

59. $\sum_{k=1}^{5} (2k + 3) = 5 + 7 + 9 + 11 + 13 = 45$

61. $\displaystyle\sum_{k=1}^{5} \frac{5}{3^k}$

63. Here $a_n = 1 + 4n$, so $a_{14} = 1 + 4(14) = 57$

65. Here $a_n = \dfrac{10}{2^{n-1}}$, so $a_{12} = \dfrac{10}{2^{11}} = \dfrac{5}{1024}$

67. Here $a = -5$, $n = 100$, $d = 3$, so:

$$\begin{aligned} S_{100} &= \frac{n}{2}[2a + (n-1)d] \\ &= 50[-10 + 99(3)] \\ &= 50[287] \\ &= 14350 \end{aligned}$$

69. By inspection:
$S_1 = 7$; $S_2 = 77$; . . . ; so $S_{10} = 7{,}777{,}777{,}777$

71. $S = \dfrac{\dfrac{3}{5}}{1 - \dfrac{1}{5}} = \dfrac{3}{4}$

73. $S = \dfrac{\dfrac{1}{9}}{1 + \dfrac{1}{9}} = \dfrac{1}{10}$

75. $.45\ldots = .45 + .0045 + .000045 + \ldots$

This is a geometric sequence with $a = .45$, $r = \dfrac{1}{100}$, so:

$$.45\ldots = \dfrac{.45}{1 - \dfrac{1}{100}} = \dfrac{45}{99} = \dfrac{15}{33} = \dfrac{5}{11}$$

77. $S_n = \dfrac{n}{2}\left(2(1) + (n-1)1\right)$

$= \dfrac{n}{2}(2 + n - 1)$

$= \dfrac{n}{2}(1 + n)$

$= \dfrac{n^2}{2} + \dfrac{n}{2}$

$= n + \dfrac{n^2}{2} - \dfrac{n}{2}$

$= n + \dfrac{n(n-1)}{2}$

79. $S_n = \dfrac{n}{2}\left(2(1) + (n-1)3\right)$

$= \dfrac{n}{2}(2 + 3n - 3)$

$= \dfrac{n}{2}(3n - 1)$

$= \dfrac{3n^2}{2} - \dfrac{n}{2}$

$= n + \dfrac{3n^2}{2} - \dfrac{3n}{2}$

$= n + \dfrac{3n(n-1)}{2}$

81. (a) $1^2 + 2^2 + \ldots + 50^2 \approx \dfrac{\left(50 + \dfrac{1}{2}\right)^{2+1}}{2 + 1}$

$= \dfrac{\left(\dfrac{101}{2}\right)^3}{3}$

$= \dfrac{1030301}{24}$

≈ 42929

(b) $\dfrac{50(51)(101)}{6} = 42925$

Percent error $= 100 \cdot \dfrac{4}{42925} \approx 0.00932\ \%$

(c) $1^4 + 2^4 + \ldots + 200^4 \approx \dfrac{(200.5)^5}{5} \approx 6.48040 \times 10^{10}$

(d) $1^4 + 2^4 + \ldots + 200^4 = \dfrac{200(201)(401)(120599)}{30} \approx 6.48027 \times 10^{10}$

Percent error $= 100 \cdot \dfrac{0.00013 \times 10^{10}}{6.48027 \times 10^{10}} \approx 2 \times 10^{-3}\,\%$

83. We draw a figure:

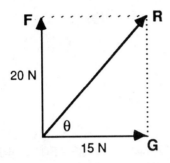

The resultant has a magnitude and direction given by:

$$|\mathbf{R}| = \sqrt{15^2 + 20^2} = \sqrt{625} = 25\ \text{N}$$

$$\theta = \tan^{-1}\dfrac{20}{15} \approx 53.1°$$

85. $v_x = 50\cos 35° \approx 41.0\ \text{cm/sec}$
     $v_y = 50\sin 35° \approx 28.7\ \text{cm/sec}$

87. We draw the figure:

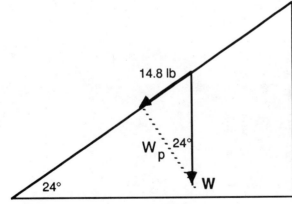

$\tan 24° = \dfrac{14.8}{|\mathbf{W}_p|}$, so $|\mathbf{W}_p| = \dfrac{14.8}{\tan 24°} \approx 33.2\ \text{lb}$

$\sin 24° = \dfrac{14.8}{|\mathbf{W}|}$, so $|\mathbf{W}| = \dfrac{14.8}{\sin 24°} \approx 36.4\ \text{lb}$

89. $|\langle 2,6 \rangle| = \sqrt{2^2 + 6^2} = \sqrt{40}$ and $|\langle -5, b \rangle| = \sqrt{(-5)^2 + b^2} = \sqrt{b^2 + 25}$
We find b by solving the equation:
$$\sqrt{b^2 + 25} = \sqrt{40}$$
$$b^2 + 25 = 40$$
$$b^2 = 15$$
$$b = \pm\sqrt{15}$$

91. $\mathbf{a} + \mathbf{b} = \langle 3, 5 \rangle + \langle 7, 4 \rangle = \langle 10, 9 \rangle$

93. $\mathbf{3c + 2a} \quad = 3\langle 2, -1 \rangle + 2\langle 3, 5 \rangle$
$$= \langle 6, -3 \rangle + \langle 6, 10 \rangle$$
$$= \langle 12, 7 \rangle$$

95. $\mathbf{b} + \mathbf{d} = \langle 7, 7 \rangle$ and $\mathbf{b} - \mathbf{d} = \langle 7, 1 \rangle$, so:
$$|\mathbf{b} + \mathbf{d}|^2 - |\mathbf{b} - \mathbf{d}|^2 = (7^2 + 7^2) - (7^2 + 1^2) = 98 - 50 = 48$$

97. $(\mathbf{a} + \mathbf{b}) + \mathbf{c} = \langle 10, 9 \rangle + \langle 2, -1 \rangle = \langle 12, 8 \rangle$

99. $(\mathbf{a} - \mathbf{b}) - \mathbf{c} = \langle -4, 1 \rangle - \langle 2, -1 \rangle = \langle -6, 2 \rangle$

101. $\mathbf{4c + 2a - 3b} = \langle 8, -4 \rangle + \langle 6, 10 \rangle - \langle 21, 12 \rangle = \langle -7, -6 \rangle$

103. $\langle 7, -6 \rangle = 7\mathbf{i} - 6\mathbf{j}$

105. $|\langle 6, 4 \rangle| = \sqrt{36 + 16} = \sqrt{52} = 2\sqrt{13}$, so such a unit vector would be:
$$\frac{1}{2\sqrt{13}}\langle 6, 4 \rangle = \left\langle \frac{3}{\sqrt{13}}, \frac{2}{\sqrt{13}} \right\rangle = \left\langle \frac{3\sqrt{13}}{13}, \frac{2\sqrt{13}}{13} \right\rangle$$

107. $u_1 = \cos\frac{\pi}{12}$
$$= \cos\left(\frac{\pi}{3} - \frac{\pi}{4}\right)$$
$$= \cos\frac{\pi}{3}\cos\frac{\pi}{4} + \sin\frac{\pi}{3}\sin\frac{\pi}{4}$$
$$= \frac{1}{2} \cdot \frac{\sqrt{2}}{2} + \frac{\sqrt{3}}{2} \cdot \frac{\sqrt{2}}{2}$$
$$= \frac{\sqrt{6} + \sqrt{2}}{4}$$

$$u_2 = \sin\frac{\pi}{12}$$

$$= \sin\left(\frac{\pi}{3} - \frac{\pi}{4}\right)$$

$$= \sin\frac{\pi}{3}\cos\frac{\pi}{4} - \cos\frac{\pi}{3}\sin\frac{\pi}{4}$$

$$= \frac{\sqrt{3}}{2}\cdot\frac{\sqrt{2}}{2} - \frac{1}{2}\cdot\frac{\sqrt{2}}{2}$$

$$= \frac{\sqrt{6} - \sqrt{2}}{4}$$

109. $3\left[\cos\frac{\pi}{3} + i\sin\frac{\pi}{3}\right] = 3\left(\frac{1}{2} + \frac{\sqrt{3}}{2}i\right) = \frac{3}{2} + \frac{3\sqrt{3}}{2}i$

111. $2^{1/4}\left[\cos\frac{7\pi}{4} + i\sin\frac{7\pi}{4}\right] = 2^{1/4}\left(\frac{\sqrt{2}}{2} - \frac{\sqrt{2}}{2}i\right) = 2^{-1/4} - 2^{-1/4}i$

113. $\frac{1}{2} + \frac{\sqrt{3}}{2}i = 1\left[\cos\frac{\pi}{3} + i\sin\frac{\pi}{3}\right]$

115. $-3\sqrt{2} - 3\sqrt{2}\,i = 6\left(-\frac{\sqrt{2}}{2} - \frac{\sqrt{2}}{2}i\right) = 6\left[\cos\frac{5\pi}{4} + i\sin\frac{5\pi}{4}\right]$

117. $5\left[\cos\frac{\pi}{7} + i\sin\frac{\pi}{7}\right]\cdot 2\left[\cos\frac{3\pi}{28} + i\sin\frac{3\pi}{28}\right] = 10\left[\cos\frac{7\pi}{28} + i\sin\frac{7\pi}{28}\right]$

$$= 10\left[\cos\frac{\pi}{4} + i\sin\frac{\pi}{4}\right]$$

$$= 10\left(\frac{\sqrt{2}}{2} + \frac{\sqrt{2}}{2}i\right)$$

$$= 5\sqrt{2} + 5\sqrt{2}\,i$$

119. $8\left[\cos\frac{\pi}{12} + i\sin\frac{\pi}{12}\right] \div 4\left[\cos\frac{\pi}{3} + i\sin\frac{\pi}{3}\right] = 2\left[\cos\left(-\frac{3\pi}{12}\right) + i\sin\left(-\frac{3\pi}{12}\right)\right]$

$$= 2\left[\cos\left(-\frac{\pi}{4}\right) + i\sin\left(-\frac{\pi}{4}\right)\right]$$

$$= 2\left(\frac{\sqrt{2}}{2} - \frac{\sqrt{2}}{2}i\right)$$

$$= \sqrt{2} - \sqrt{2}\,i$$

121. $\left[\cos\dfrac{\pi}{9} + i\sin\dfrac{\pi}{9}\right] \bullet 3\left[\cos\dfrac{4\pi}{9} + i\sin\dfrac{4\pi}{9}\right] = 3\left[\cos\dfrac{5\pi}{9} + i\sin\dfrac{5\pi}{9}\right]$

123. $\left[3^{1/4}\left(\cos\dfrac{\pi}{36} + i\sin\dfrac{\pi}{36}\right)\right]^{12} = 3^3\left[\cos\dfrac{12\pi}{36} + i\sin\dfrac{12\pi}{36}\right]$

$= 27\left[\cos\dfrac{\pi}{3} + i\sin\dfrac{\pi}{3}\right]$

$= 27\left(\dfrac{1}{2} + \dfrac{\sqrt{3}}{2}i\right)$

$= \dfrac{27}{2} + \dfrac{27\sqrt{3}}{2}i$

125. Since $\sqrt{3} + i = 2\left(\dfrac{\sqrt{3}}{2} + \dfrac{1}{2}i\right) = 2\left[\cos\dfrac{\pi}{6} + i\sin\dfrac{\pi}{6}\right]$, then:

$(\sqrt{3} + i)^{10} = \left[2\left(\cos\dfrac{\pi}{6} + i\sin\dfrac{\pi}{6}\right)\right]^{10}$

$= 2^{10}\left[\cos\dfrac{5\pi}{3} + i\sin\dfrac{5\pi}{3}\right]$

$= 2^{10}\left(\dfrac{1}{2} - \dfrac{\sqrt{3}}{2}i\right)$

$= 2^9 - 2^9\sqrt{3}\,i$

$= 512 - 512\sqrt{3}\,i$

127. Let $z = r(\cos\theta + i\sin\theta)$ and $1 = 1[\cos 0 + i\sin 0]$, so:
$z^6 = r^6(\cos 6\theta + i\sin 6\theta) = 1(\cos 0 + i\sin 0)$

Thus $r = 1$ and $6\theta = 0 + 2\pi k$, so $\theta = 0 + \dfrac{\pi}{3}k$.

When $k = 0$: $z_1 = 1[\cos 0 + i\sin 0] = 1(1 + 0i) = 1$

When $k = 1$: $z_2 = 1\left[\cos\dfrac{\pi}{3} + i\sin\dfrac{\pi}{3}\right] = \dfrac{1}{2} + \dfrac{\sqrt{3}}{2}i$

When $k = 2$: $z_3 = 1\left[\cos\dfrac{2\pi}{3} + i\sin\dfrac{2\pi}{3}\right] = -\dfrac{1}{2} + \dfrac{\sqrt{3}}{2}i$

When $k = 3$: $z_4 = 1[\cos\pi + i\sin\pi] = -1 + 0i = -1$

When $k = 4$: $z_5 = 1\left[\cos\dfrac{4\pi}{3} + i\sin\dfrac{4\pi}{3}\right] = -\dfrac{1}{2} - \dfrac{\sqrt{3}}{2}i$

When $k = 5$: $z_6 = 1\left[\cos\dfrac{5\pi}{3} + i\sin\dfrac{5\pi}{3}\right] = \dfrac{1}{2} - \dfrac{\sqrt{3}}{2}i$

So the sixth roots of 1 are $1, \dfrac{1}{2} + \dfrac{\sqrt{3}}{2}i, -\dfrac{1}{2} + \dfrac{\sqrt{3}}{2}i, -1, -\dfrac{1}{2} - \dfrac{\sqrt{3}}{2}i,$ and $\dfrac{1}{2} - \dfrac{\sqrt{3}}{2}$.

129.   Let $z = r(\cos\theta + i\sin\theta)$ and:

$$\sqrt{2} - \sqrt{2}\,i = 2\left(\frac{\sqrt{2}}{2} - \frac{\sqrt{2}}{2}i\right) = 2\left[\cos\frac{7\pi}{4} + i\sin\frac{7\pi}{4}\right]$$

Then $z^2 = r^2(\cos 2\theta + i\sin 2\theta) = 2\left[\cos\frac{7\pi}{4} + i\sin\frac{7\pi}{4}\right]$.

So $r^2 = 2$, and $r = \sqrt{2}$, and also $2\theta = \frac{7\pi}{4} + 2\pi k$, so $\theta = \frac{7\pi}{8} + \pi k$.

When $k = 0$: $z_1 = \sqrt{2}\left[\cos\frac{7\pi}{8} + i\sin\frac{7\pi}{8}\right]$

$$= \sqrt{2}\left[\frac{-\sqrt{2+\sqrt{2}}}{2} + i\frac{\sqrt{2-\sqrt{2}}}{2}\right]$$

(by the half angle identities)

$$= \frac{-\sqrt{4+2\sqrt{2}}}{2} + \frac{\sqrt{4-2\sqrt{2}}}{2}i$$

When $k = 1$: $z_2 = \sqrt{2}\left[\cos\frac{15\pi}{8} + i\sin\frac{15\pi}{8}\right]$

$$= \sqrt{2}\left[\frac{\sqrt{2+\sqrt{2}}}{2} - i\frac{\sqrt{2-\sqrt{2}}}{2}\right]$$

$$= \frac{\sqrt{4+2\sqrt{2}}}{2} - \frac{\sqrt{4-2\sqrt{2}}}{2}i$$

So the square roots of $\sqrt{2} - \sqrt{2}\,i$ are: $\dfrac{-\sqrt{4+2\sqrt{2}}}{2} + \dfrac{\sqrt{4-2\sqrt{2}}}{2}i$

and $\dfrac{\sqrt{4+2\sqrt{2}}}{2} - \dfrac{\sqrt{4-2\sqrt{2}}}{2}i$.

131.   Let $z = r(\cos\theta + i\sin\theta)$ and $1 + i = \sqrt{2}\left(\frac{\sqrt{2}}{2} + \frac{\sqrt{2}}{2}i\right) = \sqrt{2}\left[\cos\frac{\pi}{4} + i\sin\frac{\pi}{4}\right]$

Then $z^5 = r^5[\cos 5\theta + i\sin 5\theta] = \sqrt{2}\,[\cos 45° + i\sin 45°]$

So $r^5 = \sqrt{2}$ and $r = 2^{1/10}$, and $5\theta = 45° + 360°k$, so $\theta = 9° + 72°k$.

When $k = 0$: $z_1 = 2^{1/10}[\cos 9° + i\sin 9°]$
            $= (1.0718)[\cos 9° + i\sin 9°]$
            $\approx 1.06 + 0.17\,i$

When $k = 1$: $z_2 = 1.0718[\cos 81° + i\sin 81°] \approx 0.17 + 1.06\,i$

When $k = 2$: $z_3 = 1.0718[\cos 153° + i\sin 153°] \approx -0.95 + 0.49\,i$

When $k = 3$: $z_4 = 1.0718[\cos 225° + i\sin 225°] \approx -0.76 - 0.76\,i$

When $k = 4$: $z_5 = 1.0718[\cos 297° + i\sin 297°] \approx 0.49 - 0.95\,i$

So the fifth roots of $1 + i$ are: $1.06 + 0.17\,i$, $0.17 + 1.06\,i$, $-0.95 + 0.49i$, $-0.76 - 0.76i$, and $0.49 - 0.95\,i$.

133. $(\cos \theta + i \sin \theta)^3$

$= (\cos \theta)^3 + 3(\cos \theta)^2(i \sin \theta) + 3(\cos \theta)(i \sin \theta)^2 + (i \sin \theta)^3$

$= \cos^3 \theta + 3 \cos^2 \theta \sin \theta\, i - 3 \cos \theta \sin^2 \theta - \sin^3 \theta\, i$

$= (\cos^3 \theta - 3 \cos \theta \sin^2 \theta) + (3 \cos^2 \theta \sin \theta - \sin^3 \theta)\, i$

Since this is equal to $\cos 3\theta + i \sin 3\theta$, and the real and imaginary parts must be equal, we have the identities:

$\cos 3\theta = \cos^3 \theta - 3 \cos \theta \sin^2 \theta$

$\sin 3\theta = 3 \cos^2 \theta \sin \theta - \sin^3 \theta$

135.   Call $b = ra$ and $c = r^2 a$, so $a + ar + ar^2 = 70$. Since 4a, 5b, 4c are consecutive terms in an arithmetic sequence, then their common difference is the same. So:

$5b - 4a = 4c - 5b$

$10b = 4a + 4c$

$5b = 2a + 2c$

$5(ra) = 2a + 2(r^2 a)$

$5ra = 2a + 2r^2 a$

Since a is nonzero, we divide by a:

$5r = 2 + 2r^2$

$2r^2 - 5r + 2 = 0$

$(2r - 1)(r - 2) = 0$

$r = \dfrac{1}{2},\ 2$

If $r = \dfrac{1}{2}$, we find a:

$a + a \bullet \dfrac{1}{2} + a \bullet \dfrac{1}{4} = 70$

$7a = 280$

$a = 40$

So the terms are 40, 20, 10.

If $r = 2$, we find a:

$a + 2a + 4a = 70$

$7a = 70$

$a = 10$

So the terms are 10, 20, 40.

137. We assume:
$$\frac{1}{c+a} - \frac{1}{b+c} = \frac{1}{a+b} - \frac{1}{c+a}$$
Our goal is to prove that:
$$b^2 - a^2 = c^2 - b^2$$
Multiply the first equation by $(c+a)(b+c)(a+b)$:
$$(b+c)(a+b) - (c+a)(a+b) = (c+a)(b+c) - (b+c)(a+b)$$
$$(ab+ac+bc+b^2) - (ac+bc+ab+a^2) = (bc+ab+ac+c^2) - (ab+ac+bc+b^2)$$
$$b^2 - a^2 = c^2 - b^2$$

This proves the desired result.

139. (a) We must have $4 + x = r(3 + x)$ and $5 + x = r^2(3 + x)$,

so $r = \dfrac{4+x}{3+x}$. Substituting into the second equality:

$$5 + x = \left(\frac{4+x}{3+x}\right)^2 (3+x)$$

$$5 + x = \frac{(4+x)^2}{3+x}$$

Multiplying each side by $3 + x$:
$$15 + 8x + x^2 = 16 + 8x + x^2$$
$$15 = 16$$
So no such value for x exists.

(b) Here $b + x = r(a + x)$ and $c + x = r^2(a + x)$, so $r = \dfrac{b+x}{a+x}$.

Substituting:

$$c + x = \left(\frac{b+x}{a+x}\right)^2 (a+x)$$

$$(c+x)(a+x) = (b+x)^2$$

$$ac + (a+c)x + x^2 = b^2 + 2bx + x^2$$

$$(a + c - 2b)x = b^2 - ac$$

$$x = \frac{b^2 - ac}{a + c - 2b}$$

(Note that $a + c - 2b = 0$ for (a), explaining why no x could be found).

141.   (a)   Let $S = a_1 + ra_2 + r^2a_3 + \ldots + r^{n-1}a_n$, so:

$$rS = ra_1 + r^2a_2 + r^3a_3 + \ldots + r^na_n$$

Then:

$$
\begin{aligned}
S - rS &= a_1 + r(a_2 - a_1) + r^2(a_3 - a_2) + \ldots r^{n-1}(a_n - a_{n-1}) - r^na_n \\
&= a_1 + rd + r^2d + \ldots + r^{n-1}d - r^na_n \\
&= a_1 + \frac{d(r - r^n)}{1 - r} - r^na_n
\end{aligned}
$$

(b)   Continuing from (a), we have:

$$S(1 - r) = a_1 - r^na_n + \frac{d(r - r^n)}{1 - r}$$

$$S = \frac{a_1 - r^na_n}{1 - r} + \frac{d(r - r^n)}{(1 - r)^2}$$

APPENDIX

A.4 Working With Fractional Expressions

1. $\dfrac{x^2 - 9}{x + 3} = \dfrac{(x - 3)(x + 3)}{x + 3} = x - 3$

3. $\dfrac{x + 2}{x^4 - 16} = \dfrac{x + 2}{(x^2 - 4)(x^2 + 4)}$

          $= \dfrac{x + 2}{(x - 2)(x + 2)(x^2 + 4)}$

          $= \dfrac{1}{(x - 2)(x^2 + 4)}$

5. $\dfrac{x^2 + 2x + 4}{x^3 - 8} = \dfrac{x^2 + 2x + 4}{(x - 2)(x^2 + 2x + 4)} = \dfrac{1}{x - 2}$

7. $\dfrac{9ab - 12b^2}{6a^2 - 8ab} = \dfrac{3b(3a - 4b)}{2a(3a - 4b)} = \dfrac{3b}{2a}$

9. $\dfrac{a^3 + a^2 + a + 1}{a^2 - 1}$ $= \dfrac{a^2(a+1) + (a+1)}{(a-1)(a+1)}$

$= \dfrac{(a+1)(a^2+1)}{(a-1)(a+1)}$

$= \dfrac{a^2+1}{a-1}$

11. $\dfrac{x^3 - y^3}{(x-y)^3}$ $= \dfrac{(x-y)(x^2+xy+y^2)}{(x-y)^3}$ $= \dfrac{x^2+xy+y^2}{(x-y)^2}$

13. $\dfrac{2}{x-2} \cdot \dfrac{x^2-4}{x+2}$ $= \dfrac{2(x-2)(x+2)}{(x-2)(x+2)}$ $= 2$

15. $\dfrac{x^2 - x - 2}{x^2 + x - 12} \cdot \dfrac{x^2 - 3x}{x^2 - 4x + 4}$ $= \dfrac{(x-2)(x+1)}{(x+4)(x-3)} \cdot \dfrac{x(x-3)}{(x-2)^2}$

$= \dfrac{x(x+1)}{(x+4)(x-2)}$

$= \dfrac{x^2+x}{(x+4)(x-2)}$

17. $\dfrac{x^3 + y^3}{x^2 - 4xy + 3y^2} \div \dfrac{(x+y)^3}{x^2 - 2xy - 3y^2}$ $= \dfrac{(x+y)(x^2 - xy + y^2)}{(x-3y)(x-y)} \cdot \dfrac{(x+y)(x-3y)}{(x+y)^3}$

$= \dfrac{x^2 - xy + y^2}{(x-y)(x+y)}$

19. $\dfrac{x^2 + xy - 2y^2}{x^2 - 5xy + 4y^2} \cdot \dfrac{x^2 - 7xy + 12y^2}{x^2 + 5xy + 6y^2}$ $= \dfrac{(x+2y)(x-y)}{(x-4y)(x-y)} \cdot \dfrac{(x-4y)(x-3y)}{(x+3y)(x+2y)}$

$= \dfrac{x - 3y}{x + 3y}$

21. $\dfrac{4}{x} - \dfrac{2}{x^2}$ $= \dfrac{4x}{x^2} - \dfrac{2}{x^2}$ $= \dfrac{4x - 2}{x^2}$

23. $\dfrac{6}{a} - \dfrac{a}{6}$ $= \dfrac{36}{6a} - \dfrac{a^2}{6a}$ $= \dfrac{36 - a^2}{6a}$

25. $\dfrac{1}{x+3} + \dfrac{3}{x+2}$ $= \dfrac{x+2}{(x+3)(x+2)} + \dfrac{3(x+3)}{(x+3)(x+2)}$

$= \dfrac{x + 2 + 3(x+3)}{(x+3)(x+2)}$

$= \dfrac{4x + 11}{(x+3)(x+2)}$

27. $\dfrac{3x}{x-2} - \dfrac{6}{x^2-4} = \dfrac{3x}{x-2} - \dfrac{6}{(x-2)(x+2)}$

$$= \dfrac{3x(x+2)-6}{(x-2)(x+2)}$$

$$= \dfrac{3x^2+6x-6}{(x-2)(x+2)}$$

29. $\dfrac{a}{x-1} + \dfrac{2ax}{(x-1)^2} + \dfrac{3ax^2}{(x-1)^3} = \dfrac{a(x-1)^2 + 2ax(x-1) + 3ax^2}{(x-1)^3}$

$$= \dfrac{ax^2 - 2ax + a + 2ax^2 - 2ax + 3ax^2}{(x-1)^3}$$

$$= \dfrac{6ax^2 - 4ax + a}{(x-1)^3}$$

31. $\dfrac{x}{x^2-9} + \dfrac{x-1}{x^2-5x+6} = \dfrac{x}{(x-3)(x+3)} + \dfrac{x-1}{(x-3)(x-2)}$

$$= \dfrac{x(x-2) + (x-1)(x+3)}{(x-3)(x+3)(x-2)}$$

$$= \dfrac{x^2 - 2x + x^2 + 2x - 3}{(x-3)(x+3)(x-2)}$$

$$= \dfrac{2x^2 - 3}{(x-3)(x+3)(x-2)}$$

33. $\dfrac{4}{x-5} - \dfrac{4}{5-x} = \dfrac{4}{x-5} + \dfrac{4}{x-5} = \dfrac{8}{x-5}$

35. $\dfrac{a^2+b^2}{a^2-b^2} + \dfrac{a}{a+b} + \dfrac{b}{b-a} = \dfrac{a^2+b^2}{(a-b)(a+b)} + \dfrac{a}{a+b} - \dfrac{b}{a-b}$

$$= \dfrac{a^2+b^2 + a(a-b) - b(a+b)}{(a-b)(a+b)}$$

$$= \dfrac{a^2+b^2 + a^2 - ab - ab - b^2}{(a-b)(a+b)}$$

$$= \dfrac{2a^2 - 2ab}{(a-b)(a+b)}$$

$$= \dfrac{2a(a-b)}{(a-b)(a+b)}$$

$$= \dfrac{2a}{a+b}$$

37. $\dfrac{1}{x^2 + x - 20} - \dfrac{1}{x^2 - 8x + 16} = \dfrac{1}{(x + 5)(x - 4)} - \dfrac{1}{(x - 4)^2}$

$\qquad\qquad\qquad\qquad\qquad = \dfrac{x - 4 - (x + 5)}{(x + 5)(x - 4)^2}$

$\qquad\qquad\qquad\qquad\qquad = \dfrac{-9}{(x + 5)(x - 4)^2}$

39. $\dfrac{2q + p}{2p^2 - 9pq - 5q^2} - \dfrac{p + q}{p^2 - 5pq} = \dfrac{2q + p}{(2p + q)(p - 5q)} - \dfrac{p + q}{p(p - 5q)}$

$\qquad\qquad\qquad\qquad\qquad\qquad = \dfrac{(2q + p)p - (p + q)(2p + q)}{p(2p + q)(p - 5q)}$

$\qquad\qquad\qquad\qquad\qquad\qquad = \dfrac{2pq + p^2 - 2p^2 - 3pq - q^2}{p(2p + q)(p - 5q)}$

$\qquad\qquad\qquad\qquad\qquad\qquad = \dfrac{-p^2 - pq - q^2}{p(2p + q)(p - 5q)}$

41. $\dfrac{x}{(x - y)(x - z)} + \dfrac{y}{(y - z)(y - x)} + \dfrac{z}{(z - x)(z - y)}$

$\qquad = \dfrac{x}{(x - y)(x - z)} - \dfrac{y}{(y - z)(x - y)} + \dfrac{z}{(x - z)(y - z)}$

$\qquad = \dfrac{x(y - z) - y(x - z) + z(x - y)}{(x - y)(x - z)(y - z)}$

$\qquad = \dfrac{xy - xz - xy + yz + xz - yz}{(x - y)(x - z)(y - z)}$

$\qquad = \dfrac{0}{(x - y)(x - z)(y - z)}$

$\qquad = 0$

43. $\dfrac{y + z}{x^2 - xy - xz + yz} - \dfrac{x + z}{xy - xz - y^2 + yz} + \dfrac{x + y}{xy - yz - xz + z^2}$

$\qquad = \dfrac{y + z}{x(x - y) - z(x - y)} - \dfrac{x + z}{x(y - z) - y(y - z)} + \dfrac{x + y}{y(x - z) - z(x - z)}$

$\qquad = \dfrac{y + z}{(x - y)(x - z)} - \dfrac{x + z}{(y - z)(x - y)} - \dfrac{x + y}{(x - z)(y - z)}$

$\qquad = \dfrac{(y + z)(y - z) - (x + z)(x - z) + (x + y)(x - y)}{(x - y)(x - z)(y - z)}$

$\qquad = \dfrac{y^2 - z^2 - x^2 + z^2 + x^2 - y^2}{(x - y)(x - z)(y - z)}$

$\qquad = \dfrac{0}{(x - y)(x - z)(y - z)}$

$\qquad = 0$

45. $\dfrac{x^2 + x - a - 1}{a^2 - x^2} + \dfrac{x + 1}{x + a} \div \dfrac{x - a}{x - 1}$ $= \dfrac{x^2 + x - a - 1}{a^2 - x^2} + \dfrac{x + 1}{x + a} \cdot \dfrac{x - 1}{x - a}$

$$= \dfrac{x^2 + x - a - 1}{-(x^2 - a^2)} + \dfrac{x^2 - 1}{x^2 - a^2}$$

$$= \dfrac{-x^2 - x + a + 1 + x^2 - 1}{x^2 - a^2}$$

$$= \dfrac{-x + a}{(x + a)(x - a)}$$

$$= \dfrac{-(x - a)}{(x + a)(x - a)}$$

$$= \dfrac{-1}{x + a}$$

47. $\dfrac{x^2 - 2ax + a^2}{px + q} \cdot \left(\dfrac{p}{x - a} + \dfrac{ap + q}{(x - a)^2} \right)$ $= \dfrac{(x - a)^2}{px + q} \cdot \dfrac{p(x - a) + ap + q}{(x - a)^2}$

$$= \dfrac{1}{px + q} \cdot \dfrac{px - pa + ap + q}{1}$$

$$= \dfrac{px + q}{px + q}$$

$$= 1$$

49. $\dfrac{1 + \dfrac{4}{x}}{\dfrac{3}{x} - 2}$ $= \dfrac{x}{x} \cdot \dfrac{1 + \dfrac{4}{x}}{\dfrac{3}{x} - 2}$ $= \dfrac{x + 4}{3 - 2x}$

51. $\dfrac{a - \dfrac{1}{a}}{1 + \dfrac{1}{a}}$ $= \dfrac{a}{a} \cdot \dfrac{a - \dfrac{1}{a}}{1 + \dfrac{1}{a}}$

$$= \dfrac{a^2 - 1}{a + 1}$$

$$= \dfrac{(a - 1)(a + 1)}{a + 1}$$

$$= a - 1$$

53. $\dfrac{\dfrac{1}{2+h} - \dfrac{1}{2}}{h}$ $= \dfrac{2(2+h)}{2(2+h)} \bullet \dfrac{\dfrac{1}{2+h} - \dfrac{1}{2}}{h}$

$= \dfrac{2 - (2+h)}{2h(2+h)}$

$= \dfrac{-h}{2h(2+h)}$

$= \dfrac{-1}{2(2+h)}$

55. $\dfrac{\dfrac{a}{x^2} + \dfrac{x}{a^2}}{a^2 - ax + x^2}$ $= \dfrac{x^2 a^2}{x^2 a^2} \bullet \dfrac{\dfrac{a}{x^2} + \dfrac{x}{a^2}}{a^2 - ax + x^2}$

$= \dfrac{a^3 + x^3}{x^2 a^2 (a^2 - ax + x^2)}$

$= \dfrac{(a + x)(a^2 - ax + x^2)}{x^2 a^2 (a^2 - ax + x^2)}$

$= \dfrac{a + x}{x^2 a^2}$

57. $\dfrac{x + y}{2(x^2 + y^2)} - \dfrac{1}{2(x + y)} + \dfrac{x - y}{x^2 - y^2} - \dfrac{x^3 - y^3}{x^4 - y^4}$

$= \dfrac{x + y}{2(x^2 + y^2)} - \dfrac{1}{2(x + y)} + \dfrac{1}{x + y} - \dfrac{(x - y)(x^2 + xy + y^2)}{(x - y)(x + y)(x^2 + y^2)}$

$= \dfrac{x + y}{2(x^2 + y^2)} - \dfrac{1}{2(x + y)} + \dfrac{1}{x + y} - \dfrac{x^2 + xy + y^2}{(x + y)(x^2 + y^2)}$

$= \dfrac{(x + y)(x + y) - (x^2 + y^2) + 2(x^2 + y^2) - 2(x^2 + xy + y^2)}{2(x^2 + y^2)(x + y)}$

$= \dfrac{x^2 + 2xy + y^2 - x^2 - y^2 + 2x^2 + 2y^2 - 2x^2 - 2xy - 2y^2}{2(x^2 + y^2)(x + y)}$

$= \dfrac{0}{2(x^2 + y^2)(x + y)}$

$= 0$

59.
$$\dfrac{\dfrac{a+b}{a-b}+\dfrac{a-b}{a+b}}{\dfrac{a-b}{a+b}-\dfrac{a+b}{a-b}}\cdot\dfrac{ab^3-a^3b}{a^2+b^2}$$

$$=\dfrac{(a-b)(a+b)}{(a-b)(a+b)}\cdot\dfrac{\dfrac{a+b}{a-b}+\dfrac{a-b}{a+b}}{\dfrac{a-b}{a+b}-\dfrac{a+b}{a-b}}\cdot\dfrac{ab(b^2-a^2)}{a^2+b^2}$$

$$=\dfrac{(a+b)^2+(a-b)^2}{(a-b)^2-(a+b)^2}\cdot\dfrac{ab(b-a)(b+a)}{a^2+b^2}$$

$$=\dfrac{2a^2+2b^2}{-4ab}\cdot\dfrac{ab(b-a)(b+a)}{a^2+b^2}$$

$$=\dfrac{2(a^2+b^2)}{-4}\cdot\dfrac{(b-a)(b+a)}{a^2+b^2}$$

$$=\dfrac{(b-a)(b+a)}{-2}$$

$$=\dfrac{b^2-a^2}{-2}$$

$$=\dfrac{a^2-b^2}{2}$$

61.
$$\dfrac{ap+q}{ax-bx-a^2+ab}+\dfrac{bp+q}{bx-ax-b^2+ab}$$

$$=\dfrac{ap+q}{x(a-b)-a(a-b)}+\dfrac{bp+q}{x(b-a)-b(b-a)}$$

$$=\dfrac{ap+q}{(a-b)(x-a)}+\dfrac{bp+q}{(b-a)(x-b)}$$

$$=\dfrac{ap+q}{(a-b)(x-a)}-\dfrac{bp+q}{(a-b)(x-b)}$$

$$=\dfrac{(ap+q)(x-b)-(bp+q)(x-a)}{(a-b)(x-a)(x-b)}$$

$$=\dfrac{apx+qx-abp-bq-bpx-qx+apb+aq}{(a-b)(x-a)(x-b)}$$

$$=\dfrac{apx-bq-bpx+aq}{(a-b)(x-a)(x-b)}$$

$$=\dfrac{a(px+q)-b(px+q)}{(a-b)(x-a)(x-b)}$$

$$=\dfrac{(px+q)(a-b)}{(a-b)(x-a)(x-b)}$$

$$=\dfrac{px+q}{(x-a)(x-b)}$$

63. $$\dfrac{\dfrac{1}{a} - \dfrac{a - x}{a^2 + x^2}}{\dfrac{1}{x} - \dfrac{x - a}{x^2 + a^2}} + \dfrac{\dfrac{1}{a} - \dfrac{a + x}{a^2 + x^2}}{\dfrac{1}{x} - \dfrac{x + a}{x^2 + a^2}}$$

$$= \dfrac{ax(a^2 + x^2)}{ax(a^2 + x^2)} \cdot \dfrac{\dfrac{1}{a} - \dfrac{a - x}{a^2 + x^2}}{\dfrac{1}{x} - \dfrac{x - a}{x^2 + a^2}} + \dfrac{ax(a^2 + x^2)}{ax(a^2 + x^2)} \cdot \dfrac{\dfrac{1}{a} - \dfrac{a + x}{a^2 + x^2}}{\dfrac{1}{x} - \dfrac{x + a}{x^2 + a^2}}$$

$$= \dfrac{x(a^2 + x^2) - (a - x)ax}{a(a^2 + x^2) - (x - a)ax} + \dfrac{x(a^2 + x^2) - (a + x)ax}{a(a^2 + x^2) - (x + a)ax}$$

$$= \dfrac{a^2 x + x^3 - a^2 x + ax^2}{a^3 + ax^2 - ax^2 + a^2 x} + \dfrac{a^2 x + x^3 - a^2 x - ax^2}{a^3 + ax^2 - ax^2 - a^2 x}$$

$$= \dfrac{x^3 + ax^2}{a^3 + a^2 x} + \dfrac{x^3 - ax^2}{a^3 - a^2 x}$$

$$= \dfrac{x^2(x + a)}{a^2(a + x)} + \dfrac{x^2(x - a)}{a^2(a - x)}$$

$$= \dfrac{x^2}{a^2} + \dfrac{x^2}{a^2} \ (-1)$$

$$= 0$$

65. $$\dfrac{x^2 - qr}{(p - q)(p - r)} + \dfrac{x^2 - rp}{(q - r)(q - p)} + \dfrac{x^2 - pq}{(r - p)(r - q)}$$

$$= \dfrac{x^2 - qr}{(p - q)(p - r)} - \dfrac{x^2 - rp}{(q - r)(p - q)} + \dfrac{x^2 - pq}{(p - r)(q - r)}$$

$$= \dfrac{(x^2 - qr)(q - r) - (x^2 - rp)(p - r) + (x^2 - pq)(p - q)}{(p - q)(p - r)(q - r)}$$

$$= \dfrac{qx^2 - q^2 r - rx^2 + qr^2 - px^2 + p^2 r + rx^2 - pr^2 + px^2 - p^2 q - qx^2 + pq^2}{(p - q)(p - r)(q - r)}$$

$$= \dfrac{-q^2 r + qr^2 + p^2 r - pr^2 - p^2 q + pq^2}{(p - q)(p - r)(q - r)}$$

$$= \dfrac{(p^2 r - q^2 r) - (pr^2 - qr^2) - (p^2 q - pq^2)}{(p - q)(p - r)(q - r)}$$

$$= \dfrac{r(p - q)(p + q) - r^2(p - q) - pq(p - q)}{(p - q)(p - r)(q - r)}$$

$$= \dfrac{(p - q)\big(r(p + q) - r^2 - pq\big)}{(p - q)(p - r)(q - r)}$$

$$= \dfrac{rp + rq - r^2 - pq}{(p - r)(q - r)}$$

$$= \frac{p(r-q) + r(q-r)}{(p-r)(q-r)}$$

$$= \frac{-p(q-r) + r(q-r)}{(p-r)(q-r)}$$

$$= \frac{(q-r)(-p+r)}{(p-r)(q-r)}$$

$$= \frac{-p+r}{p-r}$$

$$= -1$$

67. (a) The sum and the product both equal 1/42.

(b) After adding the three fractions and combining the many like terms appearing in the resulting numerator, we obtain:

$$\frac{b-c}{1+bc} + \frac{c-a}{1+ca} + \frac{a-b}{1+ab}$$

$$= \frac{ab^2 - ac^2 + bc^2 - a^2b + a^2c - b^2c}{(1+bc)(1+ca)(1+ab)}$$

$$= \frac{(ab^2 - b^2c) + (a^2c - ac^2) + (bc^2 - a^2b)}{(1+bc)(1+ca)(1+ab)}$$

$$= \frac{b^2(a-c) + ac(a-c) + b(c^2 - a^2)}{(1+bc)(1+ca)(1+ab)}$$

$$= \frac{b^2(a-c) + ac(a-c) - b(a-c)(a+c)}{(1+bc)(1+ca)(1+ab)}$$

$$= \frac{(a-c)\left(b^2 + ac - b(a+c)\right)}{(1+bc)(1+ca)(1+ab)}$$

$$= \frac{(a-c)\left(b^2 + ac - ab - bc\right)}{(1+bc)(1+ca)(1+ab)}$$

$$= \frac{(a-c)\left(c(a-b) - b(a-b)\right)}{(1+bc)(1+ca)(1+ab)}$$

$$= \frac{(a-c)\left((a-b)(c-b)\right)}{(1+bc)(1+ca)(1+ab)}$$

$$= \frac{(c-a)(a-b)(b-c)}{(1+bc)(1+ca)(1+ab)}$$

$$= \frac{b-c}{1+bc} \bullet \frac{c-a}{1+ca} \bullet \frac{a-b}{1+ab}$$

69. For convenience, let $z = x - y$. Then $-z = y - x$, and we have:

$$(1 + a^z)^{-1} + (1 + a^{-z})^{-1} = \frac{1}{1 + a^z} + \frac{1}{1 + \frac{1}{a^z}}$$

$$= \frac{1}{1 + a^z} + \frac{a^z}{a^z} \bullet \frac{1}{1 + \frac{1}{a^z}}$$

$$= \frac{1}{1 + a^z} + \frac{a^z}{a^z + 1}$$

$$= \frac{1 + a^z}{1 + a^z}$$

$$= 1$$

THE END!